# The Ray Society

INSTITUTED 1844

This volume (No. 144 of the series) is the issue of
the Ray Society for the years 1959, 1960 and 1961,
and is sold at a price of eight guineas.

LONDON

1962

VERA FRETTER & ALASTAIR GRAHAM

# British
# Prosobranch
# Molluscs

THEIR FUNCTIONAL ANATOMY
AND ECOLOGY

LONDON
Printed for the Ray Society
*Sold by Bernard Quaritch Ltd*
*11 Grafton Street London W1*

1962

Made and printed in Great Britain by
Adlard & Son Ltd
Bartholomew Press, Dorking

Set in Monotype Bembo

Reprinted photographically
by
Jos Adam - Brussels
1965
ECM

# BRITISH PROSOBRANCH MOLLUSCS
## THEIR FUNCTIONAL ANATOMY AND ECOLOGY

# PREFACE

I N the nineteenth century there appeared three accounts of British Molluscs which have been the standard works of reference for students of these animals ever since. They were Alder & Hancock's *British Nudibranchiate Mollusca* (1845–55), Forbes & Hanley's *History of the British Mollusca, and their Shells* (1848–53) and Jeffreys' *British Conchology* (1863–69). Great as is the debt which all malacologists and conchologists owe to these authors, the fact remains that their severely systematic approach to their subject, their attitude to zoology and even their vocabulary and style are very different from their modern counterparts. The molluscs have, indeed, been shown to be excellent material for work on functional morphology and for demonstrating the adaptation of structure to function and of both to the ecological niche which the animals occupy, though they have proved less suitable for, and less productive of results in certain fields of physiology. The rich findings of this modern malacology have not as yet received any synthetic treatment, though Morton has made a brave attempt to indicate their main lines in his little book *The Mollusca* (1959). The whole molluscan field, however, is really too great to deal with except in such a brief way and we have, therefore, in preparing this attempt to present the results of all this work, limited ourselves to the prosobranch gastropods, the group with which we are most familiar, and which, to our thinking, shows the inter-relationships of structure and function and habitat in more varied and convincing ways than any other.

We have not set out to write a systematic account nor one which will permit the identification of specimens collected in the field, believing that this was a ground already adequately covered by others and one, to tell the truth, in which we were less interested than in that of functional morphology, where, too, the need for synthesis is greater. We have, however, included a list of British prosobranchs with some indication of their precise habitat and present distribution and a reference which will permit those who are interested to refer to Forbes & Hanley's or Jeffreys' works for fuller descriptions of shell and external features. These two works will, indeed, long live on for such use because of the excellence of their descriptive text and figures. We have written our account primarily on the basis of work done on those prosobranchs which live in Britain and the British seas, but when it has seemed necessary or desirable to refer to animals which are not found in these localities in order to increase the value of a discussion, we have not hesitated to do so. Whilst the text rests largely on published work much of what is included without reference to an author is new material from our unpublished investigations. Although the writing of the book was naturally started by each author undertaking the sections which his interests and experience rendered most apt, each of us has read and re-read the other's writing, and the result is (and is intended to be) a genuinely joint effort; both of us are therefore equally responsible for the shortcomings, whether of fact, style or treatment, which the discriminating reader will inevitably discover.

We have made a point of preparing new illustrations and, except where it is otherwise indicated, the drawings have all been made especially for this book. As we invariably feel more stimulated when we open a book and find new figures to illustrate it, and not just re-drawings of the old familiar ones, so we hope that readers of this will feel stimulated by its figures, though we cannot hope to rise to the artistic level achieved by some of the famous productions of the Ray Society. We have, however, used a certain number of figures previously published by ourselves or our research students and a very small number from the work of other people. For permission to reproduce these we are indebted to the following sources: the Editor of the *Journal of the Marine Biological Association* for figs. 32, 74, 99, 102, 103, 112, 118, 122B, 134, 171, 174, 175, 184, 192, 193, 194, 195, 200, 206, 209, 278, 308; the Council of the Royal Society for figs. 224, 225, 226, 227, 228, 229, 230, 231, 234A and 234D; the Council of the Zoological Society of London for figs. 119, 121, 141, 168, 188, 205, 232, 234B and 234C; the Editor of *Helgoländer wissenschaftliche Meeresuntersuchungen* for figs. 41, 131, 236 and 305; the Editor of the *Proceedings of the Malacological Society of London* for figs. 56, 130, 182, 196; the Editor of *Biological Reviews* for fig. 251; the Editor of the *Pubblicazione della Stazione Zoologica di Napoli* for fig. 199; and the Editor of *Zoologiska Bidrag fran Uppsala* for fig. 176.

It is obvious that a book of this kind has not been prepared without a great deal of help from a variety of sources. We are particularly mindful of the way in which two people, Dr D. Crofts and Dr H. Quick, have been lavish of their time and energy and generous of their very extensive knowledge of the molluscs in response to our requests for help: both have read the whole typescript and their careful attention has saved us from many mistakes. Dr C. O. van Regteren Altena of the Rijksmuseum van Naturlijke Historie, Leiden, Dr M. V. Lebour and Dr D. P. Wilson of the Marine Laboratory, Plymouth, Dr R. H. Nisbet of the Royal Veterinary College, Dr D. A. Hancock of the M.A.F.F. Research Laboratory, Burnham-on-Crouch, and Mr P. David of the National Institute of Oceanography have read and criticized certain chapters or parts of chapters where their special knowledge was invaluable, and Mr S. P. Dance of the British Museum (Natural History) and Mr G. M. Spooner, M.B.E., of the Plymouth Laboratory have both read Appendix I. The latinity of this list has also been checked for us by Professor J. M. R. Cormack of the University of Reading. Dr G. Rees and Mr B. James of the University College of Wales, Aberystwyth, have given invaluable guidance to us in the parasitological field (of which we are largely ignorant), and have been extraordinarily generous in lending preparations and in allowing us to make use of their knowledge: had it not been for their help the list of parasites in Chapter 23 could never have been so complete. Despite this help we should like to make it clear that we, none the less, are responsible for what is said in these chapters and for such errors of fact or interpretation as they contain. We are much indebted to the following for supplies of animals and for information about them: Dr Altena, Dr A. Ansell, Mr P. David, Dr J. H. Fraser, Dr D. A. Hancock, Professor L. A. Harvey, Professor A. D. Hobson, Dr C. Burdon-Jones, Dr N. S. Jones, Dr R. B. Pike, Dr F. Segrove and Mr G. M. Spooner. Figs. 3 and 14 were drawn for us by Miss A. M. Taylor, who acted for a while as research assistant to one of us (A. G.) at Birkbeck College (University of London), fig. 199 by Mr W. A. Rogers and figs. 6, 33B, 185 and 215 by Miss A. Court of the Zoology Department, University of Reading, and we received much help with photography from Mr F. C. Padley of the same department. The task of typing from our manuscript was shared by Mrs R. Hake and Mrs G. I. Smillie and we owe much in the way of secretarial help to these two persons. Much of the original work which is incorporated in the book was carried out at the Plymouth Laboratory and, like so many other marine zoologists, we owe a great debt to Dr F. S. Russell, F.R.S., for the manner in which he has so often made our stay there rewarding and encouraged us over the more dreary stretches of the way; to many members of his staff we also owe much, but to two in particular we would give special thanks—Miss L. Serpell for help in tracking references and completing the bibliography, and Mr R. Tozer for his interest in seeing that we got the animals which we wanted. The dust jacket was designed by Miss Gwyneth Solly of the School of Fine Art of the University of Reading, and we are grateful for much advice and help in designing parts of the book to Mr. M. L. Twyman of the same School. Finally we would record our thanks to successive officials of the Ray Society—for so slow has been our progress that their presidencies and secretaryships have grown long and finally been handed over to others—for the patience with which they have awaited our typescript, and the generosity with which they have listened to and met our wishes in the matter of book production. We hope that the consequence of so much activity by so many people—which lies in the later pages of this volume—may appear a worthwhile help towards further study of a phylum which we regard as one of the most interesting and successful in the whole animal kingdom.

Reading, July 1960.

# LIST OF ILLUSTRATIONS

# CHAPTER I

# INTRODUCTION TO THE MOLLUSCA

THE Mollusca are one of the great groups of the animal kingdom. If we measure the success of a stock of animals by paying attention to the number of individuals, the size to which they grow and the variety of different modes of life to which they have adapted themselves, then it is clear that not more than three or four of the numerous groups of animals known to the zoologist have proved outstandingly successful. Undoubtedly the most markedly so are the arthropods—the crustaceans, insects, spiders, centipedes, extinct trilobites and similar creatures; another successful group—which we inevitably tend to regard as the highest of all—is the vertebrates, in which fishes, amphibians, reptiles, birds and mammals are included; and a third is the phylum Mollusca, to which belong all the animals which are dealt with in this book and many more. Of these three groups the molluscan phylum is the least successful, but it has been computed by Hesse, nevertheless, that there are at least 80,000 different kinds of living animals included in it.

The word Mollusca, which is derived from the Latin *mollis*, meaning soft, may seem at first sight a curious name for animals one of the outstanding characteristics of which is a hard, calcareous shell, sometimes, as in the case of the common mussels and cockles, completely encasing the body. This apparent misnomer originated historically in that it was first used by the French naturalist Cuvier in 1798 for the squids and cuttlefish, a group of the Mollusca amongst living forms of which the shell is always (except in the pearly nautilus) either reduced and covered by the soft flesh of the animal or is altogether wanting. Since then, the relationship of the more familiar snails, slugs and bivalves to the squids and cuttles has been made certain and the name extended to them as well. Despite its seeming unsuitability, however, it was a fortunate accident which led to the group being named so as to emphasize the importance of the soft parts rather than of the shell, because although the latter is of importance to the palaeontologist—is, in fact, the only part of the animal which is usually fossilized and so preserved for his inspection—it is the soft parts which are of outstanding interest to the zoologist, whether he be anatomist, physiologist, or, simply, naturalist. Paradoxically it is the soft parts which at the start produce and mould the shell within which they are later to lie; it is the soft parts which trim away unwanted or obstructive portions of shell which inhibit growth or development, and it is, finally, the extraordinary plasticity of the soft body of the molluscs which has allowed them to become adapted for life in a great number of different ecological niches.

The ancestral mollusc must have appeared on earth many millions of years ago, too early for any fossil record of it to have been preserved, because by the time the oldest fossiliferous rocks were laid down, evolution had already produced molluscs of many different patterns. What this ancestral type may have looked like, therefore, can only be deduced from a study of these fossils and of present day forms according to the laws of comparative morphology and embryology, guides of a certain degree of trustworthiness but not by any means infallible. It would seem, on their basis, that it was marine in its habitat, creeping over the surface of the shores or sublittoral regions of an archaic sea, and had evolved from a group related to the same stock as that from which arthropods and annelids are derived and originally arising from a turbellarian-nemertine ancestry.

The turbellarian-nemertine group consists of unsegmented, acoelomate animals which, in the case of the flatworms, glide, partly by ciliary and partly by muscular action, over the substratum. The body is flat and thin in a dorsoventral direction so that the viscera have to be packed away in the limited space between the upper and lower surfaces. This shape is connected with the fact that it has neither blood system nor special respiratory organs, and the alimentary canal of the larger polyclads and triclads branches repeatedly and reaches into all parts of the body, supplying them with food; in the smaller rhabdocoels it may remain a simple sac. The leaflike shape allows oxygen to diffuse into its deepest parts. Although the brain and the major sense organs are located at one end, which normally goes first and so is the head, the mouth is often placed on the ventral surface some way behind; but there are again many smaller forms in the Rhabdocoelida in which it lies anteriorly. There is no other opening to the gut at all.

These anatomical features limit the turbellarians to a low level of metabolism and this is to some extent exaggerated by functional peculiarities. The lack of an anus prevents a continuous stream of food from passing along the gut and imposes an alternation of inward and outward movements, and it appears from the investigations of Westblad (1922) that during digestion the walls of the gut fuse with one another across the cavity so as to convert it into a solid spongy mass of tissue within the spaces of which the food is digested. When the process is completed the vacuolated syncytial mass breaks down to form a hollow tube with epithelial walls once more and the indigestible residue of the meal is left in the lumen for egestion. This essentially intracellular digestive phase clearly imposes a kind of paralysis on the digestive system and, along with the lack of respiratory organs and vascular system, limits rather strictly the size and complexity which the turbellarians have been able to reach in their evolutionary history.

The outermost layer of the turbellarian is a richly glandular and ciliated epidermis, resting on a layer of connective tissue. Many of the glands associated with the skin lie embedded in this connective tissue and discharge their secretion through long necks which lie between the epithelial cells. In the connective tissue, too, run muscle strands, some circular in direction, some longitudinal, some crossing from the upper to the lower epidermis and collectively forming a complex network of fibres differing a little in the details of its arrangement from one part of the body to another. The connective tissue also forms the matrix (parenchyma) in which the gut, the nervous system and the reproductive organs are embedded. The nervous system is centred in two cerebral ganglia placed in the head as dorsal enlargements on a ring of nervous tissue encircling the gut in those forms which have the mouth placed anteriorly, but not related to it in others. To them run sensory nerves from receptors, tactile, chemical and visual, located at the anterior end of the body, and from them arise cords which pass posteriorly. These are better developed on the ventral side, in accordance with the biological principle of neurobiotaxis, which asserts that nerve cells migrate inside an animal towards the region from which they receive most stimulation, and a nerve-net ramifies in relation to them and the musculature of the body underneath the epidermis. The movement of the animal, effected and controlled largely by this nerve-net under the direction of the cerebral ganglia, involves the simultaneous discharge of secretion from the numerous gland cells to produce a layer of mucus over which the animal glides, the rhythmic contraction of the muscles of the body and the beating of the cilia of the epidermal cells. In different circumstances the effect of the cilia may predominate or the effect of the muscles, but the secretion of the cutaneous glands always appears to be important.

The excretory organs are 'flame cells' or protonephridia, running in the parenchymatous connective tissue and discharging to the exterior.

The turbellarians, like all the platyhelminths, are hermaphrodite, and the fertilized eggs undergo spiral cleavage to give rise (in those marine forms in which a free-swimming stage occurs) to a larva of trochophoral pattern. When fully formed this is an ovoid body with a number of ciliated lobes projecting from the equatorial region by means of which it swims. A mouth opens on the ventral side leading to a blind pouch, which is the archenteron or beginning of the gut. Between body surface and gut wall is a cavity, the primary body cavity or blastocoel, within which lies a number of cells which are the rudiments of the parenchymatous material found in the adult animal. Some of these cells are derived from the ectodermal cells of the body wall and are therefore ectomesoderm. In animals which exhibit spiral cleavage true mesoderm, such as is formed from the teloblasts of annelids and is responsible for the formation of the coelom, is derived normally from cell 4$d$ (p. 416). In the turbellarians and nemertines, however, though this gives rise to endoderm, some mesenchyme, some muscles and the genital organs, no coelom sacs are formed and as a consequence the turbellarians and nemertines are acoelomate. The ducts by which their genital products are conveyed to the exterior may, nevertheless, be regarded as coelomoducts and the cavity within them as coelomic, but no part of the cavity between epidermis and gut wall is of this nature. Their excretory protonephridia, too, are to be regarded as straightforward ectodermal ingrowths without any coelomic connexions.

The nemertine members of the platyhelminth assemblage of invertebrates have advanced upon the turbellarians in a number of respects, all of which may be associated with a more active mode of life. These advances give rise to animals with bodies which mimic those of annelid worms, though they are not metamerically segmented, and have probable arisen because of the adoption by both groups of similar ways of living. The body has become worm-shaped and the alimentary canal has acquired an anus, placed terminally at the posterior end, and digestion has become partly—if not wholly—an extracellular process. Both these changes mean that a continuous stream of food can pass through the gut without the pauses for digestion and egestion which have to occur in the turbellarian.

The organization of the body wall has altered, probably in connexion with the more active wriggling and creeping by means of which nemertines move, although it still retains a ciliated and glandular epidermis. Within this there now lie, however, definite layers of circular and longitudinal muscles. The brain has enlarged, as might be expected to occur in a more active animal and two of the longitudinal nerves, one on each side of the body, are of much greater importance than the others. They are still in relation to a well developed nerve-net in a sub-epidermal position. The departure of the body from a leaf-like shape and the adoption of a cylindrical one have been permitted by the invention of a vascular system, neither extensive nor probably very efficient, but certainly permitting some transport of food and respiratory gases. The nemertines have become distinctly specialized in their invention of a proboscis as a special food-catching organ which is armed, at least in some cases, with chitinous stylets for piercing and gripping the body of their prey.

A considerable number of changes were involved in the evolution from an animal with this type of organization of any one to which the name mollusc could be given unreservedly. These changes were perhaps least in connexion with the locomotor organs, because, apart from a thickening of the musculature of the ventral part of the body to form a structure called the foot and an enrichment of the already generous equipment of gland cells with which it was furnished, the mollusc moves by fundamentally the same machinery as does the turbellarian—a combination of glandular, ciliary and muscular activity co-ordinated by a network of nerves. These are related to the main nerve centres by two principal longitudinal trunks—the pedal nerve cords.

The alimentary tract, like that of the nemertine, acquired an anus, and lost the method by which it had become converted into a solid parenchyma when actively digesting. It may be that the first and last parts of the molluscan gut are the inventions of this ancestral mollusc which put it into possession of a continuous alimentary tract, whilst the digestive gland, a voluminous mass of branching caeca, within which intracellular digestion often occurs, may represent the ancestral turbellarian system. At any rate, the bulk of this collection of viscera was now so great as to cause the animal to depart from the ancestral flattened shape and to make the body swell into a dorsal protuberance, rather like a hump on a camel, in which they were accommodated. This dorsal bulge, evolved to house the viscera, is the visceral mass or visceral hump. The skin over this important part of the body, now called the pallium or mantle, secreted a covering of conchiolin impregnated with calcareous salts, which is the molluscan shell. Once this shell had developed no significant movement of the surface of the visceral mass was possible and the original equipment of muscle fibres with which the dorsal surface of the body had been provided became superfluous and was reduced, although never totally lost. Some strands of the dorsoventrally directed musculature of the turbellarian-like ancestor not only persisted in the mollusc but enlarged and increased in importance in that dorsally they became fastened to the inside of the calcareous shell and so provided a means by which this could be pulled down over the body to give maximal protection.

The anterior end of the archaic mollusc under consideration formed a head, more distinctly separated from the foot than the head of a flatworm is separated from the rest of its body. It bore the mouth and a number of sense organs often situated on tentacle-like outgrowths from its surface. Similar tentacle-like outgrowths perhaps extended down the sides of the foot forming a structure called the epipodium. Possibly the same tendency which in nemertines produced stylets gave rise in the mollusc to a series of chitinous teeth on the lining of the buccal cavity, by means of which food could be gathered. This is the radula, which is one of the hallmarks of the mollusc. With it the first molluscs collected minute plants and animals and, perhaps, detritus off the bottom on which they crawled, for they were in all probability microphagous feeders.

At the posterior end of the visceral mass the alimentary tract opened to the exterior by an anal opening, through which faecal matter escaped. The anus opened to a groove lying around the head and foot, the pallial groove, roofed by the edge of the mantle or mantle skirt, and the shell. This cavity is possibly the most characteristic possession of the molluscs and has played an extremely important part in their evolution. Into it, in the mid-line, opened the anus, bringing faecal matter from the gut; into it, too, on either side opened the kidneys, bringing more waste, while (again on each side) the respiratory organs lay in it and reproductive cells were discharged to it.

The nervous system of the ancestral molluscan type was clearly related to that of the animals in the group from which it had sprung: its centre was two cerebral ganglia lying in the head as dorsal enlargements of a ring of nervous tissue encircling the anterior end of the alimentary tract. The beginnings of two other concentrations of nerve cells had appeared in this ring, a pleural one lying alongside the gut and a pedal one lying below on each side, and from these longitudinal cords ran back towards the posterior end of the body just as they had done in the turbellarian ancestors. Two cords (pedal cords) ran near the ventral surface and so lay in the foot, for the co-ordination of the activities of which they were responsible; cross-connexions gave a ladder-like appearance to this part of the nervous system and ensured accurate simultaneous control of the two sides of the foot. Two other longitudinal cords (lateral or pallial cords) ran nearer the dorsal surface at the edge of the visceral mass; between members of this pair transverse connexions did not occur except at the posterior end, where the right and left nerves were linked ventral to the rectal region. Possibly, transverse connexions linked pedal and pallial cords on each side.

The mollusc has been able to increase the volume and change the shape of its body from that of its ancestors largely because of two things: it has invented gills—special, thin-walled areas of the body surface, through which respiratory exchange of gas is possible; and secondly, because it has acquired a circulatory system by means of which these respiratory gases may be transported around the body in the blood, as can also food and waste. The mantle cavity, which lies, it will be recalled, under the protective cover of the shell, is a good place for the gills to lie, provided that some ventilation of the cavity goes on to ensure that they are continuously exposed to fresh water, and do not lie in a wholly stagnant mass. Some kind of movement of the blood is necessary in a vascular system which has this function to fulfil, and this calls for a contractile heart, which lies in the visceral mass of the mollusc receiving oxygenated blood from the gills to circulate to the rest of the body. The provision of heart and vascular system has involved the molluscs in a considerable amount of bodily reorganization. The body of the platyhelminths is a spongy mass of tissue in which numerous organs are embedded; it is difficult to imagine a contractile organ developing and functioning properly in such surroundings, since for successful working a contractile heart should be placed inside a cavity: the mollusc has made this out of the genital spaces which its body possesses. The bulk of the body cavity is, like that of a platyhelminth and larval mollusc, blastocoelic in origin, with ectomesodermal cells lying in it in the larval stage. At this time in the life of the animal the endomesoderm or coelom rudiment is represented in the molluscs by cell 4d. From this develop strips of cells, one right, one left, of a very transitory nature, which soon break down entirely into groups of cells scattered irregularly throughout the primary body cavity. At this stage it is, in most cases, quite impossible to tell whether any particular cell in such a situation is of ectomesodermal or endomesodermal origin. Eventually in the development of modern molluscs a double group of cells sometimes of mixed origin is formed: this is the rudiment of the heart, the gonad and genital ducts and the kidneys, all of which appear as part of one and the same cell mass. This cavitates to give rise to the pericardial cavity from which open the gonads and the kidneys, and when the heart forms it lies within the pericardial cavity which has so arisen. The kidneys, and through them the pericardial cavity and gonads, acquire a connexion to the mantle cavity. The essential nature of the pericardium, therefore, appears to be an expansion on the course of the ducts between the gonads and the exterior and it is clearly coelomic— the sole cavity genuinely of that nature in the body of the mollusc, just as the cavity of the gonads and their ducts are the only spaces in the body of a platyhelminth with which it could be regarded as homologous. The physiological necessity for the cavity is the need for a space in which the heart may beat.

The animal which we have, in imagination, created from a hypothetical flatworm-like ancestor, lived a littoral or sublittoral life, its stout shell giving it a measure of protection against the waves. The animal breathed by means of the gills in the mantle cavity. It crept about on the sole of its foot, which was sufficiently broad and flat to prevent dislodgement by waves, and it fed on minute plant or detrital material raked into the gut by the radula. It possessed now all the essential characters of the molluscs, which may be enumerated thus:

(i) a body of triploblastic, largely acoelomate organization;
(ii) the body divided into three regions—head, foot and visceral mass;
(iii) the visceral mass covered by a shell secreted by the mantle or skin over the visceral mass;
(iv) a radula in the buccal cavity;
(v) a mantle cavity under a fold of mantle and shell, in which gills lay and to which the anus, excretory and genital organs discharged.

It would appear that all molluscs evolved from some such ancestral form: let us sketch the main directions in which this has occurred. The ancestral type of mollusc has not itself survived the competition of the millions of years which have elapsed since its appearance, nor is this to be wondered at, since, like all prototypes, it was to some extent an experimental model liable to modification in innumerable ways as it was put through the tests imposed upon it by natural selection. Perhaps the nearest approach to this ancestral mollusc is the monoplacophoran genus *Neopilina*, discovered in 1952 by the Danish *Galathea* expedition in the Pacific Ocean at 9° 23′ N, 89° 32′ W at the depth of 3,570 m and described by Lemche (1957) and Lemche & Wingstrand (1959). This extraordinary find turned out to be a mollusc belonging to the group Monoplacophora previously established by Odhner in 1940 for some fossils of Palaeozoic age which were thought to be primitive limpet-like gastropods. With the results of the investigations of Lemche & Wingstrand before us, however, it is clear that the monoplacophorans are much more primitive than any gastropod, and although it is likely that they are already somewhat specialized they probably give a closer picture of the first molluscs than can be obtained in any other way. A second species, *Neopilina (Vema) ewingi*, differing only in details from *N. galatheae*, was discovered later (Clarke & Menzies, 1959).

*Neopilina galatheae* is limpet-like in shape, with a spoon-shaped shell more or less circular in outline, the largest specimen so far obtained measuring 37 mm long, 33 mm broad and 14 mm high. The apex of the shell overhangs the anterior margin of the shell and bears a dextrally coiled larval shell, though this is usually lost. The shell covers the entire animal and, like that of a limpet, has no operculum, though this might have been present in the larva. When seen in ventral view the animal shows a rather small, circular foot occupying the centre of the circle and leaving a broad pallial groove between the edge of the foot and the edge of the mantle skirt. In this lie the anus (median and posterior), 5 pairs of gills (lateral) and the animal's head (anterior).

The head bears the mouth, which is bordered in front by a transverse fold; a pair of postoral ridges which end in tufts of branched tentacle-like appendages are perhaps concerned with the capture of food. The head also bears a pair of tentacles. The foot is muscular only near its margin. The gills consist each of an axis with a single series of rather finger-shaped lamellae attached to its posterior side, though there is an indication of a second series on the anterior side of the most anterior gills.

The most interesting features of the internal anatomy of *Neopilina* relate to the muscular system, the vascular and urinogenital organs, the gut and nervous systems being less remarkable. There is a coiled radular sac and the intestine is very long and coiled as it is in some chitons. The nervous system consists of a ring round the anterior part of the gut with pedal and lateral cords on each side which are connected to each other by transverse lateropedal nerves, again as in some chitons.

The animal has two ventricles, each in its own pericardial cavity and placed right and left of the rectum on the dorsal side of the body. These receive blood from the gills and deliver it to the body. The pericardial cavities are connected to the last members of a series of excretory organs which Lemche & Wingstrand (1959) call nephridia, and which open at their other end to the pallial groove at the base of the last gills. The other members of this series of excretory organs (4–5 pairs) seem to connect with a coelom sac which lies anterior to the pericardial cavity on each side, but which does not appear to have any function apart from this. The gonads are ventral and discharge to the exterior through the middle members of the nephridial series.

Muscles run from the foot and gills to an origin on the shell. Five pairs of muscles, each double, run dorsally from the foot to the shell, and 3 further pairs pass forwards from the foot to the shell alongside the head. Each gill has also a pair of retractor muscles, one internal, one external, which likewise are attached to the underside of the shell.

Although *Neopilina* is like many molluscs in many respects it is clear from what has been said above that it departs too much in its organization from any one of the other molluscan classes to be regarded as a member of them. Its classification in the Monoplacophora along with the other animals of that group described by Knight (1952) and the elevation of that group to the rank of class follow. The animal gives us a picture of a stage much closer to the ancestral stock from which the molluscs have been derived than any other, even if it be granted that it seems more close to groups like the chitons and gastropods than to some others.

The most outstanding feature of *Neopilina*, however, and the one which seems to fit less with previous ideas of the position of the phylum within the animal kingdom is the clear indications of metamerism which it exhibits, more particularly in the gills, the excretory organs, the gonads and the musculature. These are interpreted by Lemche (1959) as proof of a closer relationship between the molluscs and the annelid-arthropod phyla than has been proposed before; in particular, in view of the presence of a digestive gland, an open circulation, a reduced coelom and the type of excretory organ known as mixonephridium in both molluscs and arthropods and the absence of digestive glands, the closed circulation, the expanded series of coelom sacs and the frequently separate coelomoducts and nephridia of annelids, he concludes that the kinship of molluscs and arthropods is much closer than that either between molluscs and annelids or even between annelids and arthropods.

The suggestion that molluscs are derived from a stem of animals possessing short segmented bodies is not new: Pelseneer (1898–99, 1906a) and Naef (1926) have both discussed it, basing their suggestion mainly on the reduplication of genital or excretory ducts of the chitons and cephalopods. It has been Lemche's good fortune to be able to study an animal exhibiting these features not just in one system but in several, and to show that the molluscan body consists of a rather longer series of segments (8 in *Neopilina*) than was originally thought likely. He may well be right, too, in considering the molluscs more closely related to arthropods than to annelids in so far as many of the more primitive arthropods are also short-bodied creatures; the elongate body of the typical annelid and its expanded coelom sacs are perhaps best regarded as modifications introduced into that group in connexion with the method of locomotion. If this idea be accepted then it may also be true that the small coelom sacs of molluscs and arthropods are primarily small, not secondarily so as was predicated by the theory of phleboedesis proposed by Lankester (1893), and that the open circulatory system found in these groups is a direct development of the primary body cavity of an ancestral platyhelminth-like animal. The almost complete loss or collapse of coelom sacs which occurs in modern molluscs and arthropods and the clearing of tissue which might otherwise have been required for support from the haemocoel are changes which are perhaps dependent upon the development of a shell and a tough exoskeleton in the modern members of these phyla.

The Monoplacophora show a number of resemblances to a second class of molluscs, the group to which the chitons, or coat-of-mail shells, belong and to which the name Loricata (= Amphineura, Polyplacophora) is given. These animals have become highly modified for a sedentary, rock-clinging life on the sea-shore and have sacrificed mobility for increased protection against wave action and the desiccating effects of the intertidal periods. They have achieved this by flattening the visceral hump so that it offers less resistance to, and less hold for, the water. As in Monoplacophora the mantle covers the whole of the animal. The size and muscular power of the foot have been increased so as to give a firm grip on the substratum to which the animal clings and the shell has been broken up into a series of 8 movably articulated sections lying one behind the other, which greatly facilitates the creeping of the animal over the rough and irregular surfaces of the rocks on which it makes its home. It also confers another benefit in that it allows the mollusc, should waves dislodge it from its rock, to roll up after the manner of a hedgehog to protect the soft underside and expose only the shell-protected back. The mantle cavity is a mere shallow groove running round the edge of the large foot, between it and the margin of the mantle. With their sedentary rock-clinging ways, the demands of chitons for oxygen can never be high, but the small mantle cavity does not allow the development of large enough gills to provide an adequate supply of oxygen even for such sluggish animals. The situation seems to have been met by increasing the number of gills so that their number is much greater than that of other possibly metameric structures in their organization (shell, urinogenital organs). As the kind of life which chitons lead might suggest, their nervous system is poorly developed, the nerve cells being mainly, as in many primitive animals, situated in the nerve trunks instead of being aggregated into ganglia as in most molluscs, and the head and foot bear neither tentacles nor eyes: this is to some extent compensated for by the development of special sensory structures called aesthetes, some of which mimic eyes in structure and function, which are developed from cells belonging to the mantle and which lie embedded in the calcareous matter of the valves of the shell.

Undoubtedly related in some way to the chitons are some worm-like animals placed in a group called the Solenogastres. These are frequently found in association with hydroid colonies, upon which they feed. The body is circular in transverse section save in the mid-ventral line along which runs a groove with a ridge within it. The body therefore approaches in transverse section the limit which a transverse section through a chiton would reach were the foot to be made progressively narrower and the mantle curved more and more ventrally to keep contact with the diminishing foot. This is, in fact, the interpretation which has been put upon these animals by the great Belgian malacologist, Pelseneer, who regarded the Solenogastres as the most advanced group of the Loricata, and thought that in the genus *Cryptoplax*, a worm-like chiton with narrow ridge-like foot and reduced shell plates, he had found an intermediate form. Most malacologists today, however, follow the lead of Thiele, Nierstrasz and Odhner, and regard these creatures as much less close to the chitons. They would, in fact, remove them from the phylum Mollusca altogether, and regard them as an early offshoot from the turbellarian-like stem from which we have derived the molluscs, which separated from the main evolutionary line at a time when some, but not all, of the essential characteristics of the phylum had been evolved. For this reason it is probably more satisfactory to follow Hoffmann (1937) and regard the Solenogastres as one class of a group called the Paramollusca, related to, but not part of the group Eumollusca, to which the true molluscs belong.

A second major evolutionary development of the eumolluscan line led to the large class called the Lamellibranchia or the bivalves. The ancestral mollusc was not an active animal—in fact one of the few current English words based on a mollusc, *sluggish*, could be better used to describe it—and this tendency was, if anything, exaggerated by the chitons. The lamellibranch molluscs have done likewise, and, with a few exceptions, spend all their life buried in sand, mud, or lying in crevices of rocks in a very slothful manner, whilst a small number, like the oyster, after a brief free-swimming life in early youth, settle down to a completely fixed existence. In order that an animal may adopt this mode of life it is essential that, somehow or other, its food shall come to it, as flies come to a spider, instead of the other way round as with most animals. Currents in the water in which animals live may well be utilized for this as in the case of barnacles, or of some insect larvae (e.g. *Simulium*, *Hydropsyche*) which sieve the currents of the water they inhabit for particles held in suspension. The lamellibranchs, however, create their own currents, using for this purpose the gills in the mantle cavity. These organs, originally evolved for respiratory purposes, also created a current of water for the ventilation of the cavity in which they lay, and this inevitably brought a certain amount of suspended particulate matter with it. Ordinarily the mollusc rejects this, but the lamellibranchs collect it and use it for food and the size of their gills increased and their structure became more complex so that they became able to pass more water through the mantle cavity and strain more food out of it. Other changes follow this new mode of life: the foot, used little, if at all, for locomotion over surfaces, loses its creeping sole and becomes axe-shaped (whence the name Pelecypoda for the group) for ploughing through sand or mud; the head, no longer used for finding, catching and manipulating food, which is now done almost automatically by the gills, becomes very much reduced in size, if not altogether lost (whence another name for the group, the Acephala). Tentacles, eyes and radula all disappear. The gills, in response to the need for increased area and complexity of structure, become relatively enormous, as must, too, the mantle cavity in which they lie, and the mantle grows down on either side of the body, which gets completely covered by it; nothing of the animal is visible in superficial view except the mantle. Since the mantle secretes shell on its outer surface wherever it goes, the body of the lamellibranch becomes totally enclosed in two large pieces of shell, one valve lying on the animal's right side and the other on its left.

The group as a whole is rather uniform in structure and most lamellibranchs are littoral or sublittoral in their habitat. A small number, like the swan mussels, have strayed via the estuaries of rivers into freshwater, and one small group, the Septibranchia, has migrated from the littoral zone down to deeper water. Their specialized mode of feeding has precluded any lamellibranch from becoming terrestrial.

The group Mollusca includes one class, the Cephalopoda, which has turned to living in a completely different way from any of the others—free-swimming life in the open waters of the ocean, where its members compete, on more or less equal terms, with such creatures as fish and the aquatic mammals. The foot of the cephalopod, originally an organ for creeping over surfaces, has grown round the head to produce the arms of the squid, beset with suckers and capable of being rapidly shot out in front of the animal to capture prey, whilst another part has become rolled up (and usually its edges fused) to form a tubular funnel leading out of the mantle cavity.

The swimming of the squid is due to the movement of fins which have developed along the sides of the visceral mass, unless the animal is disturbed, or hunting, when the water which is in the mantle cavity can be forced through the funnel by violent muscular contractions of the mantle. According to the direction in which the funnel points the mollusc will be driven through the water backwards (as would happen if it were frightened) or forwards (as when chasing prey). It will be noticed in this account of the movement of the cephalopod that the mantle is referred to as being strongly muscular. This distinct departure from the arrangement in the original molluscan stock is correlated with the reduction or loss of the shell which has occurred in all recent cephalopods with the exception of the pearly nautilus, an animal of totally different habit, which still retains a massive, external and chambered shell such as occurred in many extinct members of this class. The other recent cephalopods (*Spirula* apart) never have more than a reduced shell acting as an internal support to the dorsal (anterior) face of the visceral mass, and as an attachment for muscles, and many have none at all.

Since squids are rapidly moving animals it is not surprising to find that they are provided with well developed sense organs, their eyes, in particular, being as efficient as those of most vertebrates, their statocysts elaborate and their central nervous system probably more highly organized than that of any other invertebrate. All the ganglia are massed into a brain lying in the animal's head, supported and protected by a cartilaginous skull. In many other ways the organization of the cephalopods is at a higher level than that of other molluscs, e.g. in the presence of capillaries linking their arteries and veins, and in the use which they make of hormones to regulate their metabolism. They have adopted two main modes of life: the more primitive squids are free-swimming, pelagic creatures, often growing to an enormous size. Their bodies are thin, narrow and streamlined; those living in the deeper parts of the ocean may be provided with luminous organs. The cuttlefish, on the other hand, are a more advanced group and are littoral, though derived from pelagic ancestors. They have a more or less globular body, with no trace of shell, and they live lurking in crevices in the rocks, ready to seize with their arms any crab or prawn that swims by. To help in this the arms are frequently webbed so as to produce a bag in which the prey may be smothered; frequently, too, the web becomes an important organ of locomotion, in which case both mantle and funnel are reduced in size and importance.

The animals which are dealt with in this book belong to the class Gastropoda. The ancestral members of the group had, at first, the same tendency to a rock-clinging mode of life as had the chitons, but the whole evolutionary trend within the class has been towards greater freedom of movement and a less sedentary mode of life, ending with the production of animals devoid of shell, visceral hump and mantle cavity.

The first modification of structure which may be described as affecting the ancestral gastropod stock is an alteration in the arrangement of the mantle cavity, though it is unlikely that this occurred independently of other changes in organization. If *Neopilina* and the chitons may be taken as guides, the molluscan mantle cavity was originally a pallial groove running under the margin of the shell and mantle skirt round the head and foot and containing the gills and certain external apertures. No one part of this cavity was significantly deeper than any other. It is assumed that in the early gastropods, however, this was no longer true, for the part of the mantle cavity lying behind the visceral mass had become much deeper than the parts along its sides and anterior to it. Into this posterior enlargement the anus and the ducts from kidneys and gonad were thought to discharge and it was also to this part of the cavity that the occurrence of gills was limited, the lateral and anterior parts becoming mere gutters without contents of any importance. Because of the deepening of this part of the mantle cavity and the gathering there of organs of such diverse function as gills, anus and excretory openings, the protogastropod created for itself a number of functional problems the solving of which led to a great deal of evolutionary change within the group. Simultaneously with the development of this enlarged posterior mantle cavity it is believed that the early gastropod was also enlarging its head and foot, the former becoming increased in size to accommodate a more powerful radular apparatus than had previously been present, allowing greater quantities of food to be collected, and to house tentacles and eyes; the latter growing into a powerful muscular organ on which the mollusc could move far and relatively fast. As a consequence of the altered proportions of head, foot and visceral mass brought about by these changes the two former now appeared as the main parts of the body and not as relatively small structures projecting from the pallial groove as they had in *Neopilina*. The foot, in fact, could only be brought under the shelter of the shell because of the presence of this enlarged posterior cavity into which it could be pulled: the evolution of the gastropods into molluscs actively creeping on the sole of a powerful muscular foot and yet able to withdraw into the shell for protection depends upon the fact that the mantle cavity became excavated in this way out of the posterior face of the visceral mass and was no longer a shallow pallial groove as in *Neopilina* or the chitons. In the posterior position in which the mantle cavity lay, it was the foot which was most easily given shelter when the animal withdrew, and the head which tended to be left outside. As pointed out by Garstang (1928), the mantle cavity would clearly have had greater value as a shelter had it faced the other way and been placed looking forwards on the anterior face of the visceral mass: then, were the creature attacked, it would be the head which could be withdrawn into the mantle cavity and the thicker, tougher foot which would be left outside. A twisting, partly brought about by muscular effort and partly by a growth process, takes place during the developmental stages of all gastropods whereby the visceral hump is rotated through an angle up to 180° on the head and foot, which are unaffected by the process. These molluscs are then said to exhibit torsion; the twisting has invariably taken place in a counter-clockwise direction when the animal is viewed from above. Morton (1958) has suggested that a gastropod which has undergone torsion is also at an advantage over one which has not in that its mantle cavity is more effectively ventilated.

A second great structural trend may be traced among the gastropods: the size of the visceral mass is greatly increased to accommodate not only the viscera but also a mantle cavity big enough to shelter the gills at all times and to allow the head and foot to be withdrawn into it when the animal is disturbed or exposed to unfavourable circumstances. The posterior part of the foot, which is the last part of the body of the snail to be pulled into the shelter of the shell, and which therefore acts as an additional protection to the head, develops a plate of tough, cuticular (sometimes calcified) material on its upper side, and this operculum acts as a plug sealing the mollusc within its shell and completing the protection which it receives. Now, were this growth of the visceral mass to take place by means of a simple increase in its height, the whole visceral mass and shell would rapidly become so unwieldy as to be a hindrance rather than a benefit to its possessor. This is avoided, however, when the growth of the two sides of the visceral hump is unequal, which gives a structure coiled in a spiral, the familiar helicoid spiral of the snail shell. Normally it is the post-torsional left side of the visceral mass which grows more rapidly than the post-torsional right. Because of this differential growth rate there is much more space available for the accommodation of those organs such as gill, kidney and the like, which lie on the left than there is for their partners on the right, and this results in the right gill and other organs being often smaller than those on the other side of the body. The more tightly the visceral mass becomes coiled into a spiral the more compact does the gastropod body become, but the greater is the compression of the animal's right side which this entails, and this, in fact, becomes possible only with the complete loss of the organs on the right. There can be distinguished two grades of gastropod mollusc exhibiting torsion: a lower, in which the right and left sets of pallial organs are both present, although there may be differences of size between the right and left sets (the Archaeogastropoda or Diotocardia); and a higher grade in which the bulk of the right set has been lost (the Monotocardia or Mesogastropoda and Stenoglossa (= Neogastropoda)) so as to make a more efficient arrangement. Although shown today mainly by gastropods this tendency towards a spiral coiling of the visceral region is a very old feature of the molluscs as is indicated by the presence of a dextrally coiled larval shell in *Neopilina* and by its occurrence in cephalopods.

Most of the diotocardians alive today, especially the common littoral forms, have secondarily lost the spirally coiled shell and visceral mass characteristic of their ancestors and have simple, conical shells. This may be related to the fact that they have become adapted to a rock-clinging mode of life like chitons, and a simple, streamlined, conical shell is much less likely to be lifted off the rocks by waves than is one which is spirally coiled.

The Monotocardia include an immense variety of gastropods, the majority of which are littoral in their habitat, but they live a more active life than the archaeogastropods, their larger visceral hump permitting greater activity and, at the same time, because of the fact that the animal can now shelter during the intertidal periods by withdrawing completely into its shell, freeing them from the necessity of having to hold themselves against the surface of a rock by means of their foot after the manner of a chiton or limpet. Most are vegetarians, like the winkles, but some, like the Stenoglossa, are carnivorous. Of the British forms a few, like *Littorina neritoides*, live so high up on the beach that they are practically terrestrial and two species, *Pomatias elegans* and *Acicula fusca*, are completely so, being found in hedge-bottoms and amongst dead leaves on chalky ground in such places as the North Downs and the Chiltern Hills. A few have become at home in freshwater and may, like *Bithynia tentaculata* or *Potamopyrgus jenkinsi*, abound in appropriate places. Many have become sublittoral (many Stenoglossa). More surprisingly, a few have become adapted for a pelagic life, like the violet *Ianthina* which keeps itself at the surface of the sea by means of a float of air-bubbles entangled in mucus from the same glands on the foot as produce the slime over which more ordinary gastropods creep; or like the heteropods *Atlanta*, *Carinaria* and *Pterotrachea*, which reduce their visceral mass and shell to negligible proportions and inflate the rest of their body to form a swollen, gelatinous mass which allows them to remain at the surface of the sea.

The groups of gastropod molluscs which have just been mentioned, the Diotocardia (= Archaeogastropoda) and Monotocardia (= Mesogastropoda and Stenoglossa), show the full consequences of the process of torsion. As a result their gills, which in their untwisted ancestors lay behind the heart, projecting into the backwardly facing mantle cavity, now face forwards and lie anterior to the heart. For this reason the two groups are united in a single primary sub-division of the class Gastropoda, to which the name Prosobranchia has been given. Throughout this prosobranch group, as has already been suggested, runs a tendency to relinquish the rock-clinging habit and to adopt a more free-living one. A still more mobile life would undoubtedly be possible were the shell to be completely lost and the animal become slug-like. Clearly the shell cannot be lost without some alternative protection being given to the visceral mass: this has occurred in some gastropods with the expansion and hollowing of the foot to provide a cavity into which the visceral mass could be sunk so that it no longer appeared as a projection from the animal's back. At the same time as these changes in the organization of the animal were taking place a third one also occurred: a process of detorsion by means of which the original untwisted disposition of the parts of the body was restored. Which of these various events is the primary change and which are merely its concomitants is difficult to say: each probably contributes its own significant share to the success of the total change. The final result of this evolutionary sequence is an unshelled slug-like animal at least superficially symmetrical, though different kinds of animal show various degrees of reduction of shell, incorporation of the visceral mass in the foot and of detorsion. These gastropods, because the process of detorsion which they have undergone has restored the original relationship of gill and heart, are called the Opisthobranchia. They have all, without doubt, been derived from some monotocardian ancestor, a statement which it is possible to make because of the fact that all, whilst embryonic or larval, present a condition of torsion which has to be undone during the later stages of their development; and also because they do not possess any pallial organ belonging to the post-torsional right, a state of affairs found only in Monotocardia.

To complete this summary of the adaptive radiation of the gastropods it is necessary to mention a third group, also derived from a monotocardian ancestry, the Pulmonata. The facies of the pulmonate body is that of the monotocardian: in most a large visceral mass covered by a stout calcareous shell is still present, and there has been no detorsion, so that the mantle cavity still lies above the animal's head and faces forwards. The cavity, however, has been converted into a lung and the original gill has been completely lost, and the members of this group (which includes the common garden and most freshwater snails) breathe air. The shell is retained by these as a protection against desiccation and osmotic changes, but just as in the other evolutionary lines in gastropods, there is repeated in the pulmonates the same trend towards a naked body, a visceral hump not coiled and pulled into a foot blown out to make room for it and a slug-like shape: this gives rise to one of the most successful of all groups of molluscs, the land slugs.

# CHAPTER 2

# THE ANATOMY OF *LITTORINA* TO ILLUSTRATE PROSOBRANCH ORGANIZATION

IN order that the anatomy of a prosobranch mollusc may be understood it seems best to describe that of one animal in particular with which comparison may later be made. For this purpose we have selected the common edible winkle *Littorina littorea*.

The reasons which have led to the choice of this particular mollusc are these: it is an extremely common animal which may easily be obtained alive in any part of the country; it represents a central, rather unmodified type of prosobranch gastropod, and it is of a size which allows, with reasonable care and the help of no more than a simple lens, the checking of most of its organization by dissection.

If some living winkles are put into sea water and watched they will soon emerge from their shells and start creeping over the surface of the vessel into which they have been placed. It will be seen that the animal moves in a gliding fashion on the under surface of a wedge-shaped part of its body, which is broadly truncated at the front and tapers to a rounded point behind. This is the foot (fig. 1, f), confluent anteriorly with the head, which is a more or less cylindrical structure projecting forwards above its front end. Towards its posterior end the head carries a pair of laterally placed tentacles (t), one on on each side. These are delicate, tapering, finger-shaped structures which are mobile and contractile and are kept in frequent movement as the animal creeps. At the base of each, on the outer side, is a cushion-like bulge on which a dark spot with a lighter halo around it may be seen. This is the eye stalk, which has become fused to the outer side of the base of the tentacle, and the dark spot on it (e) is the eye. The tentacle, which is tactile and olfactory, is thus the seat of three major senses. At the end of the snout (sn) projecting in front of the tentacles lies the mouth, bordered by lips (fig. 3, ol) which are complete dorsally, but interrupted in the mid-ventral line.

On the dorsal surface of the foot posteriorly will be seen an oval, plate-like structure. This may be difficult to see because of the way in which the shell lies over it, but if the shell be gently pushed aside the animal will continue to creep and permit the hinder half of the foot to be seen. The disc of material which lies here is the operculum (op, figs. 1, 2), which serves to block the opening of the shell after the mollusc has retracted within (fig. 5). In the winkle it is made of conchiolin, and grows as the animal grows by the addition of strips of material along the edge which faces forwards on the extended foot. Here the operculum dips into a groove (oge, fig. 4) which runs transversely across the dorsal surface of the foot and it is in this that new material is secreted. The under surface of the operculum is attached to the skin of the special lobe of the dorsal part of the foot which carries it, which is called the operculigerous disc (opd), and to part of its under surface there runs a slip of muscle (columellar muscle) the other end of which is fastened to the columella of the shell; by contraction of this the operculum will be pulled against the mouth of the shell, which it fits accurately. The edge of the operculum which lies anteriorly as the winkle crawls comes against the columella of the shell (col) when the animal retracts: it is therefore called the columellar edge (ce). Similarly the edge of the operculum which is posterior when the winkle is extended comes against the outer lip of the mouth of the shell when the snail is retracted. It is therefore called the labial edge (lee). The side of the operculum on the animal's right when extended comes to lie against the upper part of the mouth of the shell in the retracted state, and that on the winkle's left against the lower part; these are known as the sutural (sus) and siphonal (sis) edges respectively.

The visceral hump of the animal is completely covered by the shell and the two structures have the same shape, though the shell is more capacious than the visceral mass

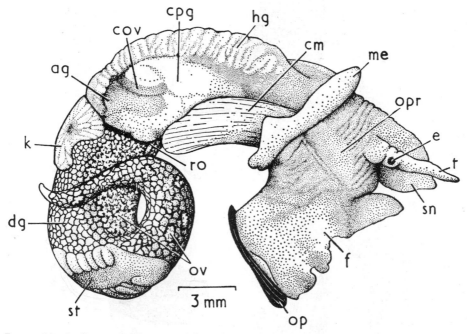

FIG. 1.—*Littorina littorea*: female removed from shell and seen from the right side.
ag, albumen gland; cm, columellar muscle; cov, covering gland; cpg, capsule gland; dg, digestive gland; e, eye on eye stalk; f, foot; hg, hypobranchial gland; k, kidney; me, mantle edge; op, operculum; opr, ovipositor; ov, ovary; ro, renal section of oviduct; sn, snout; st, stomach; t, tentacle.

since it accommodates not only that part of the body of the animal but the head and foot as well when these are retracted. The shell is made of calcium carbonate in a matrix of the protein conchiolin. The calcareous part of the shell is arranged in different layers, and the whole is covered by a layer of conchiolin known as the periostracum. In some gastropods it is very obvious, but this is not the case in *Littorina littorea*. The periostracum and the outer layer of calcareous matter can normally be added to only at the mouth of the shell, but the innermost layers are secreted by the entire surface of the visceral mass. This is necessary in order that the older parts of the shell, which were produced when the animal was young and small, should be thick enough and strong enough to protect the body of the winkle when it has grown larger and older. In theory there is perhaps no limit to the size to which gastropods may grow, but in practice there is a size which

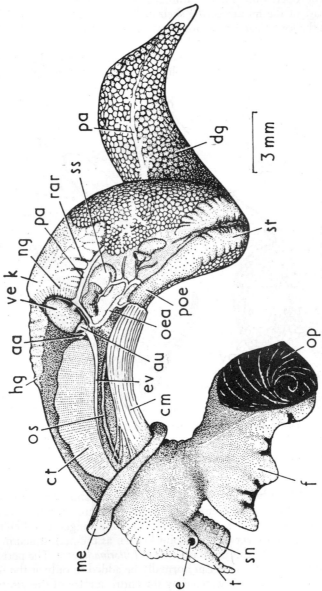

FIG. 2.—*Littorina littorea*: animal removed from shell and seen from the left side.
aa, anterior aorta; au, auricle; cm, columellar muscle; ct, ctenidium; dg, digestive gland; e, eye on eye stalk; ev, efferent branchial vessel; f, foot; hg, hypobranchial gland; k, kidney; me, mantle edge; ng, nephridial gland; oea, oesophageal artery; op, operculum; os, osphradium; pa, posterior aorta; poe, posterior oesophagus; rar, renal artery; sn, snout; ss, style sac region of stomach leading forward to intestine; st, stomach; t, tentacle; ve, ventricle.

is not exceeded by each species and when this is reached straightforward growth of the shell ceases, though other growth—in particular general thickening and the formation of teeth around the mouth—may continue for a while.

The shell of *Littorina littorea* (fig. 5) is more or less conical in shape and consists in essence of a tube of gradually expanding diameter coiled in a helicoid spiral, the direction of coiling being right-handed, that is, in the same direction as the movement of the hands of a clock. The tube is closed at its inner end, but is open at its outer end, and this opening is the mouth, through which the body of the winkle can be protruded for movement and feeding. The growth of the tube is so arranged that each successive turn

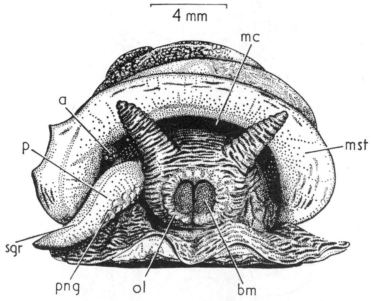

FIG. 3.—*Littorina littorea:* male, removed from shell, in anterior view. The mouth is half open. a, anus; bm, buccal mass; mc, mantle cavity; mst, mantle skirt; ol, outer lip; p, penis; png, penial glands; sgr, seminal groove.

of the spiral (a whorl) is applied to the outer surface of the previous one, which it partly conceals (fig. 6). In any one shell, therefore, there will be one turn of the spiral—the largest—the outer side of which is completely visible. This turn ends at the mouth of the shell and is the youngest (most recently secreted) part. In it, when the winkle is retracted, will be found the animal's head and foot, that is, all the body except the visceral hump: for this reason it is called the body whorl (bw, and see fig. 34). The remaining whorls of the spiral, of each of which only a part is visible, constitute the spire of the shell. The line of contact where two whorls meet is called a suture (sts).

As the animal lies in its shell the outer part of each whorl corresponds to the dorsal surface of the body, and the inner to the ventral. The lower side of each turn of the shell corresponds to the left side of the visceral mass and the upper or apical to the right— these, it will be remembered (p. 11), must have started originally the other way round and have been brought into this new position by the process of torsion. As a result of the dextral coiling of the visceral hump, much more space is available on the left-hand side of that part of the body than there is on the right, and this is reflected in the arrangement of the organs which occur there, as will be seen below.

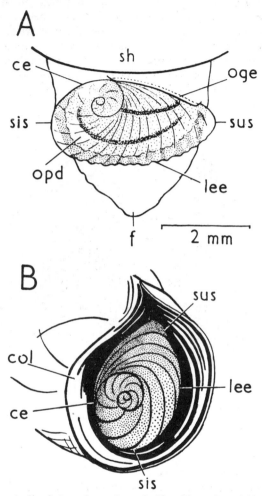

FIG. 4.—*Littorina littorea:* A, dorsal view of posterior end of foot of creeping winkle to show relationships of operculum; B, mouth of shell to show relationships of operculum when winkle is retracted.

ce, columellar edge of operculum; col, columella of shell; f, foot; lee, labial edge of operculum; oge, opercular groove of foot; opd, operculigerous disc seen through operculum; sh, shell; sis, siphonal side of operculum; sus, sutural side of operculum.

Where the inner sides of the spirally coiled whorls are brought into contact with one another there results a more or less solid central pillar round which the whorls of the shell rotate. This is the columella (col). If the contact between the concave sides of successive whorls is very intimate then it will be solid; if less so, the columella may be hollow with a small part of external space lying in its centre and opening to the outside at its base. This opening is the umbilicus (u).

The mouth of the shell is formed of an outer lip (fig. 5, ol) on the animal's left and an inner lip (il)—often inconspicuous against the columella—on its right.

The shell is added to as the animal grows, and except in a few cases, of which the winkle is not one, loses no part during its life-time. The initial shell which was present during larval life, the protoconch, forms the extreme summit of the spire and often is different in appearance, or texture, or architecture, from the shell secreted by the meta-morphosed animal: in most winkles it will have been worn away. The shell usually exhibits changes in rate of growth marked by lines (grl) representing successive positions of the mouth: these lie parallel to the columellar axis and are described as vertical. In addition, the shell of the edible winkle exhibits a number of lines which run spiralwise

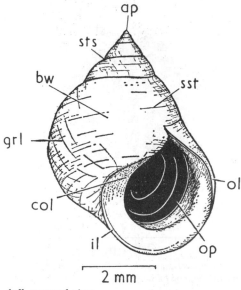

Fig. 5.—*Littorina littorea:* shell, apertural view.
ap, apex; bw, body whorl; col, columella; grl, growth line; il, inner lip; ol, outer lip; op, operculum; sst, spiral stria; sts, suture.

down the shell and are obviously due to slight differences in the rate of secretion or to irregularities of the outer lip itself. These lines are called spiral striae (sst). In the case of the edible winkle the shell is rather smooth and neither striae nor vertical lines are pronounced. The body whorl is large, as it must be when such a large body has to be enclosed, but the rest of the shell, the spire, is rather short, tapering smoothly to the apex. The sutures are visible but are not deeply marked and the upper whorls have flat sides so that the spire is rather regularly conical. The mouth is large, somewhat com-pressed from side to side and the outer lip tends to run up the body whorl so as to approach it tangentially. There is no umbilicus. The whole shell is solidly built, is of a dark colour, with brown streaks usually clearly visible near the lips; there is usually a white patch on the columellar side.

Young shells have the outer lip with a slightly crenulated margin, but with sexual maturity it becomes much thicker, and this, and possibly the effect of wear on a shell the rate of growth of which has been reduced, causes it to be smooth.

When a living edible winkle is observed moving, the head and foot are extended outside the shell, but the visceral mass does not leave its shelter: the only other part visible is a fold of tissue resting against the inside of the mouth of the shell. This is the edge of the mantle skirt (mst, fig. 3), which forms a fold round the body of the animal at the point of union of visceral mass (on one side) and the head and foot (on the other). Between the mantle skirt and the underlying body lies a space, which is the mantle cavity (mc, fig. 3), and the depth of this will be the same as the length of the mantle skirt. Further observation of the living animal will show that, except when it is completely withdrawn into the shell, a current of water passes into the cavity on the left side, and leaves it on the right.

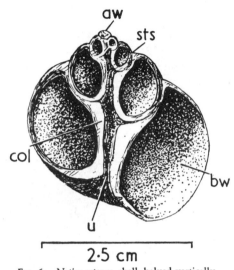

FIG. 6.—*Natica catena:* shell, halved vertically.
aw, apical whorl of shell; bw, body whorl; col, columella; sts, suture; u, open umbilicus.

To examine the extent and contents of the mantle cavity after the winkle has been removed from its shell it should be opened by a cut through the mantle skirt which starts medianly at the anterior end and bears to the animal's left posteriorly. If the two halves of the mantle skirt are then pulled apart the inside of the mantle cavity will be visible (see fig. 7). It is low in a dorsoventral direction (see fig. 8), broad at the mouth and tapering to a narrow inner end. Its floor is formed by the dorsal integument of the head and anterior part of the visceral mass and its roof by the mantle skirt. All the structures which lie partly in the head-foot and partly in the visceral mass make their way from the one part of the body to the other by a narrow connexion ventral to the innermost end of the mantle cavity. Except at its free edge the mantle skirt is everywhere delicate, but all the organs of importance in the mantle cavity lie on it, and are developments from it.

At the left side lies the gill or ctenidium (ct, figs. 2, 7), which has the form of an elongated axis lying along the mantle skirt in an antero-posterior direction from the innermost part of the cavity almost to its mouth. Attached to the axis is a series of branchial leaflets (blf, fig. 8), 50–60 in number. Each of these has a triangular shape, with one side of the triangle fused to the mantle skirt, and they all hang into the mantle cavity like a series of pages from a book. Along the axis of the ctenidium lies a blood vessel, the efferent branchial vessel (ebv, figs. 7, 8), which may be traced back from the

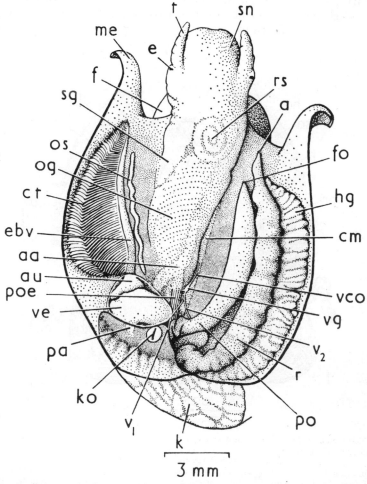

FIG. 7.—*Littorina littorea:* animal removed from shell and mantle cavity opened mid-dorsally to display its contents. Some other structures are seen by transparency.

a, anus; aa, anterior aorta; au, auricle; cm, columellar muscle; ct, ctenidium; e, eye on eye stalk; ebv, efferent branchial vessel; f, foot; fo, female opening; hg, hypobranchial gland; k, kidney; ko, kidney opening; me, mantle edge; og, oesophageal gland; os, osphradium; pa, posterior aorta; po, pallial oviduct; poe, posterior oesophagus; r, rectum; rs, radular sac; sg, salivary gland; sn, snout; t, tentacle; $v_1$, nerve to heart and kidney; $v_2$, genital nerve; vco, visceral connective; ve, ventricle; vg, visceral ganglion.

posterior end of the ctenidial axis to the heart (au, ve, figs. 2, 7). Blood reaches the branchial leaflets by way of small afferent branchial vessels (av, fig. 8) which enter the right edge of the attached side of each leaflet from the mantle skirt: they are too small to be visible except with high magnification. The gill lamellae contain a network of blood spaces through which the blood travels from afferent to efferent vessel. Each lamella is ciliated and the leaflets are collectively responsible for driving water from the infrabranchial space (ibr, fig. 8) which lies below and to the left of the gill, into the suprabranchial space (sbr) above it and to the right. This is, in fact, the driving force of the current which enters the mantle cavity on the left and leaves it on the right and which has already been referred to.

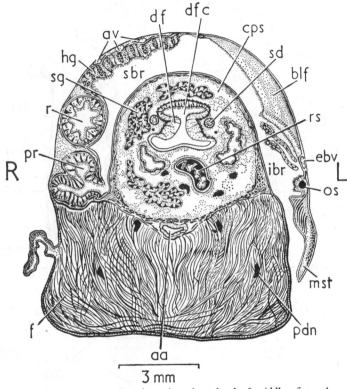

FIG. 8.—*Littorina littorea:* transverse section through male at level of middle of mantle cavity.  R, L, mark right and left sides.

aa, anterior aorta;  av, afferent branchial vessels;  blf, branchial leaflet;  cps, cephalopedal blood sinus;  df, dorsal folds of oesophagus;  dfc, dorsal food channel of oesophagus;  ebv, efferent branchial vessel;  f, foot;  hg, hypobranchial gland;  ibr, infrabranchial part of mantle cavity;  mst, mantle skirt; os, osphradium;  pdn, pedal nerve;  pr, prostate gland;  r, rectum;  rs, radular sac;  sbr, suprabranchial part of mantle cavity;  sd, salivary duct;  sg, salivary gland.

Parallel to the ctenidial axis and along its left side runs a narrow pigmented ridge. This is the osphradium (os, figs. 7, 8) one of the animal's major sense organs, and it is believed to test the water entering the mantle cavity, although the precise nature of the testing is still not known. It may be a straightforward chemical testing, or one discriminating the amount of suspended particulate matter in the water washing its surface, or perhaps both these things at once. The osphradium is certainly well placed for this.

To the right of the ctenidium lies a stretch of mantle skirt which shows little specialization immediately alongside the gill. Microscopic examination, however, reveals numerous mucous cells here and towards the right, where the epithelium is puckered and ridged, their number increases greatly. (The puckering occurs only in the edible winkle, not in other British species of *Littorina*.) This area is the hypobranchial or mucous gland (hg) and it produces secretion for trapping and cementing particulate matter sucked into the mantle cavity in the respiratory water current, prior to its expulsion on the right.

Still more to the right will be observed a tube running parallel to the right edge of the hypobranchial gland. This is the rectum (r), which emerges from the visceral hump at the inner end of the mantle cavity and runs along the mantle skirt to open at the anus (a) placed near the mouth of the cavity. To the right of the rectum lies the terminal part of the reproductive duct. This duct differs according to whether the winkle is male or female, and whether the animal is examined during the breeding season or not.

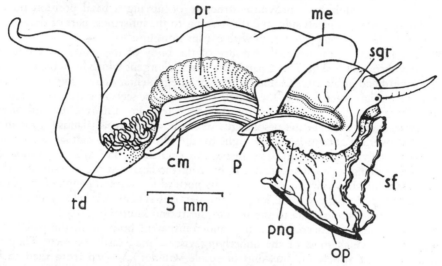

FIG. 9.—*Littorina littorea:* male, removed from shell, to show genital duct.
cm, columellar muscle; me, mantle edge; op, operculum; p, penis; png, penial glands; pr, prostate; sf, sole of foot; sgr, sperm groove; td, testicular duct acting as vesicula seminalis.

Outside the breeding season the reproductive apparatus becomes much reduced, to be re-formed when the next reproductive period approaches. In males the duct from the testis opens to the mantle cavity by a pore situated deeply within it on the right of the rectum. This discharges to a ciliated groove which runs forward along the floor of the mantle cavity until it reaches a position posterior and ventral to the right cephalic tentacle, where it runs on to the penis (p, figs. 3, 9, 10), a large, curved, paddle-shaped structure. Within the mantle cavity the groove traverses the centre of a rich glandular field which is the prostate gland (pr, figs. 9, 10).

In females conditions differ in that the section of the duct which lies on the mantle skirt is not open to the mantle cavity as in males, but is a closed tube and because of this the female aperture lies near the anus. This section of the female duct is very glandular, especially in the breeding season, when the capsule gland (cpg, fig. 1), which secretes the bulk of the wall of the capsule within which the eggs are laid, forms a large, chalk-white mass lying ventral to the rectum in the inner half of the mantle cavity. Alongside it on the outer (shell) side are two other associated glands: one of these is the albumen gland (ag), which is of a translucent buff colour and secretes the albuminous fluid in which each egg is embedded in the capsule, and the other is a special area of the capsule gland, apricot in colour (cov), which produces the covering around the egg and its albumen (ec, figs. 20IC, F). There is, of course, no penis in the female, but there is a structure occupying a corresponding position on the right side of the head, in the form of an unpigmented glandular tract running down the side towards the foot. This is the ovipositor (opr, fig. 1), a function of which is to carry the egg capsule out of the mantle cavity and launch it on its pelagic life. The precise use of the glands is not known: they must be, in part, simply lubricating, but they have also been held to form the tough outer layer of the capsule wall.

The only other structure to be directly connected with the mantle cavity is the kidney (k, figs. 1, 2, 7), a pinkish or brownish structure occupying a basal position on the visceral hump towards the left side, and discharging to the innermost part of the mantle cavity by a slit-like opening (ko, fig. 7) with conspicuous lips.

A certain amount of the internal anatomy of the body of the winkle is visible by transparency through the skin. This is particularly true of organs which lie in the posterior part of the head and in the visceral mass where the integumentary coverings are delicate. Through the unpigmented floor of the mantle cavity may be seen a number of structures which are drawn in fig. 7. These are mostly connected with the anterior end of the alimentary tract and of them the oesophagus with the oesophageal glands (og) is most conspicuous, overlaid anteriorly on the right by the spirally coiled radular sac (rs) and on the left by salivary glands (sg). The anterior or cephalic aorta (aa) is also visible by transparency running forward and to the right from the heart. At the innermost end of the floor of the mantle cavity there may also be noticed the visceral ganglia (vg) placed at the posterior end of the visceral loop of the nervous system (see below) and nerves may be traced from the ganglia to the rectum, heart and kidney ($v_1$, $v_2$).

The visceral hump is covered by a thin and transparent body wall, the pallium or mantle, through which most of the underlying viscera may easily be seen. They are shown in figs. 1, 2 which are drawings of edible winkles removed from their shells. When viewed from the left (fig. 2) the basal part of the visceral hump is seen to be occupied by the pericardial cavity containing the heart (au, ve), which receives the efferent branchial vessel (ev) from the ctenidial axis, and which sends off an anterior aorta (aa) to the head and foot and a posterior aorta to the organs lying in the visceral hump (pa). Behind the pericardial cavity (i.e. further towards the apex of the spire) is the kidney (k) and that part of it which borders the pericardial cavity may be picked out from the rest by its lighter colour as the nephridial gland (ng). The remainder of the visceral hump is mainly occupied by the tubules of the digestive gland (dg), dark brown in colour. Should the animal be breeding, however, greater or lesser areas of gonad will lie over the digestive gland, especially on the columellar (concave) side of the whorls, and obscure it from sight. The gonad (te, fig. 10; ov, fig. 1) is grey or grey-green in colour in males, but yellow or pinkish in females. On the basal, convex region of the visceral mass parts of the stomach (st, figs. 1, 2) are visible, and quite ventrally, underneath the mantle cavity, is the white band-shaped mass of the columellar muscle (cm), originating on a short length of the columella of the shell and running into the head, the foot, on to the operculum and into the mantle skirt to pull these parts into the shell for protection when the animal is disturbed.

We may now turn to an account of the internal anatomy of the winkle. This may easily be investigated by opening the body by a cut through the mid-line of the floor of the mantle cavity. The cut should be extended forwards to the tip of the snout and backwards towards the inner end of the mantle cavity, though care must be taken in the region of the visceral ganglia. The pericardial cavity may be opened together with the kidney, but it is unprofitable to attempt the dissection of the upper visceral mass unless particular information regarding such structures as lie there is being sought.

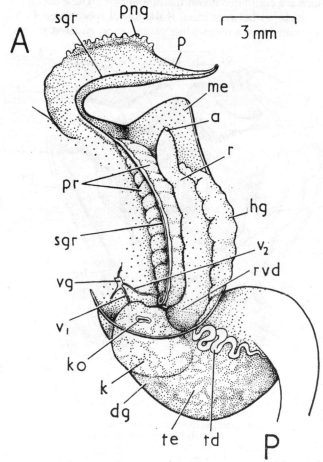

FIG. 10.—*Littorina littorea*: dissection to show male reproductive system. A, P, mark anterior and posterior ends.

a, anus; dg, digestive gland; hg, hypobranchial gland; k, kidney; ko, kidney opening to mantle cavity; me, mantle edge; p, penis; png, penial glands; pr, prostate; r, rectum; rvd, renal section of vas deferens; sgr, sperm groove; td, testicular duct acting as vesicula seminalis; te, testis; $v_1$, renoperi-cardial nerve; $v_2$, rectal and genital nerve; vg, visceral ganglion.

The mouth lies at the apex of the snout (sn, figs. 1, 2) and is bordered by lips (ol, figs. 3, 11). Dorsally and laterally these are continuous, fleshy, ridged structures, but ventrally they turn in towards the first part of the gut, the oral tube (ot, fig. 11). This is very short and is bounded internally by a ridge projecting into the cavity from the ventral and lateral surfaces, but not dorsally: this is the inner lip (il) and on its inner side lies the buccal cavity (bcv). The latter is a globular chamber connected to the oral tube in front and leading to two tubes posteriorly: of these the upper is the oesophagus (aoe) and the lower the radular sac. The roof of the buccal cavity is tied to the body wall by numerous strands of muscle. Internally its side walls show some unimportant, irregular folds, but the roof has two prominent longitudinal folds along it, one to either side of the mid-line, which are continued down the oesophagus. These are the dorsal folds (df), and the channel which lies between them is the dorsal food channel (dfc). The floor of the buccal cavity is raised into a tongue-like prominence, covered with a shining cuticle,

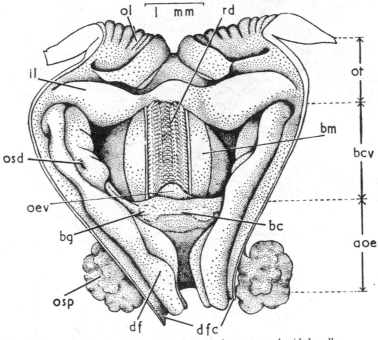

FIG. 11.—*Littorina littorea:* buccal cavity and anterior oesophagus opened mid-dorsally.
aoe, anterior oesophagus; bc, buccal commissure, seen by transparency; bcv, buccal cavity; bg, buccal ganglion, seen by transparency; bm, buccal mass; df, dorsal fold of oesophagus; dfc, dorsal food channel; il, inner lip; oev, oesophageal valve; ol, outer lip; osd, opening of salivary duct; osp, oesophageal pouch; ot, oral tube; rd, radula on upper surface of buccal mass.

fused to the floor of the cavity posteriorly but free at its anterior tip. This is the buccal mass or odontophore (bm, figs. 3, 11), a complex mass of muscles attached in part to skeletal structures called cartilages, from their histological resemblance to the cartilage of vertebrates, and in part to the body wall. It is a very mobile structure which is pushed in and out of the mouth, turned up and down and twisted right and left as the winkle feeds. Over the median part of its mid-dorsal surface runs the radula (rd, fig. 11), a belt of cuticular material bearing teeth in regular transverse and longitudinal rows. These teeth are formed at the inner end of the radular sac and are gradually moved forward along the sac and on to the surface of the odontophore as those already there are lost or broken in use. The radular sac ends blindly and lies coiled in a spiral dorsal to the oeso-phagus on the right side of the body. In length it may be as much as 50 mm or about twice the shell length. Each transverse row (fig. 12) contains a definite number of teeth of several shapes and sizes: these comprise a single medianly placed central or rachidian tooth with 3 large cusps on it (rh), flanked on each side by 3 rather similarly shaped teeth each with a number of cusps on its edge. The most median of these teeth, which is next to the rachidian, is called a lateral tooth (lat); the two others are marginal teeth (mrt). The arrangement of each transverse radular row is identical with that of its neighbours in front and behind and it can be represented by a formula

2 marginal—1 lateral—1 rachidian—1 lateral—2 marginal

or, more simply,

2—1—1—1—2.

All the cusps on all the teeth are curved so that they point inwards. As the odontophore is moved in and out of the mouth the radula is moved backward and forwards over the angled edge at the tip of the odontophore. Anterior to this edge the marginal and lateral teeth are spread sideways; posterior to it they are folded in towards the mid-line. As the

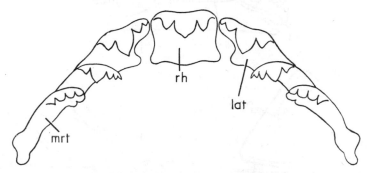

FIG. 12.—*Littorina littorea:* one transverse row of radular teeth. lat, lateral tooth; mrt, marginal tooth; rh, rachidian tooth.

radula is moved backwards and forwards the teeth spring from the one position to the other—on the inward movement moving towards the middle line. As they carry out this movement the recurved cusps rake detritus or algae into the mid-line where it gets caught on the cusps of the median rachidian teeth. These form a conveyor belt carrying the food into the gut. The process is lubricated by saliva and the two salivary glands (sg, fig. 14) which lie dorsal to the oesophagus, on the animal's left, discharge their secretion by ducts (sd, figs. 8, 14) which enter the buccal cavity at points (osd, fig. 11) on the latero-dorsal walls just lateral to the dorsal folds. The secretion is mainly mucus.

The next section of the alimentary tract is the oesophagus, which leads from the buccal cavity (in the head) to the stomach (in the visceral mass). It therefore traverses the region of the body which has been affected by torsion and it will be as well to consider what the effects of this have been before describing what is actually visible in a dissected winkle.

The pre-torsional gastropod (fig. 13A) possessed a visceral hump with the mantle cavity excavated from its posterior face. The anus (a) discharged into this cavity and was medianly placed. Between mouth and anus the oesophagus (aoe, moe, poe) ran dorsally to the stomach (st), which lay near the summit of the visceral mass, and the intestine (i) descended again to the more ventral anus. The gut was therefore U-shaped, the U being inverted and the mouth and anus marking the ends of its limbs. When torsion occurred the visceral mass rotated in an anticlockwise direction through 180° on an axis which we may suppose passed vertically through its centre, so that the posteriorly placed anus was brought forward. If, as in figs. 13B and C, we draw this new arrangement in its simplest form, it will be realized that, in order to keep the dorsal side of the oesophagus in connexion with the dorsal side of the stomach and intestine, it is necessary to introduce a twist in the course of the gut. Thus in the basal part of the visceral hump the original

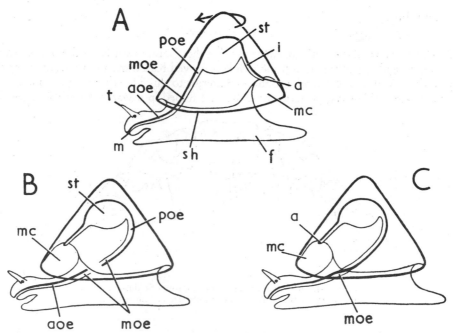

FIG. 13.—Diagrams to show the effect of torsion upon the gut. A, pretorsional stage; C, after torsion; B, for explanation see text. The morphologically dorsal surface of the gut is marked by a thicker line. a, anus; aoe, anterior oesophagus; f, foot; i, intestine; m, mouth; mc, mantle cavity; moe, mid-oesophagus; poe, posterior oesophagus; sh, shell; st, stomach; t, tentacle.

dorsal surface comes to lie topographically ventral, and the original ventral surface dorsal. This twist occurs in the oesophagus of the prosobranch mollusc, and as the oesophagus happens to be a rather elaborate part of the gut with clearly differentiated dorsal and ventral sides, the twisting is particularly easy to see.

The first part of the oesophagus, which may be called the anterior oesophagus (aoe, figs. 11, 13, 14), lies anterior to the region of torsion and is therefore normally disposed. It begins at the posterior end of the buccal cavity and dorsally, apart from the continuations of the two folds and food channel, there is nothing remarkable about its structure. Two oesophageal pouches (osp, figs. 11, 14), however, open from its lateral walls anteriorly, one on each side. They are hollow, spherical structures with lobulated walls, of unknown significance. At the posterior end of this section the gut is surrounded by a nerve ring (fig. 14).

The next part is the mid-oesophagus (moe, figs. 13, 14) and it is this which is twisted by torsion. The twist is such that the mid-dorsal line of the gut curves over to the left and eventually on to the underside, whilst the morphological mid-ventral part curves up the right side until it lies above. The course of the twist is easy to follow because the

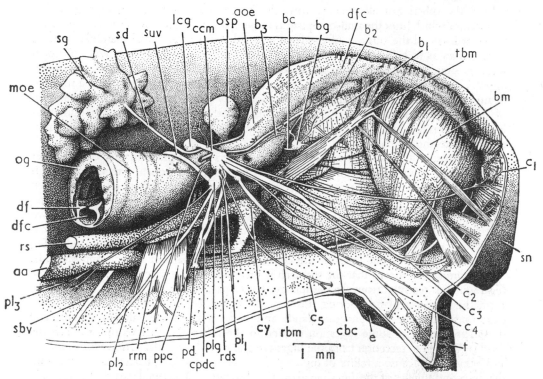

FIG. 14.—*Littorina littorea*: dissection of head from the right side. The head has been opened by a cut in a right dorsolateral position and the right body wall and tentacle pulled ventrally. The oesophageal pouch and salivary gland on the right side have been removed.

aa, anterior aorta; aoe, anterior oesophagus; $b_1$, $b_2$, $b_3$, buccal nerves; bc, buccal commissure; bg, buccal ganglion; bm, buccal mass; $c_1$, dorsal labial nerve; $c_2$, lateral labial nerve; $c_3$, ventral labial nerve; $c_4$, tentacular nerve; $c_5$, optic nerve; cbc, cerebrobuccal connective; ccm, cerebral commissure; cpdc, cerebropedal connective; cy, cephalic aorta; df, dorsal folds of oesophagus now twisted to mid-ventral position; dfc, dorsal food channel; e, eye; lcg, left cerebral ganglion; moe, mid-oesophagus; og, oesophageal gland; osp, oesophageal pouch; $pl_1$, $pl_2$, $pl_3$, pleural nerves; pd, pedal ganglion; plg, right pleural ganglion; ppc, pleuropedal connective; rbm, retractor muscles of buccal mass; rds, radular sinus; rrm, retractor muscles of radular sac; rs, radular sac in radular sinus; sbv, sub-oesophageal part of visceral loop; sd, salivary duct; sg, salivary gland; sn, snout; suv, supra-oesophageal part of visceral loop; t, tentacle; tbm, tensor muscles of buccal mass.

morphologically mid-dorsal part of the oesophagus bears the food channel and its two edging folds and these can easily be traced from an anatomically mid-dorsal position at the anterior end of this section to a mid-ventral position at the posterior end. The mid-ventral line is similarly marked by other structures to be mentioned below and its curvature may also be easily followed (fig. 14).

The mid-oesophagus is an elongated spindle-shaped structure lying between the nerve ring in front and the posterior end of the mantle cavity, where it narrows to join the posterior oesophagus (poe, fig. 7). The swelling of this section of the alimentary tract is due to the presence of oesophageal glands in the lateral and ventral walls. These are flung into a series of folds so that they present the appearance of a series of compartments one behind the other, but all opening towards the central axis of the oesophagus. The epithelium which lines the mid-oesophagus is ciliated. The direction of the ciliary beat is backwards on all the surfaces of the food channel, but in the lateral glandular areas is arranged so as to bring their secretion into the food channel, where it will be mixed with the food passed back from the mouth. This secretion has been shown to contain digestive enzymes, so that at the posterior end of the mid-oesophagus there is a mixture of mucus, food particles and digestive enzymes ready to be passed into the next section of the gut. This is the posterior oesophagus, a rather narrow tube with numerous longitudinal ridges and no special glandular equipment, which runs up the visceral mass to open into the stomach.

The stomach (st, figs. 1, 2, 15) lies entirely in the visceral mass, mainly on the outer (convex) side towards the animal's left and is an elongated pouch extending through more than one whorl of the spiral. The oesophagus opens into it about half way between its two ends (OA, fig. 15), and the intestine (I) leaves the lower end, the upper end being blind. Internally the cavity of the upper half of the stomach is almost divided into two parts by a tall longitudinal fold (FF) which ends near the summit. The oesophagus opens into the chamber on one side of this fold, whilst the ducts of the digestive gland (DD), three in number, and the intestine are connected to the chamber on the opposite side. This arrangement means that the stomach is provided with a caecum, along which the food which is received from the oesophagus has to pass before it is exposed to secretions from the digestive gland. During this time, however, the food is in contact with the secretions from the oesophageal glands and perhaps from the salivary glands, and doubtless, therefore, some digestion occurs. In the other chamber of the stomach the food is exposed to secretion from the digestive gland, and muscular action will mix food and enzyme and cause a reflux of digested food and, perhaps, of particulate matter into the ducts and tubules of the digestive gland for absorption. The distal part of the stomach, leading forwards to the intestine, may be distinguished as the style sac. Along its length run two ridges, the major (T1) and minor (T2) typhlosoles, with the intestinal groove (GI) between them. This originates at the point where the ducts of the digestive gland open into the stomach. The indigestible residue of a meal is forced into the style sac of the stomach where it comes under the influence of two sets of ciliary currents, one, on the typhlosoles, which tends to drive the mass towards the intestine; the other, on the remaining areas of the walls, which rotates the contents. As a consequence the indigestible remains are gradually compacted with mucus into a rod of faecal material and passed out of the style sac into the intestine. There will also be a certain amount of waste material which is derived from the digestive gland: this may be particulate indigestible matter which has accidentally got into the ducts of the gland along with matter for absorption, or it may be the indigestible remains of particulate food ingested during intracellular digestion (if such occurs in *Littorina littorea*), or it may be true excretory matter which is discharged from the digestive gland cells. Whatever its origin, it will escape from the ducts of the digestive gland into the intestinal groove and so make its way along the style sac and become incorporated in the rod of faecal matter which enters the intestine.

The intestine is a tube of smaller diameter than the style sac of the stomach, with

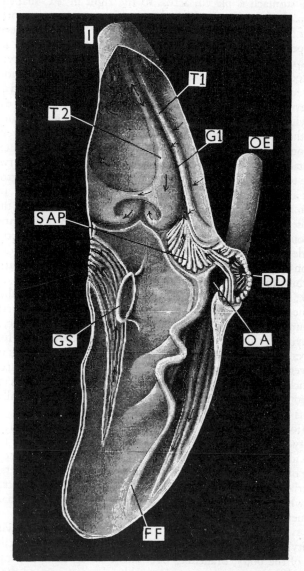

FIG. 15.—*Littorina littorea:* stomach, opened longitudinally. Arrows show direction of ciliary currents. DD, opening of ducts from digestive gland; FF, longitudinal fold; G₁, intestinal groove; GS, gastric shield; I, intestine; OA, opening of oesophagus to stomach; OE, oesophagus; SAP, posterior sorting area; T₁, major typhlosole; T₂, minor typhlosole.

numerous longitudinal folds running along its walls. It runs from the left side of the body, where the stomach is placed, across to the right in a C-shaped loop and there enters the right part of the mantle skirt, along which it passes anteriorly to open at the anus. The rod of faecal matter which it receives from the style sac becomes segmented into oval faecal pellets which are still further compacted by intestinal secretions, so that when discharged they do not easily disintegrate within the mantle cavity.

Molluscs are coelomate animals, but the extent of the coelomic cavities is small, being primarily confined, as in a platyhelminth, to the cavities of the gonad (though this may be delayed in development) and the ducts which connect this to the exterior. Molluscs differ from platyhelminths in that a circulatory system has evolved for the transport of material round the body, and the heart which this demands has developed in a cavity related to the gonads and provided with ducts connecting it to the exterior. There is therefore a genital section of the coelom, a pericardial section, and two pairs of ducts connecting these to the exterior. These are coelomoducts, that is, outgrowths of the wall of the coelomic cavity towards the animal's skin with which they fuse and through which they open. Their primary function is to convey germ cells to the outside. In the gastropod molluscs the genital part of the coelom does not develop separate coelomoducts so there is only one pair which open, internally, to the pericardial portion of the coelom and to the mantle cavity externally. In prosobranchs like the winkle one of these coelomoducts, that on the animal's post-torsional right is used for the carrying of eggs or spermatozoa, whilst the other becomes the kidney.

The kidney (k, figs. 2, 7) lies on the left side of the visceral hump abutting against the upper end of the mantle cavity to which it opens by a slit-like aperture (ko, fig. 7). Internally it communicates by means of a very fine ciliated canal (rpc, fig. 16) with the pericardial cavity. The kidney is a roomy sac with walls differentiated for varied purposes at different places. On the right there projects into the cavity a series of lobulated folds (kf), mainly covered by an excretory epithelium resting on blood spaces, but with some ciliated cells which produce currents leading excretory matter towards the outer opening, which is guarded by a sphincter muscle and may be opened by radially running dilator muscles. Over its lips beats a strong outward ciliary current.

The left anterior wall forms part of the nephridial gland (ng, fig. 2) which borders the pericardial cavity. Here a series of blind diverticula opens (ngo, fig. 16) from the main cavity of the kidney and pushes into blood spaces, so that a close intermingling is achieved. Some of the cells of this nephridial gland are excretory, others are again ciliated and drive material extracted from the blood into the kidney for excretion. The details of the way in which excretory and osmoregulatory functions are shared by these two parts of the kidney is not certain.

The vascular system of *Littorina littorea* comprises the heart, lying within the coelomic pericardial cavity, and a number of vessels and spaces. Arteries distribute the blood to the main parts of the body, branching over and over again until they are minute, and end by pouring their contents into a series of blood spaces around the main organs and in between the muscles and connective tissue layers of the body. From this series of spaces other vessels take the blood to the excretory and respiratory organs, whence it is returned to the heart. The vascular system of the winkle differs from the more familiar vertebrate pattern in a number of important respects: the heart receives, primarily, oxygenated blood to circulate to the body and is, therefore, a systemic heart whereas that of the vertebrate is originally a branchial heart pumping deoxygenated blood to respiratory organs for oxygenation; there is no capillary system between the arteries and veins but a series of indefinite haemal spaces, though these are not necessarily of dimensions very different from capillaries. All the organs are directly bathed in blood, and the circulation must be slower than in the vertebrate and less definite in its course. Many of the mollusc's movements, moreover, are hydraulic in mechanism, and it seems likely that their accomplishment will bring about vascular disturbance just as compression of our own veins does. Most gastropods have various sheets of muscle and connective tissue

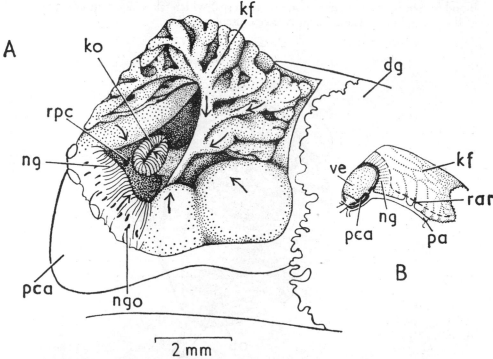

2 mm

Fig. 16.—*Littorina littorea:* A, view of the inside of the kidney sac which has been opened along the broken line marked in the inset figure B, which has been copied from fig. 2. Arrows show the direction of ciliary currents.

dg, digestive gland; kf, folded surface of kidney; ko, opening of kidney to mantle cavity; ng, nephridial gland; ngo, opening from kidney sac to tubules of nephridial gland; pa, posterior aorta; pca, pericardial cavity; rar, renal artery; rpc, opening of renopericardial canal to main kidney sac; ve, ventricle.

subdividing the haemocoelic spaces so that they have greater control over the distribution of blood in their body; these are not well developed in the winkle, except for one major one which separates the haemocoel within the visceral mass from that in the combined head and foot. This runs across the body at the level of the posterior oesophagus just anterior to the visceral ganglia.

In *Littorina littorea* the heart (au, ve, figs. 2, 7) lies in the pericardial cavity on the left side near the base of the visceral mass, anterior and ventral to the kidney. The anterior wall of the pericardium is in contact with the innermost end of the mantle cavity. The heart is composed of two chambers, an auricle and a ventricle. The auricle (au) lies anterior and slightly ventral to the ventricle (ve) which is set across the body. The two communicate by an aperture guarded by a single tongue-shaped valve (avv, fig. 17), so arranged as to permit free flow of blood from auricle to ventricle but not in the reverse direction. The two chambers are covered by an outer epithelium (vep, fig. 19), but there is no endothelial lining. Both have bundles of muscle (hm) forming a series of strands, much less elaborate in the auricle than in the ventricle. The latter opens posteriorly and ventrally to a single vessel, which is sometimes called the bulbus or truncus arteriosus (ob, fig. 17), and which splits almost at once into two, a larger anterior aorta (aa) taking blood forwards, and a smaller posterior aorta (pa) which takes blood into the upper coils of the visceral mass. These channels have muscular walls.

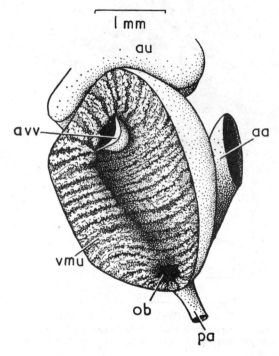

Fig. 17.—*Littorina littorea:* ventricle, opened.
    aa, anterior aorta; au, auricle; avv, auriculo-ventricular valve; ob, opening from ventricle to bulbus; pa, posterior aorta; vmu, muscles in wall of ventricle.

In most individuals the arteries have around their walls a thick investment of connective tissue laden with granules of calcium carbonate which makes them show up a brilliant white in a fresh animal. The course of the major arteries is therefore readily observable.
    The anterior aorta (aa, figs. 2, 7, 14, 18, 20) runs forward under the floor of the pericardial cavity on its way to the head and foot, lying dorsal to and left of the posterior oesophagus at this point. It gives off a branch, the oesophageal or style sac artery (oea, figs. 2, 18), which runs posteriorly, dorsal to the oesophagus, into connective tissue filling the space between the oesophageal and intestinal limbs of the stomach, to both of which structures it sends branches. The main aorta now penetrates into the cephalopedal haemocoel, lying dorsal to the mid-oesophagus (aa, fig. 20), and, like that structure, it shows here the effects of torsion, crossing the mid-oesophagus dorsally so that it comes

to lie on its right, and then curving underneath until it lies in the mid-ventral line at the level of the anterior end of the mid-oesophagus, directly below the radular sac (aa, fig. 14). At this point the anterior aorta passes ventrally through the nerve ring into the foot through a gap in the sheet of transverse muscle which separates the cephalic and pedal haemocoelic cavities; it then divides into a main pedal artery (pda, fig. 18A) and a main cephalic artery (car). The pedal artery turns backwards and branches within the muscular masses of the foot emptying the blood finally into the haemocoelic spaces of that organ (cps, fig. 18B). The cephalic artery climbs dorsally back into the head, gives off a radular artery which enlarges to form a sinus (rds) around the radular sac, and then passes into the buccal mass to supply blood to that complex—blood which then escapes to the cephalopedal haemocoel (cps).

The posterior or visceral aorta (pa, figs. 2, 18A) leaves the bulbus at its dorsal end and passes up the visceral mass along the left border of the kidney, giving off a number of renal arteries (rar) as it does so. The aorta then passes deeply into the central parts of the visceral mass, emerges on to the surface on the columellar side and runs in this position to its summit, giving off a large number of arteries to the intestine, the stomach and, principally, to the digestive gland and gonad. All these vessels pass blood into a large visceral haemocoel (vs, fig. 18B) by which these organs are surrounded.

Though the distribution of blood from the heart to the body is thus achieved in a fairly direct way, the venous return is more complex, especially when it is realized that both the kidney and the respiratory organ are incorporated in it. From the visceral mass blood may pass directly into haemal spaces in the mantle skirt (pas) mainly by way of a large vessel lying around and on the right of the rectum, and the same is also true for blood in the cephalic and pedal haemocoels, which are connected broadly to the mantle skirt on the left. Nevertheless there is a second, more important, route by which blood may return—by way of the kidney. A short cephalopedal vein (cpv) returning blood from the main cephalopedal sinus (cps) and visceral veins (vv) returning blood from the visceral sinus (vs) unite near the right side of the kidney and liberate their blood by way of one main renal vessel into the numerous blood vessels (rvn) which lie in the walls of the kidney sac. From here the blood may pass to the nephridial gland; in *Littorina*, this is then carried by an efferent vein (env) direct to the auricle, although in some other prosobranchs it may go to pallial blood spaces lying in the mantle skirt. Blood may also pass directly into these pallial spaces from the visceral sinus and from the lateral parts of the cephalopedal sinus.

The blood which has reached the haemal spaces in the mantle skirt (pas, fig. 18B) (by whatever route) will undoubtedly undergo some degree of oxygenation there, but it is gradually passed into channels which form the afferent branchial vessels (abv) leading into the right edges of the ctenidial leaflets. The blood passes through spaces within the gill lamellae and finally escapes from these into the efferent branchial vessel in the ctenidial axis (ev) along which it flows to the auricle of the heart. In *Littorina* the auricle therefore appears to receive the bulk of its blood in oxygenated form from the ctenidium and a moiety of blood from the nephridial gland and kidney which has not been oxygenated in the gill, whatever oxygen it may have acquired elsewhere.

The blood is a colourless or slightly bluish liquid, the colour being due to the blood pigment haemocyanin. It contains numerous amoebocytes (am, fig. 19). The muscle of the ventricular wall is striated (hm). Many cells laden with pigmented material, possibly excretory in nature, cling to the muscle fibres inside the heart: it is these which make both the auricle and the ventricle look brownish in colour (pgc).

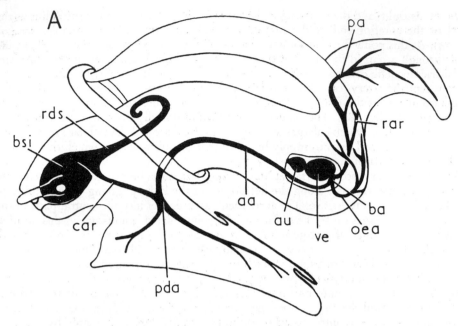

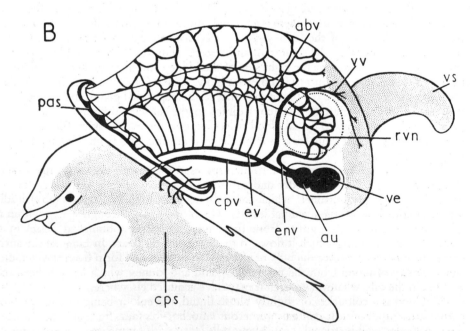

FIG. 18.—*Littorina littorea:* diagrammatic representations of A, the main parts of the arterial system and
B, the main parts of the venous system as seen in animals viewed from the left side.   The main blood
sinuses are stippled.   The proportions of the parts have been distorted for the sake of clarity.

   aa, anterior aorta; abv, afferent branchial vessels; au, auricle; ba, bulb of aorta; bsi, buccal sinus;
car, cephalic artery; cps, cephalopedal blood sinus; cpv, cephalopedal vein; env, efferent vessel from
nephridial gland; ev, efferent branchial vessel; oea, oesophageal artery; pa, posterior aorta; pas,
pallial blood sinus; pda, pedal artery; rar, renal artery; rds, radular sinus; rvn, renal vessels; ve,
ventricle; vs, visceral sinus; vv, visceral vein.

The nervous system of the gastropod consists of a number of ganglia, interlinked, and giving off nerves to various organs. The ganglia lie mainly in the head, in a group around the oesophagus, but some are placed in the visceral hump to co-ordinate the activities of the viscera. Originally the entire system was symmetrical but as a consequence of torsion and also of the asymmetry introduced by the spiral coiling of the visceral hump the final arrangement is usually quite asymmetrical.

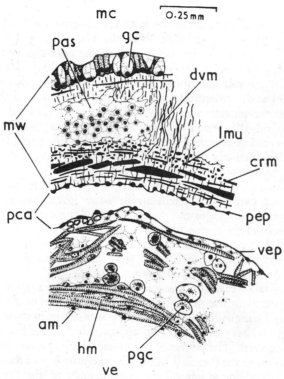

Fig. 19.—*Littorina littorea:* transverse section showing wall of ventricle and of pericardial cavity and inner epithelium of mantle skirt.

am, amoebocyte; crm, circular muscle; dvm, dorsoventral muscle; gc, gland cell in epithelium lining mantle cavity; hm, striped muscle of ventricle; lmu, longitudinal muscle; mc, mantle cavity; mw, wall of mantle cavity = inner part of mantle skirt; pas, pallial blood space; pca, pericardial cavity; pep, epithelium lining pericardial cavity; pgc, pigment cell; ve, cavity of ventricle; vep, outer epithelium of ventricle.

Around the oesophagus is a ring of six ganglia (figs. 14, 20). These are on each side: the cerebral, most dorsally; the pedal, most ventrally; and the pleural intermediately. The three ganglia on each side are linked to each other and the right and left cerebrals and the right and left pedals are linked across the mid-line of the body. Longitudinal connexions between different ganglia are called connectives; connexions between corresponding ganglia of the right and left sides are called commissures. Thus there are cerebral and pedal commissures in the nerve ring and there are cerebropleural, cerebropedal and pleuropedal connectives on each side. To these ganglia there come many nerves from sense organs such as the eyes and the statocysts, the tentacles and other structures on the head, foot and mantle skirt, and nerves go to muscles in the same situations. The muscles of the odontophore, which form an extraordinarily complex apparatus calling for delicately controlled manipulation, are provided with two special buccal ganglia, connected with the cerebrals. These are placed at the point where the anterior oesophagus and the radular sac separate from the buccal cavity and are linked by a buccal commissure which runs between the anterior oesophagus above and the radular sac below.

Another group of ganglia is associated with the innervation of the mantle skirt and the viscera. Connectives between these form the visceral loop which runs from the pleural ganglion on each side of the nerve ring in the head into the visceral mass, the two parts connecting there so as to form a complete nerve loop. On this are borne five or six ganglia, the pleurals anteriorly, the single or double visceral (or abdominal) ganglion which lies at the innermost end of the mantle cavity, and the parietal ganglia, which lie between the pleurals anteriorly and the viscerals behind. Originally, in the pretorsional gastropod, the entire loop lay ventral to the gut, but it will be realized that this part of the nervous system, like the gut and the anterior aorta, has to make its way between the head, which has not been disturbed by torsion, and the visceral hump, which has, and it will therefore be affected by the process. This has the effect of transferring ganglia which were originally on the right side of the body to the left, and vice versa, and of turning part of the system upside down just as happens to the mid-oesophagus. As a consequence of this the visceral loop of the nervous system comes to lie dorsal to the gut behind the region of torsion, though not anteriorly, and it is also flung into a figure-of-eight shape where the nerves cross from their original right and left position in the head to their new left and right positions in the visceral hump. This twisted state of the visceral loop is called streptoneury.

Once torsion has taken place the visceral loop is twisted at a point which lies between the two pleural ganglia in the nerve ring anteriorly and the two parietal ganglia posteriorly. The pleural ganglia, being cephalic in position, retain their original situations; the parietals, however, have come to lie on opposite sides of the body, the original right on the left and vice versa. The course of the visceral loop is now, therefore, as follows: right pleural ganglion to the (original right) parietal (now left of the oesophagus), to the (original right) visceral (now left of the oesophagus), to the (original left) visceral ganglion (now right of the oesophagus), to the (original left) parietal ganglion (now right of the oesophagus), and it is completed by a connexion to the left pleural ganglion in the nerve ring. Because torsion also involves the turning upside down of the posterior half of the visceral loop the connexion between right pleural and parietal ganglia now crosses the oesophagus dorsally, whereas the connexion between left pleural and parietal ganglia lies ventral to the oesophagus. The two visceral ganglia and the commissure which links them are now dorsal to the oesophagus. It is largely because of these new relationships to the alimentary canal that the parietal ganglia are given the names by which they are generally known in gastropods—the original right parietal, now lying left of the oesophagus and connected to the right pleural by a connective which lies dorsal to the oesophagus is called the supra-oesophageal (or, sometimes, but less happily, the supra-intestinal) ganglion; the original left parietal, now lying right of the oesophagus and connected to the left pleural by a connective which lies ventral to the oesophagus is called the sub-oesophageal (or sub-intestinal) ganglion.

The supra- and sub-oesophageal ganglia are concerned in the innervation of the mantle skirt and the organs which are situated there, such as the gill and the osphradium, for which the supra-oesophageal ganglion in particular is important: there may, indeed, be special ganglia, osphradial and branchial, connected to it. The pleural ganglia themselves may be involved in some control over the lateral parts of the mantle lying contiguous to and joined to the side of the foot and the head, which are controlled by the pedal and cerebral ganglia respectively. Since the head-foot has not undergone torsion, whereas the visceral mass—and so the mantle skirt—has, this would mean that neighbouring areas of mantle skirt would be controlled by ganglia the nervous pathways between which might be quite lengthy. As an example we may consider the control of part of the mantle edge on the animal's left side. The anterior part of this might be innervated by fibres originating in the left pleural ganglion (and would be in working relationship with pedal structures controlled by the left pedal ganglion), the posterior part by fibres connected to the supra-oesophageal ganglion. To ensure proper nervous co-ordination it is clear that links between the left pleural and the supra-oesophageal ganglia—and possibly the left pedal ganglion—are desirable. There is, however, no direct initial contact with these two nerve centres and the shortest route by which a connexion can in fact be established is by way of the left cerebropleural connective, left cerebral ganglion, cerebral commissure, right cerebral ganglion, right cerebropleural connective, right pleural ganglion and the connective between that and the supra-oesophageal ganglion, a route which almost certainly involves at least four synaptic junctions, or by way of the visceral ganglion, which is no shorter, and less likely. Gastropods are not noted for the rapidity of their reactions, but they need more efficient nervous pathways than this, and many of them modify the original plan of the visceral loop so as to bring about direct connexions between the right pleural ganglion and the sub-oesophageal ganglion on the one hand, and between the left pleural and supra-oesophageal ganglia on the other. Occasionally connexions with the pedal ganglia are also established. These are called zygoses or zygoneuries and they occur more frequently on the right side of the nerve ring (between right pleural and sub-oesophageal ganglia) than on the left. A second way in which the gastropod may attempt to co-ordinate the control of these pallial organs is by means of what is known as a dialyneury; this is a peripheral fusion between the pallial nerves emanating from the two ganglia involved and it would seem to achieve a result which is possibly physiologically similar to what a zygoneury does.

In *Littorina littorea* the nervous system is illustrated in figs. 14, 20, 21, 22. The cerebral ganglia (lcg, figs. 14, 20) lie behind the buccal mass, one on either side of the oesophagus, which is narrow at this point. Each is connected to the other cerebral ganglion by the cerebral commissure (ccm, figs. 14, 20, 21) which passes dorsal to the anterior oesophagus, and to the pleural (lpl, plg, figs. 14, 20B) and pedal (pd) ganglia by connectives. The pleural ganglia lie close behind and a little ventral to the cerebrals, so that the cerebropleural connectives (cpc, fig. 21) are short. The pleural ganglia are slightly smaller than the cerebrals, and, like them, are connected to the pedals by a pleuropedal connective (ppc, figs. 14, 20) which runs alongside the cerebropedal (cpdc). The pedal ganglia lie side by side ventral to the anterior aorta in the blood spaces of the foot. The connectives to the dorsal ganglia are therefore long.

From each cerebral ganglion (fig. 21) there originate four connexions to other ganglia: (*a*) the cerebral commissure (ccm); (*b*) the cerebropleural connective (cpc); (*c*) the cerebropedal connective (cpdc); and (*d*) the cerebrobuccal connective (cbc). This runs forward from the ganglion with one of the nerves going to the superficial muscles of the buccal mass.

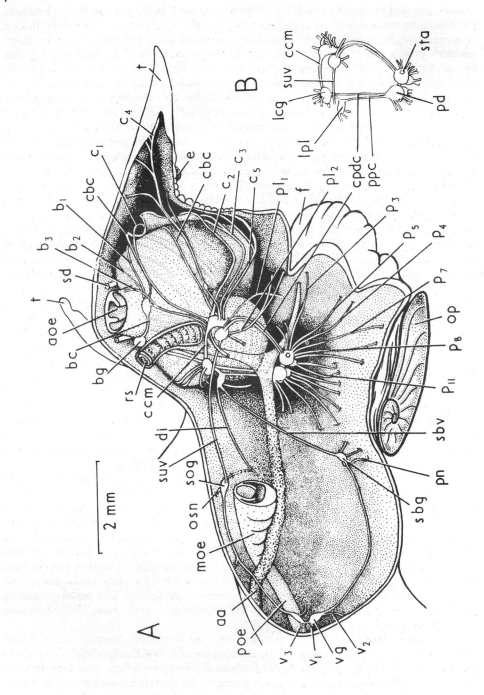

In addition, each cerebral ganglion gives off 5 nerves (figs. 14, 21). These are:

$c1$ A nerve of moderate size to the dorsal integument and muscles of the snout; this leaves the anterior border of the ganglion medially and somewhat ventrally, near the origin of the cerebral commissure.

$c2$ A stout nerve to the lateral integument and muscles of the snout; this leaves the ventral side of the anterior border of the ganglion lateral to the origin of nerve $c1$.

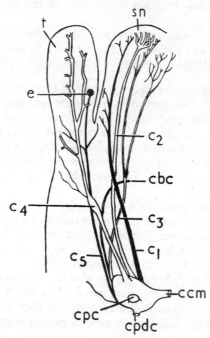

FIG. 21.—*Littorina littorea:* left cerebral ganglion and nerves (modified from Leyon, 1947).
$c_1$, dorsal labial and integumentary nerve; $c_2$, lateral labial and integumentary nerve; $c_3$, ventral labial and integumentary nerve; $c_4$, tentacular nerve with ganglion; $c_5$, optic nerve; cbc, cerebrobuccal connective; ccm, cerebral commissure; cpc, cerebropleural connective; cpdc, cerebropedal connective; e, eye; sn, snout; t, tentacle.

FIG. 20.—*Littorina littorea:* A, dorsolateral dissection of head, foot and base of visceral mass to show the nervous system. The gut has been cut at the level of the anterior oesophagus; the greater part of the radular sac has been removed. Both anterior oesophagus and radular sac have been pulled forwards through the nerve ring and turned dorsally, and the two salivary glands have been cut out. The mid-oesophagus has been displaced posteriorly. B, diagram to show ganglia in nerve ring.

aa, anterior aorta dividing anteriorly into pedal and cephalic arteries; aoe, anterior oesophagus; $b_1$, $b_2$, buccal nerves; $b_3$, anterior branch of oesophageal nerve, the posterior branch being cut behind the nerve ring; bc, buccal commissure; bg, buccal ganglion; $c_1$, dorsal labial nerve; $c_2$, lateral labial nerve; $c_3$, ventral labial nerve; $c_4$, tentacular nerve with ganglion; $c_5$, optic nerve; cbc, cerebro-buccal connective; ccm, cerebral commissure; cpdc, cerebropedal connective; di, dialyneury on left linking supra-oesophageal and left pleural ganglion; e, eye; f, foot; lcg, left cerebral ganglion; lpl, left pleural ganglion; moe, mid-oesophagus; op, operculum; osn, osphradial and branchial nerve; $p_3$, $p_4$, $p_5$, $p_7$, $p_8$, $p_{11}$, pedal nerves; pd, left pedal ganglion; $pl_1$, $pl_2$, pleural nerves; pn, pallial nerves; poe, posterior oesophagus; ppc, pleuropedal connective; rs, radular sac in radular sinus; sbg, sub-oesophageal ganglion; sbv, sub-oesophageal part of visceral loop; sd, salivary duct (cut); sog, supra-oesophageal ganglion; sta, statocyst; suv, supra-oesophageal part of visceral loop; t, tentacle; $v_1$, visceral nerve to heart and kidney; $v_2$, visceral nerve to rectum and genital duct; $v_3$, columellar nerve; vg, visceral ganglion.

c3 A large nerve to the ventral integument and muscles of the snout, which divides into two branches of equal size about half way to the skin of the snout; it arises from the ventral surface laterally and its basal section is bound with part of the cerebrobuccal connective by tissue.

c4 The tentacular nerve: this bears a small ganglionic enlargement a short distance from the cerebral ganglion; it originates from the dorsal surface of the ganglion and gives off numerous branches to the skin of the tentacles. It is olfactory in function.

c5 The optic nerve; a nerve of moderate size which arises from the ventral surface of the ganglion lateral and posterior to the nerve c4. It goes to the eye and the skin in its neighbourhood.

The pleural ganglia (plg, fig. 14; lpl, fig. 20B) lie close to the cerebrals, but slightly more posterior and ventral. Each gives off 3 connexions to other ganglia: (a) the cerebropleural; (b) the pleuropedal (ppc); and (c) the pleuroparietal connectives. The right pleural ganglion (plg, fig. 14) gives rise to a connective (suv, figs. 14, 20) which runs (dorsal to the oesophagus) to the supra–oesophageal ganglion (sog, fig. 20) lying on the left; the left pleural ganglion gives rise to a connective (sbv) which runs (ventral to the oesophagus) to the sub-oesophageal ganglion (sbg) lying on the right. There is no zygoneury in *Littorina littorea*.

The right pleural ganglion gives rise to 3 nerves (*pl*1, *pl*2, *pl*3, fig. 14) which innervate tissue at the right mantle edge, where it joins the side of the cephalopedal mass. The left pleural ganglion innervates a corresponding region on the left, but in this case one of the nerves joins another which has come from the supra-oesophageal ganglion so as to give rise to a dialyneury (di, fig. 20) on the animal's left.

From each pedal ganglion (pd, fig. 20; see also fig. 22) arise 3 connexions to other ganglia: (a) a very short pedal commissure (pcm); (b) a much longer pleuropedal connective (ppc); and (c) a cerebropedal connective (cpdc). Each also gives rise to 11 nerves to various parts of the foot. These tend to arise in groups from lobe-like expansions of the ganglion. They are:

$\left.\begin{array}{l} p1 \\ p2 \\ p3 \end{array}\right\}$ A group of small nerves arising from a median lobe posterior to the pedal commissure: they run to the median part of the anterior border of the foot.

$\left.\begin{array}{l} p4 \\ p5 \\ p6 \\ p7 \end{array}\right\{$ This group of nerves originates mainly from the lateral margin of the ganglion. (5) divides into 3 branches; and (6) and (7) each into 2. The anterior ones run to the antero–lateral border of the foot, the posterior ones to the posterior part of the sole. (4) links with a nerve from the sub-oesophageal ganglion so as to complete a dialyneury on the animal's right. (4) also innervates the penis.

$\left.\begin{array}{l} p8 \\ p9 \\ p10 \\ p11 \end{array}\right\}$ This group of stout nerves arises in a posterior lobe of the ganglion. They run posteriorly to the back of the sole and to the operculigerous disc.

The buccal ganglia (bg, figs. 14, 20) are placed lateral to the gut at the point where oesophagus and radular sac originate from the buccal cavity. Each is the source of 2 connexions to other ganglia: (a) the buccal commissure (bc); and (b) the cerebrobuccal connective (cbc). Each ganglion also sends 2 nerves (*b*1, *b*2) which pass forwards into the muscles of the buccal mass and a third ($b$3) which curves backwards along the oesophagus running alongside the salivary duct. It sends branches to this duct, to the dorsal food channel in the roof of the buccal cavity, and continues under the nerve ring. Here it again divides, one half passing under the supra-oesophageal connective and following the oesophagus as far as the stomach; the other passes above the connective and goes to the body wall, where it innervates the muscles suspending the oesophagus.

The visceral loop contains ganglia from each of which a number of nerves takes origin. From the supra-oesophageal, connectives run forwards to the right pleural and posteriorly to the visceral ganglia; this ganglion is also the origin of pallial nerves and of the branchial and osphradial nerves. The sub-oesophageal ganglion is connected to the left pleural and the visceral ganglia and gives off 3 nerves (pn, fig. 20A) to the mantle edge on the right and to the anus and reproductive aperture. Occasionally a circum-pallial nerve is formed, running round the edge of the mantle skirt, by the fusion of the pallial nerves from these 2 ganglia. The 2 ganglia lie on the floor of the haemocoelic space in which the oesophagus and anterior aorta run and are partly buried in the muscles which form it. The connectives which link them to the visceral ganglia are similarly situated so that the posterior part of the visceral loop is less easy to see and dissect than the anterior half.

The visceral ganglia (vg, figs. 7, 10, 20) are represented by a single structure lying below the integument forming the floor of the mantle cavity almost at its innermost end. A smaller ganglion is sometimes visible close to this on the course of the connective which passes over the posterior oesophagus and anterior aorta on its way to the supra-oesophageal ganglion. Two main nerves originate from the larger ganglion: one goes to the heart and excretory organ ($v$1), whilst the other is a genital nerve ($v$2) passing to the oviducal region in the female and to the male pore in the opposite sex. From the smaller ganglion nerves pass to the columellar muscle ($v$3).

The most important sense organs of the winkle are probably local tactile and similar sensory structures in the skin, but in addition to these the animal possesses at least three other major sense organs—the eyes, the statocysts, and the osphradium.

The eyes (e, figs. 1, 2) are situated at the base of the tentacles, on their outer side. Strictly speaking they are on stalks which have become secondarily fused to the tentacles. Each eye is a hollow vesicle, formed in development by intucking of the skin, and within the cavity of the organ is a spherical cuticular lens. The retina is formed of light perceptive cells shielded by black pigmented ones. The skin over the eye is clear and forms a kind of conjunctiva. How good these may be as image-forming organs is not known: the winkle certainly reacts to a shadow falling on the eyes by a contraction into its shell.

The statocysts (sta, fig. 22) lie near the pedal ganglia, though not, in *Littorina littorea*, as close to their surface as is often the case. That on the left is further forwards than that on the right, and both are surrounded by connective tissue containing granules of calcium carbonate. Each statocyst has the form of a small, spherical sac, completely closed in the adult state and filled with fluid. In this is found a statolith, a spherical mass of calcium carbonate embedded in an organic matrix and often showing concentric shells, perhaps due to rhythms in the animal's growth. The statoliths fall under the influence of gravity on to the sensory epithelium which lines the cavity.

The osphradium (os, fig. 7) is usually regarded as a receptor for chemical stimuli, although some writers believe that it may be also, or, instead, sensitive to the amount of particulate matter which is carried in suspension in the water to which it is exposed.

In *Littorina littorea* it forms a ridge projecting from the mantle skirt into the mantle cavity and lying alongside and parallel to the ctenidial axis. It contains numerous sensory cells and ganglionic enlargements of the osphradial nerves. It is sometimes said that the nerve fibres which run to the osphradium start in the cerebral ganglia although they reach their destination in nerves which originate in the supra-oesophageal. This is known to be true of the nerves supplying the statocysts: although running in nerves from the

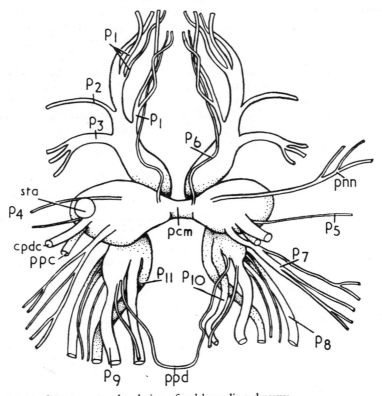

Fig. 22.—*Littorina littorea*: posterodorsal view of pedal ganglia and nerves.
    cpdc, cerebropedal connective; p1, p2, p3, p4, p5, p6, p7, p8, p9, p10, p11, pedal nerves; pcm, pedal commissure; pnn, penial nerve; ppc, pleuropedal connective; ppd, posterior pedal commissure; sta, statocyst.

pedal ganglia the fibres have their real origin in the cerebral ganglia. The cerebral ganglia thus have direct information not only from the snout, the tentacles and the eyes, but also from the statocysts and, possibly, from the osphradium as well, on which to base the behaviour which the winkle will exhibit in any particular situation.

  Edible winkles are either male or female. The former may easily be distinguished, at least during the breeding season, by the presence of a penis (p, fig. 3) lying on the side of the head behind the right tentacle. Females have a smooth, unpigmented patch of skin in the same region, the ovipositor (opr, fig. 1). When the animals are not breeding both the penis and the ovipositor are greatly reduced in size and conspicuousness, but they never vanish completely.

In males the testis (te, fig. 10) is a large, diffuse, branching organ which lies in the upper parts of the visceral mass, mainly more superficial than the digestive gland, but thrusting itself, wherever space is available, between the lobules of that gland. It is commonly a greyish, grey-green or grey-brown colour. The tubules of the testis join along the columellar (inner) side of the visceral mass to produce a duct which is formed from the walls of the gonad itself: this is the testicular duct (td, figs. 9, 10) which runs towards the mantle cavity. Its course, at first straight, becomes more convoluted as the cavity is approached, and this part is used as a seminal vesicle for the storage of spermatozoa. During the breeding season it appears for this reason as a chalk-white tube. The duct then narrows (rvd, fig. 10) and opens to the inner end of the mantle cavity at the male pore. The narrower section of the male duct is presumably derived embryologically from the kidney of the right side and it may therefore be distinguished as the renal section of the vas deferens.

From the male opening a ciliated sperm groove (sgr) runs forward on the floor of the mantle cavity on to the side of the head and to the base of the penis (p). Along the pallial stretch of this groove its walls are tall and hypertrophied by the development of folds of glandular tissue which produce a well developed prostate gland (pr).

The penis is conical, slightly flattened from side to side and carries the sperm groove to its summit along the dorsal edge. When at rest it forms a sickle-shaped structure lying behind the right tentacle and hidden within the mantle cavity, but at times of copulation it becomes engorged with blood and greatly extended. On the ventral border of the penis, though not extending right to the tip, lies a row of mammilliform structures which give the penis a serrated edge: these are glands (png, figs. 3, 9, 10) the secretion of which is said to hold the penis in position during copulation when only the elongated tip passes through the female pore and enters the bursa copulatrix, into which the spermatozoa are discharged.

The reproductive organs of the female winkles (figs. 1, 23) are more elaborate than those of the male. This is due to the facts that not only do they have to provide for the elaboration of female gametes and lead them to the exterior, but must also make provision for their fertilization in the course of this journey and for enclosing them, plus food, in a protective capsule within which the earliest developmental stages are undergone.

The ovary (ov, fig. 1) lies in the visceral hump in a position similar to that occupied by the testis in males. It may be recognized by its colour, which is yellow to pink or violet, and is very similar to that of the kidney. The ovary extends into the first part of the oviduct, which is therefore an ovarian duct; this runs to the inner end of the mantle cavity along a straight path. At one point along this part of the duct a side branch opens to the pericardial cavity. This is the gonopericardial duct, and it is said to be the inner part of the right kidney. The part of the oviduct between the ovary and the gonopericardial duct is therefore gonadial in origin, whereas the next section between the gonopericardial duct and the mantle cavity is the renal section of the oviduct (ro, figs. 1, 23). The female winkle differs from the male in retaining the original connexion between the renal section of the genital duct and the pericardial cavity, possibly because ova are large and immobile whilst—were it retained in the male—small, motile spermatozoa might travel along such a connexion and block it.

The female winkle also differs from the male in that the original opening of the renal section of the genital duct to the mantle cavity is not retained. Instead the oviduct opens at this point into a further section of duct which has been formed by the folding off of the wall of the mantle skirt to form a tube. In this way a third section of genital duct has been produced in the female, which may be distinguished as the pallial section of the oviduct. This lies alongside, and to the right of, the rectum and has brought the female pore near the anus, close to the mouth instead of in the depths of the mantle cavity.

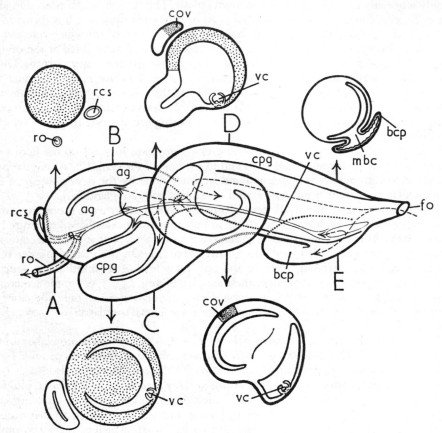

Fig. 23.—*Littorina littorea*: diagram of the female genital tract represented as a transparent object seen from the right side. A, B, C, D and E are transverse sections across the duct at the levels indicated. The arrows within the main diagram are intended to show channels of communication between sections of the duct: they are not related to the movements of germ cells or secretions. In the sections the albumen gland has been coarsely stippled; the covering gland has been finely stippled; the capsule gland is unshaded. To prevent obscurity the covering gland has not been shown in the main diagram.
   ag, albumen gland; bcp, bursa copulatrix; cov, covering gland; cpg, capsule gland; fo, female opening to mantle cavity; mbc, mouth of bursa copulatrix; rcs, receptaculum seminis; ro, renal section of oviduct; vc, ventral channel.

The pallial section of the female genital tract is composed of a series of glands, which become extremely large and prominent at the height of the breeding season, and, in addition, of chambers for the reception and storage of spermatozoa received in copulation.

The renal section of the oviduct opens ventrally to the upper end of the pallial section. From here to near the female pore there stretches a ciliated groove which marks the morphological ventral side of this part of the female genital tract. This is the ventral channel (vc, fig. 23). Also at its upper end opens a small blind tubule, the receptaculum seminis (rcs), whilst between its lower end and the external aperture there opens to it a large blind sac, the bursa copulatrix (bcp), which extends below and to the left of the rest of the duct. These three parts of the female apparatus are concerned primarily with the reception and storage of spermatozoa. During copulation the penis is placed into the bursa copulatrix and spermatozoa and prostatic secretion are discharged. The spermatozoa then swim along the ventral channel of the female duct to the receptaculum seminis, which is usually visible at the upper end of the mass of glandular tissue as a refringent white streak due to the spermatozoa within it. They are arranged with their heads stuck to or embedded in the surface of the cells lining the receptaculum and they may receive nourishment from these.

The upper end of the ventral channel is thus a region which eggs, descending from the ovary, have to traverse in close proximity to a store of spermatozoa. It is, therefore, the most likely site of fertilization, and we may imagine a stream of fertilized eggs passing into the glandular mass which the female duct forms at this point. Perhaps because of the presence of the rectum immediately to the left of the female tract almost all its glandular development occurs on the right side; this is the explanation of the fact that the ventral channel lies on the left side.

The albumen gland (ag) is the most posterior section of the pallial duct. It has a translucent buff appearance in the fresh state and secretes material available for the feeding of the developing egg. Anteriorly it is followed by a second gland which is opaque white in the living animal. This is the capsule gland which at first lies ventro-lateral to the albumen gland, but nearer the genital aperture expands to form a great mass (cpg). Across the right side of this gland runs a strip of orange or orange-pink tissue which secretes a kind of shell around the albumen which covers the fertilized egg. This 'shell' is usually called the egg covering and the gland may therefore be referred to as the covering gland (cov). The three glands co-operate to produce the egg capsule of the edible winkle.

A number of eggs, usually 3–5, enters the upper end of the ventral channel from the upper oviduct. There they are fertilized and passed forward. Their presence stimulates the albumen gland to secrete so that they become embedded in a mass of albumen from this source. At this point the eggs may be travelling in a group, but it is equally possible that they may be progressing down the duct singly, because the next thing which happens is that each, with its coat of albumen round it, becomes enclosed in an egg covering secreted by the covering gland. After this, however, the eggs become grouped, because it is in groups of 1–5 that they are to be found enclosed in the egg capsule, the material for which is produced by the capsule gland.

The capsule is of a disc shape, about 1 mm diameter or rather less, with a swelling in the centre in which the eggs are accommodated, each with its own covering and supply of albumen. The peripheral parts of the capsule form a flat flange to the central swelling and the whole has a somewhat hat-like shape. The outermost skin of the capsule is much tougher than the inner layers, although it retains its glass-like clarity. The hardening has been said to be due to the effect of the secretion of glands on the ovipositor. The ovipositor (opr, fig. 1) is a broad belt of tissue, slightly raised above the general level of the skin of the head, but made most obvious by the fact that it is almost completely unpigmented. It is ciliated and undoubtedly helps in carrying the capsules forward out of the mantle cavity. The capsules are pelagic, and give rise to planktonic veliger larvae. They are laid 2–12 hrs after copulation has occurred, usually at a high tide period and by night, until an estimated total of about 500 capsules has been produced. There may then be a pause after which laying may be resumed. The breeding season is long, January to July (Millport), or, at Plymouth, between November and May, the males ripening a little before the females. The breeding season has a peak in spring, during which each female may lay several lots of capsules, so that the total number produced in the whole breeding period may total about 5,000 per individual (Tattersall, 1920).

After laying, the capsules sink slowly, the rate being determined by the number of eggs they contain: this allows them to be well distributed by surface currents. The cleavage of the egg is completed after the first day and the larvae hatch on the sixth day as free-swimming veligers. The larva (fig. 235) has a yellowish spiral shell of one and a half turns and no definite architectural markings apart from faint spiral striae. Around the head the body is drawn out into two semicircular velar lobes (from which it is named) edged by strongly beating cilia, which are its main locomotor organs. The anterior parts of these lobes are marked with dark purple pigment, by means of which it may be recognized as the veliger of *Littorina littorea*. These are also visible as two hemispherical patches showing through the shell when the animal is retracted. The larva swims in the plankton for a period of about two weeks by which time the shell has grown to two whorls and darkened in colour to a brownish hue. At metamorphosis the velum is lost and as a consequence the young winkle falls to the bottom and assumes a crawling mode of life.

# CHAPTER 3

# THE SHELL

THE body of a mollusc is typically enclosed within a shell, and to many this dead product of the animal's secretory activity is more familiar than the living organism itself. Because of their beauty of shape and colour, molluscan shells have for long been collected with eagerness and at much expense; indeed, until a recent period within the last 200 years a 'cabinet' of shells gathered from all the world over was regarded as one of the main features of a naturalist's collection (Dean, 1936). Shells were sought from many sources and beautiful rarities like *Conus gloria-maris* sometimes changed hands at very high prices (see Cooke, 1895, p. 121). Today, collections of this nature are no longer regarded so highly, though many people still derive great pleasure from the contemplation of small private stocks or more extensive ones in public ownership in museums.

The molluscan shell is secreted by the mantle, or pallium, that is, by the epithelial covering of the visceral hump and mantle skirt and it has, therefore, the same shape as that part of the animal's body. The processes by which it is secreted are discussed elsewhere (p. 127); it is enough here to recall that after the laying down by the larval shell gland of a larval shell (known as the protoconch), growth proceeds by the addition of new rings of conchiolin impregnated with calcium carbonate to the edge of the shell, and by the addition of calcium carbonate over the whole of its inner surface. The marginal accretion represents the formation of new shelly substance to accommodate the increased volume of the visceral hump of a larger animal; the addition to the inside thickens it so as to give the extra strength which is called for in a larger structure. Normally, the calcareous material secreted at the pallial edge is in the crystalline form of prisms of calcite lying normal to the surface of the shell, whereas the inner part is made of layers of crystals of aragonite parallel to the shell surface. In lower prosobranchs this part is often known as nacre, or mother-of-pearl, and much of the lustrous appearance of molluscan shells, especially their blue, or blue-green refulgence, depends upon the refraction of light by this inner layer. The relative extents of these layers and their precise microstructure vary within the prosobranch series and have been described by Bøggild (1930) in some detail. External to the whole mass of calcareous matter there lies a layer of conchiolin not impregnated with mineral material: this is the epidermis or periostracum. Sometimes, perhaps usually in prosobranchs, it is so delicate as to be all but invisible; sometimes, as in *Capulus* (fig. 24), it forms a distinct layer over the rest of the shell and imparts its own colour to the whole; sometimes, as in *Trichotropis* (fig. 95), *Velutina* or young *Viviparus* (fig. 56), it not only covers the shell but is drawn out into hairlike processes standing erect on the surface; usually it becomes worn off the older parts of a shell, and it is often absent from all but the youngest. The thickness of the periostracal layer is related to the habitat in which a mollusc lives, being greatest in animals from freshwaters or high latitudes and least in those coming from the warmer seas. Where it is lost in terrestrial or freshwater animals erosion often follows, so that it has a clear protective function.

Since it is generally assumed that the visceral hump of the ancestral gastropod was conical or cap-shaped, it follows that the shell which it produced was similar. With evolutionary advance, however, the visceral hump elongated and became coiled into a helicoid spiral, with the necessary consequence that the shell became similarly elongated and coiled: it can, in fact, be regarded as a long tube, approximately circular in transverse section and of gradually increasing diameter, which is rolled into a helicoid spiral coil. This, it has been suggested by Cox (1955), should be known as the helicocone; it is sometimes known as the conchospiral. The mathematical properties of the plane

3 cm

FIG. 24.—*Capulus ungaricus:* the Hungarian cap shell.    Note the thickened and spiny periostracal layer.

logarithmic or equiangular spiral are discussed by D'Arcy Thompson (1942). We may imagine a tube coiled so that the centre of each turn (or whorl) lies in a plane (fig. 25A). This would produce a shell which is disc-like in shape, actually biconcave because of the fact that the helicocone increases in diameter from the central part outwards (fig. 25B). In the vast majority of prosobranchs, however, the coil of the helicocone is not in one plane but is such as would be produced by winding it round the surface of a cone from apex to base: it is this shape which is a helicoid spiral, and a shell with that configuration is known as conispiral (figs. 25C, D). According to the size of the apical angle of the cone round which we imagine the helicocone to grow a great number of shapes may be produced, with the planispiral shell as that limiting case where the apical angle equals 180°. Normally the direction of coiling is right-handed, or in a clockwise direction when

FIG. 25.—Diagrams to illustrate the coiling of gastropod shells.    A represents a plane on which a spiral line marks the centre of a helicocone coiling dextrally;  B represents a vertical section through such a shell along the line xy.    This type of shell is planispiral.

C represents a plane on which a spiral line marks the centre of a helicocone coiling dextrally; a cone has been pressed upwards through the plane from below, its apex coinciding with the centre of the spiral.    D represents a vertical section through such a shell along the line xy.    This type of shell is conispiral and orthostrophic.

E represents a plane on which a spiral line marks the centre of a helicocone coiling dextrally; a cone has been pressed downwards through the plane from above, its apex coinciding with the centre of the spiral.    F represents a vertical section through such a shell along the line xy.    This type of shell is conispiral and hyperstrophic.    Note that although the coiling of the spiral is unchanged it appears to be reversed when the shell is viewed in the conventional way.

G is a logarithmic or equiangular spiral; note that the angles $\theta$ between a line drawn through the central point of the spiral and tangents at the points where it intersects the spiral, are constant.    H is a logarithmic or equiangular spiral in which two triangles linking the origin with the points bc and b'c' respectively are inscribed, by joining corresponding points in successive turns;  note that these figures are similar.    The line lmn, which is a radius vector, is cut by the spiral into lengths which are in geometrical proportion.

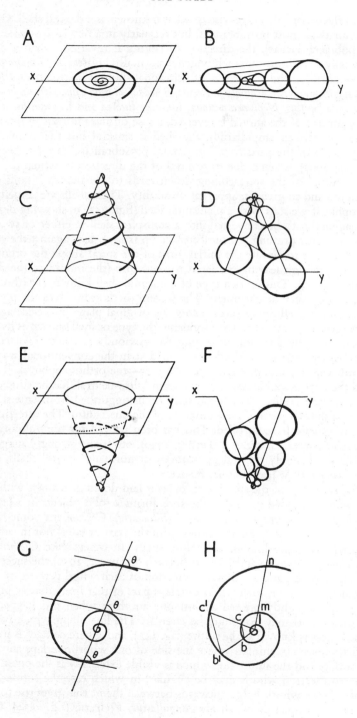

viewed from the origin: this gives rise to what is known as a dextral shell. Occasionally, as an abnormality in most prosobranchs, but regularly in a few species when adult (and in all opisthobranch larvae), the direction of coiling is reversed, when a sinistral shell results. The only British prosobranch which is normally sinistral is *Triphora perversa*, but Ancey (1906) recorded the occurrence of occasional sinistral specimens in the following species: *Viviparus viviparus*, *Valvata piscinalis*, *Theodoxus fluviatilis*, *Acicula fusca*, *Buccinum undatum*, *Nucella lapillus*, *Neptunea antiqua*, *Littorina littorea* and *L. saxatilis*. In these cases the entire symmetry of the animal is reversed, a case of *situs inversus*; in some, however, like *Lanistes* (an African ampullariid), the shell is sinistral but the animal retains the normal disposition of the parts found in dextral prosobranchs. This has been explained (Simroth, 1896–1907) as being due to reversal of the direction in which the apex of the shell points. Instead of the spire coiling downwards to the mouth it coils downwards from the mouth and so gives an apparent sinistrality. These shells are sometimes known as hyperstrophic. If we start with a planispiral shell (figs. 25A, B) showing dextral coiling we may imagine this to be converted into a conispiral shell in either of two ways. The first of these involves pressing a conical surface up from below against the centre of the planispiral shell so as to elevate the initial turns of the spiral above the original plane in which they lay, though leaving the latest formed turn (the mouth of the shell) in that position (figs. 25C, D). This gives a type of conispiral shell known as orthostrophic and is the usual prosobranch arrangement. The second method involves the pressing of the central turns of the shell downwards below the original plane but, once again, leaving the last turn there (figs. 25E, F) and so producing the type of shell known as hyperstrophic. In both these cases the direction of coiling has obviously not been affected, yet if the shells produced by the two methods are looked at in the conventional way—with the apex upwards and the mouth facing the observer—the orthostrophic shell will appear dextral and the hyperstrophic sinistral. The term 'ultra-dextral' has been used to describe this kind of sinistral coiling, which can only be distinguished from true sinistrality by examination of the soft parts of the animal, or of the operculum. The direction of coiling is presumably genetically controlled. This has been proved for the pulmonate *Lymnaea peregra* (Boycott, Diver, Garstang & Turner, 1930), but is also strongly suggested by the local occurrence of purely sinistral populations of normally dextral shells, such as that of *Neptunea antiqua* at St Jean de Luz, France.

Normally, each turn of the spiral as it forms is laid down in contact with the wall of the whorl which preceded it, so that the shell forms a solid object. In a few genera of prosobranchs such as *Vermetus*, *Tenagodus* (=*Siliquaria*), *Caecum* and some trichotropids the successive turns of the spiral are (either from the start or later) not in contact, giving an open spiral: these are known as evolute shells. In others, like *Clathrus* (fig. 142), *Pomatias*, *Valvata*, *Cirsotrema* and its allies (Clench & Turner, 1950) the successive whorls just touch one another, and the transverse section of each whorl is more or less circular. In many genera, however, each whorl overlaps part of that immediately preceding and successive ones are tightly pressed against one another; when this happens, the cross section of each whorl may no longer be circular. The line along which two successive turns of shell meet is known as the suture (fig. 34A), and where contact is just made this will be strictly linear. In animals where the side of one whorl overlaps another, contact is along a surface and the suture line which is visible externally is the outer edge of that surface. In cross section whorls may be circular, in which case the suture lines will be deeply sunk and the whorls bulge outwards between them: this gives rise to a ventricose shell (fig. 26A), examples of which are *Ampullarius*, *Viviparus* (fig. 183A), *Clathrus* (fig.

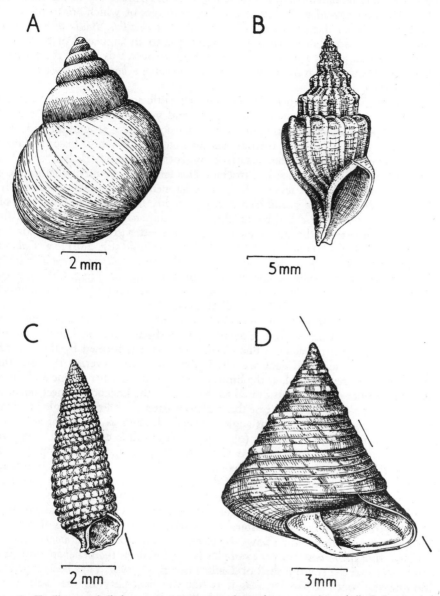

FIG. 26.—To illustrate shell shape. A, *Littorina saxatilis*, to show a ventricose shell; B, *Lora turricula*, a turreted shell; C, *Cerithiopsis tubercularis*, a cyrtoconoid shell; D, *Calliostoma zizpyhinum*, a coelo-conoid shell. In C and D lines are drawn from the apex to form a tangent to the outer lip in order to reveal the convexity of the spire in C and its concavity in D.

142), *Valvata* (fig. 310), *Littorina saxatilis*, *Hydrobia ventrosa*. Alternatively, the outer side of the whorl may be flattened, when there is no (or only little) dip to the suture lines: this gives rise to a flat-sided shell (figs. 26C, D), examples of which are to be found in the trochids, *Littorina littorea*, *Hydrobia ulvae*, *Cingula cingillus*, *Balcis alba*, *Turbonilla elegantissima*. Other shapes of shell tube can give rise to an angulated or turreted shell (fig. 26B), when the upper part of each whorl projects outwards below the suture line. Shells of this shape are seen in *Alvania carinata*. *Trichotropis borealis*, *Trophon barvicensis* and *Lora turricula*.

Further major factors in giving a shell its characteristic appearance are also dependent upon the relationship of each whorl to its older and younger neighbours. As the shell grows, it can be regarded as rotating in three-dimensional space around the protoconch, which acts as origin. With each rotation the diameter of the whorl becomes larger. If the rate of increase is constant then a surface tangential to the whorls is a regular cone, and this type of shell is conical, as in a trochid. This term may be used whether the sides of the whorls are flat or ventricose. It frequently happens that the rate of increase is not regular, but becomes either steadily greater, or steadily less, as the mollusc gets older. Shells of this type may be called conoidal, in that their shape is nearly conical. In the former group the sides of the cone are concave, in the latter group convex: Cox (1955) suggested that those with concave sides be called coeloconoid (fig. 26D) (e.g. *Calliostoma zizyphinum*, *Littorina littorea*, *Aclis supranitida*, *Pelseneeria stylifera*, *Neptunea antiqua*), whilst those with convex sides be known as cyrtoconoid (fig. 26C) (e.g. *Gibbula cineraria*, *G. umbilicalis*, *Rissoa parva*, *Bittium reticulatum*, *Triphora perversa*, *Cerithiopsis tubercularis*, *Eulima trifasciata*). The term 'extraconical' is sometimes used instead of coeloconoid. Successive whorls may also vary in respect of the extent to which an older one is overlapped by a younger: if the amount of overlap is very slight then, necessarily, a rather tall shell results, the height of which is due to the fact that it is formed by the sum of the separate heights of the constituent whorls. If the amount of overlap is great, then a much squatter shell results until, at the limit, all whorls lie together in one and the same plane. In the former case tangents drawn to the sides of the helicocone meet beyond the apex at a small angle; in the latter case the angle is greater than a right angle and may be in the neighbourhood of 180°. This angle is usually known as the apical angle and is represented by $\alpha$. *Turritella communis* (fig. 37A) is an example of a prosobranch with a small apical angle (about 17°), whereas *Conus* spp. (fig. 37B), *Ianthina* spp. (fig. 299), *Valvata* spp. (fig. 310) and *Velutina* spp. exemplify shells with a rather wide apical angle. In the final case, where the coiled tube of the shell lies symmetrically in a single plane the shell will obviously have the form of a biconcave disc, because of the fact that the diameter of the tube grows steadily greater with age. This type of shell, as pointed out by Cox (1955), has been called planispiral or isostrophic. No British prosobranch has a shell which is strictly isostrophic, however, except perhaps *Omalogyra atomus* (fig. 206B) and *Valvata cristata*, the best known examples being found in the bellerophonts. It may be noted here that the sinistral shell of *Lanistes* (see p. 52) which has been explained as an 'ultra-dextral' one—a bad term as it is not the dextrality of the shell which is excessive, but the apical angle—is, in fact, a shell in which the apical angle is obtuse, and in this genus exceeds 270°.

In certain cases where the helicocone is comparable to a screw of low pitch, its early turns are visible at one pole, dipping to the apex of the shell, but the last turn conceals all the others at the other pole of the shell: this type of shell is known as involute (fig. 27). No British prosobranch has a truly involute shell, though those of *Velutina velutina* and some species of *Lacuna* are very nearly so; the opisthobranch *Cylichna truncata* bears a genuine involute shell. Still another relationship of the whorls of a shell is that in which the youngest turn grows so as to conceal all those that have gone before: this condition is known as convolute and may be illustrated by the shells of *Trivia* spp. (fig. 28) or *Simnia patula* (fig. 296).

In the various formations of the helicocone which have been described above attention has been directed primarily to the degree of overlapping of the whorls. The general appearance of a gastropod shell, however, is also much affected by another aspect of this to which no reference has yet been made: this is the relation of the whorls to the axis round which the turns of the spiral revolve. As the helicocone grows from the protoconch its configuration may be regarded as due to the movement of the generating circle of mantle skirt which secretes it (*a*) around the origin in a spiral, and (*b*) along an axis at

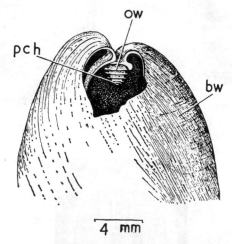

FIG. 27.—*Bulla ampulla:* an involute shell broken open to show the spire covered over by the body whorl. bw, body whorl; ow, broken edge of older whorl now covered by body whorl; pch, position of protoconch.

right angles to the plane of the spiral. In certain cases the inner walls of the whorls may all rest on the central axis around which the shell lies, forming a solid spiral; in others these walls come to lie at greater and greater distances from it so that a hollow spiral results. In shells conforming to the former plan it is naturally not possible to see the inner walls of the whorls except by breaking the shell: in the latter group they may be looked at from the base of the shell, where there is an opening which allows one to look up the centre of the series of turns comprising it (fig. 282). This opening is the umbilicus, or, more accurately, the inferior umbilicus. In some shells (e.g. *Architectonica, Valvata cristata, Skeneopsis planorbis*) almost the whole extent of the inner sides of the whorls of the shell is visible through a wide umbilical opening (figs. 29A, 290), but this is distinctly unusual: these shells are phaneromphalous. In most prosobranchs the shell is hemiomphalous with the umbilicus reduced to a chink (*Gibbula magus* (fig. 29C), *Clathrus, Monodonta lineata* (fig. 281), *Lacuna* spp., *Viviparus*) or crack (*Natica*, fig. 6) or it is lost altogether (cryptom-phalous, anomphalous) because of the tightness of the spiral coiling of the shell, or by its closure with secreted shelly material known as callus.

In involute and isostrophic shells there may be not only an inferior umbilicus produced as described above, but also a superior or apical umbilicus produced by the later coils uprising (because of their greater diameter) around earlier ones (fig. 27).

The inner walls of the rotating tube which makes up the helicocone may, as just mentioned, come into contact with one another where there is no umbilicus, and produce a central pillar around which the different whorls spiral. This central axis of the shell is

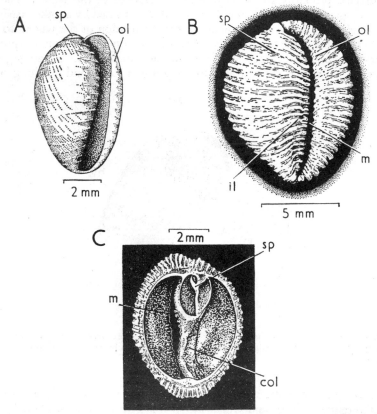

FIG. 28.—*Trivia monacha:* A, shell of young animal showing exposed spire; B, shell of adult with concealed spire (convolute); C, shell of adult halved to show internal spire.
col, columella; il, inner lip; m, mouth of shell; ol, outer lip; sp, spire.

the columella and to it is attached the great columellar muscle by contraction of which the head and foot of the animal may be withdrawn into the shell. In most species the surface of the columella is smooth, but in some, such as *Monodonta* and *Odostomia*, there is a tooth on the columella, i.e. a tooth-shaped projection on its lower end, visible when the intact shell is examined (tcl, fig. 281). This will, obviously, be the end of a ridge which runs the length of the columella and provides extra surface for the origin of the columellar muscle. In some species (Harpidae) more than one such fold may occur, when the columella may present a plaited appearance. These 'teeth' or plications are probably due to secretion of material over the surface of the columella by a mantle which has outgrown the space available for it and which has therefore become folded. Folds will be most marked when the mollusc is withdrawn into the shell and this will in turn depend in part upon whether the origin of the columellar muscle (which pulls upon the mantle edge) is remote—far up the columella—or near. It will also be related to the pull of the muscle and is a more likely development where that is excessive, as in animals with a long proboscis.

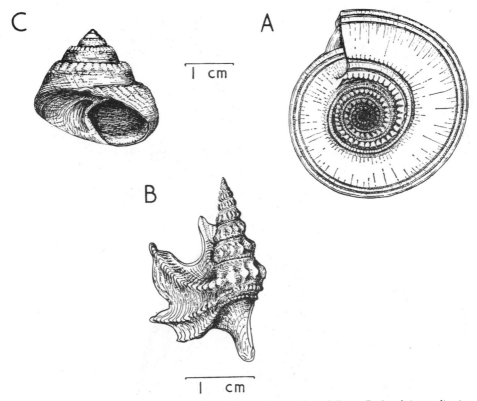

FIG. 29.—Shells: A, *Architectonica* sp., seen from below to show wide umbilicus; B, *Aporrhais pespelicani*, to show expanded outer lip; C, *Gibbula magus*, to show adapical ribs, and reduced umbilicus.

At the lower end of the helicocone lies the mouth or aperture (fig. 34A) of the shell, through which the body of the gastropod extends during life. The edge of the mouth, the growing zone of the shell, is known as the peristome and may be considered as composed of an outer lip or labrum (lying away from the axis of the shell) and an inner or columellar lip or labium (lying close to the axis of the shell). The degree of development of the margin of the mouth varies greatly from one kind of gastropod to another rarely indeed does it project as a free edge all round as it does in *Pomatias elegans*. More commonly the right side of the aperture (as viewed in dextral shells seen in apertural view) is complete, forming the outer lip, but the left, forming the inner or columellar lip, is much less well developed, and may be reduced to little more than a callus or glaze detectable on the outside of the previous whorl of the shell. Indeed, in some animals, even this sign of inner lip appears to be absent and the peristome can then be regarded as composed of a U-shaped edge, the circle being completed by the wall of the previous whorl applied to the arms of the U. This is an area known frequently as the parietal wall—as Cox (1955) commented, a most unfortunate term which he suggested might be replaced by the term parietal region. That part of the inner lip which runs over the surface of the previous whorl is also known as the parietal lip.

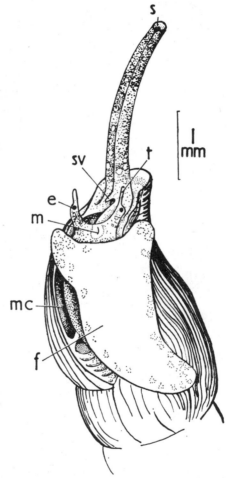

FIG. 31.—*Mangelia powisiana:* alive, in ventral view, with extended siphon.
e, eye; f, foot; m, mouth; mc, mantle cavity; s, siphon; sv, valve at base of siphon; t, tentacle.

The peristome may be, and in some primitive shells is, a plane structure. With advance in evolution, however, this may no longer be true and the peristome exhibits a complex tridimensional curvature; some of the changes leading to this are given below and it is clear that they have a functional basis and may be understood in terms of the animal's way of living. Other changes, however, which cannot so far be interpreted in any such way also affect the peristome, although these seem somehow to be concerned with the

FIG. 30.—Shells. Top left, *Emarginula reticulata*, × 11. Top right, *Diodora apertura*, × 4. Bottom right, *Patina pellucida pellucida*, from fronds of *Laminaria*, × 7. Bottom left, *Patina pellucida laevis*, from holdfast of *Laminaria*, × 6.

(*facing p.* 58).

change from primitiveness to an advanced state. One of these, mentioned by Davies (1939), is the angle which the plane of the peristome makes with the axis of the helicocone round which it rotates: in shells like those of *Calliostoma*, *Gibbula* (fig. 34B) or *Haliotis* the peristomial plane cuts the central axis at an angle of about 70°, whereas in most higher prosobranchs, mesogastropods and stenoglossans (fig. 34C) alike, the angle becomes very small. Davies remarked that this change in angle seems to be a necessary prerequisite for such further evolution in the peristome as the formation of siphonal canals, though the underlying functional significance is not apparent.

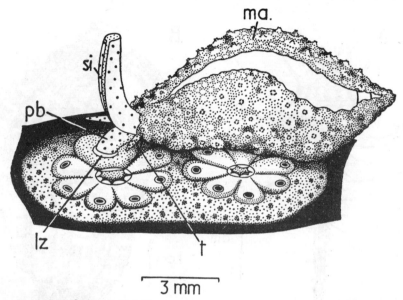

FIG. 32.—*Erato voluta:* feeding on *Botryllus*.
lz, lip of mouth of zooid; ma, mantle extended over outer surface of shell; pb, proboscis thrust into oral siphon of zooid of *Botryllus*; si, siphon; t, tentacle.

In the majority of prosobranchs the peristome is entire, that is, it forms a smooth curve from one end to the other. In a few of these animals, however, this curve is interrupted either by an ingrowth or by an outgrowth corresponding to similar changes in the shape of the edge of the underlying mantle skirt. An embayment there gives rise to a marginal slit at the lip of the shell as in *Emarginula* (fig. 30), *Scissurella* (fig. 256A), young specimens of *Puncturella* and *Diodora* and at times, *Haliotis* (see below, p. 69).

An outgrowth of the mantle edge occurs locally on the left side in prosobranchs of the families Cerithiidae, Cerithiopsidae, Triphoridae, Lamellariidae, Eratoidae, Muricidae, Buccinidae, Nassariidae, Fasciolariidae and Turridae and the shell is expanded correspondingly. In the first three families (fig. 26C) the degree of outgrowth is slight, forming a spoon-shaped bulge on the mantle edge and an expansion of similar shape on the peristome where the outer lip runs on to the lower end of the columella. In the other families this expansion of the mantle edge forms a long outgrowth which is kept rolled into a tubular form and which is mobile and muscular (s, fig. 31): it is an inhalant siphon and allows the gastropod to draw water into the mantle cavity either whilst it burrows, or from a spot remote from that which its movement or its feeding may be fouling. In these siphonate forms the shell is usually drawn out into a siphonal tube for the accommodation of the pallial siphon (sit, fig. 33A), though this has not happened in eratoids (fig. 32) and lamellariids. The length of the siphonal or anterior canal of the shell and of the pallial siphon do not necessarily correspond—*Buccinum undatum* (fig. 277) and *Nassarius reticulatus* (fig. 274) for example, have long siphons and short canals, whereas in some species of *Trophon*, and more particularly in some foreign species of *Murex* (fig. 33A), the siphonal canal may be very long and the siphon not protrude much from it.

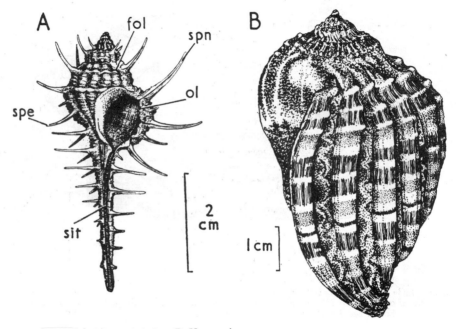

FIG. 33.—Shells: A, *Murex tenuispina*; B, *Harpa major*.
    fol, former position of outer lip; ol, outer lip; sit, siphonal tube; spe, spine which will be removed because it obstructs aperture when growth next occurs; spn, spine on outer lip.

The siphonal canal is normally open along one side like the siphon, but may, as in *Ocenebra erinacea* (figs. 36, 271), be closed by fusion of the edges.

At the opposite end of the aperture, where the outer lip abuts adapically against the surface of the body whorl, a posterior notch or canal is occasionally developed as an outgrowth of the peristome (e.g. some conids). This accommodates the right side of the mantle edge where the rectum ends and so permits the faecal products to be directed away from the body on discharge. This corresponds functionally to the slit or hole of zeugobranchs but has been separately evolved.

It will be useful at this stage to introduce some other terms used in the topographical description of the gastropod shell before turning to the question of what ornamentation its surface may bear (fig. 34A). In the majority of shells the constituent whorls are visible, but all except the youngest are partially concealed by overlap of later formed turns.

When the mollusc retracts itself within the shelter of the shell the most recently formed whorl naturally contains its head and foot, whereas older whorls never contain anything except the visceral mass: for this reason the youngest whorl, the whole external surface of which is visible, is called the body whorl. It extends back from the aperture for one complete turn of the helicocone, and its height is to be measured by the distance between the lowest point on the apertural rim and the point nearest the apex of the shell (its

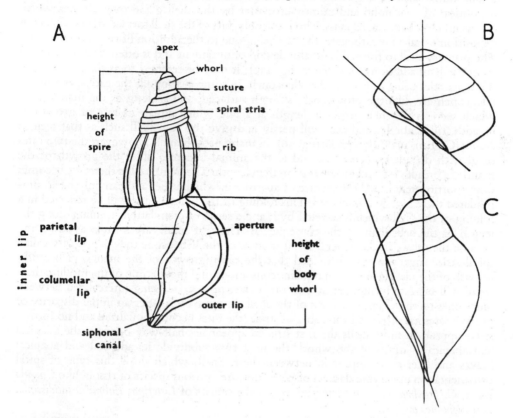

FIG. 34.—A, diagram of gastropod shell to explain some of the terms used in its description; B, shell of a trochid compared with C, shell of *Nucella*, to show difference in the angle made by the outer lip and vertical axis.

extreme adapical point) at the level at which the body whorl begins. The remainder of the shell is known as the spire. Its height is to be measured by the distance between the apex and the lowest visible point (the extreme abapical point) on its youngest whorl. The basis of measurement of the whorls in these two cases is thus different, but is justifiable on the fact that much of the general appearance of a shell is linked with the ratio between the height of the body whorl and the height of the spire and the latter is, in turn, largely dependent upon the degree to which each of the whorls is covered by its successor in the helicocone. A further measurement of the shell which helps to express its general appearance is the degree of swelling exhibited by the helicocone, that is, the diameter of its constituent tube. This may be measured by the size of the broadest part of the body whorl, which is known as its periphery, and which is clearly equal to twice the greatest radius of the body whorl. This measurement will also be related to the apical angle $\alpha$.

The initial shell of a gastropod is secreted during embryonic or larval life by the deposition of conchiolin and calcareous matter by the shell gland over an area which covers much of the visceral mass. This is the only part of the shell formed by simultaneous deposition of calcium carbonate, the rest being due to the addition of rings to its mouth. The primary shell so formed is usually devoid of ornament and is often clearly separated from the later additions (*Aclis minor*, fig. 239); it may be referred to as the protoconch, the remainder being known as the teleoconch. In some gastropods the early parts of the teleoconch are, like the protoconch, smooth surfaced, and so long as the mantle skirt which secretes the shell grows in length at a rate which equals its rate of growth in breadth, this smooth condition will persist and give rise to a shell such as that seen in *Natica* (Grabau, 1928) or *Tricolia* (fig. 36). In many prosobranchs, however, the two rates of growth do not remain equal and as the animal becomes older the growth of the mantle in breadth is greater than its growth in length. The mantle edge therefore becomes disproportionately broad for the size of aperture in which it lies and can only be accommodated there by being puckered. This folding of the mantle edge will be reflected in a folding of the shell which is secreted by it and a series of crenulations running along the length of the helicocone is the consequence. These, if small, are known as striae and because they share in the general spiral motion of the helicocone they are usually called spiral striae (figs. 34A, 35). Provided that the ratio (growth of the mantle in breadth/ growth of the mantle in length) remains constant during the lifetime of the mollusc these striae will increase in number at a constant rate, new striae being intercalated between older ones on the younger whorls of the shell. In some cases, after an initial disparity of growth rates has produced a number of striae, the rates become equalized and no further striae appear. In most shells the first stria to appear lies half-way between the adapical and abapical margins of the whorl, the next two subdivide its adapical and abapical halves and later series appear in between these. Shells which show this type of spiral ornamentation in varying degrees of perfection are: various species of rissoid like *Cingula alderi, C. proxima, C. semistriata* (fig. 293B); the species of *Littorina*; *Eulimella nitidissima*, and *Neptunea antiqua*.

In a further series of prosobranchs the spiral striae do not remain of equal prominence but some become exaggerated in height and appear more prominent than others. This is particularly noticeable in the shells of some trochids, such as *Calliostoma zizyphinum* (fig. 26D), and it is also to be seen in *Alvania carinata, Turritella communis* (fig. 37A), *Aclis minor* and *Trichotropis borealis*. One particular form taken by this exaggeration of spiral striae is that in which the first formed one becomes simultaneously exaggerated and angulated. This may often occur along with a flattening of the rest of the surface of the whorl, especially of that part which lies adapical of the angulated stria; the wall of the whorl below the main stria may also flatten on occasion, but does so much more seldom. This arrangement suggests that the exaggerated stria results from the presence of one large fold of the edge of the mantle skirt which accommodates all the surplus breadth. The result is an angulated shell, showing a shoulder projecting around the adapical part of each whorl, with or without other spiral striae abapically. The appearance of the shell varies greatly with (a) the position on the whorl—adapical or abapical—of the angulated

FIG. 35.—Shells.  Top left, *Nucella lapillus*, abapertural view,  × 2.  Top right, *Nucella lapillus*, mature, apertural view,  × 2.  Bottom left, *Nassarius reticulatus*, mature, apertural view,  × 2.  Bottom right, *Nassarius incrassatus*, young, apertural view,  × 4.

(facing p. 62).

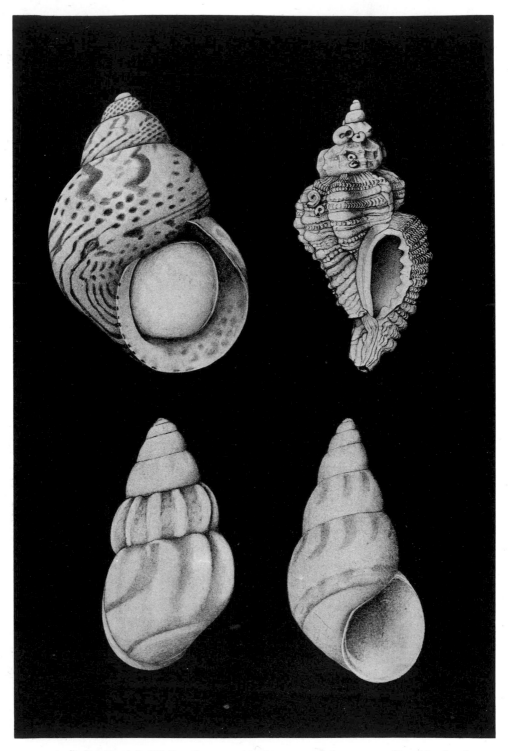

Fig. 36.—Shells. Top left, *Tricolia pullus*; note the calcareous operculum, × 10. Top right, *Ocenebra erinacea*, × 2. Bottom left, *Rissoa parva*, ribbed shell, abapertural view, showing characteristic comma-shaped pigment streak on upper part of outer lip, × 18. Bottom right, *Rissoa parva* var. *interrupta*, smooth shell, apertural view, × 18.

(facing p. 63).

stria and (*b*) the relationship between this and the degree of overlap of two successive whorls. When the angle is low down on the whorl and is placed at the suture line with the next whorl a straight-sided trochoid shell results (fig. 26D). If the angle made by the stria is obtuse the effect on the body whorl is such that the shell tapers at the base (e.g. *Turritella communis*, fig. 37A); if it is acute the base may be flat, as in *Calliostoma*, or even concave. The angle may, however, be placed high up on the whorl. If this is, again, coincident with the suture line between whorls then a straight-sided spire results, but this time the spire is short in relation to the length of the rest of the shell as in *Conus* (figs.

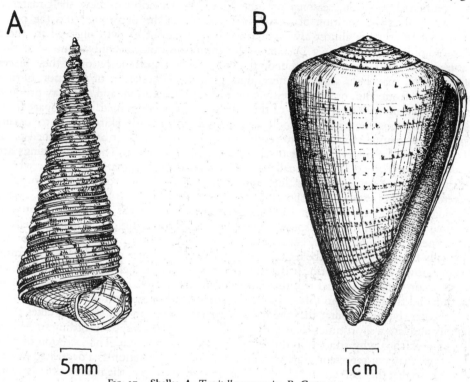

A

B

5mm

1cm

Fig. 37.—Shells: A, *Turritella communis*; B, *Conus* sp.

37B, 38A); if the succeeding whorl embraces the older coil below the angle then an angulated or turreted shell results, the length of its spire varying with the degree of whorl left exposed at each turn and also with the angle made by the shell adapical of the angle and the axis. If the shoulder slopes then the spire will be tall (fig. 26B); if the shoulder angle comes to lie at right angles to the axis of the shell then a pagoda-like outline may be produced. Not many British shells can be used to illustrate these varieties of angulated shells, but a few show them complicated either by the presence of subsidiary striae in the abapical half of each whorl or by the presence of other types of ornamentation to be described below. Shells of this type are exemplified by *Alvania carinata*, *Aporrhais pespelicani* (fig. 29B), *Trophon barvicensis*.

The spiral striae running along the course of the helicocone represent a continuous element in the architectural ornamentation of the shell. There is, in addition, a discontinuous element represented by structures which lie across the helicocone and which, therefore, are elongated in a direction more or less parallel to the axis of the shell. If they are precisely parallel to it they may be described as orthocline, if they are inclined at their adapical end towards the direction of growth of the helicocone they are called prosocline, if in the opposite sense, opisthocline. Prosocline structures are of much commoner occurrence than opisthocline.

The occurrence of this element in shell architecture is due to the fact that the fundamental growth process is discontinuous and may be made more so by its reaction to environmental variation, seasonal or otherwise. The secretion of new shell material always involves the addition of a strip of substance to the peristome, and the outer surface of the shell is almost always marked by a series of growth lines where these strips adjoin one another (e.g. *Natica*, where they constitute the only element of this nature in the shell). Superimposed upon the more or less regular secretion of these pieces of new shell may be a seasonal effect, due, perhaps, to cessation of secretion during hibernation from cold, or during aestivation to avoid desiccation, and this may produce marks by means of which the age of the animal may be determined. Quite apart from seasonal rhythms, however, periodic swelling of the mantle skirt seems to occur, especially in marine species, and to result in the formation of a greatly thickened piece of shell placed at intervals along the length of the helicocone. These thickenings are known as ribs (fig. 34) and are usually spaced with complete regularity along the whorls of the shell, suggesting that the thickening of the mantle edge, or the hypertrophied secretory activity which is responsible for their occurrence, is a rhythmical event, although it is difficult to see any underlying reason for it as it is clearly not related to seasonal change and there are some species, e.g. *Rissoa parva* (fig. 36) in which shells of two types, ribbed and ribless, occur. In almost every individual shell in which ribs are normally found one rib will be found to coincide with the outer lip of the shell aperture: this is known as the labial rib. It is extremely rare to find a shell of a species in which these occur without a labial rib, that is to say, in the period between the secretion of one rib and the next. From this it may be deduced that the growth of the helicocone is not regular, but spasmodic; that the growth between one rib and the next takes place rapidly and lasts a short time—only 2 days in the case of *Murex* spp. according to Abbott (1954)—which is why animals in this state are only rarely found. The secretion of ribs, therefore, may not represent so much an increased rate of secretion as a decreased rate of growth, so that the shelly material which is produced piles up as the mantle skirt remains stationary. Some prosobranchs found in this country which show shells bearing ribs (with or without spiral striae) are: *Rissoa parva*, *R. inconspicua*, *Alvania crassa*, *Turbonilla elegantissima*, *Nassarius incrassatus* (fig. 35) and *Mangelia coarctata*.

Although it is possible to explain the formation of labial and other ribs as due either to an increased rate of secretion of shelly material recurring periodically, growth remaining constant, or, alternatively, to a decreased rate of growth recurring periodically whilst secretion remains constant, there are other events occurring in the formation of some shells which are more complex and seem to involve simultaneous change in both rate of growth and rate of secretion. These are structures such as varices and spines, which are advanced types of shell ornamentation evolved from ribs. They are exhibited by few British gastropods—indeed none shows either type of decoration in anything except a rudimentary form, and it is necessary to refer to exotic shells in quoting typical examples of both. Just as the secretion of shelly substance at the outer lip of the shell produces a labial rib (the position of the secretory mantle edge being constant), so a varix arises when the mantle edge turns outwards while still secreting. This produces an out-turned outer lip projecting more or less at right angles to the rest of the body whorl, perhaps ending smoothly, or in a number of points, or in a number of spines. Examples of this may be seen in *Clathrus* spp. (fig. 142) and in *Aporrhais pespelicani* (fig. 29B) amongst British shells and (particularly clearly) in such others as *Pterocera* and various species of the genus *Murex* (fig. 33A). In *Aporrhais* and *Pterocera* the expansion of the outer lip occurs only in the fully grown shell of which it is a permanent feature, but like the formation of ribs, the formation of out-turned lips may occur at regular intervals during the lifetime of the gastropod and the outer surface of the whorls will therefore be marked by a series of out-turned flanges, with or without spines, indicating previous positions occupied by the outer lip. It is these structures which are termed varices. They may be seen beautifully in *Clathrus* spp. and (on a small scale) in young specimens of *Nucella lapillus* (fig. 270) and in adults which have been living in deep water where the shell has not been worn smooth, and on shells of *Ocenebra erinacea*. *Trophon barvicensis* shows them, equally small, but partly decorated by spines. For the best examples of this type of structure, however, it is again necessary to quote from animals which are not found in this country: *Harpa* spp. (fig. 33B) show well formed, but simple varices, whilst species of *Murex* such as *M. tenuispina* (fig. 33A) or *M. palma-rosae* show them in a much more elaborate and spiny form. In the formation of these it is clear that a very considerable growth in the mantle edge has occurred, leading to a great increase in the amount of calcareous matter produced.

The secretion of varices or of spine rows which run across the whole breadth of a whorl, from its adapical to its abapical border, is clearly going to complicate the formation of the shell when, in the process of growth, the next turn of the helicocone brings the inner lip to lie alongside the former outer lip. In this position the varix will block much of the aperture and interfere with the movements of the animal in and out of the shell: in some cases indeed (*Murex tenuispina*) the length of the spines is so great that they project completely across the aperture and beyond the outer lip. In these circumstances it is necessary for the spines or the varix to be removed from that part of the older whorl about to be overgrown by the younger. How this is undertaken is not known, but it is presumably by the same process as erosion of shell (though on a much less impressive scale) is known to be achieved in other instances (see p. 68).

If a shell exhibiting ribs or varices or spine rows is examined (fig. 142) it will be noticed that successive varices are not arranged in rows the projection of which on an axial plane would be parallel to the axis of the shell, but that they run in spirals which coil in a direction opposite to that in which the shell itself is turning. This indicates a steady decrease in the proportional amount of shell which is laid down between the 'quiescent' periods—or, alternatively expressed, the periods during which the animal makes new shell become progressively shorter. This has been regarded by Grabau (1902) as an indication that Minot's law of senescence applies to these animals, which show signs of ageing from the very start of their existence. This may be so, but it is well to remember that the size of ribs, varices, spines and other outgrowths gets progressively greater as the size of a shell increases and it may be that the total physiological activity of the animal, in the secretion of shell plus ornamentation, increases steadily throughout its lifetime.

The two types of structure described above, spiral striae and ribs, are the bases of ornamentation of the gastropod shell: the former is in Davies' phrase (1939) a 'space-rhythm', the latter a 'time-rhythm'. Either may occur alone, but more frequently both

4

kinds are present and the definitive structure of the shell is achieved by means of the interaction of the two types of architecture. In many cases there is produced in this way a simple network or reticulation over the surface of the shell; sometimes, as in many of the Stenoglossa, the spiral striae run clearly over the surface of the ribs of the shell, sometimes, as in *Chrysallida* and *Turbonilla*, the ribs run equally obviously over the striae, but in many others the two reinforce one another at the nodes of the reticulation and produce a surface elevated into bosses or short tubercles where ribs and striae cross. This is well seen in many British shells: *Cantharidus striatus*, *Alvania cancellata*, *Bittium reticulatum*, *Triphora perversa*, *Cerithiopsis tubercularis* (fig. 26C), *Nassarius reticulatus* (fig. 35) and *Philbertia asperrima* will serve as examples. In other shells such as those in which spines occur it will be discovered that these also are located at points where ribs and striae cross (e.g. *Murex* spp.) and the points on the expanded lip of *Aporrhais* (fig. 29B) and *Pterocera* are similarly related to striae. This reticulation or cancellation of the surface is also related to the colour pattern of the shell (see p. 75).

In the examples which have been discussed so far the decorative elements of the shell surface have been supposed to affect the entire extent of the whorls. This, however, is by no means necessarily so, and it is common to find that the adapical part is decorated in a different way from the abapical half. This will, in most cases, be detectable only on the body whorl because that is normally the only coil of which the abapical half is visible. A common difference of this sort is the disappearance of ribs over the abapical part of the whorl so that they form small projections limited to the adapical region. Frequently, too, their interaction with striae is graded from a maximum in the adapical region to a minimum abapically. This tendency is particularly noticeable in angulated shells where the primary stria is exaggerated, and if this interacts with ribs (which may also be exaggerated adapically) there is produced a series of prominent tubercles or spines on the keel of the whorl.

Some examples of British prosobranchs showing a limitation of ribs to the adapical part of the whorls are: *Gibbula magus* (fig. 29C), *Rissoa parva* (fig. 36), *Cingula semicostata* (fig. 293A). *Buccinum undatum* and many other Stenoglossa show ribs on the shell which become less and less prominent towards the abapical parts of the whorls, finally disappearing. *Lora trevelliana*, *L. turricula* (fig. 26B), *Trophon barvicensis*, are native shells showing an approach to a turreted outline, but few British shells show this distinctly; for examples of these one must again have recourse to prosobranchs from abroad, e.g. *Tectarius pagoda*, *Melanatria fluminea*, *Melania amàrula*, *Cerithium nodulosum*, and some cones, like *Conus marmoreus*.

In addition to the striae, ribs, spines and other kinds of external processes which may appear on the shell of a prosobranch gastropod a certain amount of similar growth is also found to occur internally, though normally to a much lesser extent. This is in addition to the secretion of aragonite which goes on over the whole of the internal surface, and, in most cases, is limited to the inner region of the lips and to mature animals. So long as the animal is immature and further shell growth is likely to occur the outer lip remains thin and sharp-edged. When maturity is reached, growth of the helicocone ceases at least in some cases and the only further deposition of calcareous matter leads to the formation of a thicker lip to the aperture of the shell and to the appearance of bosses, tubercles or teeth projecting into the mouth. This takes place in a very distinct way in the dog whelk *Nucella lapillus*, young specimens of which (fig. 27D) are found to have a thin lip devoid of internal processes, whereas mature specimens (fig. 35) show a thick, blunt-edged outer lip carrying a number of rounded projections internally. Those on the inside of the outer lip are often related to the striae on its external surface, as if the same overactive parts of the mantle skirt were responsible for both sets of structures (*Nassarius*, fig. 35). The appearance of these ingrowths at maturity is not, perhaps, widespread amongst prosobranchs though they are visible in many Stenoglossa and in *Trivia*, but the thickening of the outer lip at maturity is common.

Changes in the shape of the aperture with age and in the development of a labial rib have been correlated with stages in the maturity of the reproductive system of *Rissoa parva* by Gostan (1958). He has shown a correspondence between the appearance of the shell and sexual development summarized in Table 1.

TABLE I

| Shell | Reproductive system |
|---|---|
| No ribs | Rudimentary |
| 1st rib; angulated outer lip, no labial rib | Gonad and duct unlobed, solid Gonad lobed, duct hollow |
| Ribs; rounded outer lip, no labial rib | Sexes recognizable |
| Ribs; labial rib | Mature |

Other changes may also occur with the onset of maturity. In animals of the genus *Trivia* (and of the Cypraeidae) the young shell shows a short spire with a large, smooth body whorl. When mature, however, the pattern of coiling changes and the shell becomes convolute, the mature body whorl enveloping all those of greater age (fig. 28). In addition to this the eratoids and cypraeids differ from other prosobranchs in that the mantle skirt extends beyond the edge of the shell and may completely cover the entire external surface (figs. 32, 214). Like any other part of the mantle this secretes shell, but adds it to the outer surface of the body whorl, not the inner. As a result this becomes overlaid by a polished sheet of material which obscures much of the irregularity normally seen on the outer surface of a prosobranch shell, and results in the smooth, glossy surface familiar in the shell of all cowries, although in *Trivia* it bears striae. Pelseneer (1932) called this the epiostracum. The same overgrowth of the mantle, but followed by fusion of the right and left halves, gives the wholly internal shell of *Lamellaria* (fig. 294), which is also glossy.

In addition to these internal growths on the lips or columella which, according to Dall (1889), take place because the mouth has become too large for the animal living within, but which might equally be due to folding of the mantle for the very reverse reason, similar ingrowths may occur throughout the inner surface of the helicocone. Alternatively septa may be laid down to separate the uppermost whorls of the spire, into which the visceral hump no longer extends, from the lower ones which it occupies, or within these whorls so as to exclude a peripheral part of their volume and leave only a central part alongside the columella for the visceral mass to lie in. These changes are particularly common in shells with tall spires. Ingrowths from the columella encroaching on the cavity of the whorls are particularly well known in prosobranchs of the family Cymatiidae (e.g. *Distortrix*), whilst the formation of septa is seen in the shells of terebrids, melaniids, vermetids and cerithiids (fig. 38A). In *Caecum* (fig. 38B) and a few other genera such as *Truncatella* (figs. 314A, B) a septum is laid down, when the animal has grown to a certain size, in such a way as to close off completely the upper coils of the shell, which are then broken off and lost. This truncated shell is said to be decollated. In the case of *Caecum*, the shell of which is coiled in an open spiral, this occurs twice or several times and gives the animal the appearance of living inside a shell which is a

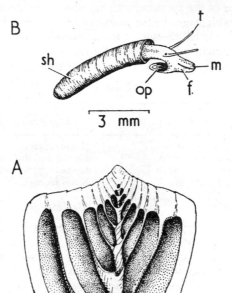

FIG. 38.—A, *Conus* sp., shell in longitudinal section to show internal septa; B, *Caecum glabrum*, from life. f, foot; m, mouth; op, operculum; sh, shell; t, tentacle.

slightly arched tube, bearing little resemblance to the coiled spiral shell of the typical prosobranch.

It is well known that the molluscan mantle has not only the power of secreting shelly substance but is equally capable of removing what has already been secreted: examples of this have already been given in dealing with shells possessing varices and spines. In addition to removing such obstructive growths the mantle may also remove internal parts of the shell, either as part of a remodelling, or wholly, so as to give the animal greater freedom of movement within the shell. These alterations must, of course, not interfere radically with the mechanical strength of the shell, although they may in certain cases be relatively extensive, as in the pulmonates of the family Ellobiidae described by Crosse & Fischer (1882) and by Morton (1955), in which the whole of the older part of the columella and the internal parts of the upper whorls are absorbed. The same thing has been shown to occur in many neritids (Woodward, 1892) and in some cones, though in these animals the internal partitions are not removed, but merely reduced in thickness.

The above description of the formation and decoration of the prosobranch shell has been written primarily with reference to the shape of shell which is most commonly found in that group of gastropods, the spirally coiled helicocone. There are, however, a number of special cases to be considered, in which the shell appears—at least superficially—to possess not this shape, but some other. One of these has already been mentioned in referring to the genus *Caecum*, the shell of which is a short curved tube, related to the more usual prosobranch shell as explained above. Many prosobranchs have conical shells with, in the adult condition, little or no apparent sign of spiral coiling, and the question may be asked how these shells have been produced. They vary amongst themselves, too, in that some (*Patella, Propilidium, Patina* (fig. 30), *Acmaea*) are simple cones, others (*Calyptraea, Crepidula* (fig. 39A)) have internal partitions, whilst still others have apical holes (*Diodora* (fig. 30), *Puncturella*) or marginal slits (*Emarginula*, fig. 30). The first and last of these have all been derived from a spirally wound helicocone of which they represent the body whorl, the whole of the spire having been lost. This shape is due to the fact that increase in the radius of the helicocone occurs very rapidly, so that the initial turns of the spiral are minute and disappear easily. In young limpets of any one of these genera (figs. 40A, D) the spire of the shell is visible as a small coil at the apex of the expanded terminal part in which the body of the animal is housed, but it has no internal cavity, which has been early sealed off by shelly substance, and it is usually rapidly eroded so as to be no longer visible. Since the conical shell of a limpet represents the body whorl of the helicocone with the aperture clamped against the substratum, the spiral striae are represented by the ribs which radiate from its apex, and the growth lines by lines parallel to the mouth of the shell. As in more typical prosobranchs these frequently interact to give a reticulated pattern over the surface, particularly well seen in *Emarginula* spp. (fig. 30) and in *Diodora apertura* (fig. 30), less clearly in *Patella* spp. and hardly at all in such smooth-shelled animals as *Patina* (fig. 30), *Acmaea* or *Calyptraea*.

In *Emarginula* the slit which extends from the margin is due to the mantle underneath being similarly split, the opening overlying the anus and excretory apertures and allowing escape of the respiratory water current from the mantle cavity. With growth of the shell the slit becomes filled in with shelly material at its upper end, its previous positions being marked by this, forming a feature on the shell known as the slit band. A similar appearance is to be found on the shells of *Scissurella* (fig. 256) and the pleurotomariids, which have the usual spiral shape. In *Puncturella* and *Diodora* (figs. 40A, B) the young shell looks like an *Emarginula*, with a marginal slit, but with further growth the mantle edges come together again at the lower end of the slit, re-unite and so convert what was an emargination into a perforation through the mantle skirt. In *Puncturella* this lies on the anterior face of the shell, but in *Diodora* it comes to occupy the summit of the cone. In both it serves as an exit for the pallial water stream. In *Haliotis* (fig. 85) a series of such holes forms with growth of the shell, of which the 5–6 youngest are open, older ones being sealed internally by nacre. In *Puncturella* and *Diodora* only one hole exists. As it grows in size with growth of the shell it is clear that its margins must be resorbed by the mantle which lines it.

The remaining limpets, *Calyptraea* (fig. 40D) and *Crepidula* (fig. 39A), have shells which are derived from the ordinary spiral gastropod shell in a different way, giving a simple conical shell in the former genus (Chinaman's hat) but one retaining a distinct

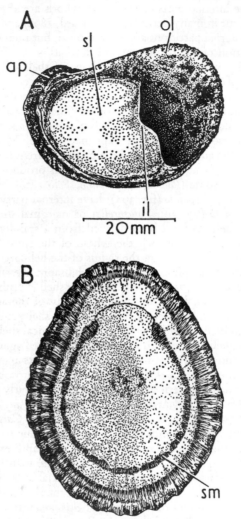

FIG. 39.—Shells of limpets in ventral view: A, *Crepidula fornicata*, the slipper limpet; B, *Patella vulgata*, the common limpet.
    ap, apex of shell; il, inner lip of shell; ol, outer lip of shell; sl, shelf; sm, attachment of shell muscle.

spiral coiling in the latter (slipper limpet). Both are easily distinguished from the shells of other limpets by the occurrence of a shelf or septum partially subdividing the internal cavity (fig. 39A). This is a specialization due to the behaviour of the mantle during development, well described by Werner (1955). The unhatched larval stage of *Crepidula fornicata* possesses a shell (fig. 41A) which is formed partly of a single conical piece secreted by the shell gland, and which is the protoconch, and partly of a number of pieces added to this by secretion from the edge of the mantle skirt. The result is a shell coiled spirally in a plane, the mouth, before torsion, overhanging the posterior end of the animal and the apex the anterior end (exogastric coiling), after torsion these positions being reversed (endogastric coiling). At this stage the shell is symmetrical, its plane of symmetry being

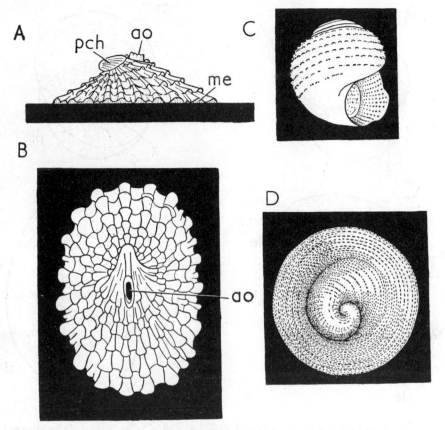

FIG. 40.—Shells of recently metamorphosed animals. A, *Diodora apertura*, from life, in side view from the right; B, *Diodora apertura*, shell of the same specimen in apical view; C, *Alvania punctura*, from life; D, *Calyptraea chinensis*, apical view showing protoconch.
ao, apical opening; me, mantle edge; pch, protoconch.

coincident with the sagittal plane of the body. The veliger hatches and takes up a pelagic existence, and during this shell growth continues, but becomes asymmetrical. The right side of the mantle skirt starts to grow much more rapidly than the left, the growth rate of which is very slow, and the shell secreted by the mantle also becomes asymmetrical. The result is the formation of a shell (fig. 41B) which is greatly expanded laterally but of low height, possessing a relatively enormous mouth and resembling that of *Haliotis* in general shape. At this stage the left half of the mantle skirt has come to lie ventrally and the whole of the dorsal, right and left parts of the mouth of the shell are lined by the expanded right half. As a consequence of the restricted space available to it because of this change in orientation, the left half of the mantle expands posteriorly underneath the older part of the shell in that area. It does not cease from the production of shelly material in this position, however, and so gives rise to a small ledge of calcareous material running round the posterior part of the body whorl at the level to which its edge reaches (fig. 41C).

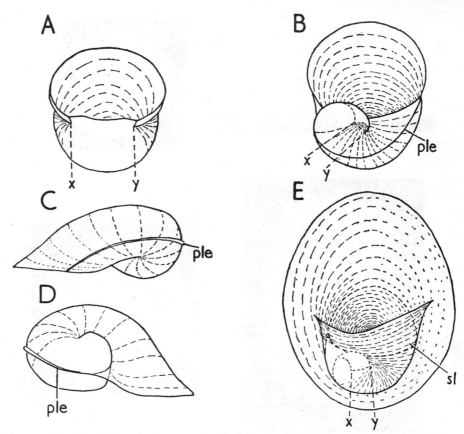

FIG. 41.—*Crepidula fornicata:* development of adult shell.   A, shell of veliger stage ready for hatching, from below; B, shell of older veliger, from below; C, shell of veliconcha stage, from left; D, shell of veliconcha stage from right; E, shell of young metamorphosed animal, from below.   After Werner.

   ple, mantle line (the beginning of the septum); sl, septum; x and y mark corresponding points in figures A, B and E.

This is the so-called pallial line (ple) on the shell, but it is, in fact, the beginning of a pronounced calcareous ledge which is gradually built on to the posterior part of the shell and which comes to link itself anteriorly with the right and left edges of the greatly expanded mouth of the shell derived from the right half of the mantle (fig. 41D). In this way the beginnings of a limpet-like shell are achieved, the bulk of it from the activity of the right pallial half, the smaller posterior half from the shell edge ('rim' of Moritz, 1939) produced by the posterior tip of the back-turned left pallial half ('accessory mantle fold' of Moritz, 1939). When this stage is reached the two parts of the mantle become fused and are no longer distinguishable one from the other.

When this fusion of the different parts of the mantle has occurred it follows that the posterior part of the shell, on the underside, is now covered by mantle both inside and out—the former by the proximal part of the mantle skirt, the latter by the posteriorly reflected distal part—and at the mouth of the shell these two layers join one another at an angle approaching 360°. Over all this surface calcareous matter continues to be secreted and results in the complete covering over of the original spire of the shell, so as to render it invisible from below, and also, at the point where the mantle is bent backwards, in the formation of a sheet of calcareous material gradually growing forwards towards the anterior end. This is the septum (sl), which gives the shell of all members of the family Calyptraeidae a characteristic appearance and which also provides, on its underside, a surface for the insertion of the pedal muscles by means of which attachment to the substratum is secured.

As has been seen, the production of shell material by a gastropod mollusc is not necessarily a steady process continuing throughout the lifetime of the animal: it merely seems so in the same way as a man's movement looks steady though made up of a number of separate steps. In addition to this regular discontinuity (as it may be called) there may also occur a certain number of more complete changes in the shell, which affect its ornamentation to a considerable degree, often changing it from one style to another, apparently quite sharply. These changes are connected primarily with the animal's age, and not, it would seem, with changes in the environment to which it is exposed, except that they are absent from all non-marine prosobranchs, the shell of which, like that of pulmonates, never shows anything but a gradual change from whorl to whorl. In others, the first occurs, not unexpectedly, at the point where the protoconch joins the teleoconch, no growth lines being visible on the former whereas they are on the latter, and the transition being also marked by a difference in opacity. The change takes place whilst the animal is still a larva or embryo and is therefore not due to changes occurring at metamorphosis. That event may, nevertheless, be marked by a rather abrupt change in the shell, either in the style of ornamentation, or by a varix, or, as in opisthobranchs, Pyramidellidae, Eulimidae, by a reversal of the direction of coiling, so that the initial turns are sinistral and the remainder dextral, a condition known as heterostrophy. Since it appears that the body of the animal within the sinistral coil is organized on a dextral basis, like that of *Lanistes*, this perhaps should also be regarded as a case of 'ultra-dextral' coiling. On the other hand, metamorphosis from a planktonic existence to a bottom dwelling life may leave no obvious mark on the shell, nor may the adoption of a free-living life after emergence from the egg capsule (*Aclis minor*, fig. 239).

During larval life and early metamorphosed life, however, the ornamentation of the shell may change abruptly at several points, each of these, in general, representing the addition of an extra element of ornamentation. One of these steps represents the final stage of decoration and this stage will then be retained for the remainder of the animal's lifetime, perhaps complicated at maturity by the formation of teeth or spines as cessation of ordinary growth takes place. Examples of this are to be seen in *Cingula vitrea* (=*Onoba vitrea* of Thorson, 1946) where the shell shows first an unornamented protoconch which changes abruptly to a shell showing spiral striae. In *Alvania punctura* (fig. 40c) a protoconch with a few spiral striae passes suddenly to a shell showing spiral striae on its abapical half but with small raised spots adapically; this changes to one with delicate ribs which finally interact with the striae to give a shell with a reticulate ornament. In *Tur-

*ritella communis* the protoconch develops as an unsculptured shell, but later whorls show the development of spiral striae some of which become exaggerated in still younger parts of the shell. *Bittium reticulatum* shows the same growth sequence, but adds to it a final stage in which ribs develop and combine with the striae, some of which are exaggerated, to produce the series of tubercles which characterize the shell of this species. A particularly clear case is that of *Lora trevelliana* (=*Bela trevelyana* of Thorson, 1946): in this species the initial part of the shell has a few dots on it, and the succeeding whorl develops spiral lines some of which eventually become transformed into exaggerated striae. At the beginning of the third turn ribs appear and give rise to a reticulated pattern on its surface. Further examples could be multiplied, but it is clear that there is a regular sequence in the development of sculpture on the shell of a gastropod. This has been claimed (e.g. by Grabau, 1928) to be a recapitulation of ancestral shell characteristics, but it is not safe to interpret the shell structure in this way. In so far as some aspects of patterning are essential prerequisites for the development of others, however (e.g. the presence of both spiral striae and ribs for the appearance of a reticulated or cancellated sculpture) these stages do have a certain ordinal significance and the sculpture may be of value as a sign of either primitiveness or advancement. Grabau's stages are as follows: smooth, round-whorled stage (naticoid); primitive ribbed, spiral stage; angulated, with nodes where ribs and striae cross; keeled stage; secondary round-whorled stage (by loss of sculpture); spinous stage; smooth stage (by loss of spines); loose spiral stage (by loss of power to coil, e.g. *Vermetus*). These later stages show gerontism in the disappearance of the sculptural characteristics of the shell.

The gastropod shell is frequently coloured. In some the predominant colour is that of an overlying periostracal layer, but in addition to that—and in animals where the periostracum is not evident—the calcareous material is usually pigmented by the inclusion of coloured substance. This is found in the outer layer of the shell only, which is, it will be recalled, the part secreted by the edge of the mantle skirt. This does not mean that the inner surface of the gastropod shell is inevitably colourless because, as is well known, the inner side of a shell like *Haliotis* or a top shell shows beautiful mother-of-pearl tints. However, this effect is physical in origin and it is the colouring of the shell by means of pigments of chemical nature which is confined to its outer layer. The chemical nature and possible origin of these substances are discussed on p. 135: here it is their relationship to the sculpturing of the surface of the shell which is of interest.

Like the ornament on the shell, its colour often shows specialization in space and time; and since its mere presence must mirror the activity of chromogenic cells in the mantle skirt, there must be a spatial differentiation of that part of the body with or without a superimposed temporal rhythm. If no pigmentation at all is produced at the mantle edge then the resulting shell is white, although it may be sufficiently translucent to acquire a spurious colour from the underlying viscera. If pigment is incorporated into the shell by adding secretion from pigment glands to the calcareous secretion, and if these glands lie uniformly along the length of the mantle skirt, then a uniformly coloured shell will result, the tint depending upon the nature and amount of pigment secreted. Uniformly coloured shells of this sort may be found, for example, in *Littorina littoralis* and *Barleeia rubra*. They are, however, unusual, and it is much more common to find a pattern in the colouring of the shell, which implies a secretion of pigment which is not uniform. If manufacture of pigment is localized at points or stretches of mantle edge which secrete continuously then the result is a series of spiral lines or bands of pigment as in *Eulima glabra*, *E. trifasciata*, *Lacuna parva*, *Cingula cingillus* and some specimens of

*Nucella lapillus* (fig. 35). Should the secretion of pigment be rhythmical and occur in outbursts of activity separated by rest periods, then these bands will be interrupted and appear as a line of dots or blocks of pigment as may be seen in *Alvania punctura* and *Natica catena* (fig. 304A).

In many other prosobranchs the ability to manufacture pigment for incorporation in the substance of the shell is present along the entire length of the mantle edge but only intermittently. As a result axial lines of colour may be produced in the shell, and if spiral lines are also present there may be produced a criss-cross of coloured lines precisely comparable to the reticulation of spiral striae and ribs in its sculpturing. Coloured 'ribs' of this sort are well seen in many trochids, *Rissoa guerini*, *Turritella communis* and *Neptunea antiqua*, whilst a reticulation due to interaction of the continuous spiral and discontinuous axial elements may be seen in some toxoglossans. Occasionally these axial lines fail to be complete, more particularly at the periphery of the whorls, an event which gives the impression that they are crossed by a light spiral band as in *Rissoa parva* (fig. 36). As with true ribs or spine rows these coloured lines or reticulations are set spirally down the whorls of the spire.

The two types of pigmentation referred to seem at first sight to be brought about by two different kinds of event in the edge of the mantle skirt. There are, however, a number of shells which show a type of pigment marking which links the one with the other. In *Tricolia pullus* (fig. 36), for example, the shell often bears a number of zigzag or V-shaped lines lying with the point of the V pointing up the helicocone towards the apex. This kind of mark suggests that at a particular instant of time a group of cells in the edge of the mantle skirt, previously quiescent or incapable of manufacturing pigment, suddenly burst into activity; and further, that a wave of secretion then passed along the edge of the mantle skirt away from this point, all cells relapsing into quiescence after a short burst of secretion. If the spread of the wave of metabolic activity is slow in relation to the rate of shell growth a long and narrow V mark results; if the reverse relationship holds, a wide V will be formed; if spread is more rapid in one direction than another then the V will be asymmetrical; whilst if the rate of propagation of the disturbed metabolism is one subject to acceleration or deceleration then a mark which is not rectilinear but curved will be the visible consequence. If the activity starts and stops abruptly the lines will be sharp; if either is slow then the lines may fade gradually into the background. This kind of marking is of frequent occurrence and may be seen on many trochids (fig. 26D) as well as on *Tricolia pullus* (fig. 36), *Rissoa parva*, *Theodoxus fluviatilis*, some specimens of *Littorina littoralis*, *Natica alderi*, and—perhaps the best known examples—such exotic shells as those of *Harpa major* (fig. 33B), *Cypraea zic-zac*, *Oliva porphyria* and *Conus geographus*. Where these zigzag lines may be traced across the entire breadth of a whorl, as in some specimens of *Tricolia pullus*, and as in some of the lines on *Harpa major*, they presumably represent a single transverse line which differs from the straight line seen in *Viviparus* (fig. 183A) only in that the ability to secrete pigments has not been developed at all points in the mantle edge simultaneously. In many cases, however, as in some shells of *Tricolia pullus* or those of *Oliva porphyria*, the jumble of short zigzags is so complicated and they are mixed with so many spots, blotches and short curves that it is difficult to decide whether the decoration results from the disorganization of axial lines or from the spreading of attempts to produce spiral lines.

The pigmentation of the shell in relation to its sculpture has been well examined by Wrigley (1932, 1934, 1942 and general discussion in 1948). From his work it is clear that there is, in general, an inverse relationship between pigment formation and excess secretion of calcareous matter. Where tubercles, spines, varices, teeth and similar out-growths occur, the secretion of pigment is reduced and these parts stand out as light coloured projections against the generally darker background of the rest of the shell. Pigment abounds in the areas between them. This is well seen in many shells: *Gibbula magus*, *Clathrus* spp., on ribbed specimens of *Rissoa parva*, *Aporrhais pespelicani*, *Bittium reticulatum*, *Cerithiopsis tubercularis*, *Nassarius* spp. and many toxoglossans. The physio-logical basis underlying this is obscure and it may be that better understanding would be obtained of the relationship were it thought of, not as a negative correlation between secretion of pigment and the formation of calcareous outgrowths, but as a positive correlation between pigment formation and the growth of the mantle skirt; for it will be recalled from the discussion above that the formation of tubercles, ribs and the like occurs during a period when shell and pallial growth has been arrested, whereas the areas between these—which are, as Wrigley points out, the pigmented parts—coincide with periods during which growth is maximal. If the formation of pigment were in any way connected with the increased metabolism which affects the mantle skirt during these periods, then it might be possible to assume that that is the cause of the material being added to the shell then, but not at other times.

Although much of the general structure, decoration and sculpture of the gastropod shell appears to be wholly unrelated to the environment in which the animal lives, this is not entirely so, as indicated by Berner (1942). He pointed out that *Murex brandaris* has long spines on muddy bottoms but only short ones on sand and rocks. This may, how-ever, be a spurious adaptation in that wear of the spines is less in the one case than in the other, just as it is possible to find shells of *Nucella lapillus* with an imbricated surface when they have grown in deep waters and on softer substrata, whereas those living on intertidal rocks suffer enough abrasion to remove these. The only difference between the case of *Nucella* and that of *Murex* is that the latter is susceptible of interpretation as an adaptation, the former is not. Other examples of the effect of the environment producing adaptations—or apparent adaptations—are variations in the height of *Patella* shells at different levels of the beach (see p. 501) and a thickening of the shells of *Nucella lapillus*, *Nassarius reticulatus* and some others in brackish habitats.

Because both the shell which covers the visceral hump of a prosobranch and the operculum which lies on the dorsal surface of its foot are made of a basis of conchiolin, more or less impregnated with salts of calcium, many malacologists have tried to show that the two structures are merely parts of one single shell. This view was originally put forward by the French naturalist Adanson (1757), and was supported by his compatriot Dugès in 1829, by the British worker Gray in 1850 and may still be encountered in conchological literature, as, for example, in Fleischmann (1932) and Pruvot-Fol (1954). On this theory the only univalves would be the cephalopods (unless the aptychus of ammonoids represents a second valve): gastropods and lamellibranchs would agree in being bivalved and the columellar muscle of the former could be equated with the adductors of the latter. The chitons remain distinct with a multivalvular shell difficult to homologize with that of the other molluscan classes, though Simroth (1896–1907) made the statement that he would like to homologize the gastropod shell with the anterior valves of a chiton and the operculum with the most posterior were it not for the fact that the last chiton valve is morphologically dorsal to the anus, whereas the gastropod operculum lies ventral to it.

De Blainville and Lamarck denied Adanson's proposition that the operculum and shell were homologous, on the ground that the one was a pallial secretion and the other pedal, but Dugès overcame this objection by supposing that the operculum was in fact secreted by the mantle skirt when the mollusc had withdrawn into the shell and was only secondarily associated with the foot. Doubtless this theory was the more easily tenable in view of the fact that the epiphragm produced by hibernating pulmonates, which looks and acts very much like a temporary operculum, is largely pallial in origin and is produced by stylommatophoran snails when retracted.

No real light was shed on the origin of the operculum and the different types which could be found in prosobranchs until the work of Houssay (1884), the majority of whose findings are current today, though a more recent re-investigation by Kessel (1942) has extended our knowledge considerably and corrected some mistakes of Houssay's. There is room, however, for a proper histochemical investigation of the secretion and regeneration of the prosobranch operculum.

Not all prosobranchs have an operculum when adult, but it seems to be ubiquitous in their larval stages. All those with a final limpet shape (*Haliotis, Emarginula, Puncturella, Diodora, Acmaea, Lepeta, Propilidium, Patina, Patella, Calyptraea, Crepidula* and *Capulus*) lose their operculum at metamorphosis, as do, also, a number of pelagic forms like *Ianthina* (Graham, 1954b) and the heteropods (Franc, 1949). In these cases the loss of the operculum can easily be related to the animals' mode of life, but the reason for its loss in a further series is obscure. In *Lamellaria*, with an internal shell, an operculum is clearly pointless and its absence understandable, whilst in the case of *Trivia* the narrowness of the mouth of the shell may perhaps render an operculum superfluous, but it is difficult to suggest any reason why some genera of stenoglossans (*Philbertia, Mangelia*) should have no operculum, whilst others—of almost identical structure and habits so far as is known—should possess one (*Lora, Haedropleura, Typhlomangelia*). The absence of an operculum in the eulimids and pyramidellids may be because of their parasitic habits, or because they have relations with the opisthobranchs within which group a trend towards loss of the operculum regularly occurs, even when the shell persists.

Houssay distinguished two types of operculum on a basis of whether they showed a spiral or a non-spiral construction. Kessel also distinguished two types of operculum, but based these on the material of which they were made—horny and calcareous. As all opercula turn out to be fundamentally similar, neither classification is wholly happy, but perhaps the division into spiral and other types is the better. A description of the operculum of a single species of prosobranch, *Littorina littorea*, has already been given (p. 14, fig. 4) and it will be recalled that the bulk of the operculum has its origin in a groove (oge) lying transversely across the dorsal surface of the foot. Here secretion goes on steadily throughout the lifetime of the mollusc, but although the foot is a bilaterally symmetrical part of the body the secretion of opercular material proceeds at a greater rate on the right side than on the left. The result of this is that the operculum is gradually pushed round in a clockwise direction (when examined in dorsal view) on the opercular disc on the foot. To its underside are attached muscle fibres belonging to the columellar muscle: as clockwise rotation of the growing operculum occurs these fibres must migrate, though the mechanism by which this is brought about seems to be completely unknown. As in other similar situations the muscle fibres end on epithelial cells through which tonofibrillae run to transmit the pull from muscle to operculum. Houssay (1884) believed epithelial cells were absent at the attachment of the operculum, but this was shown to be wrong by Fischer (1940a).

A further consequence of the asymmetrical addition of opercular material to its columellar edge (ce) and of the fact that the breadth of the added strip increases with growth of the mollusc, is that the operculum has a spiral structure with a nucleus representing the beginning of its formation. In an animal such as *Littorina* this lies towards the left side or siphonal edge (sis). The spiral, like the spiral of the shell, is an equiangular spiral and the rates of growth of the two structures are so adjusted that the operculum is always of approximately the same size as the mouth of the shell. Whereas the shell coils dextrally, however, the operculum coils sinistrally and vice versa, and this remains true even in hyperstrophic shells.

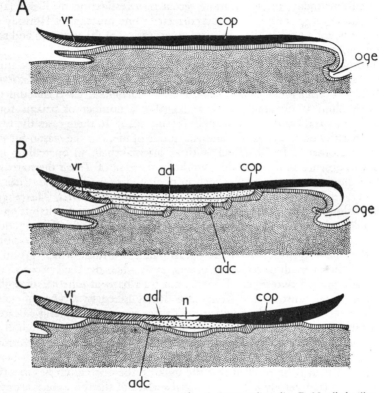

Fig. 42.—Diagrammatic sagittal sections of opercula: A, *Littorina littoralis*; B, *Nucella lapillus*; C, *Viviparus viviparus*. After Houssay and Kessel. Conchiolin layer is shown in solid black, varnish with diagonal hatching, adventitious layers stippled.
    adc, cells secreting adventitious layers; adl, adventitious layer; cop, conchiolin layer; n, nucleus; oge, opercular groove; vr, varnish.

The conchiolin or 'horny' material which is secreted in the opercular groove produces the bulk of the material out of which the operculum of *Littorina* is made, but not all. In addition a second substance is secreted from a groove placed across the foot underneath the posterior (sutural) edge of the operculum (vr, fig. 42A). This substance is therefore applied underneath the horny material. It is shiny and is for this reason known as the varnish or gloss; its chemical composition appears to be unknown.

The processes which have been described—secretion of conchiolin anteriorly, of varnish posteriorly and rotation—account for the production of the operculum in

*Littorina* and probably most of the prosobranchs in which a similar, spiral, horny operculum is to be found. Complication is limited to a stratification of alternate layers of conchiolin and gloss in older specimens. This is brought about by the rotation of the operculum. When the posterior edge, which has an outer layer of conchiolin and an under layer of gloss, rotates forward through 180°, the new conchiolin material will lie under the gloss; when that, at a still later stage, has rotated through a further 180° another layer of varnish will be applied under that again, so that a sandwich structure of alternating layers of conchiolin and gloss is finally produced.

In the cases so far mentioned the opercular groove stretches across a large part of the dorsal pedal surface. There appears, according to Kessel (1942), to be a trend leading to the shortening of this groove so that it becomes only a short slit on the right side of the foot. This is common in trochids (fig. 43A) and has the effect of producing an operculum of spiral pattern, but with a large number of turns instead of the small number found in animals like *Littorina* (fig. 43B). These opercula are known as polygyrous, whereas those of *Littorina* pattern are called oligogyrous. Apart from this difference in the size of opercular groove and the effects which stem from it the two kinds of operculum are identical.

The edges of the opercula described above, except for the columellar one which is buried in the opercular groove, are free and therefore flexible to some extent, since the conchiolin out of which they are made is not rigid. This means that some variation in the extent to which the animal withdraws into the shell is permissible, the opercular edge bending outwards as the animal withdraws further. With animals which possess a siphonal canal, it has been claimed that a more precise fitting of the opercular edge to the shell mouth is required and that this is achieved by an operculum which is not of spiral construction but which has a marginal or terminal nucleus and which grows in size by the addition of new material to the opposite edges. This style of operculum is that exhibited by the Stenoglossa, and is well shown by *Nucella* (fig. 42B) and *Nassarius* (fig. 43D). On its external face it presents a series of markings lying around the terminal nucleus (n) which represent growth lines. On its underside there shows a series of concentric marks related to an eccentric nucleus but bearing no relationship to the growth marks on the opposite side. In addition, the underside shows areas of different texture, one part (the greater) being roughened and representing the area of attachment of the columellar muscle, the other (limited to a strip around the labial margin drawn out to fine lines at the siphonal and sutural ends) being glossy and marking where varnish has been secreted. Over this area the concentric marks have been covered and lie under the gloss. Sections show that the conchiolin which forms the outer layer is secreted in an opercular groove as before, but that this does not cause a rotation of the operculum on the opercular disc, but merely a transverse gliding so ensuring that the projection which fits into the siphonal canal of the shell is not displaced. Gloss, therefore, never comes to be added all round the conchiolin but only along its labial edge which lies at the posterior end of the opercular disc, and the alternation of layers of conchiolin and varnish which occurs in spiral opercula is therefore never encountered in this type. It may also be seen from an examination of sections that the concentric markings on the underside of the operculum are due to the presence of plates of conchiolin lying below the main one. These are known as adventitious layers (adl, fig. 42B) and they presumably add strength to the operculum over the area to which the columellar muscle is attached. They are secreted by circles of gland cells in the epithelium of the opercular disc (adc). In the literature these are usually known as 'chitinogenous' cells, but this is a bad name and derives from times when anything of a cuticular nature was regarded as 'chitin' by the zoologist.

A certain number of opercula contain calcareous material as well as conchiolin. The amount of this may be relatively small as in *Pomatias elegans*, or considerable as in *Theodoxus fluviatilis*, or may constitute so prominent a part of the operculum as to leave

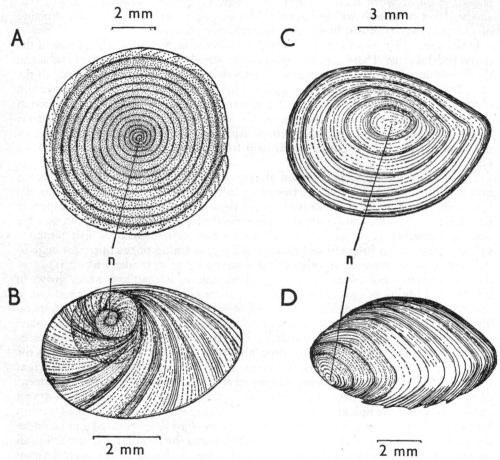

FIG. 43.—Opercula.   A, *Gibbula cineraria*, polygyrous spiral type;   B, *Littorina littorea*, oligogyrous spiral type;   C, *Viviparus viviparus*, concentric type;   D, *Nassarius reticulatus*, with marginal nucleus. n, nucleus.

it in doubt as to whether any other constituent can occur. This is the type of operculum found in turbinids in general, and in *Tricolia pullus* (fig. 36), the only British member of the family, which is immediately identifiable on this single feature. The two first of these are, in effect, simple spiral opercula in which the matter which is secreted is partly conchiolin, partly calcareous, as in the shell, but in the turbinids, according to Kessel, the secretion of the operculum follows a rather different course. The calcareous matter is produced, not by the opercular groove, but by the expanded margin of the opercular disc which forms the posterior lip of the groove, a structure which he calls the *Deckelsaum* or opercular flange. The conchiolin part of the operculum comes in the normal way from the opercular groove, but is applied underneath the calcareous operculum by an eversion of the opercular groove brought about by blood pressure and taking place in a rhythmical way. The whole structure rotates like any spiral operculum and this may give rise to a spiral keel of calcareous matter on the outer surface of the operculum as in *Turbo rugosus*. In other cases (*Tricolia pullus*) the outer surface may be completely smooth, whilst in others again (*Turbo sarmaticus*) the outside may be irregularly roughened. In all of these a varnish underlies the calcareous matter.

Some other opercula appear to be built on a pattern which is different from those already described. These are the concentric opercula, of which by far the best known is that of *Viviparus* (figs. 42C, 43C). Superficially, this type appears to be made of concentric rings of conchiolin which may (in other genera) often be impregnated with salts of calcium. When examined in sections, however, the apparent simplicity vanishes and the operculum is found to consist of several different components, each of which occupies its own characteristic fraction of the whole area. In *Viviparus* the central areole turns out to be made of an embryonic nucleus (n); anterior to that the operculum is made of conchiolin (cop), posterior to it of varnish (vr), whilst underneath there will probably be found adventitious layers of further conchiolin (adl). In the early embryos of *Viviparus* an opercular groove occurs as a shallow invagination along the anterior edge of the opercular disc, secreting conchiolin, whilst at the posterior end is a gland secreting varnish: at this stage, therefore, conditions in *Viviparus* are precisely comparable to those in other prosobranchs. Later, however, the groove everts, its secretory epithelium forming a line across the anterior border of the opercular disc, and from this stage the edge of the operculum projects freely all around the opercular disc. With growth this group of secretory cells transforms into the anterior half of a circle the posterior half of which is formed by the cells which manufacture the varnish, so that from this time on, growth of the operculum depends upon the expansion of 2 semicircles, one of varnish, the other of conchiolin. The structure of the operculum is further complicated by the presence of cells secreting adventitious conchiolin. These are at first placed together centrally, underneath the operculum, but with time the group of cells expands and becomes converted into a circle of ever-increasing radius (adc), the central cells losing the ability to secrete, and ultimately becoming only loosely attached to the operculum. The circle of secreting cells lays down the material of the adventitious layer as it expands under the overlying operculum. From this it follows that the relative dispositions of varnish and adventitious layers vary in the two types of operculum which have them: in opercula with marginal and terminal nuclei (e.g. *Nucella*) the varnish underlies the adventitious layers, but in concentric opercula with a central nucleus the adventitious layer lies under the varnish. Hubendick (1948) has shown that the rings in the operculum of *Viviparus* are related to overwintering but because other factors may produce them they cannot be used to measure the age of a snail with certainty.

Like the shell, the operculum may be repaired when damaged, or even replaced should it be altogether lost. The ability to do this seems to vary from species to species, since Techow (1910) got no regeneration in *Viviparus viviparus*, though Hankó (1913) obtained positive and similar results with *Murex brandaris* and *Nassarius mutabilis*. Not unnaturally, snails from which the operculum (or parts of it) had been removed spent much time withdrawn into the shell and secreted quantities of mucus; the operation was not, however, fatal except in one instance. The exposed surface of the opercular disc was completely re-clothed with epithelial cells 10 days after the removal of the oper-culum; many of the cells were immigrants from the surrounding surface of the foot, but some were derived from the circles of secreting cells responsible for producing the adventitious layers found in the opercula of these animals. Dedifferentiation of these cells occurred so that the wound was covered with a uniform epithelium of unspecialized cells. This condition persisted for about a further 3 weeks, when the cells transformed to a columnar secretory type filled with granules which passed out and produced a cuticular covering. This was repeated so that a multilayered operculum was formed. The produc-tion of cuticle started centrally and gradually passed peripherally until the entire oper-culum had been replaced, the new structure being thickest centrally and tapering to its margin. It showed no differentiation of structure apart from being laminated, and neither varnish nor calcareous material was present. The entire process—which was carried out in a Mediterranean spring—took from 21 March to 5 June.

# CHAPTER 4

# THE MANTLE CAVITY

THE mantle cavity is one of the features diagnostic of the molluscs, and throughout the group retains such a standard pattern as to indicate that it must have been arranged in much the same way in the original members of the phylum, whatever changes may have taken place as adaptive radiation occurred. In gastropods the cavity (fig. 44) is fundamentally a pocket on the posterior face of the visceral mass, which comprises its anterior wall and floor. The roof and sides are formed of a fold of body wall hanging down from the more dorsal parts of the visceral hump, forming a structure called the mantle skirt (mst). Within the mantle cavity lies an assemblage of structures which collectively constitute the pallial complex. In the primitive mollusc these comprised (a) the anus; (b) 2 excretory openings; (c) 2 genital apertures; (d) right and left osphradia; (e) right and left gills; and (f) right and left hypobranchial glands. These are disposed in a relatively constant way. The anus lies medianly towards the inner end of the cavity, which primitively was perhaps not a very deep one, and it was flanked on either side by the excretory openings. To the outer side of these lay the gills and lateral to these again, or possibly on them, were the osphradia. The inner epithelium of the mantle skirt between the gill and the anus was extremely glandular and formed the hypobranchial glands. The position of the genital openings can be stated less certainly as they may have been situated on either the median or the lateral side of the gills: evidence suggests the former since they lie median to the gills in chitons, bivalves and cephalopods.

In the gastropods the mantle cavity has been rotated by the process of torsion which the members of that class undergo during development so that it lies anteriorly on the visceral mass. Strictly, it is not confined to that area, because the mantle skirt extends as a frill round the whole of the stalk by which the visceral mass is connected to the head and foot. At all points except directly behind the head, however, the mantle skirt is very brief and the cavity which lies underneath is correspondingly shallow. If we exclude the very drastic modifications which have taken place within the class in adaptation to different ways of life, the sole other difference between the pallial complex of gastropods and that of other molluscs is that the gonads do not discharge by openings separate from those of the kidneys.

The following description of the mantle cavity of the earliest gastropods is based mainly on the conclusions of Yonge (1947). It was perhaps not very deep (see fig. 44), and the 3 openings (anus (a) and kidney apertures (eo)) lay at the innermost end, whilst the gills (ct) arose at a similar level but projected forwards towards its mouth. Each gill, known as a ctenidium because of its comb-like structure, was composed of an axis (cta) carrying a double row of leaflets, set alternately. The axis of each ctenidium stretched obliquely forwards across the lateral parts of the cavity, so that one row of leaflets lay below and towards the mid-line whilst the other lay above and more laterally. Along the inner part of its length it was fastened by a membrane (called a suspensory membrane) to the side wall of the mantle cavity laterally (efm), and to the mantle skirt in the neighbourhood of the mid-line medianly (afm). The distal, anterior part of the ctenidial axis, however, projected freely into the mantle cavity and was not supported by membranes, although a supporting endoskeleton (fs, figs. 44, 49) in the form of chitinous rods was often

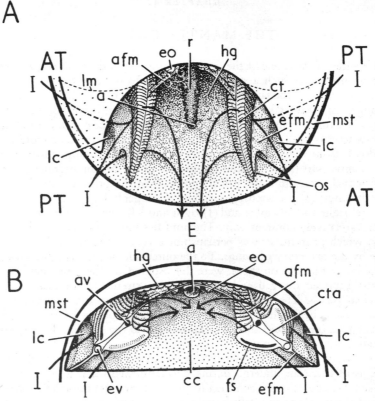

Fig. 44.—A. Diagrammatic representation of the contents of the mantle cavity of a gastropod and a possible pretorsional ancestor seen by transparency through the mantle skirt. The reference letters AT, PT, on the left mark the anterior and posterior ends of the pretorsional stage; those on the right refer to a gastropod which has undergone torsion. Arrows show direction of water currents.

B. View of the contents of the inner half of the mantle cavity of a primitive gastropod. The outer half has been cut away and the deeper part is seen through the cut. Arrows show direction of water currents.

a, anus; afm, afferent membrane of ctenidium; av, afferent branchial vessel; cc, central compartment of mantle cavity; ct, ctenidium; cta, ctenidial axis; E, exhalant; efm, efferent membrane of ctenidium; eo, excretory opening; ev, efferent branchial vessel; fs, skeletal rod in ctenidial leaflet; hg, hypobranchial gland; I, inhalant; lc, dorsolateral compartment of mantle cavity; lm, inner limit of mantle cavity; mst, mantle skirt; os, osphradium; r, rectum.

developed in the axis and in the leaflets it bore. Because of the way in which the ctenidia were attached to the walls of the mantle cavity this was divided in its deeper parts into 3 compartments—a left dorsolateral one (lc, figs. 44, 48A, 54) between the axis of the left gill and the left wall of the mantle cavity; a right dorsolateral compartment with similar relations to the right gill; and a central compartment (cc) into which discharged the anus and the right and left kidney apertures, one of which was also the outlet for reproductive cells. In the left compartment lay the left row of leaflets belonging to the left gill; in the right lay the right row of leaflets of the right gill; in the central lay both the other rows. For functional reasons explained below the membrane on the dorsal (median) side (afm) of the axis usually extended less far forward than the membrane connecting the gill axis to the floor of the mantle cavity (efm).

The hypobranchial glands (hg, lhg, rhg) developed particularly on the inner wall of the mantle skirt in the deeper parts of the central compartment, but extended on to the gill membranes and anal papilla.

Since the respiratory organs—delicate structures which could not be directly exposed on the surface of the body of the gastropod—were housed within the mantle cavity, they had also to be ventilated. It was, in fact, largely the ciliated surfaces of the ctenidia themselves which became responsible for this task. Since, in addition, there had to be an escape route for the faecal and excretory matter from the anus and kidney openings, it was convenient to use the outgoing stream of water from the ctenidia for carrying this material out of the mantle cavity, though contraction of the shell muscle, pulling the visceral mass down on to the head and foot, would also forcibly eject water from the mantle cavity carrying this material with it.

In all, or almost all, respiratory organs the circulation of the blood is so arranged that the efferent blood vessels lie on the side of the respiratory surface which is bathed by the incoming stream of water: in this way the blood leaving the respiratory organ is in equilibrium with the water of highest oxygen content and minimal carbon dioxide tension. The gastropods are no exception to this rule though its efficiency has been measured only by Hazelhoff (1938), who showed that *Haliotis* removed 56% of the oxygen from the incoming water and *Murex brandaris* 38%. Not all of this passed necessarily through the ctenidium. In the primitive gastropods the incoming current of water (I, fig. 44) entered the mantle cavity lateroventrally and left (E) in a more median and dorsal position, the 2 ctenidia lying across the stream. The efferent blood vessels of the ctenidia (ev) were situated on their ventrolateral sides and the afferent ones (av) on the upper side. Water passed between the ctenidial leaflets and accumulated in the dorsal half of the mantle cavity. As a consequence of this arrangement of the water currents, the suspensory membrane of the ctenidial axis which fastened it to the floor of the mantle cavity could be quite elongated without interfering with the flow of water, and the osphradia (os), lying partly on the anterior edge of these membranes and partly on the ventral edges of the free ctenidial axis, were well placed to test the water which was coming into the mantle cavity. Because of this, too, the supporting gill endoskeleton (fs) developed along the ventral part of each ctenidial axis and its lateral leaflets. On the upper side of each ctenidium, where the water emerged into the main mantle cavity from the inter-lamellar spaces, an extensive dorsal supporting membrane would probably interfere with the circulation of the water, especially in view of the fact that it was this water which had to remove waste (from kidneys or gut) and reproductive products. The upper suspensory membrane (afm) of the early gastropod gill was, therefore, reduced or even lost. Thus water tended to pass from the right and left lateral compartments of the mantle cavity into the central one and so augmented the volume available for washing waste away.

Essentially the same relationships exist between the ctenidia and the rest of the body in other molluscs, although the details of the arrangement vary. In Loricata (chitons) (fig. 45) (Yonge, 1939b) the ctenidia (ct) are so short because of the need to fit into the narrow and shallow mantle cavity (mc) which these molluscs possess, that they have become very much more numerous, though this may be better interpreted as, in part, a vestige of metamerism, as in *Neopilina* where the gills also lie in a narrow and shallow mantle

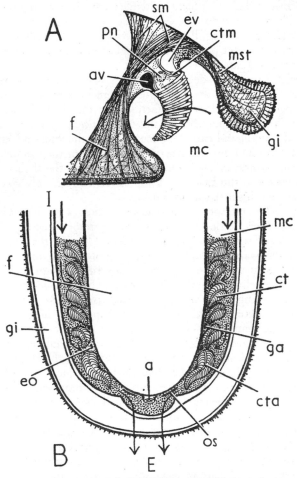

FIG. 45.—A. Part of a transverse section through body of a loricate (chiton) to show a ctenidium hanging into the mantle cavity. The arrow shows direction of water current.

B. Ventral view of posterior half of the body of a loricate (chiton) to show the contents of the mantle cavity; the gills have been pulled apart to show these more clearly. Arrows show direction of water currents.

a, anus; av, afferent branchial vessel; ct, ctenidium; cta, ctenidial axis; ctm, ctenidial muscle; E, exhalant; eo, excretory opening; ev, efferent branchial vessel; f, foot; ga, genital opening; gi, girdle; I, inhalant; mc, mantle cavity; mst, mantle skirt; os, osphradium; pn, pallial nerve; sm, shell muscle.

cavity. Each consists of an axis (cta) bearing a number of leaflets on either side. The axis arises from the point where mantle skirt (mst) and body join and projects outwards and downwards into the pallial cavity, its position in this being slightly variable and under the control of muscles. The leaflets which it bears are flattened and project backwards and forwards. They are ciliated and the cilia direct water from the outer channel between mantle and gill into the inner channel between gill and foot (f) along which it flows to the posterior end of the body. After washing over the genital (ga), the excretory (eo) and the anal openings (a) the water leaves the mantle cavity at the posterior end (E). The osphradia (os) lie in the pathway of the efferent current near the anus. In conformity with most respiratory organs the main efferent blood vessel (ev) lies facing the incoming current and is therefore on the outer, or dorsolateral side of each ctenidium. The gills are so small as to be effectively controlled by their musculature (ctm), and suspensory membranes are absent: they would, in fact, interfere considerably with the flow of water within the mantle cavity. There is no hypobranchial gland.

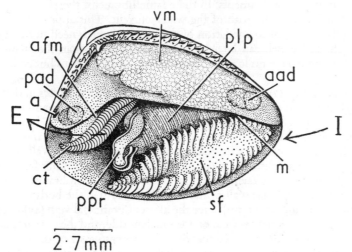

FIG. 46.—*Nucula* sp.: the right valve of the shell and the right mantle skirt have been removed to show the contents of the mantle cavity. Arrows show direction of water currents.

a, anus; aad, anterior adductor muscle; afm, afferent membrane of ctenidium; ct, ctenidium; E, exhalant; I, inhalant; m, mouth; pad, posterior adductor muscle; plp, palp lamella; ppr, palp proboscis; sf, sole of foot; vm, visceral mass.

The relationship of the conditions found in the two other large classes of the Mollusca, the bivalves and cephalopods, to those already described has been discussed by Yonge (1947), to whose paper the reader may be referred for fuller information.

The ctenidia (ct, fig. 46) lie in the mantle cavity of a bivalve such as *Nucula* in a steeply oblique position and consist of an axis attached by a suspensory membrane (afm) dorsally and posteriorly, but free elsewhere, bearing a double row of leaflets very similar to those of the gastropods or chitons. In other bivalves the ctenidial axis may be set at a smaller angle to the longitudinal axis of the animal and may, as in *Ensis* or *Teredo*, come to lie parallel to it. The flow of water through the mantle cavity of *Nucula* is an anteroposterior one (I, E) so that the ctenidia lie across its path and water circulates between the leaflets into the suprabranchial cavities dorsal and posterior to them. The efferent blood vessel lies on the anteroventral side of the ctenidial axis, the afferent one on the posterodorsal side, and, since this is the only side of the ctenidium attached to the body by membrane it is to be noted that the membrane of the bivalve is what may be called an afferent membrane (attached to the side of the ctenidial axis in which runs the main afferent blood vessel), whereas in the gastropod the principal attachment of the ctenidial axis is by an efferent membrane. This is due simply to the retention of the one part of the original (supposedly) complete membrane in the one class and the retention of the other half in the other.

In the filibranchs and eulamellibranchs the arrangement of the ctenidia is more complex than in the protobranchs because of their progressively greater specialization in connexion with the gathering of food from the water current. In adaptation to this the leaflets have elongated from their mid-points so as to give rise to filaments of a V-shape. In addition to this change of shape the vascular arrangements have altered so that whilst the afferent vessel remains in the ctenidial axis the efferent one has given rise to two which now run in the distal margins of the filaments. In these lamellibranchs, therefore, the afferent and efferent vessels alike lie in the path of the water current. This appears to be less related to improving the degree of oxygenation of the blood—which need not be great in such inactive animals, and which can be achieved in places other than the ctenidia—than to the fact that the ctenidia are no longer primarily respiratory organs but collectors of food particles.

The cephalopods (fig. 47) depart from the practice of other molluscs in that they pump water through the mantle cavity by muscular movements of the mantle skirt or funnel rather than by means of the ctenidia themselves. Water appears to be drawn into the cavity on the anteroventral side (I), passed across the gill leaflets (ct) and sent out (E) by way of the funnel (i). Strictly this belongs to the anteroventral wall, being pedal in origin, but it projects sufficiently into the mantle cavity to drain water from the exhalant, posterodorsal, chamber. The ctenidia (ct) are anchored by membranes extending along the ctenidial axis to the dorsal wall of the mantle cavity (i.e. the body) and these membranes are afferent membranes (afm) since the afferent branchial vein (av) runs along that side of the ctenidial axis. It lies, indeed, on the inhalant side, and the cephalopod ctenidium would appear, therefore, to break the rule that the efferent vessel of the respiratory organ leaves on the inhalant side. But the precise behaviour of the water within the mantle cavity of the cephalopod is doubtful and it may well be that eddies take the water through the gill in more than one way.

In most respects, then, the ctenidial relationships of all the groups of the molluscs are identical, although the detailed arrangements of the parts vary from group to group.

The gastropods and the protobranchiate bivalves are the only two groups of the molluscs in which a well developed hypobranchial gland occurs, and, when its function is known, this is not surprising. It serves to cement particles sieved out of the water current by the ctenidia so that they may be swept out in the exhalant current of water. Cephalopods, with their powerful muscular mantle, can eject any particles which might enter and they are often less benthic in their mode of life and so less liable to pick up particles; lamellibranchs exploit these particles as food and therefore get rid of them from the mantle cavity by eating them or by forcing them out by the contraction of the shell muscles overcoming the relatively feeble ciliary currents. Their disposal becomes a problem only in the gastropods and protobranchs which live where particles may enter easily and which have a current strong enough to suck them in. Only these animals therefore possess this type of gland. Chitons might be expected to display hypobranchial glands in their mantle cavity on this theory, and it is perhaps surprising that they have none. There are, however, on the side of the foot, glandular epithelial strips which appear to carry out the same function though they are not homologous with the hypobranchial gland of the other molluscan classes.

In the primitive gastropod the mantle cavity lay mainly in the visceral hump posteriorly (fig. 44). Water was sucked in laterally (I) and somewhat ventrally by the ciliated epithelium of the ctenidial filaments and escaped medianly and somewhat dorsally (E). In the early gastropods torsion brought this whole apparatus forwards. In this situation water entered and left as before so that the outgoing stream, though normally clearing the head because it was leaving the mantle cavity dorsally rather than

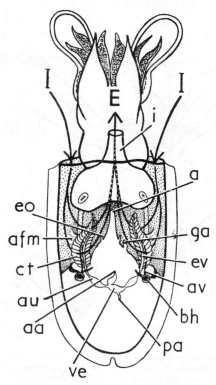

Fig. 47.—Ventral view of a decapod cephalopod showing the contents of the mantle cavity and some other organs by transparency.   Arrows show direction of water currents.

a, anus; aa, anterior aorta; afm, afferent membrane of ctenidium; au, auricle; av, afferent branchial vessel; bh, branchial heart; ct, ctenidium; E, exhalant; eo, excretory opening; ev, efferent branchial vessel; ga, genital opening; I, inhalant; i, infundibulum; pa, posterior aorta; ve, ventricle.

ventrally, was liable to carry the faecal and excretory water stream into its close proximity. This condition is represented in fig. 48A and is such an insanitary arrangement that it has been superseded in all living groups of gastropods. The ciliary currents in the mantle cavity of gastropods have been particularly investigated by Yonge (1938, 1947). On the assumption that what he described for living prosobranchs can be applied to the extinct ancestral types now under consideration then the picture of what went on within their mantle cavity is this.

Each gill filament may be taken as corresponding to that of *Haliotis* (fig. 49) and be regarded as a triangular leaflet fastened to the ctenidial axis (cta) by its base. On each of the flat surfaces of the filament is a delicate epithelium occasionally ciliated over the major part, but richly so over a strip overlying the endoskeletal support (fs) near the lower (efferent) margin. These are the lateral cilia (ltc), and it is they which are responsible for driving water from one side of the gill to the other and so for creating the current through the mantle cavity.

The water enters through a narrow slit into the relatively spacious mantle cavity (fig. 48A). When this happens the speed of the current decreases and the larger particles

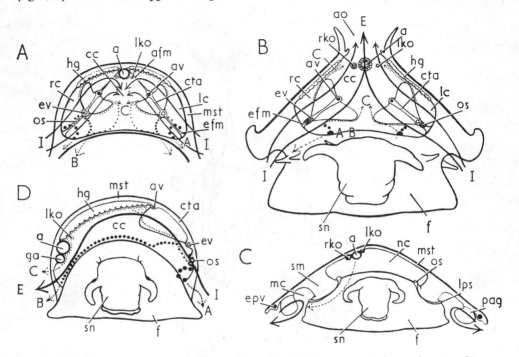

Fig. 48.—Diagrammatic transverse sections to show water and ciliary currents in the mantle cavity of A, a hypothetical, primitive gastropod; B, *Diodora*; C, *Patella*; D, a mesogastropod. Continuous arrows show the direction of water currents; broken arrows show the direction of ciliary currents A, B and C, and the particles affected by them are indicated by dots of three sizes.

a, anus; afm, afferent membrane of ctenidium; ao, apical opening of mantle cavity; av, afferent branchial vessel; cc, central compartment of mantle cavity; cta, ctenidial axis; E, exhalant; efm, efferent membrane of ctenidium; epv, efferent pallial vessel; ev, efferent branchial vessel; f, foot; ga, genital opening; hg, hypobranchial gland; I, inhalant; lc, left dorsolateral compartment of mantle cavity; lko, left kidney opening; lps, lateral pallial streak; mc, mantle cavity; mst, mantle skirt; nc, nuchal cavity; os, osphradium; pag, pallial gill; rc, right dorsolateral compartment of mantle cavity; rko, right kidney and genital opening; sm, shell muscle; sn, snout.

suspended in it fall on to the floor, where they encounter a ciliated epithelium which carries them to the mouth of the cavity and outside (see legend to fig.). This is the current called current A by Yonge (1938). Medium-sized particles do not drop on to the floor of the mantle cavity until a later stage and so tend to fall nearer the mid-line, whence currents also carry them to the mouth of the cavity (B). The most minute particles, however, stay in suspension until they reach the gill filaments, over the surface of which stretches a sheet of mucus on which they are trapped. Frontal cilia (fc, fig. 49) on the efferent edge of the leaflet and abfrontal cilia (aci) on the afferent edge then sweep the mucus and embedded particles by a variety of routes on to the mantle skirt and the surface of the hypobranchial gland (hg, fig. 48A). The secretion of this cements them together so that they remain in the main exhalant stream (C) in which they are swept out of the mantle cavity along with excretory and faecal matter, and, in the appropriate season, the reproductive cells.

In the original disposition of the body of the primitive gastropod, as indicated above, this exhalant stream, laden with waste, left the mantle cavity anteriorly in the mid-line over the animal's head. Such an arrangement is not encountered in any living gastropod, and it may therefore be assumed that its apparent insanitary effects had some degree of reality. In all living gastropods alternative means of disposing of the waste matter have been introduced, which have the effect of diverting the stream away from the head, and

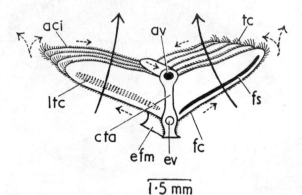

FIG. 49.—*Haliotis tuberculata:* stereogram of portion of ctenidium showing a short length of axis bearing leaflets. The nearest leaflet on the right has been cut open longitudinally. Continuous arrows show the direction of water currents; broken arrows show the direction of ciliary currents.

aci, abfrontal cilia; av, afferent branchial vessel; cta, ctenidial axis; efm, efferent membrane of ctenidium; ev, efferent branchial vessel; fc, frontal cilia; fs, endoskeletal support of branchial leaflet; ltc, lateral cilia; tc, terminal cilia.

which in some animals also involve the separation of the sanitary and the respiratory aspects of the activity of the cavity.

The first of these devices which may be mentioned is that used by Zeugobranchia (e.g. *Pleurotomaria, Haliotis, Puncturella, Diodora, Emarginula*); in some cases it permits of an almost perfect external bilateral symmetry, more perfect, perhaps, than that achieved by any other prosobranch. In these animals one may imagine with Garstang (1928) that the impact of the exhalant stream of water, laden with metabolites, against the edge of the mantle skirt, has slowed down its rate of growth so that a bay is formed in the mid-point anteriorly, directly over the head. This bay in the mantle skirt has consequential effects upon the shell, with the result that a slit-like emargination appears (fig. 30) at this point, and it is through this slit in the mantle skirt and shell that the outgoing stream of water now passes. The edge of the mantle skirt may be turned outwards a little through the slit in the shell so as to form a kind of incomplete siphon (fig. 40A), which may be used to direct the water upwards, or sideways—in any direction except towards the head. This is the state of affairs in *Pleurotomaria* and *Scissurella* (fig. 256B). A further evolutionary step separates the opening of the mantle cavity into two parts by the fusion of the anterior edges of the mouth of the slit. When this has occurred there are two unconnected pallial openings, the main one over the animal's head and neck, which is now an inhalant aperture (for water currents), and the separated slit through which the outgoing current passes. At first located near the anterior margin of the shell (*Emarginula* (figs. 30, 253B), *Puncturella* (fig. 254)) it may be moved by secondary growth of the shell

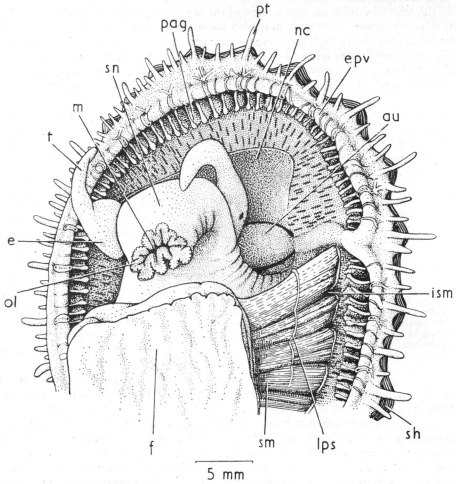

FIG. 50.—*Patella vulgata:* anterior half in ventral view.
    au. auricle; e, eye; epv, efferent pallial vessel; f, foot; ism, interstice between bundles of shell muscle; lps, lateral pallial streak; m, mouth; nc, nuchal cavity; ol, outer lip; pag, pallial gill; pt, pallial tentacle; sh, shell; sm, shell muscle; sn, snout; t, tentacle.

so that it comes to lie further back, when the outgoing current may be directed completely away from the head (*Diodora*, fig. 40A). Despite the changes in pallial arrangements shown by zeugobranchs particulate matter may still be removed from the mantle cavity by the main inhalant aperture either by ciliary currents A and B, which cannot be separately distinguished, or by the animal pulling the shell down on the head and foot by contraction of the shell muscle, a movement which has the effect of washing water and particles forcibly out of the cavity. The arrangements in this case are shown in fig. 48B.

As explained elsewhere (p. 12), the gastropod visceral mass is normally wound in a right-handed spiral. This involves differential growth along its two sides, the left hypertrophying, the right atrophying. This tendency is marked in some of the zeugobranchs (*Pleurotomaria*, Scissurellidae), is much less marked in others (*Haliotis*) and has been completely lost with the assumption of a limpet-like shape by the Fissurellidae. This evolutionary trend is perhaps to be linked with the fact that the animals have found a workable means of ventilating the mantle cavity by apical or sub-apical openings in the shell. It presupposes, however, the adoption of a particular ecological niche in that it decreases the value of the shell as a protection against desiccation.

Alternative solutions of the problem of the ventilation of the mantle cavity have been found by such gastropods as are not occupants of this niche. One of the simplest of these is that adopted by the majority of members of the Patellacea (=Docoglossa). In these (e.g. *Patina*, *Patella*, figs. 266, 48C, 50) the mantle cavity has given up its respiratory function and the ctenidia have been lost. The main site of exchange of respiratory gases is now provided by secondary gills (pag) which are developed on the pallial skirt near its edge. Superficially these resemble the ctenidial leaflets, but they are new structures, and the cilia on their surface create a local current of water which enters dorsally and leaves ventrally. The main anterior part of the mantle cavity (the nuchal cavity (nc), lying over the animal's neck) is now concerned only with accommodating the head when that is retracted, and in housing the anus (a), the osphradia (os) and the openings of the two kidneys (lko, rko). Hardly any current of water is maintained through it in the adult and faeces and other material are led out by ciliary means (fig. 267B). Presumably it is for this reason that the faeces (fig. 127H) are highly compacted by the elaborately coiled intestine which these animals possess (fig. 125). All members of the Patellacea have apparently lost the hypobranchial gland—presumably functionally replaced by the gland cells of the intestine (see p. 232). *Acmaea* (=*Patelloida*) (figs. 51, 258, 259) still retains a single ctenidium (ct) (although some workers believe this to be a new pseudo-ctenidium) and therefore resembles the animals of the next section.

Most prosobranchs (Monotocardia) have altered the arrangements within their mantle cavity in relation to the different growth rates of the right and left sides of the visceral mass already referred to. In a primitive gastropod the exhalant part of the mantle cavity is marked by the anus and it lies in a median position, inhalant streams of water converging on it from right and left. Could the animal push the mid-line over to one side, so to speak, the anus and exhalant stream would then be lateral. This is precisely what the spiral coiling allows: the hypertrophy of the organs of the animal's (topographical) left side makes them occupy almost the entire breadth of the mantle cavity, pushes across the left kidney opening and the anus, which is morphologically median, so that they come to lie at the extreme topographical right of the mantle cavity, whilst the organs of the right side atrophy almost completely. The original, double, lateral to median current in the mantle cavity is thus replaced by a single transverse current which enters the mantle cavity on the left, washes across the animal's back and emerges, with its waste, on the right (fig. 48D).

Associated with this change in the general disposition of the pallial complex of mesogastropods go changes in its detailed arrangement. The general trend to replace double water currents by a single one involves the suppression of one whole row of ctenidial leaflets.

Only the left ctenidium survives in Monotocardia, and only the right series of ctenidial leaflets remains attached to the axis in most species. In the Trochacea and Neritacea, which are diotocardian but have only one gill, the left, there exists a state of affairs which shows how this may have arisen. The ctenidium is bipectinate with right and left rows of leaflets attached to the axis. In the Neritacea (fig. 52) it (ct) projects rather freely into the mantle cavity and its suspensory membranes (afm, efm) are weakly developed, especially on the dorsal side, so that water can flow freely above it and below. The right ctenidium is reduced to a small vascular knob (ho), the so-called 'organe creux' of

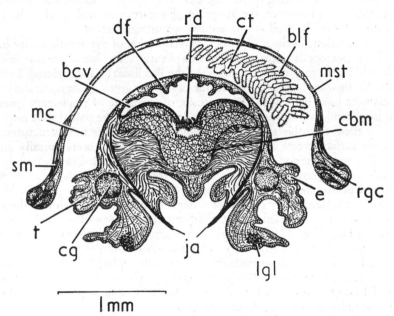

FIG. 51.—*Acmaea virginea:* transverse section at level of base of tentacles.
bcv, buccal cavity; blf, branchial leaflet; cbm, cartilage of buccal mass; cg, cerebral ganglion; ct, ctenidium; df, dorsal fold of buccal cavity; e, eye; ja, jaws; lgl, labial glands; mc, mantle cavity; mst, mantle skirt; rd, radula; rgc, repugnatorial glands of edge of mantle skirt; sm, shell muscle; t, tentacle.

Lenssen (1899). In most Trochacea, however (figs. 53, 54), only the anterior third of the ctenidium is free, the posterior part being tied above to the mantle skirt by an afferent membrane (afm) and to the wall of the mantle cavity below by an efferent one (efm). The free tip is stiffened by an internal skeleton (fs).

In this region and in the middle third of the gill two sets of leaflets are carried on the axis. In the anterior third these project into the main mantle cavity; in the middle third only those on the right side of the axis can do this, those on the left being cut off from it by the suspensory membranes. They therefore project into a small cavity (lc, fig. 54) cut off from the main one, and obviously difficult to ventilate effectively, though Clark (1958) has been able to show that the same kind of circulation exists within it as within the main pallial chamber. The left leaflets rapidly become small and die out towards the base of the gill where the cavity in which they lie also disappears. In its most posterior third, therefore, the trochacean gill consists of an axis fused broadside to the mantle skirt and carrying a single row of leaflets which project from its right side into the general mantle cavity. This is, in fact, the condition in which the ctenidium exists throughout its entire length in all the monotocardian gastropods which Thiele (1929–35) placed in the Mesogastropoda and Stenoglossa. As a result the ctenidial axis appears to be attached to

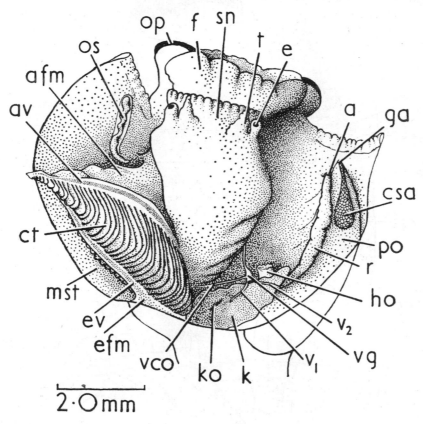

FIG. 52.—*Theodoxus fluviatilis:* dissected to display the contents of the mantle cavity.
a, anus; afm, afferent membrane of ctenidium; av, afferent branchial vessel; csa, crystal sac on oviduct; ct, ctenidium; e, eye; efm, efferent membrane of ctenidium; ev, efferent branchial vessel; f, foot; ga, genital opening; ho, 'organe creux' of Lenssen, vestigial right ctenidium; k, kidney; ko, kidney opening; mst, mantle skirt; op, operculum; os, osphradium; po, pallial oviduct; r, rectum; sn, snout; t, tentacle; $v_1$, renopericardial nerve; $v_2$, genital nerve; vco, part of visceral loop; vg, visceral ganglion.

the mantle skirt not only by its dorsal and ventral edges, but along its whole breadth and the triangular leaflets which it bears are apparently joined to the mantle skirt along the whole of one side.

A second change which is to be associated, but less certainly, with the trend towards more effective ventilation and cleansing of the mantle cavity, is the altered position of some or all of the apertures which lie within it. In most of the lower Diotocardia (figs. 257, 258, 259, 266) the anus lies well back from the edge of the mantle skirt near the inner end of the mantle cavity and it is flanked by small papillae on which the right and

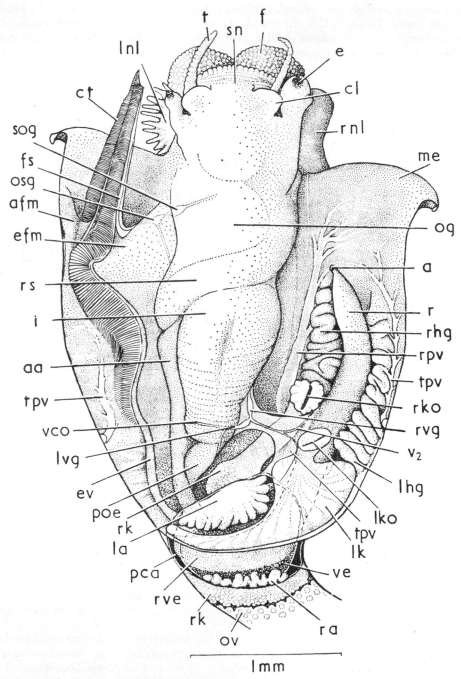

Fig. 53.—*Monodonta lineata*: dissected to display the contents of the mantle cavity.

a, anus; aa, anterior aorta; afm, afferent branchial membrane; cl, cephalic lappet; ct, ctenidium; e, eye on eye stalk; efm, efferent membrane of ctenidium; ev, efferent branchial vessel; f, foot; fs, skeleton of gill; i, intestine, by transparency; la, left auricle; lhg, left hypobranchial gland; lk, left kidney or papillary sac; lko, left kidney opening; lnl, left neck lobe; lvg, left visceral ganglion; me, mantle edge; og, oesophageal glands, by transparency; osg, osphradial ganglion, by transparency; ov, ovary; pca, pericardial cavity; poe, posterior oesophagus, by transparency; r, rectum; ra, right

left kidney openings are placed, the former acting also as a genital pore. In the Zeugo-branchia (fig. 257) these are in close proximity to the slit or hole in the mantle through which the exhalant current of water passes. They lie in corresponding positions in the

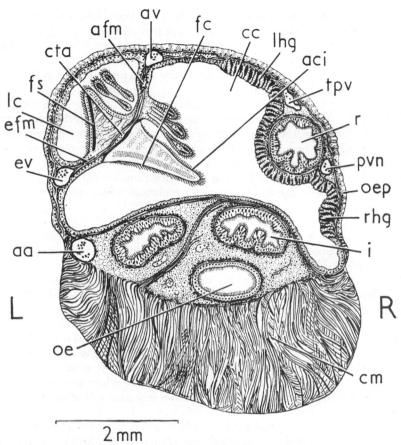

FIG. 54.—*Monodonta lineata*: transverse section at level of middle third of mantle cavity.
aa, anterior aorta; aci, abfrontal cilia; afm, afferent membrane of ctenidium; av, afferent branchial vessel; cc, central compartment of mantle cavity; cm, columellar muscle; cta, ctenidial axis; efm, efferent membrane of ctenidium; ev, efferent branchial vessel; fc, frontal cilia; fs, skeleton of branchial leaflet; i, intestine; L, left; lc, left compartment of mantle cavity; lhg, left hypobranchial gland; oe, oesophagus; oep, outer epithelium of mantle skirt; pvn, pallial vein; R, right; r, rectum; rhg, right hypobranchial gland; tpv, transverse pallial vein.

Patellacea (figs. 258, 259, 266) where there is no hole. In the Trochacea (fig. 53) and Neritacea (fig. 52), however, a change has occurred which is met with again in the mesogastropods and stenoglossans: the anus in the first group, and the genital duct

---

auricle; rhg, right hypobranchial gland; rk, right kidney; rko, right kidney and genital opening; rnl, right neck lobe; rpv, right pallial vein; rs, radular sac, by transparency; rve, rectum in ventricle; rvg, right visceral ganglion; sn, snout; sog, supra-oesophageal ganglion; t, tentacle; tpv, transverse pallial vein ; $v_2$. genital nerve; vco, part of visceral loop; ve, ventricle.

(extending from the right kidney aperture) in addition in the others, now open to the mantle cavity close to its mouth so that faeces and gametes are no longer shed into the deeper parts. The purely renal opening stays as a pore in the deepest part of the mantle cavity.

How this extension of rectum and genital duct has been achieved can be deduced from the fact that in some species the genital duct is merely a ciliated gutter stretching along the mantle skirt (sgr, fig. 10), and from the fact that even when it forms a closed duct traces of its origin from a gutter are occasionally discernible (fig. 181J). It is there-fore possible that the anus has been brought forward to its new position in the same way, though traces of this are not discoverable.

Another factor to be considered is this: with the alteration in growth rates between right and left sides the extension of the mantle skirt is maximal on the left, minimal on the right, and of intermediate extent between. The altered position of the anus may be merely relative and the real change a deepening of the left half of the cavity. However it has been brought about, the forward position of the anus and the genital pore has the effect at one and the same time of keeping faeces from contaminating the mantle cavity, leading germ cells to the edge and facilitating copulation, which might otherwise prove too difficult a process.

The various changes which have accompanied and permitted the evolution of the ciliary method of food collecting in prosobranch gastropods have been well discussed by Yonge (1938) and by Werner (1952, 1959). This particular trend seems to have been limited to the sedentary monotocardians, and does not occur among the diotocardians, despite the limpet-like mode of life which many of these have adopted, nor is it found in the Stenoglossa. In the case of the last the explanation may be sought in their specialized carnivorous habits, but it seems difficult at first glance to explain why no diotocardian is a ciliary feeder. The reason for this in zeugobranchs is most likely to be found in the disposition of the currents within the mantle cavity—so long as there are two sets of these, right and left, converging in the mid-line, it will prove impossible for the material which they carry in suspension to be collected into a place where the gastropod may use it. It is only when the water current is the transverse stream of the mesogastropod that this happens.

As explained above, suspended material which enters the mantle cavity of a meso-gastropod is normally sorted into three lots (fig. 48D), each of which is treated differently by the animal. The basis of the sorting is size and weight, the largest and heaviest particles settling out of the water current soonest, therefore to the left side of the mantle cavity, the smallest ones being trapped only when they reach the gill surface. Those of the first group are led out of the mantle cavity by a tract along the left side of the animal's neck which takes them to the side of the foot, from which they fall off or are swept away. This, it will be recalled was called current A by Yonge. The others, medium-sized, which fall on to the floor of the inner part of the mantle cavity, or the smallest, on the gills, are carried by currents B and C respectively—on the floor of the mantle cavity in the case of B, over the hypobranchial gland in the case of C—and ultimately reach the right side of the cavity and are carried out.

In the evolution of a ciliary feeding mechanism the main step which had to be taken was the diversion of at least some of the material carried by these three currents, A, B and C, to the animal's mouth, a diversion which clearly had to occur before they joined the faecal and excretory stream. One of the simplest of the alterations is found in *Bithynia tentaculata* (Schäfer, 1953*a*, *b*; Lilly, 1953): here (fig. 55) the material from current B is carried down the right side of the mantle cavity along a line which forms a distinct ciliated groove (fg). The material which emerges from the front end of this passes on

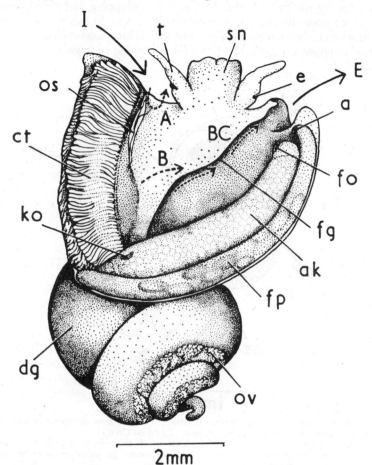

2mm

FIG. 55.—*Bithynia tentaculata:* dissection to show contents of mantle cavity. Continuous arrows show the course of water currents; broken arrows show the course of ciliary currents A, B and C (for explanation see text).

a, anus; ak, anterior diverticulum of kidney overlying pallial oviduct; ct, ctenidium; dg, digestive gland; E, exhalant; e, eye; fg, food groove; fo, female opening; fp, faecal pellets in rectum; I, inhalant; ko, kidney opening; os, osphradium; ov, ovary; sn, snout; t, tentacle.

to the propodial region in front of the snout (sn), from where it may be raked into the gut by the radula. Material from current A is not collected and it appears as if material from current C were diverted so as to join B (BC). This is a regular feature of ciliary feeding prosobranchs (fig. 61) and in other genera involves the elongation of the ctenidial filaments until their free tips rest on the floor of the mantle cavity. This is thus split into two sections, an inhalant chamber on the left (ibr), and an exhalant chamber on the right (sbr). The two are separated by the ctenidium which forms an incomplete barrier through which water is driven by the beat of the lateral cilia. Over the surface of the ctenidium there is now secreted a net of mucus (bf) from goblet cells lying in the ctenidial epithelium and this net, continuously renewed, is continuously driven down the leaflet edge by the frontal cilia (fc, fig. 62), entrapping suspended particles from the water which passes through its interstices as it does so. In this way there is produced by the prosobranch the two essential parts of any ciliary food-collecting mechanism— (*a*) something to create a water current, and (*b*) something to strain suspended particulate matter from it.

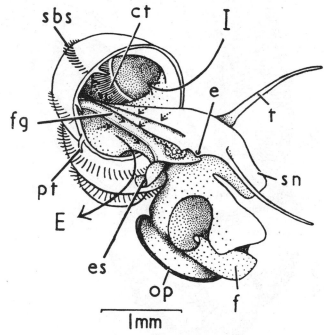

FIG. 56.—*Viviparus contectus:* young specimen.   Continuous arrows show the course of water currents; broken arrows show the course of ciliary currents.   Based on Cook.
ct, ctenidium; E, exhalant; e, eye; es, exhalant siphon; f, foot; fg, food groove with accumulation of food at anterior end; I, inhalant; op, operculum; pt, pallial tentacle; sbs, bristle on shell; sn, snout; t, tentacle.

With further elaboration of the food-collecting apparatus a number of changes appears. One of the most widespread is the conversion of the tract on the right of the mantle cavity, along which the food particles are led to the mouth, into a deep gutter. A groove is visible in *Bithynia, Calyptraea, Crepidula,* but has become converted into a distinct gutter in *Viviparus* (fg, fig. 56) and reaches its maximal development in *Turritella* (fg, fig. 57) where it forms a great trough, with high, upraised sides, which runs across the whole of the floor of the mantle cavity to a point just under the right cephalic tentacle. These devices help to keep food and faeces separate. A second change affects the size and efficiency of the ciliated surface which creates the current: by increasing the length of the mantle cavity it is possible to house a longer ctenidium and so create a greater current; and by elongating the ctenidial leaflets the same end is achieved. These

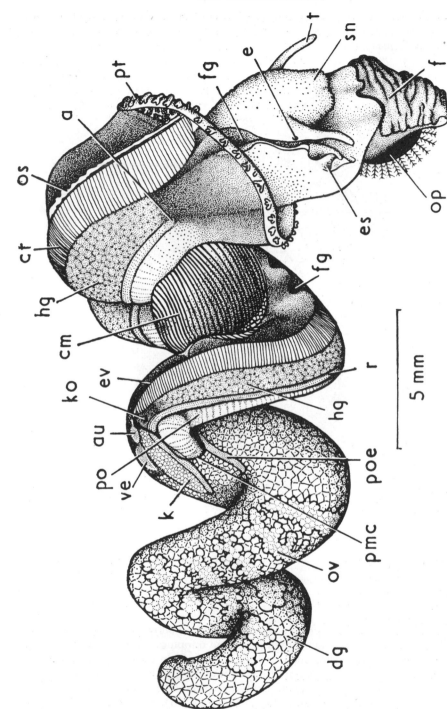

FIG. 57.—*Turritella communis*: animal removed from shell, seen from the right.
a, position of anus; au, auricle; cm, columellar muscle; ct, ctenidium, by transparency; dg, digestive gland; e, eye; es, exhalant siphon; ev, efferent branchial vessel; f, foot; fg, food groove; hg, hypobranchial gland; k, kidney; ko, kidney opening, by transparency; op, operculum; os, osphradium; ov, ovary; pmc, posterior limit of mantle cavity; po, pallial oviduct; poe, posterior oesophagus; pt, pallial tentacle; r, rectum; sn, snout; t, tentacle; ve, ventricle.

changes may be noted by comparing the mantle cavity and ctenidium of *Bithynia* (fig. 55), which is not particularly specialized, with those of *Calyptraea*, *Turritella* (fig. 57), and (especially) *Crepidula* (fig. 58) which are.

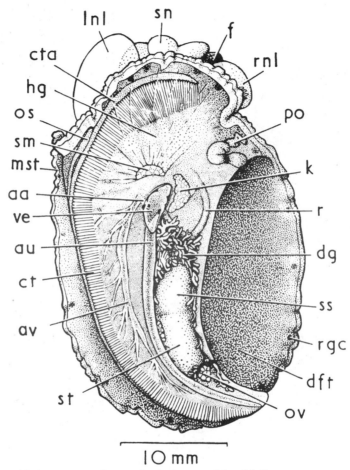

FIG. 58.—*Crepidula fornicata*: dorsal view of animal removed from shell.
aa, anterior aorta; au, auricle; av, afferent branchial vessel; ct, ctenidium; cta, ctenidial axis; dft, dorsal surface of foot; dg, digestive gland; f, foot; hg, hypobranchial gland; k, kidney; lnl, left neck lobe; mst, mantle skirt; os, osphradium; ov, ovary; po, pallial oviduct; r, rectum; rgc, repugnatorial gland; rnl, right neck lobe; sm, shell muscle; sn, snout; ss, style sac region of stomach; st, stomach; ve, ventricle.

Increased gill area produces a greater water current and allows the animal to sieve a greater volume in a given time, but for effective food trapping, this necessitates a greater production of mucus. This is provided, at least in part, from the increased gill surface itself, but in some of the more elaborate forms this appears to be inadequate and has to be supplemented by the development of totally new sites. The most important of these is the 'endostyle' of the Calyptraeacea (fig. 59; ens, fig. 61), first described by Orton

(1912*a*, *b*; 1913*b*), and so called because its function is a precise parallel to that of the
endostyle of the protochordates, in that it provides mucus out of which a sheet is made,
stretched (in these animals) over the gill slits to sieve the water current which escapes

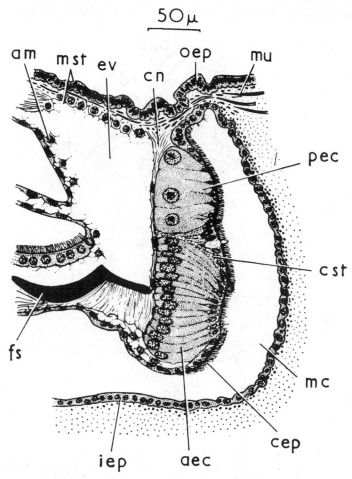

FIG. 59.—*Crepidula fornicata:* transverse section of ctenidial axis to show endostyle.
        aec, anterior gland cells of endostyle; am, amoebocyte; cep, ciliated epithelium of ctenidial axis;
cn, connective tissue; cst, strip of ciliated cells between two parts of endostyle; ev, efferent branchial
vessel; fs, skeleton of branchial filament; iep, inner pallial epithelium; mc, mantle cavity; mst,
mantle skirt; mu, muscle fibre; oep, outer pallial epithelium; pec, posterior gland cells of endostyle.

from the pharynx to the atrial cavity. The histology of the endostyle has been described
in detail by Werner (1953), who showed that it is composed of two longitudinal strips
of gland cells (aec, pec, fig. 59) alternating with ciliated cells. Between these groups of
gland cells runs a tract composed predominantly of ciliated cells (cst) within which an
occasional goblet cell may be found. The whole structure overlies the efferent branchial
vessel (ev) the cavity of which is kept open partly by the gill skeleton (fs). The cilia beat

forwards, that is across the endostyle, so that its secretion is carried on to the ventral face of the ctenidial filaments.

A third change which may affect the mantle cavity in the evolutionary trend towards ciliary food collecting is the inclusion of Yonge's current A amongst the sources of particulate food: this has been managed only in the more advanced types. In *Capulus*

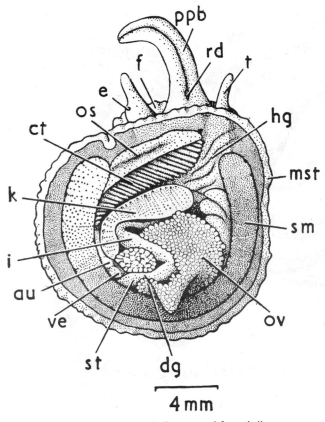

FIG. 60.—*Capulus ungaricus:* dorsal view of animal after removal from shell.
au, auricle; ct, ctenidium; dg, digestive gland; e, eye; f, foot; hg, hypobranchial gland; i, intestine; k, kidney; mst, mantle skirt; os, osphradium; ov, ovary; ppb, proboscis; rd, radula; sm, shell muscle; st, stomach; t, tentacle; ve, ventricle.

(fig. 60) the material collected from the right side of the mantle cavity is assembled on the propodium (f), anterior to the mouth, on which the proboscis (pb) rests. To this, too, comes the material which is collected from the floor of the mantle cavity on the left by current A, and food from both sources is taken to the mouth by the proboscis.

The most complex of the devices for exploiting current A, however, is that described by Werner (1953) for *Calyptraea, Crepidula* and some other members of the Calyptraeidae. In these ciliary feeders may be seen the apex of the trend amongst gastropods (figs. 58, 59, 61, 62, 63): the mantle cavity is very long, the gill extensive, its filaments elongate, an endostyle is present and there is, in addition, what is called by Werner a pallial filter (pfr, figs. 61, 63) as well as the branchial one (bf, figs. 61, 62). This lies across the mouth of the mantle cavity on the left of the head as a web of mucous threads, secreted by glands at the point where the mantle skirt joins the head-foot, which strain the bigger particles out of the incoming water current and transport them to a food pocket in the anterior part of the mantle skirt. From there they may be withdrawn by the radula.

In the calyptraeids, Werner (1953) has described the elaborate mechanisms responsible for the collection and transportation of the food caught on the branchial filter. This, as

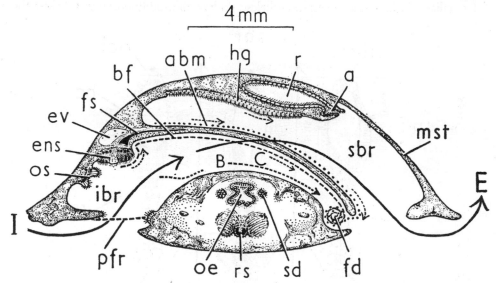

Fig. 61.—*Crepidula fornicata:* transverse section to show currents in the mantle cavity. Continuous arrows show direction of water currents; broken arrows show direction of ciliary currents, B, C (for explanation see text).

a, anus; abm, abfrontal mucous stream; bf, branchial mucous filter collecting fine particles; E, exhalant; ens, endostyle; ev, efferent branchial vessel; fd, food and mucous string in food groove; fs, skeleton in branchial filament; hg, hypobranchial gland; I, inhalant; ibr, infrabranchial part of mantle cavity; mst, mantle skirt; oe, oesophagus; os, osphradium; pfr, pallial mucous filter collecting coarse particles; r, rectum; rs, radular sac; sbr, suprabranchial part of mantle cavity; sd, salivary duct.

shown in figs. 61, 62 (bf), is a sheet of mucus secreted from the endostyle (ens), supported by the gill filaments and carried towards their tip by the beating of the frontal cilia (fc). The bulk of the small food particles entering the mantle cavity in the inhalant water current is caught in this filter; a few may succeed in passing between the filaments into the suprabranchial space (sbr) but these then fall either on the abfrontal mucous membrane (abm) and are carried by the abfrontal cilia (aci) to the tip of the filament, or on to the hypobranchial gland (hg). It is only the small fraction of the total suspended matter in the water entering the mantle cavity making up the last of these groups which eludes the food-collecting apparatus. The remainder moves to the tips of the filaments which, in these animals, rest on the food groove on the floor of the mantle cavity on the right. Here the detailed arrangement of the cilia on gill tip and food groove rolls the mucus and its attached food particles into a cylinder rather like a Swiss roll, with the mucus

corresponding to the sponge, and the food particles to the jam (fd). This is carried forwards along the groove (fg, fig. 63), along the base of the neck lobe (nl) on the right,
ventral to the tentacle (t) to its end by the mouth (efg).

There are a few other features of the mantle cavity of ciliary feeding prosobranchs,
and other modifications of their structure, which may be conveniently referred to here.
Most of these animals are sedentary and live on bottoms which are hard: if too much
suspended matter were to enter the mantle cavity there is danger of the filter becoming
clogged and certainly its efficiency being decreased even if it is not actually damaged.
A few ciliary-feeding gastropods, nevertheless, do live on muddy bottoms. Of these the

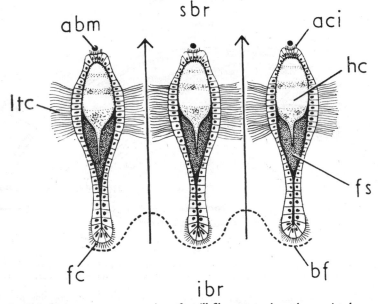

FIG. 62.—*Crepidula fornicata:* transverse section of 3 gill filaments to show the associated mucous food
trap. Continuous arrows show direction of water currents. Based on Werner.
    abm, abfrontal mucous stream; aci, abfrontal cilia; bf, branchial mucous filter collecting fine
particles; fc, frontal cilia; fs, skeleton in branchial filament; hc, haemocoelic space; ibr, infrabranchial part of mantle cavity; ltc, lateral cilia; sbr, suprabranchial part of mantle cavity.

best known is perhaps *Turritella* (fig. 64) in which the mantle edge has been thickened,
especially on the left side, and drawn out into pinnately branched tentacles (pt). These
project dorsally a little way over the mouth of the shell, but their greatest length is
directed over the inhalant aperture of the mantle cavity, across which they stretch as a
coarse filter. By means of this device the amount of suspended particulate matter which
does find its way into the mantle cavity is kept within manageable limits. *Crepidula
fornicata* and *Calyptraea chinensis* may also live in silty situations, but these animals are
attached by the sucker-like foot and contrive to raise themselves to a position where
there is no danger of mud fouling their feeding mechanism by settling on shells and
stones.

All particles which are caught in the mantle cavity are trapped in mucus and transported towards the mouth embedded in this material. The radula licks lengths of it into

the buccal cavity and may, in prosobranchs which feed entirely by this means, never be used for manipulating any more abrasive substance. As a consequence wear on the radular teeth is minimal, as has been shown by Peile (1937). The salivary glands, too, which usually produce the mucus required for the lubrication of the radular movements, find themselves replaced functionally by the glands of the mantle cavity and in molluscs like *Crepidula* form two tubular structures, and in *Capulus* or *Turritella* two tufts of acini discharging to the buccal cavity, much smaller than the voluminous glands of prosobranchs which feed in other ways.

These changes in the various parts of the pallial complex and the associated changes in the first part of the alimentary canal (see also p. 220) are, in general, parallel to those

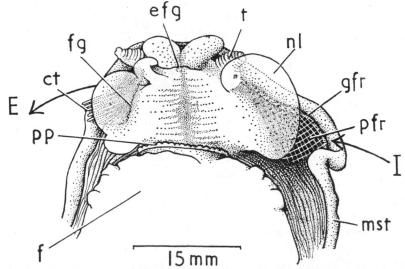

FIG. 63.—*Crepidula fornicata:* ventral view of the anterior half of the body. Arrows show direction of water currents. Details added from Werner.

ct, ctenidium; E, exhalant; efg, anterior end of food groove; f, foot; fg, food groove, by transparency; gfr, groove along which food and mucus from pallial filter travel to food pouch; I, inhalant; mst, mantle skirt; nl, neck lobe; pfr, pallial mucous filter; pp, propodium; t, tentacle.

which have also occurred in the lamellibranchs, and point clearly to the way in which the structure of this second class of molluscs has been reached.

Amongst the prosobranchs a ciliary feeding process has been described for the following animals found in the British Isles:

*Viviparus contectus* (Cook, 1949, *V. viviparus* in error), *Bithynia tentaculata* (Schäfer, 1953a; Lilly, 1953), *Turritella communis* (Graham, 1938), *Capulus ungaricus* (Yonge, 1938), *Calyptraea chinensis* (Orton, 1912b; Werner, 1953), *Crepidula fornicata* (Orton, 1912a, b; Werner, 1953).

*Viviparus* and *Bithynia* are freshwater animals (see pp. 588–593). The former tends to bury itself in muddy detritus at the bottom of the streams in which it lives, and feeds, at least partly, on what it collects from its mantle cavity. It seems to be able to live in this habitat without the specialized filters required by *Turritella*. *Bithynia*, whilst normally feeding on detritus and small algae collected by the radula, supplements this by eating what it collects in the mantle cavity. This seems to be true of specimens living in certain habitats only, and observers of the animal (Starmuhlner, 1952; Lilly, 1953; Werner, 1953) agree that it cannot be its primary feeding method.

*Turritella* (Yonge, 1946) is found in mud and sometimes muddy gravel at a depth of a few fathoms, living just below the surface but maintaining connexion with the overlying water by means of two openings. One of these is inhalant and is made by the foot; the other is exhalant and is due to the outflowing current from the mantle cavity. This is given momentum enough to make and keep open the hole by the fact that it is ejected from an exhalant siphon formed from the right side of the pallial skirt. Through this waste water and faecal pellets are ejected clear of the inhalant opening.

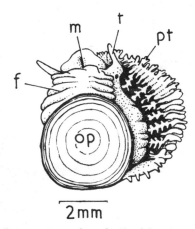

Fig. 64.—*Turritella communis:* to show details of the inhalant pallial aperture.
f, foot; m, mouth; op, operculum simplified; pt, pallial tentacle; t, tentacle.

*Crepidula* and *Calyptraea* are to be found, often in enormous numbers, the latter on stones in the lower parts of the beach and below, the former in clumps of individuals attached to one another in chains (see p. 374). *Capulus* is also sublittoral and has been shown by Sharman (1956) to be particularly common on shells of *Pecten*, living on the edge of the valve, which its presence distorts, and supplementing what it collects by means of the water current through the mantle cavity by thrusting its proboscis into the mantle cavity of the bivalve and appropriating what it can of that animal's food (see p. 506).

All these ciliary feeding gastropods, it will be noted, have become exceedingly sedentary in their mode of life and this is, indeed, an essential corollary of the ciliary feeding habit. Schäfer (1953b) has made some quantitative estimations of the efficiency of ciliary feeding in *Bithynia tentaculata* and shown that one individual filters about 400 ml of water in a day and extracts about 8 mg of suspended matter from a suspension containing 20 mg/l. More effective feeders must extract still greater quantities.

# CHAPTER 5

# THE SKIN

THE skin of an animal is invariably an interesting part of the body in that it has to provide protection for the living protoplasm within against the rigours of the environment without and at the same time allow the animal to become aware of its surroundings so that it may move successfully through them. The more thoroughly does the skin provide protection—and in the case of freshwater or terrestrial animals the need for this may be great—the more difficult will it be for it to allow communication with the outside world. These two cutaneous functions are therefore fundamentally antagonistic and some compromise becomes necessary. In many molluscs the matter becomes more acute in that a great extent of the exposed surface of the body is covered by a shell and is therefore frankly protective and almost devoid of sense organs, save in a few special cases like the chitons and perhaps the extinct tryblidiaceans. This has the effect of concentrating sense organs on other parts.

In gastropod molluscs, not only is this true, but in addition another area, the sole of the foot, becomes preoccupied with locomotor activity, whilst elsewhere, especially in the mantle cavity, other parts are involved in the transport of such material as genital products, excretory matter, faeces and other waste. The skin of gastropods is therefore concerned not only with the ordinary functions of protection and sensation, but with a number of other activities which are special to the group.

The fundamental structure of the skin is an epidermal epithelium resting on a mat of connective tissue through which run muscle fibres. No gastropod has become terrestrial in the sense that some arthropods and vertebrates have become land dwellers: the epidermis never becomes waterproofed either by the growth of a cuticle or the keratinization of the surface layers as it does in these two groups, and molluscs are terrestrial only in the narrow sense that they are not aquatic, and they survive on land only by avoiding truly xerotic conditions and by being active only in restricted habitats of high humidity. The modifications of structure shown by the skin are therefore mainly in relation to its glandular equipment, the height of the cells and their equipment with cilia. In ordinary circumstances (fig. 65A) the epidermis is a low columnar epithelium (epc), the cells of which are ciliated, and it includes a number of gland cells of the goblet cell type (gc). From this state the skin may depart towards a taller ciliated epithelium (as on the sole of the foot (fig. 66)) or one which is almost squamous (as on the lining of the mantle cavity and visceral hump (fig. 82B)) and the proportion of gland cells may be either high or low. In places, too, cilia may be absent (fig. 65C).

The gland cells which are present in the more simple cases (sole of the foot; skin of the head) are goblet cells (gc, figs 65A, C), most of which secrete mucus. The secretion is stained metachromatically by toluidine blue and by alcian blue and other mucous stains. It is therefore comparable to the epithelial mucins of many other groups of animals and is probably an acid mucopolysaccharide. Some other types of secretion are also produced by a second type of goblet cell; these are not so frequent in the sole of the foot as in epithelia in other situations. In this case the staining reactions suggest that the secretion is protein.

On the head, over most of the floor of the mantle cavity and on the upper surface of the foot the gland cells usually lie in the thickness of the epithelium. In other situations, however, where the amount of secretion which is called for is greater, they often become sunk into the underlying connective tissue (sgc, fig. 66) and open to the exterior by long

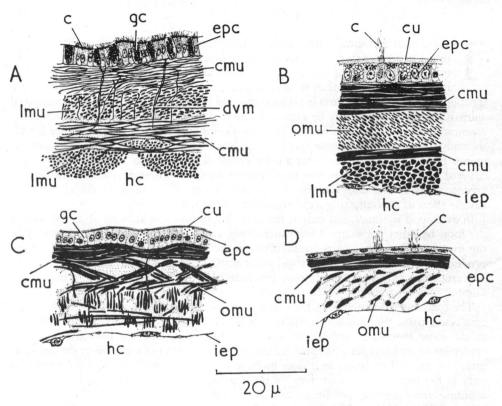

FIG. 65.—Structure of the body wall as shown by transverse sections of dorsal surface of head.
A, *Gibbula cineraria*; B, *Emarginula reticulata*; C, *Diodora apertura*; D, *Calyptraea chinensis*.
c, cilia; cmu, circular muscles; cu, cuticle; dvm, dorsoventral muscles; epc, epidermis; gc, gland cell; hc, haemocoelic cavity; iep, inner epithelium; lmu, longitudinal muscles; omu, oblique muscles.

necks lying between the epidermal cells. In this way the local concentration of glands may be greatly increased. Gland cells arranged in this way may be found on the sole and sides of the foot, in the shell gland at the edge of the mantle skirt (p. 128 and fig. 81), often in the roof of the mantle cavity and in a number of other, special, situations. These cells are alleged to differ from corresponding cells in other phyla in being derived from connective tissue cells, at least in some species.

There are three areas of skin which call for lengthier treatment because of the particularly important part which they play in the life of a prosobranch mollusc. These are the skin over the foot, that over the visceral hump and that at the mantle edge.

The foot is not only the main locomotor organ by means of which the gastropod creeps over the surface of the substratum, but it is also involved in a number of other activities since it bears the operculum, is, on occasion, sensory, is often concerned with the manipulation of egg capsules and almost always forms the penis in such males as have one. In Neritidae and Viviparidae the penis is cephalic (p. 350).

Primitively the molluscan foot is arranged in three sections lying one behind the other and separated from one another by transverse grooves. These are the propodium, the mesopodium and the metapodium. This arrangement is very rarely seen in its entirety, some of the more primitive heteropods being the only gastropods in which it is clearly visible. Except in a few cases, of which the Naticidae are the most obvious (fig. 304), the propodium loses its identity by merging into the front end of the mesopodium (pp,

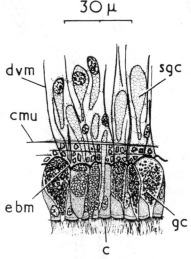

FIG. 66.—*Calyptraea chinensis:* vertical section through epidermis and underlying tissue of sole of foot. c, cilia; cmu, circular muscles; dvm, dorsoventral muscles; ebm, basement membrane; gc, gland cell in epidermis; sgc, gland cell in subepithelial connective tissue.

msp, fig. 67), from which is formed the flat surface on which the gastropod creeps, and the metapodium (mpt), which is the posterior lobe on which the operculum (op) is carried, becomes similarly fused to its dorsal surface.

The foot is equipped with a number of glands most of which are primarily concerned with lubricating the locomotion of the animal, but it also contains others which have nothing to do with this activity. The descriptions given by Lang (1896), Thiele (1897) and Pelseneer (1906a) are inaccurate because of the failure of these workers to realize that these glands are not all locomotory. The following classification of the glands present in the foot of prosobranchs is modified from Touraine (1952).

The *anterior pedal mucous gland* (apg, fig. 68) is a collection of gland cells opening to the sole of the foot at the anterior end of the mesopodium. The openings of the glands may be to the general surface of the foot so that its anterior margin shows no macroscopic evidence of the presence of this gland (*Calyptraea chinensis*; *Crepidula fornicata* (fig. 63); trochids, e.g. *Cantharidus clelandi* (fig. 69)); but in the majority of species the gland cells

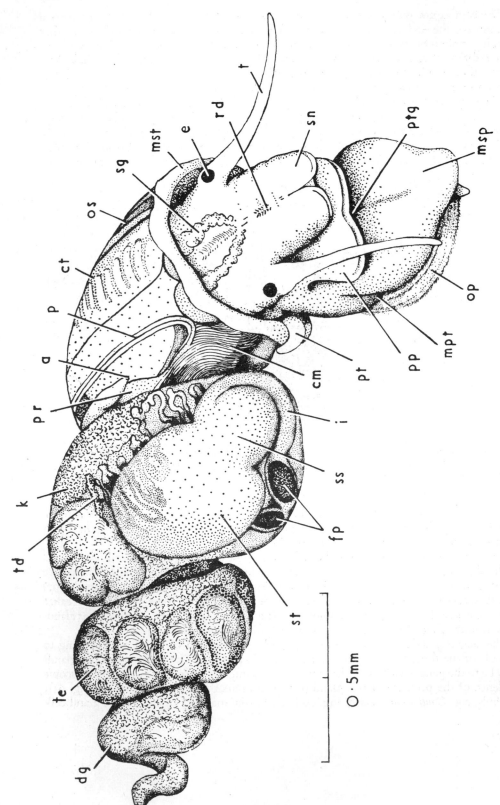

FIG. 67.—*Cingula semicostata*: animal removed from shell, seen from the right.
a, anus; cm, columellar muscle; ct, ctenidium; dg, digestive gland; e, eye; fp, faecal pellets in rectum; i, intestine; k, kidney; mpt, metapodium; msp, mesopodium; mst, mantle skirt; op, operculum; os, osphradium; P, penis with penial duct; pr, prostate; pt, pallial tentacle; ptg, mouth of posterior pedal gland; pp, propodium; rd, radula, by transparency; sg, salivary gland, by transparency; sn, snout; ss, style sac region of stomach; st, stomach; t, tentacle; td, testicular duct; te, testis.

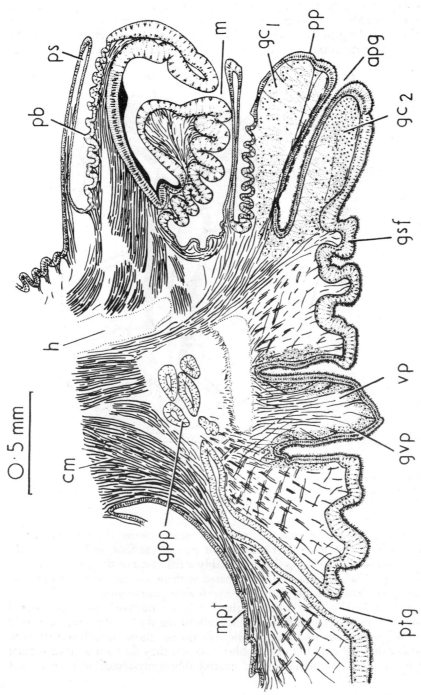

FIG. 68.—*Trivia* sp.: parasagittal section through head and foot to show pedal glands and proboscis. The animal had been narcotized before fixing; otherwise the papilla of the ventral pedal gland would have been retracted. $^{a}$pg, mouth of anterior pedal mucous gland; cm, columellar muscle; gc$_1$, first type of gland in anterior pedal mucous gland; gc$_2$, second type of gland in anterior pedal mucous gland; gpp, gland cells of posterior pedal mucous gland; gsf, gland cells of sole gland; gvp, gland cells of ventral pedal mucous gland; h, haemocoelic space; m, mouth; mpt, metapodium; pb, proboscis; pp, propodium; ps, proboscis sheath; ptg, mouth of posterior pedal mucous gland; vp, papilla of ventral pedal gland, partly protruded.

discharge into a transverse furrow which runs across the anterior end of the sole, separating the mesopodium behind from the reduced propodium in front (pp, fig. 68). In *Calliostoma* the groove occurs but gland cells are confined to its lips. In some cases this furrow is the mouth of an invagination which may run some way into the deeper parts of the foot in a longitudinal direction. This is known as the sagittal canal of the gland and it is slightly developed in Lacunidae, Cerithiopsidae and the Stenoglossa (fig.

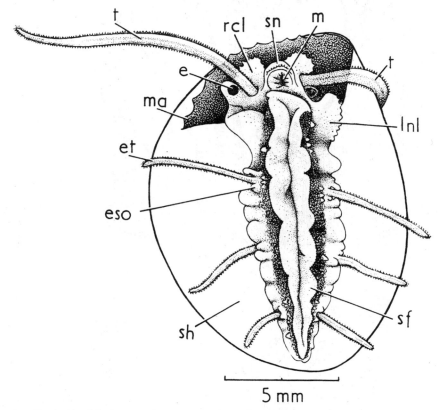

5 mm

FIG. 69.—*Cantharidus clelandi:* ventral view; the shell is left unshaded.
e, eye;  eso, epipodial sense organ;  et, epipodial tentacles;  lnl, left neck lobe;  m, mouth;  ma, mantle;  rcl, right cephalic lappet;  sf, sole of foot;  sh, shell;  sn, snout;  t, tentacle.

269), but much more in the eratoids (fig. 68). In *Pomatias elegans* the canal runs into tubules lying deep in the haemocoel of the anterior part of the foot, and it is also well developed in *Acicula fusca* (Creek, 1953)—presumably a reflection of the greater need for mucus in the locomotion of a terrestrial as compared with an aquatic animal and leading on to the great development of this gland in the terrestrial pulmonates.

Although it is referred to as a 'mucous' gland it is not the same mucous material which is produced here as in the ordinary goblet cells of the skin. Only some of its cells produce acid mucopolysaccharide: most of the cells do not show metachromasia with toluidine blue nor do they stain with alcian blue, whereas they do stain so as to suggest that their secretion might be mucoprotein, neutral mucopolysaccharide or even not 'mucus' at all. Possibly in relation to this difference in the staining of the cells of the gland it is to be noted that most of them are not simple goblet cells, but are arranged in nests in subepithelial spaces. The epithelium which lines the transverse furrow or the sagittal canal is not normally glandular, but is composed of columnar ciliated cells, between which the true gland cells discharge. The anterior pedal gland is the normal source of most of the mucus over which an aquatic prosobranch creeps.

The *sole gland* is the name which may be given to the collection of glands which pour secretion on to the surface of the sole on which the animal moves. The name is given by Touraine (1952) only to those cells which are subepithelial in position, and he does not use it to include those goblet cells which lie within the epithelium. It seems somewhat illogical to separate these two collections of gland cells on this basis alone, even if, as is mentioned below, they may be to some extent chemically different, and it is therefore proposed to use the term 'sole gland' for the sum of all the gland cells opening here, whatever their position in the foot. As might be expected, there is a relationship between the development of the sole gland and the degree of locomotor activity which the animals exhibit. In the Zeugobranchia and Patellacea, most of which have adopted a limpet-like mode of life and do not wander far from a 'home', there are only rare glands in the epithelium of the pedal sole and most of those are subepithelial, mainly single cells scattered evenly over the surface, though concentrated in anterior and posterior masses in *Emarginula*, and laterally in *Patella*. Their secretion appears to be in some cases (the Patellacea) an acid mucopolysaccharide comparable to the secretion of goblet cells; in others (the Zeugobranchia) a mucoprotein or neutral mucopolysaccharide.

Many prosobranchs possess goblet cells in the epithelium of the sole of the foot (gsf, fig. 68) in addition to the subepithelial ones, and they seem to be exclusively given over to the secretion of an acid mucopolysaccharide and any other kind of secretion has its origin in the deeper cells. The number of goblet cells in the epithelium may be quite low (Zeugobranchia, Patellacea, *Theodoxus fluviatilis*), moderate (*Calyptraea chinensis* (fig. 66), *Crepidula fornicata*, *Natica catena*), or very high (*Trivia* (fig. 68), *Nassarius reticulatus*). The trochids, *Bittium* and *Littorina* spp., on the other hand, have no goblet cells at all in this position. The subepithelial cells of the monotocardians do not usually secrete acid mucopolysaccharides, and in most animals are scattered in an irregular way throughout the interstices of the muscular feltwork which lies under the pedal epithelium. In some, however (*Littorina littorea* is a good example), these cells are arranged in bundles.

Occasionally the sole gland is constructed to a pattern; thus in *Lacuna* spp. the gland cells are confined to two lateral bands and the centre of the foot has none. Special arrangements are also to be found in *Ianthina* in relation to the habit this animal has of enclosing air in bubbles of mucus to form a float, a process which has been described by Fraenkel (1927*b*). Across the anterior edge of the foot in this animal runs a cleft marking the position of the anterior pedal mucous gland. Along the centre of the anterior half of the mesopodium (msp, fig. 299) runs a groove into which the sole gland discharges mucus; this groove is called the funnel and posteriorly it ends in a transverse fold covered with smaller longitudinal grooves and rich in gland cells. It is here that air, trapped from the atmosphere, is covered with mucus to make the bubbles of the float (see p. 562).

The *posterior pedal mucous gland* opens by a pore in the middle of the sole of the foot (ptg, figs. 68, 70), and there frequently runs a groove from that point to the posterior end (gv, fig. 70) along which its secretion flows. It does not occur in more than a limited number of prosobranchs which are especially those of small size like the rissoids, *Rissoella*, *Skeneopsis*, *Omalogyra*, Cerithiopsidae, triphorids and eratoids. The animals which have it tend to use its secretion, which assumes the form of a thread, in much the same way as a spider uses the thread of silk which it spins, and they climb up and down it from one water level to another. It may also act as an accessory lubricating gland in general locomotion, or as a source of adhesive mucus preventing the mollusc from being dislodged by water currents. The pore leads by way of a duct lined by a ciliated epithelium to a number of secretory tubules (gpp, fig. 68) which lie in the pedal haemocoel at a rather deep level. In some species (rissoids, *Omalogyra atomus*, *Skeneopsis planorbis* (ptg,

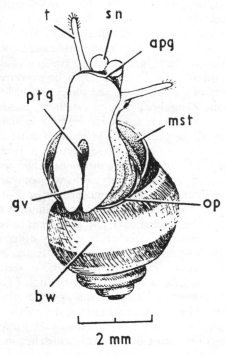

FIG. 70.—*Cingulopsis fulgida*: ventral view.
apg, mouth of anterior pedal mucous gland; bw, body whorl of shell; gv, groove from pedal gland conducting mucus to posterior tip of foot; mst, mantle skirt; op, operculum; ptg, mouth of posterior pedal gland; sn, snout; t, tentacle.

fig. 184B)) these tubules extend dorsally into the head and even into the visceral hump, lying around the nerve ring and alongside the oesophagus. In most cases the tubules are lined by goblet cells regularly alternating with supporting cells and their secretion is identical with that from the epithelial goblet cells of the pedal sole.

It may be that this posterior pedal mucous gland is homologous with the posterior pedal gland found in some slugs, the secretion of which also emerges as a thread and which can be used as a means of climbing or descending from one level to another.

The last gland of widespread occurrence in the foot is the *ventral pedal gland*, which occurs, in the female sex only, in some of the higher Mesogastropoda (Lamellariacea) and in the Stenoglossa. It has no relation to the locomotor activities of the animals, but is concerned with the attachment of egg capsules to the substratum on which they are laid. In such lower prosobranchs as attach their eggs to a substratum this is effected by the foot. The use of the gland for this purpose is an advance from this.

The establishment of the true function of this gland was long delayed. Pelseneer (1910) suggested that it was the place in which the egg capsule was actually secreted around eggs and albumen received from the female genital duct. That this could not be the true story was shown by Kostitzine (1940) who discovered a capsule, more or less fully

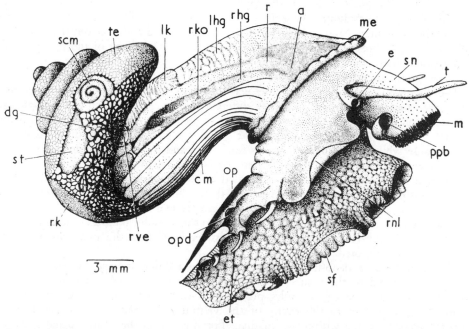

FIG. 71.—*Calliostoma zizyphinum:* male removed from shell and seen from right side; some organs are seen by transparency.

a, anus; cm, columellar muscle; dg, digestive gland; e, eye; et, epipodial tentacle; lhg, left hypobranchial gland; lk, left kidney or papillary sac; m, mouth; me, mantle edge; op, operculum; opd, operculigerous disc; ppb, pseudoproboscis; r, rectum; rhg, reduced right hypobranchial gland; rk, right kidney; rko, opening of right kidney (urinogenital); rnl, right neck lobe; rve, rectum within ventricle; scm, spiral caecum of stomach; sf, sole of foot; sn, snout; st, stomach; t, tentacle; te, testis.

formed, within the genital duct of a female whelk (*Buccinum undatum*). At the same time doubt was also thrown on Pelseneer's account of the function of the gland by Fischer's discovery (1940b) that there were no mucous cells in the ventral pedal gland of *Nucella lapillus*, although parts of the wall of the capsule are made of that material. He suggested that the ventral pedal gland was responsible for imparting its final shape to the capsule rather than for its production. Pelseneer's view, however, was re-affirmed by Franc (1941b) who observed the eggs of *Thais haemastoma* emerge from the genital pore encased only in a transparent, lens-shaped membrane and enter the ventral pedal gland. The mollusc remained with this pressed against the substratum for about 15–20 min at the end of which time the animal rose and left a fully formed egg case *in situ*. It had, in fact, already been shown by Ankel (1929), of whose work the French writers were apparently not aware, that the ventral pedal gland of *Nassa mutabilis* shapes a capsule which is received from the genital duct and attaches it to the substratum, and this was also confirmed for a variety of Stenoglossa by Fretter (1941).

In Stenoglossa the gland lies within the muscles and haemocoel of the foot, opening by a pore in the mid-line slightly nearer the front than the hinder end. The pore leads to a deep cavity with folded walls, which is lined by a ciliated columnar epithelium. In the epithelium lie gland cells, but the bulk of these is to be found in clusters of cells placed under the epithelium. The secretion of the cells is sometimes partly mucus, partly some other substance. Muscle fibres form a network around and between the groups of cells and radial fibres also run outward from the folds. The shape of the cavity of the gland resembles that of the egg capsule which emerges from it, and there is no doubt that the one is caused by the other.

The Lamellariacea amongst the mesogastropods possess ventral pedal glands, and these are constructed on a plan rather different from that on which the stenoglossan gland is built. This may be correlated with the slightly different uses to which the gland is put in the two cases. In Stenoglossa the gland is used for shaping the wall of the egg capsule while it is still soft into its final form and for pressing it against stone or weed or whatever substratum is appropriate for its attachment. During this process some of the material of the capsule wall is moulded by the muscles around the gland, and by the general pressure exerted by the body of the mollusc, into a small attachment plate which fits any irregularities in the substratum closely and allows of a good grip. It is doubtful whether the gland cells add anything to the capsule: their secretions are more concerned with lubricating the fixation process, or hardening the materials of which the capsule is composed.

The Lamellariacea deposit their egg capsules in a different way, embedding them in holes excavated in the tissues of compound ascidians. These cavities are bitten out by the radula and the egg capsules pushed into them. The capsules are transferred from the genital duct to the cavity of the ventral pedal gland and ejected from it into their resting place within the ascidian. For this reason the ventral pedal gland of these mesogastropods is not a simple cavity as in Stenoglossa but is provided with a central region (vp, fig. 68) which is protrusible and acts as a ramrod for pushing the capsule home and perhaps shaping its mouth. The gland, like those of stenoglossans, is lined by a ciliated columnar epithelium which contains goblet cells and has groups of gland cells in the subjacent tissue (gvp), although the secretion is not mucus as in members of that group. The protrusible papilla contains similar glands, but is not ciliated, and the whole structure is strongly muscular.

The gastropod foot has other glandular structures associated with it in addition to those that have just been mentioned, but these are located on the sides rather than upon the sole, and are not normally concerned with the locomotor activities of the animals. Such a structure is the lateral glandular streak (fig. 72) which lies along the side of the foot at the level of the shell muscle anteriorly, in young specimens of *Patella*, and which recurs in a number of other genera. The secretion from the lateral pedal glands of prosobranchs, whether irregularly scattered over the general surface or not, is partly mucous and partly protein. The function of these glands is probably, in the broad sense, repugnatorial, a first indication that it may be so being provided by the fact that they tend to be located in exposed situations, and that corresponding glands are particularly abundant at the mantle edge of those gastropods the shape of which qualifies them for the name of 'limpet'; they also abound all over the skin of those gastropods which have become naked by reduction or loss of the shell.

In the Zeugobranchia and Patellacea the cells on the side of the foot are mainly large subepithelial cells secreting material which is protein or mucous in nature; cells of a similar sort do not occur on the mantle edge in most genera. In *Acmaea*, however, the mantle edge becomes laden with an agglomeration of gland cells of three types (figs. 73, 74). The first ($rg_1$, $gc_1$) is a large cell, deeply sunk in the connective tissue and haemo-

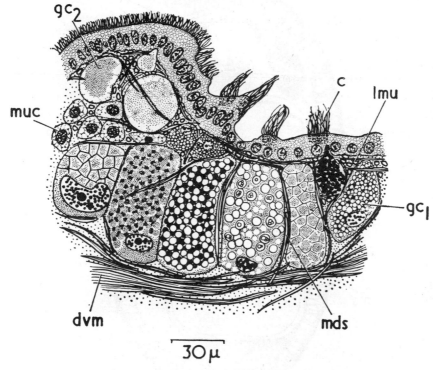

FIG. 72.—*Odostomia unidentata:* transverse section through lateral glandular streak.
c, cilia; dvm, dorsoventral muscles of foot; $gc_1$, $gc_2$, gland cells of two types; lmu, longitudinal muscles of foot; mds, muscles for discharge of secretion; muc, mucous cell.

coelic spaces of that region and discharging by a long neck between the epithelial cells of the edge. The contents of the cells reflect the light and appear white in living animals, giving a white edge around the mantle skirt. Their secretion emerges from the mouth of the gland as a viscid, white thread which does not disperse quickly. The second type of gland ($gc_2$) is similarly situated and smaller, so lying closer to the mantle edge. It is not visible in the living state but in sections has homogeneous contents which stain readily. The third type of gland cell ($rg_3$, $gc_3$) has bright red contents and may therefore be seen in the living animal. It is the smallest of the three and the gland cells appear in life as small red streaks running between the necks of the cells of the first type. The nature of the secretion and the cause of the colour are not known.

The mantle edge of molluscs of the genera *Crepidula* and *Calyptraea* contains multi-cellular glands (rgc, fig. 75). These lie at regular intervals round the edge of the mantle skirt and may be seen in the living animal as a series of whitish objects buried in its thickness (rgc, fig. 58). From the gland, which is more or less spherical, a narrow duct

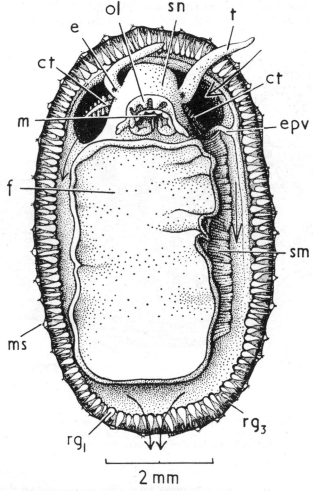

FIG. 73.—*Acmaea virginea:* ventral view.
ct, ctenidium in mantle cavity; e, eye; epv, efferent pallial vessel; f, foot; m, mouth; ms, cilia on sensory processes of mantle edge; ol, outer lip; $rg_1$, large repugnatorial glands; $rg_3$, small repugnatorial glands; sm, shell muscle; sn, snout; t, tentacle.

runs to open (drg, fig. 75) at the surface of the mantle skirt on the ventral surface of the middle pallial fold (p. 128). The cells in the gland are large and their secretion is protein, not mucus. The body of the gland and the duct are surrounded by muscle fibres which probably help in the discharge of the secretion. As in *Acmaea* and some opisthobranchs in which similar glands occur this happens only after rather drastic stimulation and gives rise to persistent threads. Similar glands are found in *Onchidella celtica*, *Acteon tornatilis*, *Haminea* and other opisthobranchs, the secretion of which has been shown to be distinctly toxic to other animals, and it therefore seems proper to assume that in such prosobranchs as have them these glands are repugnatorial too. It may be, of course, that whilst the skin glands of an opisthobranch like *Acteon* are positively dangerous to a small predator, the skin glands in other gastropods are simply the cause of a bad taste, and the glands which occur on the sides of the foot of *Diodora* may be better called antiseptic rather than truly repugnatorial.

Another conspicuous glandular field on the surface of the prosobranch body is the hypobranchial gland. A considerable amount of effort has been put into attempts to

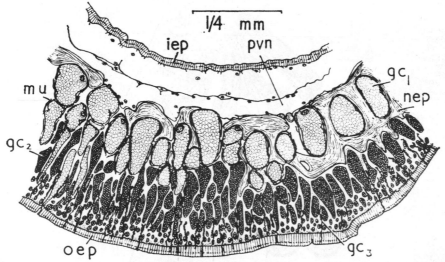

FIG. 74.—*Acmaea virginea:* tangential section of part of edge of the mantle skirt showing the nerve plexus, gland cells and muscle fibres around gland cells. The sensory organs on the outer pallial epithelium do not occur at this level.

gc₁, gc₂, gc₃, different types of pallial gland cells; iep, inner pallial epithelium; mu, muscle fibre; nep, nerve plexus; oep, outer pallial epithelium; pvn, pallial vein.

prove that it produces a toxic secretion and Dubois (1909) has gone so far as to claim that dog whelks are helped to overcome their prey by its use, a claim recently repeated by Clench (1947). A similar claim has been made for the purple secretion of the hypobranchial gland of *Ianthina* feeding on *Velella* (Hardy, 1956). It is true that extracts of the whole gland of stenoglossans have been shown by Dubois (1909) and Jullien (1948) to be poisonous to some animals when injected, but the latter has also shown in experiments with fish that the secretion of the hypobranchial gland does not diffuse freely into the water round an uninjured dog whelk and that although this does occur when the dog whelk has been injured the concentration of secretion never rises to a level which is sufficiently high to act as an external poison. More recently Erspamer (1952) and Whittaker & Michaelson (1954) have identified this poisonous substance in *Murex* spp. and in *Urosalpinx* and *Nucella* respectively as urocanylcholine. Fischer (1925) claimed that the hypobranchial secretion in *Nucella* has sexual significance in that it leads to aggregations of animals attracted by its odour, but the most reasonable assumption as to its significance in the life of the prosobranch is that, as described on p. 91, it is concerned solely with the production of a glairy slime which will cement particles together as they are being swept out of the mantle cavity, and simultaneously provide a conveyor belt moved by the beating cilia. Mucous cells, mainly of the goblet cell type, abound for this reason on most parts of the wall of the mantle cavity and are especially abundant on

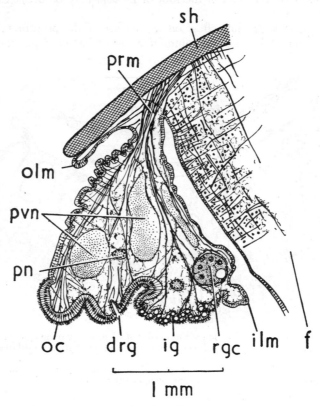

Fig. 75.—*Calyptraea chinensis:* transverse section through mantle edge.
    drg, opening of duct from repugnatorial gland; f, foot; ig, inner glandular zone of middle pallial lobe; ilm, inner pallial lobe; oc, outer ciliated zone of middle pallial lobe; olm, outer pallial lobe; pn, pallial nerve; prm, pallial retractor muscle; pvn, pallial blood vessels; rgc, repugnatorial gland; sh, shell.

the ctenidial leaflets, but the hypobranchial gland is a particularly rich source of this and other secretions.

In some of the Diotocardia the hypobranchial gland is double and lies right and left of the rectum (hg, fig. 76). The two parts are equally developed in some Zeugobranchia (fig. 76), but vary considerably within the Trochacea. In this group the right half is somewhat reduced in *Gibbula, Monodonta* (rhg, fig. 53) and most species of *Cantharidus*, but in *C. clelandi* the left half is reduced and in *Margarites* (hg, fig. 168) there is only a right gland present. In *Tricolia pullus* (fig. 77) a remnant of the left gland occurs along with a well developed right one. Clark (1958) has attempted to rationalize this distribution by relating it to the course of the rectum: a right gland develops only where the rectum curves to the left (see also p. 325). Hypobranchial glands seem to have been completely lost in the Patellacea (fig. 48c). The Neritacea (at least *Theodoxus fluviatilis*

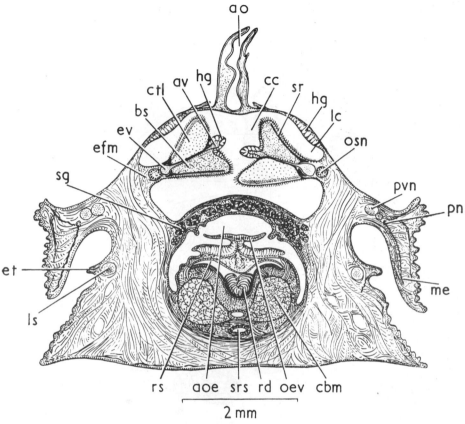

FIG. 76.—*Diodora apertura:* transverse section at level of apical mantle opening.
     ao, apical opening of mantle cavity; aoe, anterior oesophagus; av, afferent vessel of ctenidium; bs, blood space in ctenidial leaflet; cbm, cartilage of buccal mass; cc, central compartment of mantle cavity; ctl, ctenidial leaflet; efm, efferent membrane; et, epipodial tentacle; ev, efferent vessel of ctenidium; hg, hypobranchial gland; lc, dorsolateral compartment of mantle cavity; ls, lateral pedal sinus; me, mantle edge; oev, oesophageal valve; osn, osphradial nerve; pn, pallial nerve; pvn, pallial vein; rd, radula; rs, radular sac; sg, salivary gland; sr, skeletal rod in ctenidial leaflet; srs, subradular space.

(fig. 52)) possess no undoubted hypobranchial gland but on the extreme right of the mantle cavity posteriorly a few glandular tubules open. These are lined by an epithelium which secretes mucus and they have been claimed (Thiele, 1897; Bourne, 1908) as the homologue of the right hypobranchial gland. Mucous cells in the mantle skirt between the ctenidium and the rectum represent a reduced left hypobranchial gland.

The monotocardians have all apparently lost the right hypobranchial gland but retain that of the left side more or less well developed. It occupies the field between the attachment of the ctenidial axis on the left and the rectum on the right on the inner side of the mantle skirt. In some the degree of development is slight (*Crepidula*, fig. 58; *Turritella*, fig. 57), in others it is sufficiently well developed to fling this part of the epithelium into irregular low folds (*Littorina*, fig. 7; *Aporrhais*, fig. 179; *Nassarius*, fig. 116) whilst in

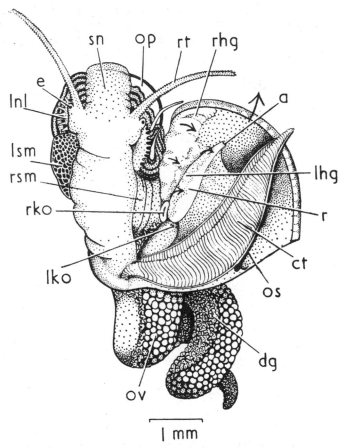

FIG. 77.—*Tricolia pullus:* dissection to show contents of mantle cavity. Arrows show direction of ciliary currents.

    a, anus; ct, ctenidium; dg, digestive gland; e, eye; lhg, left hypobranchial gland; lko, opening of left kidney; lnl, left neck lobe; lsm, left shell muscle; op, operculum; os, osphradium; ov, ovary; r, rectum; rhg, right hypobranchial gland; rko, opening of right kidney; rsm, right shell muscle; rt, right tentacle; sn, snout.

some genera (*Buccinum*) the development is considerable and the gland is a conspicuous folded structure on the roof of the mantle cavity.

    The nature of the secretion of the hypobranchial gland has not been investigated with modern histochemical methods to the extent that that of some other glands in gastropods has been. Some of its cells secrete mucus apparently identical with that produced by goblet cells elsewhere in the skin, but these may not be the commonest kind; it is because of their presence, however, and because of the fact that the secretion in general resembles mucus, that this gland is occasionally called the mucous gland.

In *Diodora*, the hypobranchial gland of which has been examined histochemically by Gabe (1951*b*), mucous cells are relatively few and are limited to the part of the gland lying on the upper surface of the ctenidial axis and to the anal papilla (mh, fig. 78A). Elsewhere the cells of the (fixed) gland usually appear very empty although occasional granules of secretion occur (gc); they give no clear staining reaction and Gabe, like previous workers, came to no clear conclusion as to what they do secrete. *Emarginula* (fig. 78B) and *Puncturella* show glands with identical staining reactions. In *Scissurella*,

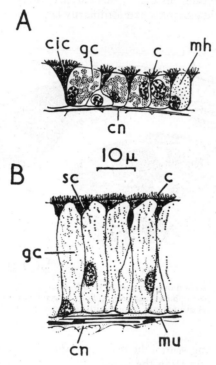

FIG. 78.—Transverse sections of part of hypobranchial gland: A, *Diodora apertura*; B, *Emarginula reticulata*.

c, cilia; cic, ciliated cell; cn, connective tissue; gc, gland cells; mh, mucous cell of hypobranchial gland; mu, muscle fibres; sc, supporting cells.

where the left gland is much smaller than the right, mucous cells occur along with a second type with minutely granular contents (Bourne, 1910). These gland cells (gc) alternate regularly with slender supporting cells (cic, sc), some of which are ciliated. In *Diodora* and its relatives the binding properties of the secretion of the hypobranchial gland are possibly less than in many monotocardian prosobranchs because of the more thorough ventilation of the mantle cavity allowed by the apical hole in the shell. Crofts (1929) reported the presence of two types of cell in the hypobranchial gland of *Haliotis*: both of these were said to secrete mucus.

In many gastropods true mucous cells are relatively more abundant than they are in the zeugobranchs and they form in some species the major constituent of the hypo-branchial gland. This is true of the Calyptraeacea, Lamellariacea and Cypraeacea. In the last two of these groups the hypobranchial gland is very extensive, in *Velutina* covering the entire surface of the mantle cavity right of the gill. In most mesogastropods, however, other cells secreting protein material are added to the mucous cells and in some genera (*Turbonilla*, fig. 79; pyramidellids; *Omalogyra*; *Skeneopsis*), these are the common type of cell in the hypobranchial gland and mucous cells occur very sparsely, although it is as well to add that most of these animals are probably opisthobranchs (see p. 639) or have strong opisthobranch affinities. In these genera hypertrophy of the protein gland cells (pc, hy) is apt to occur; they become extraordinarily large and have, indeed, on occasion

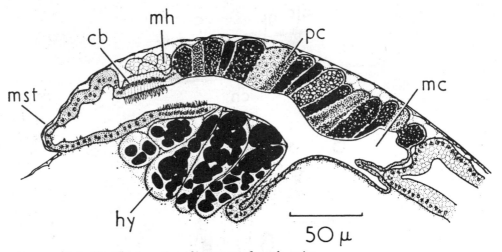

FIG. 79.—*Turbonilla jeffreysi:* section of inner part of mantle cavity.
cb, ciliated strip; hy, hypertrophied gland cells on floor of mantle cavity; mc, mantle cavity; mh, mucous cell of hypobranchial gland; mst, mantle skirt; pc, protein cell of hypobranchial gland.

been mistaken for eggs lying within the mantle cavity. What is involved in the changing proportions of the secretions from the hypobranchial gland is by no means clear. It is worth noting, however, that the hypobranchial secretion tends to contain more mucus in those gastropods which have a ctenidium in the mantle cavity, whereas it tends not to be mucus in animals where this has been—for whatever reason—replaced by ciliated strips (cb). In these (e.g. *Turbonilla*) such mucous cells (mh) as do occur lie in close relation to the ciliated strips and the remainder of the hypobranchial gland has none. It may be that the current of water maintained by ciliated strips through the mantle cavity is less powerful than that maintained by a ctenidium and requires a different kind of lubricant and transport medium for the particles which have to be moved. The nature of the varying hypobranchial secretions is a point for further investigation.

In a number of prosobranchs the secretion of the hypobranchial gland is coloured. This occurs, for example, in *Cirsotrema*, *Nucella lapillus*, *Ocenebra erinacea* and probably all muricaceans, *Clathrus* spp. and *Ianthina janthina*. In all these animals the secretion is purple in its final form, but in the stenoglossans it is a greenish-yellow colour when first liberated. This gradually turns to a red hue and then deepens to purple. The change is dependent on the presence of oxygen and light and will not occur in their absence, although this appears to happen in *Murex trunculus* (Dubois, 1909). Chemically the purple pigment (the Royal or Tyrian Purple of the ancients, made in classical times from species of *Murex*) is 4-4'-dibromindigo or 6-6'-dibromindigo, related to natural indigo or woad and presumably manufactured by the mollusc from a tryptophane source. The production of the coloured secretion has been fully investigated by Letellier (1889, 1890) and Dubois (1902a, b; 1903a, b), Erspamer (1947) and Bouchilloux & Roche (1955). Letellier and Dubois suggested that a colourless chromogen was acted upon in the light by an enzyme which Dubois called purpurase, and converted into dibromindigo. Erspamer showed that the source of the substances involved was the median part of the hypobranchial gland, the enzyme being produced in the anterior third of the gland and the chromogen (or a prochromogen) in the posterior part. Like Dubois before him, Erspamer found that whilst the chromogens varied from species to species, the enzyme was identical in all. The study of the secretion has been taken further by Bouchilloux & Roche using chromatography: they have shown the presence of three prochromogens in *Murex*, *M. trunculus* having prochromogen 1 and prochromogen 2; *M. brandaris* prochromogen 3. The prochromogens consist of a sulphate group linked to an indoxylic group, which contains bromine in prochromogens 2 and 3, and is probably 6-bromoindoxyl, but has no bromine and is probably indoxyl in the case of prochromogen 1. The origin of the indoxyl compounds is not known. Prochromogen 1 of *M. trunculus* is converted by the removal of the sulphate radicle by a sulphatase called purpurase into a blue pigment which is indigo itself; prochromogen 2, in the same species, is similarly converted into a red-mauve pigment which is bromindigo and is very similar to the 6-6'-dibromindigo of *M. brandaris* made from prochromogen 3. The pigments of *Ocenebra erinacea* and *Nucella lapillus* have not been similarly investigated but are no doubt closely related. Little work has been done on purple pigments from other prosobranch sources. The familiar purple pigment which can be obtained from animals of the genus *Aplysia* is chemically quite different from the prosobranch purples, being a haem derivative.

One major activity of the molluscan integument is to give rise to a shell and it is now recognized that this is secreted by the mantle (Réaumur, 1711; Tullberg, 1881) and is not the result of a direct transformation of the animal's tissue as supposed by von Nathusius-Königsborn (1877). This activity is confined to the skin which forms the outer covering of the visceral mass or hump, though in exceptional cases something corresponding to a shell may be produced from skin over other parts of the body (*Teredo*, *Hipponyx*). If this does happen, however, the structure of the secreted material is invariably simpler than true shell.

The secretion of the shell is undertaken by special areas of the mantle. The shell is composed, in a general way, of an organic base, conchiolin, which is impregnated with inorganic salts of calcium, predominantly calcium carbonate, and which may exist as a separate layer, not so impregnated, over the outer surface, where it is known as the periostracum. The secretion of the organic base and of the initial calcareous material of the shell takes place normally only at the free edge of the mantle skirt, and it is the gradual growth which occurs along this line which generates the shell. The total secretion at this place, however, does not produce more than a thin shell and later deposition of extra calcareous matter thickens and strengthens it. This secondary growth involves the addition of calcareous salts and conchiolin over the whole of the inner surface of the shell and is undertaken by the whole outer pallial epithelium. In many cases the crystalline character of the calcareous matter produced at these two sites is different, the edge of the mantle skirt producing prisms, the general pallial epithelium, on the other hand, laying down plates which alternate with conchiolin.

There are, therefore, three problems to be discussed: (a) the site and mechanism of conchiolin production; (b) the site and mechanism of the production of the outer prismatic layer; and (c) those of the inner material. It must be confessed, at the outset, that no clear account can be given of the ways in which the whole shell is produced in the case of any mollusc. What work has been done on the secretion of the shell in gastropods relates predominantly to species of the genus *Helix*, and much of the work is concerned with the secretion of the shell in lamellibranchs. It is likely that there is no fundamental difference between the two classes in this respect, but this has not yet been proved, and, as Bøggild (1930) has shown, the organization of the shell tends to differ in the two classes.

In most lamellibranchs, and in some gastropods like the Zeugobranchia (fig. 80), the free edge of the mantle skirt is flung into three folds, the outer (olm), middle (mlm) and inner (ilm) pallial folds. In lamellibranchs the periostracum originates from the groove between the outer and middle folds and there has been debate as to whether the site of secretion is the lateral aspect of the middle fold, or the medial aspect of the outer. Older workers (Tullberg, 1881; de Villepoix, 1892; List, 1902; Manigault, 1939) have mainly chosen the former situation; more recent ones (Kessel, 1944; Brown, 1952) have favoured the latter. The calcareous matter, on the other hand, is produced from the lateral surface of the outer fold and from the rest of the pallial surface. There is, therefore, at the edge of the mantle folds a small gap between the newly secreted periostracum and the ventralmost edge of the calcareous part of the shell. In gastropods the same general relationships hold, but the proportionate sizes of the folds are different and the production of periostracum often much less. The most important change in the relative sizes of the pallial folds of gastropods in the present context is the reduction of the outer pallial fold which has the effect of bringing the groove in which the periostracum is secreted into close proximity to the site of secretion of the calcareous matter of the shell, and the two processes appear to go on more or less side by side.

Conchiolin is the name given to the non-calcareous matrix of the shell. It is perhaps a complex of substances rather than one substance in the strict chemical sense; it appears to be protein (Friza, 1932) and to vary from animal to animal and even from part to part of the shell (Beedham, 1958b). The protein also appears to be tanned (Trueman, 1949). Bevelander & Benzer (1948), working with oysters, have shown that a great mass of glands, which lie with ducts opening to the groove where the periostracum is formed, have protein and polysaccharide contents. These may, therefore, be assumed to be the source of the conchiolin of the shell. In gastropods they are much less conspicuous and, in some genera, it is difficult to find any glands at all in this position. In most, they occur in small groups of cells embedded in the connective tissue of the mantle edge and discharging to its margin (fig. 81).

The secretion of the calcareous layers of the molluscan shell is still, frankly, improperly understood and little help towards its understanding is to be obtained from the histology of the parts which appear to be involved. The outer surface of the outer pallial fold, it is true, is usually covered by a columnar epithelium rather taller than that which occurs on other external pallial surfaces, just as has been described by Trueman (1942) in the lamellibranch *Tellina tenuis*, and by Yonge (1953) in *Pinna*; this is particularly marked in trochids (fig. 54), where it may extend on to the general surface of the visceral mass. In other situations the mantle epithelium is a thin and delicate layer of low cells (pe, figs. 82, 83), often loaded with pigment granules (pgr) and lying over a layer of connective tissue and muscle fibres (mu). The presence of calcareous granules has been shown in a

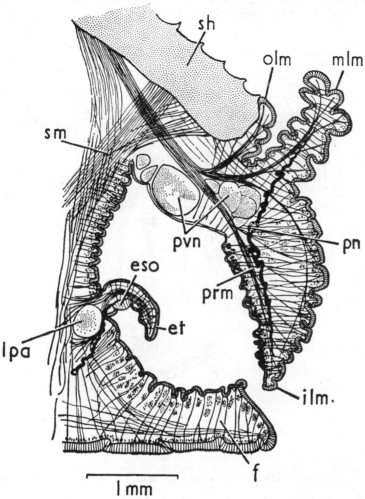

Fig. 80.—*Diodora apertura:* transverse section through lateral part of foot and mantle edge.
eso, epipodial sense organ; et, epipodial tentacle; f, foot; ilm, inner pallial lobe; lpa, lateral pedal artery; mlm, middle pallial lobe; olm, outer pallial lobe; pn, pallial nerve; prm, pallial retractor muscle; pvn, pallial vein; sh, shell; sm, shell muscle.

few animals, mainly bivalves, suggesting that these cells contain precursor material which could be liberated at the right moment for the formation of new shell, but calcium is certainly not present in many gastropods in recognizable quantities, at least normally, nor do the nuclei look as if they were those of metabolically active cells. Even if it be agreed that the secretion of the shell may well be a rhythmical activity, tied to the

6

seasons of the year, no significant features can be detected in the epithelium to suggest this. Its general appearance, in fact, suggests metabolic inactivity and free permeability to fluid and dissolved material of small molecular size and possibly, like a vertebrate capillary wall, to amoebocytes or other wandering cells. McGee-Russell (1954) suggested (in *Helix aspersa*) the occurrence of stoma-like apertures in the epithelium through which cells could escape from the internal blood spaces. These facts tend to support the idea

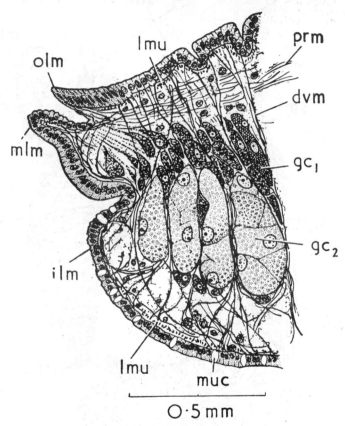

FIG. 81.—*Siphonaria* sp.: transverse section of mantle edge.
    dvm, dorsoventral muscle; $gc_1$, $gc_2$, cells of shell gland; ilm, inner pallial lobe; lmu, longitudinal muscle; mlm, middle pallial lobe; muc, mucous cell; olm, outer pallial lobe; prm, pallial retractor muscle.

originating with de Waele (1930) that shell secretion does not call primarily for activity on the part of the pallial epithelium, but that it is essentially a physicochemical phenomenon and that the pallial epithelium is merely the outside surface of the animal adapted for allowing the free passage of the materials which are necessary for the process. The same idea is supported by the work of Manigault (1933) and of Dotterweich & Elssner (1935). The supposition made by these workers is that at the time when secretion of shell material is about to occur there is formed between the mantle and the shell a layer of fluid, the extra-pallial fluid, in which an alleged protein-calcium salt complex

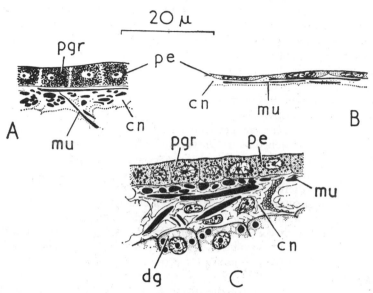

FIG. 82.—Transverse sections of mantle from surface of visceral hump: A, *Patella vulgata*; B, *Emarginula reticulata*; C, *Nassarius reticulatus.*
    cn, connective tissue; dg, digestive gland; **mu**, muscle fibre; pe, mantle epithelium; pgr, pigment granule.

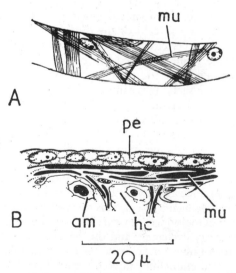

FIG. 83.—*Ocenebra erinacea:* mantle from surface of visceral hump; A, surface view; B, transverse section.
    am, amoebocyte; hc, blood space; mu, muscle fibre; pe, mantle epithelium.

occurs and from which calcareous matter is precipitated on to the inner side of the shell, during growth (= thickening), or on to the inner side of the periostracum during the formation of new shell near the mantle edge. This might happen without any vital activity at all, that being confined to making the precipitation of calcium salts possible by facilitating the production of the extra-pallial fluid or of the salts which it contains in solution. Many observers have noticed that the mantle becomes turgid with blood at the times when growth or repair of shell is going on (Manigault), an occurrence which would probably increase diffusion through the mantle epithelium into a space between it and the shell, and it is obvious to all who have extracted gastropods from their shell that there is no close attachment between mantle and shell except where pallial and columellar muscles are fastened to it. On the other hand, as pointed out by Robertson (1941), there is no real basis for the alleged protein-calcium complex, and ordinary extra-pallial fluid is many times richer in organic matter than the shell into which it is allegedly converted, and has a different enzyme content (Florkin & Besson, 1935).

The source of the calcium which is used in the manufacture of shell does not normally appear to be the cells of the mantle, which have little stored within them, and various workers have looked for this in a variety of places. It has often been sought in the mucous glands of the mantle, a view reproduced as recently as 1948 by Bevelander & Benzer and by Korringa (1952) for *Ostrea*. Though these occur in the outer pallial epithelium of lamellibranchs they are not common in the epithelium covering the visceral hump of gastropods which is responsible for the production of the inner layers and for repair. They do occur in trochids. Prenant (1924b) and Manigault (1933) looked for the source of calcium in subpallial connective tissue cells which migrate through the mantle and liberate calcareous material in extra-pallial fluid or on the inner surface of pre-existing shell. According to Manigault these cells were markedly eosinophile. Prenant thought of the mitochondria of the connective tissue cells as being responsible for making a hyaline substance which was precipitated with calcium salts. Wagge (1951), working with *Helix aspersa* which, being a terrestrial pulmonate, may have to make more elaborate arrangements for the storage of calcium salts than a marine prosobranch, found the source of the calcium in cells of the digestive gland, which become loaded with calcium carbonate whenever circumstances lead to an increased consumption and a lowered use of calcium salts. She described the removal of this calcareous matter from the digestive gland by amoebocytes and its transport to an extra-pallial fluid during the repair of damage done to the shell. This cannot be generally true of prosobranchs since they have no large store of calcareous salts in the digestive gland. This view has been criticized by McGee-Russell (1954) (also working on *H. aspersa*) who believed that extra-vasation occurs through pores in the pallial membrane and that the calcium is in solution in the blood along with polysaccharide and protein. He believed that such cells as appear in this extra-pallial fluid have been accidentally detached from the body of the mollusc. This is not in agreement with the earlier work of Sioli (1935) on *H. pomatia*, who found no increase in blood calcium accompanying loss of liver stores at a time when extensive shell repair was going on. Manigault (1939) was the first to report the presence of phosphatase in molluscs, an enzyme which can enrich body fluids in calcium salts and may also be involved in all energy exchanges and this has been confirmed by later workers who assume that it is responsible for accelerating transport of calcium in the body of snails. It occurs in the pallial epithelium in considerable, but locally varying quantities.

The general conclusion of these workers appears to be that from stores of calcium in connective tissue or other depots what is required for growth or repair is brought into an extra-pallial fluid, either in solution, or in the cytoplasm of amoebocytes, or through the protoplasm of the epithelial cells of the mantle, from which it is probably passed into solution. All recent workers, with the possible exception of Wagge (1951), agree that the final deposition of the calcium is likely to be a physicochemical event occurring extra-cellularly. Manigault (1939) has shown that it depends upon the partial pressure of carbon dioxide in the atmosphere to which the extra-pallial fluid is exposed and that no deposition of calcareous matter occurs unless this is 15% or less. Thus where the partial pressure of carbon dioxide is high, as it would be near the body of the mollusc, no precipitation of calcium salts occurs, but where it is low, as it would be further from the body, especially if the shell had been damaged and the extra-pallial fluid was in direct contact with the external medium, there new shell material would be laid down. It is a common observation, too, that in natural waters with a high tension of dissolved carbon dioxide erosion—or even solution—of molluscan shell may take place.

There is a general tendency on the part of workers on shell formation to state that the deposition of the calcareous material occurs only on a special matrix which is laid down first, both in growth and repair. This may be the conchiolin material secreted at the mantle edge in the case of new calcareous shell, but this cannot be so with the repair of damage to the higher parts of the coil of the shell. It may be remarked at this point that if the damage which has been done to the shell is near enough to the mantle edge to allow it to be drawn back into the broken piece of shell, then that will happen, and the greater part of the repair of the damage will be brought about by the secretion initiated by this region; only if the damage is so high up the spire of the shell that this readjustment of position on the part of the mantle edge is impossible does the gastropod regenerate shell in other ways. In these circumstances no participation by conchiolin in the repair can occur unless there is a localized formation of that substance. This would impute the potentiality of secreting conchiolin to the entire covering of the visceral hump instead of to the mantle edge alone, and there is little evidence for that in gastropods (Andrews (1934, 1935a) and Wagge (1951) deny it for *Theodoxus* and *Helix*; Boutan (1923) and van Deinse (1913) describe it in *Haliotis* and *Buccinum*), although it is known to occur in lamellibranchs (Rassbach, 1912a, b). The matrix which precedes the deposition of shell is usually described as 'calcaffine', is made of chondroprotein or glycoprotein (Manigault, 1939), and is, in fact, the first seal over the break in the shell which the mollusc manufactures. It may be that it appears as a film of protein on the surface of the extra-pallial fluid, which, as a derivative of the blood of the animal, almost certainly contains some protein, and its appearance could then be dictated by purely physical and chemical factors—its formation, like that of the calcareous part of the shell later, is an event taking place external to the animal over which it has little control.

Wagge's account of the events in *Helix aspersa* differs from that of others in that she believed that the material for the calcaffine matrix, like the calcareous matter deposited in it, is also transported by amoebocytes, different in characteristics from those that are responsible for carrying the calcium salts. According to Wagge, successive waves of the two types of amoebocyte deposit protein matrix and calcareous material until the whole structure is thick enough to plug the gap. This point would appear to be reached, according to Berner (1942), when the mantle meets a certain critical resistance from the overlying shell: this could act by opposing the tendency of extra-pallial fluid to accumulate by escape from the gorged blood lacunae of the mantle. Work on lamellibranchs suggests that the pallial epithelium may play a greater role in the formation of shell material than this account of investigations on gastropods assumes; and in view of the probability that there is an underlying similarity in the two groups, it would clearly be worthwhile to apply some of the newer histochemical methods of investigating cell metabolism to the mantle epithelium of gastropods. The calcareous matter is said to be deposited as carbonate by such investigators as Villepoix (1892), de Waele (1930), Robertson (1941) and Wagge (1951), but as phosphate, which will be later transformed to carbonate, by Manigault (1939), Bevelander & Benzer (1948) and Bevelander (1952). Abolinš-Krogis (1958) suggested that organic polymer crystals are first laid down and that these are then mineralized by the deposition of calcium carbonate. The material of the initial crystalline deposit she showed to be an acid mucopolysaccharide, probably chondroitin sulphuric acid, on the basis of its staining reactions. This material is that which takes up $P^{32}$ rapidly (Bevelander, 1952) whereas $Ca^{45}$ is taken up by the inorganic crystal.

The whole process of shell formation is possibly much more easy in marine than in either freshwater or terrestrial molluscs, although in gastropods it has been studied almost exclusively in the last of these groups. All the calcium which terrestrial gastropods require has to be obtained from the food which they eat and if this is deficient the shell may be thin and transparent and less extensive than is necessary to make a complete covering to the visceral hump (e.g. *Helix aspersa* reared on a diet lacking calcium or fed on lettuce). In freshwater molluscs the water itself may be a source of calcium in addition to the food, and in marine animals calcium abounds in this source. It is not surprising, therefore, that the shells of gastropods differ from species to species in relation to their environment, and also from individual to individual in one and the same species for the same reasons, marine shells always being thicker and heavier than those of freshwater or terrestrial forms, and those of marine animals living in quiet localities more likely to have spines or other outgrowths than those living in rougher situations—e.g. *Nucella* (Moore, 1936).

A further factor which may influence the secretion of the calcareous molluscan shell is the enzyme carbonic anhydrase. This affects the rate of the reaction

$$H_2O + CO_2 \rightleftharpoons H_2CO_3$$

and it was suggested by Freeman & Wilbur (1948) that it might be involved in the manipulation of carbonate since it is known to occur in the tissues of the mantle. Wilbur & Jodrey showed later (1955) that if the enzyme be poisoned in the oyster by the specific inhibitors 2-benzothiazolesulphonamide and diamox (2-acetylamino-1,3,4-thiadiazole-5-sulphonamide) then the rate of deposition of new shell was correspondingly lowered. Abolinš-Krogis (1958) has shown that the conversion of organic to inorganic crystals of calcium carbonate involves carbonic anhydrase. Nevertheless, this mechanism cannot be an essential part of the machinery of shell deposition because it appears to be totally absent from a number of gastropods (e.g. *Crepidula*), and in others it occurs in many places in addition to the pallial epithelium—although that does not necessarily deny it value in the treatment of shell material.

The processes by which calcium carbonate is deposited in the molluscan shell, whatever they may precisely be, lead generally to the growth of the shell at the mouth, and to its thickening at all other parts. In addition accessory pieces may be added, such as septa separating empty upper whorls from the more basal ones in which the animal lives. They are also reversible, and just as calcium salts may be laid down, so may they also be resorbed. A swan mussel, for example, fed on a calcium-free diet and kept in water lacking calcium will nevertheless grow, and produce new shell, the material for which is obtained by removal of calcium from thicker, older parts of the shell and its transport to the mantle edge to form new material. Precisely how this is managed is not known, but the mantle epithelium must be involved and amoebocytes may be. In certain cases the removal of calcareous material may be extensive, as when ellobiids erode the entire columella (see p. 69) or when spines decorating one whorl of a shell are removed during overgrowth by the next, as occurs in muricids (see p. 65).

Most molluscan shells are coloured, and inspection shows that this is limited to the outer layer of the shell, such colour as occurs in the inner layers being of physical origin. This location of the colour therefore implies the presence, at the mantle edge, of glands which secrete pigments at the time and near the place where the calcareous material of the outer layer is being formed. The nature of the pigment which is produced in such situation is often unknown, but has been investigated in a number of animals. In the following account the findings of Comfort (1951) are mainly relied upon.

There is a difference between the lower prosobranchs and the higher in that the shell pigments of the latter are bound to protein material incorporated in the shell, whereas those of the diotocardians are not and so may be obtained in solution by dissolving the shell. The bound pigments have not been properly investigated chemically as no methods for their extraction have yet been elaborated. They may be chromoproteins with melanin groups incorporated. The only pigments which have been demonstrated in these shells without doubt are pyrroles, though it has been suggested that indigo-like pigments and melanins also occur, and there are numerous others, still chemically unknown.

Indigo and 6-6'-dibromindigo have already been discussed in relation to the hypo-branchial gland of Stenoglossa. Some of these animals, on occasion, display violet tints in their shell, and the assumption is readily made that these are chemically identical or related. There is no proof, however, that this is so, and the statement that ianthinine, the pigment which gives the purple colour to the shell and hypobranchial secretion of *Ianthina* spp., is indigoid (Moseley, 1877) appears unlikely to be true.

Melanins are likely substances to be responsible for various shades of yellow, through brown, to black, in the pigmentation of shells as in other parts of the body, but they have never been demonstrated in any prosobranch.

Pigments of pyrrole type are apparently the most abundant source of colour of chemical origin in the shells of the lower prosobranchs. These may be of two types: (a) where the pyrrole rings form a ring: these are porphyrins; and (b) where the pyrrole rings form a chain: these are bilins. The latter are much less common than the former, but are responsible for the green colour of certain shells (*Turbo, Haliotis*). The porphyrins are the usual source of colour in the shells of the lower prosobranchs, the principal one which is found being uroporphyrin I, which occurs in a pure state, but in marine forms only. Another porphyrin encountered in many shells is conchoporphyrin. According to Comfort (1951) these porphyrins are to be found in the following British species of gastropods: *Acmaea virginea, Gibbula magus, G. cineraria, Cantharidus striatus, Monodonta lineata, Velutina velutina, Erato voluta, Trivia monacha, Acteon tornatilis*.

This list suggests a general distribution in the Trochacea and Lamellariacea, and, although investigations are not numerous, they suggest that porphyrins are also found in the shells of Zeugobranchia, Cypraeacea and of *Tricolia*. They do not occur in *Patella*.

The origin of the porphyrins is not known. In other animals porphyrins are usually held to be chlorophyll derivatives, and if this were true of gastropods, their deposition in the shell could be regarded as fundamentally an excretion of material otherwise unmanageable. There is, however, no evidence of a biochemical kind that this is indeed the case so that the source of the pigment remains unknown. That dietary factors can, on occasion, affect the colour of the shell by altering the kind of pigment which is laid down in it, has nevertheless, been shown to be true of some prosobranchs. Dr D. R. Crofts tells us that month-old *Haliotis* fed on red weeds develop red shells and Moore (1936) has brought evidence to suggest that the stenoglossan *Nucella lapillus* makes shell which is predominantly grey in colour, though yellow may also occur, where the diet is of barnacles; where the diet includes mussels, however, brown or even purple pigment is deposited in the shell. If an animal be reared first on the one food and then on the other a sharp change in colour will be recorded in the shell at the point corresponding to the changed diet. This is, however, unlikely to be the full story (see p. 514). More recently Ino (1949) has shown that the type of food eaten influences the colour of the shell of the turbinid *Turbo cornutus*. If these animals eat calcareous algae then the shell is coloured; if they are not allowed to eat this type of food their shell is white, and there are incidental changes in spinyness. Blinded animals behave in the same way as intact ones, showing that there is no visual response such as might be part of a procryptic coloration.

# CHAPTER 6

# THE MUSCULAR SYSTEM

THE body wall of the gastropod is dermomuscular (fig. 84) and shares in the locomotor activities of the animal as in annelids, the haemocoelic fluid acting as an internal skeleton. Whereas the arrangement of the muscles in the annelid is regular, with outer layers of fibres running in a circular direction and inner layers running longitudinally, the two sets forming antagonistic pairs, this is not so obvious in gastropods, where greater irregularity of arrangement is found (figs. 65, 84). In annelids the coelomic fluid is separated by metamerically arranged septa into compartments and the septa are usually numerous. In gastropod molluscs septa are also developed with the same effect of limiting the movement of the fluid in the body cavity, but they are few in number, never the simple transverse partitions that they are in annelid worms and not the walls of coelomic sacs. As might be expected, the degree of development of the muscles in the body wall can be correlated with the use to which each area is put: it is minimal in the mantle (figs. 82, 83), underneath the shell, where movement is negligible, greater in the mantle skirt (figs. 75, 80, 81), still better developed over the surface of the head (fig. 84B), the sides of the foot and the floor of the mantle cavity, and reaches the highest development in the muscles developed in the sole of the foot in connexion with locomotion (figs. 68, 294). All these muscles are histologically plain, except in *Scissurella*.

In addition to the muscles of the body wall described above the gastropod possesses muscles which are attached to the inner surface of the shell which acts as an exoskeleton. The inner ends of these shell muscles have, therefore, a fixed origin unlike the muscles of the body wall. They are, presumably, simply special groups of dermal muscles which have secondarily acquired this connexion. The most important is that known as the columellar muscle. It originates on the columella of the shell in those prosobranchs where this is spirally coiled, runs down the concave side of the visceral hump to a ventral position slightly to the right side of the body (cm, figs. 1, 2, 157, 272, 273). From there it runs into the head-foot. In that region it splits into bundles which spread into the head, into the anterior and posterior halves of the foot and on to the inner surface of the operculum (cm, figs. 68, 134, 269). The part which enters the head sends branches to the skin and snout, the tentacles, the buccal mass and radular sac (ort, pmr, fig. 108); the sections which enter the foot fan out into bundles which are inserted on the inner surface of the pedal epithelium, and the opercular branch is linked to the underside of that structure. When the columellar muscle contracts all these parts of the body are pulled within the shelter of the shell. Bozler (1930) has shown that in *Helix pomatia* this muscle can contract to a tenth of its relaxed length.

A few fibres from the columellar muscle fan from its dorsal surface into the right side of the mantle skirt in the region of the anal and reproductive apertures, and a few separate from it on the left side to run into the mantle skirt near the anterior end of the osphradium and ctenidium (figs. 2, 157). Neither of these groups of fibres, however, provides adequate contractility for the free edge of the mantle skirt where there is present a series of muscles lying at right angles to its anterior edge and originating from the shell a little way in from its mouth: these are retractor muscles of the pallial edge

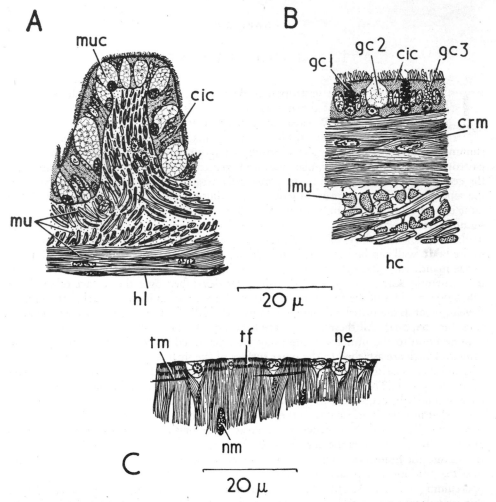

FIG. 84.—A & B, *Nucella lapillus*: histology of body wall, A, basal part of introvert; B, body wall dorsal to introvert; C, *Emarginula reticulata*: histology of insertion of shell muscle on to shell, part of a transverse section.

cic, ciliated cell; crm, circular muscle; $gc_1$, $gc_2$, $gc_3$, three different types of gland cell; hc, haemocoel; hl, layer of cells lining haemocoel; lmu, longitudinal muscle; mu, muscle fibres; muc, mucous cell; ne, nucleus of pallial epithelial cell; nm, nucleus of muscle cell of shell muscle; tf, tonofibrillae of epithelial cell; tm, transverse muscle fibre.

(prm, figs. 75, 80). All of them, like the columellar muscle, are composed of fibres histologically plain.

At other situations within the body of the gastropod other muscles are to be found. The gut, the reproductive ducts and some of the major arteries have plain muscles in their walls which propel their contents. Sphincter muscles lie around the external kidney opening (rsp, fig. 152) and at various places on the gut and reproductive tracts. Two situations, however, deserve special mention in connexion with the muscular system, in that the fibres which occur there are not histologically plain, but striated, though probably with a spiral pattern rather than the more complex structure of vertebrate striped muscle (Hanson & Lowy, 1957). These are the ventricle (fig. 19) and the buccal mass, both places in which more rapid and powerful contraction is called for. The arrangement of the musculature in these places is dealt with elsewhere (pp. 279, 179).

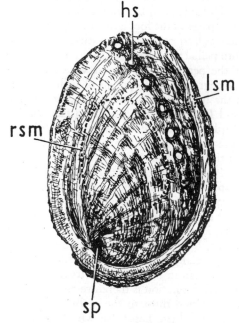

FIG. 85.—*Haliotis tuberculata:* shell, seen from below.
hs, hole in shell; lsm, impression of left shell muscle; rsm, impression of right shell muscle; sp, spire.

In the case of the muscles of the buccal mass, skeletal attachment is provided by the cartilage-like material which occurs there.

Some prosobranchs have not spiral shells, and in these the columellar muscle tends to be replaced by one (sm, fig. 252) running from the inner surface of the shell (lsm, rsm, fig. 85; sm, fig. 39B) into the foot and head, to the same destinations as before except that in these limpet-like animals the operculum has been lost. In most of these prosobranchs the muscle has a horseshoe-shaped origin on the shell, the open part of the shoe facing anteriorly and marking the situation of the mantle cavity (sm, figs. 60, 253, 254, 257, 266). From its origin fibres spread downwards into the head and the foot (sm, fig. 268), not so much to bring about the withdrawal of these parts of the body into the shell as to pull the shell down to the substratum. The fibres of the shell muscle do not run for any distance in distinct bundles, but radiate into fans which spread into head and foot. From both right and left origins of the shell muscle fibres spread to the entire breadth of the foot so as to produce a decussation in the mid-line of the body. As in other prosobranchs, the radular sac and the cartilages of the buccal mass are connected to the shell by slips of muscle. Slightly different arrangements exist in connexion with the retractor muscles of the mantle edge: in limpets these muscles run into the shell muscle and originate from the shell in the same region as that, either immediately on its lateral margin (*Emarginula*, Patellacea (prm, fig. 268)) or, after crossing over some of the more lateral fibres of the shell muscle, intermingled with its fibres (*Diodora*, prm, fig. 80).

The columellar muscle of prosobranchs appears to be attached to the shell as a single bundle of fibres: the shell muscle of these diotocardians is not. It is arranged in a series of bundles separated by narrow clefts, and this pattern is often visible in the scar left by the muscle on the shell. Thiem (1917*b*) has shown that these clefts allow for the passage of blood from the venous spaces in the foot and amongst the viscera into the blood spaces of the mantle skirt, where at least partial oxygenation may occur. From the mantle edge the blood is collected into pallial veins and sent to the auricle. The degree of oxygenation which occurs here, or the percentage of blood which is exposed to the water here, depends partly upon the degree of development of pallial gills and partly upon whether ctenidia are present in the mantle cavity. In Zeugobranchia such as *Diodora* (fig. 257), *Emarginula* (fig. 253) and *Puncturella* (fig. 254) two ctenidia are present, no particular development of pallial gills occurs, and, although some division of the shell muscle is to be noted, this is not great, and presumably the bulk of the respiratory exchange occurs within the main part of the mantle cavity over the head. The muscle is little divided in some members of the Patellacea e.g. *Lottia*, *Patina* and *Patella*: these have either no ctenidia but well developed pallial gills (the Cyclobranchia, e.g. *Patina* and *Patella* (fig. 50)), or one ctenidium and less well developed pallial gills (*Lottia*); because of the high degree of development of the pallial gills oxygenation is easily effected and only a small number of afferent vessels is required. The shell muscle is therefore little split. In other members of the Patellacea, however, pallial oxygenation is less easily brought about because of the absence of special gills on the mantle edge (*Acmaea*, fig. 73) and although the animal possesses a ctenidium in the nuchal cavity this may not always be capable of effective functioning. Pallial respiration is therefore essential, but not easy, and has to be facilitated by bringing the blood through the shell muscle in many small vessels. The same is also true for the abranchiate Lepetidae which, perhaps because they are small, have neither ctenidia nor pallial gills (fig. 262). In all these animals the shell muscle is much interrupted for the passage of afferent pallial veins.

It is now necessary to enquire what relationship exists between the single columellar muscle which is found in most prosobranch molluscs and the single horseshoe-shaped shell muscle which is found in the limpet-like forms. Knight (1947) has shown that the extinct Bellerophontacea, the earliest known prosobranchs, had two muscles inserted on the columella of the shell, which ran across the body of the animal from side to side, one at its right extremity and the other at its left. The two muscles were equally developed and the animal apparently completely bilaterally symmetrical. Two columellar muscles may still be found in some living prosobranchs, but in all these the shell is coiled in a helicoid spire, which introduces a lateral asymmetry, instead of in a plane spire as was the case in the bellerophonts. Associated with the asymmetry of the shell is an asymmetry of the columellar muscles and that on the (post-torsional) right is always larger than that on the left. Two unequal muscles of this nature are to be found in the following archaeo-gastropods: Haliotidae (lsm, rsm, fig. 85), Scissurellidae (lsm, rsm, fig. 255), *Tricolia* (lsm, rsm, fig. 77) and possibly other turbinids, Neritidae, Helicinidae, and in the meso-gastropods *Rissoella*, *Lamellaria* (lsm, rsm, fig. 86), *Trivia* and *Velutina*. In the genus

*Hydrocena* (Neritacea), according to Thiele (1929–35), the columellar muscle is single in the head and foot, but splits into right and left halves which embrace the visceral mass before being inserted on the shell: this might represent a partially double state. Where only a single columellar muscle exists it is the right member of the pair which persists and the left which has disappeared. The double muscle is of importance in many proso-branchs in helping to bring about torsion and may persist into the adult of primitive forms and of those monotocardians in which the body whorl is expanded.

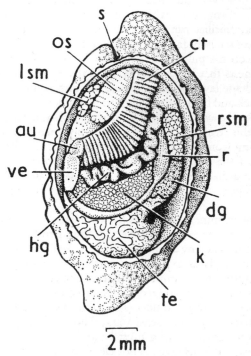

**2 mm**

Fig. 86.—*Lamellaria perspicua:* dissection to show animal after removal of the shell and the mantle overlying it.

    au, auricle; ct, ctenidium seen through mantle; dg, digestive gland; hg, hypobranchial gland; k, kidney; lsm, left shell muscle; os, osphradium; r, rectum; rsm, right shell muscle; s, siphonal notch at edge of mantle; te, testis; ve, ventricle.

The shell muscle of the patelliform prosobranchs never shows any trace of doubleness in the adult animal. Nevertheless it is usually believed that it has been produced by two muscles, one on each side, increasing in size and gradually extending their insertion on the shell backwards until they join to form the definitive horseshoe-shaped mass. A suggestion as to how this may have happened is given by the two elongated columellar muscles of the limpet-like *Septaria* (Bourne, 1908) and is also supported by Crofts' account (1955) of their development in *Patella*.

    Since it is by means of the contraction of the fibres of the columellar or shell muscles that a prosobranch mollusc retracts within the shelter of the shell, and withdraws the edge of the mantle skirt before that is trapped between the lip of the shell and the operculum or substratum, it is necessary for the fibres to have a firm attachment to the substance of the shell. Over the area where attachment occurs the calcification of the shell is interfered with and, as a consequence, it appears as a slight depression on the surface of the shell—the muscle scar (sm, fig. 39B). The fibres of the muscle do not make direct contact with the material of the shell, however, nor do they penetrate into its substance (fig. 84C). The muscle fibres end at the inner surface of the mantle epithelium which covers the whole area of attachment just as it lines the whole of the rest of the shell. At this point, however, the mantle cells are low, squamous cells and contain fibrillae (tonofibrillae) (tf, fig. 84C) which are continuous with the myofibrillae of the muscle cells. These tonofibrillae run across the pallial epithelium to the outer surface of the cells where they are securely fastened to the inner surface of the shell. Recent work by Hubendick (1958) on the pulmonate *Acroloxus lacustris* has shown the details of this arrangement and suggests that it is probably generally applicable to all molluscs. Here the muscles end in a dense layer of connective tissue underlying the epidermal cells, the bases of which interlock and interdigitate with it. Neighbouring epidermal cells similarly interlock, so as to make the epithelium and underlying tissue a cohesive whole. The most remarkable detail of this structure, however, is the presence of vast numbers of finger-like processes projecting from the outer surface of the cells and dipping into depressions on the inner surface of the shell. These form a brush border of what Hubendick calls microvilli. They have a diameter of $0 \cdot 05 - 0 \cdot 1$ $\mu$ at their base, a length of about $2 \cdot 5$ $\mu$ and number 25–100 per sq $\mu$ (25–100 $\times$ $10^6/mm^2$). The tonofibrillae enter these microvilli.

That the attachment of muscle to shell is by no means easily broken is illustrated by the well known ability of animals like limpets to cling firmly to their home, especially after they have been stimulated by an unsuccessful attempt to dislodge them. This ability allows limpets to live in places exposed to currents so strong that other gastropods cannot withstand them (see, for examples, Lilly et al., 1953). The force which a limpet is able to withstand before being dislodged has been known since the time of Réaumur (1711) and has often been investigated since (see Aubin, 1892; Lawrence-Hamilton, 1892; Menke, 1911; Krumbach, 1918; Loppens, 1922; Thomas, 1948): various investigations have suggested that a weight of 6–7 kg must be applied to a limpet before it looses its hold on the rock. How this is achieved is not clear, except that it is not due to the foot as a whole acting as a sucker actuated by atmospheric pressure, as Woodward (1875) believed, although this may be part of the mechanism. The foot may act as a whole, or part of it may grip whilst the remainder is free, and injuring the sole by radial cuts does not affect its ability to grip the substratum. It is clear that muscular contraction is involved since, if a limpet attached to a sheet of glass is watched, it will be seen that the area of the foot increases when an unsuccessful attempt to remove the animal is made; but it is often assumed that some kind of glandular cement may help, partly by giving increased contact between foot and substratum, partly by the very stickiness of the secretion. As Ankel (1947) has suggested, the release of the grip on the substratum would then be a more complicated matter than if muscular contraction alone were the cause, because whereas a simple relaxation would stop the grip in this case, the sticky secretion would have to disperse or be dispersed in the other. Alkalinity of sea water might be sufficient to disperse an acid secretion or at least destroy its effect, and this has been found to be an actual deterrent to the adhesion of limpets (Réaumur, Menke) and chitons (Hoffmann, 1938). Evidence of the secretion of such a substance has been offered by Ankel (1947) in connexion with *Gibbula cineraria*, a mollusc which wanders over surfaces and feeds by rasping diatoms and detritus as it goes. As it does this it leaves no trail of slime, yet, if knocked off a glass plate which is then stained, an impression of the sole of the foot will be left at the place where the mollusc was dislodged, in the form of many oval drops of mucus representing the mouths of glands, from which long fibrous threads spread in all directions. This secretion must be produced in response to the force used in removing the animal from the glass and Ankel regards it as a reflex. If this be accepted as a major activity of the glands on the prosobranch foot, it may be that it is an important function of much of the sole gland, especially in the more sedentary types.

The main locomotor organ of the gastropod is the foot, and it is characteristic of the class that this has become flattened ventrally to form a sole by the activity of which the animals creep over the ground on which they dwell. It is only in exceptional cases (e.g. some heteropods) where the animal has become free-swimming, that this is no longer true.

It has an elaborate system of muscles. The extrinsic musculature is the columellar muscle, but in addition to this the foot has many muscles confined to itself, longitudinal, transverse and dorsoventral bundles running in a rather irregular manner to produce a feltwork. Amongst these muscles lie glands, connective tissue cells, nerves and blood vessels. The vessels are largest near the central parts of the foot where they constitute part of an extensive sinus fed with blood from the pedal branch of the anterior aorta. As a result the musculature tends to be thicker laterally and the whole is roughly bilaterally symmetrical. Dorsally the musculature thins markedly and is restricted to the sides of the foot; centrally at this level viscera may be found. The foot is therefore divisible into a dorsal visceral part and a ventral muscular part in its middle region. Anteriorly and, in particular, posteriorly the whole thickness of the foot may be filled with the muscular network, and it is this which is used as the animal's means of locomotion.

If a snail of any sort be allowed to creep over the surface of a glass plate it may be inverted and the sole of the foot examined through the glass. A series of waves of local contraction and relaxation of the pedal musculature will then be seen to travel along the sole, their number and their direction of travel depending upon the kind of mollusc which is being examined (fig. 87). Vlès (1907) distinguished direct waves and retrograde waves according to whether their direction of travel was in the same sense as that in which the mollusc moved or the reverse. Direct waves therefore travel along the sole from the hind end forwards, retrograde waves from the front end backwards. The waves may be monotaxic when they occupy the entire breadth of the foot, ditaxic if there is a double series out of phase with one another, each occupying half the foot, or tetrataxic in which no less than four sets of waves travel along the sole. Some examples are given in Table 2.

TABLE 2

| Direct | | Retrograde | |
|---|---|---|---|
| Monotaxic | Ditaxic | Monotaxic | Ditaxic |
| Pulmonates | *Haliotis* | Chitons | *Nucella lapillus* |
| *Hydrobia ulvae* | Trochids | | *Littorina littorea* |
| | *Patina pellucida* | | *L. littoralis* |
| | *Patella vulgata* | | *L. saxatilis* |
| | | | *L. neritoides* |

Carlson (1905*a*), Parker (1911) and Copeland (1922) have shown that these rhythmical waves are the cause of the animals' locomotion forwards, but not only failed to show how the passage of waves over the pedal surface brought this about, but were also uncertain whether the waves, which appear as dark bands moving over the sole, were furrows or ridges on its surface and whether a given point on the foot was in continuous

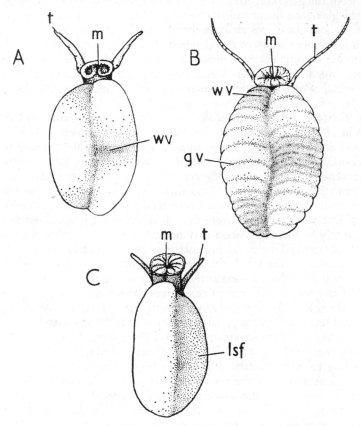

FIG. 87.—Ventral views of 3 prosobranchs to show locomotor waves on the sole of the foot; A, *Littorina saxatilis*; B, *Gibbula cineraria*; C, *Pomatias elegans*. In all cases the animal is progressing towards the top of the page, but in A and B the ditaxic waves travel to the posterior end of the foot. In *Pomatias*, which steps alternately with right and left halves of the foot, the left half is shown raised from the substratum.

gv, transverse groove on foot, characteristic of trochids; lsf, left half of sole of foot raised from ground; m, mouth; t, tentacle; wv, wave of contraction on foot.

though fluctuating movement, or whether its motion was intermittent. Van Rijnberk (1919) and ten Cate (1922) believed the waves were protrusions from the surface, whereas Olmsted (1917) and Bonse (1935) regarded them as grooves; Biedermann (1905) may be mentioned as one who thought of the movement as continuous, whereas Bonse believed that a forward movement of a given point occurred only as a wave passed over it. Once this had happened, he thought that it then remained motionless relative to the substratum until the next wave in the series arrived.

More recent work by Lissmann (1945, 1946) has provided answers to most of these questions and the following is largely based on his account. In *Helix pomatia* a monotaxic series of direct waves passes along the sole of the foot: by tracing the position of such natural reference points on the sole as mucous glands or of marked points in cinephotographic records, Lissmann was able to show that the waves passing forwards over the foot are waves of contraction and that normally a point moves only during the passage of such a wave. Between waves a particular point on the sole is characteristically at rest, but may in certain cases slip a little backwards under the influence of the wave of contraction next behind, or be dragged a little forward under the residual effect of the wave of contraction ahead. He was also able to show that coincident with the wave of contraction of the longitudinal muscles, visibly marked by a dark band on the sole, the surface of the foot was locally lifted clear of the substratum, an effect perhaps produced by contraction of the dorsoventral musculature. The snail is thus resting, at any given moment, on a series of transverse ridges formed on the sole of the foot, just as a long-bodied arthropod is held up on numerous legs.

The same kind of statement may be made about other gastropods. In *Haliotis*, which exhibits ditaxic direct waves, or *Littorina* (fig. 87A) with retrograde waves, there tend to be three interlinked areas of the sole—two on one side and one on the other—on which the animal is supported, as in an insect. In *Pomatias* (fig. 87C) a slightly different mechanism appears to exist, in that the two halves of the foot work independently of one another and out of phase, so that the animal appears to shuffle along first with the one side of the foot and then with the other, the tip of the snout also being involved and acting as a prop or third support during the stepping. If one half of the foot be watched it will be seen that the stepping starts by a lifting of the lateral margin and then of the whole breadth at the posterior end. This lifting is accompanied by a contraction of the longitudinal muscles which shortens the posterior half. The lifting and shortening continue until the whole half-foot is off the ground. Once this has been achieved it is then replaced, the posterior end regaining contact first, at a position in advance of that from which it was lifted because of the contraction of the longitudinal muscles. From this point forwards the foot gradually comes to rest on the ground, elongating as it does so, with the result that the anterior end is one step ahead of the starting position. This process is then repeated by the other half of the foot.

The study of *Pomatias* is useful in that it provides evidence as to how the forward movement of the snail is achieved by the events which occur in the foot. It will be noted that in each half-foot three factors are important in bringing movement about. At first the half-foot moves so as to bring the posterior part forwards, gripping the substratum in the meantime with the anterior end; later the posterior part grips the substratum and the anterior end is protracted. The three essential parts of the process are therefore the mechanisms responsible for adhesion to the ground, for contracting and for elongating the sole. The first of these is probably in part the close fit which is possible between the soft under surface of the foot and the substratum and, in part, the secretion of slime from the pedal glands; the contraction of the foot is brought about by contraction of the musculature, but the elongation is due to a mechanism still not clear but probably involving the hydrostatic pressure of the blood. What causes increased blood pressure is not certain.

The locomotion of *Helix*, though more like that of the majority of prosobranchs, is less easy to analyse. The alternating waves of contraction and relaxation which sweep along the foot have the result of keeping a state of tension in the posterior part so that it is pulled forwards, whilst a thrust exerted on the anterior end pushes it forwards; a central point acts to some extent as an anchorage. Lissmann points out that as the fastening of the snail foot to the ground is achieved predominantly by the extent of the area of contact this is best done by applying the relaxed parts to the substratum, whereas in worms, which grip by setae, the areas of contact may be contracted areas. Movement of the sole therefore coincides with longitudinal contraction and therefore with direct waves. It is interesting to note, nevertheless, that some prosobranchs do progress forwards by means of retrograde waves, notably all the common species of *Littorina*.

The use of the foot in two halves, as in *Pomatias*, is a common occurrence in many rissoaceans and is reflected, presumably, in the division of the foot into right and left halves by a median groove. In these animals, too, the anterior half of the foot tends to be separated from the posterior half by a constriction and this again seems to reflect a degree of independence in the use of the two parts, the anterior part operating by itself when the snail is negotiating corners or passing on to the surface film. These creatures, particularly the hydrobiids, use their proboscis as an accessory locomotor device just as *Pomatias* does; this is very noticeable when the animals are creeping out of water and they are denied the support which it would give. The same habit is emphasized in snails of the genus *Truncatella* (Clench & Turner, 1948, and see p. 584) which are therefore known as 'looping snails'.

In a certain number of prosobranchs no muscular waves can be detected on the surface of the foot as the animal moves and it seems to glide over the substratum, presumably by means of the cilia with which the sole of the foot is covered. This may be seen in *Hydrobia ulvae* when it is under water and moving horizontally over a smooth surface; when moving vertically waves become apparent in the posterior half of the foot. The smaller *Nassarius* species, *incrassatus*, can similarly move without any visible contractions, as observed for the related *Alectrion* by Copeland (1919) and for *Polinices* (Copeland, 1922). This is probably true for many small gastropods as noted by Gersch (1934) for *Skeneopsis*, where, when the animal stops creeping, the pedal cilia are found to have stopped beating, an observation which suggests that they may be under nervous control.

If the movement of a prosobranch is indeed dependent upon waves of contraction passing along the pedal musculature from one end to the other or upon metachronal waves affecting the pedal cilia, then reversal of the direction of motion would seem to involve a reversal of the nervous impulses upon which these waves depend and of the direction of the effective ciliary beat. This is a somewhat difficult thing to envisage and it has been commonly stated that prosobranchs cannot in fact move backwards. Ten Cate (1923), for example, put slugs into blindly ending tubes of so narrow a bore that they were unable to turn round in them; in these circumstances the slugs moved towards the blind end of the tubes and stayed stuck there. Nevertheless Gersch (1934) devised situations in which animals of *Gibbula cineraria* held between glass plates were compelled to turn if they were going to make any further progress. This they managed by producing the normal direct waves on one half of the foot and a series of retrograde waves on the other, so as to produce a rotatory effect. He also reported that *Patina pellucida* which, like other limpets, has direct ditaxic waves, can move backwards and that when it does so the foot shows retrograde waves moving over its sole. This reversal of activity in the muscles, which would apparently involve a reversed polarity in the pedal nerve net, must be centrally controlled from the pedal ganglia, but the nervous control of the locomotion of gastropods is very little understood.

The shape of the foot has been investigated in relation to the habitat and way of life by Rotarides (1934), who gave figures for the ratio between the height and breadth of the foot in a number of gastropods (Table 3).

TABLE 3

Ratio between height and breadth of foot. 1 = breadth in each case

| Patella caerulea | 1 : 0·4 | Calyptraea chinensis | 1 : 0·7 |
| Haliotis tuberculata | 1 : 0·8 | Murex brandaris | 1 : 0·8 |
| Littorina neritoides | 1 : 0·7 | Nassa mutabilis | 1 : 0·3 |
| Pomatias elegans | 1 : 1 | | |

All of these except *Pomatias* are aquatic. In *Pomatias* the equality of the height and breadth agrees with the figures obtained from the terrestrial pulmonates and is presumably related in some way to the need for supporting a heavier body in an aerial environment. Rotarides also believed that in animals with a heavier body the distinction between the visceral and the muscular parts of the foot is more pronounced. This is exaggerated where the animal moves over soft bottoms, where, presumably, the difficulty of movement becomes greater; this may also be partly overcome by having a broad sole (e.g. *Buccinum*, *Natica*). A circular foot tends to occur in limpets, where the problem of holding on to the substratum is often made worse by the roughness of the water in which the animals live; the adhesive power of the foot is increased by a number of factors of which the broad attachment to the shell and the insertion of the muscle splayed over the whole foot are perhaps the most important.

Simroth (1882) gave a few relative rates for the movement of prosobranchs: *Viviparus viviparus* 2–3, *Bithynia tentaculata* 2, *Pomatias elegans* 0·7. He pointed out that the difference between *Pomatias* and the two others reflected the fact that it has to carry its own full weight: it may also reflect different locomotor mechanisms. Stephenson (1924) recorded a speed of 5–6 yards/min in *Haliotis*, but this is maintained only momentarily.

# CHAPTER 7

# THE ALIMENTARY SYSTEM—1

THE alimentary canal of the gastropod mollusc consists of a stomodaeal section of ectodermal origin, a central stretch derived from the embryonic endoderm and of a terminal proctodaeal length which has been formed from the ectoderm of the underside of the mantle skirt. The mouth lies on the animal's head, terminally, and the anus discharges into the mantle cavity, primitively in the mid-line, but in most cases more or less displaced to the right side. In a few genera of Docoglossa the anus lies at the innermost end of the mantle cavity, but in most prosobranchs the rectum runs along the mantle skirt and opens closer to the mouth of the cavity.

The mouth leads into a short tubular part of the gut, of variable length, the oral tube. This enlarges into a more spherical cavity, the buccal cavity, from the posterior end of which arise two tubes lying one directly over the other. The lower one is the radular sac, the dorsal one the oesophagus. Into the buccal cavity discharge buccal glands, mostly goblet cells, but there are in addition one or two pairs of larger salivary glands provided with ducts. All the apparatus up to the beginning of the oesophagus is of ectodermal origin and so is stomodaeal and may be distinguished as the fore-gut, and it may be that in some prosobranchs the oesophagus is also stomodaeal.

The oesophagus leaves the posterior end of the buccal cavity dorsally and runs to the stomach, which is placed near the base of the visceral mass, commonly rather to the left. The anterior part of the oesophagus may carry lateral outpouchings, but the mid-oesophagus is primitively the seat of extensive secretory epithelium, especially in its lateral walls, which constitutes the oesophageal glands. The posterior oesophagus is not glandular and leads, primitively, to the upper end of the stomach as it lies in the visceral mass.

The stomach of the prosobranch gastropod (fig. 88) is a complex structure into which open the ducts of the digestive gland, which is arranged in two lobes, one on the right and the other on the left, the two usually being unequally developed. In the more archaic prosobranchs the stomach is pear-shaped with the swollen base of the pear towards the upper end of the visceral mass and receiving the oesophagus (oe) and the ducts of the digestive gland (dd). It is often drawn out near its upper end into a spirally coiled caecum (scm). Internally its walls bear in part a ciliated epithelium (sap) responsible for the movement—and often the sorting—of the particulate matter within, in part a cuticle which is frequently raised into a tooth-like eminence, the gastric shield (gs), helping in the trituration of food. One ciliated groove, which is called the intestinal groove ($g_1$), is a permanent feature of this part of the stomach, lying alongside a fold which is called the major typhlosole ($t_1$). Both these structures are often related to the duct from the larger liver lobe and run into the second part of the stomach (corresponding to the narrow end of the pear) which lies lower in the visceral mass. This is a cylindrical or conical section connected to the main part of the stomach dorsally and leading into the intestine ventrally, and known as the style sac (ss). The intestinal groove and major typhlosole run along its walls in the majority of animals and continue into the intestine (i). This runs forward, looping to the neighbourhood of the kidney and pericardial cavity—in the archaeogastropods, indeed, passing through the ventricle—and thereafter passing into the mantle skirt. After a more or less extended course in this the intestine opens at the anus at the summit of a short papilla. Occasionally a rectal or anal gland may

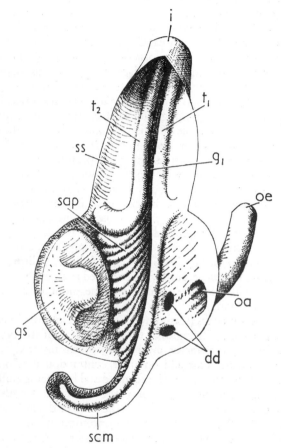

FIG. 88.—Diagram of the stomach of a generalized prosobranch, opened mid-dorsally.
dd, openings of ducts of digestive gland; $g_1$, intestinal groove; gs, gastric shield; i, intestine; oa, oesophageal aperture; oe, oesophagus; sap, posterior sorting area; scm, spiral caecum; ss, style sac region; $t_1$, major typhlosole; $t_2$, minor typhlosole.

occur. It is certain that some part of this intestinal region is of ectodermal, proctodaeal origin; it may be only the small papilla hanging freely into the mantle cavity at the summit of which the anus opens, or it may be the entire stretch which is embedded in the mantle skirt.

The mouth lies on the underside of the snout. In most gastropods this means that because of the downward curvature of the snout, it lies in a horizontal plane just clearing the substratum over which the animal moves; in some of the higher prosobranchs, however, the snout is straighter and the mouth then lies obliquely. In Stenoglossa and in such higher mesogastropods as possess a proboscis, the aperture visible on the underside of the head is not the true mouth but the opening of a proboscis sac within which the proboscis lies. The formation of a proboscis has occurred in animals which feed on material not immediately accessible: it occurs in prosobranchs which bore into other animals to find their food (*Natica*, Doliacea, Muricacea); in those which are carrion feeders and must use their proboscis to reach or probe into the body of the prey (Buccinacea); in those which seek access to the most nutritious parts of the body of their prey by way of natural apertures (Lamellariacea, Cypraeacea, Cerithiacea); by those with still more specialized ways of feeding (Toxoglossa—see p. 205; Pyramidellidae—see p. 251). The formation of a proboscis has not taken place among all prosobranchs in exactly the same way. When a proboscis is fully everted the true mouth lies at its tip and the apparent mouth—really that of the proboscis sac—disappears. The proboscis is then seen in its true morphological relations, as an elongation of that part of the snout lying anterior to the tentacles, an exaggerated example of what Amaudrut (1898) called snout formation or pretentacular elongation: all forms agree in this. It is in respect of the way in which this elongated snout is disposed of within the body on retraction that they differ. The simpler case appears to be the acrembolic type (figs. 89C, D), which is a simple introvert or inturned part of what is truly outer body surface. Here the retractor muscles (rmp) are inserted primarily at the tip of the proboscis and to a lesser extent along its side walls; when retraction occurs it is the apex of the proboscis which is pulled in first so that it comes to be the most deeply invaginated part and the whole process is like turning a stocking outside in by putting one's hand in and pulling the toe towards the top. This type of proboscis is found in the families Scalidae, Aclididae, Eulimidae, Pyramidellidae, Naticidae, Lamellariidae, Eratoidae. It may be regarded as an exaggeration of a tendency in all prosobranchs to withdraw the mouth into the snout to a certain extent when subject to noxious stimulation.

In more advanced prosobranchs (Cassididae, Doliidae, Columbellidae and Tritoniidae amongst mesogastropods, and Stenoglossa) the proboscis is of the type called pleurembolic (figs. 89A, B). Here the retractor muscles (rmp) are inserted on the sides of the proboscis mainly towards the base and on their contraction it is only this basal part which is invaginated to form the proboscis sac, the distal half being pulled into the shelter of that without turning inside out. Since only about half the length of the proboscis, when retracted, has to be accommodated within the head of the gastropod with this type of proboscis, it is clear that this is a device more economical of space than the acrembolic type in which the entire invaginable length has to be stored. Or, from another point of view, the pleurembolic type of proboscis may be relatively longer than the acrembolic type when a given volume of storage space is used. It is also mechanically more efficient.

The mouth is a rounded or slit-like opening on the end of the snout in the primitive gastropods, usually elongated in a transverse direction, a fact more easily seen in the preserved than in the living animal. Around the actual opening lies a ridged outer lip, the ridges marking the outer ends of longitudinal folds in the tube to which the mouth leads. Frequently this ring-like tip is interrupted in the mid-ventral line so that it becomes horseshoe-shaped (*Patella* (fig. 50), *Littorina* (fig. 3), *Lacuna* (fig. 90)), but this is due to an inturning of the lip at that point rather than to a true interruption to its course. In many Trochidae, on the other hand, an eversion of the outer lip is to be found at this spot and a gutter-like process projects from the mid-ventral line of the mouth. It is short and tied to the mid-ventral wall of the snout in *Gibbula cineraria* (vlp, fig. 91), still shorter in *G*.

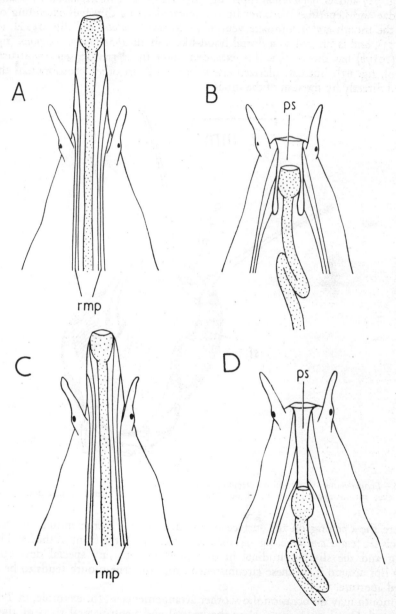

FIG. 89.—Diagrams showing proboscis structure: A, pleurembolic type extended; B, pleurembolic type retracted; C, acrembolic type extended; D, acrembolic type retracted. The gut is stippled. ps, proboscis sheath; rmp, retractor muscles of proboscis.

*umbilicalis*, well developed and turned to the right neck lobe in *Calliostoma zizyphinum* (ppb, fig. 71) and *C. papillosum* (ppb, fig. 92), but absent in *Monodonta lineata*. In the Acmaeidae and Lepetidae the outer lip is elongated into a thin frill extending outward around the mouth and incomplete ventrally (*Acmaea tessulata*: ool, fig. 93; *A. virginea*: ol, fig. 73), and is limited to a dorsal hood-like veil in *Propilidium exiguum* (fig. 262). Thiem (1917b) has shown that this extended outer lip is rich in sensory structures in parts (ool, fig. 93), but cuticularized elsewhere (mol). In other prosobranchs the lip is bordered directly by the skin of the snout.

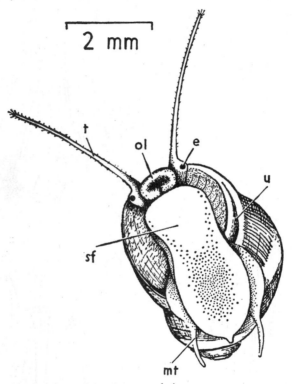

FIG. 90.—*Lacuna vincta*: young animal creeping, ventral view.
e, eye; mt, metapodial tentacle; ol, outer lip; sf, sole of foot; t, tentacle; u, umbilicus.

Where the opening on the surface of the head is not a true mouth but leads to a proboscis sac (e.g. *Lamellaria*, fig. 94, m; *Balcis*, fig. 140B), the front of the head is usually tapering and the slit longitudinal in direction without any special development of sensory lips around it. In these circumstances, too, the true mouth tends to be a simple rounded aperture.

The mouth may on occasion show other arrangements as, for example, in *Trichotropis borealis* and *Capulus ungaricus*. Here the ventral and ventrolateral parts of the lips are drawn out to form a long proboscis (ppb, figs. 95, 60), in *Capulus* almost equal in length to that of the shell, with a groove extending along the whole of its dorsal side at the proximal end of which the mouth is placed and rather resembling the proboscis of the trochids. It is used in connexion with the peculiar feeding arrangements of these animals.

In *Trichotropis borealis* the proboscis appears to be kept permanently turned towards the right part of the mouth of the mantle cavity (Graham, 1954*a*), as was first thought to be true of *Capulus* (Orton, 1912*b*). Yonge (1938) has shown that the proboscis of *Capulus* is actually freely movable.

The mouth leads to the first part of the alimentary tract, a tube of short length, the oral tube (ot, fig. 11). Along it run continuations of the folds which marked the outer lip, except on the ventral side. It is lined by an epithelium bearing a cuticle and its walls are

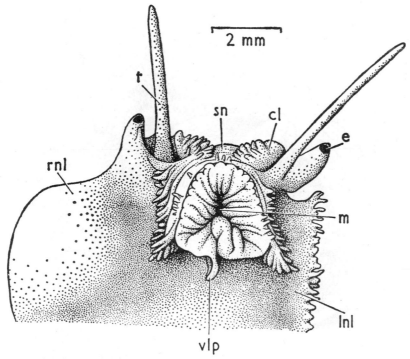

FIG. 91.—*Gibbula cineraria:* head, ventral view.
cl, cephalic lappet; e, eye; lnl, left neck lobe; m, mouth; rnl, right neck lobe; sn, snout; t, tentacle; vlp, ventral lip drawn out into median projection.

muscular and may be partly glandular. It leads into an expanded chamber which is the buccal cavity (bcv). A number of characteristic structures lie here. Embedded in the dorsal or lateral walls of the cavity at its anterior end may be a pair of jaws (ja, fig. 101), or they may be replaced by a single median one. Behind the level of the jaws there extends into the buccal cavity from the ventrolateral walls a pair of inner lips (il, fig. 11), which may be drawn across the buccal cavity like a curtain so as to separate it more or less completely from the oral tube. Projecting into the buccal cavity from the posterior floor, like a tongue, is the great buccal mass, or odontophore (bm), over the dorsomedian surface of which runs the radula (rd). The buccal mass is free dorsally, laterally, and ventrally near its tip. The space between the ventral surface of the buccal mass and the floor of the buccal cavity is the sublingual space or cavity; the space between the sides of the buccal mass and the lateral walls of the buccal cavity—often roomy—may sometimes be referred to as buccal pouches. These parts of the buccal cavity are partly cuticularized but especially on the inner lips and in parts of the lateral pouches are also partly glandular; the surface of the buccal mass, however, is almost wholly covered with a thick cuticle and presents, therefore, a glistening appearance on dissection.

The roof of the buccal cavity is more elaborately built than any other part. Its most conspicuous feature is a pair of longitudinally directed folds which lie on either side of the mid-dorsal line (df, fig. 11); they begin some little way behind the jaw and run

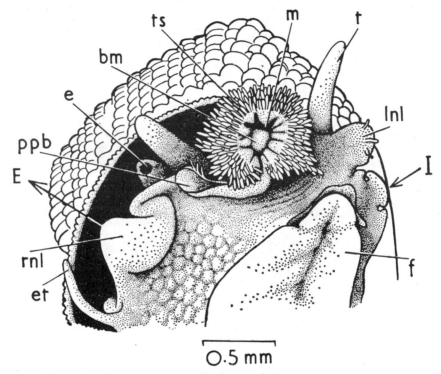

FIG. 92.—*Calliostoma papillosum:* anterior part of body, ventral view.
    bm, anterior tip of buccal mass; e, eye; E, direction of exhalant water current; et, epipodial tentacle; f, foot; I, direction of inhalant water current; lnl, left neck lobe; m, mouth; ppb, pseudo-proboscis formed from ventral lip; rnl, right neck lobe; t, tentacle; ts, tentacles on snout.

posteriorly out of the buccal cavity into the oesophagus, forming the lateral walls of a trough-like space which occupies the dorsomedian wall. These are the dorsal folds of the fore-gut enclosing the dorsal food channel (dfc). Frequently each fold appears double where it runs on the buccal roof into which it fades away anteriorly. In contrast to the rest of the buccal walls the epithelium which lines these folds and the channel is, in most prosobranchs, richly and strongly ciliated, the cilia on the folds beating into the channel and those in the channel maintaining a strong current backwards into the oesophagus.

Arising from the lateral wall of the buccal cavity on each side, ventral to the dorsal folds, is a sheet of tissue which sweeps horizontally across the buccal cavity to meet its partner from the opposite wall. This forms a septum (oev) which is at one and the same time the floor of the oesophagus and the roof of the radular sac. Ventral to this septum the buccal cavity is continued into a narrow tube, the radular sac, which extends backwards ventral to the oesophagus to a varying distance, ending blindly. Within it is secreted the radula (see p. 173). The septum is sometimes said to mark the inner limit of the stomodaeal region which is then coincident with the inner end of the buccal cavity, the oesophagus behind it being of endodermal origin, but many observers regard the whole gut as far as the posterior end of the oesophagus as being ectodermal (see p. 429).

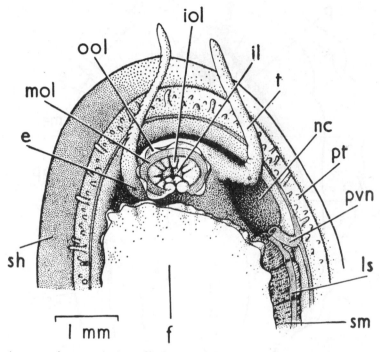

FIG. 93.—*Acmaea tessulata:* anterior part of body, ventral view.
e, eye; f, foot; il, inner lip; iol, inner zone of outer lip; ls, lateral blood sinus; mol, middle zone of outer lip; nc, nuchal cavity; ool, outer zone of outer lip; pt, pallial tentacle; pvn, pallial vein; sh, shell; sm, shell muscle; t, tentacle.

It is right to add at this point that in the view of Nisbet (1953), the line separating buccal cavity and oesophagus should be drawn, not vertically across the gut of the animal as has just been suggested, but obliquely, so that whilst its ventral end would coincide with the mouth of the radular sac its dorsal end would cut the roof of the buccal cavity at the anterior end of the dorsal folds and dorsal food channel, posterior to the point of entry of the salivary ducts. This would separate the whole of the food conducting apparatus (food channel and folds) from the buccal cavity. This may be a better arrangement anatomically, and is certainly so from the functional point of view, than that which divides it partly into a buccal section and partly into an oesophageal half.

In connexion with the buccal cavity is a number of glands which may be dealt with before the complexities of the buccal mass are treated. Most of these glands are unicellular goblet cells lying in the buccal epithelium secreting mucus. They are particularly abundant on the inner lips and in the lateral parts of the buccal walls, but may occur in some animals in other positions. Thus in *Diodora* and *Haliotis* there is a concentration at

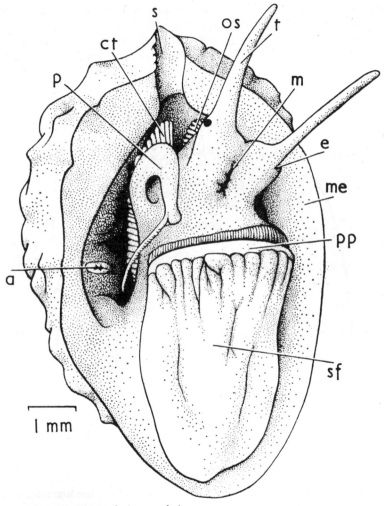

Fig. 94.—*Lamellaria perspicua:* male, in ventral view.
    a, anus; ct, ctenidium; e, eye; m, mouth; me, mantle edge; os, osphradium; p, penis, with flagellum; pp, propodium; s, siphon; sf, sole of foot; t, tentacle.

the base of the jaw (Ziegenhorn & Thiem, 1926) in the roof of the buccal cavity, and *Theodoxus* (Whitaker, 1951) and *Septaria* (Bourne, 1908) show a pair of blind tubules of a glandular nature discharging to the inner end of the space ventral to the buccal mass.
    The most important of the glands connected to the buccal cavity, however, are the salivary glands, which discharge to its roof just anterior and lateral to the ends of the dorsal folds. In the more primitive groups such as the Zeugobranchia these glands (sg,

fig. 96) are not conspicuous, but form a single pouch or a tuft of a few short tubes discharging by a common opening, which hardly merits the name of duct, to the buccal cavity. All the epithelial tissue, including that of the duct, is secretory, apart from occasional ciliated cells wedged between the gland cells (fig. 97D). Most of the cells secrete mucus, though some secrete other substances: in neither case is the secretion digestive and in these lower prosobranchs the gland appears to be concerned solely with producing a lubricant for the feeding processes and an adhesive for the food particles. In the Trochacea the salivary glands resemble those of the Zeugobranchia. In the Patellacea (sg, fig. 261) and most mesogastropods, however, the salivary glands are much increased in complexity and have become bulky masses of secretory tissue. The glands are now

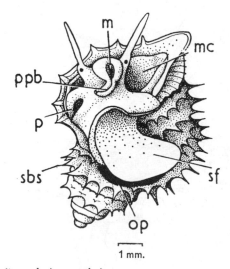

1 mm.

FIG. 95.—*Trichotropis borealis:* male, in ventral view.
m, mouth; mc, mantle cavity; op, operculum; p, penis; ppb, pseudoproboscis formed from ventral lip; sbs, bristles on shell; sf, sole of foot.

found in the posterior part of the head, or even in the basal part of the visceral hump, and are connected to the buccal cavity by ducts which run along the roof of the oeso-phagus and buccal cavity lateral to the attachment of the dorsal folds, thus avoiding the congestion which they would produce if they remained in the snout. In most cases the ducts run through the nerve ring. In the Patellidae each gland has two ducts running parallel to one another and opening close together. In the Acmaeidae two histologically distinct types of so-called salivary glands occur: the ordinary ones which open to the roof of the buccal cavity by ducts alongside the dorsal folds (the 'pharyngeal salivary glands' of Thiem (1917b)), and a number of tubules which open separately to the buccal pouches or even to the oesophagus (these are not present in *Acmaea virginea*). The double pair of *Patella* and its relatives probably represents a doubling of the first type rather than two different sorts, since their histology is identical. In all these cases the glandular tissue is confined to the main mass of the gland and the duct is a purely conducting tube, leading the secretion to the buccal cavity, and lined, in relation to this function, with a ciliated epithelium which, together with secretion pressure, appears to be the main means of transporting the secretion, muscle fibres being notably rare. The secretory cells, as in zeugobranchs, alternate with ciliated cells and produce predominantly mucous substance although basic protein secretions are also of frequent occurrence (fig. 97c). Few prosobranchs secrete digestive enzymes in their saliva, which appears to be primarily a lubricant for the food-collecting and swallowing activities of the animal. Hirsch (1915)

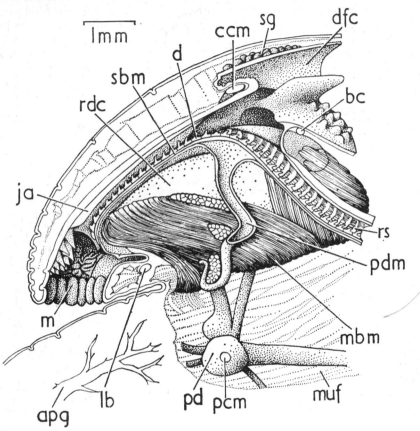

FIG. 96.—*Diodora apertura:* right sagittal half of head and part of foot, seen from median side.
  apg, anterior pedal gland; bc, buccal commissure; ccm, cerebral commissure; d, radular tooth; dfc, dorsal food channel; ja, jaw; lb, labial commissure; m, mouth; mbm, muscles of buccal mass; muf, muscle fibres; pcm, pedal commissure; pd, pedal ganglion; pdm, diverticulum extending ventrally between two halves of buccal mass; rdc, radular cartilage; rs, radular sac; sbm, subradular membrane; sg, salivary gland.

and Mansour-Bek (1934) recorded the occurrence of a variety of proteolytic enzymes in the glands of species of *Murex*, and Jenkins (1955) recorded amylase in those of *Littorina littorea*. Welsh (1956) has shown that the salivary glands of *Buccinum* produce 5-hydroxy-tryptamine, and Fänge (1957, 1958) has recorded a similar substance in those of *Cassidaria* and an acetylcholine-like substance, possibly neurine, in those of *Neptunea antiqua*. He suggested that in addition to its well known carrion feeding, this animal may also use its toxic saliva to permit the capture of active prey.

In the Stenoglossa (Muricacea, Buccinacea) the salivary glands lie in a position which is different from their location in less advanced prosobranchs. In the diotocardians (fig. 96) the glands (sg) lie usually over the buccal roof and posterior to the point at which the

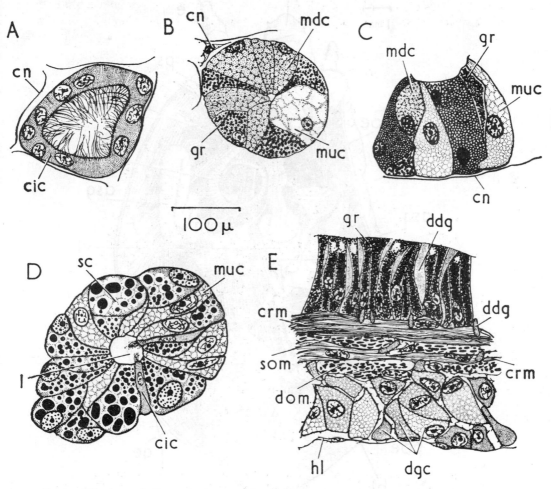

FIG. 97.—Histology of salivary glands.    A, *Nassarius reticulatus*, transverse section of salivary duct;  B, *Nassarius reticulatus*, section of lobe of gland;  C, *Diodora apertura*, section of salivary cells;  D, *Patella vulgata*, section of lobe of gland;  E, *Nucella lapillus*, section of part of accessory gland.

cic, ciliated cell; cn, connective tissue; crm, circular muscle layer; ddg, duct of deep gland cell; dgc, deep gland cell; dom, deep layer of oblique muscles; gr, granule of secretion; hl, limit of haemo-coelic space; l, lumen; mdc, mucoid cell; muc, mucous cell; sc, secreting cell; som, superficial layer of oblique muscles.

cerebral commissure (ccm) runs. In the monotocardians the point of entry of the salivary duct into the buccal cavity shows that the fundamental morphology of the glands is the same, but as a consequence of the backward shift of both gland and cerebral commissure the salivary duct (sd, fig. 14) runs through the nerve ring. The Stenoglossa (fig. 98) have

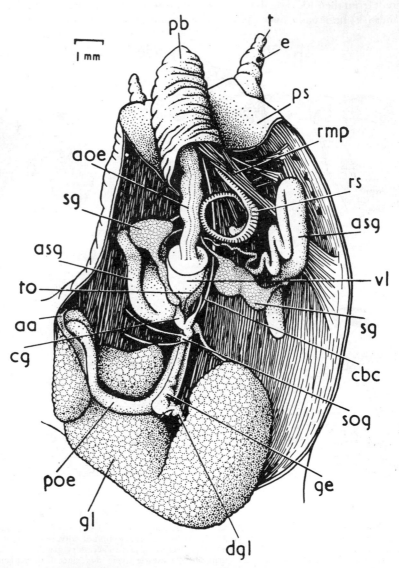

FIG. 98.—*Nucella lapillus:* dissection to show anterior part of gut. The proboscis sheath has been opened to show the proboscis and the anterior part of the body cavity dissected.

aa, anterior aorta; aoe, anterior oesophagus; asg, accessory salivary gland; cbc, cerebrobuccal connective; cg, cerebral ganglion; dgl, duct of the gland of Leiblein; e, eye; ge, 'glande framboisée'; gl, gland of Leiblein; pb, proboscis; poe, posterior oesophagus; ps, proboscis sheath; rmp, retractor muscle of proboscis; rs, radular sac; sg, salivary gland; sog, supra-oesophageal ganglion; t, tentacle; to, line marking site of separation of glands from rest of oesophagus; vl, valve of Leiblein.

elongated the anterior part of the gut in the course of making a proboscis (pb) and this elongation lies anterior to the nerve ring. As a consequence of differential growth rates involved in this process the salivary glands (sg) have been pulled anteriorly through the nerve ring and now lie in front of the cerebral commissure and so their ducts do not pass through it. Despite this, because of the need to exclude bulky glands from a slender, retractile proboscis, considerable elongation of the ducts has occurred and the glands lie

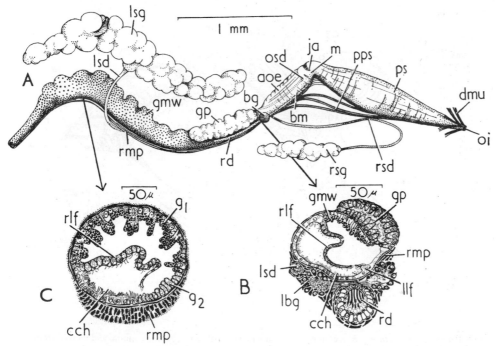

FIG. 99.—*Cerithiopsis tubercularis:* A, anterior part of alimentary canal removed from animal and viewed from the right; B, transverse section at level indicated by arrow; C, transverse section at level indicated by arrow.

   aoe, anterior oesophagus; bg, right buccal ganglion; bm, buccal mass; cch, ciliated channel; dmu, dilator muscles; $g_1$, first type of gland cell of mid-oesophagus; $g_2$, second type of gland cell of mid-oesophagus; gmw, glandular wall of mid-oesophagus; gp, glandular diverticulum of oesophagus; ja, jaw; lbg, left buccal ganglion; llf, left longitudinal fold; lsd, left salivary duct; lsg, left salivary gland; m, position of mouth; oi, opening of proboscis sheath; osd, opening of salivary duct; pps, protractor muscles of proboscis; ps, proboscis sheath; rd, radular sac; rlf, right longitudinal fold; rmp, retractor muscles of proboscis; rsd, right salivary duct; rsg, right salivary gland.

at the inner end of the proboscis in the neighbourhood of the nerve ring. The production of a proboscis in the mesogastropods seems to have been accompanied merely by an elongation in the length of the salivary duct allowing the gland to remain alongside the nerve ring in the body of the mollusc when the proboscis is everted (eratoids: Fretter, 1951a). In *Cerithiopsis tubercularis* (Fretter, 1951b) the slimness of the animal has caused the right (rsg, fig. 99) and left (lsg) glands to be staggered to permit better packing, as has occurred with the internal organs of snakes. The arrangement of the salivary glands in *Triphora perversa* is discussed below (p. 219).

The size and shape of the salivary glands vary within the prosobranchs to a consider-

7

able extent. The normal structure of the gland is acinous but it may depart from this and tubular glands occur in a number of families (hydrobiids, rissoids (fig. 67), assimineids, Ptenoglossa (fig. 100), Calyptraeidae, Pyramidellidae (fig. 134)). The size of the gland may be related to the amount of lubrication called for, and where this is slight, the glands may be quite small. This is noticeable where the lubricant is provided by other glands such as those in the mantle cavity, as occurs in ciliary feeders: then the salivary glands

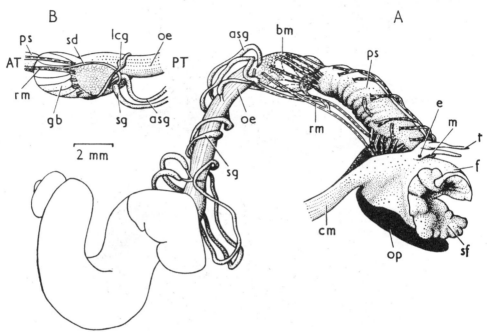

FIG. 100.—*Clathrus clathrus:* A, anterior part of alimentary canal removed from animal and viewed from the right; B, buccal region, seen from the left.

asg, accessory salivary gland; AT, anterior; bm, buccal mass; cm, columellar muscle; e, eye; f, foot; gb, glands in wall of buccal cavity; lcg, left cerebral ganglion; m, mouth of proboscis sheath; oe, oesophagus; op, operculum; ps, proboscis sheath; PT, posterior; rm, retractor muscle; sd, salivary duct; sf, sole of foot; sg, salivary gland; t, tentacle.

may be very small (*Capulus, Turritella*). In other animals the glands may be wholly absent (Neritacea, Eulimidae) and in these animals secretion of lubricating substances is probably sufficient at other places to compensate for their loss, though it is not always certain where these places are. On the other hand, the salivary glands have become hypertrophied in some prosobranchs: they are particularly large in Ampullariidae and in some families of the Doliacea. In *Dolium* itself, Weber (1927) has shown that this is due to the fact that they secrete a moderate concentration of sulphuric acid in the saliva, which is used to poison the prey which the animal attacks. The gland is covered with a layer of muscle tied to the foot and on contraction this squeezes the gland against the solid background provided by this part of the body and so ejects the acid saliva through the long duct and into the body of the prey under considerable pressure. *Dolium* and *Cassis* both show an accessory salivary gland on the course of the duct near its origin from the main gland; its significance is not known.

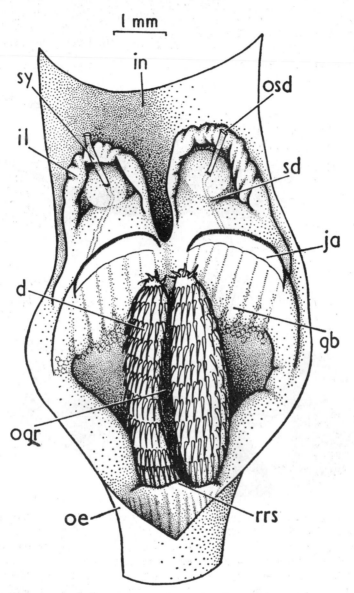

FIG. 101.—*Clathrus clathrus:* dissection showing the base of the introvert, the buccal cavity and the anterior part of the oesophagus opened mid-dorsally.

d, radular tooth; gb, glands in wall of buccal cavity; il, inner lip; in, introvert; ja, jaw; oe, oeso-phagus; ogr, groove on mid-dorsal surface of buccal mass; osd, opening of salivary duct; rrs, roof of radular sac; sd, salivary duct; sy, stylet on which salivary duct opens.

In a few prosobranchs special arrangements affect the organization of the salivary glands. In the family Scalidae, for example, *Clathrus clathrus* (fig. 100A) and other species possess a pair of long, tubular salivary glands (sg) tied to the oesophagus at their inner ends by muscle strands. They narrow to form ducts at the level of the nerve ring. The

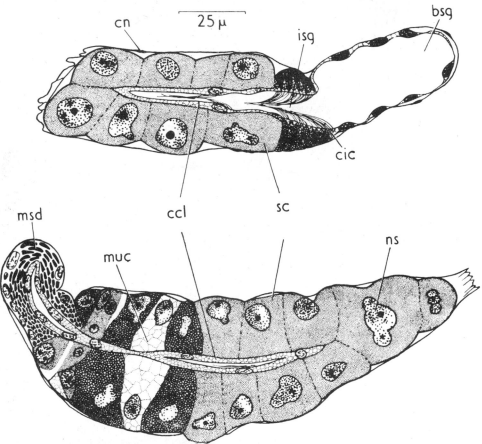

FIG. 102.—*Odostomia lukisi:* longitudinal sections through the salivary gland; the upper section cuts the proximal half of the gland, the lower the distal half and the initial part of the duct.

bsg, bladder of salivary gland; ccl, ciliated epithelium of lumen; cic, ciliated cell; cn, connective tissue; isg, intermediate section of salivary gland; msd, circular muscles of salivary duct; muc, mucous cell; ns, nucleus of secreting cell; sc, secreting cell.

ducts (sd, figs. 100B, 101) penetrate this and then run forwards alongside the buccal mass and oral tube. Here they expand somewhat to form reservoirs which open to the exterior on the inner lips (il), each of which carries a mammiform swelling on its inner surface. Projecting from the centre of this is a hollow chitinous stylet (sy) which bears the opening of the salivary duct at its summit (osd). As the scalids possess an acrembolic proboscis this apparatus is normally hidden at the base of the introvert (in), but will project when the proboscis is everted. Its precise use is unknown, as the feeding of these animals has not been observed, but it seems likely that it forms part of a device for overwhelming prey, perhaps by the injection of a poisonous salivary fluid.

A somewhat similar device is employed by the pyramidellids, although its anatomical basis is different. In these animals the salivary glands (sg, fig. 134) are, again, tubular, the innermost part of the tube being a thin-walled bladder (bsg). Next to that is a small section (isg, fig. 102) in which small gland cells alternate with ciliated cells (cic). This section is brief and the bulk of the rest of the wall of the tube is lined by ciliated cells of a squamous shape (ccl) overlying large gland cells (sc) the secretion of which enters the gland between the ciliated cells. The gland produces very little mucus and the nature of its secretion is not known. A very muscular duct (msd) leads the secretion to the buccal cavity. Here (fig. 103), in the mid-dorsal line, the two ducts (sd) unite and open into the central cavity of a hollow stylet (sy) which in this case, however, is the animal's jaw, which has been rolled into a hollow cylinder with a tip tapered like a hypodermic needle. When the mollusc feeds, this is thrust through the skin of the prey and saliva injected. As pyramidellids appear to feed primarily on fluid sucked from the body of their prey, the salivary secretion may well be an anticoagulant.

Along with the salivary glands which have just been described a number of proso-branch gastropods possess other glands of a salivary type. Some of these are merely exaggerations of the glands already mentioned in the walls of the buccal cavity. Others, however, are additional structures and of these, the most important are perhaps the tubular salivary glands of Stenoglossa (asg, fig. 98). These occur with the ordinary acinous type alongside which they lie as white tubules, somewhat bent. They narrow anteriorly into ducts which do not traverse the nerve ring but run forwards to the underside of the proboscis, where they unite to form a median duct of very fine diameter which runs to open on the mid-ventral line of the mouth. The gland (fig. 97E) is lined by a columnar epithelium containing spherules of secretion (gr) which seem to be of a protein nature. This epithelium rests on a thick layer of muscle made of two sheets of fibres running diagonally and at right angles to one another and arranged in outer and inner sets (crm, som, dom). External to this are gland cells (dgc), three or four layers thick, which send long necks (ddg) through the muscle coat and between the epithelial cells, to discharge secretion to the central space. The function of these gland cells is not known. They do not occur in Buccinacea, which do not bore into the shells of other molluscs, whereas they do occur in most Muricacea, which are active borers. They have been recorded in *Oliva* (Küttler, 1913) but it is not certainly known to what extent they occur in other volutaceans nor what the feeding habits of the animals may be. They do not seem to produce an acid which might help in boring (Graham, 1941) nor a 'calcase' such as has been suggested by Ankel (1937a) might help in the process. It is possible that their secretion may have some toxic effect on their prey, or contribute towards an external digestion of it (though Graham (1941) failed to find either proteolytic or amylo-lytic enzymes in their secretion in *Nucella*) or—most probably—they may be simply a source of further lubrication for the radula during the boring process, the opening of the duct being well placed for this function.

This second pair of salivary gland of the Muricacea leads to a discussion of the poison gland of another group of Stenoglossa, the Toxoglossa, which are well known for their ability to inflict a poisonous bite on their prey. Four species of the genus *Conus*, *C. geographus*, *C. tulipa*, *C. aulicus* and *C. textile*, all from the Indopacific region, are known to be actively poisonous and to have harmed and killed man. Most toxoglossans, in-cluding the Mediterranean species (*C. mediterraneus*) and the British species of *Philbertia*

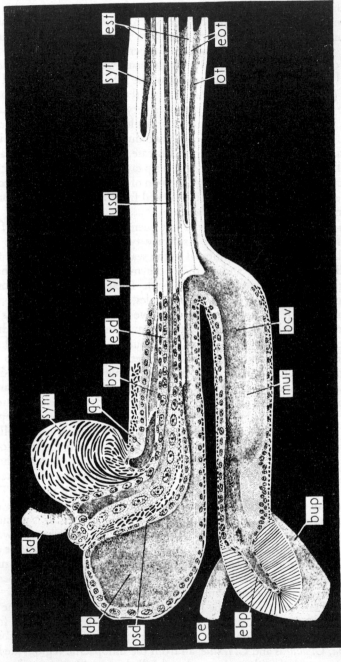

FIG. 103.—*Odostomia:* stereogram of a sagittal half of the base of the stylet and associated structures. bcv, buccal cavity; bsy, base of stylet; bup, buccal pump; dp, dorsal pouch of buccal cavity; ebp, epithelium of buccal pump; eot, epithelium of oral tube; esd, epithelium of salivary duct; est, epithelium of stylet tube; gc, gland cell; mur, mucous ridge; oe, oesophagus; ot, oral tube; psd, projection containing salivary ducts; sd, salivary duct; sy, stylet; sym, muscles moving stylet; syt, stylet tube; usd, united salivary ducts.

and *Mangelia* described by Robinson (1955), have the same apparatus and, presumably, the same toxic powers, though their small size prevents them from being troublesome to man. In *Mangelia* the animal possesses a long and muscular, but slender, proboscis (pb, fig. 104) retractile into a proboscis sac. The proboscis is again folded on itself to produce a second cover for the apical region on which the mouth is situated, a part called the supporting sheath (ssh) by Robinson. The mouth leads to an oral tube (ot) of considerable

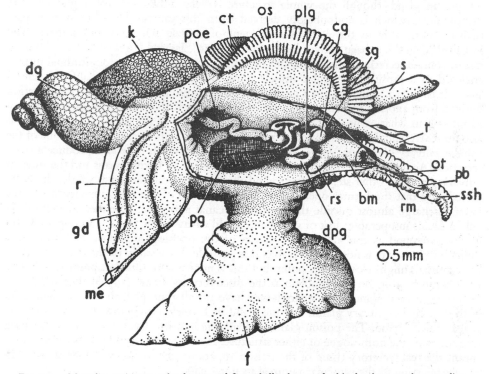

Fig. 104.—*Mangelia powisiana:* animal removed from shell; the mantle skirt has been cut by a median longitudinal incision and the halves deflected and the anterior part of the body dissected. The proboscis has been pulled out from the proboscis sheath and its tip and the oral tube are seen by transparency through the walls of the suspensory sheath.

bm, buccal mass; cg, right cerebral ganglion; ct, ctenidium; dg, digestive gland; dpg, duct of poison gland; f, foot; gd, genital duct; k, kidney; me, mantle edge; os, osphradium; ot, oral tube; pb, proboscis; pg, muscular sac, the so-called poison gland; plg, right pleural ganglion; poe, posterior oesophagus; r, rectum; rm, retractor muscle of proboscis; rs, radular sac; s, siphon; sg, salivary gland; ssh, suspensory sheath; t, tentacle.

length which dilates into a buccal cavity with muscular walls (bm) from which a short radular sac (rs) and the oesophagus (poe) pass back. The glands connected with this region are three in number: two salivary glands (sg), which are poorly developed, and a much bigger structure, the so-called poison gland (pg), connected to the buccal cavity at a point near the origin of the radular sac by a long and convoluted duct (dpg). According to Alpers' analysis (1931*b*) of these organs in the Mediterranean cone the poison gland is the left salivary gland; according to Amaudrut (1898) it is an oesophageal gland separated from the main oesophageal channel (see below, p. 218), whilst Robinson is of the opinion that it may be related to the second pair of salivary glands of the Muricacea and other Stenoglossa. Against Alpers' homology with the left (ordinary) salivary gland stands the occurrence of a pair of these structures in *Mangelia*, in the form of small acinous glands, asymmetrically placed in the neighbourhood of the nerve ring at the posterior end of the buccal cavity, to which they discharge. Their secretion is primarily mucus. More may be said in favour of Amaudrut's theory of an oesophageal origin for the poison gland, though the whole structure is very unlike any other gland in the prosobranchs which is undoubtedly derived from this source. This difference is particularly noticeable in the great development of muscle which is found there. The so-called 'gland' has been shown by Hermitte (1946), Jaeckel (1952) and by Robinson not to contain secreting cells, but to be composed almost entirely of longitudinal muscle enclosed in a capsule of circular muscle lying around an extremely confined central space. It is, in fact, a pump, not a gland, and its main use must be to force the secretion derived from another source towards the exterior. The real site of secretion is a mass of gland cells in what earlier workers regarded as the 'duct' of the gland. This structure is also muscular, and the combination of muscle and gland cells forcibly reminds one of the tubular salivary glands of *Nucella* and similar animals, which may also produce a toxic secretion. Against this homologizing of the poison gland of toxoglossans and the anterior salivary glands of other stenoglossans stand the facts that the former is single, the latter paired, and that the former opens to the innermost end of the buccal cavity whilst the latter discharge almost outside the alimentary canal altogether. Neither of these difficulties seems insuperable: loss of one gland could easily occur in such a congested area of the gastropod as this and the migration of the opening of the duct, whilst more difficult to imagine, is not inconceivable. It is possible that a study of the embryology of these animals might clear up the point, but this is not known. One last point which may have some bearing on the problem is the discovery by Franc (1952*b*) that whilst the ordinary salivary glands of a stenoglossan have no alkaline phosphatase in their cells, both the tubular salivary glands and the gland of Leiblein (see below, pp. 165, 218) are rich in this enzyme. The poison gland of *Philbertia purpurea* has none and on this basis might not be the homologue of either structure. It is not clear, however, whether Franc meant the real secretory tissue of the poison apparatus (the 'duct') when he wrote this, or was referring to the muscular pump at its inner end.

In the roof of the buccal cavity of many prosobranchs, anteriorly, lie the jaws or jaw. These are primitively placed right and left of the mid-line, but in some species they may become approximated and fuse to a single piece. When double, they may be used in a scissor-like way to shear pieces off the prey, as in *Natica*, but more usually—and always when single—they form a stiff edge against which pieces of food may perhaps be pressed by the buccal mass and bitten or broken. The name 'jaw' unfortunately suggests this type of biting action, but as pointed out by Starmuhlner (1952) and Nisbet (1953) the jaw is much more important in manipulating the radula, or in preventing food escaping from the buccal cavity than in biting. Each jaw is an exaggeration of the cuticular covering present on the walls of much of the buccal cavity and is secreted by the cells there. Chemically it appears to be chitinous. Each cell secretes numerous threads of material which may be seen, in fixed and stained sections, as cilia-like structures extending from the outer surface of the cell across a narrow space (presumably an artefact) to the jaw. Each cell thus produces a piece of material which joins on to those secreted by neighbouring cells, though retaining its independence to a sufficient degree to make the jaw look as if composed of numerous rods. This arrangement (or differential wear at the free edge of the jaw) often produces a serrated edge. The whole structure is deeply embedded in a groove running along or across the anterodorsal wall of the buccal cavity. Muscles run from the base to the body wall and buccal mass which may protract or retract it. In Docoglossa the (single) jaw does not show either the rod-like structure or the serrated edge.

In a number of prosobranchs, in correlation with a mode of feeding which does not call for any kind of biting, jaws have vanished. This is true of the Trochidae, for the most part, the Neritidae, Lacunidae, Pomatiasidae, Acmidae, Assimineidae (where they are vestigial), Eulimidae, the parasitic forms, Calyptraeidae, and all Stenoglossa, though vestiges may appear in some of this last group. The heteropods have also lost jaws as part of their adaptation to pelagic life. In a few groups (Docoglossa, Ampullariidae, Cerithiopsidae, Scalidae and Pyramidellidae) the jaws have united to a single piece, in the pyramidellids a tubular structure penetrated by the single salivary duct. In other families the jaws are paired.

The most characteristic structure of the molluscan buccal cavity is the radula, one of the hallmarks of the phylum. It is a chitinous ribbon continually added to at its inner end, which is placed at the posterior end of the radular sac, a blind diverticulum from the posterior end of the buccal cavity, and stretching forward from there over the dorsal surface of the buccal mass on the floor of the buccal cavity. The ribbon bears teeth placed regularly alongside one another in transverse rows and regularly behind one another in longitudinal series and the number of these and the shape of the teeth differ from species to species, though remaining fairly constant within one species. As a consequence of this and the fact that they are imperishable and may be extracted from dried bodies, the radula is an important organ from the taxonomic point of view. From the functional viewpoint, however, there are many important questions arising in connexion with it to which it is still impossible to give any adequate answer.

Each row of teeth on the radula normally repeats precisely the number and shape of the teeth in the rows in front of it and behind. In it there is usually an odd number of teeth due to the fact that the row consists of a single tooth, centrally placed, with a series of others on either side, those on the right being the mirror image of those on the left. The middle tooth is the rachidian or central; those on either side of it are broadly known as the laterals. These usually diminish in size from the mid-line laterally, sometimes in an even gradation of similar teeth, but, more commonly, a group of teeth nearer the rachidian (the lateral or intermediate teeth) is distinguishable from a group lying further away (the marginal teeth). The biggest lateral tooth may be called the dominant. Since the number of teeth in a row is a specific character it is customary to represent it by means of a formula in which either figures representing the number of teeth of each kind in a single row are given, or figures for the rachidian and the right half-row, the left half being assumed to be the mirror image of the right. Thus we may write either $30 + 4 + 1 + 4 + 30$ or $R + 4 + 30$. Occasionally figures $(1, 2, 3 \ldots)$ under the tooth number give their relative sizes. If the number of teeth of one kind is high and variable it may be denoted by $n$; if very high or virtually uncountable by $\infty$. D may be used to show the dominant; * a tooth which has no cusp. A few examples of uses of this sort are given here:

$$\infty + D + 4 + R + 4 + D + \infty \quad \text{(Rhipidoglossa)}$$
$$3 + R + 3 \quad \text{(Taenioglossa)}$$
$$n + O + n \quad \text{(Dorid)}$$
$$R \quad \text{(Ascoglossa)}$$

The various patterns of radular structure which are encountered among the proso-branchs are these:

1. Rhipidoglossan (from the Greek *rhips, rhipidos*, a fan) (fig. 105A): formula

$$\infty + 1 + 4 + R + 4 + 1 + \infty \quad \text{or} \quad \infty + 1 + D + 3 + R + 3 + D + 1 + \infty.$$

The rachidian tooth (rh) is large and often not cusped. On either side of it lies a fan of smaller teeth which can be divided into five laterals (lat) with the outermost dominating; beyond comes a vast array of needle-like marginals (mrt) the most median of which is sufficiently differentiated to be counted as unlike the rest. The half rows on one side alternate with those on the other. A rhipidoglossate radula is met with in the Zeugo-branchia, Trochacea and Neritacea. It is in all probability the most primitive type of gastropod radula.

2. Docoglossan (from Greek *dokos*, a beam or spear) (figs. 105B, C): formula

$$3 + D + 2 + R + 2 + D + 3.$$

R may be absent (Acmaeidae) and is usually small and unpigmented (rh) and therefore not easily seen in those families (Patellidae) in which it occurs. The marginals (mrt) are also uncoloured except for the dominant (plu) which is pigmented black like the laterals (lat). The teeth are unicuspid except the dominant which is pluricuspid, possibly due to fusion, though this is not evident in the Lepetidae. This type of radula occurs in the Patellacea and would seem to be derived from the rhipidoglossate type by reduction or loss of the marginal and rachidian teeth.

3. Taenioglossan (from Greek *tainia*, a band) (fig. 105D): formula

$$3 + R + 3 \quad \text{or} \quad 2 + 1 + R + 1 + 2.$$

The teeth which lie on either side of the rachidian (rh) are usually distinguishable into two marginal (mrt) and one lateral (lat) on each side, but it is very doubtful whether this division corresponds to the similar one in rhipidoglossate types: it is more likely that the teeth known here as laterals and marginals correspond only to the lateral teeth of the rhipidoglossate forms. On this interpretation the teeth corresponding to the marginal teeth of the rhipidoglossate radula are regarded as not present at all. It may be, however, that fusion of the marginal teeth has occurred to give a reduced number. Radulae of taenioglossate pattern occur in all the families of monotocardian proso-branchs which are placed by Thiele in the group Mesogastropoda, except for those which have become secondarily devoid of a radula, and the few families which are ptenoglossan.

4. Ptenoglossan (from Greek *ptenos*, feathered) (fig. 101): formula

$$n + O + n.$$

This type of radula is clearly modified from a taenioglossate type and is the main support for the supposition that the few lateral teeth of that pattern have been evolved by a fusion of the more numerous teeth of an ancestral rhipidoglossan type. All the teeth are of similar, rather simple, hook-like shape and give rise to a very efficient grasping organ. This type of radula occurs in Ianthinidae and Scalidae amongst British prosobranchs.

5. Rachiglossan (from **Greek** *rhachis*, a spine) (fig. 105E): formula

$$1 + R + 1.$$

This narrow type of radula is found in the Muricacea and Buccinacea amongst British members of the Stenoglossa.

6. Toxoglossan (from **Greek** *toxon*, a bow or *toxotes*, an archer) (figs. 105F, G): formula

$$D + O + D \quad \text{or} \quad 1 + O + O + O + 1.$$

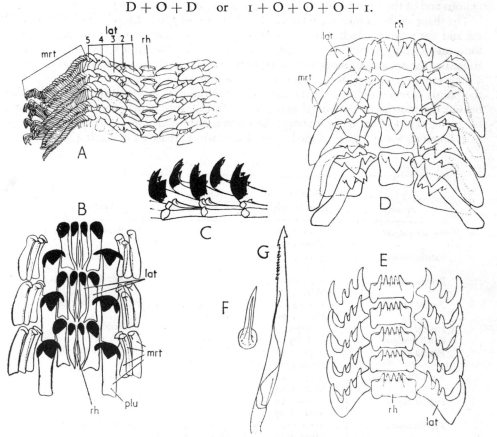

FIG. 105.—Radulae.  A, rhipidoglossan (*Haliotis*), dorsal view; B, docoglossan (*Patella*), dorsal view; C, docoglossan (*Patella*), side view (rh, not seen); D, taenioglossan (*Littorina*), dorsal view; E, rachiglossan (*Buccinum*), dorsal view; F, toxoglossan (*Mangelia*), single tooth; G, toxoglossan (*Conus*), single tooth. To facilitate comparison all are drawn with the anterior end above except E, in which it is below. lat, lateral tooth; mrt, marginal tooth; plu, pluricuspid tooth; rh, rachidian or median tooth.

The 2 teeth in each row alternate and are in use only one at a time. They are of complex structure (see p. 204).

These six types of radulae show a gradual evolution from the polyodont rhipido-glossan, with an extremely large number of teeth in each row, to a number of patterns with few teeth per row (oligodont) reaching as a climax the toxoglossan where only a half row, containing a single tooth, is in use at any particular time. This evolutionary change, it appears, has taken place at least twice, since a study of the functioning of the

radula shows that whilst it is possible to put the rhipidoglossan—taenioglossan—rachiglossan—toxoglossan radulae together, the docoglossan type differs fundamentally from
these and must be looked upon as a separate line of change (see p. 200). The ptenoglossan
type would appear as a regression from the taenioglossan towards the ancestral rhipidoglossan type, at least in part, whilst the rhipidoglossan radula is itself reminiscent of the
broad ribbon of little specialized teeth which is to be found in the buccal cavity of
chitons and of the basal families of the tectibranchs (e.g. Acteonidae).

The shape of the radular teeth is directly related to the kind of food which the animals
eat and the way in which it is manipulated, just as the dentition of a mammal and its
food and feeding habits are correlated. The length of the radula appears also to be
related to the amount of work which has to be done in feeding: where wear is extensive
a long radula is present, where wear is less (because softer food is eaten) the length of
the radula is much reduced. In the latter case the radular sac forms only a small bulge
behind the muscles of the buccal mass; in the former case it may loop backwards and
forwards, as it does in *Patella*, amongst the viscera, or be coiled in a spirally wound heap,
as in *Littorina*. Some figures of the length of the radula are given in Table 4.

TABLE 4

| Animal | Radula length / Shell length | Radula / ∛Shell volume | Author |
|---|---|---|---|
| *Patella vulgata* . | 1·30–2·30 Mean 1·75 | — | Fischer-Piette, 1935b |
| *Patella vulgata* . | 1·13–2·00 Mean 1·51 | — | Eslick, 1940 |
| *Patella vulgata* . | 1·20–2·20 Mean 1·75 | — | Fischer-Piette, 1941a |
| *Patella vulgata* . | 1·40–2·00 Mean 1·60 | 3·20–4·80 Mean 3·90 | Fischer-Piette, 1948 |
| *Patella vulgata* . | 1·80 | — | Pelseneer, 1935 |
| *Patella vulgata* . | 1·69 | — | Evans, 1953 |
| *Patella aspera* . | 0·95–1·40 Mean 1·15 | — | Fischer-Piette, 1935b |
| *Patella aspera* . | 0·93–1·25 Mean 1·05 | — | Eslick, 1940 |
| *Patella aspera* . | 0·80–1·40 Mean 1·15 | — | Fischer-Piette, 1941a |
| *Patella aspera* . | 1·00–1·10 Mean 1·05 | 2·50–3·50 Mean 2·90 | Fischer-Piette, 1948 |
| *Patella aspera* . | 1·11 | — | Evans, 1953 |
| *Patella intermedia* . | 1·60–2·50 Mean 2·10 | — | Fischer-Piette, 1935b |
| *Patella intermedia* . | 1·60–2·70 Mean 2·10 | — | Fischer-Piette, 1941a |
| *Patella intermedia* . | 1·40–2·00 Mean 1·60 | 4·10–5·70 Mean 4·71 | Fischer-Piette, 1948 |
| *Patella intermedia* . | 1·88 | — | Evans, 1953 |
| *Gibbula cineraria* . | 1·31 | — | Pelseneer, 1935 |
| *Littorina littorea* . | 2·00 | — | Pelseneer, 1935 |
| *Littorina saxatilis* . | 2·33 | — | Pelseneer, 1935 |
| *Buccinum undatum* . | 1·00 | — | Pelseneer, 1935 |
| *Nucella lapillus* . | 0·30 | — | Pelseneer, 1935 |

In some exotic prosobranchs the radula may be still longer, e.g. in *Tectarius pagoda* it is said to be not less than seven times as long as the animal's shell. Although the length of the radula has always been assumed, since the days of Simroth (1896–1907), to be correlated with the degree of hard usage to which it is put, no proof of this has ever been given, nor is there any clear idea of how the effect would be brought about. Peile (1937) has certainly shown that the effects of wear are visible on radular teeth, but no one has convincingly shown for any one species that differences in the food, or in the substratum from which the food is collected, make differences to the length of the radula.

In the young animal the radula appears as a secretion from the inner end of the radular sac, a finger-shaped caecum which grows out from the posterior end of the buccal cavity and is usually slightly bifid at its tip. Its floor opens on to the dorsal surface of the buccal mass, its roof turns over to the floor of the oesophagus. Both are lined by a columnar epithelium which presents the same histological appearance as that into which it is continued in the rest of the gut: that is to say, the upper epithelium has no special characteristics, but the lower secretes a cuticle like that overlying the buccal mass. This is known (for reasons which will appear later) as the subradular or elastic membrane. The upper wall of the sac becomes folded inwards so as to bulge like a typhlosole into its cavity and, except near its mouth, the lumen of the sac is wholly or almost wholly obliterated by this, so that it is shaped like a broad U in transverse section. The gutter which runs externally along the roof of the sac is filled in with a characteristic spongy connective tissue and the whole structure is surrounded by a blood sinus (rds, fig. 106) connected to the cephalic branch of the anterior aorta. The outer walls of this are muscular and various muscle strands originating in the walls of the head, or the columellar muscle or the buccal mass are inserted upon it. This outer wall is the radular sheath.

The copious blood supply and the connective tissue rich in stored nutritive materials seem to be related to the fact that throughout the lifetime of a prosobranch a continuous secretion of radular teeth is occurring in which the greater part of the walls of the sac would appear to be involved, only the tissues nearest to the buccal cavity not actively helping in this process. The cells in the sac which are responsible for the initiation of tooth production are the odontoblasts, which lie at the innermost end of the radular sac, rather more ventrally than dorsally, so that the terminal wall of the radular sac is clothed by a backward extension of the same epithelium as covers the roof. In any one animal these odontoblasts are of various size, the cells known as $\alpha$ and $\beta$ cells, which are most posterior in position, being small and the $\gamma$ cells, the biggest, being more anterior (fig. 106, $\beta$ cells not labelled). They also vary in size and number from group to group, there being many small odontoblasts in prosobranch gastropods, but only a small group of relatively giant cells (somewhat unnecessarily distinguished as odontophytes) in pulmonates and opisthobranchs: for this reason almost all work upon the secretion of radular teeth has been carried out on the latter two groups, although there is no reason to suppose that the process is any different from that occurring in prosobranchs. The odontoblasts appear to be arranged in groups each of which is responsible for the production of one tooth.

There have long been two views as to the way in which the odontoblasts produce a radular tooth, which parallel the two views which have been held regarding the manufacture of the molluscan shell. Trinchese (1878) and Pruvot-Fol (1925, 1926) have both assumed that each group of odontoblasts is directly transformed into a tooth and thereby extinguished as a productive unit. The next tooth in that series must, therefore, be due to the activity of a new group of odontoblasts, as will every successive one. This con-

tinual production of new nests of odontoblasts they see in a periodic transformation of
cells from the upper epithelium of the radular sac which is assumed to migrate over the
terminal wall of the sac and change rhythmically into odontoblasts, the rhythm coinciding with that of tooth production. Most investigators of this subject, however, have
regarded the formation of a radular tooth as merely an exaggerated local secretion of
cuticular material such as goes on to a lesser extent in many other sites in the body of
the animal. These investigators still differ among themselves, nevertheless, on the matter

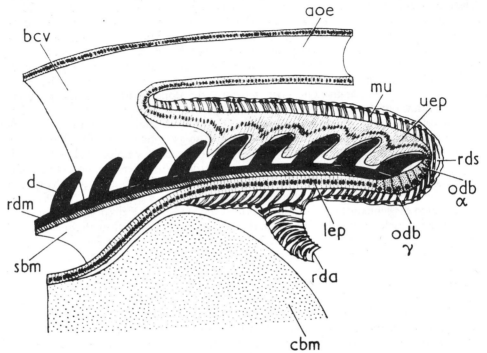

Fig. 106.—Diagrammatic longitudinal section of the radular sac and of the radula with related parts of the
alimentary canal.
aoe, anterior oesophagus; bcv, buccal cavity; cbm, cartilage of buccal mass; d, radular tooth; lep,
lower epithelium of radular sac; mu, muscles in wall of radular sinus; odbα, α odontoblasts; odbγ,
γ odontoblasts; rda, radular artery; rdm, radular membrane; rds, radular sinus; sbm, subradular
membrane; uep, upper epithelium of radular sac.

of the renewal of odontoblasts; Rössler (1885), Beck (1912), Spek (1921) and Prenant
(1925) believed that each group of odontoblasts persists throughout the life of the
mollusc and produces all the teeth; Rücker (1883), Rottmann (1901), Schnabel (1903)
and Sollas (1907) believed that a group of odontoblasts is exhausted by the secretion of
one tooth, as did Pruvot-Fol (1925), and therefore believed in their rhythmical replacement as described above. Bloch (1896) also believed in their replacement, but not in the
same regular way after the secretion of each tooth. Although we have no personal
experience of this problem this seems to us the less likely happening.
The secretory process may, perhaps, resemble that which produces chaetae in annelids.
This has been described in a number of genera by Schepotieff (1903, 1904), in *Nereis* by

Pruvot (1913), *Myzostomum* by Jägersten (1937), *Sabellaria* by Ebling (1945) and, in oligochaets, by Bourne (1894) and Vandebroek (1936). The most interesting of these studies is by Ebling, who showed how the secretion of a chaeta is carried out within the chaetal sac primarily by the activity of one cell lying at its base. To the primary core produced by this cell the other cells on the opposite wall of the sac add a secondary, superficial layer so that the final chaeta has a double structure. As the chaetae mature they migrate up the chaetal sac along its ventral wall, and since their primary cells travel with them it is clear that there must be a continuous production of new chaetoblasts at the base of the sac, apparently from the same cell population on the dorsal wall as gives rise to the cells adding the secondary material to the primary core of the chaetae.

The resemblances between what happens here and what may be happening in the gastropod are very close and it may be that in the mollusc, as in the annelid, a migration of cells from the dorsal wall of the sac in one direction keeps up the supply of odonto-blasts for the manufacture of successive new teeth, whilst the same cells, moving in the opposite sense, lie over the radular teeth and add secondary material to them as they migrate from the radular sac into the buccal cavity.

The secretion of a single tooth has been described for several euthyneurous gastropods (fig. 106). It involves a group of odontoblasts (odb) lying ventrally at the inner end of the radular sac. These decrease in size from the large $\gamma$ cells anteriorly to the small $\alpha$ cells posteriorly. This gradient of size coincides with gradient in the amount of secretion produced, the $\alpha$ cells producing minimal quantities, the $\gamma$ cells maximal. As a result of this a wedge-shaped mass of secretion accumulates over the odontoblasts, its tip pointing posteriorly and overlying the $\alpha$ cells. A further difference between the large $\gamma$ cells on the one hand and the smaller $\beta$ and $\alpha$ cells on the other is that secretion is continuous in the former but periodic in the latter. When the secretory phase has finished in the $\alpha$ and $\beta$ cells the continued secretion of material by the $\gamma$ cells causes the material lying over the $\alpha$ and $\beta$ cells to be pulled away from their surface, and when the next phase of secretion occurs in these cells a discrete mass of secretion is formed which is not connected to the mass previously produced in that situation. The $\gamma$ cells, however, secrete continuously and the sum of the activity of all the cells is a ribbon of material (the product of the $\gamma$ cells) from which, at regular intervals, rise up the tapered blocks which have come from the $\alpha$ and $\beta$ cells. The continuous ribbon is called the radular membrane (rdm), the blocks (from $\alpha$ and $\beta$ cells) are the teeth (d). Jones, McCance & Shackleton (1935) have shown that the body of the radula in *Patella* is made partly of a protein and partly of a polysaccharide strengthened by salts of iron and silicon. Although the salts may vary from animal to animal the body of the radula probably remains substantially the same.

With successive waves of tooth production the teeth attached to the radular membrane are inevitably pushed forward on the floor of the radular sac away from the site of secretion. In this position they meet and over-ride the cuticle which lies there and which is an extension of that covering the buccal mass, so that the two cuticular layers, one above (the radular membrane), the other below (the cuticle) are in contact, with the upper appearing to slip forward over the lower. This arrangement persists so long as the radula grows, and because of its position the lower cuticular layer is, in this situation, called the subradular membrane (sbm). Amaudrut (1898) called it the elastic membrane. Like so many cuticular secretions in gastropods it looks fibrous, this structure being apparently due to the escape of the secretion in thread-like masses from the upper surface of the cell.

This is the classical interpretation of the fact that the membrane to which the radular teeth are attached shows a distinct double layering with different staining properties. Recent work by Runham (personal communication), however, suggests that there is only a single cuticle the upper part of which is tanned where the radula lies; the source of the tanning material is probably the overlying epithelium. This interpretation would imply that not only the radular teeth and the 'radular' membrane, but also the whole of the 'subradular' membrane would be gradually moving forwards from the posterior towards the anterior end of the buccal mass. Indeed, it has been suggested that a roughened pile of cuticular material lying ventrally at the tip of the buccal mass of top-shells and limpets and known as the 'licker' might be the accumulated heap of cuticle produced by this mass migration.

The teeth recently produced by the activity of the odontoblasts do not present the same appearance to the eye as do those which lie nearer the buccal cavity, and it is clear that between their initial formation and their appearance on the buccal mass they change. This alteration, it is agreed by all workers on the subject except Rottmann (1901) and Schnabel (1903), is due to the activity of the cells forming the epithelium of the dorsal wall of the radular sac (uep). After the teeth have broken away from the groups of odontoblasts and have moved forward in the radular sac, their upper surface is in contact with the epithelium on the roof of the radular sac. The activity of these cells adds to the composition of the teeth and is responsible for the final form which they assume and their ultimate chemical constitution and physical consistency (Prenant, 1924a). It is at this stage, probably, that are added the salts of iron and silicon shown by Jones, McCance & Shackleton (1935) to be responsible for much of the hardness of the teeth in Patella. Although this much may be said about the secretion of the gastropod radula, many details of the process remain unknown and it is clear that this is a problem which urgently calls for proper histochemical investigation.

When the radula is first formed it inevitably lies within the radular sac. As the animal grows it is found to lie over the dorsal surface of the buccal mass. A continuous secretion of new teeth occurs at the inner end of the radular sac: those teeth which lie at the tip of the buccal mass show signs of wear and can be seen to be torn off during feeding. Small individuals have a small buccal mass and would seem to require small-sized teeth, whilst fully grown animals have a larger buccal mass and, presumably, larger teeth. All these things would point to a steady forward movement of the radula out of the sac on to the buccal mass during the lifetime of the mollusc, and to a gradual increase in the size of the teeth present on it. That an increase in the size of the teeth with age occurs is undoubted: it can be seen by looking at a preparation of the radula of the cephalopod Eledone, but in most prosobranchs (e.g. Patella) the teeth have to be carefully measured before this is detected, even in animals with a long radula of many rows. Nevertheless in a young Patella, Pruvot-Fol (1926) recorded that the teeth are only one-seventh the length of the teeth of a typical adult: from this it may be deduced that between youth and maturity a very large number of rows of teeth are used, broken off and replaced by others which have been formed within the radular sac.

The question therefore arises as to how these teeth move out of the radular sac on to the buccal mass, and this is a question to which it must be admitted there is no generally agreed answer. A number of causes have been supposed to bring it about. First is a slipping forwards of the radular membrane, plus the teeth it bears. This may be the way in which the movement takes place but it can hardly be supposed to occur spontaneously: some pull from the front or push from behind must set it in motion. Both these things have, in fact, been imagined as acting: the forces exerted on the front of the radula as the animal feeds have been suggested by Rücker (1883) and others as pulling the radula forwards over the buccal mass and out of the radular sac, and a variety of other muscular tractions on the radula in its sac have been supposed to act in the same way. Similarly the secretion of new teeth at the inner end of the radula will push those already formed forwards. To what extent this force exists is not known, but Hoffmann (1932) has suggested that its effect will be felt no further forward than the innermost 3 rows of teeth. Migration of the radular teeth forwards out of the radular sac on to the buccal mass would seem to involve a gliding or slipping of the teeth on the radular membrane over the underlying subradular membrane, or of teeth and membrane together over the epithelium, and although measurements such as those given by Pruvot-Fol (1926) for *Patella* (mentioned above) would seem to have this as a necessary consequence, no proof of this movement has ever been obtained.

One further factor is undoubtedly involved in the change of position of the radular teeth—the relative rates of growth in the buccal cavity and radular sac. If the buccal cavity extends backwards more rapidly than the radular sac grows, then the posterior wall of the buccal cavity will uncover a stretch of radula previously enclosed within the sac, and so produce an apparent forward movement. This is known to occur (Pruvot-Fol, 1926), but it must be confessed that to say that the forward movement of the radula is due to such an extent to this factor and to such an extent to another is an impossible task.

The radular teeth may be immovably fixed to the membrane of which they form part, or they may be movably articulated with it. The former condition is characteristic of all rachidian teeth and of all teeth in a docoglossate radula: the latter applies to the lateral and marginal teeth of the other types. It is important in connexion with the use of these teeth in feeding, and will be described in the section dealing with that (p. 187). The teeth are also adapted in shape and size for the use to which they are put by their owner and this too will be best illustrated when their use is considered.

Before this can be done, however, attention must be turned to the buccal mass, which is an elaborate apparatus of great complexity evolved for the manipulation of the radula in the process of feeding. It is a tongue-shaped structure lying on the floor of the buccal cavity from the back of which it projects freely. It is obviously composed of a right and a left half connected across the mid-line where, on its dorsal side, runs a groove in which lies the radula. The whole of this, and the bulk of the rest of the surface is covered with a thick and shining cuticle, though this is thinner towards the ventral side, where it may disappear and be replaced by glandular epithelium. Internally the buccal mass is usually supported by 'cartilages', pieces of tough, resilient material which earn this name because of the resemblance which they exhibit to vertebrate cartilage from the histological point of view. The number of cartilages varies from 5 pairs (*Patella*) to 2 (most prosobranchs) or even a single bilobed piece (*Ianthina*). They are wrapped in layers of tough connective tissue and not only contribute towards the maintenance of the shape of the buccal mass— which they are able to do because of the turgor of the cells out of which they are com- posed, like a notochord—but also give origin to a great number of muscles which are concerned with the movement of the buccal mass and of the radula upon it.

The histology of these has been described most carefully by Nowikoff (1912) in *Patella caerulea*, *Diodora apertura* and *Haliotis tuberculata*. In the two last genera and in the posterior cartilages of *Patella*—as indeed in the majority of prosobranchs—the cartilages are made of highly vacuolated cells containing a peripherally placed nucleus and a few granules. Each cell secretes matrix which is frequently fibrous. The cells lying centrally in the cartilage mass are polyhedral and large, those lying peripherally are small and flattened and merge into the perichondrium, a dense mass of fibrous material. In the anterior cartilages of *Patella* the cells are less vacuolated, richer in cytoplasm and granules and the matrix is alveolar: these differences may be related to differences in the stresses to which the cartilages are exposed.

The muscles of the buccal mass may be arranged in series according to the functions which they subserve: there are protractors of the buccal mass, which will project it towards, or through, the mouth; retractors of the buccal mass, which will bring about the reverse effect; intrinsic muscles of the buccal mass, which affect the shape; and a series of tensor muscles of the buccal mass which have the effect of immobilizing it in any particular position. In addition to these muscles a further series of radular muscles is attached to the radula and to the radular sheath.

Some account of the musculature of the buccal mass has usually been given by most investigators of different forms of prosobranchs, though few of these except Amaudrut (1898) have been particularly thorough. More recently a small number of more complete investigations has been made, especially by Carriker (1943) for *Urosalpinx*, and by Nisbet (1953) for *Monodonta*. The second of these is particularly important in that it approaches the problem from a physiological as well as an anatomical viewpoint and so gives a more complete picture of the functioning of the buccal mass than does the work of any other author. The muscles appear cross-striated but this may perhaps be another case of 'double striation' or helical arrangement of myofibrils rather than the true striation of vertebrates (Hanson & Lowy, 1957). They also contain haemoglobin (Lankester, 1872) and for this reason often appear as a red mass shining through the body wall, and Ball & Meyerhof (1940) have shown in *Busycon* the presence of a complete cytochrome system. Fänge & Mattisson (1958) have described a high concentration of mitochondria in the buccal muscles of *Buccinum undatum* and have shown that the oxygen consumption is very high and that their respiratory enzymes are not easily poisoned by cyanide or carbon monoxide. These characteristics would permit a high level of activity even if conditions are not particularly favourable.

# CHAPTER 8

# THE ALIMENTARY SYSTEM—2

THE musculature which is associated with the movements of the buccal mass and radula of *Monodonta* is complex and Nisbet (1953) distinguished no less than 33 different muscles. In addition some strands of stout connective tissue, which he called tendons, are involved. These immobilize certain areas. Three are important: the mid-ventrally placed nuchal tendon (nt, figs. 107, 108) which runs from the inner end of the sublingual pouch to the musculature of the foot (f), and the dorsal buccal tendon (dbt) on each side, which runs from the base of each jaw outwards to the musculature of the side of the head. As a result of the presence of these tendons the three points from which they run remain more or less unchanged during the various feeding movements. In addition a pair of ventrolateral buccal tendons steadies the lateral buccal areas.

The feeding process may be divided into a cycle of operations each of which involves the primary activity of a group of muscles and the synergic action of many others. The different phases of the cycle (which has also been described for the related *Gibbula cineraria* by Ankel (1938*a*) and his pupil Eigenbrodt (1941)) were given by Nisbet as follows: (1) the opening of the mouth, along with which occurs an uncovering of the cuticularized edges of the two jaws; (2) the protraction of the buccal mass and, simultaneously, a backward movement of the subradular membrane over the tip and sides of the anterior end of the odontophore; (3) the opening of the radula; (4) the closing of the radula; (5) the retraction of the buccal mass; and (6) the shutting of the mouth. These actions—which are not separated in performance by the animal but flow together and overlap in one continuous movement—may now be investigated one by one.

(1) *Opening of the mouth* (figs. 108A, B, C). The tip of the snout of *Monodonta* shows, at rest, a circular surface crossed by a vertical cleft which is the closed mouth, lying between the lateral lips. Diagonal extensions from the mouth dorsally mark off a dorsal lip (dlp) or premandibular fold and similar extensions ventrally mark off a ventral lip (vlp). These are mobile and move during the opening of the mouth, but the outer rim of the circular end of the snout is not involved in this process. When the mouth opens the dorsal and lateral lips move swiftly, the ventral lip less so. These movements are produced by synchronous contraction of (i) the mandibular protractor, (ii) the mandibular retractor and (iii) the inner ventral buccal protractor muscles.

The mandibular protractor muscle (mpm) has its origin primarily in the oral rim of the snout dorsally, but secondarily in the dorsal lip (dlp). From these places it runs to be inserted on the dorsal (anterior) surface of the jaw (ja) towards its base. Its contraction will either protract the jaw (if the retractor of the jaw synchronously relaxes) or will retract the dorsal lip (if the jaw is immobilized by simultaneous contraction of its retractor).

The mandibular retractor muscle (mr) runs from an origin in the dorsal wall of the snout to the dorsal (anterior) surface of the jaw, being inserted near the lower free edge.

Some of its fibres run to the more fleshy parts of the jaw. When it contracts it pulls these away so as to expose the edge and (if the mandibular protractor simultaneously relaxes) will retract the jaw. The simultaneous contraction of mandibular protractor

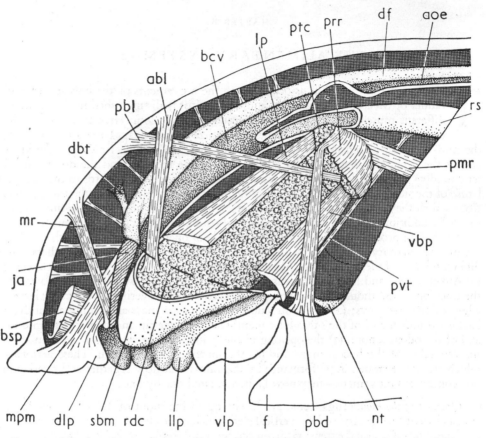

FIG. 107.—*Monodonta lineata:* diagram of lateral dissection of the anterior part of the head and foot, showing the anterior part of the alimentary tract and some of the muscles associated with it. Radular teeth are omitted. All cut surfaces are left white; the haemocoel is cross-hatched; the jaw is diagonally hatched and the cavity of the gut stippled. After Nisbet.

abl, anterior buccal levator muscle; aoe, anterior oesophagus; bcv, buccal cavity; bsp, buccal sphincter muscle; dbt, dorsal buccal tendon; df, dorsal fold; dlp, dorsal lip; f, foot; ja, jaw; lp, lateral protractor muscle; llp, lateral lip; mpm, mandibular protractor muscle; mr, mandibular retractor muscle; nt, nuchal tendon; pbd, posterior buccal depressor muscle; pbl, posterior buccal levator muscle; pmr, postmedian retractor muscle of the radula; prr, posterior retractor muscle of the radula; ptc, posterior radular cartilage; pvt, posterior ventral radular tensor muscle; rdc, anterior radular cartilage; rs, radular sac; sbm, subradular membrane; vbp, ventral buccal protractor muscle; vlp, ventral lip.

and retractor which occurs at this stage of the feeding cycle means that the jaw is steadied and the dorsal lips withdrawn.

The inner ventral buccal protractors (ivp) run from the lateral and ventral lips dorsally and posteriorly along the underside of the buccal mass on each side, and end by being attached to the ventral end of each posterior cartilage. In so far as the opening of the mouth is affected by these muscles it is the attachment to the cartilage which acts as the origin of the muscle and its endings within the lips which behave as its insertion.

(2) *Protraction of the buccal mass and of the subradular membrane* (figs. 108C, D). These actions are occurring whilst the mouth is being opened: their separation here is purely to simplify description. If an animal feeding on a glass plate be watched it will be seen that the radula appears in the mouth before that is fully opened, having been brought to this position by a forward movement of the buccal mass within the buccal cavity. This movement continues until the tip of the odontophore, and the radula which lies over it, are pressed against the substratum. As this happens the radula opens and is in the open state when actually brought into contact with the substratum.

The forward movement of the odontophore will be discussed in this section and the factors which open the radula in the next.

The forward movement of the odontophore is achieved by means of the lateral and ventral buccal protractor muscles, and the posterior buccal levator and depressor muscles.

The lateral protractors (lp) have each a triple origin and are inserted on the dorsal third of each posterior cartilage (ptc). The most dorsal of the 3 sections into which this muscle is divisible runs forward from the cartilage into the lateral wall of the buccal cavity, passing obliquely round that to its dorsal side. There it spreads forward and is attached to the wall of the head (fig. 108B). The second section lies ventral to the first and its fibres, running forwards in the lateral wall of the buccal cavity, join those of the outer buccal constrictor muscle (obi, see below) which are also running there (fig. 108A). The third section, still more ventral and deeper, joins the inner buccal constrictor (ibm, see below) in exactly similar fashion (fig. 108E). These points are all relatively fixed, with the result that when the protractor contracts the posterior cartilage is pulled forward, and, as it is cupped against the posterior surface of the anterior cartilage, and joined to it by groups of muscles, this forward pull is transmitted to the anterior cartilage and the whole mass moves forward.

The same effect is achieved by the simultaneous contraction of the ventral buccal protractor (vbp, fig. 107). One slip of this has already been described in connexion with the withdrawal of the lateral and ventral lips during the opening of the mouth; the bulk of the muscle, however, helps to protract the buccal mass. The fibres of this major part are inserted like those of its smaller section, on the posterior cartilage (ptc) ventrally. From there they run forward and fan out to give a number of slips which end on the walls of the head, laterally and ventrally.

The posterior buccal levator muscle (pbl) lies on each side. It has its origin dorsolaterally on the wall of the head and from there passes round the side of the buccal cavity to be inserted on the ventral part of the posterior cartilage (ptc). Since its course is obliquely backwards and downwards it not only raises the posterior end of the buccal mass but has a protractor effect. The posterior buccal depressor (pbd) is, likewise, a paired muscle which originates in the musculature of the ventral body wall in the neck region and runs thence dorsally to the posterior cartilage. Some fibres are inserted on the cartilage but most join the posterior retractor muscle of the radula (prr). Like the levator this muscle has a protractor action in addition to its depressor one and simultaneous contraction of both levator and depressor will cause a moderate degree of protraction alone.

The simultaneous contraction of the ventral and lateral protractors and the posterior levators and depressors will produce a drive of the buccal mass forwards and downwards

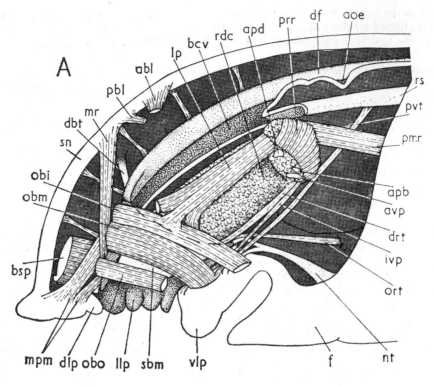

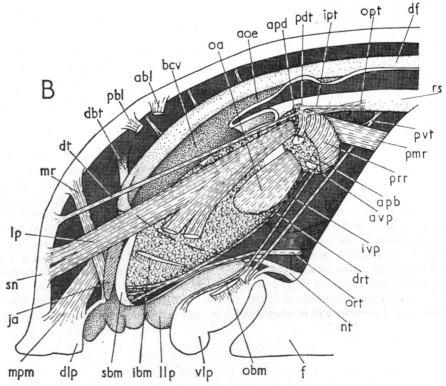

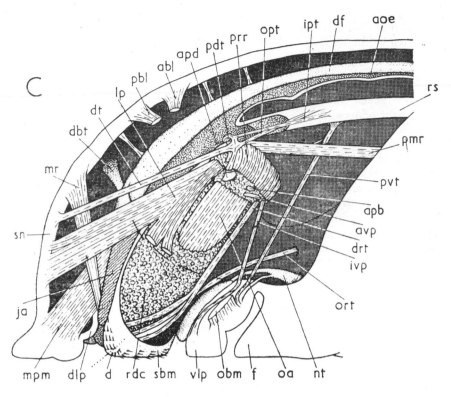

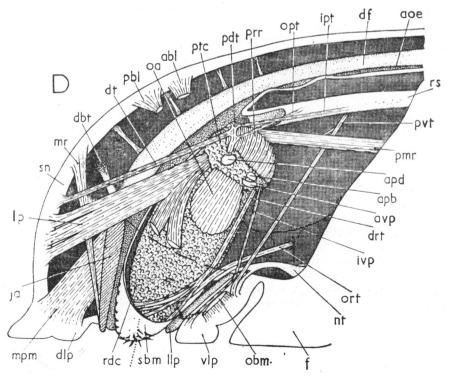

which brings its tip up to and through the mouth, and with it will be brought the radula and subradular membrane. The buccal mass, however, is not like a piston, wholly unconnected to the walls of the cylinder within which it moves, but at certain points the subradular membrane, which forms its outer covering, is reflected on to the walls of the buccal cavity. This occurs, in particular, at the inner end of the sublingual pouch underneath the buccal mass, and at the inner ends of the lateral buccal pouches at the sides of the radula. These lines are kept more or less fixed in position by the tendons running to the body wall. As a consequence of this the forward movement of the carti-lages within the buccal mass causes the subradular membrane to be pulled backwards and downwards to a certain extent because of its connexions with the buccal epithelium at these places. The movement of the subradular membrane is possible because it is invaginated within a deep groove in the mid-dorsal line of the odontophore where it bears the radula, and this invagination is pulled out and the groove obliterated. The effects which this movement of the subradular membrane has upon the radula are dealt with in the next section. In addition to the purely mechanical effects of the tendons in causing this movement, it is actively promoted by the contraction of muscles, the most important of which are the tensor muscles shown in figs. 108B, C, D. The direct tensors (drt) are relatively thin bands originating in the anterior surface of the posterior cartilage close to the origin of the ventral protractors (avp). Each passes forwards ventrally towards the tip of the anterior cartilage (rdc) where it splits into two or three bands which curve dorsally round the front of the cartilage and are inserted dorsally, in a somewhat recurved way, on to the subradular membrane (sbm). The oblique tensors (ort) are inserted alongside the direct ones and the first part of their course is almost identical; instead of originating on the posterior cartilage, however, these muscles are tied to the columellar muscle, of which, indeed, they are best regarded as slips.

Whilst this anterior movement of the buccal mass and the simultaneous movement of the subradular membrane are occurring a further action takes place which has the effect of pressing the jaw against the dorsal side of the odontophore as it moves forward within the buccal cavity. This presses the jaw against the groove in which the radula lies and so appears to antagonize the effect of the tendons and tensor muscles in pulling this open: it at least prevents it from being effective until a level more anterior than the tip of the jaw has been reached. This pressure of the jaw against the advancing odontophore is produced by the contraction of the outer and inner buccal constrictor muscles (figs. 108A, E).

The outer buccal constrictor muscle is in reality triple, the three parts being placed successively behind one another. The outermost (obo) has its insertion in connective tissue between the 2 jaws mid-dorsally and thence curves round the wall of the buccal cavity in a ventral direction, ending on the lateral borders of the mouth. The innermost of the three (obi) begins in the same area of connective tissue, but overlies the base and not the apex of the jaw, and then curves ventrally in a similar fashion. With its fibres are amalgamated those of the middle part of the lateral protractor (lp) muscle (fig. 108A). The middle section of the outer buccal constrictor (obm) is unpaired and runs sphincter-wise round the wall of the buccal cavity at about the level of the middle of the jaw. It is not a complete ring of muscle, having a gap mid-ventrally. On contraction these muscles pull the jaw backwards.

The inner buccal constrictor muscle (ibm, fig. 108E) has a similar course to the outer but lies at a deeper level. Each muscle is fastened to the cartilaginous material of which the jaw is made and then runs round the lateral wall of the buccal cavity to the point

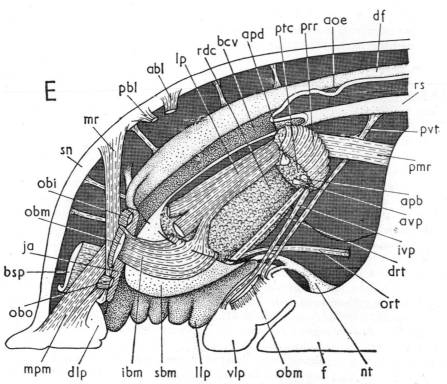

Fig. 108.—*Monodonta lineata:* a series of diagrams of lateral dissections of the anterior part of the head and foot showing the cycle of operations in the feeding process. A, the mouth is shut and the buccal mass retracted in the position of rest. B, the mouth is opening, the dorsal lip is withdrawn and the buccal mass is beginning to protract. C, the mouth is open, the dorsal lip withdrawn, the buccal mass is protracted and the subradular membrane pulled forwards; note the contact between the jaws and the dorsal surface of the buccal mass, and the different position taken up by the radular teeth according to whether they lie outside the bending plane (to the right of the dotted line) or within it (to its left). D, the mouth is open, the dorsal lip withdrawn, and the radula has been closed by the backward movement of the anterior radular cartilages and therefore of the bending plane (marked by the dotted line). E, the mouth is open, the dorsal lip protracted and the buccal mass is almost fully retracted. Radular teeth are shown diagrammatically in C and D only. All cut surfaces have been left white, the haemocoelic cavities are cross-hatched, the jaw diagonally hatched and the cavity of the gut and the buccal tendons stippled. The broken line stretching acoss the buccal mass from the dorsal end of the jaw to the inner end of the subradular part of the buccal cavity marks the boundary of the buccal cavity laterally and is a fixed line maintained by the dorsal buccal and nuchal tendons. Based on Nisbet.

abl, anterior buccal levator muscle, cut; aoe, anterior oesophagus; apb, attachment of posterior buccal levator muscle to posterior cartilage; apd, attachment of posterior buccal depressor muscle to posterior cartilage; avp, attachment of ventral protractor muscle to posterior cartilage; bcv, buccal cavity; bsp, buccal sphincter muscle; d, radular tooth just external to the bending plane; dbt, dorsal buccal tendon; df, dorsal fold; dlp, dorsal lip; drt, direct radular tensor muscle; dt, dorsal buccal tensor muscle; f, foot; ibm, inner buccal constrictor muscle; ipt, inner posterior tensor muscle of the radula; ivp, inner ventral buccal protractor muscle; ja, jaw; lp, lateral protractor muscle; llp, lateral lip; mpm, mandibular protractor muscle; mr, mandibular retractor muscle; nt, nuchal tendon; oa, outer approximator muscle of the cartilages; obi, inner part of outer buccal constrictor muscle; obm, median part of outer buccal constrictor muscle; obo, outer part of outer buccal constrictor muscle; opt, outer posterior tensor muscle of the radula; ort, oblique radular tensor muscle; pbl, posterior buccal levator muscle, cut; pdt, posterodorsal tensor muscle of the cartilages; pmr, postmedian retractor muscle of the radula; prr, posterior retractor muscle of radula; ptc, posterior radular cartilage; pvt, posterior ventral radular tensor muscle; rdc, anterior radular cartilage; rs, radular sac; sbm, subradular membrane; sn, wall of snout; vlp, ventral lip.

where that joins the side of the odontophore. It then bends sharply forwards under the subradular membrane and ends on the outer surface of the anterior cartilage. To it are joined the fibres of the most ventral part of the lateral protractor.

(3) *Opening of the radula.* As explained above (p. 169) the radula consists of a continuous ribbon of cuticular material carrying rows of teeth. This extends forwards out of the mouth of the radular sac over the mid-dorsal line of the buccal mass on top of the sub-radular membrane, which is the name given to the cuticle of the buccal mass itself. When the buccal mass is in the retracted position the subradular membrane dips into a longitudinal groove which lies over the gap between the two pairs of cartilages. As an accompaniment of the movement of protraction this groove is pulled open so that the radula comes to lie flush with the general surface of the buccal mass instead of sunk in a groove. This is due to three separate factors: (i) the pull on the subradular membrane maintained by the fixed posterior walls of the buccal cavity laterally and ventrally; (ii) the direct action of the tensor muscles, and (iii) the hydrostatic pressure of the blood within the haemocoelic spaces of the buccal mass creating turgor pressure.

In addition to the stretching of the subradular membrane which abolishes the gully within which the radula lay, there is an actual backward and downward movement of the subradular membrane sideways and over the tip of the cartilages within the buccal mass. At the point where the radula passes over the cartilages a change occurs in the position of the teeth relative to the surface of the buccal mass: internal to this point (i.e. on the buccal cavity side) the teeth lie flat, one over the other, approximately parallel to the surface. As they move forwards over the points of the anterior cartilages the teeth erect themselves, the rachidian and lateral teeth rotating forwards through an angle of about 90° so as to stand almost vertically erect on the surface of the buccal mass, and the marginal teeth swing sideways and forwards through an arc of about 90° so as to form a series of fan-like structures on either side of the central tract of rachidian and lateral teeth. As the radula is pulled forwards this movement will be seen to affect each row of teeth as it turns over the line marked by the anterior horns of the anterior cartilages. As a result the teeth lying at the tip of the odontophore and on its underside are in the opened condition and rest over a broad area of substratum. This behaviour of the radular teeth was first adequately described by Ankel (1936b), who named the level at which it occurred the 'Knickkante', a term which may be translated as the bending plane.

(4) *Closing of the radula* (fig. 108D). Just as the movement of the radula over the bending plane formed by the stationary anterior horns of the anterior cartilages produces a change in the orientation of the radular teeth, so may the same result be achieved by a movement of the anterior cartilages underneath the stationary radula. In fact, relative movement of cartilages and radula at the bending plane, however produced, will result in a change in the position of the radular teeth. When the movement transfers teeth from within the bending plane to the outside, then an erection and outward rotation of the teeth will occur; when the movement is in the opposite sense then an infolding and flattening results.

It is interesting to note that these movements of the radular teeth, which are the critical events in the feeding action of the radula, are due not so much to the pull of muscles on the structures which do the actual movement, as to the reaction of these structures to changing tensions in the cuticular sheet to which they are attached. These are achieved partly by the pull of muscles on the cuticular material at other places, partly by tensions created in it by stretching over cartilages and partly by tension created by blood pressure. This effect is reminiscent of similar movements of cuticular structures in arthropods (e.g. insect wings, butterfly proboscis) and may be a characteristic feature of this kind of structure wherever it occurs.

Opening of the radula and erection of its teeth occur in *Monodonta* primarily because the subradular membrane is pulled forwards over the bending plane by muscular action; but the closing of the radular teeth into the resting position is achieved by a movement of the bending plane from an anterodorsal to a posteroventral position. This is brought about by a downwards and backwards movement of the anterior tips of the anterior cartilages, so that they swing across the opened mouth from the neighbourhood of the dorsal lip to the neighbourhood of the ventral lip. As this happens one row of radular teeth after another closes, the rachidian and lateral teeth collapsing on to the radular membrane and successive rows of marginal teeth sweeping inwards towards the middle line and folding down in the same way, brushing any particulate matter which may be lying in their path into a median heap as they do so. This action constitutes the main food-collecting action of the radula.

The movement of the cartilages within the buccal mass is due to the intrinsic muscles of the odontophore only to a very slight extent: most of it is brought about by a movement of the jaws which press on to the upper surface of the buccal mass and so cause motion of the cartilages within. The jaws are pulled ventrally by the action of 3 muscles: (i) the inner buccal constrictor (ibm, fig. 108E); (ii) the outer buccal constrictor (obi, obm, obo, fig. 108A); and, (iii) the buccal sphincter (bsp, figs. 108A, E). The first two of these muscles have already been described and the movement which they bring about at this point in the feeding cycle is clearly only a continuation and enhancement of the effect described in section (2). The buccal sphincter muscle, despite its name, is not connected to the buccal mass at any point on its course. It forms a band passing round the anterior wall of the buccal cavity over the muscles of the jaws, the fibres decussating posteriorly. It emerges from the side walls of the neck region on the right and left and probably properly belongs to the columellar muscle. It therefore is shaped like an open figure-of-eight with the open limbs pointing backwards, and its contraction will tend to close the mouth and to press the jaws against the buccal mass. Although the bulk of the movement of the anterior cartilages is effected by pressure from the jaws, for which these muscles are responsible, some of the movement is due to intrinsic muscles of the buccal mass, the outer approximators of the cartilages (oa, figs. 108B, C, D). These form a sheet of muscle, on each side, of which the fibres originate along the anterior edge of the posterior cartilage (ptc) and run forwards for varying distances to be inserted on the anterior cartilages (rdc). Since the posterior cartilages are held firmly at this stage of the feeding cycle by tonus of the protractor muscles, contraction of the less powerful approximator muscles will cause movement of the anterior cartilages on the posterior ones and, in fact, a backward rotation.

(5) *Retraction of the buccal mass* (fig. 108E). After the posterior movement of the odontophoral cartilages just described the radular teeth have scraped particulate matter off the surface against which they have been applied and in their in-swinging closing motion have grasped it and swept it towards the lateral and rachidian teeth. The next movement of the feeding cycle involves the withdrawal of the buccal mass into the buccal cavity along with whatever the radular teeth have plucked from the substratum. This movement is due to the contraction of the retractor muscles of the radula, the paired posterior retractors (prr) and the paired postmedian retractors (pmr).

Each posterior retractor muscle of the radula has its origin on the outer face of the posterior cartilage. Each is partly continued into the posterior buccal depressor (pbd, fig. 107) at its dorsal end and into the ventral protractor (vbp) at its ventral end. From their origin the fibres of the muscle extend round the posterior face of the cartilage and then run forwards to be inserted on the lateral and ventral walls of the radular sac (rs). Contraction of the muscle will pull the radular sac back until the level of the muscle insertions has reached the level of the posterior face of the posterior cartilage. This effect, however, depends upon the contraction of the postmedian radular retractors anchoring the buccal mass to the columellar muscle: if this does not occur then the role of the muscle is changed and its contraction causes a partial protraction of the buccal mass.

The postmedian retractors of the radula are united to one another to form a single band, except at two points along their course, the first anteriorly, where the right and left muscles separate to allow another muscle to pass between them, the second posteriorly, where, after entering the columellar muscle, the two run to separate origins amongst the fibres of that muscle. The insertions of the muscle are on the ventral surface of the radular sac, posterior to those of the posterior retractors. Their action is to provide a posterior anchor to the whole buccal apparatus and to withdraw the radula, and so the subradular membrane and the buccal mass.

(6) *Shutting the mouth.* This is not, in general, an action which is due to direct muscular action. The movements of the jaw, however, which have been described in section (4) have, as one of their results, the gradual shutting of the mouth and, as soon as the buccal mass has been retracted, relaxation of the muscles which had opened the mouth allows it to close. The closed mouth is the resting state and therefore does not involve extensive muscular contraction.

In feeding, the cycle of operations just described would be repeated in a regular way as the animal creeps over a suitable substratum, and loose detritus would be brushed off the surface by the rotating marginal radular teeth which act somewhat after the style of the brushes of an electric polisher. This material is then pulled into the buccal cavity on the retraction of the buccal mass. It will be noticed that the marginals are the only teeth that move extensively over the substratum and, therefore, that they are the only ones which can brush it. Since this is an important part of the collection of food the teeth must not be pressed too tightly against the substratum in case the whole apparatus jams. This implies that the central and lateral teeth, when erected, do not scratch deeply into the substratum: in fact, they show little signs of movement in this stage of the feeding cycle and are more concerned with pulling into the buccal cavity the material gathered by the marginal teeth than with collecting food material themselves. As a consequence of the weakness of the jaws, too, these are not used to any extent as a means of biting: their real importance has to do with holding the radula shut during protraction and moving the cartilages after it has been applied to the substratum, and these are crucial features of the feeding process. On all these grounds it is clear that the radula of *Monodonta* (and, indeed, of other rhipidoglossans) is a sweeping or brushing radula rather than a scraping or gnawing type, and, because of this, the animals must be microphagous, feeding on protophyte and protozoan material and detritus of all sorts. This is recognized in the name which Ankel (1938a) has applied to the rhipidoglossan radula—Randbursten-radula—which may be translated as a 'border-brush radula'.

Before any survey of the other types of prosobranch buccal masses is made it is worth while remarking one other feature of that of *Monodonta* and, therefore, presumably of all other rhipidoglossan prosobranchs. As remarked above, the buccal mass of *Monodonta* is used in such a way that the marginal teeth must be free enough to move and yet close enough to the substratum to sweep fine particles from it. A certain amount of mobility is also necessary to allow for irregularities in the surface against which the rotating teeth might get caught. The feeding operations therefore call for nice manipulation of the buccal mass. This appears to be controlled by a further series of muscles shown in figs. 108B, C, D. These are fine strands of muscle, not powerful enough to be capable of moving the buccal mass, but associated with structures which, according to Nisbet (1953), are proprioceptive sense organs. This series consists of 4 muscles, 3 of which are paired, all interconnected, and related to the cartilages, the wall of the snout and the radular sac so as to form a kind of sling suspending the buccal mass in the head. The alleged proprioceptors are placed mainly at the points where the unions and intersections of the members of the sling occur, and they are, therefore, in a position where they may, perhaps, measure the relative tensions in the parts of the sling. Since these are determined largely by the main protractors and retractors this system acts as a kind of monitor system, giving the animal information of the precise state of affairs in the buccal mass and allowing a delicate control which would permit the radula to be applied to the substratum with the correct degree of pressure for the collection of food.

The muscles which act thus are the posterodorsal tensor, the inner and outer posterior radular tensors and the dorsal buccal tensors, of which all are paired except the first.

The posterodorsal tensor (pdt, figs. 108B, C, D) is a thin band of muscle which runs transversely over the dorsal surface of the buccal mass above the radular sac (rs), but below the oesophagus (aoe), from the outer surface of one posterior cartilage (ptc) to the outer surface of the other. It can therefore directly control the degree of approximation of these two cartilages, or, by measuring tension generated in its fibres by the separation of the cartilages, reflexly stimulate other more powerful muscles to control this separation.

The inner and outer posterior radular tensors (ipt, opt) run posteriorly to an insertion on the walls of the radular sac from an anterior origin. In the case of the inner muscle the origin is on the posterodorsal tensor (pdt); in the case of the outer muscle it is on the dorsal surface of the posterior cartilage (ptc). These muscles will, therefore, be stretched on protraction of the buccal mass and can signal to the central nervous system the extent of this process.

The dorsal buccal tensor (dt) is also inserted on the posterodorsal tensor (pdt) and runs forward from there to an origin on the anterior wall of the snout. It antagonizes the posterior radular tensors in that it is stretched when the buccal mass is retracted and may, therefore, provide a measure of this process. During protraction and retraction tonic contraction and relaxation keep all the members of this system taut and appear to allow the animal to gauge the position of the whole buccal apparatus, a matter of significance to any animal with the type of radula possessed by *Monodonta*.

It is unfortunate that, although descriptions of the buccal mass in other rhipidoglossan prosobranchs have been published (e.g. by Woodward (1901a) for *Pleurotomaria*, and Crofts (1929) for *Haliotis*) these do not include a sufficiently detailed account of the musculature to say whether corresponding tensor muscles occur. Woodward's account of the musculature of *Pleurotomaria* allows it to be said that muscles homologous with the lateral and ventral protractors of *Monodonta* occur as well as those corresponding to the main retractors, from which it may be concluded that protraction and retraction of the buccal mass are achieved similarly in both animals. No description of the musculature in the walls of the buccal cavity is given, which makes it impossible to decide whether there is a movement of the subradular membrane over the cartilages or of the cartilages within the subradular membrane such as to cause opening and closing of the radular teeth, nor is there any mention of muscles which might behave as tensors.

On turning to the account given by Crofts of *Haliotis* it is noticeable that there is a greater resemblance to *Monodonta*. Protractor muscles and retractor muscles appear to correspond in both molluscs, though a greater number of protractors occurs in *Haliotis*. These are related to a third pair of cartilages which are placed near the mouth. More important, a tensor system of muscles is described and a number of buccal muscles, from the arrangement of which it seems likely that the buccal mass and radula of *Haliotis* function in a way very similar to those of *Monodonta*. Although no account has been given of the details of the buccal mass in *Gibbula* spp. it is, nevertheless, likely that in these gastropods, too, the mode of functioning is similar to that of *Monodonta*. This is based partly on the fact that Nisbet (1953) recorded *Gibbula* as being structurally similar to *Monodonta*, partly on Eigenbrodt's description (1941) of the movements of the radula of *Gibbula*, and partly on the photographs of the results of the radular action given by Ankel (1938a). This last author investigated the appearance of a sheet of glass covered with algal growth after it had been grazed by a variety of molluscs, including *Gibbula*. Where feeding has occurred the radular teeth scrape the algae off the surface of the glass and so expose it and from the pattern which the feeding leaves the action of the various teeth involved may be deduced. In the case of *Gibbula* feeding leaves a broad track, broader than the radula in the buccal cavity, which is marked by innumerable fine scratches each of which is the arc of a circle running more or less transversely across the track. Few marks are visible in the central part of the track apart from the central ends of these arcs. From this it may be deduced (1) that the marginal teeth open outwards, making the radula much broader when set against the substratum than in the buccal cavity; (2) that the substratum is scratched by the rotary movement of these teeth; and (3) that the rachidian and lateral teeth either do not touch the substratum at all or do so very lightly —though it is possible that whatever marks they may make on it are later obliterated by the raking action of the marginals.

One feature of the buccal mass of some rhipidoglossan prosobranchs (the family Fissurellidae) remains to be mentioned. This is a caecum which lies in the haemocoelic space in the mid-line of the buccal mass between the two sets of radular cartilages and their associated muscles (pdm, fig. 96). The caecum is lined by an epithelium which is an extension of that over the general surface of the buccal mass (fig. 109), but the cells are modified for secretion. The nucleus lies basally in dense cytoplasm whilst the distal part of the cell is vacuolated and contains granules which may be seen discharged in the cavity of the caecum. The walls are not muscular. The significance of this structure is unknown, and what part it plays—if any—in the functioning of the buccal mass is equally uncertain. It must, presumably, be formed at a late stage of development in the animals which possess it, as the subradular membrane is complete over its mouth. That this membrane is complete, in fact, speaks for the idea that it must be secreted towards the posterior end of the buccal mass and move forward from there, perhaps sharing in the radular movement. In this region, indeed, radular and subradular membranes could be regarded as merely the differentiated inner and outer layers of one and the same structure.

The prosobranchs which are not rhipidoglossan have radulae which appear to function in a different way, and may therefore have buccal masses in which the musculature is differently arranged. The first of these groups which may be dealt with is the Taenio-glossa, a group which has what Ankel (1938a) called a 'spreading-tooth radula' or 'splay-tooth radula' and which corresponds, approximately, to the group Mesogastropoda of Thiele. The conditions in this type (fig. 105D) are readily derivable from the rhipido-glossan. The radula is characterized by the presence of a bending plane marked by the anterior horns of the cartilages of the buccal mass and at this the teeth behave as in the rhipidoglossan radula. The marginal teeth, however, are much fewer, though they execute the same kind of outward sweep on passing forwards over the bending plane and an inward sweep on being withdrawn, and so are less efficient as sweeping agents. This is, perhaps, compensated by one important difference, however, discernible on comparing the trace of a taenioglossan radula with that of a rhipidoglossan, in that the impress of the rachidian and lateral teeth is clearly visible on the substratum. It appears,

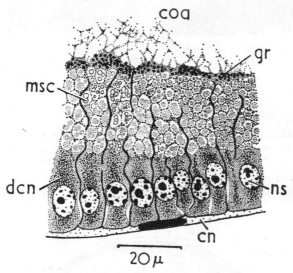

FIG. 109.—*Diodora apertura:* part of the wall of the buccal caecum.
cn, connective tissue; coa, coagulum of secretion in lumen; dcn, dense cytoplasm; gr, granule of secretion; msc, mass of secretion within vacuole; ns, nucleus of secreting cell.

therefore, that the marginal teeth of the taenioglossan radula may still brush loose material towards the centre of the radula, but that this is not such an important part of the feeding mechanism as it is in *Monodonta*: it may be that as its importance diminished so did the number of marginal teeth. Its diminution has accompanied, and, possibly, been caused by the activity of the more centrally placed teeth which may gather material directly from the substratum, or loosen it for the marginals to brush together, or both. In many of these gastropods, too, a cuticularized jaw exists and the action of the rachidian and lateral teeth against this may allow something resembling a bite to be taken.

The form and musculature of the buccal mass has been rather superficially examined in a number of taenioglossan prosobranchs, usually without any reference to the way in which the apparatus functions. The most important of these works is possibly that in which Johansson (1939) described the buccal musculature of *Littorina* and some rissoids, more particularly since the working of the radula of *Littorina* has been carefully

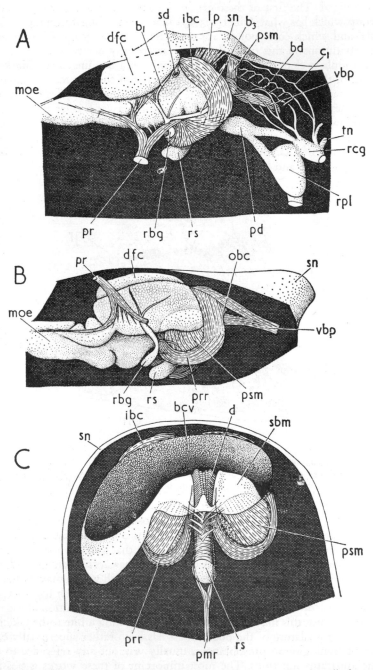

FIG. 110.—*Viviparus viviparus:* dissections of head to show buccal mass.   A, dorsolaterally from the right; the nerve ring has been cut mid-dorsally and the right half pulled ventrally to the right; the oeosophageal dilator muscle on the right has been cut and pulled ventrally and away from the nerve ring;   B

described by Ankel (1937c). The buccal mass of some rissoaceans has also been described by Bregenzer (1916) and Krull (1935), and Nisbet (1953) has included references to *Littorina*. The working of the radula and the feeding movements have also been described in *Viviparus* by Eigenbrodt (1941) who stated that they are similar to those seen in *Littorina*. The musculature has also been described by Starmuhlner (1952) and this therefore allows anatomy and function to be correlated.

The buccal mass of *Viviparus* is small and globular, with an inflated dorsal food channel extending along its dorsal surface (dfc, fig. 110). The sides of the food channel overlap the sides of the buccal mass and the duct of the salivary gland (sd) runs between these two structures with lobules of glandular tissue lying around a central lumen. The dorsal and lateral walls of the food channel are connected to the side and dorsal walls of the snout by a large number of small strands of dilator muscle (bd), which may also help in protraction. One larger muscle (pr) runs from the base of the dorsal folds to the body wall, passing between the cerebropedal connective in front and the pleuropedal connective behind as it does so: it acts as a main retractor and simultaneously dilates the oesophagus.

The buccal mass itself is anchored to the body wall by a number of muscles. These include the following paired muscles.

(1) Lateral buccal protractors (lp): these originate on the lateral walls of the snout well forward and run, as several converging strands, to be inserted on the posterior edge of the cartilage which forms the support of the odontophore on each side.

(2) Ventral protractors (vbp): these also originate on the lateral walls of the snout on each side, ventral to the origin of the previous muscle, and pass to an insertion near the anterior end of each cartilage, somewhat ventrally. The action of these two muscles is to protrude the buccal mass. The same effect is partly achieved by a third pair of muscles which also originate from the wall of the snout. These are the protractor muscles of the subradular membrane (psm). Their origin lies on the snout wall anterior and ventral to those of the other protractors: from there they run to the lateral aspect of the cartilage, pass dorsally to its upper end and then medially, where they are inserted on the under surface of the subradular membrane (sbm). The effect of their isolated contraction is (*a*) to pull the buccal mass forward and (*b*) to stretch the subradular membrane laterally, which helps to open the radular teeth. A few fibres apparently belonging to this muscle run only between subradular membrane and the dorsal part of the cartilage: these would limit the extent of stretching of the membrane and enhance the protraction effect.

The combined effect of all these muscles, which appear to act synergically, is to pull the buccal mass forwards from the buccal cavity, through the oral tube, so that it may

---

similar view; nerve ring completely removed, the oesophageal dilator muscle lies in its normal position but has been cut from the body wall and the superficial muscles over the posterior end of the radular cartilages dissected away to expose the posterior retractor of the radula and the protractor of the subradular membrane muscles; C, dorsal view, the buccal cavity and the posterior half of the buccal mass opened.

$b_1$, $b_3$, buccal nerves; bcv, buccal cavity; bd, buccal dilator muscle, cut; $c_1$, dorsal snout nerve; d, radular tooth; dfc, dorsal food channel; ibc, inner buccal constrictor muscle; lp, lateral protractor muscle; moe, mid-oesophagus; obc, outer buccal constrictor muscle; pd, pedal ganglion; pmr, post-median retractor muscle of the radula; pr, posterior retractor and oesophageal dilator muscle, cut; prr, posterior radular retractor muscle; psm, protractor muscle of the subradular membrane; rbg, right buccal ganglion; rcg, right cerebral ganglion; rpl, right pleural ganglion; rs, radular sac; sbm, subradular membrane; sd, opening of salivary duct to buccal cavity; sn, snout; tn, tentacular nerve; vbp, ventral buccal protractor muscle.

be applied to the surface of the ground on which the animal is feeding. At the same time, because the posteriorly inserted protractors have a dorsal origin anteriorly and the anteriorly inserted ones have a more ventral origin, the odontophore is also upended so that its anterior tip is applied to the substratum more or less at right angles. This has already been noted by Eigenbrodt (1941).

Another set of muscles is concerned with a movement of the subradular membrane outwards over the cartilages, which occurs simultaneously with the combined rotation and protraction already described. This is due to the action of muscles inserted ventrally on the subradular membrane and originating on the cartilages of the buccal mass and the radular sac itself. The latter consists apparently of a median muscle, the median radular protractor, which is inserted on the mid-ventral part of the subradular membrane near the tip of the buccal mass and which runs posteriorly between the two cartilages to an origin on the underside of the radular sac near its posterior end. The former comprise a pair of muscles, the lateral radular protractors, inserted on the subradular membrane one to either side of the median protractor and running back alongside that muscle to the ventral end of the cartilage, to which they are fastened posteriorly. When these muscles contract the subradular membrane will be pulled out of the buccal cavity and down over the apex of the buccal mass; as it does so it is tensed by the spreading effect exerted by the protractor of the subradular membrane and passes, in this stretched state, over the bending plane marked by the anterior horns of the cartilages. This has the effect of causing the radular teeth to rotate outwards as they are protruded.

The tip of the odontophore is thus brought into contact with the substratum after the opening of the mouth in such a way that the horns of the odontophore lie at the level of the dorsal lip; the radular teeth which are in contact with the ground have, therefore, been drawn over that and so are in the outspread position.

The next event in the feeding cycle, as recorded by Eigenbrodt (1941), is the passage of the horns of the cartilages across the mouth from the level of the dorsal lip to that of the ventral lip. Since they move behind the radula this moves the bending plane behind the teeth which are exposed and in contact with the substratum. Nisbet (1953) observed that a to and fro movement of the cartilages behind the radular teeth may occur so that they open and close several times in succession, rasping the substratum each time. Finally, however, a backward movement occurs corresponding to the single one described by Eigenbrodt and, simultaneously with this, the radular teeth are drawn into the buccal cavity so that whatever material they may have grasped as they shut at the instant the bending plane moved behind them, is ingested. The two components of this movement appear to be due to another series of muscles, as follows:

(*a*) Posterior retractor of the radula (prr): this comprises a pair of muscles which originate in a mass of muscle lying at the anterior end of the cartilages and in the roof of the buccal cavity at the same level. From this origin they pass backwards along the outer face of each cartilage, rather ventrally, curve medianly round the posterior end and thence run forwards through the space between the cartilages, and end by inserting on the wall of the radular sac and on the subradular membrane underneath the radula.

(*b*) Postmedian retractor of the radula (pmr): this is an apparently single muscle posteriorly but is composed of separate right and left halves anteriorly, where it runs within the buccal mass. The muscle originates in the mid-line of the foot where it separates from the bundles of columellar muscle which lie there: it then runs to the ventral side of the posterior end of the radular sac and bifurcates into right and left halves before penetrating the sheath of circular muscle which lies around the sac. Within this the two parts of the muscle run forwards underneath the radular sac and end by becoming inserted on the ventral surface of that structure. This muscle acts not only as a means for withdrawing the radula over the horns of the cartilage, but also as a retractor of the entire buccal mass. It is by virtue of the tone of this muscle, too—steadying the radular sac—that contraction of the median protractor of the radula is able to bring about its full effect.

(c) The retractor (pr) which runs from the skin of the snout to the posterior end of the cartilage on each side, and which also sends branches to the oesophageal wall.

The mechanism by which movement of the cartilages within the buccal mass is brought about is not clear in *Viviparus*. It may be that their backward drive is managed by the same means as in *Monodonta*, i.e. by pressure exerted on them by musculature in the roof of the buccal cavity in the neighbourhood of the jaws, but it is not easy to find muscles which would translate their tips anteriorly again and so permit the to and fro rocking observed by Nisbet. The muscles which do seem able to do this (not confirmed by observation) are the inner buccal constrictors (ibc), a pair which have their attachments to the roof of the buccal cavity far forwards at one end and to the outer face of the anterior end of the cartilages at the other. On the assumption that the roof of the buccal cavity can be immobilized by contraction of other muscles, these would then pull the horns of the cartilages dorsally when they contracted. Anterior to these, other muscles, the outer buccal constrictors (obc), will press the jaws against the buccal mass and so effect the backward movement of the horns of the cartilages in the same manner as in *Monodonta*.

The following table (p. 196), in which Starmuhlner's names (1952) are italicized, suggests homologies between the muscles of *Monodonta* and those of *Viviparus*. To what extent these homologies are justifiable is uncertain in view of our relative ignorance of their comparative anatomy and our total ignorance of their development.

A study of this table shows that a number of homologies can apparently be established between the muscles of the two gastropods under discussion, with a general identity of function as well as of arrangement. Since Nisbet has described no less than 33 separate muscles in *Monodonta* it is clear that the taenioglossan has undergone a considerable simplification of its buccal mass and many muscles have vanished: as suggested above, this may perhaps be correlated with the fact that the rhipidoglossan has to poise its buccal mass rather accurately over the substratum in order that the marginal teeth may function properly, and to do this the system of tensor muscles is necessary. With the more coarse type of activity displayed by the taenioglossan, which sets its odontophore down on to the substratum without the same degree of adjustment, these are unnecessary and have gone.

The evolution from rhipidoglossan to taenioglossan radula has involved a number of other changes: the buccal mass has shortened and is supported by only a single pair of cartilages, whilst the marginal teeth are reduced in number. These changes are continued, and to some extent increased, in the Stenoglossa, a group which receives its name from the fact that marginal teeth are not found on the radula at all, and the number of lateral teeth is reduced to one on each side or none. Each row of teeth in the radula of a rachiglossan (fig. 105E) consists of only three teeth, a rachidian flanked by a single lateral tooth on each side. The radula behaves like the rhipidoglossan and taenioglossan types in that it possesses a bending plane and movement of the teeth outwards over the bending plane (or of the bending plane inwards under the teeth) will cause the teeth to erect themselves instead of lying flat on the surface of the subradular membrane, whilst the lateral teeth also curve outwards. Movement of the radula or of the bending plane in

TABLE 5

| Monodonta | Use | Viviparus | Use |
|---|---|---|---|
| Lateral protractor | Protracts buccal mass | Lateral protractor<br>*Protractor of buccal mass* | Protracts buccal mass and rotates ventrally |
| Ventral protractor | Protracts buccal mass | Ventral protractor<br>*Protractor of buccal mass* | Protracts buccal mass and rotates ventrally |
| ? | — | Protractor of the sub-radular membrane<br>*Radular tensor and radular folder* | Protracts buccal mass and spreads sub-radular membrane |
| ? | — | Branch of above | Protracts buccal mass. |
| ? | — | Median radular protractor<br>*Radular protractor* | Pulls radula outwards |
| Direct anterior radular tensors | Pull radula outwards | Lateral radular protractors<br>*Radular protractor* | Pull radula outwards |
| Posterior retractor of radula | Retracts radula | Posterior retractor of radula<br>*Elevator of buccal mass* | Retracts radula |
| Postmedian retractor of radula | Retracts radula and buccal mass | Postmedian retractor of radula<br>*Radular retractor* | Retracts radula and buccal mass |
| Inner buccal constrictor | Moves cartilages back and constricts buccal cavity | Inner buccal constrictor<br>*Buccal constrictor* | Moves cartilages back and constricts buccal cavity |
| Outer buccal constrictor | Moves cartilages back and constricts buccal cavity | Outer buccal constrictor<br>*Buccal constrictor* | Moves cartilages back and constricts buccal cavity |
| Buccal sphincter | Closes oral tube | Buccal sphincter<br>*Buccal constrictor* | Closes oral tube |
| Buccal dilators | Dilate buccal cavity | *Buccal dilators* | Dilate buccal cavity |
| Oesophageal dilators + ? | Dilate dorsal food channel | Oesophageal dilators and *retractor of buccal mass* | Dilate dorsal food channel |
| Retractor of transverse fold | Retracts oesophageal valve and transverse fold | Retractor of oesophageal valve | Retracts oesophageal valve and subradular membrane below |
| Ventral approximator of cartilages | Pulls cartilages together ventrally | *Ventral approximator of cartilages* | Pulls cartilages together ventrally, separates them dorsally |

the opposite direction causes the reverse effects, and, in particular, a biting or gripping action as the lateral teeth curve inwards towards the mid-line. This biting effect is exaggerated by the fact that the radula lies outspread on the under surface of the buccal mass but in a deep groove running over the dorsal surface. The rotation which occurs as each tooth swings over the bending plane is therefore caused partly by the movement from the erect to the supine position and partly by infolding of the subradular and radular membranes on passing from the outspread condition into the groove. It is, therefore, a wide arc, and as the teeth are provided with sharp fangs they pierce and pull on the food which is being eaten.

The movement of the radula of a gastropod in relation to the underlying cartilages was likened by Huxley (1853) to the movement of a rope over a pulley, whereas Geddes in 1879 regarded the two structures as so closely united that movement in the one could only be caused by movement in the other. If there is any group in which the second kind of movement occurs it is not the Rachiglossa: they are, contrariwise, a group in which all the movement of the radula appears to be of the type described by Huxley, and to be achieved by the radular retractor and protractor muscles pulling the subradular membrane backwards and forwards over the bending plane created by the anterior horns of the cartilages, and the ties between subradular membrane and cartilages are few and loose to permit this to occur. There appears to be little or no activity due to the movement of the cartilages behind the subradular membrane.

The buccal mass has been described in a number of Stenoglossa—in *Buccinum* by Dakin (1912) and Brock (1936), in *Sycotypus* (= *Busycon*) by Herrick (1906), by Wilsmann in *Buccinum undatum* (1942), and by Carriker in *Urosalpinx* (1943). The muscles mentioned by Carriker lie in and around the buccal mass, a relatively small structure which lies at the apex of the proboscis, whether that be withdrawn or extended. Most of the surface of the buccal mass and of the buccal cavity and anterior oesophagus is moored to the inner surface of the proboscis by numerous slender bundles of muscle called buccal or oesophageal tensors by Carriker: these also act as dilators of the buccal cavity and dorsal food channel. The buccal mass is kept under tension by a sheet of circular muscle running around it and the buccal cavity at a rather anterior level: this will constrict the buccal cavity and press the jaws down over the dorsal surface of the odontophore. It may, therefore, help to fold the radular teeth away into the dorsal groove as they are withdrawn into the buccal cavity, or prevent their precocious uprising as they move in the opposite direction.

Protraction of the buccal mass is brought about by two pairs of muscles which originate on the lips around the mouth and are inserted, one pair dorsally, the other pair ventrally, at the posterior end of each buccal cartilage. Retraction is due to the action of two other pairs of muscles which run back from the buccal mass to more posterior origins. One of these pairs originates on the proboscis wall ventrally and laterally and is inserted on the other muscles of the buccal mass; these are the lateral retractors of the odontophore. The second pair, the odontophoral retractors, originates, according to Carriker, on the walls of the cephalic haemocoel, well behind the base of the proboscis: this may indicate a real attachment on the columellar muscle. From there the muscles run to the ventral part of the buccal cartilages posteriorly, but a slip passes further forward and is treated by Carriker as a separate, powerful muscle, the dorsal subradular membrane retractor. A slip from the lateral odontophoral retractor on each side is also involved in the formation of this muscle, which is inserted on the subradular membrane on the dorsal side of the buccal mass. Some of its fibres, however, originate on the posterior ends of the buccal cartilages. The action of this muscle is to pull the subradular membrane dorsally and posteriorly into the buccal cavity over the bending plane. It is helped in this by the contraction of another muscle on each side, the lateral retractor of the subradular membrane, which runs from the posterior end and outer side of the cartilage on to the subradular membrane over the buccal mass. This complex of muscles, therefore, separately or simultaneously retracts the buccal mass and the subradular membrane over it and so is responsible for the effective feeding action of the radula.

The outward movement of the subradular membrane over the bending plane, which is responsible for the opening of the teeth of the radula, is primarily due to the action of a pair of ventral retractors of the subradular membrane, to give them Carriker's name. These originate on the buccal cartilages posteriorly and run forwards, ventral to each cartilage, to be inserted on the subradular membrane near the posterior end of the sublingual cavity. They are probably aided in their work by an increased tension in the subradular membrane which is produced by the contraction of the divaricator muscles of the cartilages. These run from the lateral wall of each cartilage out to the side walls of the proboscis: their contraction will clearly stretch and tauten the subradular membrane over the dorsal surface of the odontophore, will tend to open the groove in which the radula lies there and so make it more susceptible to the forces which open it as it passes over the bending plane.

The other muscles which are mentioned by Carriker in his account of *Urosalpinx* are oral sphincters, oral retractors and tensors of the radular sac. The first of these forms a ring of circular muscle round the mouth, the second a cone of muscular strips which radiate from the lips back to the wall of the snout, and the third, which run from the innermost end of the radular sac to the buccal artery, serve as a means of securing the sac in the proboscis haemocoel during protraction and retraction.

The apparent homologies of these muscles with those of *Buccinum* (Wilsmann, 1942), *Viviparus* (Starmuhlner, 1952) and *Monodonta* (Nisbet, 1953) are given in Table 6.

On comparing this list of muscles active in *Urosalpinx* with those in the taenioglossan and rhipidoglossan it will be seen that their modification can be linked with the modification in the use of the radula. Broadly speaking, the stenoglossan has selected a few of the varied movements of which the buccal mass of the rhipidoglossan is capable and has developed an effective feeding mechanism out of them and the taenioglossan has done the same. But whereas in the taenioglossan it is the rotary phase of the total pattern of rhipidoglossan activity which has been exaggerated, it is the movement of the subradular membrane over stationary cartilages which is the most important feature of the working of the stenoglossan buccal mass, and it is, therefore, the muscles which allow this to occur which are best developed. Since it is the retraction of the subradular membrane which is the effective working stroke in the feeding cycle it is the muscles which bring this about (dorsal and lateral retractors of the subradular membrane) which are the best developed and most powerful in the buccal mass. It is difficult to see what muscles in *Viviparus* or *Monodonta* correspond to these, partly because the closure of the radular teeth is brought about by a completely different mechanism in these animals, partly because the entry of the food into the buccal cavity is managed by the retraction of the whole odontophore rather than by that of the radula alone, and partly because there is so little evidence, comparative or embryological, on which to build firm homologies.

In carnivores the musculature must be normally greater than in herbivores and in biters transverse forces must be greater than longitudinal ones. In prosobranchs which gnaw or scrape with the radula longitudinal forces predominate and this is particularly evident in a second evolutionary trend in radular function which may be traced in another group of the prosobranchs, the Docoglossa. These are certainly derived from a rhipidoglossan ancestry, but their radula is distinct from the rhipidoglossan type in a

TABLE 6

| Urosalpinx | Buccinum | Viviparus | Monodonta |
|---|---|---|---|
| Buccal tensor | (Buccal dilators) | Buccal dilators | Buccal dilators |
| Oesophageal tensors | ? | Oesophageal dilators | Oesophageal dilators |
| Buccal circular muscles | Buccal circular muscles | Buccal constrictor | Buccal constrictors |
| Lateral odontophoral retractor | Retractor pharyngis? | ? | ? |
| Odontophoral retractors | Median retractor of radula | Postmedian retractor of radula? | Postmedian retractor of radula? |
| Dorsal odontophoral protractors | Posterior jugal muscle | Lateral buccal protractor | Lateral buccal protractor |
| Ventral odontophoral protractor | Anterior jugal muscle | Ventral buccal protractor | Ventral buccal protractor |
| Oral sphincter | ? | Buccal sphincter | Buccal sphincter |
| Oral retractors | ? | ? | ? |
| Radular sac tensors | ? | ? | Posterior ventral radular tensors? |
| Ventral subradular membrane retractors | Radular retractors | Lateral radular protractors | Direct anterior radular tensors |
| Dorsal subradular membrane retractors | Ventral tensors | ? | Ventrolateral tensor of buccal membrane? |
| Lateral subradular membrane retractors | Lateral tensors | ? | ? |
| Divaricators of cartilages | ? | Protractor of the subradular membrane? | ? |
| Transverse muscle | Horizontal muscle | Approximator of cartilages | Ventral and outer (?) approximators of cartilages |
| ? | Dorsal protractor of radula | ? | ? |

number of ways: the rachidian tooth is minute or absent, the marginals do not exceed three in number and are not prominent, and, most important, a bending plane is either totally absent or its effect is so slight as not to be important.

The working of the radula has been described for *Patella* and *Patina* by Ankel (1938*a*) and again (for *Patella*) by Eigenbrodt (1941). A number of previous workers have also described in less detail how limpets feed (Davis & Fleure, 1903; Orton, 1913*b*) and the former of these and Geddes (1879) and Amaudrut (1898) have given brief accounts of the cartilages and associated musculature. There are at least 4 pairs of cartilages, anterior, posterior, anterolateral and ventrolateral. Of these the first two are held firmly together by tough membrane and, as they articulate with one another by flat surfaces, it does not seem likely that much movement between them is possible. The third and fourth pairs lie anteriorly, lateral to the anterior cartilages and are not in contact either with them or with one another: instead they are attached by muscle to a variety of structures in the head.

No adequate account of the musculature of *Patella* has ever been given: preliminary investigations undertaken by us show that it is much more complex than the previous descriptions would suggest. It is also noticeably more powerful than that of the various prosobranchs so far dealt with, this being due to two main causes, a hypertrophy of the muscles which interconnect the cartilages and of those which protract the buccal mass and radula. The consequence of the first of these changes is that the buccal mass is protruded as a very stiff and inflexible pad, and the consequence of the second is that it is protruded with very great power. This, in turn, may be related to the fact that since there is no effective bending plane in the radula (although some movement of tooth on radular membrane does occur at the apex of the buccal mass), the action of the teeth in a docoglossan radula is fundamentally different from that of any of the other types which have been so far dealt with. In these, each radular tooth, with the possible exception of the rachidian, scrapes the substratum only as it pivots through an arc of a circle on its base, as that moves over the bending plane. In other words, the bending plane and the working place coincide. In the docoglossan, on the other hand, the tooth and the buccal mass move together without any pivoting of the one on the other. In the first case, therefore, the muscular equipment need be powerful enough only to move the subradular membrane over the horns of the cartilages (or vice versa) with sufficient force to move against the substratum the radular teeth of the one or two rows that lie over the bending plane: contact between teeth and substratum is limited to the immediate neighbourhood of that plane, as may be seen by reference to the feeding tracks left by these animals. In the docoglossan, however, a large part of the underside of the protracting buccal mass, with numerous rows of teeth, is applied to the substratum and the whole structure forced across it like a rasp: in this action the working place lies (morphologically) anterior to the bending plane and it clearly calls for much more muscular power; this is responsible for the hypertrophy of the buccal musculature mentioned above.

A further important difference exists between the docoglossan and the other prosobranchs in respect of the use of their buccal mass. It will be recalled that the effective food-gathering part of the feeding cycle in *Monodonta* occurred at the end of the protraction of the buccal mass and radula, which had the effect of laying the radula down on the substratum with its teeth open. Then the backward movement of the cartilages and the retraction of the radula caused the rotation of the marginal teeth which brushed the substratum and their withdrawal into the buccal cavity. The same kind of movement is the essential part of the feeding of a taenioglossan, and it is the retraction of the radula which is again the basis of feeding in a stenoglossan. The docoglossan differs from this, as shown by Ankel (1938a) and Eigenbrodt (1941) in that the important part of the feeding cycle is the phase of protraction: the buccal mass is everted through the mouth so that it strikes the substratum near the ventral lip, with a number of radular rows applied to the substratum. The whole structure is then moved forwards across the substratum to the region of the dorsal lip, the tips of the teeth scoring the substratum with a number of parallel lines (showing absence of rotation) as this happens. This movement then merges into the beginning of retraction, with the subradular membrane being pulled into the buccal cavity close to the dorsal lips and the jaw. The muscles which require to be well developed for carrying out such an action are, therefore, those which stiffen the entire buccal mass against the vibration and shocks of a forceful application of the radula to the substratum, and those which will drive the buccal mass forwards despite the friction engendered by so many teeth rasping the substratum on which the animal is feeding. This need explains the great development of the protractor muscles, of the muscles binding cartilage to cartilage and, also, the very large size of the buccal mass.

Some other peculiarities of the radula and feeding of Docoglossa may be noted here and correlated with what has just been pointed out. The radular teeth in many Doco-glossa, especially the laterals (figs. 105B, C), are often provided with dark, pigmented denticles: this appears to indicate hardness. All the teeth differ from those of other prosobranchs in having a broad base of attachment to the radular membrane instead of a more or less linear one: this is clearly linked with the lack of rotatory movement. Finally it is obvious that this kind of use must expose the teeth to a very high degree of wear and is probably the reason why limpets possess such long radulae. All the Docoglossa appear to be able to apply considerable pressure on the substratum on which they feed: *Patina* easily excavates great caves under the stipe of *Laminaria* in which to shelter and feed, whilst *Patella* leaves clear rake-like markings where it has been feeding on the surface of even moderately hard rocks.

The above sections deal with the buccal mass in the most important subdivisions of the Prosobranchia, the Rhipidoglossa, the Docoglossa, Taenioglossa and the rachiglossan Stenoglossa. They have not included a number of minor groupings within the subclass, such as the Ptenoglossa and the toxoglossan Stenoglossa. It is, indeed, impossible to treat either of these groups in a comparable way in view of the almost complete lack of knowledge of the musculature of the buccal mass. It is almost true to say that there is no definite information at all about the way in which many toxoglossan prosobranchs use their radula, some accounts stating that the radular teeth are shot out of the mouth into the body of the prey, whereas others infer that the teeth come into operation within the proboscis or even the buccal cavity (see p. 205). It is, therefore, unprofitable to discuss the functional morphology of their buccal mass.

The same is true of the Ptenoglossa in so far as the musculature of the buccal mass is concerned; but the general mode of functioning of the radula is known. Ptenoglossa is the name given to a small group of prosobranchs (which make up the families Ianthinidae and Scalidae) which are in the habit of swallowing their prey whole. This is, at least, true for the Ianthinidae which are known to capture and swallow whole specimens of the siphonophore *Velella*, but the feeding habits and food of the scalids are only partly known, though it may be deduced from the structure of their buccal mass that they can ingest their prey whole. Ankel (1938a) and Thorson (1958) have stated that they, too, ingest coelenterates, though from the fact that they occur in sand or mud and have special stylets for leading a toxic saliva into the body of their prey, this seems perhaps not the whole truth.

In *Ianthina* (and *Clathrus* (fig. 101) is similar) the mouth leads through an oral tube past a sphincter muscle into a capacious buccal cavity in the lateral walls of which are embedded jaws and on the floor of which lies a large odontophore occupying the greater part of the available space. Dorsally, over the odontophore, it opens widely into the oesophagus, which is a simple folded tube without any trace of the dorsal folds or other features usually found in the prosobranch. No clear radular sac is visible and the radula appears to be secreted in the posterior part of the buccal cavity rather than in a separate sac.

The odontophore is supported by a single piece of cartilage on each side which is composed of highly vacuolated cells and extends across the mid-line from side to side. There is also cartilage developed in the roof of the buccal cavity and in its floor, below the sublingual pouch. The odontophore is deeply cleft mid-dorsally and rises into two halves placed right and left of the mid-line; the two halves also extend forwards from the anterior end of the bridge which links them together ventrally. The whole structure thus forms a trough-like structure with steep sides and an incomplete floor, which projects forwards into the buccal cavity from its posterior wall and can, when necessary, be everted through the oral tube and mouth, the two halves then diverging. All its surfaces bear radular teeth, all of which are alike—curved, fang-like structures set on the radular ribbon by an elongated, narrow base in such a way that all the teeth point inwards, the arrangement being reminiscent of the teeth on the jaws of a non-poisonous snake. Indeed, the whole feeding mechanism is comparable to that of a python or similar creature. The teeth are movable on the radular ribbon in such a way as to bend inwards, but they cannot bend outwards: as the mollusc feeds, therefore, and protracts the buccal mass, the teeth swing inwards and lie flat on its surface so as to slip under the body of the prey; when the buccal mass is retracted, however, the teeth erect themselves and pull the prey into the buccal cavity. Any outward movement on the part of the prey, too, will be stopped by the recurved points of the teeth, whereas inward movement will be facilitated by their downfolding. The grip is intensified by the approximation of the two halves, like a hand grasping. It may be that, although this is a competent enough piece of apparatus for dealing with relatively inactive prey such as the coelenterates upon which *Ianthina* mainly feeds, a more lively kind of animal would be able to make its escape. If this were so, then the need for paralysing the prey, which is presumably the effect of the saliva injected by scalids, becomes obvious.

The form of the radular teeth is usually closely related to the use to which they are put, and to the type of food eaten. It has been discussed by Cooke (1895, 1920) and Peile (1937) amongst others. The typical radular tooth is recurved at its apex, where it is frequently denticulate, so as to form an efficient rasping tool and also a structure adapted for the retention of the material rasped from the substratum, like a hand scraping up sand or snow. Since the precise use of the teeth varies from animal to animal and from one type of radula to another the matter may be approached on that basis.

The Docoglossa, as has been shown above, differ from other prosobranchs in that their radula is moved from behind forwards over the substratum. Since it is the teeth lying on the underside of the buccal mass which are brought into contact with the ground, this forward movement means that their recurved tips dig into the substratum and rasp off threads or particles which can then be carried over the tip of the odontophore into the buccal cavity. Loose particles may also be gathered. *Patina* appears to be able to rasp weeds effectively in this way, but *Patella* and *Acmaea*, to judge from their gut contents, seem rather to take unicellular algae than parts rasped from larger plants. Davis & Fleure (1903) suggested these types of food for *Patella*, but added a method of feeding in which pieces of weed are held in the lips whilst the radula rasps them, and they believed that, whilst the anterior end of the radula is rasping on the substratum, the next inner piece is triturating the food already gathered against the jaw. Peile (1937) recorded little sign of use on the most anterior teeth, but assumed, since the teeth detach readily from the radular ribbon when it is being manipulated, that worn teeth fall off readily in nature, and are replaced by fresh ones moving forward. No wear on the teeth in from the tip is to be seen, so that no support from this source is available for the idea that the limpet chews its food between radula and jaw. From another point of view it seems unlikely that this action, if it occurs at all, is extensive—the occurrence of uncrushed fragments of vegetable material in the gut and even in the faeces.

In the case of the rhipidoglossan type of radula working place and bending plane coincide and the bulk of the action of the radular teeth is due to the sweeping action which they have on the substratum, whilst the rachidian and lateral teeth appear to be more important as a conveyor belt for the material gathered by the other teeth than as collectors of food themselves. These facts also may be related to the form of the teeth, the marginals being long bristle-like structures, very numerous, and well adapted for the use to which they are put. Gwatkin (1914) was one of the earliest to note this, talking of a 'whirlpool motion' of the radula when the small trochid *Margarites helicinus* feeds. It may also be observed in the other trochids and in the turbinid *Tricolia pullus*. All these appear to feed mainly by collecting diatoms and detrital matter from the substratum. Peile (1937) noted that the tip of the radula is formed from a few rows containing marginal teeth only, from which the more median teeth have been lost. He suggested that these marginals may not only gather up small particles, but also exclude large ones and act as a filter allowing water to escape, but not the particles. As discussed above, it is not known to what extent the lateral and median teeth of a rhipidoglossan are involved in the collection of food: some evidence bearing on this may be obtained from a study of the radula, in that examination shows a blunting of the most anterior lateral teeth, suggesting that they hit and move over the substratum. This is also borne out by Crofts' account (1929) of feeding in *Haliotis*, which, she said, feeds on minute encrusting algae and, also, by rasping fragments from the surface of weeds by means of the narrow lateral teeth. She also, like Davis & Fleure, supposed that the radula can chew food against the jaw once it has been rasped from the substratum, but wear from this cause (if it occurs) is too slight to be detectable. Other rhipidoglossans also show blunting of the lateral teeth of the radula, so that it appears probable that some scraping of the surface of the substratum is carried out in addition to the brushing due to the marginals.

Most taenioglossans have a feeding method fundamentally similar to that of rhipidoglossans, with the brushing minimized and the scraping exaggerated. This may be responsible for the signs of wear exhibited by the teeth of *Littorina* and for the length of the radula in species of that genus. In some Taenioglossa the primary effect of the movement of the radular teeth which occurs as they pass over the bending plane appears to be grasping rather than rasping or scraping and in this case one would naturally expect to find less signs of wear. This lack of wear has been shown to occur in *Pila* (Prashad, 1932), *Viviparus contectus*, *V. viviparus*, *Bithynia tentaculata* and *Pomatias elegans* (Peile, 1937) and, in at least some of these animals (*Viviparus, Bithynia*), may be correlated with the fact that they are ciliary feeders, and the radular teeth are used for no harder work than grasping the mucous string laden with food particles which is elaborated in the mantle cavity. The same is also true of *Crepidula fornicata*, *Calyptraea chinensis* and *Capulus ungaricus*, which are also ciliary food collectors, and in which little wear is detectable on the radula.

On the other hand the radula of taenioglossans may show signs of excessive wear as in *Natica*, a fact which puzzled Peile, since at the time at which he was writing this gastropod was supposed to bore through the shells of the bivalves which it ate by means of acid secreted from a gland placed below and behind the mouth (Schiemenz, 1891). Since then the work of Ziegelmeier (1954) and Carriker (1959) has shown that all the removal of shell is apparently due to rasping by the teeth on the radula and the degree of wear which these exhibit is not surprising.

For the same reason, the teeth of those rachiglossans which feed after boring through the shells of other molluscs, show much damage and those in the most anterior rows of the radula of *Nucella*, *Ocenebra* and *Urosalpinx* are often completely devoid of cusps, so intensely have they been ground down. In other groups of Rachiglossa, however, the fact that the animals are carnivores which do not bore or are carrion feeders (Buccinacea) is reflected in the lesser degree of wear exhibited by the teeth, which are used as grasping and pulling organs rather than as rasps. In these the cusps are not worn down in the smooth, rounded way found in *Nucella*, for example, such as regular wear on a hard substance would produce, but, if not complete, show irregular fractures, such as would happen on accidental contact with hard material.

The Toxoglossa have radular teeth quite unlike those met with in any other prosobranch (figs. 105F, G), and their function is as different from those of other prosobranchs as their shape is aberrant. It is true that there is still some doubt as to the precise way in which they are used, but it is at least certain that they do not act either as rasping or grasping organs. The most primitive type of toxoglossan radula is that found in *Spirotropis* and *Drillia*, in which each row contains 5 teeth, so that the formula is $1 + 1 + R + 1 + 1$. The central teeth are small and insignificant and are flanked by the laterals which are broad and have serrated edges, whilst on the outer side of these lie long tapering marginals bearing some resemblance to the teeth found in the more advanced toxoglossans such as *Conus*. From these Cooke (1895) derived the teeth of the cones, the dental formula of which he therefore gave as $1 + o + o + o + 1$. With this interpretation Simroth (1896–1907) agreed and he gave the teeth of *Mangelia* as examples of intermediate forms in which the tapering point of the tooth of *Spirotropis* is reduced to a hook-shaped base whilst the original base grows into a spine. In *Bela* this spine becomes grooved and its apex is provided with a recurved hook. Continued elongation and rolling of the edges of the groove with development of the barb are supposed to give the typical scroll-like, harpoon-shaped teeth of the more advanced *Conus*. A further evolutionary trend has converted the normal movable attachment of the tooth to the radular membrane into a long stalk so that the resemblance to a harpoon is still more exact, in that the tooth lies at the end of a long, mobile, attaching thread.

The method by which these teeth are used is still a matter of conjecture, especially in the small British toxoglossans, although Shaw (1915), Alpers (1931a, 1932), Clench (1946), Hermitte (1946), Jaeckel (1952) and Kohn (1956, 1959) have discussed the problem in connexion with various species of the genus *Conus*, and Risbec (1953a) in relation to terebrids, some of which resemble *Conus* in having a radula and poison gland (e.g. *Terebra cancellata*) whilst in others the poison gland is lost and in a few (e.g. *Terebra muscaria*) the radula has vanished as well. Clench (1946) noted that neither turrids nor terebrids are known to 'bite' or 'sting' their prey: only the Conidae are capable of doing this. In all these animals the gut ends in a proboscis normally withdrawn into a proboscis sheath (see p. 167 and fig. 104). From the apex of the proboscis the mouth leads to an elongated oral tube expanding to a buccal cavity into which open the radula sac, the poison gland and the salivary glands. No real odontophore is found, though there are muscles attached to the radular teeth. No cartilage lies in relation to them, nor do jaws occur. The opening of the radular sac is narrow, and the sac itself bears a deep dorsal diverticulum, so that it is Y-shaped and joined to the gut by the tip of one of the arms of the Y. In both arms lie the long arrow-shaped teeth. How they get out of the sac, and how they are bent through the 90° angle between the radular sac and the buccal cavity is not known, though Jaeckel (1952) argued that they must be rotated by muscular means, and this may be the function of what odontophoral musculature still persists.

The next point of argument is the site at which the teeth are brought into operation. In terebrids it seems that, if they are used at all, then it must be within the buccal cavity or oral tube, on prey which has been engulfed by the muscular proboscis and swallowed whole (Risbec, 1953a), as Alpers (1932) said that the cones also did. In the case of the cones, however, it seems more likely that the radular teeth come into operation in a more external situation.

The proboscis of the Toxoglossa is exposed partly by the retraction of the sheath which lies around it. Indeed, Alpers went so far as to suggest that not only does the proboscis sheath retract thus, but also the greater part of the wall of the proboscis, so that the whole oral tube and buccal cavity are everted, with the result that a 'mouth' is formed at the level where poison gland, salivary glands and radular sac are all opening more or less together. This description cuts across the line of thought of other workers who have argued that the coiling of the so-called 'duct' of the poison gland was slack, which would straighten on the protrusion of the proboscis, and as Jaeckel (1952) noted that in *Conus geographus* the 'gland' was 2 cm long and its 'duct' 28 cm—equal to several times the length of the gastropod—it was assumed that the extension of the proboscis would be considerable. Now that it is known, however, that the alleged duct is really the secreting part of the poison apparatus, it may well be that its length is not due to the provision of slack to straighten when the proboscis extends, but is simply the only way in which adequate secretory surface can be produced in a gland which has to be linear in form since its secretion is ejected by pressure from a muscular bulb at its innermost end.

Alpers' description of the feeding of *Conus* mentions how worms which were attacked suddenly contracted and stood still although they were not in contact with the proboscis of the cone: this he believed was due to the fact that they had been struck by a jet of poison projected from a radular tooth held in the mouth of the predator. Thereafter the immobilized prey was ingested and butchered within the gut. Jaeckel (1952) would like to interpret these observations of Alpers to mean that the tooth, laden with poison, is shot out of the cone's mouth and fired into the body of the prey—likening the action to the firing of a poisoned arrow rather than to a spitting of poisonous fluid, and in support of this idea mentions the frequency with which loose radular teeth are found in the proboscis of animals examined in the preserved state, which previous workers regarded as an artefact brought about by contraction of muscles at death. Clench (1946), dealing with the biting of *Conus citrinus* in a paper briefing U.S. Army troops about to proceed to the Pacific area during World War II, described how the proboscis is extended from the proboscis sheath, the tip of a radular tooth emerges from the mouth, the proboscis is raised in the air like the head of a snake about to strike and then suddenly jabbed forwards and downwards. If allowed to strike a non-absorbent surface, fluid, milky white and viscous, exudes from the tooth and forms a pool about a quarter-inch in diameter. A much more detailed account of the feeding of some species of *Conus*, however, has been given recently by Kohn (1956, 1959). Some of these eat worms, others molluscs and still others catch fish. In certain species eating worms (*C. abbreviatus* and *C. ebraeus*) the proboscis, grasping a tooth at its apex, is extended to 'sting' the prey. The proboscis is retracted, leaving the tooth embedded in the body of the prey which is thus anaesthetized and swallowed at leisure. In other species the cone does not lose its grip on the prey after stinging by loss of the tooth, and the contraction of the proboscis therefore draws the immobilized prey towards it. In all cases the mouth appears capable of enormous dilatation and the body of the prey is ingested whole. In cones which feed on other molluscs (*C. pennaceus*) several teeth may be discharged in succession into the prey.

All these accounts vary, but are not necessarily incompatible provided that it be allowed that different species of toxoglossan may have evolved different uses for their radular apparatus.

Another matter still in doubt is how the poison, which is a powerful neurotoxic substance allied to curare, reaches the teeth. It is secreted by cells lining the 'duct' of the poison 'gland' (see p. 168) and can be forced under pressure from the musculature of the 'gland' into the buccal cavity, the point of entry being close to the mouth of the radular sac. Whether the buccal cavity becomes filled with secretion which then enters any radular tooth that may be passed out of the radular sac, or whether the radular tooth is brought into position and then filled with poison is not known. Though normally used to attack prey the poison appears to be also employed in self-defence, and it is likely that most attacks on man (see Yasiro, 1939) arise from this cause.

# CHAPTER 9

# THE ALIMENTARY SYSTEM—3

THE part of the gut which lies behind the mouth of the radular sac is the oesophagus. Whilst this landmark conveniently sets off its ventral anterior limit, its dorsal one is by no means so clear and is perhaps best regarded as lying still further forwards over the buccal mass at a point just behind the opening of the salivary ducts. The posterior limit of the oesophagus is its entry to the stomach which lies in the visceral mass. It is this section of the gut, therefore, which, in a prosobranch, has to traverse the part of the body in which the effects of torsion are obvious; as the dorsal and ventral sides of the oesophagus carry characteristic structures, it is easy to follow the twist which has been imposed by torsion. Graham (1939), investigating the oesophagus in a variety of prosobranchs, has suggested that it is divisible into 3 sections. These are: (1) the anterior oesophagus, lying directly behind the posterior end of the buccal cavity, but in front of the region affected by torsion; (2) the mid-oesophagus, which includes the whole length of the part involved in torsion and usually sections anterior and posterior to that; and (3) the posterior oesophagus, which runs to the stomach. Since this division coincides with the separation of a mid-region characterized by the development of much glandular tissue not present in either of the other two parts, it has much to recommend it.

The dorsal wall of the anterior oesophagus and of the mid-oesophagus in an animal like *Patella* (Graham, 1932) or a trochid (Randles, 1905; Nisbet, 1953), is marked by the fact that along it run two great folds separated by a deep channel. These have been called the dorsal folds (df, fig. 111B) by Graham and the channel between the dorsal food channel (dfc). In some prosobranchs the dorsal folds show signs of being bifid. Along the ventral wall of the mid-oesophagus in these animals runs an apparently single fold of tissue (vf), but in the anterior oesophagus this can be seen to arise as two separate ridges lying right and left of the mid-line and converging and uniting posteriorly. In the mid-oesophagus of a limpet or an animal like *Calliostoma*, too (fig. 111C), the ventral fold can be shown to be double, so retaining traces of the two folds of the anterior oesophagus. In that part of the gut the anterior end of the diverging halves of the fold and the lip of the radular sac demarcate a triangular area which is often raised into a flap-like structure drawn into an anteriorly directed point. This may be called the oesophageal valve (oev, fig. 11) and it acts like the mammalian epiglottis in preventing the entry of food to the radular sac; it may also prevent regurgitation of food from the oesophagus when the animal is feeding, an occurrence which protraction of the buccal mass might facilitate.

In the anterior oesophagus the lateral walls, which lie between the oesophageal valve ventrally and the dorsal fold dorsally, are often drawn out into capacious pouches (osp, fig. 11), which may communicate widely with the rest of the cavity (*Patella*, Zeugobranchia, Trochidae) or be connected to it only by a narrow mouth, as is the case in winkles. However this may be, these side walls are not adapted for the production of digestive juices, although they may contain plentiful goblet cells secreting mucus. Presumably they provide a certain amount of loose wall and space for the accommodation of food during feeding, and for easing the movements of the buccal mass and radula.

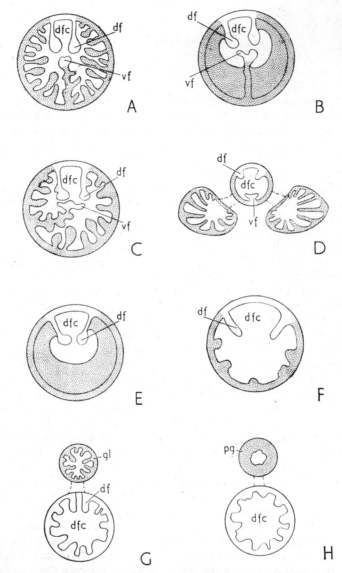

Fig. 111.—A series of diagrammatic transverse sections of the mid-oesophagus of prosobranchs. A, zeugobranch; B, patellacean; C, trochacean; D, *Theodoxus fluviatilis*; E, *Littorina littorea*, and also typical of most mesogastropods; F, mesogastropods with a crystalline style; G, rachiglossan; H, toxoglossan. In these sections the dorsal folds, the ventral fold and the other walls of the dorsal food channel are not stippled; the glandular epithelium of the oesophageal gland and of structures homologous with it, is. Broken lines indicate connexions between glands and the main part of the oesophagus not occurring at the level of the sections.

df, dorsal fold; dfc, dorsal food channel; gl, gland of Leiblein of rachiglossan; pg, poison gland of toxoglossan; vf, ventral fold.

A mid-ventral pouch found in *Erato voluta* by Fretter (1951*a*) should perhaps be regarded as comparable to these paired oesophageal pouches. It opens to the oesophagus behind the nerve ring and extends forward from there through the nerve ring and along the proboscis (mud, fig. 112). As in other oesophageal pouches its walls are lined by mucous cells alternating with ciliated supporting cells.

In the mid-oesophagus, however, the lateral walls are expanded to form a pouch-like extension of the gut cavity on either side and their surface is further increased in area by the development of finger-like outgrowths from the inner surface (Zeugobranchia, fig. 111A; Trochacea, fig. 111C) or by the formation of lamellae (Patellacea, figs. 111B, 261; Littorinacea, fig. 111E; Cypraeacea; Lamellariacea; Doliacea). Both kinds of outgrowth and the wall between are covered by a glandular epithelium not found in other parts of the gut, which is responsible for secreting digestive enzymes. It forms a gland,

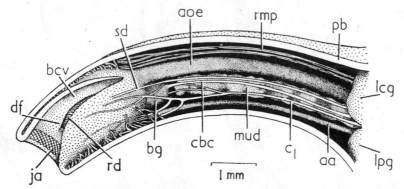

Fig. 112.—*Erato voluta:* longitudinal section through the proboscis, partly extended. The left wall of the proboscis has been removed and part of the left lateral wall of the buccal cavity. The haemocoel is black.

aa, anterior aorta; aoe, anterior oesophagus; bcv, buccal cavity; bg, buccal ganglion; $c_1$, cerebral nerve to muscles of buccal mass; cbc, cerebrobuccal connective; df, dorsal fold; ja, jaw; lcg, left cerebral ganglion; lpg, left pedal ganglion; mud, mucous diverticulum of anterior oesophagus; pb, proboscis; rd, radula; rmp, retractor muscles of proboscis; sd, salivary duct.

the oesophageal gland, which, since the saliva is usually devoid of digestive action, is normally the first digestive secretion which the food meets on its course along the alimentary canal.

By comparison with the two parts of the oesophagus which lie in front of it, the posterior oesophagus is relatively simple. The two dorsal folds and the ventral fold of the anterior and mid-oesophagus die out, or merge into other folds, and the glandular epithelium of the lateral walls disappears. Consequently the diameter of the oesophagus is much reduced and the posterior oesophagus is a narrow tube with an internal surface raised into a series of longitudinal folds none of which is more prominent than any other, and all of which contain only mucous goblet cells.

The most interesting part of this oesophageal region is the mid-oesophagus, which, because of the dilatation caused by the lateral glands is a conspicuous object, easily seen on dissection, and often known as the crop. Within the prosobranchs it has undergone an extensive evolutionary change and, as Amaudrut (1898) was the first to point out, it is an easy structure to investigate from the point of view of comparative anatomy since its relationships with other structures in this area, also affected by torsion, are almost

constant. The effects of torsion on the mid-oesophagus itself are plain to see (fig. 113):
the dorsal folds and food-channel (dfc'), which mark the morphological mid-dorsal line,
curve over the left side until they come to lie in the topographical mid-ventral line.
Simultaneously the fold which lies mid-ventrally at the anterior end of the mid-oeso-

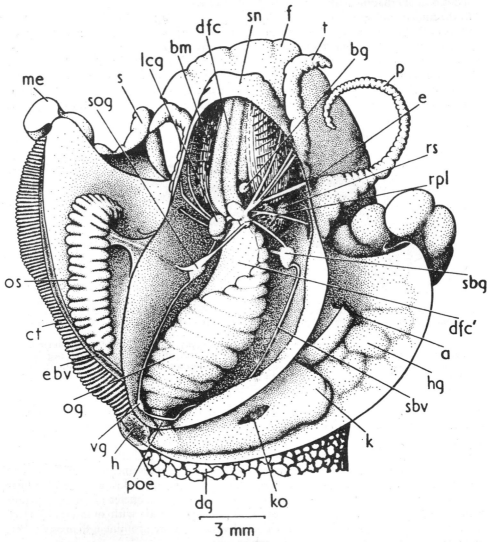

FIG. 113.—*Trivia monacha*: dissection of anterior part of body. The mantle skirt has been cut medianly
and the two halves deflected laterally.

a, anus; bg, buccal ganglion; bm, buccal mass; ct, ctenidium; dfc, dorsal food channel of buccal
cavity seen by transparency; dfc', dorsal food channel in mid-oesophagus seen by transparency; dg,
digestive gland; e, eye; ebv, efferent branchial vessel; f, foot; h, heart; hg, hypobranchial gland;
k, kidney; ko, opening of kidney; lcg, left cerebral ganglion; me, mantle edge; og, oesophageal
gland; os, osphradium; p, penis; poe, posterior oesophagus; rpl, right pleural ganglion; rs, radular
sac; s, siphon; sbg, sub-oesophageal ganglion; sbv, sub-oesophageal part of visceral loop; sn, snout;
sog, supra-oesophageal ganglion; t, tentacle; vg, visceral ganglion.

phagus curves round the right side until it lies in the topographical mid-dorsal line. The glandular areas (og) also curve across so as to lie on the opposite side of the body from that to which they actually belong. The anterior limit of the area affected by torsion is marked by the supra-oesophageal part of the visceral loop, which curves over the oesophagus from the right pleural ganglion (rpl) on its way to the supra-oesophageal ganglion (sog) on the left, while the posterior limit of the area involved in the twist is similarly marked by the anterior aorta, which curves over the oesophagus from a dorsal position on the left, where it has emerged from the heart (h), to a ventral position on the right, where it breaks into cephalic and pedal branches. Whilst both these structures curve over the mid-oesophagus the precise part of that organ where this happens varies from animal to animal: it may be far forward, close to the posterior end of the anterior oesophagus, as in *Calliostoma* and *Pomatias*, or it may be relatively close to the posterior end of the mid-oesophagus, as in *Gibbula* or the Stenoglossa.

From the functional point of view the mid-oesophagus divides itself into two clear parts: the glandular lateral outpouchings and the rest, which is so arranged that the ventral fold (vf, figs. 111A, B, C) fits over the dorsal food channel (dfc) between the dorsal folds (df) and converts that trough into a virtually closed channel. The histology of these structures is related to the different parts which they play in this process. Thus the epithelium which lines the dorsal food channel, the median faces and summits of the dorsal folds and the summit of the mid-ventral fold is a tall columnar ciliated epithelium rich in mucous cells. The direction of the beat of the cilia on the walls of the food channel is towards the stomach, as it is also on the summit of the ventral fold. Since that structure forms, in effect, the floor of the channel into which the food is passed from the radula, this arrangement makes the dorsal food channel into a food-carrying tube transporting it back to the stomach, and secreting mucus to bind the food particles together and to lubricate their travel.

On the summit of the dorsal folds, and for a very short part of their lateral wall over which the same type of epithelium spreads, the direction of the ciliary beat is transverse—out of the lateral pouches of the mid-oesophagus into the food channel. This brings whatever substances may be produced there into the food channel where they may be mixed with the food. In the lateral pouches, or on the villi, a wholly different type of epithelium is found, in which 2 types of cell occur, one glandular, the other ciliated. The glandular cells are low in height and, in *Patella* (fig. 114A), where the pouches contain lamellae, they alternate more or less regularly with ciliated cells (cic). Their cytoplasm is vacuolated (gc), lobed superficially and almost always contains spherules of secretory material (msc). In *Gibbula*, where the pouches contain villi, the glandular cells appear on the sides of the villi, intermingled with ciliated cells as in *Patella* and resembling the gland cells of that animal. The apex of the villus is devoid of ciliated cells but is covered with an epithelium of cells looking like the glandular ones but with a firm, almost cuticularized surface, which does not support the idea that they are secretory. In all these animals the direction of the beat of the cilia in the lateral glandular pouches is such as to drive material either towards the dorsal or the ventral folds, where they can be directed into the food channel. Since many workers have shown that the secretion of these pouches contains digestive enzymes the whole apparatus allows for the transport of food from the buccal cavity back to the stomach and for the simultaneous mixing of the food and the enzymatic secretion of the lateral pouches during the transport.

As has already been described, the mid-oesophagus has two folds running along its dorsal wall and a double, or potentially double, fold running along its mid-ventral line.

The doubleness of this fold and the way in which it is formed by the approximation and more or less complete fusion of two folds in the anterior oesophagus suggest that the primitive organization of the ventral half of the oesophagus mirrored that of its dorsal half, and that a ventral food channel separated a right glandular mass from a left one just as does a dorsal channel. No living prosobranch, however, possesses an oesophageal

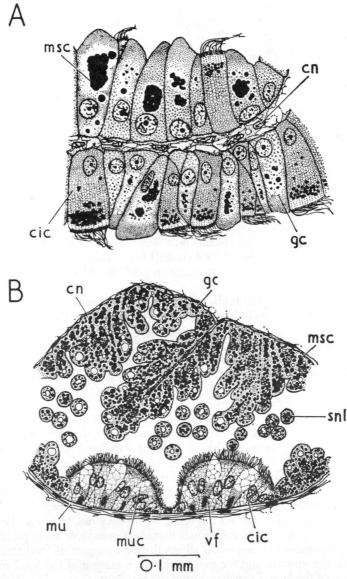

Fig. 114.—Histology of oesophageal glands.  A, *Patella vulgata*;  B, *Nucella lapillus*, gland of Leiblein. cic, ciliated cell; cn, connective tissue; gc, gland cell; msc, mass of secretion; mu, muscle fibre; muc, mucous cell; snl, secretion in lumen of gland, nipped off from tip of gland cell; vf, ventral fold.

structure of this sort, though in development Fischer (1892) has shown that the oesophagus is marked by lateral glandular strips separated by non-glandular conducting strips in the mid-dorsal and mid-ventral lines. All the diotocardian prosobranchs (the Neritacea excepted) and many mesogastropods show a mid-oesophagus with, at most, a double fold along the mid-ventral line to mark where a ventral food channel may once have stood. In many of the monotocardians, however, even this is lost and in *Littorina*, for example, the right and left glandular areas are connected without interruption across the mid-ventral line (fig. 111E).

Considerable evolutionary change has affected the oesophageal glands in the Stenoglossa, and these seem to have undergone a completely different kind of alteration in the rachiglossan members of the group from what has affected them in the Toxoglossa. In the Rachiglossa much of the evolution must be set down to two things: (1) the elongation of the snout to form a proboscis, and (2) the production of a gland set off from the main course of the gut and connected to it by a duct instead of lying along it as in a mesogastropod—perhaps a more efficient arrangement.

The formation of a proboscis not only calls for an elongation of the body wall in gastropods (a group in which the proboscis is an introvert) but inevitably also for an elongation of the gut which lies within the body wall. In the Rachiglossa (figs. 115, 116) it is easy to see that the part of the gut which has been elongated is almost entirely derived from the anterior oesophagus: the buccal cavity bears the normal relationships of a prosobranch buccal cavity and shows no signs of increased size, and, at the level of the nerve ring, lies the part affected by torsion and therefore mid-oesophageal in origin. Between these two levels, stretching along the whole length of the proboscis, lies a part of the gut (aoe) which is posterior to the mouth of the radular sac, anterior to the point of torsion and marked by a small number of longitudinal folds of which two are outstandingly large and spread forwards dorsal to the buccal mass. Ciliary currents stream backwards on and between these two folds dorsally and the ducts of the normal salivary glands (sd) lie along their bases and open to the buccal cavity at their anterior ends. Between them, on the ventral side of the gut, lies a shallow groove which opens anteriorly on to a triangular area forming the roof of the radular sac. From these relationships it is evident that the two main folds are the dorsal folds, that the broader dorsal channel between them is the dorsal food channel, and that that section of the gut which has contributed the bulk of the elongation involved in the formation of the proboscis is the anterior oesophagus. When the proboscis is retracted it is flung into an S-bend; when the proboscis extends it straightens.

This part of the gut ends at the base of the proboscis by expanding into a pear-shaped structure which is known as the pharynx of Leiblein (vl, figs. 98, 115, 116, 117), the broad base of the pear being anterior and its narrower end tapering posteriorly. It narrows to a part of the gut which is surrounded by the nerve ring almost immediately behind which (since the rachiglossan nervous system is partly concentrated) the supra-oesophageal nerve crosses the gut from right to left and the anterior aorta (aa, fig. 115) from left to right, the two almost in contact. The oesophagus, after traversing the nerve ring, expands a little in diameter and in the Muricacea, but not the other groups, bears a mass of lobed glandular tissue (ge, figs. 98, 117) called the 'glande framboisée' by Amaudrut (1898) and the 'median unpaired fore-gut gland' by Haller (1888). Immediately behind this, in all groups, a duct (dgl, figs. 98, 116) leaves the oesophagus and runs to a brown or yellow mass of glandular tissue which is wrapped around the oesophagus and the anterior aorta. This is the gland of Leiblein (gl, figs. 98, 115, 116) and it has been shown, by numerous workers on different animals, to be a source of powerful digestive enzymes. From the point of entry of the duct from the gland of Leiblein a relatively narrow tube, with walls flung into several longitudinal folds, runs back to the stomach. This is the posterior oesophagus (poe, fig. 98) and the problem which calls for discussion is whether all that

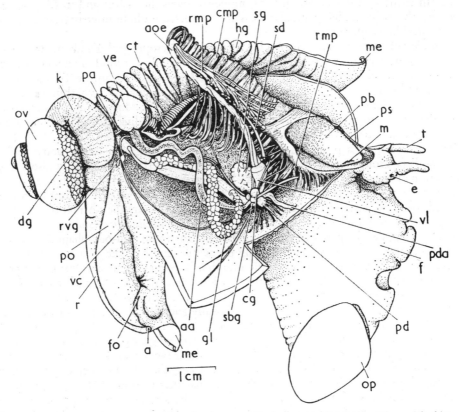

FIG. 115.—*Buccinum undatum:* dissection of anterior part of body from the right side. The mantle skirt has been cut medianly and deflected above and below, and a window cut in the proboscis sheath.

a, anus; aa, anterior aorta; aoe, anterior oesophagus; cg, right cerebral ganglion; cmp, circular muscles of proboscis; ct, ctenidium; dg, digestive gland; e, eye; f, foot; fo, female opening; gl, gland of Leiblein; hg, hypobranchial gland; k, kidney; m, mouth; me, mantle edge; op, operculum; ov, ovary; pa, posterior aorta; pb, proboscis lying in proboscis sheath; pd, pedal ganglion; pda, pedal artery; po, pallial oviduct; ps, cut wall of proboscis sheath; r, rectum; rmp, retractor muscles of proboscis; rvg, right visceral ganglion; sbg, sub-oesophageal ganglion; sd, right salivary duct, cut; sg, left salivary gland; t, tentacle; vc, ventral channel within capsule gland, seen by transparency; ve, ventricle; vl, valve of Leiblein.

lies between the anterior oesophagus in front and the posterior oesophagus behind is homologous with the mid-oesophageal region of the lower prosobranchs; and, if it is, how the transformation which it has undergone in the stenoglossans has been effected.

If the oesophageal region of *Nucella lapillus* be slit longitudinally the appearance which is obtained is seen in fig. 117. The two dorsal folds (df) continue into the pharynx of Leiblein and run across it, spiralling from a lateroventral position at its anterior end, round the right side, to a mid-dorsal position at its posterior end. As they do so they draw close together so that they lie alongside one another at the posterior end of the pharynx, with only the narrowest of clefts between. Now here is certainly an appearance which suggests torsion, but at first sight it seems that it cannot actually be torsion since we are talking of folds twisting dorsally round the right side of the oesophagus, whereas in *Patella*, a trochid or *Littorina* they twist ventrally round the left side. Nevertheless the

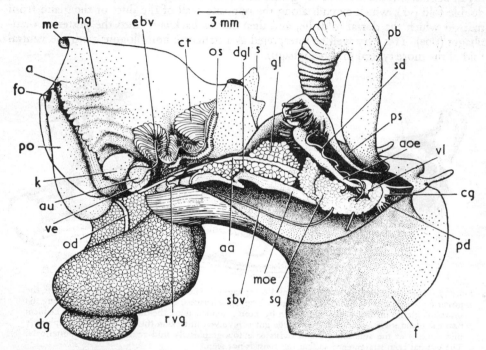

FIG. 116.—*Nassarius reticulatus:* dissection of anterior part of body from the right side. The mantle skirt has been cut along the right side and raised dorsally and the proboscis sheath opened and the proboscis pulled out of it.

a, anus; aa, anterior aorta; aoe, anterior oesophagus; au, auricle; cg, right cerebral ganglion; ct, ctenidium; dg, digestive gland; dgl, duct of the gland of Leiblein; ebv, efferent branchial vessel; f, foot; fo, female opening; gl, gland of Leiblein; hg, hypobranchial gland; k, kidney; me, mantle edge; moe, mid-oesophagus; od, ovarian duct; os, osphradium; pb, proboscis; pd, right pedal ganglion; po, pallial oviduct; ps, proboscis sheath; rvg, right visceral ganglion; s, siphon; sbv, sub-oesophageal part of visceral loop; sd, right salivary duct; sg, salivary gland; ve, ventricle; vl, valve of Leiblein.

connexions of these folds anteriorly, their histology (tall columnar ciliated cells with numerous intermingled mucous cells) and the direction of the ciliary currents over them, all agree with the idea that they are the homologues of the dorsal folds of other prosobranchs. They have, however, migrated ventrally down the side walls of the oesophagus until they now lie ventrolaterally or even ventrally. In so doing they have expanded the dorsal food channel and constricted the lateral and ventral walls of the oesophagus. The course which they now follow is therefore, quite properly, one that corresponds to the course taken along the mid-oesophagus of *Patella* or *Gibbula* by the ventral fold.

If the folds are traced behind the pharynx of Leiblein, along the narrow stretch which runs from there through the nerve ring and back to the duct of the gland of Leiblein, they will be found to run along the dorsal side of the oesophagus and become greatly folded and expanded. It is, in fact, these expanded convolutions of the dorsal folds which produce the 'glande framboisée' (ge) in this situation. Finally the folds enter the duct of the gland of Leiblein (gl) and die away near the point where the glandular tissue of that organ begins. On the walls of the gland, however, starting near its posterior tip, runs a double fold (vf), which extends along the opposite wall of the duct of the gland from that on which the dorsal folds lie, and then curves backward into the posterior oeso-phagus (poe). This may well be interpreted as a structure homologous with the ventral fold of the more typical mid-oesophagus.

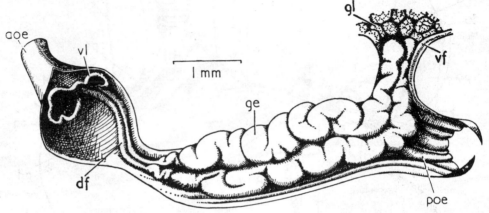

FIG. 117.—*Nucella lapillus:* dissection of the mid-oesophagus. The anterior oesophagus lies to the left, the posterior oesophagus to the right. The mid-oesophagus between has been opened by a cut along the morphologically median dorsal line, which has been extended along the duct of the gland of Leiblein into the gland itself. Since this part of the gut is involved in torsion this cut starts topographically mid-dorsally at the anterior end and twists to a topographically mid-ventral position posteriorly. The gut has been straightened so that this twist is not seen.

aoe, anterior oesophagus; df, dorsal fold; ge, 'glande framboisée'; gl, gland of Leiblein; poe, posterior oesophagus; vf, ventral fold; vl, valve of Leiblein.

If we now turn attention to the cleft which separates the two dorsal folds in their new, ventral position we ought to find something which corresponds to the ventral half of the normal mid-oesophagus. What we do find, in fact, is a strip of oesophageal wall lined by an epithelium of squamous cells, contrasting completely with that which forms the lining of the remainder of the oesophagus. The cells are featureless and show no trace of glandular activity, or, indeed, of being more than a membranous seal to the gut cavity stretched between the dorsal folds.

In all probability, the correct interpretation which should be placed upon this part of the alimentary tract (fig. 111G) is this. In the formation of the rachiglossan proboscis, as has been seen, great elongation of the anterior part of the gut is necessary, largely accomplished by extension of the anterior oesophagus, but needing still further alteration in the arrangement of the parts. That the elongation of the anterior oesophagus has not been adequate to keep pace with the growth rate of the proboscis is shown, for example, by the fact that the (ordinary) salivary glands now lie anterior to the nerve ring, their ducts not passing through that structure: the ducts have grown less fast than the body wall and so the glands have been pulled forwards. Similarly, part of the mid-oesophagus, represented by the pharynx of Leiblein, has been pulled forwards through the nerve ring by the traction exerted on it by the growing body wall: this can be recognized as mid-oesophageal by the torsion of the gut shown in that position. Now the mid-oesophagus is normally a dilated region of the gut by virtue of the glandular pouches attached to it, a configuration which does not lend itself to movement through a relatively narrow gap like the nerve ring. The rachiglossan has therefore undergone an evolution in the course of which the lateral glandular pouches of the mid-oesophagus and the ventral fold which runs between right and left halves, have been torn off backwards from the food channel so that they are now connected to the mid-oesophagus only at its posterior end. To fill the hole in the oesophageal wall the dorsal folds have migrated ventrally until they come into contact with one another in the mid-ventral line, but, even so, there is left between them a narrow gap which is filled in with a scar tissue represented by the thin epithelium described above. It is extremely unlikely, partly because of the close contact maintained between the two dorsal folds, partly because of the way in which the cilia on the dorsal folds maintain their original direction of beating—out of the lateral parts of the oesophagus into the food channel and therefore out of the cleft between the folds—that food particles ever reach this epithelium, which might easily be broken by their impact.

One further elaboration of this region of the alimentary canal in *Nucella* remains to be described. At the anterior end of the pharynx of Leiblein each dorsal fold is expanded into a flap-like structure which hangs freely into the cavity of the gut (vl, fig. 117), and into a pad of mucous cells lying at the base of the flap. The two flaps normally project backwards into the lumen of the pharynx, which is dilated at this spot largely to accommodate them. Their free surfaces are fringed with extremely long cilia which beat, however, very languidly. This structure acts as a valve, reacting partly mechanically in preventing regurgitation of food from the more posterior parts of the gut during the elongation of the proboscis, and probably also chemically, since Brock (1936) has shown that in the whelk *Buccinum undatum* stomach contents or secretion from the digestive gland stimulate the flaps to come together and prevent forward movement. Since the pharynx of Leiblein is a more or less constant feature of the rachiglossan gut it is probable that it acts in the same way in each animal and it is proposed to refer to it as the valve of Leiblein, as a more appropriate name than pharynx.

The conditions which have just been described apply in particular to *Nucella*, but would be equally true for any member of the Muricacea. A certain number of differences are noticeable in the Buccinacea and Volutacea. In the Buccinacea the valve of Leiblein is reduced or even absent (*Galeodes, Semifusus, Busycon*) and so are the dorsal folds, which never give rise to a 'glande framboisée'. More important, perhaps, is the fact that the part of the mid-oesophagus which shows the effects of torsion is not the part which forms the valve of Leiblein, but the length behind that, which runs through the nerve ring and back to the opening of the duct of the gland. This is marked in *Neptunea* and *Buccinum* by a groove, lined with scar tissue, which represents the original line of attachment of the gland and which twists from the mid-ventral line up the right side to a dorsal position; in *Nassarius* even this vestige has been lost.

In the Muricacea the gland of Leiblein (gl, fig. 98) is a large and solid mass of glandular tissue lying rather compactly behind the nerve ring and shown by Hirsch (1915) (and probably by Mansour-Bek, 1934) to secrete digestive enzymes in the Mediterranean

*Murex trunculus*. In the Buccinacea it appears (*Buccinum*, gl, fig. 115; *Nassarius*, gl, fig. 116) much less solid, its walls more transparent, and it extends backwards along the posterior oesophagus as a thin finger-shaped caecum the walls of which are not glandular at all. This tendency of the organ to become less glandular appears to extend to other members of the Buccinacea and the Volutacea: Vanstone (1894) described *Semifusus* spp. as having only a small caecum to represent the gland and *Galeodes melongena* as having lost it altogether, whilst Woodward (1901*b*) described *Volutocorbis abyssicola* as having only a sac-like gland. This would seem to suggest an evolutionary trend within the Rachiglossa towards the suppression of the gland of Leiblein, possibly associated with the assumption of greater activity by the digestive gland.

From the histological point of view the mid-oesophagus of these stenoglossan prosobranchs shows an advance on that of lower forms. The main tubular part of the gut is lined by a tall, ciliated, columnar epithelium with numerous mucous cells interspersed, especially in the valve of Leiblein and where the dorsal folds are elaborated in the Muricacea to form the 'glande framboisée'. The epithelium rests on a wall with a little circular and longitudinal muscle in it, but the cilia appear to be responsible for much of the movement of food. The gland (fig. 114B), in the forms where it is well developed, has a central cavity into which a large number of partitions project. In the partitions and in the outer walls lie a few muscle fibres (mu), but there is no muscular capsule around it. The epithelial cells which clothe the inner walls are mainly club-shaped and bulge into the cavity, and their distal tips appear to be nipped off when secretion occurs (snl). The nuclei lie centrally, and the cytoplasm is usually stuffed with large numbers of protein spherules (msc). The cells are very fragile and burst readily on handling. Occasional mucous cells are intermingled with the other gland cells. Sometimes the gland cells have a striated distal border which may indicate a change of phase. Franc (1952*a*) has shown the gland to be rich in alkaline phosphatase in *Tritonalia* (= *Ocenebra*) *aciculata*.

The second group of the Stenoglossa is the Toxoglossa, a group which has achieved some notoriety by containing the animals known as cone shells, capable of inflicting a severe, poisonous bite even on man. The poison gland of these animals has been taken to be the homologue of the gland of Leiblein (fig. 111H), and therefore of the oesophageal pouches of lower prosobranchs, since the days of Amaudrut (1898). The arrangements which occur in a toxoglossan have already been described (p. 167, fig. 104) and need not be repeated, and it is clear that the whole oesophageal region has been profoundly modified so that it is difficult to see any resemblance between what is found here and what occurs in other animals. Nevertheless authors such as Franc (1952*b*) and Robinson (1955) talk about a 'pharynx of Leiblein', which implies a structure comparable to that of the Rachiglossa, and therefore a separation of the gland of Leiblein from the conducting channel of the oesophagus; as pointed out by Amaudrut, however, this separation must have been from the back forwards in the Toxoglossa, since the duct from the gland opens anteriorly. No scar tissue like that which has been found in the Rachiglossa has ever been described in a toxoglossan, though this is not perhaps a serious matter since it cannot be found in the rachiglossan *Nassarius*. Most authors, however (Bouvier, 1885; Amaudrut, 1898; Shaw, 1915; Alpers, 1931*b*, 1932; Hermitte, 1946; Clench, 1946), do not describe anything which could be regarded as comparable to a valve of Leiblein, and in view of the fact that these animals have an elongated proboscis, it is possible that a similar valvular arrangement may have been independently evolved. Although it is tempting to homologize the poison gland of the Toxoglossa with the gland of Leiblein of the Rachiglossa there is little supporting anatomical evidence for it, and such histological evidence as is available is distinctly unfavourable. In fact the entire homology rests as much upon the fact that there is this gland present in a position where some closely related gastropods have the gland of Leiblein as upon anything else, and it is clear that much more careful work is called for before the homology can be regarded as undoubtedly true.

There still remain to be dealt with a few cases where the mid-oesophageal region of the gut has undergone some special modification. The most puzzling example of this is shown by the sinistral prosobranch *Triphora perversa* described by Fretter (1951b) (fig. 118). In this animal, which has a long proboscis correlated with its habit of feeding on sponges amongst other things, there are two large salivary glands which open by a single

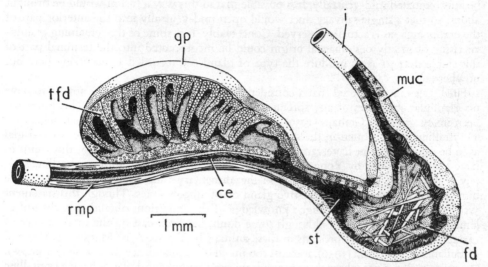

FIG. 118.—*Triphora perversa:* diagrammatic longitudinal section through the posterior oesophagus, stomach and part of the intestine.
ce, ciliated epithelium of oesophagus; fd, food in stomach; gp, glandular pouch; i, intestine; muc, mucous cells of intestine; rmp, retractor muscles of proboscis; st, stomach; tfd, transverse fold.

duct into the ventral part of the oesophagus. The part of the duct near the glands has secretory cells in it like those found in the glands themselves, but the distal part, near the oesophagus, contains other types of gland cells different from anything in the salivary gland or the oesophagus. The oesophagus itself is a tube of small diameter, lined by a ciliated columnar epithelium: no sign of dorsal folds, ventral folds, lateral glandular pouches or of torsion can be detected. Overlying it, however, and connected to it by a duct, is a gland (gp), the internal cavity of which is lined by a glandular epithelium flung into septate folds (tfd) and which is therefore reminiscent of many a mid-oesophageal gland. The duct leaves the posterior end of the gland and opens to the oesophagus not far from the point where that enters the stomach (st).

It may be that here, again, a separation of the glandular equipment of the mid-oesophagus has occurred in relation to the formation of a lengthy proboscis, but, as in Toxoglossa, this would appear to have occurred in *Triphora* without leaving any scar along the line of separation between oesophagus and gland. Perhaps, therefore, it is a new structure which has been evolved in *Triphora* for its own special functions. That would, to a certain extent, fit in with the unusual arrangements which the salivary glands exhibit. Fretter, however, offered an explanation of the salivary arrangement which involves the glandular equipment of the mid-oesophagus, and, if this is accepted then the posterior oesophageal pouch must have originated *de novo* or a split of the oeso-phageal glands into anterior and posterior halves must be postulated. In the lower prosobranchs the salivary ducts run dorsolaterally along the wall of the anterior part of the oesophagus at the insertion of the dorsal folds (sd, fig. 14). If the latter be supposed to migrate round the oesophageal wall ventrally—as they have already been shown to do in the rachiglossan stenoglossans—then they and the two salivary ducts will come to be approximated mid-ventrally. It is possible that in this way a fusion would be brought about, so that a single salivary duct would open mid-ventrally into the anterior part of the oesophagus, as is actually observed. Conceivably, too, some of the remaining glandu-lar tissue of strictly oesophageal origin could be incorporated into the terminal part of this single duct so as to produce the type of gland cell recorded as occurring here but nowhere else.

Finally, it must be noted that a considerable number of prosobranchs appear to have no glandular structures of any sort in connexion with the oesophagus. This point has been investigated by Graham (1939) and it appears to be generally true that, whenever a crystalline style is found in the stomach, the oesophageal glands are either so vestigial as to be functionless, or have vanished altogether (fig. 111F). The reason for this seems to have been discovered by Yonge (1930), who stated that molluscs with a crystalline style never had a free proteolytic enzyme in the alimentary canal: such as did occur were intracellular enzymes of the digestive gland or of amoebocytes. Though this statement was based primarily upon Yonge's knowledge of the conditions obtaining in the gut of lamellibranch molluscs, and although some doubt has been cast on the total absence of extracellular digestion of proteins in these animals by the work of Mansour (1945) and of Ballantine & Morton (1956), it seems too much of a coincidence that, with few known exceptions, all the prosobranch gastropods without oesophageal glands have a crystalline style, for the theory not to embody some truth. One exception appears to be *Tornus* (=*Adeorbis*) *subcarinatus* which, according to the description given by Woodward (1899), has both oesophageal glands and a crystalline style. It has never, to our knowledge, been examined alive—and not at all since that date—so that whether a style really exists or, as the words of Woodward might be taken to imply, merely a style sac region in the stomach, is not known for sure.

The British prosobranchs which are known to possess a style and, therefore, to have no oesophageal glands are these: all Rissoidae; *Hydrobia ulvae*; *H. ventrosa*; *Potamopyrgus jenkinsi*; *Bythinella scholtzi*; *Pseudamnicola confusa*; *Bithynia tentaculata*; *B. leachi*; *Assiminea grayana*; *Pomatias elegans*; *Turritella communis*; *Aporrhais pespelicani*; *Crepidula fornicata*; *Calyptraea chinensis*; *Capulus ungaricus*. A fuller list of gastropods with a style is given by Yonge (1954).

A few other prosobranchs which have no crystalline style, but are, in fact, either pronounced carnivores or parasites, have also lost all trace of oesophageal glands. These include animals such as *Ianthina*, *Clathrus*, *Balcis*, *Eulima* and the pyramidellids; as all these show opisthobranch affinities this loss of oesophageal glands is probably a matter of inheritance rather than of adaptation.

The posterior oesophagus, the section of gut which follows the mid-oesophagus is, in contrast to that length of the alimentary canal, a simple tube carrying food and such

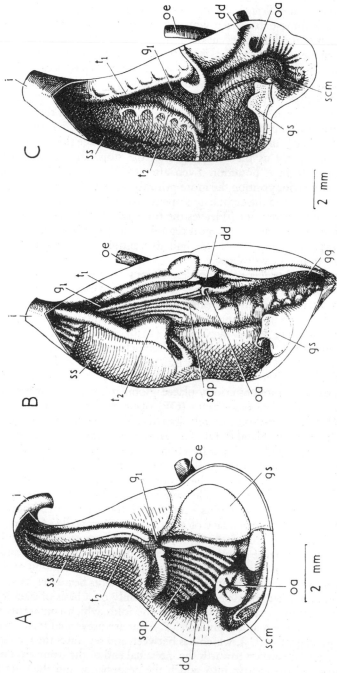

Fig. 119.—Dissections of stomachs, opened by a dorsal longitudinal cut.  A, *Diodora apertura*;  B, *Theodoxus fluviatilis*;  C, *Bithynia tentaculata*.  dd, opening of ducts of digestive gland;  g₁, intestinal groove;  gg, posterior groove;  gs, gastric shield;  i, intestine;  oa, oesophageal aperture;  oe, oesophagus;  sap, sorting area;  scm, spiral caecum, reduced;  ss, style sac region;  t₁, major typhlosole;  t₂, minor typhlosole.

enzymes as are produced by the salivary and oesophageal glands towards the stomach.
The only development of this region which calls for comment is the pouch-like caecum
attached to it in *Buccinum* and *Neptunea*. This appears to be a simple expansion of the gut,
presumably providing some extra space which may help to counteract any tendency
towards regurgitation of food in the event of elongation of the proboscis.

The next section of the alimentary canal is the stomach, which lies in the visceral hump
usually towards the left side. Much of it is invisible in surface view because of the way
in which it is covered by other viscera, of which kidney, digestive gland and gonad are
the most important. As has been indicated above (p. 28) the alimentary canal of gastropods is primitively U-shaped when seen from the side, rising from the mouth to the
stomach in the visceral hump and then falling again to the point where the anus discharges to the mantle cavity. In the hypothetical pre-torsional stage the mantle cavity was
posteriorly placed, the entry of the oesophagus to the stomach was anterior and the
origin of the intestine from it posterior. Even after torsion has displaced the mantle
cavity and anus to an anterior position the more primitive groups (fig. 119A) still maintain
this orientation of the parts and the oesophagus opens (oa) at the topographically posterior
end of the stomach and the intestine (i) leaves the topographically anterior end. Because
of the twist which occurs in the oesophageal region of the gut the dorsal surface of the
stomach is the morphologically dorsal side and its ventral surface is morphologically
ventral, as reference to fig. 13 will show.

A large number of more or less extensive descriptions of the anatomy of the stomach
of various prosobranchs have been published, the value of which is diminished by the
fact that they have often been opened in different ways in different states of contraction
and almost always described in inadequate detail. The following descriptions rest mainly
on the comparative account given by Graham (1949). The most primitive type of
stomach which is apparently present in the prosobranchs is that of the Trochacea (see
Owen, 1958): that of *Monodonta* is shown in fig. 120A. It is an ovoid sac embedded in
digestive gland, lying near the base of the visceral hump, on the animal's left. It is
divisible into two parts, a more posteriorly placed globular part, and a more cylindrical
anterior, the style sac (SS). The oesophagus (OE) opens near the posterior end of the
globular portion on to a groove on the right gastric wall. Into this groove discharges a
single duct from the digestive gland (DD). The groove, bounded by a marked fold ($T_1$)
on its left, runs into the mouth of a spirally coiled caecum (SCM) which extends from
the posterior end of the stomach amongst the tubules of the digestive gland. Almost the
whole of the remainder of the wall of the posterior globular part of the stomach is
covered by a thick cuticle, the gastric shield, which is raised near the middle of the left
side into a prominent boss (GS). Along its ventral edge the gastric shield borders a fold
(FF) and this, in turn, forms the boundary of a strip of stomach wall (SAP) edged by the
fold $T_1$ already referred to and, like it, disappearing into the mouth of the spiral caecum.
This strip is crossed by a large number of parallel grooves and ridges and extends
anteriorly into the base of the cylindrical part of the stomach. Examination of this region
in a living animal shows that diverse, vigorous, ciliary currents beat over its surface, and
that it is, in fact, an area where particles are sorted, mainly on a basis of size. It has been
called the posterior sorting area of the stomach. The folds which run across it do not
make actual contact with the major typhlosole ($T_1$), but are prevented from so doing by
a groove, the intestinal groove ($G_1$), which lies between and separates the two structures.
Along this a fast ciliary stream sets towards the intestinal end of the stomach. Posteriorly,
like the sorting area and the groove into which the oesophagus and the duct from the

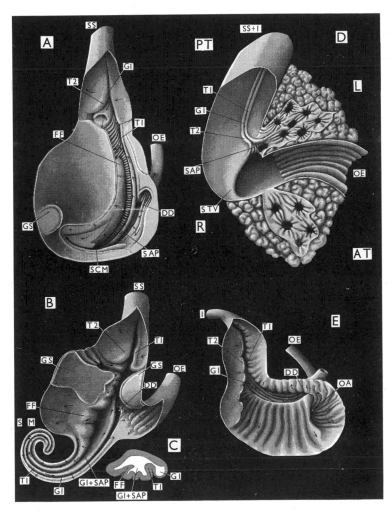

FIG. 120.—Dissections of stomachs, opened by a dorsal longitudinal cut. A, *Monodonta lineata*; B, *Calliostoma zizyphinum*; C, *Calliostoma zizyphinum*, T.S. spiral caecum; D, *Patella vulgata*; E, *Nucella lapillus*. Arrows show the course of ciliary currents. All × about 13.

AT, anterior end; DD, opening of duct of digestive gland; FF, fold emerging from spiral caecum; $G_1$, intestinal groove; $G_1 + SAP$, area representing fusion of intestinal groove and sorting area; GS, gastric shield; I, intestine; L, left; OA, oesophageal aperture; OE, oesophagus; PT, posterior end; R, right; SAP, sorting area; SCM, SM, spiral caecum; SS, style sac region; SS + I, part of gut formed from style sac or intestine—boundaries not detectable; STV, fold in stomach acting as valve; $T_1$, major typhlosole; $T_2$, minor typhlosole.

(*facing p.* 222.)

digestive gland open, the intestinal groove disappears into the mouth of the spiral caecum. If that be slit open (figs. 120B, c) the relations of the structures within it may be seen, and it is obvious that the major typhlosole ($T_1$) extends to the very tip of the caecum, where it ends, whereas the intestinal groove ($G_1$) curves round its tip and so becomes continuous with the groove connected with the oesophagus and digestive gland—they are, in fact, one and the same groove.

The only other feature which calls for mention in the posterior part of the stomach of a trochid is another groove which emerges from the caecum on the side opposite to that on which the ingoing and outcoming intestinal groove runs: this curves across to the base of the boss on the gastric shield and cilia on it beat in that direction.

The intestinal end of the stomach (SS) is cylindrical or conical in shape, broader where it is fitted to the posteriorly placed globular part, narrower anteriorly where it runs into the intestine. Along its ventral wall the intestinal groove extends from the posterior part of the stomach, with an extension of the major typhlosole ($T_1$) on its right. On the left it is bordered by a second typhlosole ($T_2$), the minor, which resembles the major but does not pass into the posterior half of the stomach. At the base of the style sac these typhlosoles diverge somewhat, and in the triangular space so formed are wedged the tip of the sorting area and a special area rich in mucous glands.

On the basis of this description and a comparison between the trochid stomach and that of other molluscs it is possible to say that the generalized prosobranch stomach (fig. 88) may be expected to show the following features. The oesophagus (oe) opens on the right side near the posterior end, the intestine (i) emerges from the anterior end of the style sac (ss), and the duct, or ducts, from the digestive gland (dd) open near the oesophageal aperture (oa). From the posterior end of the stomach there extends a spiral caecum (scm). Internally the fundamental features of the stomach wall appear to be: (1) the extensive cuticularized area, the gastric shield (gs), lying over the dorsal and left walls; (2) the intestinal groove ($g_1$) along the major typhlosole ($t_1$), the latter extending across the whole length of the stomach from the intestine to the apex of the spiral caecum, the former curving round that and running to the duct of the digestive gland; (3) the sorting area (sap) which lies in relation to the intestinal groove between it and the gastric shield; and (4) the minor typhlosole ($t_2$) which forms a second lip to the intestinal groove in the style sac.

Within the prosobranch gastropods it is possible to trace a relatively small number of evolutionary trends which affect the organization of the stomach. One of these is the gradual disappearance of the spiral caecum. Although this structure is clearly recognizable in most cephalopod and lamellibranch molluscs and therefore appears to be a fundamental feature of molluscan gastric organization, it is, in fact, only the Trochacea and the families of Zeugobranchia with spirally coiled shells (Pleurotomariidae, Haliotidae, Scissurellidae) which possess it in a well formed state amongst the Prosobranchia. In the remaining Zeugobranchia, e.g. *Diodora* (fig. 119A), *Emarginula* (Graham, 1939), the stomach shows the usual division into a globular posterior portion and a narrower anterior style sac, with the oesophagus opening into the former on a prominent papilla (oa) flanked by large ducts (dd), right and left, from the digestive gland. From these, sorting area (sap), intestinal groove ($g_1$) and major typhlosole run in characteristic fashion towards the style sac (ss), but behind there lies only a slight depression (scm) which could be held to represent the spiral caecum. A greater representation of the caecum may perhaps be recognizable in the Neritacea, if the conditions in *Theodoxus fluviatilis* (fig. 119B) are at all typical of the group. In this animal the oesophagus opens on the right (oa), into the posterior chamber, between the openings of two ducts from the digestive gland (dd) and from these apertures a pronounced groove (gg) leads to the posterior apex of the stomach. This is edged on both sides by folds, one of which runs along the base of the gastric shield (gs), which is not an extensive cuticularized area but covers only a limited part of the stomach wall, though it is raised into a curved crest in its middle. The fold which borders the other side of the groove is not obviously connected with the major typhlosole ($t_1$), which appears to originate at the mouth of one of the ducts from the

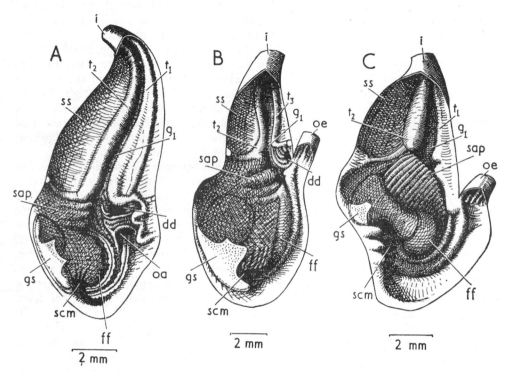

Fig. 121.—Dissections of stomachs, opened by a dorsal longitudinal cut. A, *Crepidula fornicata*; B, *Calyptraea chinensis*; C, *Turritella communis*.

dd, opening of duct of digestive gland; ff, fold emerging from spiral caecum; $g_1$, intestinal groove; gs, gastric shield; i, intestine; oa, oesophageal aperture; oe, oesophagus; sap, sorting area; scm, spiral caecum, much reduced; ss, style sac region; $t_1$, major typhlosole; $t_2$, minor typhlosole; $t_3$, fold on major typhosole.

digestive gland. From the posterior apex of the stomach a groove leads towards the base of the gastric shield, and more anteriorly a grooved and ridged sorting area (sap) lies at the base of the style sac, wedged between the two typhlosoles which run there, and in this area, too, lies a pouch-like depression from which mucus is secreted. This stomach obviously bears resemblances to that of *Monodonta* and, in particular, the slightly protuberant upper apex has a number of points in common with the spiral caecum of the trochid, though it is much less well developed and not at all spirally wound. In similar fashion it is possible to suggest that small pockets which lie at the upper end of the stomach of *Bithynia tentaculata* (fig. 119C), *Turritella communis* (fig. 121C), *Aporrhais pes-*

*pelicani, Bittium reticulatum, Calyptraea chinensis* (fig. 121B) and *Crepidula fornicata* (fig. 121A) are vestiges of the elaborate caecum of the trochids. In most of the prosobranch stomachs, however, not even this persists, and it is not possible to see any trace of it in the Docoglossa (fig. 120D), Architaenioglossa, Valvatacea, Littorinacea, Rissoacea, the higher groups of the mesogastropods or Stenoglossa (fig. 120E). The explanation of this is partly functional, as will be seen below.

A second evolutionary trend which is discernible in the prosobranchs is the gradual migration of the oesophageal opening from its morphologically anterior but topographically posterior position to a point which is topographically anterior. This involves a gradual shifting along the ventral side of the stomach and brings it much closer to the base of the style sac, so that the intestine and the style sac appear to be coming off the posterior part of the stomach together, and, at least in some cases, that part then looks like a caecum extending up the visceral hump. The changed position of the oesophageal opening is probably due as much to the mechanical traction of the more anterior parts of the alimentary canal as to any other cause, but, as a discussion of function will show later, it is also tied up with the altered importance of the spiral caecum and may be partly responsible for the disappearance of that structure in most prosobranchs, though it is difficult to disentangle cause and effect in this connexion. Associated with these changes is an alteration in the importance of the major typhlosole: with the reduced size or even absence of the caecum there is correlated a tendency for the typhlosole to stop near the base of the style sac, and this is, indeed, almost a necessary condition for the migration of the oesophageal opening towards the same point. This is indicated even in the trochids because the stomach of *Calliostoma zizyphinum* (fig. 120B) shows the oesophagus moving forwards and a breaking of the major typhlosole $(T_1)$ into 2 sections, an anterior one which is confined to the style sac (SS) and a posterior one which is restricted to the caecum (SCM). It is across the break in the typhlosole which has been made in this way that the oesophagus, and, to some extent, the ducts of the digestive gland too, migrate forwards.

A third change in the stomach of prosobranchs is definitely connected with a change in feeding habits. The more archaic members of the sub-class are all herbivorous and mainly microphagous, collecting algae and detritus of all kinds by means of their radula; a few may, in addition, bite or scrape small pieces off larger plants by means of the radula acting against the jaw. Most of the higher monotocardians, however, are carnivores, and the problems of digestion are different. There may, too, be a greater emphasis on extra-cellular digestion in the carnivorous forms and a greater emphasis on the sorting of material for ingestion and intra-cellular digestion by the cells of the digestive gland in the case of the microphagous herbivores. Whichever of these may be the effective cause there is a pronounced simplification of the stomach in the higher prosobranchs and it is reduced to little more than a sac to which oesophagus, intestine and the ducts of the digestive gland open, with only vestiges of intestinal groove and typhlosoles and often no trace at all of caecum, sorting area or gastric shield. This is seen, for example, in the stomach of *Nucella lapillus* (fig. 120E) (Graham, 1949), *Natica catena* (fig. 122A) and *Buccinum undatum* (Brock, 1936).

The same kind of evolution, more unexpectedly, has occurred in the Patellacea (fig. 120D), where the morphologically anterior part of the stomach can be regarded as almost wholly lost, a mere trace sandwiched between the well developed oesophagus (OE) on the one hand and the equally prominent style sac (SS) on the other. Two typhlosoles $T_1$, $T_2$) run along the latter with a vestigial sorting area (SAP) between, but all the

9

other features of this part of the prosobranch stomach have disappeared. It is difficult to suggest a convincing reason for their loss in these animals.

Throughout, the stomach is lined by a columnar epithelium which, in certain areas, contains mucous goblet cells. Other types of gland are not common. The height of the epithelium is variable and it is principally to this that may be attributed the lesser folds

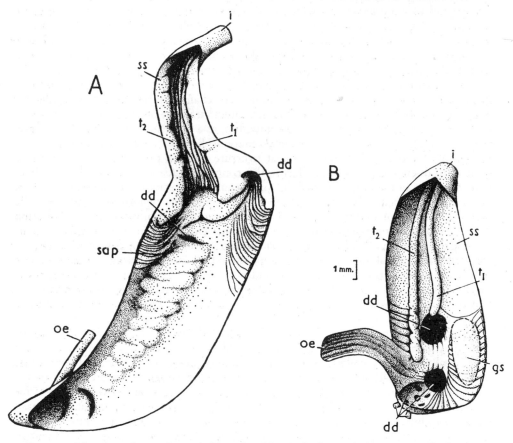

FIG. 122.—Dissections of stomachs, opened by a dorsal longitudinal cut.   A, *Natica catena*;   B, *Capulus ungaricus*.
    dd, opening of ducts of digestive gland; gs, gastric shield; i, intestine; oe, oesophagus; sap, sorting area; ss, style sac region; $t_1$, major typhlosole; $t_2$, minor typhlosole.

and grooves which are so prominent over its inner surface. The cells are not noteworthy in any way except in so far as they may be either ciliated (cic, fig. 123E) or cuticularized (gs, fig. 123D). In the latter case they exhibit the same structure as in the jaw—a fibrous layer interposed between the distal surface of the cell and the overlying cuticle, suggesting that the secretion escapes from pores in the cell surface and that the individual threads coalesce to form a sheet over the epithelium.

The style sac is marked off from the rest of the stomach not only anatomically but also histologically. The typhlosoles, major and minor, bear tall, columnar, ciliated cells interspersed with which are gland cells, mainly mucous. The rest of the sac is lined by an extremely characteristic epithelium the like of which is not found in any other situation. The cells are cubical or columnar and are filled with rather dense cytoplasm in which a large, rounded nucleus is centrally placed. The distal surface is densely clothed with long, close-set cilia each with a prominent basal granule. From the basal granules intracellular fibrillae converge fanwise to the side of the nucleus and can, on occasion, be traced even as far as the basal surface of the cell.

In gastropods with a crystalline style it appears to be the gland cells on the typhlosolar regions of the style sac which are responsible for the secretion of the substance out of which the style is made, just as they are in lamellibranchs (Nelson, 1918). The evolutionary step which has occurred in so many bivalves whereby the typhlosoles fuse across the intestinal groove and so separate that (as an intestine) from the main cavity of the style sac, has occurred much less commonly in prosobranchs and is found only in *Tornus* (Woodward, 1899), *Typhobia* (Robson, 1922*b*) and *Pterocera* (Yonge, 1932). It is well to remember in this connexion, however, that whereas all bivalves (save the protobranchs) possess a crystalline style, only a very small number of gastropods do, and it is probable that more advanced structure will be found only in the former class.

Opening into the stomach lies the digestive gland which fills the greater part of the visceral hump except, possibly, during the breeding season when the gonad is large. The digestive gland is the organ most clearly visible on the surface of the visceral mass when a prosobranch is removed from its shell. Superficially examined, it appears as a vast mass of branching tubules; more carefully seen, it is found to be composed of 2 lobes of unequal size each connected to the stomach by a single duct. Of these lobes that on the left is by far the larger. Much modification of the ducts may occur: in many Trochacea and Docoglossa, for example, the 2 ducts from the 2 lobes unite before reaching the stomach so that only a single aperture appears on the stomach wall. In others the reverse kind of change seems to have occurred and each lobe may open to the stomach by several apertures as if multiple ducts were present. This is presumably due to the opening out of the main ducts on to the walls of the stomach.

The tubules of which the gland is composed extend into the visceral haemocoel and so are bathed in blood (fig. 123). Only a very thin layer of connective tissue (cn) appears to separate the digestive cells from the blood (hc), and, in places, even this may be absent. A few muscle fibres are normally present around them; cells containing glycogen may be found in the connective tissue. The amount of material which is stored here depends not only upon such obvious factors as the degree of starvation of the animal but also upon the season and the sexual state. Linke (1934*b*) has shown that in a prosobranch such as *Littorina littorea* (fig. 124) the bulk of the visceral hump is occupied by digestive gland (dg) and gonad (t) during the breeding season with a minimal amount of connective tissue (cn) containing reserve food separating the tubules of these 2 organs. During the resting period which intervenes between two breeding periods, however, much of the reproductive system is broken down and, at these times, the visceral hump is primarily made up of digestive gland and a voluminous connective tissue rich in stored foodstuffs in which only vestiges of gonad may be traced.

In most prosobranchs, at least the main ducts of the digestive gland are lined by a ciliated, columnar epithelium similar to that lining the stomach (ste, fig. 123E): it may be that it is an eversion of the stomach wall which has given rise to them. The tubules of the gland, however, are lined by a totally different type of epithelium within which at least two different types of cell may always be distinguished. One of these appears to correspond, broadly, to the digestive cell described by Yonge (1925b) in the digestive gland of bivalves, but the second sort is different from the 'young' cells which occur in the crypts of the tubules in members of that class.

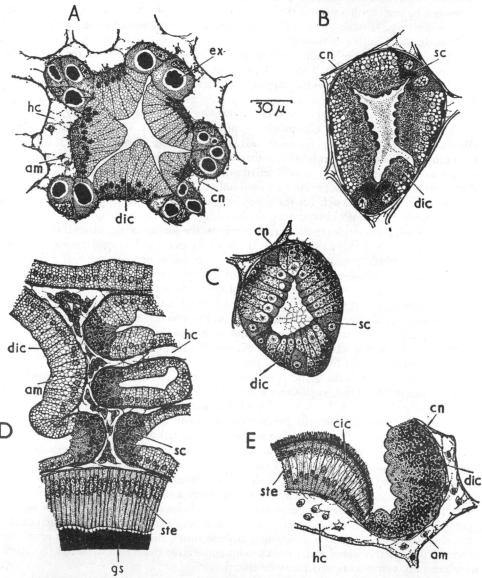

FIG. 123.—Histology of the digestive gland. A, *Bithynia tentaculata*; B, *Lacuna vincta*; C, *Patella vulgata*; D, *Gibbula cineraria*; E, *Natica catena*. Fig. D contains a piece of cuticularized gastric wall, and fig. E a piece of ciliated duct.

am, amoebocyte; cic, ciliated cell; cn, **connective tissue**; dic, digestive cell; ex, excretory cell; gs, cuticle of gastric shield; hc, haemocoelic space; sc, secretory cell; ste, epithelium of stomach wall.

The histology of the digestive gland varies considerably from animal to animal amongst the prosobranchs. This may be partly due to genuine specific differences related to such questions as the animal's food and whether ingestion of particulate food is carried on, but some of the differences may be due to a rhythmical cycle of activity related to secretion, ingestion and the like, such as has been described for *Helix pomatia* by Krijgsman (1925, 1928).

The diotocardian prosobranchs all appear to be microphagous herbivores, occasionally supplementing this diet by rasping pieces off larger plants, though others, like *Diodora* and *Emarginula*, have the habit of feeding on sponges. It is not surprising, therefore, that there is a broad resemblance between the digestive glands of these animals (figs. 123C, D). The commonest cell is the digestive cell (dic), a tall, columnar cell with highly vacuolated cytoplasm which rarely stains at all intensely. The distal border is often denser than the rest of the cell, may show signs of striations normal to the surface and, in life, is often

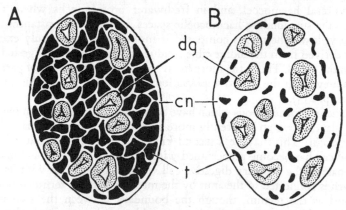

FIG. 124.—*Littorina littorea:* diagrammatic transverse sections of the visceral hump. A, during the breeding season; B, in non-breeding period. After Linke.
cn, connective tissue; dg, digestive gland; t, testis.

ciliated, though the cilia either drop off or are withdrawn on fixation and so do not appear in sections (see Owen, 1956). It may, on the other hand, be lobed, and suggest the nipping off of part of the cell with secretion: the nucleus may be central or basal and has not a prominent nucleolus. These cells can, in some animals (*Patella, Acmaea*) be shown to ingest particulate food into vacuoles and to digest it intracellularly, and to take it up from solution in most prosobranchs. The second type of cell (sc) is less numerous and tends to occur in groups in the crypts located at the angles of the tubules. In it the cytoplasm is dense, though it may be somewhat vacuolated, and always stains darkly. It is not recorded by workers in this field as taking up food, either in solution or in particles, from the lumen of the gut. The cell is triangular in section, with a broad surface set along the base of the epithelium and abutting against the blood space beyond, and tapers to a fine point where it reaches the cavity of the tubule. The nucleus is basal, large, and contains a prominent nucleolus, whilst darkly staining spherules often abound in the cytoplasm. In trochids and some other groups these cells have often been seen to project into the intertubular haemocoelic spaces. They seem, therefore, adapted for the uptake of material from the blood by way of their expanded bases and for elaborating it into some secretion which would be then shed to the lumen of the tubule. Both types of cell seem able to manufacture secretion of some sort: presumably these are unlike and in view of the greater number of the first type of cell it seems more likely that they would be the source of any digestive enzymes that might be secreted.

Whilst this appears to be the general histological structure of the digestive gland not only in the diotocardians but in most prosobranchs, some depart from it. In the rissoids, hydrobiids, *Littorina*, naticids, *Bittium*, and calyptraeids there frequently occur large yellowish concretions, usually spherical but frequently quite irregular in shape. Their real nature is unknown, but as they may often be found, apparently unaltered, in the faeces, they appear to be excretory matter of some sort. In sections of the digestive gland of these animals (fig. 123A) these concretions are found to occur in the cells which lie in the crypts of the gland and, therefore, to correspond to the glandular cells of a limpet which have a special relation to the vascular system: this is especially well seen in *Bittium* where these cells occupy almost the whole of the peripheral wall of the tubules abutting against the visceral haemocoel, and in freshwater prosobranchs where they project markedly into the surrounding haemocoelic spaces. In these circumstances the material of which the yellow spherules is composed is more likely to be truly excretory than faecal matter derived from the indigestible residue of what has been ingested by the first type of cell in the gland. This is the more likely, too, in that ingestion of particulate food is not a certain event in the digestive physiology of some of the molluscs that produce such spherules (p. 235).

In some higher mesogastropods which have become carnivorous and in the Stenoglossa the digestive gland shows an apparently more elaborate histology in that a third kind of cell seems to occur. This may be a second kind of gland cell, introduced because the original gland cell has become preoccupied with excretory activity, or it may be simply a secretory phase of the ordinary digestive cell which is out of step with its neighbours.

The stomach is connected to the anus by the intestine and the terminal portion of this is distinguished as the rectum, though the boundary between the two is somewhat arbitrarily drawn. The rectum usually shows considerable longitudinal folds on its walls, whereas the intestine is normally smooth. The intestine leaves the stomach at the distal end of the style sac, the point being marked by the disappearance of the ciliated epithelium characteristic of that part, by a decrease in diameter and, in some animals, by a slight sphincter muscle. The intestinal groove and the 2 typhlosoles, major and minor, normally continue along the intestine, dying away after greater or lesser distances, but occasionally continuing as far as the anus.

The length of the intestine varies considerably: in *Diodora* it is relatively short—in *D. apertura* measuring only 4 times the length of the shell—whereas in the Docoglossa it is vastly longer—in *Patella vulgata* equalling 8 times the shell length (fig. 125). The reason for this difference in intestinal development appears to be the need for consolidation of the faecal material before it is passed into the mantle cavity. The dangers of fouling this are evident, but may be minimized by the elaboration of the faecal matter into pellets as it travels along the intestine from stomach to anus. The length of the intestine may, perhaps, be regarded as proportional to the urgency of this requirement in relation to the kind of faecal matter produced, for few signs of other activity on its part have ever been recorded (see p. 234). The brevity of the intestine in *Diodora* would then be correlated with the presence of an apical pallial aperture through which the exhalant current from the mantle cavity escapes, washing over the anus as it does so, and carrying faecal matter from contact—or likelihood of contact—with the ctenidia.

In a general way most herbivorous prosobranchs have a longer intestine than do carnivorous forms. In *Trivia*, *Lamellaria*, *Ianthina*, *Balcis*, *Nucella*, *Buccinum* and *Mangelia*, for example, the intestine runs straight from style sac to anus and is not long. In *Diodora* it forms a simple loop between stomach and anus, in *Emarginula* a large loop, with a smaller loop superimposed near the anus. In the trochids the intestine runs forward from the stomach, loops tightly on itself once and then passes forwards towards the head (i,

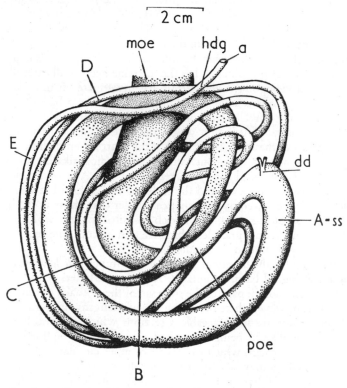

FIG. 125.—*Patella vulgata:* diagram of the course of the alimentary canal lying within the visceral mass. a, anus; dd, ducts of the digestive gland; hdg, hind gut or rectum; moe, mid-oesophagus; poe, posterior oesophagus; A = ss, proximal section of intestine homologous with style sac of stomach; B, C, D, E, sections of intestine.

fig. 170); from this position it bends back towards the stomach and curves on to the mantle roof to reach the anus (a). In the herbivorous monotocardian prosobranchs it is more or less possible to discern an underlying plan for the intestinal coiling: in many, on emerging from the style sac the intestine is flung into an S-bend, the initial loop towards the animal's right, by the kidney, the second towards the left and the neighbourhood of the pericardial cavity from where it runs on to the mantle skirt. This pattern of intestinal coiling is found, for example, in littorinids, lacunids, rissoids, calyptraeids, capulids, turritellids, and aporrhaids. In the Docoglossa—at least the larger ones—the intestine becomes much more elaborately coiled and forms, in *Patella vulgata*, 6 loops around the visceral dome before running to the anus (fig. 125).

In the Zeugobranchia, Trochacea and Neritacea the intestine runs through the ventricle of the heart before running on to the mantle skirt to open at the anus (rve, figs. 53, 71). During development it starts ventral to the heart but the ventricle wraps round it as growth occurs. This region is generally referred to as the rectum, but, in forms where penetration of the ventricle does not occur, there is very little reason for separating one part from another. The whole intestinal length is clothed with a columnar epithelium the cells of which vary in height and so often give rise to shallow longitudinal folds. These, especially in the rectum, are often raised on connective tissue masses so that folds of considerable dimensions run along the gut. The cells are usually ciliated and gland cells abound, becoming more frequent in the neighbourhood of the anus, though a zone rich in this type of cell may occur near the style sac as well (e.g. *Trichotropis*).

In only a few species of prosobranch has the intestine been at all carefully investigated from the histological viewpoint. Gabe (1951b) has investigated it in *Diodora* and shown that several segments are discernible. The epithelium rests on a basement membrane of collagen and on a double muscle layer, of circular fibres internally and longitudinal and oblique mixed externally. This is thin where the rectum lies within the ventricle but becomes thicker towards the anus. At the level of the heart the epithelium is low (15–20 $\mu$) and its cells contain neither iron-containing granules nor alkaline phosphatase. The chondriome is poorly developed and gland cells are sparse. A second region may be distinguished lying between the heart and the style sac and a third between the heart and the anus. The former is covered by epithelial cells taller than those in the heart (35–40 $\mu$) and ciliated. The base of the cytoplasm is rich in mitochondria whilst the more distal parts contain numerous yellow granules which are rich in iron. The anal region has gland cells and alkaline phosphatase in the epithelium.

Graham (1932) divided the intestinal region of the limpet *Patella vulgata* (fig. 125) into 5 sections on a histological basis, designated by reference letters A, B, C, D and E. Of these section A corresponds, in part, to the style sac of the stomach of other prosobranchs. To the remaining 4, however, there falls to be added a lengthy hind-gut, so that between stomach and anus, there are still traceable 5 sections which are histologically differentiated, though all are alike in being composed of a columnar epithelium resting on a connective tissue basis through which run layers of inner circular and outer longitudinal muscles. Section A, which may be compared with the style sac of the stomach, nevertheless shows some signs of difference from the usual appearance of that region, in that the component cells are tall and narrow (28–30 $\mu$), with only short cilia. They contain, distally, numerous yellow-green pigment granules, and seem to secrete some mucoid substance. Section B is narrower in diameter and marked by shallow longitudinal folds. Its epithelium (18 $\mu$) resembles that of section A in most respects, but contains fat droplets. Section C, which forms 2 of the 6 loops into which the intestine is flung, is lined by an epithelium (16–20 $\mu$) mainly similar to that of previous sections, save for the absence of fat droplets, but, in addition, it contains gland cells which are wedged between the bases of the ciliated cells and connected to the lumen of the gut by long, slender necks. Their cytoplasm is packed with numerous minute granules which are very refringent in fresh material and stain so as to suggest that they are protein. In section D these glands also occur, but so does a second sort, the clavate gland, which produces large spherules of secretion with the same refringency and staining properties as the much more minute granules of the basal glands. Section E is, in general, reminiscent of section C, with basal glands alone, but its cilia are very short and its pigmentation greater. The hind-gut, on the other hand, is almost unpigmented, and its walls are flung into several longitudinal folds, two of which largely subdivide the cavity into dorsal and ventral channels, the faeces always, for some reason, using the latter. Mucous cells occur here.

In some prosobranchs a rectal or anal gland is to be found. The occurrence of this has been wrongly attributed to some Zeugobranchia: in *Diodora* and *Emarginula*, but not *Haliotis* nor *Scissurella* apparently, a long tube runs alongside the intestine and rectum, with which it communicates near the anus. This was described first by Haller (1884) who called it a genital duct, but later Pelseneer (1906a) regarded it as an anal gland. It is, in fact, a siphon, and it rejoins the intestine just distal to the point where that leaves the style sac. Investigation shows that it is in reality the intestinal groove which has been separated from the main intestinal lumen by the fusion of the 2 typhlosoles over it. It retains a ciliated epithelium, but what its significance in the life of the animal may be is still unknown, though it always appears empty in sections. It may be that it offers an escape for intestinal fluid if the animal has to pull the shell suddenly over the viscera, but the resistance which would be offered to the flow of fluid by a tube of such inconsiderable dimensions makes its use in this way rather improbable.

A genuine anal gland in the form of a caecal outgrowth from the rectum in the neighbourhood of the anus, is known to occur in *Murex*, *Ocenebra*, *Nucella* (rgl, fig. 149), *Urosalpinx* and *Trophon* and may well occur in other, or all, genera of muricacean stenoglossans. According to Pelseneer (1906a) an anal gland also occurs in the Naticidae and Simroth (1896–1907) stated that *Puncturella* possesses one. These, however, are doubtful: Fretter (1946a) failed to find any gland in *Natica catena*, whilst that alleged to occur in *Puncturella* may well be the end of the siphon found in other conical-shelled zeugobranchs and described above.

In *Nucella lapillus* (fig. 126) the anal gland has the form of a group of caeca which unite with one another to form a duct leading to the rectum just within the anus. In young *Nucella* the gland is a simple diverticulum from the rectum lying between the rectum and mantle and extending back to the level of the posterior end of the mantle cavity. The gland is surrounded by the same blood sinus as lies around the rectum. Whilst the animal is young the epithelium is a simple, ciliated, columnar epithelium like that covering the rectum. Later as outpouching of the walls occurs, the cells begin to develop small brown granules: these two processes continue, to give rise to the dark brown or even black gland of the adult. The cells remain ciliated even when full of granules, the cilia beating gently towards the duct. The granules come to lie in vacuoles and finally break away and are lost. Experimental work shows that injected materials such as trypan blue or iron saccharate are picked out of the blood and expelled through the cells of the gland.

In a certain number of other prosobranchs a simpler type of rectal or anal gland occurs in the form of an enlargement of the terminal part of the intestinal groove or as a pouch on the side of the end of the rectum. The former condition occurs in some trochids and has been described by Fretter (1955b) and by Deshpande (1957); the latter is found in *Scissurella crispata*. The degree of development of the gland of the trochids varies, being greatest in *Margarites helicinus*, moderate in *Gibbula umbilicalis*, small in *G. cineraria* and absent elsewhere. In all the animals in which it occurs this type of rectal gland seems to be different in function from that of the stenoglossans and is to be regarded as a lubricant of the terminal part of the gut rather than as an excretory organ.

The function of the intestinal part of the gut appears to be primarily the formation of semi-solid, compacted faeces which will not disintegrate within the mantle cavity. Little absorption of the products of digestion seems to take place through its walls, and its length is rather to ensure that the incipient faeces receive a sufficient coating of cementing secretion than to provide a great area of absorptive surface. Nevertheless it is improbable that the intestinal contents are not altered in some way during their sojourn in this part of the gut, as is true of the intestine of *Helix*, where no true absorption occurs, but through the walls of which soluble substances may diffuse (Jordan & Lam, 1918; Hörstadius-Kjellström & Hörstadius, 1940), even those with molecules as large as disaccharide sugars (Jordan & Begemann, 1921). Gabe & Prenant (1949) have made similar suggestions for chitons, and Fretter (1952), using radioactive phosphorus and iodine, showed that salts could diffuse through the intestinal wall of snails and slugs.

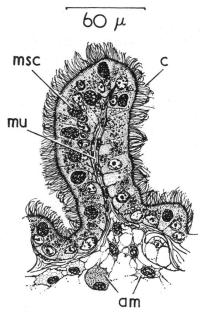

FIG. 126.—*Nucella lapillus:* histology of anal gland.
am, amoebocytes;  c, cilia;  msc, mass of secretion within cell;  mu, muscle fibre.

The formation of faeces begins in the stomach, the style sac region of that organ (ss, fig. 88) having this as its primary function. Within it there may be distinguished 2 spaces incompletely separated from one another by the 2 typhlosoles, major and minor ($t_1$, $t_2$), which run along it. Of these much the smaller is the intestinal groove ($g_1$), which arises at the main opening of the digestive diverticula into the stomach (dd) and runs thence to the style sac; the main channel of the style sac, however, is merely an analward extension of the principal part of the stomach, to which the oesophagus and digestive gland ducts open and on the walls of which lies the gastric shield (gs). Food is led into this chamber mixed, in most prosobranchs, with digestive enzymes derived from the oesophageal glands, and to this mixture is added further enzymatic material in the secretion of the digestive gland. The mixture of food and enzyme is then acted upon by the ciliary currents and by the muscular wall of the stomach, which is extensively protected against abrasion in the lower gastropods by the cuticular gastric shield. This may be correlated with the tendency of these animals to be (at least incidentally) detritus feeders; in the higher prosobranchs, which tend to be more exclusive carnivores, the gastric shield is reduced or lost as the need for its protection is minimal. When digestion has occurred the same processes of muscular squeezing and ciliary streaming press a solution of digested food material out of the mass in the stomach into the ducts and tubules of the digestive gland, where it is taken up by the absorbing digestive cells (dic, fig. 123). In certain cases (diotocardians and some lower monotocardians) minute particulate matter which enters the gland may be phagocytosed by the cells and digested intracellularly in vacuoles. These processes, however, leave in the main chamber of the stomach a mass of indigestible material which is gradually moved into the style sac. In the style sac it comes under the influence of two sets of ciliary currents, the main one (on the greater part of the walls) rotating the mass, the others (on the typhlosoles) moving it along the style sac towards the anus, the combined effect being a rotatory movement in the direction of the intestine. On the typhlosoles and in an area at the point where the style sac springs from the main part of the stomach mucous cells abound and the material in the style sac is gradually rolled and cemented into a rod of firm gelatinous consistency. In many proso-branchs provision is made for the return to the main cavity of the stomach of particles which fail to become incorporated in this rod by means of a ciliary current on the typhlosoles running in that direction. The occurrence of this current is a matter of some theoretical importance in considering the origin of the crystalline style (see below). The rod manufactured in the style sac moves out of that part of the gut into the intestine where it may undergo further cementing with secretion from intestinal glands, further compacting and perhaps a final segmentation into pellets.

In addition to material which enters the style sac from the main part of the stomach there is a second stream which passes into the intestinal groove and comes predominantly from the ducts of the digestive gland. It is composed partly of particulate matter which has failed to be incorporated in the main mass in the stomach and which has been passed into the ducts of the digestive gland, partly of a certain amount of true excretory matter which has been extracted from the blood by the excretory cells of the digestive gland, and sometimes of the indigestible residue of food undergoing intracellular digestion. These 3 kinds of material become intermingled in the intestinal groove and pass along the style sac to enter the intestine, where they become associated with the faecal rod emerging from the main part of the sac. The faecal rod in the intestine, therefore, is made up of 2 kinds of material: the bulk from the stomach, the second from the digestive gland. Using the terminology suggested by Carriker (1946), the former may be called the stomach string, and the latter the liver string. They are frequently different in con-sistency (the liver string containing only microscopic particles) and in colour, so that when both become associated in the intestine it is still possible to distinguish the parts of the faecal rods or pellets to which they give rise.

The stomach string may have no particular form apart from that imparted to it by the compacting and rolling which it has undergone in the stomach and style sac. In those prosobranchs which possess a spirally coiled gastric caecum, however (Haliotidae, Scissurellidae, Trochidae, Turbinidae), the presence of this structure affects the organiza-tion of the stomach string. In these animals, as shown by Graham (1949), the string of material which enters the stomach from the oesophagus is passed over the entrance of the ducts of the digestive gland into the mouth of the caecum (see figs. 120A, B). It travels along this to the apex of the coil and then back to the main cavity of the stomach where it is added as a thread-like structure to the end of the mass of material which fills that space. This treatment ensures a very thorough admixture of food and enzymes of both oesophageal and other origin. Although some of this structure is modified by the treatment which the food mass receives in the style sac it can usually still be recognized in the faeces even after discharge.

As a consequence of the differential origin of the faecal material and of the various treatments which it receives in different parts of the gut, the faecal rods or pellets which leave the anus are sometimes objects of considerable complexity, the architecture of which was first shown by Moore (1931–32) to have some value as a specific character. These differences are most marked in the lower gastropods, the faeces in the higher being often simple oval pellets without surface markings, enclosed in a superficial

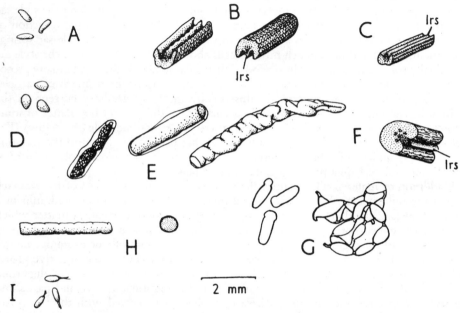

Fig. 127.—Faeces. A, *Acmaea virginea*; B, *Gibbula cineraria*; C, *Gibbula magus*; D, *Turritella communis*; E, *Calliostoma zizyphinum*; F, *Monodonta lineata*; G, *Natica alderi*; H, *Patella vulgata* in side view and T.S.; I, *Bittium reticulatum*.
     lrs, liver string.

mucous layer. Of these faecal masses Moore (1939) regarded the simple rod of *Patella vulgata* (fig. 127H) as the most primitive: here there are only segmental markings and the faecal matter lies within a skin derived from intestinal glands (Graham, 1932). The rod, which may be up to 1·7 cm long, segments fairly readily along the line of the markings but does not easily undergo further break down. Moore suggested that the extremely common pellets of higher gastropods (*Turritella*, fig. 127D; *Bittium*, fig. 127I) have been derived from the segmentation of a rod such as this. The fissurellids produce somewhat similar rod-shaped faeces, but these are flattened in section. Much more elaborate are the faeces of trochids: these consist of a rod (e.g. *Monodonta lineata*, fig. 127F) composed of a stomach string, U-shaped in section, with a liver string (lrs) plugging the opening of the U and running like a keel along one side of the rod. In the intestine this lay in the intestinal groove. The stomach string shows a regular gradation of material, the superficial layers always being composed of the finest particles and the largest invariably occurring centrally in the area where stomach and liver strings are in contact: this may perhaps be related to the rotatory movement in the style sac to which is due the initial shaping of the rod. The rod also shows a series of sinuous ripple-like markings over its surface. Similar faecal rods occur in other trochids (*Gibbula cineraria*, fig. 127B; *G. magus*, fig. 127C). *Calliostoma zizyphinum*, however, differs in that the faeces produced comprise an irregular rod containing sand, calcareous or vegetable detritus embedded merely in a mass of mucus (fig. 127E).

As mentioned above, a certain number of prosobranch gastropods possess the structure known as a crystalline style. The way in which this has arisen may now be briefly dealt with. When the anatomy of the stomach of these animals is investigated the style is found to lie in a structure which is so directly comparable with the style sac region of other gastropods in respect of its anatomical relationships, its histology and the direction of the ciliary currents along its walls as to leave little doubt that the one is homologous with the other. Inside each lies a cylindrical structure composed largely of mucus, but in the one group it is the beginning of a faecal rod travelling to the intestine, and in the other has adsorbed enzymes which are being carried to the stomach for release. If the style sacs are homologous then it is worth asking whether their contents are not equally so: Yonge (1939a) and Graham (1939, 1949) have both concluded that this is so and that the crystalline style is, indeed, merely a transformation of the faecal rod. In addition to the points already mentioned in support of their homology there may also be mentioned the facts that food particles are often embedded in the mucus of the style—just as they are in the faecal rod—and that the bulk of the mucus in both cases is derived from gland cells on the typhlosoles. It appears that in the evolution of a few groups of monotocardians, as in the evolution of the lamellibranchs, the adoption of a rigorous microphagy emphasized the phase of intracellular digestion within the digestive gland at the expense of the extracellular digestion which occurred within the stomach. When this happened the stomach string became relatively free of food particles and detritus because these now all passed to the digestive gland and, therefore, became incorporated in the liver string. The stomach string was thus susceptible to a transformation into a mucous rod with adsorbed enzymes and gave rise to the structure which we know as the crystalline style. The direction of movement which it underwent changed from a rotatory posterior to a rotatory anterior one, ciliary currents which could bring this about being already present, and the end of the rod which lay alongside the gastric shield in the main part of the stomach was no longer the place at which the rod was being formed, but the site of its solution in the gastric contents to liberate the enzymes which it contained. These appear to be simple amylases, though the style has been less thoroughly explored from this point of view than that of lamellibranchs, where it is known to contain glycogenase and oxidase as well (Yonge, 1926). *Oncomelania* (=*Hypsobia*) *nosophora* has a cellulase in its style (Winkler & Wagner, 1959). In addition to the liberation of enzymes in the gastric cavity the solution of the style helps to control the pH of the gut (being normally the most acid substance present) and its rotation helps the transport of food through the stomach.

So far as other digestive enzymes in the gut of prosobranch gastropods are concerned there is not a great deal of information in the literature, the choice of those animals which have been investigated being obviously dictated by the need for adequate supplies of tissue or gut juice for this type of physiological work. Thus the animals used have been mainly *Patella vulgata*, *Haliotis* spp., *Natica* spp., *Viviparus* spp., *Vermetus novae-*

*hollandiae*, *Pterocera crocata*, *Pterotrachea* spp. and some of the larger stenoglossans belonging to the genera *Murex*, *Nucella*, *Buccinum*, *Neptunea* and *Busycon*.

In the diotocardians amongst these it is likely that the saliva is solely lubricatory and that the salivary glands secrete no enzymes (*Patella*: Graham, 1932). On the other hand the oesophageal and digestive glands in these animals seem to secrete a digestive fluid capable of attacking proteins, fats and carbohydrates (*Patella*: Roaf, 1906, 1908; Rosén, 1937; *Haliotis*: Albrecht, 1921, 1923). Graham (1932) found no evidence of the secretion of digestive enzymes from the digestive gland of limpets though he did record the secretion of an amylolytic enzyme from the oesophageal gland. All writers, however, are agreed that the intestine is not responsible for secreting enzymes and that the uptake of digested food occurs in the digestive gland, within the cells of which intracellular digestion may also take place. Although little work has been done to demonstrate it, it is likely that this pattern of digestive activity is the common one amongst the herbivorous and microphagous prosobranchs (except where a crystalline style is found). The enzymes, apart from a lipase extracted from the digestive gland of *Viviparus viviparus* by Rosén (1932), have not been purified so that their properties are only vaguely known: they appear to work best at pH 5–6, which is the pH of the parts of the gut in which they naturally occur (Yonge, 1925a). Rosén (1937) has shown that the proteinase of the digestive gland of *Patella vulgata* requires to be activated by hydrogen sulphide or similar reducing agent and that it is inhibited by iodoacetic acid: this suggests that the enzyme is probably a cathepsin, and may, therefore, be intracellular.

In herbivores with a crystalline style free proteolytic enzymes do not normally occur because they would digest the style itself (Yonge, 1930); in them, however, free carbohydrases and lipases may be found (*Vermetus novae-hollandiae*: Yonge, 1932; *Pterocera crocata*: Yonge, 1932) derived from the salivary or digestive glands. *Pterocera* and *Strombus* also secrete a cellulase, though the site of its manufacture is not known, and in this respect they differ from all the other prosobranchs. Dodgson & Spencer (1954) reported the occurrence of sulphatases in a number of prosobranchs (*Patella*, *Monodonta*, *Calliostoma* and *Littorina littorea* in particular) which may help in the digestion of polysaccharide sulphates in the algal food which they ingest.

In carnivorous prosobranchs the investigation of digestive enzymes has been more closely pursued. Amongst the mesogastropods the most complete account is the one given by Hirsch (1915) for two species of *Natica*, *N. hebraea* and *N. millepunctata*. Here enzymes are absent from the salivary glands but a proteinase occurs in the secretion of the oesophageal glands whilst the digestive gland secretes proteolytic, amylolytic and lipolytic enzymes. The secretion of these is timed so that the digestive gland is, on the whole, active after food has been caught but does not secrete in a starved animal. This is particularly noticeable in the case of the proteolytic enzymes which might otherwise attack the gut wall. More thorough examinations of the digestive enzymes—some using modern methods for purification—have been made in the case of some Stenoglossa. Amongst the first of these to be investigated was the American *Busycon canaliculatum* by Mendel & Bradley (1905a, b, 1906). These workers found a proteolytic enzyme in the saliva, another (or the same) and a diastase in the gastric contents, whilst an extract of the digestive gland contained enzymes capable of attacking starch, glycogen, sugars and some proteins. Roaf (1906) obtained similar results with the digestive glands of *Nucella lapillus* and *Neptunea antiqua* and gave the further information that the enzymes were most active in acid media. Hirsch (1915) gave an account of digestion in *Murex trunculus*. Here the salivary glands ('kleine Vorderdarmdruse') secrete a proteolytic enzyme but not an amylolytic one; extracts of the gland of Leiblein ('grosse Vorderdarmdruse'), on the other hand, were found to digest starch but apparently to be without action on other types of food; the fluid in the stomach and extracts of the digestive gland, however, contained enzymes which were effective on proteins, carbohydrates and fats. Frequently, as in *Natica*, these were absent from a starved animal and were secreted only after feeding. A more elaborate investigation of the related species *M. anguliferus* was made by Mansour-Bek (1934). Here the saliva was shown to contain a proteinase most active at pH 8·2 and also a dipeptidase; the same enzymes were found in extracts of the gland of Leiblein, in the stomach fluid and in extracts of the digestive gland. The gland of Leiblein and the digestive gland also manufacture a carboxypolypeptidase and an aminopolypeptidase. In the fluids in which they normally occur these have an optimum pH at 7·6 or 8·2; this is unchanged when purified. The proteinase does not require either zookinase or entero-kinase for activation, which seems to suggest that it is not an enzyme of the cathepsin type and, if a trypsin, is different from the familiar type of vertebrates. The cyclical production of enzyme in step with the feeding activity of the mollusc may partly be related to the activity of the enzyme.

Brock (1936) and Mansour-Bek (1934) have given an account of the enzymes—and, in the case of the former, of much of the physiology of the alimentary tract—of the common whelk, *Buccinum undatum*. The salivary glands in this animal secrete saliva containing enzymes attacking peptone and glycylglycine at a neutral pH (water extract) or at pH 8·0-8·2 (glycerol extract); no enzyme of carbohydrase type occurs in their secretion nor in that of the gland of Leiblein, which secretes proteolytic enzymes. The fluid in the stomach, on the other hand, contains an amylase, a lipase and enzymes capable of attacking proteins and their breakdown products: these are presumably derived from the digestive gland since they may also be detected in extracts of that structure. These enzymes work optimally around neutrality, the natural pH of the stomach being slightly lower.

In all these carnivorous prosobranchs extracellular digestion in the stomach appears to be the rule, followed by an absorption of the products of digestion by the digestive gland. This also seems to be true of many of the herbivores though it may be supplemented by a phagocytosis of particulate matter in the digestive gland of these animals. In the zeugo-branchs and in the Patellacea intracellular digestion seems to be relatively more im-portant still. As in all groups of the animal kingdom diet and enzymes are correlated, proteolytic enzymes being more marked in carnivores and those of a diastatic type predominating in herbivorous animals. In contrast to the lamellibranchs and to some opisthobranch gastropods wandering amoeboid or phagocytic cells seem to play little part in the digestive processes of prosobranchs.

# CHAPTER 10

# FEEDING

THE molluscs have exhibited such ability to adapt themselves to life in so many different types of habitat that it is not surprising that they have learned how to feed in a variety of different ways. Adaptive radiation in the Mollusca, as in other phyla, has involved adaptation to feeding niches. As a first approach towards the description of some of the ways in which prosobranchs feed it may be useful to mention some of the classifications of types of feeding mechanism which have been proposed by previous writers. Of these the earliest, and one of those most commonly used, is that of Jordan (1913). This recognizes three types of animal:

(1) Strudler (a whirler or eddymaker) —a ciliary feeder.

(2) Schlinger (a snarer or swallower) —an animal feeding either by the ingestion of the bodies of plants and animals, which it eats whole, or by breaking them down into smaller particles.

(3) Sauger (a sucker) —an animal which feeds by the sucking of liquid food.

It will be noted that there is no clear separation of microphagous from macrophagous types of animals on this classification. Ciliary feeders must, it is true, be microphagous, but so, too, can be some of the animals classified in group (2), such as the prosobranch which collects detrital material or rasps minute particles from the surface of a larger organism. The classes into which the animals are grouped are so wide that this classification requires considerable subdivision before it becomes useful.

Hirsch (1915) accepted Jordan's classification as the starting point for one of his own, which adds a fourth group to the three previously established and which has the merit of distinguishing the kind of microphagous animal which Jordan placed in group (2) from the other (macrophagous) animals occurring in that group. An animal in this fourth group Hirsch called a scratcher or scraper (Kratzer).

More recently Jordan & Hirsch (1927) have together proposed a more elaborate classification of feeding mechanisms as has Yonge (1928), the latter being adopted by Prosser et al. (1950). The former is elaborate and comprehensive but has some unusual features. It is:

A. Microphagous animals
  1. Particle feeders: either filter feeders, entanglers in mucus or those with appendages like holothurians.
  2. Suckers.

B. Macrophagous animals
  1. Snarers, e.g. coelenterates.
  2. Those that chew their food.
  3. Scrapers.
  4. Animals with external digestion.

C. Animals without a gut, feeding by uptake of food in solution.

Yonge's classification differs from those of the other cataloguers in that it is primarily a classification of types of feeding mechanism rather than of animals. It may be given thus:

A. Mechanisms for dealing with small particles

   1. Pseudopodial.
   2. Ciliary.
   3. Tentacular.
   4. Mucoid.
   5. Muscular.
   6. Setous.

B. Mechanisms for dealing with large particles or masses

   1. For swallowing inactive food.
   2. For scraping and boring.
   3. For seizing prey
     (*a*) For seizing and swallowing.
     (*b*) For seizing, chewing and swallowing.
     (*c*) For seizing and holding during external digestion.

C. Mechanisms for taking in fluid

   1. For piercing and sucking.
   2. For sucking only.
   3. For absorption through surface of body.

The gastropods appear to be equipped fundamentally with apparatus permitting them to take in particles of food which are either inactive (like detrital deposits) or which are scraped from the surface of a plant or animal. They would, therefore, be classified under the headings $B_1$ and $B_2$ in Yonge's classification, and the way in which different types of gastropod are enabled to do this by means of their radula has been described above. Perhaps the only point which requires mention at this stage is the way in which they graze the vegetation, moving forwards and oscillating from side to side as they progress (ftr, fig. 206B). This has been called 'pendulum feeding' by Ankel (1938*a*). Several species have also evolved a ciliary means of collecting their food, out of the series of ciliary currents which is primarily concerned with the maintenance of a water stream through the mantle cavity and the transport of such particulate material as accidentally enters in that way: this, too, has been dealt with above (p. 98). There still remain, however, other prosobranchs with feeding mechanisms which do not belong to either of these types, or with feeding mechanisms of such complexity as to merit fuller treatment. Of these, those which have to extract their food from the deeper parts of the bodies of other animals, those which bore through shells of other molluscs to get to their food, and those which pierce the bodies of their prey to suck blood or other fluid are the most important.

Of the first group the members of the Lamellariacea and Cypraeacea are the most important, feeding on sedentary animals of a variety of sorts, mainly tunicates, though *Simnia patula* eats the coelenterates *Alcyonium digitatum* and *Eunicella verrucosa*, and *Velutina plicatilis* eats *Tubularia indivisa* (Ankel, 1936*a*). Molluscs of the genera *Lamellaria*, *Erato* and *Trivia* all eat colonial tunicates and use the proboscis to do so. *Erato* is the most

selective of these in that it thrusts the proboscis through the oral aperture of a zooid of
the tunicate *Botryllus* or *Botrylloides* and so reaches directly to the more nutritious and
tasty parts of the body (fig. 32); *Trivia*, on the other hand, which also eats botryllid and
didemnid ascidians, tears and devours the test so as to expose these parts, which it then
eats, though it cannot digest the polysaccharide material out of which the test is made.
*Velutina velutina* (fig. 128) attacks the solitary ascidians *Ascidia* and *Phallusia* (Ankel,
1936*a*) and also *Styela coriacea* (Diehl, 1956). It lives on or near the ascidians, resembling
the last in colour and surface texture, and appears to feed like *Lamellaria* and *Trivia*,
biting holes in the tunicate and rasping with the proboscis.

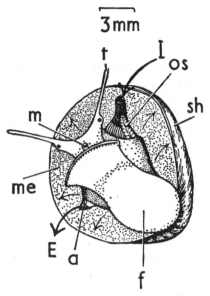

FIG. 128.—*Velutina velutina:* animal in ventral view. Arrows show direction of ciliary currents.
a, anus; f, foot; E, exhalant water current; I, inhalant water current; m, mouth; me, mantle
edge; os, osphradium; sh, shell; t, tentacle.

Two groups of prosobranchs feed on animals the bodies of which are enclosed within
shells. These are the naticids and the rachiglossans belonging to the group Muricacea,
including the British genera *Nucella*, the dog whelk, *Ocenebra*, the rough tingle, and
*Urosalpinx*, the American whelk tingle or oyster drill. The naticids eat almost entirely
bivalves, especially *Donax*, *Tellina*, *Macoma* and *Mactra*, but *Mya*, *Abra*, *Spisula*, *Venus*,
*Aloidis* and *Nucula* are known to be eaten, and probably any shell of appropriate shape
and size will be attacked, though *Natica* certainly seems to prefer bivalves with thin and
incompletely closing shells to those with thick shells which shut firmly. *Nucella lapillus*
feeds largely on mussels and limpets, or on barnacles; it is able to force barnacle shells
apart by muscular action of the proboscis without boring. *Ocenebra erinacea* attacks
*Paphia*, *Cardium*, *Venus* and oysters, though it will also bore through gastropod shells.
*Urosalpinx* eats the young of bivalves, especially oysters and *Venus*, in the spat stage, to
which it is very destructive. It has also been recorded (Galtsoff, Prytherch & Engle,
1937) as eating large numbers of barnacles, preferring them to all other kinds of food.
Hancock's observations (1954) at Burnham-on-Crouch, however, showed *Urosalpinx*

boring shells of molluscs which were covered with barnacles, apparently preferring the less accessible mollusc to the more easily entered crustacean: he cautions, however, that the barnacles belonged to the genus *Elminius* and were therefore only recently established in Essex waters and so may not yet have been appreciated as possible food by the oyster drill. There is, in fact, a considerable body of evidence (Orton, 1929*a*; Orton, 1950*b*; Hancock, 1957) that *Ocenebra*—and presumably the other genera as well—have feeding

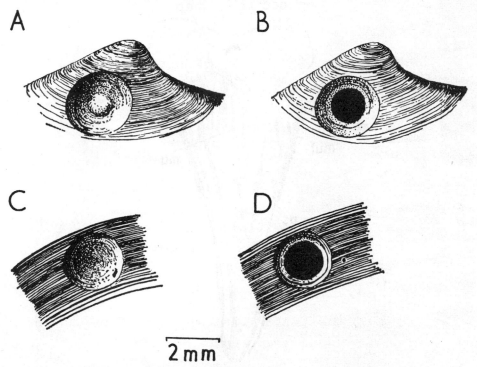

A    B

C    D

**2 mm**

Fig. 129.—Shells bored by prosobranchs. A, shell of bivalve incompletely bored by *Natica*: note the boss in the centre; B, shell of bivalve perforated by *Natica*; C, shell of bivalve incompletely bored by *Nucella*: note absence of boss; D, shell perforated by *Nucella*.

habits and preferences and take some time to appreciate the value of strange sources of food.

In all the cases described above (except barnacles) the body of the prey is reached only after a hole has been drilled in its protective shell, and valves of gastropods and lamellibranchs with holes of this nature may often be picked up on beaches (fig. 129).

The mechanism of boring in these gastropods has been repeatedly debated, especially in the naticids, but since the recent work of Carriker (1959) it now seems likely that the drilling is done by a combination of chemical and mechanical activity. *Nucella lapillus* produces a cylindrical hole up to 1·75 mm deep in 10 hrs' boring of a shell of a *Patella* or after 2 days' work on the shell of *Mytilus*. In the case of *Ocenebra erinacea* figures given by Fischer (1865) suggest a similar rate of working—3–4 hrs to bore an 'average' oyster, but more recent records by Orton (1927) and Piéron (1933) imply a much lower rate of penetration: Orton gave an average of 134 hrs for boring and eating an oyster, or 75–100 hrs for boring alone. Piéron's figures are:

7·5 hrs per 0·1 mm of shell bored (*Cardium*).
8·3 hrs per 0·1 mm of shell bored (*Cardium*).
8·3–13·3 hrs per 0·1 mm of shell bored (*Paphia*).

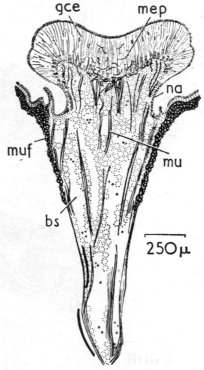

Fig. 130.—*Urosalpinx cinerea:* diagrammatic longitudinal section of the everted accessory boring organ. bs, blood space; gce, glandular and ciliated epithelium; mep, muscle fibres penetrating between epithelial cells; mu, muscles controlling movement of organ; muf, other muscles of foot; na, epithelium on neck of boring organ.

Hancock (1957) gave figures of 144 hrs for boring and eating a mussel, 168 for *Paphia* or a small oyster, and 216–240 hrs for a medium sized oyster—in June at 16–20°C. The holes which are made by this mollusc are very like those of *Nucella* but tend to be shallower (1–1·25 mm deep).

Piéron has also shown that holes made by *Ocenebra* and by *Nucella* and left unfinished have a flat base (fig. 129C). This state of affairs is commoner in thick than thin shells, as if the task of boring had exhausted the mollusc.

Mechanical boring has been advocated not only by Pelseneer (1925) and Graham (1941) among recent writers but also by Jensen (1951) and Korringa (1952). Carriker (1955, 1959) is the only recent worker to propose that some chemical activity is also involved in the process. This he has shown to be due to the accessory boring organ, a sucker-like structure (fig. 130) which lies in the mid-ventral line of the foot a little posterior to the anterior edge. This structure was first described by Fretter (1941) and was later dealt with by Carriker (1943) who then called it the accessory proboscis. It normally lies withdrawn into a sac lying in the pedal tissue; when everted, however, it swells into a large, rounded projection of diameter comparable with that of the true proboscis. It is covered by a tall epithelium containing alternate gland and ciliated cells (gce), the former secreting spherules of some material which is not mucus. Fretter's ideas as to the use to which this structure was put centred mainly on its functioning as a sucker which would help to steady the body of the predator on that of the prey during the boring process, a need which was increased by the fact that much of the anterior end of the foot is used to steady the true proboscis during boring and feeding rather than for gripping the substratum: she also found no evidence of its secretion having any action on calcareous material. Carriker (1955), on the other hand, believed that this structure has a chemical effect on the substance of the shell which, without dissolving it, nevertheless makes it easier for the radula to remove it by rasping. He has brought impressive evidence (1959) in support of this chemomechanical theory of boring with experiments involving the amputation of the proboscis and of the accessory boring organ in the muricids *Urosalpinx cinerea* and *Eupleura caudata*. Both structures are regenerated with surprising rapidity, but only those animals with both organs bore, suggesting their co-operation in this process. He has also been able to show that the accessory boring organ, like that of *Natica* (Ankel, 1937a), will etch calcareous shells when closely applied to them.

When *Nucella* is about to feed it attaches itself to the body of the prey by means of the foot, the anterior end of which is contracted and turned dorsally off the prey. The median part of the edge is particularly contracted and comes to form a groove along which the proboscis extends. The anterior corners of the foot then curve dorsally and meet above the proboscis which is therefore completely embraced and held by the foot.

The behaviour of the radula of a feeding *Nucella* is almost impossible to observe because of the way in which the proboscis is hidden; nevertheless it can be exposed by gentle removal of the foot, when it will be seen that the tip of the buccal mass is being continually pushed out of the mouth so that the radular teeth can rasp at the surface of the shell. After executing a number of rasping strokes the mollusc rests a little and it is during this period that the accessory boring organ is placed in the hole. When boring is begun again it will be noticed that the buccal mass has been rotated to one side so that the direction of rasping is altered. So far as can be seen the rotation is predominantly one of the buccal mass within the proboscis rather than of the proboscis itself. As the rasping proceeds a straight-sided cavity is produced with finely polished walls (fig. 129D), examination of which fails to reveal the marks made by the radular teeth. There is no doubt about the reality of the rasping, however, because if a dog whelk be disturbed in the middle of its drilling, killed, and its gut opened, innumerable sickle-shaped flakes of crystalline material can be found there, which prove to be calcium carbonate.

Carriker (1955) gave a similar account of the boring of oysters by *Urosalpinx*, using a method which allowed of observation of the drilling with a binocular microscope. At first the radular teeth made little impression on the shell but after the process had proceeded for a little the gastropod altered its position on the bivalve, creeping forwards until the accessory boring organ lay over the point at which the proboscis had been active. When this movement has occurred it was everted into the mark made by the proboscis and left thus for a little time. It is then retracted, the animal backs, the proboscis everted and drilling begun again. This rhythm persists throughout boring. Precisely what is going on during the period when the accessory boring organ is applied to the shell it is not possible to say: there is clearly no real solution of the calcareous matter as the chips (in *Nucella*) from the gut are still soluble with evolution of $CO_2$ in acid. If, as seems possible and as Carriker thinks, some secretion from the accessory organ occurs, then the function of this would seem to be that of softening the shell material for easier treatment by the radula. The same might also be true of similar structures in other members of the Muricacea. Carriker (1959) has suggested that the organ might produce, not an acid, but a chelating agent or, possibly, an enzyme attacking the conchiolin matrix of the shell. The role of other glands, such as the accessory salivary glands, in boring is still unclear.

Much more argument has surrounded the question of how naticids bore the shells of the bivalves which they eat. Some authors have assumed that this was done by chemical means: the first of these was Réaumur (1711), but Schiemenz (1891) was the first to support the idea with any proper evidence. He argued that the radular teeth were not hard enough, nor the proboscis mobile enough, to bore a cylindrical hole, but he was, perhaps, primarily urged towards the chemical theory of boring by the discovery of a hemispherical boss lying under the ventral lip, which he called a 'boring gland' and which, he believed, produced acid for making a hole in the shell. The secretion of the gland, he showed, reddened litmus. Other workers have upheld this theory. Hirsch (1915) showed that the diameter of the gland and the diameter of the hole bored were identical and therefore assumed that the one had been made by the other. Boettger (1930) and Ankel (1937a) also supported this idea, the latter showing that glands removed from *Natica* etched the gloss from the surface of a shell of *Trivia*. Repeating the experiment later Ankel (1938a) got no similar result and therefore suggested the presence of an enzyme, 'calcase' (which is very reminiscent of what Carriker (1955) says of *Urosalpinx*), although what precise effect this might have on the material of which the shell is composed is left vague. Giglioli (1949) has also supported this theory.

Another group of workers has suggested that boring is mechanical and is accomplished entirely by radular action. Fischer (1922) investigated the 'boring gland' of *Natica* and found it composed mainly of muscle, without obvious gland cells, and its surface had no effect on litmus. For these and other reasons he argued that it could have no part in the process of boring. Pelseneer (1925) and Loppens (1926) came to the same conclusion. Jensen (1951) discovered egg cases of *Raia* sp. and *Sipho* sp. bored by a mollusc which was probably either *Natica affinis* or *N. pallida*, though the identifications are admittedly not proved. These show clear markings of radular teeth on their edges and round the periphery, suggesting a mechanical drilling by the radula, though it may, of course, be true that naticids could bore such horny objects with the radula but must have recourse to chemical agents when attempting to drill the calcareous shell of another mollusc. Turner (1953) has also taken this view. Wheatley (1947) has gone so far as to suggest that naticids can devour certain types of prey without boring the shell at all, but this remains a rather mysterious proceeding.

The most full description of the boring of shells by naticids has been given recently by Ziegelmeier (1954), who concluded that the hole is made entirely by mechanical means. He was able to reach this conclusion because he managed to overcome the very great difficulty of seeing what the mollusc was doing to its prey during the feeding process by keeping starved specimens of *Natica* in aquaria. This difficulty, which had defeated previous observers, arises partly from the fact that *Natica* wraps its prey in its foot during the process of boring (to such an extent that Pelseneer believed that the bivalve died of suffocation) and also because it will bore only when buried in sand.

*Natica* feeds mainly on *Donax, Tellina* and *Mactra* (Piéron, 1933) but Ziegelmeier found that it would also bore holes in the shells of numerous other tellinids and of *Abra alba, Spisula solida, S. subtruncata, Venus gallina, Mya arenaria, Nucula nucleus, N. nitida* and *Aloidis gibba*. Giglioli (1949) also recorded the boring of gastropods and gave examples of cannibalism. The bivalve is gripped in the foot during boring and is almost invisible. Because of the way in which it must be held, boring is usually confined to a limited number of positions and, sometimes, because their asymmetry allows a better grip on the prey, the bivalves are bored through one valve more frequently than the other. Ziegelmeier investigated about 200 borings, almost all of which were made in the mid-region of the valve where that was broadest, and very few near its angles. Stinson's observations (1946) support this, but Belding (1930) noted that most shells had been bored towards the posterior end of the valves. *Aloidis* is regularly bored through this right valve, which is thicker than the left, but offers *Natica* a better grip. Piéron gave the following figures for shells of *Donax* entered by *Natica*:

TABLE 7

| Animal | Site of boring | | | | | |
|---|---|---|---|---|---|---|
| | Right valve | Left valve | Ant. third | Mid third | Post. third | Near hinge |
| *Donax* (Atlantic) . . | 54·3% | 45·7 | 22·3 | 73·4 | 4·3 | 29·1 |
| *Donax* (Mediterranean) . | 57·0% | 43·0 | 29·5 | 60·0 | 10·5 | 27·0 |

These figures suggest that there are privileged positions for boring, almost certainly related to the way in which the prey is held, and are in agreement with earlier figures given by Boettger (1930). Schiemenz (1891) stated that 63·6% of valves bored by *Natica* were left valves; corresponding figures given by Pelseneer (1925) are 43·75% and by Piéron (1933), 43–45%, and these may also have the same explanation. According to Pelseneer (1925) and Verlaine (1936) the site of boring is often related to the position of the underlying gonad. Verlaine has published evidence suggesting that *Natica alderi* learns how to locate its hole so as to reach the gonad: thus of a series of shells of *Tellina* (=*Macoma*) *balthica* bored by that prosobranch the dimensions of the hole (and therefore the age of the animal which bored it) and its situation in relation to the gonad are as follows:

TABLE 8

| Size of hole | % over gonad | % at edge of gonad | % not over gonad |
|---|---|---|---|
| 0·5 mm or less . | 45 | 18 | 36 |
| 0·5–1 mm . . | 78 | 9 | 13 |
| 1–1·5 mm . . | 91 | 9 | 0 |
| 1·5 mm or more . | 91 | 9 | 0 |

The hole made by *Natica* on boring is recognizably different from that made by the muricacean borers (figs. 129A, B), in that the lips show an initial abrasion and the walls are curved; incomplete ones are easily recognized by the presence of a small upgrowth arising from the centre of a concave base. Ziegelmeier's account (1954) of the boring process shows how this arises.

The bivalve is held by the propodium (fig. 305). As in the muricaceans the mid-anterior region of the propodium retracts deeply so as to form a groove into which the

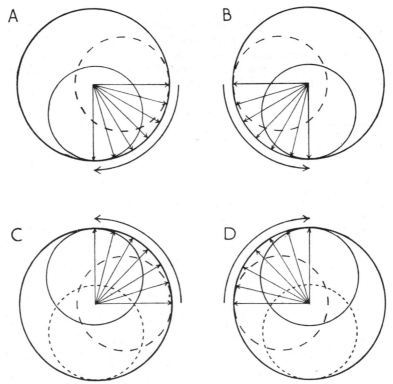

Fig. 131.—Diagrams to show the method of using the radula employed by *Natica* whilst boring. The borehole is dealt with in bursts of activity separated by rests; boring is done sector by sector represented here as the four quadrants of a circle, A, B, C and D. In each diagram the large circle represents the edge of the borehole, the small broken circle the initial position taken up by the tip of the proboscis applied to the shell, the small complete circle its final position; intermediate positions are not shown. In C and D the dotted circles represent the resting position of the proboscis. Within the small circles continuous arrows represent the pathways followed by the radula during each burst of rasping. Note that the final position of the proboscis is always straight, the initial one always twisted; the continuous arrow outside the large circle gives the direction of movement during untwisting. From Ziegelmeier.

proboscis everts and its tips then curve dorsally to hold this steady. The proboscis is rotated through 90° to right or left and applied to the shell surface against which the radula works; as successive radular strokes follow one another the proboscis gradually rotates back from the twisted to the normal position (fig. 131). After this a rest period ensues, of 2–3 min if the mollusc has just started boring, of about 5 min if it has been active for some time. During the resting period the proboscis is lifted off the shell and the accessory boring organ which lies under the ventral lip is brought close to the hole. Ziegelmeier never saw it enter it. The proboscis is then applied to the hole in a twisted position so as to allow the radula to scratch at another sector. The proboscis is always twisted so that the first scratchings are from right to left or vice versa at the beginning of a working period, and it always untwists itself so that the radula is scraping in an anteroposterior direction at the end. The central knob is obviously left because it lies at a spot where the radular action is least effective.

During the process of boring Ziegelmeier was able to see white shell material passing down the oesophagus. After the boring is completed (at the rate of 0·1 mm/4 hrs) the prosobranch begins to feed—a process which may last anything up to 60 hrs, and which may involve the animal in the ingestion of its own weight of bivalve flesh. During this defaecation occurs and up to 12 isolated, white pellets are passed, which are composed mainly of shell fragments. Later a chain of pellets is seen to escape from the anus which are dark green in colour and slimy to the touch. They are oval and measure about 1 mm long by 0·2–0·3 mm in diameter. Some figures for the amount of food eaten by naticids are given in Table 9 taken from Giglioli (1949). They refer to the American species *Polynices heros* and *P. triseriata*.

TABLE 9

| Animal | Bivalves/day | Bivalves/month | Investigator |
|---|---|---|---|
| *Polynices triseriata* (young) . | 0·34 | 10·2 | Stinson (1946) |
| *P. triseriata* (adult) . . | 0·4 | 12·0 | Stinson (1946) |
| *P. heros* (adult) . . . | 0·22 | 6·6 | Wheatley (1947) |
| *P. triseriata* (adult) . . | 0·07 | 2·1 | Wheatley (1947) |

Ziegelmeier has supplemented the information given by Fischer (1922) on the histological nature of the accessory boring organ. He described it as covered by a cuticle the thickness of which is greatest centrally, and which appears unperforated by pores through which the secretion of such gland cells as are present could escape, and it appears to have no effect on calcareous material with which it is brought into contact. Ziegelmeier, indeed, concluded that it may well be primarily a tactile sense organ giving information necessary for boring in view of the fact that this process is invariably carried out by *Natica* as it lies buried in the sand. In this respect Ziegelmeier's observations (made on *Natica* (*Lunatia*) *nitida*) are not in agreement with ours on *N. catena* (fig. 132) in which it is quite apparent that secretion from the gland cells (msc) can pass through the cuticle, which is more accurately interpreted as a rodlet border (rb).

In view of the similarity which exists between the structure on the ventral lip of *Natica* and that on the sole of the foot of muricids it is difficult to believe that the boring process is not fundamentally similar, or even identical, in the two groups of prosobranchs. Carriker's latest observations and experiments (1959) make it seem highly probable that a combination of chemical and mechanical attack allows boring in muricids and it seems likely that the same alternation occurs in naticids as well. Ziegelmeier noted the same rhythm of radular activity and 'rest' during which the accessory organ is brought near to the hole which is being made: it seems probable that during this phase some chemical attack is made which depends, like that of muricids, on the secretion of the accessory boring organ.

The Buccinacea among the rachiglossan Stenoglossa are provided with a long proboscis but do not bore, being primarily feeders on dead, but fresh animals (figs. 133, 277). Some of them, nevertheless, can open the shells of bivalves in order to feed on the animal within. This has been described by Colton (1908) and by Carriker (1951) for the American genus *Busycon* (= *Sycotypus*). The prosobranch appears to detect the lamellibranch by means of the exhalant current of water emerging from the dorsal siphon; it then climbs

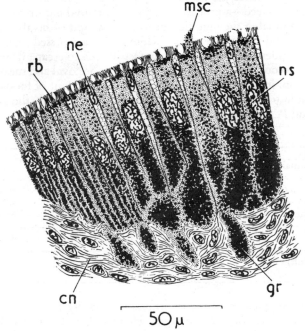

FIG. 132.—*Natica catena*: part of a vertical section through the accessory boring organ; the more lateral part of the organ is to the left.

cn, connective tissue; gr, granules of secretion; msc, mass of secretion escaping through rodlet border; ne, nucleus of supporting epithelial cell; ns, nucleus of secreting cell; rb, rodlet border.

on to the shell and grips it in the foot so that the ventral edges of the 2 valves lie under the outer lip of its own shell. By pulling this down with a slow contraction of the columellar muscle the lip is forced between the 2 valves until a piece of one of them is broken off. When this hole is large enough the proboscis is everted, passed through it and the process of feeding begun. *Busycon* eats bivalves such as *Mytilus, Venus, Mya* or *Ensis* at the rate of 4–5/week; oysters are eaten at a rate of 0·84/week in winter, but 2·7/week in spring. *Venus mercenaria* is eaten at a rate of 0·86 in winter, but 0·35 in spring, suggesting that the animal's taste or appetite varies from season to season. *Buccinum undatum*, finding bivalves with their shell open, will prevent the valves from closing by wedging them apart with the anterior end of its own shell and then will start to feed on the helpless prey. Dakin (1912) said that they incapacitate it by first attacking the adductor, but this is contrary to the general behaviour of these animals.

The food consumption of the boring muricaceans has also been measured in a number of instances. Hancock (1957) has carried out experiments with *Ocenebra erinacea* which show that feeding is most intense during July and August off the coast of Essex and does not occur at all when the temperature falls to less than 10–11 °C, which would appear to involve the animals in a starvation period extending from the beginning of December to April in the latitude of the British Isles. *Ocenebra*, however, is known to be particularly sensitive to low temperatures and related genera may not be so much affected: *Buccinum* is certainly not. Cole (1942) gave a feeding rate of 0·165 oyster spat per tingle per day. The same worker found that *Urosalpinx cinerea* devoured oyster spat at an average rate of 0·438 per day or 2·92 per week. The figures given by Carriker (1955) are higher.

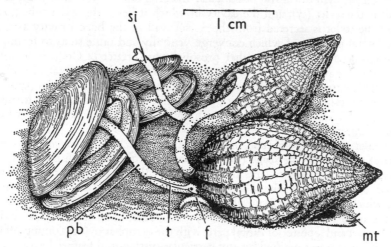

FIG. 133.—*Nassarius reticulatus:* eating dead bivalves of the species *Tellina crassa.*
    f, foot; mt, metapodial tentacle; pb, proboscis thrust into bivalve; si, extended siphon of the gastropod; t, tentacle.

Animals measuring 2–4 mm ate 33·6 oyster spat per week, whereas those 21 mm in height ate 0·05 oysters (53 mm long) per week. Like *Ocenebra*, *Urosalpinx* is affected by temperature and appears to starve during the coldest months of the year (Cole, 1942) and to feed voraciously during the warmer months and especially whilst spawning.

In contrast to the prosobranchs which have just been dealt with in the preceding section stand those gastropods which have developed a method of sucking liquid food into their gut from the body of their prey. This has been achieved mainly by those placed in the family Pyramidellidae, which are dealt with here although they have recently been shown to belong to the group Opisthobranchia rather than to the proso-branchs. To this end their gut has been highly modified since it requires not only pump-ing machinery for the sucking of the blood but also piercing apparatus to make the fluid available. The genera *Odostomia*, *Chrysallida* and *Turbonilla* have all undergone a very similar process of specialization.

The animals are provided with an elongated acrembolic proboscis (figs. 134, 135; see also fig. 103) normally withdrawn into a proboscis sheath. The elongation of the gut which is involved in the production of this affects the oral tube (ot), the buccal cavity

(bcv) and the oesophagus (oe), all of which are consequently much longer than in an
an ordinary gastropod. At the apex the proboscis is converted into a sucker with
opening and closing muscles by means of which it can be anchored to the body of
the prey after elongation. In the exact centre of the sucker in the genus *Turbonilla* lies
the only aperture which occurs, the mouth; in the genera *Odostomia* and *Chrysallida* an
opening is also to be found centrally placed on this sucker (lsa) but, in addition there is a
second, a short, crescentic slit, lying on the surface of the sucker about half way between
the centre and the ventral edge. This second opening is the mouth (m), which leads
into the oral tube, whereas the opening in the centre of the sucker leads into another
tube which is separate from the oral tube, except at its extreme inner end, and which
lodges a hollow, cylindrical rod of cuticular material tapered to a fine point at its outer
end. This is the stylet (sy), and the cavity in which it lies is the stylet tube (syt). At its
inner end the stylet is secreted from the dorsal wall of the buccal cavity as a cuticular
layer the lateral margins of which converge ventrally and unite so as to form a tube. It
is homologous with the jaw of other prosobranchs (Fretter & Graham, 1949). Into it
runs a single tube formed from the union of the 2 ducts from the salivary glands (sd),
and the whole apparatus can be moved by a complex series of muscles (sym) fastened
to its base. The stylet can be thrust out of the mouth of the stylet tube and forms a hypodermic needle which can be forced through the skin of the prey and along which saliva
can then be injected.

At the inner end of the oral tube, near the point at which (in *Odostomia* and *Chrysallida*)
that part of the gut and the stylet tube are connected, the one with the other, arises the
buccal cavity. As it passes inwards this splits into a dorsal part (dp) in which the stylet
is secreted, and into which the tube formed by the union of the salivary ducts projects
(sd), but which otherwise leads nowhere, and a ventral part (bcv), which is the continuation of the main channel of the alimentary tract. This, in its turn, can be divided into
an anterior part and a posterior caecal part, with the oesophagus (oe) coming off between.
The anterior part is not marked by any particular histological feature beyond an abundance of mucous cells; the posterior pouch, however, forms a buccal pump (bup). Its
walls are thick, but little of this is due to the epithelial lining, which is formed of featureless, squamous cells only 2 $\mu$ high (ebp, fig. 103). These rest directly on the muscle of
the walls, which is composed of radial fibres inserted on the proximal faces of the
epithelial cells and originating on a deeper layer of connective tissue, and of transverse
sheets of fibres which run rather more than half-way across the walls of the tube. The
radial fibres will clearly distend the lumen of the pouch and the transverse fibres will
constrict it. All the fibrillae within the muscle cells show marked striation. Similar
muscle fibrillae are to be seen lying around the ducts of the salivary glands and are
presumably used to force the salivary secretion along the ducts and through the fine
central canal of the stylet into the body of the prey.

The salivary glands (sg, fig. 134; and see fig. 102) are tubular structures, anchored to
the body wall by muscular strands and differentiated along their length into areas with
varying function. The innermost part is sac-like (bsg), with thin walls, and appears to
act as a store for the secretion; next outermost lies a brief region lined by ciliated cells
and containing small gland cells. The next region occupies the greater length of the
gland and is the major source of saliva; its walls are covered by a squamous epithelium
of ciliated cells under which lie the secreting cells in the form of large, cubical masses.
Few of these secrete mucus: most produce a protein.

The process of feeding in pyramidellids has been described by a number of workers

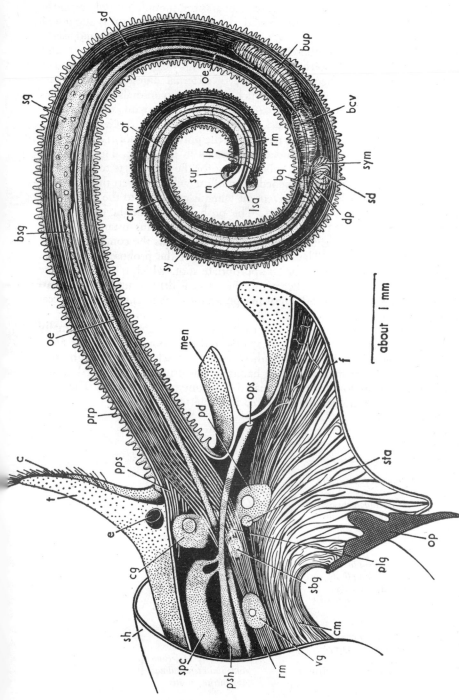

Fig. 134.—*Odostomia unidentata*: sagittal half of the anterior end of a specimen which is protruding head and foot from the shell and has its proboscis extended. This is shown in a conventional position. The haemocoel is black.
bcv, buccal cavity; bg, buccal ganglion; bsg, bladder of salivary gland; bup, buccal pump; cg, cerebral ganglion; c, cilia; cm, columellar muscle; crm, circular muscles; dp, dorsal pouch of buccal cavity; e, eye; f, foot; lb, labial commissure; lsa, lip of stylet aperture; m, mouth; men, mentum; oe, oesophagus; op, operculum; ops, opening of penial sheath; ot, oral tube; pd, pedal ganglion; plg, pleural ganglion; pps, protractor muscles of proboscis; prp, papilla on epithelium of proboscis; psh, penial sheath; rm, retractor muscle; sbg, sub-oesophageal ganglion; sd, salivary duct; sg, salivary gland; sh, shell; spc, sperm sac; sta, statocyst; sur, sucker; sy, stylet in stylet tube; syn, muscles moving stylet; t, tentacle; vg, visceral ganglion.

and it has long been known that these animals are ectoparasites, though it is only recently that the details of the feeding act have been made known. Pelseneer (1914) suggested that *Odostomia scalaris*, which normally lives in close association with *Mytilus edulis* (fig. 138), feeds by extending its proboscis into the mantle cavity of the mollusc and sucking mucus or similar material, food or pseudo-faeces, possibly by the aid of secretion of salivary enzymes which might effect some degree of external digestion. Rasmussen (1944) published a figure (without comment) which showed two animals of this species feeding on mussels, and it was left to Ankel (1948) and Fretter & Graham (1949) to show that pyramidellids were blood and tissue suckers. Ankel and Fretter & Graham made observations mainly on species of *Odostomia* feeding on the polychaete worm *Pomatoceros*, *O. plicata* in Ankel's case and *O. lukisi* and *O. unidentata* in the other. These animals lurk (fig. 135) near the opening of a worm tube waiting for the polychaete to expand its crown of tentacles (tw). When this has happened the mollusc will then evert the proboscis (pb), which moves with a slightly spiral movement when it gets close to the worm as if it were carrying out exploratory movements. The proboscis is brought close to the tentacle with great caution until it rests on one of the filaments. At this instant the worm may react slightly by jerking the tentacle, but normally it permits the contact with the proboscis without any movement. The sucker at the end of the proboscis then slides along the tentacle, appearing to search for an appropriate spot, which is usually on the inner side. When this is assured the sucker grips, the stylet is driven outwards so as to penetrate the body of the worm and vigorous pumping movements of the buccal apparatus suck fluid into the mollusc's gut.

Fretter & Graham (1949) have suggested that each species of pyramidellid is normally associated with a particular host (figs. 136, 137, 138) and does not usually occur apart from the neighbourhood of the host. Although Cole & Hancock (1955) thought that pyramidellids are not so precise in their feeding habits as was originally suggested, it still seems that each species is predominantly associated with one particular host. The associations which have so far been recorded are listed in Table 10.

TABLE 10

| Pyramidellid | Host |
| --- | --- |
| *Chysallida obtusa* | *Ostrea edulis* |
| *Chrysallida spiralis* | *Sabellaria* spp. |
| *Chrysallida seminuda* | *Crepidula fornicata* |
| *Odostomia unidentata* | *Pomatoceros triqueter* |
| *Odostomia conoidea* | *Astropecten irregularis* |
| *Odostomia lukisi* | *Pomatoceros triqueter* |
| *Odostomia plicata* | *Pomatoceros triqueter* |
| *Odostomia scalaris* | *Mytilus edulis* (small) |
| *Odostomia eulimoides* | *Pecten maximus* |
| | *Chlamys opercularis* |
| | *Ostrea edulis* |
| *Odostomia trifida* | *Mya arenaria* |
| *Turbonilla jeffreysi* | Some coelenterate, probably *Halecium* sp. |
| *Turbonilla elegantissima* | *Audouinia tentaculata* |
| | *Amphitrite gracilis* |

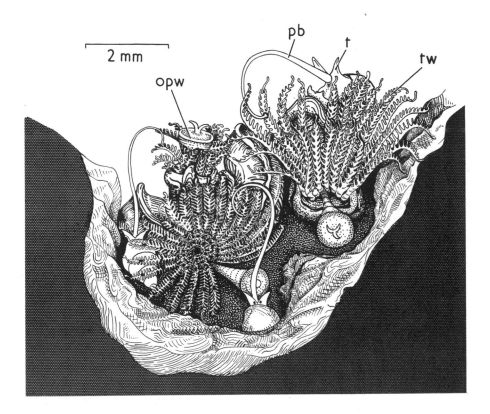

FIG. 135.—*Odostomia unidentata:* feeding on the tubicolous polychaete worm, *Pomatoceros triqueter.* opw, operculum of worm; pb, proboscis of gastropod; t, tentacle of gastropod; tw, tentacle of worm.

(*facing p.* 254.)

Other gastropods besides the Pyramidellidae have become parasitic, but few of these are British and few of them have been sufficiently adequately investigated for it to be known how they feed. Of the British forms *Pelseneeria* and some of the eulimids (or

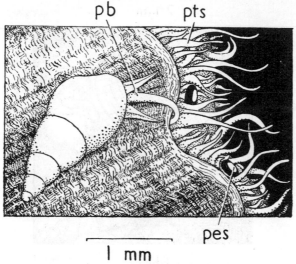

FIG. 136.—*Odostomia eulimoides:* feeding on the scallop, *Pecten maximus.*
pb, proboscis of gastropod; pes, pallial eye of scallop; pts, pallial tentacle of scallop.

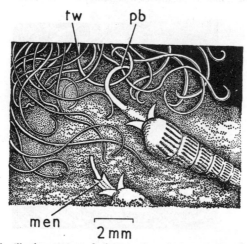

FIG. 137.—*Turbonilla elegantissima:* feeding on the polychaete worm, *Cirratulus cirratus.*
men, mentum; pb, proboscis of gastropod; tw, tentacle of worm.

melanellids) may be mentioned. These have a stout proboscis which is passed deep into the tissues of the host, unlike the superficial attachment of the pyramidellid, and appears to be able to attach the mollusc to its host without the help of the foot.

*Pelseneeria* lives on echinoids and appears to digest the epidermis by means of enzymes secreted over the body of the host. Their source is unknown. The eulimids are also associated with echinoderms and *Balcis devians* (=*Eulima distorta*) has been found on *Mesothuria intestinalis, Echinus esculentus, Strongylocentrotus drobachiensis* according to Pelseneer (1928) and also on *Antedon bifida* according to Fretter (1955*a*) (fig. 139). The

2 mm

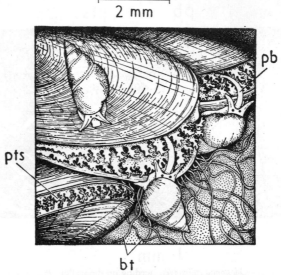

FIG. 138.—*Odostomia scalaris:* feeding on small specimens of the common mussel, *Mytilus edulis.* bt, byssus threads of mussel; pb, proboscis of gastropod; pts, pallial tentacle of mussel.

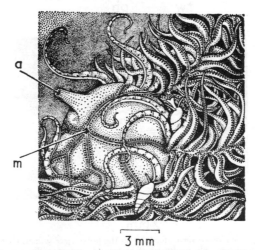

3 mm

FIG. 139.—*Balcis devians:* on the surface of the crinoid, *Antedon bifida.* a, anus of crinoid; m, mouth of crinoid.

echinoderms which are parasitized by other species of eulimid such as *Balcis alba* are not known, though this species occurs abundantly with *Spatangus purpureus* at Plymouth. The alimentary tract of these animals has been extraordinarily modified in connexion with their parasitic mode of life and has been described to a certain extent by Koehler &

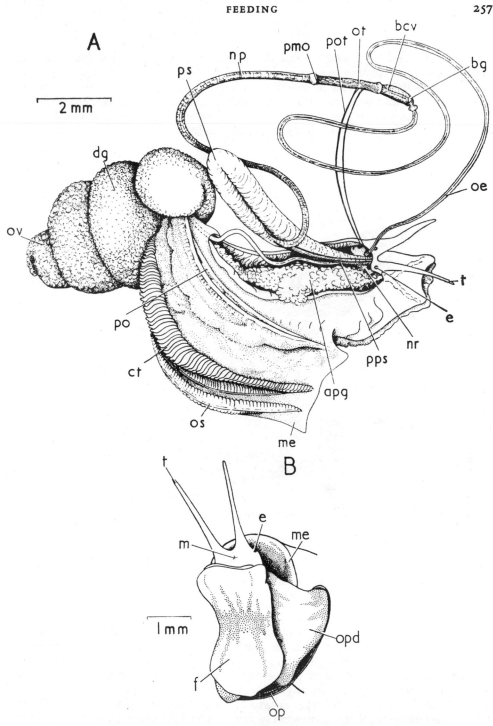

Fig. 140.—*Balcis alba:* A, dissection of animal removed from shell. The mantle skirt has been cut along the left side and folded to the right, the anterior haemocoelic space has been opened and the anterior part of the gut lifted out and displayed; B, the whole animal in ventral view.

apg, anterior pedal gland; bcv, buccal cavity; bg, buccal ganglion; ct, ctenidium; dg, digestive gland; e, eye; f, foot; m, mouth; me, mantle edge; np, narrow part of proboscis; nr, nerve ring; oe, oesophagus; op, operculum; opd, operculigerous disc; os, osphradium; ot, oral tube; ov, ovary; pmo, position of true mouth; po, open pallial oviduct; pot, protractor muscle of oral tube; pps, protractor muscle of proboscis; ps, proboscis sheath; t, tentacle.

Vaney (1912) for *Eulima equestris* and some other species, by Risbec (1954) for *E. acutissima* and an unidentified species, and by Fretter (1955a) for *Balcis devians* and *B. alba*.

The foot of *Balcis alba* and *B. devians* is well developed compared with that of the more specialized molluscan parasites of echinoderms, some of which are embedded in the tissues of the host and have lost the foot as they have no need to move about in search of food. The opercular lobe (opl, fig. 297) is large and the pedal glands which

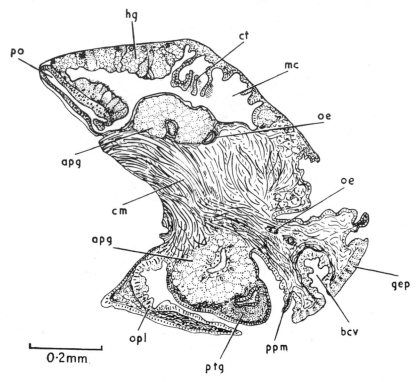

FIG. 141.—*Balcis devians:* oblique transverse section passing through the extended proboscis, the pedal glands and the mantle cavity.

apg, anterior pedal gland; bcv, buccal cavity; cm, columellar muscle; ct, ctenidium; gep, glandular epithelium; hg, hypobranchial gland; mc, mantle cavity; oe, oesophagus; opl, operculigerous lobe of foot; po, pallial oviduct; ppm, pseudopallium; ptg, posterior pedal gland.

secrete mucus have become much enlarged (apg, ptg, figs. 140A, 141) the anterior having hypertrophied to a greater extent than the posterior, and spread backwards in the general body cavity, alongside the oesophagus, as far as the base of the visceral mass. The glands are also enlarged in other parasitic prosobranchs such as *Eulima equestris*, *Pelseneeria* and *Mucronalia* (Vaney, 1913) and in *Megadenus* (Rosen, 1910), but not in *Stilifer* (Hirase, 1932) nor in the endoparasitic types in which, indeed, the foot is wholly lost. When *B. devians* is feeding the foot is contracted so that the glandular tissue is bunched together, with the openings of the 2 glands not far from one another nor from the wound made by the proboscis. The secretion may help to keep the parasite in position whilst it is fixed by the proboscis, though the possibility of it producing some toxic or digestive effect on the tissues of the host has not yet been explored.

*Balcis devians* and *B. alba* possess a long acrembolic proboscis, withdrawn into the haemocoel when not in use (fig. 140). When protruded it can excavate the tissues of the host to a depth equivalent to the length of the shell or more. In *B. alba* it is proportionately even longer, for the oesophagus, which is drawn through the introvert on its protrusion is many times the length of the shell (fig. 140A), suggesting that it passes well into the body of the host, perhaps seeking the gonad. At its inner end the proboscis (ps) opens into a narrower tube (np), rather abruptly in *Balcis alba*, but gradually in the unidentified species of *Eulima* described by Risbec (1954), and this leads to a distinct boundary which apparently marks the position of the true mouth (pmo). Behind this, specimens of *Eulima* sp. (Risbec, 1954) exhibit 2 sections of gut, one, anterior, which is clearly buccal, the second, posterior, which must be the oesophagus. As the animal has no radula, no salivary glands, no oesophageal glands and as Risbec does not describe the position of any buccal ganglia, it is difficult to relate this featureless tube to the alimentary tract of less specialized animals. The work of Fretter (1955a), however, permits this. In *Balcis devians* and *B. alba* 3 sections are discernible in this stretch, two relatively short, but the third, which passes through the nerve ring (nr), greatly elongated. There are, once again, no salivary glands, nor radula nor oesophageal glands to help in identifying parts, but at the posterior limit of the second section are to be found the buccal ganglia (bg). This, therefore, allows the second section to be identified as the buccal cavity (bcv) and the greatly elongated third part as the oesophagus (oe), whilst the first part, immediately behind the true mouth, must be the oral tube (ot).

Histologically all these sections of the gut are very much alike and strikingly devoid of gland cells. The oesophagus is ciliated, the other parts not, and all are extremely muscular. It is difficult to tell how much of this apparatus can be everted into the body of the prey: certainly not the oesophagus which passes through the nerve ring and is there, and in that neighbourhood, securely attached to surrounding tissue. It is probable, however, that the true mouth comes to lie at the summit of the proboscis when that is fully extended. Feeding must clearly be by sucking and by eating such particulate material as the muscular region round the mouth can manage to tear from the prey. From the minute size of the oesophagus (oe) where it passes through the nerve ring (nr), it seems likely that these parasitic eulimids are primarily feeders on fluids.

From the nerve ring the oesophagus runs to a stomach embedded in the visceral mass. As in pyramidellids its separation from the digestive gland is not clear and it appears more as an excavation in that than a more normal stomach. The cells in the digestive gland are much laden with darkly staining spherules, again as in the pyramidellids.

Rosen's statement (1910) that *Eulima polita* (= *Balcis alba*) is free-living, not parasitic, and has a radula and an oesophagus with attached glands is clearly based on a misidentification.

A few other prosobranchs perhaps deserve a mention at this point, mainly because the anatomy of their alimentary tract suggests unusual modes of feeding, though these are, in most cases, still not known. These animals are sometimes placed together in a group called the Ptenoglossa, and include, among British genera, *Ianthina*, *Cirsotrema*, *Clathrus*, *Graphis*, *Aclis*, *Pherusina* and *Cima*. Of this list *Ianthina* and *Clathrus* are the only animals not almost wholly unknown except for their shells. The anatomy of *Clathrus* has been described by Bouvier (1886) and Thiele (1928) and that of *Ianthina* by Thiele (1928) and Laursen (1953). Thiele (1928) gave a few details of *Aclis* and Dall (1889) described its shell as heterostrophic, which suggests a link with the pyramidellids, but apart from this our knowledge of this group of little prosobranchs is extremely meagre.

In *Ianthina* a small proboscis is developed (pb, fig. 299), the tip of which is normally inturned. The buccal mass and its covering of recurved teeth, all alike, have already been described. Thiele (1928) described 2 pairs of salivary glands on each side discharging by a common duct opening far forward on the dorsal wall of the buccal cavity: in *I. janthina*, however, the 2 salivary glands on each side open to the buccal cavity by separate ducts, one, from a posterior pair almost mid-dorsally, the second, from an anterior pair, very laterally and anterior to the cutting edge of the jaw. What degree of variation occurs within the genus is not known. The glands themselves are tubular. In the related genus *Recluzia* there are also 2 pairs of salivary glands the ducts from which lead to a pair of cuticular stylets surrounded by a sheath of muscle. These run along the

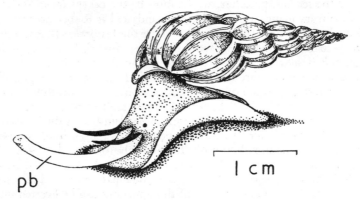

FIG. 142.—*Clathrus clathrus:* animal crawling with partly extended proboscis.
pb, proboscis.

lateral walls of the buccal cavity and open near the mouth. This is reminiscent of the genus *Clathrus* (figs. 100, 101), in which again there are 2 pairs of tubular salivary glands, dorsally and ventrally placed. Of these the dorsal pair (asg, fig. 100) open to the dorsal wall of the buccal cavity a short distance in front of the nerve ring, in a position not dissimilar to that occupied by salivary ducts in most prosobranchs. The second, ventral pair (sg), however, send ducts which pass through the nerve ring, travel in the lateral wall of the buccal cavity, expand into reservoirs and finally open (osd, fig. 101) through cuticular stylets (sy) which arise from the centre of mammiform swellings lying, apparently external to the mouth, in a lateral position. The mouth, however, lies at the base of a long proboscis (pb, fig. 142) of acrembolic type and as no one, apparently, has ever seen *Clathrus* feeding, the precise arrangement of these parts in the everted condition is not known. The buccal mass is very like that of *Ianthina* and the mollusc has 2 sharp-edged jaws (ja, fig. 101) in the neighbourhood of which the buccal wall appears to contain still other masses of glandular tissue (gb). The introvert is very muscular and, in its apical region, rich in gland cells; it is lined by a cuticle apically, but is ciliated at its base.

Beyond the fact that *Clathrus* is clearly adapted for a carnivorous mode of life and, perhaps, for the ingestion of entire animals, it is not possible to say much about its feeding, which remains one of the most interesting points in this connexion yet to be cleared up. The jaws perhaps permit us to conclude that *Clathrus* bites pieces off the body of the prey and hauls them in with the radula. Ankel (1936a) said that this mollusc eats coelenterates, and Thorson (1958) described a related American species as feeding by sucking fluid from sea anemones (see p. 575).

Thiele (1928) stated that *Aclis* is related to *Clathrus* and has a long, retractile proboscis, a pair of jaws and a radula with needle-like teeth. So far as the other animals in the group are concerned nothing appears to be certainly known of their structure or habits, a gap which would undoubtedly be interesting to fill.

The food of British prosobranchs (so far as known) is given in the following list:

*Haliotis tuberculata:* algae, especially *Delesseria, Griffithsia, Chondrus; Corallina* and *Lithothamnion* when young (Crofts, 1929).

*Emarginula reticulata, E. crassa:* sponges, especially monaxonids; perhaps also detritus.

*Diodora apertura:* sponges, especially *Halichondria* and *Hymeniacidon*; perhaps also detritus.

*Gibbula umbilicalis, G. cineraria, Monodonta lineata, Calliostoma zizyphinum* and trochids in general: mainly algal detritus and small algae.

*Tricolia pullus:* diatoms, especially those on *Chondrus.*

*Patella* spp.: algae, diatoms.

*Patina pellucida: Laminaria,* diatoms.

*Acmaea virginea, A. tessulata:* red algae, *Lithothamnion* (Ankel, 1936a).

*Theodoxus fluviatilis:* green protophytes; sponges (Ankel, 1936a).

*Viviparus viviparus, V. contectus:* microscopic algae, detritus (Cook, 1949).

*Littorina littorea, L. littoralis:* fucoids, washed up weed, algal detritus, diatoms, lichens.

*Littorina saxatilis, L. neritoides:* algal detritus, diatoms.

*Lacuna parva: Chondrus crispus, Nitophyllum laciniatum, Ceramium rubrum, Gigartina mammillata* (Ankel, 1936a).

*L. vincta: Fucus, Laminaria.*

*Pomatias elegans:* dead leaves (Kilian, 1951).

*Acicula fusca:* vegetable detritus (Creek, 1953).

*Valvata* spp.: water weeds, detritus; snail faeces (Wesenberg–Lund, 1939; Cleland, 1954).

*Hydrobia ulvae: Ulva,* blue-green algae, detritus (Ankel, 1936a).

*H. ventrosa:* microfauna and microflora of brackish water plants (Robson, 1922a).

*Potamopyrgus jenkinsi:* detritus.

*Bithynia tentaculata:* vegetable detritus (Wesenberg–Lund, 1939); filamentous algae, diatoms (Lilly, 1953).

*B. leachi:* vegetable detritus, diatoms.

*Cingula* spp.: detritus.

*Alvania crassa: Corallina* (Pelseneer, 1935).

*A. carinata:* red algae (Pelseneer, 1935).

*Rissoa parva: Corallina,* algae, detritus (Pelseneer, 1935).

*R. guerini: Codium* (Ankel, 1936a).

*R. membranacea: Zostera* (Ankel, 1936a).

*Barleeia rubra:* detritus, diatoms.

*Assiminea grayana:* diatoms (Ankel, 1936a).

*Bythinella scholtzi:* diatoms, detritus.

*Tornus* spp.: algae (Pelseneer, 1935).

*Skeneopsis planorbis: Cladophora, Pylaiella, Ectocarpus, Polysiphonia, Plocamium* (or the diatoms thereon) (Ankel, 1936a).

*Rissoella opalina, R. diaphana: Delesseria* and other fine weeds (or the diatoms thereon) (Ankel, 1936a).

*Omalogyra atomus: Ulva* (or the diatoms thereon).

*Caecum* spp.: diatoms (Götze, 1938).

*Bittium reticulatum:* general detritus.

*Cerithiopsis tubercularis: Halichondria, Hymeniacidon;* to a less extent *Grantia;* detritus, especially when young.

*Triphora perversa: Halichondria, Hymeniacidon;* animal detritus.

*Ianthina janthina: Velella, Physalia.*

*Eulima* spp.: parasitic on echinoderms.

*Balcis devians:* parasitic on *Holothuria forskali, Antedon bifida.*

*Pelseneeria stylifera:* parasitic on *Echinus esculentus* and other echinoids.

*Trichotropis borealis:* detritus.

*Capulus ungaricus:* ciliary feeder, mainly phytoplankton and floating detritus; often inquiline of bivalves, especially *Pecten maximus.*

*Calyptraea chinensis:* ciliary feeder, mainly phytoplankton and floating detritus.

*Crepidula fornicata:* ciliary feeder, mainly phytoplankton and floating detritus.

*Turritella communis:* ciliary feeder, mainly phytoplankton and floating detritus.

*Aporrhais pespelicani:* microphagous, diatoms and algal detritus.

*Natica* spp.: bivalves, especially *Tellina, Mactra, Venus.*

*Velutina velutina: Phallusia, Styela* (Ankel, 1936a), *Styela coriacea* (Diehl, 1956).

*V. plicatilis: Tubularia indivisa* (Ankel, 1936a).

*Lamellaria perspicua:* tunicates, especially *Leptoclinum, Polyclinum.*

*Erato voluta: Botryllus, Botrylloides.*

*Trivia monacha, T. arctica: Botryllus, Botrylloides, Diplosoma, Trididemnum, Polyclinum.*

*Simnia patula: Alcyonium, Eunicella.*

*Nucella lapillus:* barnacles, prosobranchs, *Mytilus; Spirorbis* when young (Moore, 1938b).

*Ocenebra erinacea: Ostrea,* barnacles, *Paphia.*

*Urosalpinx cinerea: Ostrea, Venus.*

*Neptunea antiqua:* dead fish.

*Buccinum undatum:* fresh carrion, crabs, crayfish, worms, scallops and other bivalves.

*Nassarius reticulatus, N. incrassatus:* carrion; faeces.

# CHAPTER 11

# THE VASCULAR SYSTEM

THE vascular system of the gastropod molluscs consists of a central contractile heart which is linked to the various parts of the body by a series of distributing vessels, the arteries, and by a series of collecting vessels, the veins. The arteries and the veins are connected to each other partly by means of small channels which almost deserve to be regarded as capillaries, but partly also by large cavities, the venous sinuses. These differ from the other parts of the vascular system in that in at least some places they are not lined by any special endothelium, and the blood comes into direct contact with the cells of the organs amongst which they lie. The main arteries and veins, and, on occasion, some of these sinuses, are lined with endothelium.

The heart is a systemic heart, that is, it is placed so as to pump blood through the arteries to the body, collecting it from the respiratory organs to do so. The kidney and its blood vessels occupy a particularly important place in the circulation, being intercalated between the main organs and the respiratory capillary bed. There is thus a renal portal system with afferent renal veins, draining blood from the body to the kidney, and efferent renal veins taking blood from the kidney to the respiratory organs.

The general plan of the circulatory system in most prosobranchs (fig. 18) is as follows. Blood leaves the heart by one or other of 2 main arteries, an anterior aorta and a posterior (or visceral) aorta. The anterior aorta runs forward to end in a series of sinuses in the head and foot; the posterior aorta runs up the visceral hump, usually on the outer, convex, side of the spiral and opens into visceral sinuses. From those sinuses which are placed in the head and the foot the blood is collected into a vessel which lies near the visceral ganglia and in relation to the kidney. Into it there also comes blood from the visceral sinuses, by way of a vessel running along the inner, concave, side of the visceral hump. All this blood is drained into the kidney whence most of it is taken to the mantle skirt, distributed to the ctenidium, and so returned to the heart. A part of it, however, passes from the kidney to the nephridial gland (see p. 285) and is then drained, not into the roof of the mantle cavity, but directly to the heart, so that it does not pass through the ctenidium.

In the diotocardian prosobranchs the course of the circulation is affected by the duplicity of the pallial organs which occurs in these animals and also by the asymmetry of the kidneys which they show. It has been described for a number of animals: for *Haliotis*, by Milne-Edwards (1846), Wegmann (1884) and Crofts (1929), for *Acmaea* by Willcox (1898) and Thiem (1917b), for fissurellids by Ziegenhorn & Thiem (1926), for *Patella* by Milne-Edwards (1846), Wegmann (1887), Haller (1894) and Boutan (1900), and for trochids by Robert (1900), Nisbet (1953) and Deshpande (1957).

In *Monodonta* and other trochids the heart lies in a pericardial cavity placed transversely across the basal part of the visceral mass (la, ra, ve, figs. 53, 157). It is composed of a ventricle (ve, fig. 143A), through the centre of which runs the rectum (r), flanked anteriorly by a left auricle (la), and posteriorly by a right auricle (ra). From the left end of the ventricle there emerges a single vessel, which may be called the bulb of the aorta (using

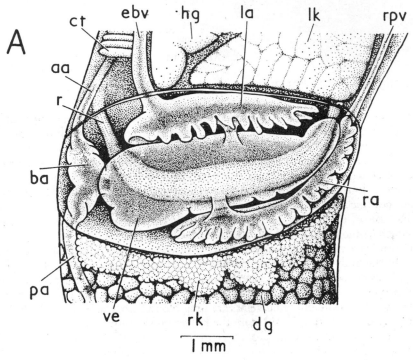

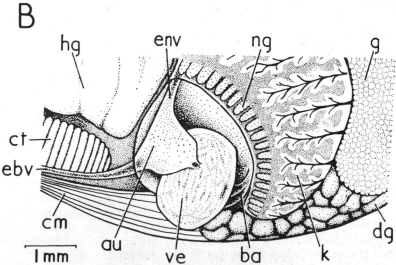

FIG. 143.—A, *Monodonta lineata:* heart and surrounding organs. Note that the roof of the pericardial cavity has been removed and that the anterior end is at the top of the figure. B, *Nucella lapillus:* heart and surrounding organs. Note that the roof of the pericardial cavity has been removed, that the ventricle is displaced and that the anterior is to the left.

aa, anterior aorta; au, auricle; ba, bulbus aortae; cm, columellar muscle; ct, ctenidium; dg, digestive gland; ebv, efferent branchial vein; env, efferent vein of nephridial gland; g, gonad; hg, hypobranchial gland; k, kidney of monotocardian; la, left auricle; lk, left kidney or papillary sac; ng, nephridial gland; pa, posterior aorta; r, rectum; ra, right auricle; rk, right kidney; rpv, right pallial vein; ve, ventricle.

Boutan's term) (ba). As soon as it has left the pericardial cavity this divides to form 2 vessels which are the anterior (aa) and posterior (pa) aortae.

The posterior aorta (pa, fig. 157B) climbs the visceral mass giving off vessels to such sections of the alimentary and reproductive systems as are to be found in that part of the body. These end by opening to the visceral haemocoelic spaces lying amongst the acini of the gonad (ov) and digestive gland (dg). The anterior aorta (aa, fig. 53) passes forwards, on the left side of the body, at the level of attachment of the mantle skirt, ventral to the line of the efferent branchial vessel (ev). It penetrates the muscular wall of the body and so comes to lie alongside a forwardly directed loop of intestine (i) placed in this area. At the anterior end of this loop the artery penetrates a muscular partition, the transverse septum (trs, figs. 144, 145, 150), which forms a boundary between the haemocoelic space in which the intestine lies and other anterior ones in the head. Having penetrated this, the aorta runs across the body, closely adherent to, or even embedded in the septum, until it reaches the right side, where it again turns and resumes its forward course, enlarging in diameter as it does so, and comes to lie underneath the buccal mass, in a space called (by Nisbet, 1953, whose nomenclature is being followed here) the cephalopedal sinus (cps, fig. 144). This forms a distributive centre from which blood passes to a further series of structures lying at the anterior end of the body: (1) an anterior pedal artery (apa) passes downwards and forward in the mid-line, supplying the anterior part of the foot; (2) paired lateral pedal arteries (lpa) pass backwards one on either side of the foot; (3) a connexion (ppa) takes blood to a cavity placed directly under the cephalopedal sinus, the pleuropedal sinus, so called because it surrounds the pleuropedal ganglionic mass, from which blood spaces extend backwards through the foot alongside the pedal nerve cords; (4) similar spaces pass dorsally alongside the cerebropleural (cpl) and cerebropedal (cpdc) connectives, pouring blood into a large haemocoelic cavity, the dorsal cephalic sinus, situated in the dorsal part of the head; (5) extensions pass forwards to the snout, the eye stalks and the tentacles; (6), (7) and (8) 3 routes by which blood can pass into the sinuses of the buccal mass. These are: a dorsal buccal sinus lying dorsally in the buccal mass and extending into the oesophageal valve (the sheet of tissue lying between the anterior oesophagus above and the radular sac below) and a ventral buccal sinus filling most of the space between the more ventrally placed muscles and cartilages of the odontophore.

Blood from these different destinations ultimately drains into a small number of sinuses lying around, or in relation to, the oesophagus and anterior loop of intestine already described. All the blood from the buccal sinuses is gathered into one called the ventral cephalic sinus (vcs). This lies around the buccal sinuses, between the outer surface of the buccal mass and the lateral walls of the head, and it extends backwards around the radular sac (rs) to where that ends anterior to the transverse septum. Blood from this sinus, however, cannot escape directly backwards at this point, because of this and other septa, but must pass dorsally into another sinus, the dorsal cephalic sinus (dcs), already referred to; into this also drains all the blood from the other haemocoelic spaces in the head. The dorsal cephalic sinus lies morphologically dorsal to the mid-oesophagus, and extends with it as far as the transverse septum, where it ends. The transverse septum is thus an important landmark, coinciding not only with the posterior, blind ends of the 2 cephalic blood sinuses, dorsal and ventral, but also marking the posterior end of the radular sac and, incidentally, the point at which the mid-oesophagus runs into the posterior oesophagus. Since the dorsal cephalic sinus overlies the mid-oesophagus it is also, like that part of the gut, twisted to the left as it passes backwards, and divided into

3 parts by double sheets of muscle and connective tissue; these run between the bases of the dorsal folds and the overlying body wall, so as to produce lateral haemocoelic compartments over the lateral glandular areas and a median channel over the food groove, which may be called the median dorsal channel of the dorsal cephalic sinus. The muscular curtains which separate it from the lateral compartments are incomplete and

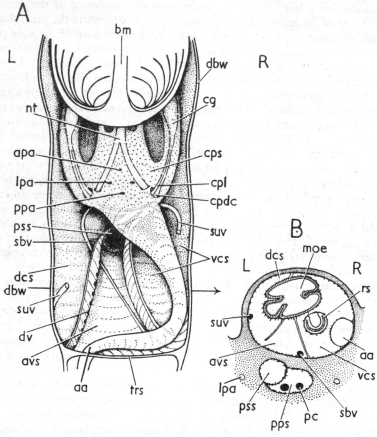

FIG. 144.—*Monodonta lineata:* A, semidiagrammatic representation of the anterior part of the body lying between the transverse septum (trs) posteriorly and the buccal mass (bm) in front; the buccal mass has been turned forwards to expose structures beneath and the radular sac and oesophagus have been removed. Some nerves and muscular partitions have also been partly taken away opening some haemocoelic spaces. The ventral cephalic sinus (vcs) is following the twist of the mid-oesophagus round the right body wall from a ventral position anteriorly to a dorsal position near the level of the transverse septum. The dorsal cephalic sinus (dcs) is similarly curving from a dorsal position anteriorly to a ventral position posteriorly where it connects with the anterior ventral visceral sinus (avs) by means of holes in a muscular partition (dv). B, transverse section at level marked by arrow in A.

aa, anterior aorta; apa, opening to anterior pedal artery; avs, anterior ventral visceral sinus; bm, buccal mass; cg, cerebral ganglion; cpdc, cerebropedal connective; cpl, cerebropleural connective; cps, cephalopedal sinus; dbw, dorsal body wall cut; dcs, dorsal cephalic sinus; dv, connexions between the dorsal cephalic and anterior ventral visceral sinuses; lpa, opening to lateral pedal artery; moe, mid-oesophagus; nt, nuchal tendon; pc, pedal cord; ppa, opening to pleuropedal sinus; pps, pleuropedal sinus; pss, opening of pedal sinus to the anterior ventral visceral sinus; rs, radular sac; sbv, sub-oesophageal part of visceral loop cut; suv, supra-oesophageal part of visceral loop cut; trs, transverse septum; vcs, ventral cephalic sinus.

allow blood to enter the dorsal channel, which it does because there is no other outlet from the lateral spaces. The median channel thus collects the blood which is returning from all parts of the head, leads it backwards and ventrally, following the torsion of the gut, and finally spills it into a sinus which extends posteriorly below the ventral edge of the transverse septum and ventral to the oesophagus and anterior intestinal loop, though dorsal to the columellar muscle. This is called the anterior ventral visceral sinus (avs) into the anterior end of which a large pedal sinus (pss) returns blood from the foot. It is thus a collector of all blood emerging from the head and foot.

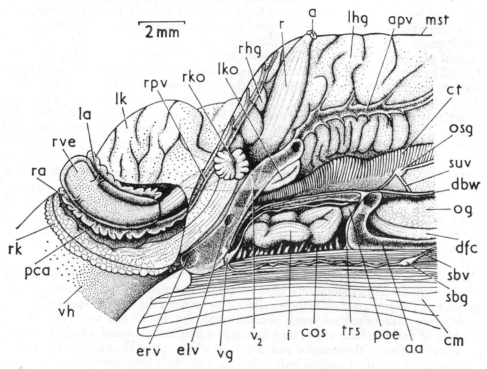

FIG. 145.—*Monodonta lineata:* dissection to show the relationships of the vascular system to other structures at the inner end of the mantle cavity. The pericardial cavity has been opened and exposes the heart and the posterior part of the right kidney. The body wall on the right side has been removed and some dissection done to display the venous sinus and posterior part of the visceral loop. The mantle skirt has been cut along the extreme right side and lifted dorsally.

a, anus; aa, anterior aorta; apv, anterior pallial vein; cm, columellar muscle; cos, collecting sinus; ct, ctenidium; dbw, cut edge of dorsal body wall; dfc, dorsal food channel of oesophagus; elv, opening of vein from left kidney to transverse pallial vein; erv, opening of vein from right kidney to transverse pallial vein; i, anterior loop of intestine; la, left auricle; lhg, left hypobranchial gland; lk, left kidney; lko, opening of left kidney; mst, cut edge of mantle skirt; og, oesophageal gland; osg, osphradium overlying osphradial ganglion; pca, pericardial cavity; poe, posterior oesophagus; r, rectum; ra, right auricle; rhg, right hypobranchial gland; rk, right kidney; rko, opening of right kidney; rpv, right pallial vein; rve, rectum within ventricle; sbg, sub-oesophageal ganglion; sbv, sub-oesophageal part of visceral loop; suv, supra-oesophageal part of visceral loop; trs, transverse septum; $v_2$, rectal and genital nerve (the guide line ends on the nerve within the transverse pallial vein at the point where it divides giving branches to the two kidney openings and the rectum, and at a point where the duct of the left kidney may be seen by transparency under the vein); vg, visceral ganglion lying at the point where the collecting sinus opens to the transverse pallial vein; vh, visceral hump.

Behind the transverse septum the roof of the anterior ventral visceral sinus (avs) is formed of a stout sheet of muscle, continuous with the transverse septum anteriorly and with a similar vertical sheet posteriorly, the vertical septum, which separates all the cephalic and pedal blood spaces so far mentioned from the major visceral blood sinuses. This sheet lies horizontally under the oesophagus and anterior intestinal loop, and is there a complete septum, but on the right it is perforated by a large number of openings through which blood passes dorsally from the anterior ventral visceral sinus into a space called the collecting sinus by Nisbet (1953) (cos, fig. 145).

Posteriorly on the right, the lateral body wall, the vertical and horizontal septa and the dorsal body wall come together to form the corner of body cavity into which the collecting sinus runs, and it is at this point that there arises a large and important vein which passes on to the mantle skirt; this is the transverse pallial vein, inside which the visceral ganglia (vg) lie and through which some of the visceral nerves (v$_2$) run. It is formed by the union of the collecting sinus (cos) from the cephalopedal regions in front, and a large vein (erv) which emerges from the right kidney (rk). The T-junction where the 3 vessels converge is traversed by strands of muscle and tough connective tissue which may permit some control of the blood flow at this point in the circulation. The transverse pallial vein, so formed, now runs on to the mantle skirt, following a forward course more or less ventral to the rectum (r), though actually crossing that structure diagonally from right to left, and flanked as it does so by the ducts and openings of the right (rko) and left (lko) kidneys (papillary sac). It therefore occupies a position which is morphologically median, a fact of some importance from the point of view of comparative anatomy. Into it, at this point, flow 3 vessels: one, according to Deshpande (1957), from the rectum, another from the left kidney (elv), and the third from the region of the right hypobranchial gland, along which it flows parallel to, and to the right of, the rectum. Small vessels leave the main channel and spread between the lobes of the gland and others ramify in the mantle skirt in front of the anterior end of the gland. The main channel of the transverse pallial vein crosses left of the rectum and then turns forward to run through the left hypobranchial gland, where it is sometimes known as the anterior pallial vein (apv); it gives off branches which pass between the lobes of the gland. Some of these are small, others are vessels of considerable size, but all pass to the left towards the base of the ctenidium where they flow into a longitudinal vessel which runs along the dorsal surface of the ctenidial axis and from which spring the numerous capillaries leading blood into the branchial leaflets (ctl, fig. 146). This longitudinal vessel is, therefore, clearly the afferent branchial vein (abv).

Whilst there can be no doubt that blood is passing into the transverse pallial vein from the right renal vein—that this is, in other words, a renal efferent vessel—there can be no similar certainty about the vessel connected to the papillary sac (the left kidney), in view of the fact that the vascular system of that kidney is also directly connected to the left auricle. It may, therefore, be possible for blood to flow from the transverse pallial vein to the left auricle either by way of the ctenidium and the efferent branchial vessel, or by way of the left kidney. At first sight it may seem that a similar doubt must also exist regarding the direction in which blood flows along the anterior pallial vein, since this might be either a tributary or distributary of the transverse pallial. This matter appears to be resolved by the occurrence of another vein, the efferent or right pallial vein (rpv, figs. 143A, 145), which runs along the mantle skirt at its extreme right margin, ventral to the right hypobranchial gland (rhg) and just dorsal to the right edge of the columellar muscle (cm). It connects anteriorly with the branches of the anterior pallial vein (apv) and carries blood to the right auricle of the heart (ra). In view of this it seems reasonable to conclude that the anterior pallial vein is, in fact, distributing blood from the transverse pallial vein to the right part of the mantle skirt which will then be collected into the efferent pallial vein.

Now the efferent pallial vein has been regarded by several writers (e.g. Thiele, 1897) as the homologue of the right efferent ctenidial vessel, the right gill having vanished, though its efferent has persisted. This view would be strengthened by the description just given, from which it would appear that the anterior pallial vein is a part of the transverse pallial vein system distributing blood by way of the right hypobranchial gland to a right ctenidium and by way of the left hypobranchial gland to the left ctenidium.

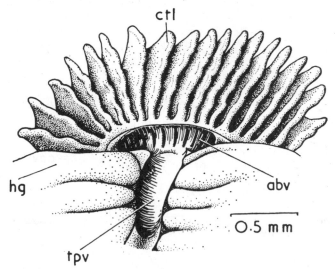

FIG. 146.—*Calliostoma zizyphinum:* a dissection to show the relationship of the transverse pallial vein to the afferent branchial vein.

abv, afferent branchial vein showing openings to blood spaces in ctenidial leaflets; ctl, ctenidial leaflet; hg, hypobranchial gland; tpv, transverse pallial vein.

The basal part of the transverse pallial vein is a (morphologically) median vessel bringing blood to what was originally a symmetrically arranged respiratory area in the roof of the mantle cavity.

The only remaining part of the vascular system to be described in *Monodonta* (fig. 147B) is the venous return of blood from the sinuses in the visceral mass. This is also achieved by way of the kidneys, and is, in fact, the main source of the blood which enters the transverse pallial vein by way of the right efferent renal vein (erv) and, perhaps, by the vein connecting the transverse pallial vein and the left kidney as well.

The historical origin of the system which has just been described would appear to lie in a gastropod in which there were two equally developed hypobranchial and ctenidial areas in the mantle roof. It is, therefore, interesting to compare the arrangement of the vascular system in trochids with what is found in the other diotocardians. Of these the zeugobranchs are, from this aspect, clearly the more important and the members of the Patellacea not so significant. In *Haliotis* (fig. 147A) the anterior aorta (aa) takes blood

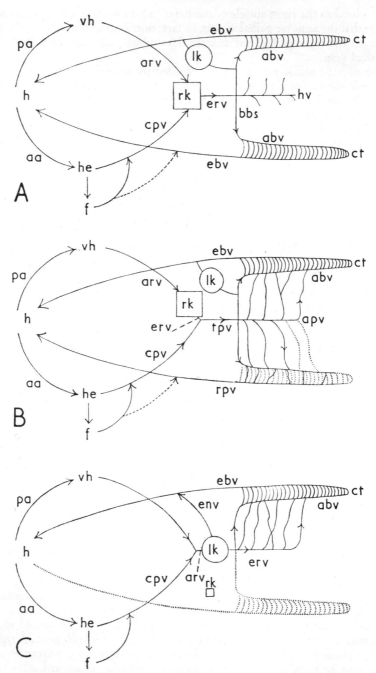

FIG. 147.—Diagrams of the vascular system of: A, *Haliotis*, based on Crofts; B, a trochid; C, a monotocardian. Solid lines indicate vessels occurring; pecked lines mark vessels which probably exist;
dotted lines are vessels which have been lost.

aa, anterior aorta; abv, afferent branchial vein; apv, anterior pallial vein; arv, afferent renal vein;
bbs, basibranchial sinus; cpv, cephalopedal vein; ct, ctenidium; ebv, efferent branchial vein; env,
efferent vessel of nephridial gland; erv, efferent renal vein; f, foot; h, heart; he, head; hv, hypobranchial vessels; lk, left kidney; pa, posterior aorta; rk, right kidney; rpv, right pallial vein; tpv,
transverse pallial vein; vh, visceral hump.

to the anterior part of the body (he, f), whence it is collected into venous sinuses: un-fortunately, these have not been described in detail comparable to what is known about *Monodonta*, so that a closer comparison is not possible. They are said, however, to open into the 'abdominal' visceral sinuses, from which they reach afferent veins leading to the right kidney (rk): if this is so, there is then a major difference between *Haliotis* and the trochids, because in the former all blood would traverse the right kidney, whereas in the latter the blood from the head-foot by-passes the excretory organ and passes straight to the mantle skirt, and only blood from the viscera traverses the kidney.

From the right kidney blood passes along the efferent renal vessel (erv) to one known as the basibranchial sinus (bbs) which lies transversely across the mantle skirt at its attach-ment to the visceral mass, between the bases of the ctenidia (ct). It lies ventral to the rectum, crossing it from side to side in what is a morphologically median situation, and in addition to its main factor (the right renal efferent) it also receives vessels related to the rectum and the left kidney or papillary sac. From its ends arise the afferent ctenidial vessels (abv) running one along the axis of each gill. There seems no difficulty, after the recital of these facts, in homologizing the transverse pallial vein of trochids with this so-called basibranchial sinus of *Haliotis* (as suggested by Bernard, 1890), and the condi-tions in this animal would also support the idea that the efferent pallial vein is the homo-logue of the right efferent ctenidial vessel.

Whereas *Haliotis* shows a departure from the trochids as regards the situation of the right kidney in the circulatory system the fissurellids appear to occupy an intermediate position, according to Spillmann (1905) and Ziegenhorn & Thiem (1926). In *Fissurella crassa* and *Glyphis graeca* (=*Diodora apertura*) the anterior aorta carries blood, as usual, to the head, foot and anterior viscera, and the posterior aorta carries blood to the visceral mass. Whereas all the blood from the visceral mass is carried to the right kidney, as in *Haliotis* and the trochids, and all the blood from the cephalic and pedal region passes straight to the basibranchial sinus as in trochids, some blood from the anterior viscera goes to the right kidney as in *Haliotis*.

Whilst in these zeugobranchs the left kidney can be omitted from consideration as it is all but a vestige embedded in the anterior pericardial wall, it is difficult on the basis of its blood supply to decide what part it plays in the life of *Haliotis*. According to the diagram given by Crofts (1929) it appears to receive only a supply of oxygenated blood from the 2 efferent ctenidial vessels and this, after traversing its tissues, is then returned to the basibranchial sinus and sent to the gills: this seems to argue that it can have little excretory function comparable to that exercised by the right kidney and, perhaps, that it is carrying out some physiological activity which calls for a high supply of oxygen (see p. 286).

In view of the reduction or absence of ctenidia in the Patellacea and their replacement by secondary pallial outgrowths, it is not surprising to find that the plan of the vascular system in these animals has been modified. In *Acmaea*, in which one ctenidium still persists, some blood is sent directly there and so to the heart, but there are other routes by which blood may reach the auricle (Willcox, 1898; Thiem, 1917b). From the head most of the blood is collected into sinuses related to the nerve ganglia, the pleural sinus, the anterior neural sinus and the posterior neural sinus. These connect with pedal veins into which also passes the blood from the major spaces of the foot, and this volume of blood is then passed through gaps in the shell muscle into the mantle edge and collected into a vein running around the free edge of the mantle skirt which leads to the auricle (epv, fig. 73). Although there are no true pallial gills set around the mantle edge in these animals there must, nevertheless, be a considerable degree of oxygenation of the blood possible in this situation and it is likely that this blood is as well oxygenated as that which passes through the ctenidium. In fact, according to Thiem (1917b), there is a correlation between the degree of folding in the mantle edge, the number of vessels passing through gaps in the shell muscle and the presence or absence of a ctenidium: thus in scurriids, with a well developed ctenidium and well developed folds on the mantle edge, these breaks are few; in acmaeids, which have no folds but still retain the ctenidium, they are numerous, whilst in the lepetids, which have neither marginal pallial folds nor ctenidium, the gaps through the shell muscle, and therefore the break-up of the blood flow into a large number of small vessels permitting ready oxygenation, are very frequent.

In addition to the two routes by means of which venous blood may be returned to the heart—both of which are so arranged as to introduce respiratory surfaces *en route*—the acmaeids also show a third way, but this does not include any significant respiratory organ. It drains blood from some of the anterior viscera (such as salivary glands, digestive gland and parts of the intestine) which abut against the posterior wall of the nuchal cavity, and passes it by means of channels which lie in the floor of the mantle cavity to the heart. Little, if any, respiratory exchange appears to be likely to occur in this situation, but the vessels are small and the amount of blood transmitted by them is probably not great. Some of the blood from these organs, however, and also apparently all from the posterior part of the visceral mass, drains through the right kidney and is then added to the stream which is passing through the shell muscle to be oxygenated in the mantle edge prior to its return to the heart. A minute fraction of this is said (Thiem, 1917b) to make its way through the left instead of the right kidney.

It is clear from this description of the acmaeid circulatory system that the ctenidium plays a significantly less important part than it did in either *Haliotis* or the trochids, and, also, that the right kidney is not incorporated into the circulation in such a strategic way as in these animals. It is not surprising, therefore, to find that the cyclobranchs, the patellids, have been able to lose their ctenidia wholly, and compensate for their loss by an expansion of the pallial branchial equipment, and to find the kidneys equally unimportant. In *Patella* (Milne-Edwards, 1846; Wegmann, 1887; Boutan, 1900; Davis & Fleure, 1903) the heart (au, ve, figs. 261, 266) lies at the anterior end of the visceral mass well to the left, near the anterior end of the shell muscle (sm). Three apparent chambers lie parallel to one another across the breadth of the pericardial cavity: the auricle (au) most anteriorly, the ventricle (ve) in the centre and a bulbus aortae (ba) (considered by Wegmann (1887) to be a subdivision of the ventricle) posteriorly. From the left side of the bulbus arises a vessel, often called the genital artery, which runs posteriorly over the visceral hump supplying the gut and gonad: this is clearly the posterior aorta. From its right side leaves a vessel which curves ventrally, under the rectum, and then runs forwards into the head, where it opens to a large cephalic blood space. This, in turn, gives rise to anterior and posterior pedal arteries and to arteries which supply the more ventrally placed viscera and those which lie to the animal's right. The vessel which originates from the right side of the bulbus corresponds to the anterior aorta of the other types described. From all these parts the blood eventually makes its way into visceral sinuses lying in the visceral mass and it is from these that the venous return starts. The blood passes through interstices in the shell muscle (ism, fig. 50) into an afferent branchial vein which runs round the base of the mantle skirt on the outer side of the shell muscle and is interrupted only anterior to the head. From this the blood is passed through the spaces in the gill leaflets (pag) into an efferent branchial vein (epv) running round the complete circle of the mantle skirt near its outer edge. At one point on the left side, near the anterior end of the shell muscle, this ring vessel gives rise to a large trunk which runs to the auricle (au). Two subsidiary routes may be added to this principal one just described, exactly comparable to those found in acmaeids. Some blood from the visceral sinuses passes through the right kidney and is led from it to the afferent branchial vein by an efferent renal vessel which crosses the rectum near the anus, crosses the kidney duct and makes its way on to the mantle skirt at the anterior end of the right half of the shell muscle. The relationships of this vessel suggest that it may well be the homologue of the basibranchial sinus of *Haliotis* and the transverse pallial vein of the trochids. What part the reduced left kidney plays in the circulation is obscure, but it may contribute some blood to this vessel. Lastly, there exists a pathway by which blood from visceral spaces can pass into the floor of the nuchal cavity, from which it is drained directly into the auricle. The quantity of blood which does this is not great, and it seems unlikely that much oxygenation can occur in such a position in a limpet.

It is now necessary to turn to the remaining prosobranchs, the mesogastropods and stenoglossans (fig. 147C). In these, as the name Monotocardia implies, there is only a single auricle in the heart (au, fig. 143B), which corresponds to the left auricle of the diotocardians and, like it, receives blood from the left ctenidium (ct) and left kidney (k, fig. 143B; lk, fig. 147C). With the disappearance of the right auricle the right or efferent pallial vein disappears too, and the whole of the right vascular complex of the roof of the mantle cavity is lost. The right kidney (rk) remains only as an element in the organization of the genital duct, and as the glandular sections of this appear to take the place of, and may have arisen from the right hypobranchial gland and have been folded off the surface of the mantle skirt, there is nothing to prevent the rectum from coming to lie well over to the right side of the body. This allows for the expansion of the left ctenidium and left hypobranchial gland in the mantle skirt and for the increased volume of the left kidney as that replaces the right as the main excretory organ. Associated with this—perhaps a necessary prerequisite of it—the rectum no longer penetrates the ventricle as it does in so many diotocardians, a fact which allows its migration to the right to occur readily; and the heart now lies more along the longitudinal axis of the body on the left, in proximity to the base of the gill, rather than across it. This allows the base of the efferent branchial vessel (ebv) to be quite short and the auricle often gives the appearance of being attached almost to the last ctenidial filament.

In *Littorina littorea* a bulbus aortae (ba, fig. 148A) lies in the posterior part of the pericardial cavity and anterior and posterior aortae (pa) diverge from it, the former passing to the head and the latter climbing up the visceral hump. Both end by passing blood to cephalic, pedal or visceral haemocoelic spaces. The anterior aorta is affected by torsion in the mid-oesophageal region and passes from the left to the right ventral side of the oesophagus before dividing, near the nerve ring, into cephalic and pedal branches (see fig. 14). As in the trochids, the blood from the sinuses to which these lead is collected into a venous sinus which lies alongside the posterior half of the mid-oesophagus. This sinus is separated by a vertical septum on its posterior side from the visceral parts of the body, but there is a gap in the septum ventrally on the right (ocp, fig. 148B). Through this, which is controlled by muscle, blood passes into a vein which runs vertically towards the mantle skirt and in which lie the visceral ganglia (vg). Across it run a number of strands of muscle and stout connective tissue (cn) which suggest valvular control of the blood flow, and nerves to the viscera leave the ganglia and travel along it. Into this vessel there opens another which can be traced along the concave side of the visceral

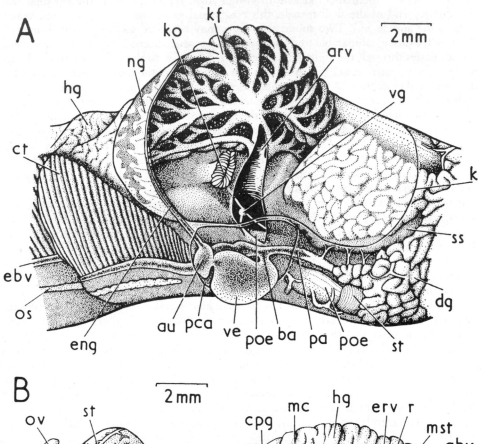

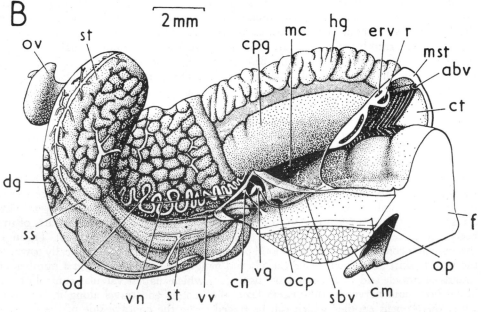

hump, running between the posterior oesophagus below and the digestive gland and genital duct above. This is a visceral vein (vv) into which blood collects from all the numerous irregular haemocoelic channels which ramify among and between the lobules of gonad and digestive gland. The union of these vessels in the neighbourhood of the visceral ganglia collects almost all the blood from head, foot and visceral mass into a single channel. This proves to be an afferent vein of the left kidney (arv, fig. 148A): it may be traced into the wall of the kidney, entering ventrally and towards the left, close to the bulbus aortae (ba). From there it runs dorsally, passing near the external aperture (ko) and projecting broadly into the cavity of the kidney sac. Nearing the dorsal wall it starts to branch, subdividing in pinnate fashion to supply the folds of excretory tissue (kf) which run over the inner and dorsal walls of the kidney, and breaking down into vessels of almost capillary dimensions.

From these renal capillaries the bulk of the blood is collected into a prominent vein which emerges from the kidney dorsally and to the right and runs forwards on the mantle skirt more or less dorsal to the rectum and genital duct (erv, figs. 148B, 149). It gives rise to a series of vessels which pass to the left in the roof of the mantle cavity between the lobes of the hypobranchial gland, which are, indeed, largely due to their presence. They ramify and anastomose among themselves and from this network arise the different channels passing into the ctenidial leaflets.

Not all the blood which has entered the kidney follows this particular course, however. A fraction of it passes out of the lamellae of the kidney sac into the capillary-like spaces of the nephridial gland and from this is collected into another vessel which runs directly to the auricle (eng, fig. 148A) without traversing the ctenidial leaflets at all; the amount of blood involved in this part of the circulation is probably not a significantly great part of the total volume so that the fact that it appears to escape oxygenation is not very important.

This plan of the vascular system seems to be general not only amongst the meso-gastropods but also in the Stenoglossa (*Buccinum*: Dakin, 1912; *Nucella*: present authors). It presents a clear resemblance to the circulatory system of the diotocardians with a number of equally marked differences, of which the most important appear to be that all blood (except a relatively small part which makes its way from visceral hump or foot directly into vessels lying in the peripheral parts of the mantle skirt) passes through the kidney on its way to the heart; and that this kidney is the left rather than the right.

---

FIG. 148.—*Littorina littorea:* A, dissection from the left to show vessels in relation to the kidney. The pericardial cavity has been opened to expose the heart. The kidney sac has been opened and the afferent renal vein slit from the point where it is formed ventrally by union of veins from head-foot and visceral mass, to the point where it branches into the kidney folds. B, dissection from the right to show vessels in relation to kidney. The animal is represented with the anterior end removed. A venous space above the columellar muscle is opened as well as the base of the afferent renal vein.

abv, afferent branchial vein; arv, afferent renal vein; au, auricle; ba, bulbus aortae; cm, columellar muscle; cn, connective tissue strut; cpg, capsule gland; ct, ctenidium; dg, digestive gland; ebv, efferent branchial vein; eng, efferent vessel of nephridial gland; erv, efferent renal vein overlying rectum; f, foot; hg, hypobranchial gland; k, cut edge of kidney sac; kf, folded surface of kidney; ko, opening of kidney to mantle cavity; mc, mantle cavity; mst, cut edge of mantle skirt; ng, nephridial gland; ocp, opening of cephalopedal vein; od, ovarian duct; op, operculum; os, osphradium; ov, ovary; pa, posterior aorta; pca, cut edge of pericardium; poe, posterior oesophagus; r, rectum; sbv, sub-oeso-phageal part of visceral loop; ss, style sac region of stomach; st, stomach; ve, ventricle; vg, visceral ganglion lying in blood space where the cephalopedal vein, visceral vein and afferent renal vein unite, and giving off the visceral loop anteroventrally, a nerve to the kidney opening anterodorsally and a visceral nerve posteriorly; vn, visceral nerve; vv, visceral vein.

These matters raise the question of the homologies of the vessels in the neighbourhood of the kidney.

When a specimen of *Monodonta* is dissected from the right side in the region around the vertical and transverse septa the view shown in fig. 145 is obtained: the visceral ganglia (vg) lie at the point where the collecting sinus, the renal vein and the transverse pallial vein all join. If the same dissection be carried out on a monotocardian (e.g. *Littorina* or *Nucella*) the appearance obtained will be that shown in fig. 148B. The two arrangements are so nearly identical in the relationships between blood vessels and ganglia, muscles and mantle skirt that it is difficult to avoid the conclusion that homologous vessels form the T-junction in each case. Yet the functions of these vessels and their relationships to the kidney are not the same in the 2 animals: the vessel emerging from the direction of the visceral hump is an efferent renal vein in the case of the trochid (erv, fig. 145), but a visceral vein in the monotocardian (vv, fig. 148B), whilst the vessel passing dorsally is running on to the mantle skirt in the diotocardian but is an afferent vein of the kidney in the monotocardian. This seems to suggest that the homologies are spurious. Nevertheless it is likely that this is not so: the anatomical relationships between vascular and other structures are too intimately identical for there to be real doubt as to this, and the explanation of the changes in the flow of blood in these channels must be looked for elsewhere, and, in particular, in the fact that in the one case the kidney is the right kidney and in the other it is the left. Reference to the series of diagrams in fig. 147 will make this clear. In fig. 147A the vascular system of *Haliotis* is shown with the right kidney (rk) placed so as to intercept the main blood flow from both anterior and posterior halves of the body. The efferent vessel from this (erv) leads to the basibranchial sinus (bbs) and so to the gills (ct), and it also connects with a rectal vessel (hv). It is not easy to determine how the hypobranchial glands receive their blood supply, but they seem to be related to a pallial vein which leads to visceral sinuses and so to the right kidney. The left kidney or papillary sac is connected to the basibranchial sinus and left efferent ctenidial vessel, but the route which the blood takes through these vessels can only be surmised.

Fig. 147B shows the arrangement in the trochids, in which it seems that the system is fundamentally similar except in 3 main points: (1) the right kidney (rk) invades the vascular system draining only the visceral hump (arv) and does not penetrate that which is running back from the head and foot (cpv); (2) the transverse pallial vein (= basibranchial sinus) sends blood to the afferent ctenidial vessel on the left through the hypobranchial gland; and (3) with the disappearance of the right ctenidium the blood from the transverse pallial vein on that side makes its way directly through the anastomoses of the right hypobranchial gland to the efferent pallial vein (= right efferent ctenidial vessel (rpv)). As a result of the new relationship between the right kidney and vascular system the anterior end of the visceral venous return now appears as a renal efferent (erv). The left kidney (lk) is still, as in *Haliotis*, somewhat ambiguously sited between transverse pallial vein and left efferent ctenidial blood stream (in this case the connexion is with the auricle and not the efferent vessel).

In the monotocardians a fundamental alteration has occurred in that the right kidney (rk) is reduced and the left (lk) expanded to form the main excretory organ. In its hypertrophy this kidney, too, has come to invade the afferent ctenidial flow of blood from head, foot and visceral hump, but the right kidney is no longer related to it. It is not an unlikely assumption that contact between the expanding left kidney and the vascular system came about at a place different from that at which the right kidney and bloodstream had commingled, and if we suppose that it occurred (as shown in fig. 147c) in front of the junction between the converging vessels from head-foot (cpv) and visceral hump then both of these would unite to form a single afferent renal vein (arv) which is made from the ventral part of the vessel known respectively as transverse pallial vein or basibranchial sinus in the two diotocardians. In these circumstances the vessel bringing blood from the head and foot will look the same in trochid and monotocardian (cos, fig. 145; ocp, fig. 148B), but the vessel returning blood from the visceral mass will be

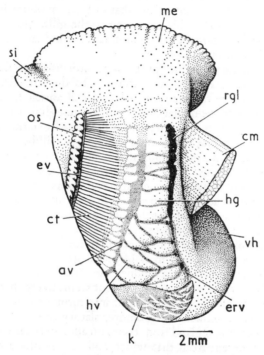

FIG. 149.—*Nucella lapillus:* dorsal view of mantle skirt and base of visceral hump.
av, afferent vessel of ctenidium; cm, columellar muscle; ct, ctenidium; erv, efferent renal vein; ev, efferent vessel of ctenidium; hg, hypobranchial gland; hv, hypobranchial vessel; k, kidney; me, mantle edge; os, osphradium; rgl, rectal gland; si, siphon; vh, visceral hump.

an efferent renal vessel in the trochid (erv, fig. 145), but, because of the disappearance of the right kidney, a simple visceral vein in the other (vv, fig. 148B). The circulation on the mantle skirt has also been modified, and not merely by the simple abolition of the entire right moiety. The main vessel emerging from the kidney runs dorsal to the rectum (erv, fig. 149) and sends branches (hv) through the hypobranchial gland towards the ctenidium, sometimes forming an afferent ctenidial channel (av) at or near the base of the gill leaflets, sometimes, however, apparently running directly into these without any longitudinal vessel intervening. From its situation over the rectum the main vessel looks as if it might be interpreted as a hypertrophied rectal vein, but it might also be regarded as the main left half of the transverse pallial vein with a new orientation, and it appears unprofitable to attempt to discriminate between these two points of view.

The last point to which attention should be directed in this discussion is the idea held by some zoologists that the kidney of monotocardians is in fact the right, and that the left has vanished (Haller, 1894). Although now primarily of historical interest, because of the clear demonstration that part of the genital duct is of renal origin and may still retain its pericardial connexion, it is easy to understand how this misinterpretation could have arisen in view of the almost identical appearance and structure of the right kidney of *Monodonta* and the single kidney of monotocardians, the lack of similarity between the left kidney of *Monodonta* and the single kidney of monotocardians and the fact that the right kidney of the trochid and that of the monotocardians are both placed so as to filter much (or all) of the blood passing to the gills. There is, however, in the organization and vascularization of the monotocardian kidney one detail which is of especial significance in this connexion.

It will be recalled that the left kidney of the diotocardians apparently receives its blood supply from the basibranchial sinus and returns it to the left efferent ctenidial vessel (*Haliotis*) or is related to the transverse pallial vein and auricle (*Monodonta*). This connexion is found to persist in the higher prosobranchs, though in a restricted sense. If the kidney of a mesogastropod or stenoglossan be examined externally on the surface of the visceral mass, the appearance represented in fig. 143B will be seen. Over most of the surface run the insertions of the main folds of the walls on which lies the excretory tissue and into which run the branches of the afferent renal vein. Along the side of the kidney sac which borders the pericardial cavity, however, the appearance of the kidney is quite different: this marks the position of a specialized part usually known as the 'nephridial gland' (ng)—an unfortunate name in that the kidney of molluscs is technically a coelomoduct and not a nephridium, but perhaps acceptable until knowledge of the functional importance of this part of the kidney provides a basis for a better one.

The nephridial gland consists of a mass of blood spaces into which projects a large number of blind tubules from the main kidney sac. These tubules are of small diameter and are lined by cells some of which are ciliated: it seems likely that the liquid from the main kidney sac and the blood can be brought into intimate contact in this part of the kidney and it may, therefore, act as an osmoregulatory organ. The blood reaches the haemal spaces of the nephridial gland from the main afferent renal vessel, but it is drained away into a separate efferent from that which collects the blood from the rest of the kidney. This vessel, the efferent of the nephridial gland (env, figs. 143B, 147C), passes directly to the auricle and so by-passes the circulation of the mantle skirt. This is clearly reminiscent of the blood supply of the left kidney of the diotocardians; that it has persisted into the monotocardians offers a proof, from the unexpected angle of its vascular supply, that the sole functional kidney of the higher gastropods is indeed the left.

Attention may now be briefly directed to the histology of the vascular system (fig. 19). The heart is muscular, the auricle less so than the ventricle, and the muscle in all prosobranch hearts which we have observed is striped in the ventricle though not in the auricle. Both chambers are bounded against the pericardial cavity by a squamous epithelium, but no epithelium lines the internal cavity. Apparent glandular cells are often adherent to the muscle cells, sometimes in such abundance as to give the heart a pigmented appearance: the colour depends on pigmented granules in the cytoplasm of the cells, which probably become free and give rise to blood cells. They do not appear to be comparable to the pericardial glands of other molluscs since these are developments of the epithelium lining the pericardial cavity. Even where these have been described in Rhipidoglossa (Grobben, 1891) it is doubtful whether their existence is real. Grobben described them as forming fringes on the edges of the auricles of these animals. Undoubtedly the margin of the auricles is lobed (see figs. 53, 143A, 157), but this is merely the shape of these parts of the heart and is not due to the occurrence of papilliform outgrowths from the surface of the heart, which is what would have to occur before the structure could properly be regarded as a pericardial gland. Such cells as occur there do not line the pericardial cavity and are no more than the same type of connective tissue cell laden with inclusions as are to be met with in other parts of the heart. Despite statements to the contrary (Ankel, 1936a) it seems doubtful whether true pericardial glands occur in the prosobranchs; their function may have been usurped by the nephridial gland or papillary sac where these occur.

The muscle fibres of the chambers of the heart appear to branch so as to form an irregular network. According to Spillmann (1905), the rhipidoglossans show a more precise arrangement in the ventricle, where the musculature is stratified into 3 layers, an outer layer of circular fibres, an intermediate one of fibres longitudinal in direction and an inner, looser layer some fibres of which may traverse the lumen. In contrast the auricles are very thin-walled and have little or no muscle. In the Monotocardia a similar arrangement is not easy to discern, the muscles forming an irregular network which is denser peripherally and more open towards the lumen. The auricle is always muscular, but less so than the ventricle. Muscular valves occur at the auriculo-ventricular junction (avv, fig. 17) and again, sometimes, between ventricle and bulbus aortae, arranged so as to keep the blood flowing from auricle to ventricle and thence to the bulbus.

The heart is innervated by nerves from the pleurovisceral loop or from the visceral ganglion, almost invariably on the right side (crn, fig. 173). In the more primitive genera the auricles are said to receive an innervation which is different from that reaching the ventricle, the nerve to which passes along the aorta (Zeugobranchia and Trochacea: Haller, 1884, 1894; Patellacea and Neritacea: Bouvier, 1887). In higher animals the different parts of the heart are all innervated by branches of the same nerve (*Natica*: Carlson, 1905b; *Ianthina, Hipponyx*: Suzuki, 1934, 1935). As in vertebrates, these nerves have the function of altering the rate at which the heart is beating, the propagation of the beat within the heart itself being myogenic. Which part acts as pace-maker is not known, although Zubkov (1934), like others before him, attributed this function to a small ganglion placed in the region of the junction between ventricle and bulbus aortae in a number of genera. On the other hand, any part of the heart appears capable of initiating the beat in *Haliotis*. The function of the cardiac nerves in prosobranchs appears to be both inhibitory and excitatory.

The molluscan heart is very sensitive to pressure and stretching of its muscles and the excised heart may be completely inactive so long as it is empty and not under tension; when filled, however, it starts to beat and the strength and even the rate of the contraction appear, within limits, to be related to the degree of distension. Over-distension, however, may cause the heart to stop and it has been suggested that one function of the pericardial fluid is to avoid the possibility of overstretching of the muscles. It is likely that the pericardial fluid is also important in causing auricular diastole. Krijgsman & Divaris (1955) suggested that the total volume of the pericardial fluid plus ventricular contents plus auricular contents must remain constant. When the auricle contracts the contents are transferred to the ventricle, a change which involves no alteration in the volume of the system; when the ventricle contracts its contents are transferred to the aorta and to preserve the total volume of the heart an equal volume of blood will be sucked into the auricle from the veins, the pericardial fluid acting as intermediary.

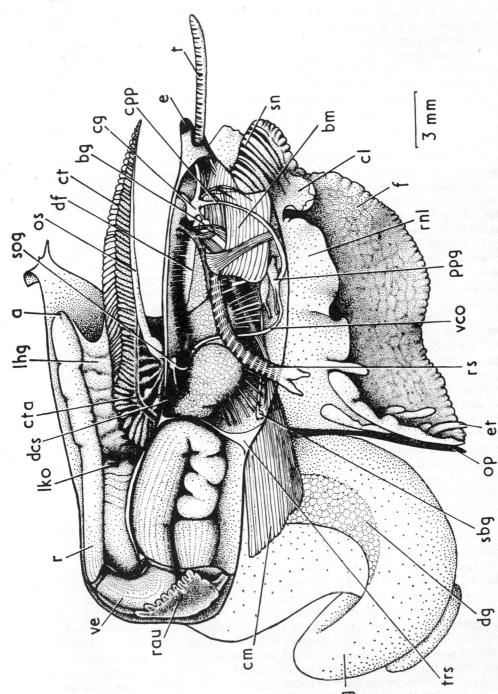

3 mm

FIG. 150.—*Gibbula cineraria*: lateral dissection of mantle cavity, base of visceral mass and head. a, anus; bg, buccal ganglion; bm, muscles of buccal mass; cg, cerebral ganglia; cl, cephalic lappet; cm, columellar muscle; cpp, cerebropleuropedal connective; ct, ctenidium; cta, ctenidial axis; dcs, dorsal cephalic sinus; df, line of dorsal fold on oesophageal wall; dg, digestive gland; e, eye; et, epipodial tentacle; f, foot; g, gonad; lhg, left hypobranchial gland; lko, opening of left kidney (papillary sac); op, operculum; os, osphradium; ppg, pleuropedal ganglion; r, rectum; rau, right auricle; rnl, right neck lobe; rs, radular sac; sbg, sub-oesophageal ganglion; sn, snout; sog, supra-oeso-phageal ganglion; t, tentacle; trs, transverse septum; vco, visceral connective; ve, ventricle.

As in other animals the heart is affected by the chemical milieu in which it beats, although prosobranchs are not animals which have been extensively used in this kind of research. Morin & Jullien (1932) reported that the following solution keeps the heart of *Murex trunculus* in normal activity for many hours: NaCl 0·482 M, KCl 0·005 M, MgCl$_2$ 0·07 M, CaCl$_2$ 0·005 M. The heart is sensitive to drugs: atropine accelerates the heart of *Pterotrachea* as do adrenaline in low concentration, strychnine and cocaine (Hykeš, 1929, 1930, 1932); that of *Murex* is also accelerated by atropine (Morin & Jullien, 1932). The hearts of *Murex* and *Pterotrachea* have both been shown to be sensitive to acetylcholine 1 : 10$^6$ (Morin & Jullien, 1931; Jullien & Vincent, 1938) which inhibits their action. They do not, however, exhibit the same acetylcholine-atropine antagonism as vertebrates, and eserine seems to have little effect; curare, however, can antagonize ACh as in vertebrates.

The physiology of the heart and circulation of molluscs has been discussed by von Skramlik (1941) and by Krijgsman & Divaris (1955) to whom the reader may be referred for further information on this topic.

Except for the main aortae the blood vessels of prosobranch gastropods are provided with thin walls apparently devoid of muscle. In these, particularly the anterior aorta, muscle fibres are found embedded in connective tissue. The connective tissue may be used for the deposit of reserve material such as fat or calcium salts, sometimes giving the arteries a very conspicuous appearance. This happens, for example, in *Littorina littorea*, the principal arteries of which are easily seen as white threads because of the calcareous matter lodged in their walls.

The blood of prosobranchs has been investigated by Cuénot (1891), Kollmann (1908), Cuénot (1914) and George & Ferguson (1950), most attention being directed to the nature of the blood cells which occur. According to Cuénot only one type of amoebocyte can be found, amoeboid and containing granules of enzymatic or metaplastic nature. Kollmann, on the other hand, denied the presence of granular cells in any gastropod other than *Viviparus viviparus* and described a young stage with hyaline cytoplasm and a spherical nucleus which acquires relatively more cytoplasm and a polymorphic nucleus as it matures. George & Ferguson described 3 types in the various stenoglossan molluscs which they examined: (1) a slightly amoeboid lymphocyte with clear, basophile cytoplasm occasionally containing some granules or vacuoles; (2) a granular phagocyte with basophile cytoplasm containing many small spherules, or vacuoles in which material is being digested, very rapidly moving and amoeboid, with an oval or bilobed nucleus; (3) a granular amoebocyte, the granules being numerous and staining with eosin, the nucleus oval and eccentric.

The origin of these cells is doubtful. George & Ferguson found no organ which seemed to be the site of manufacture of blood cells and therefore concluded that their second and third types were made from the lymphocytes, though the origin of these is itself doubtful. The main activity of these cells is presumably phagocytic and no coagulation of the blood is found to occur. The cells occupy only 1–2% of the total blood volume.

The plasma of prosobranchs varies in colour but usually shows some trace of blue because of the haemocyanin which it contains. This may amount to 9% of the blood.

# CHAPTER 12

# THE EXCRETORY SYSTEM

EXCRETORY organs of prosobranch gastropods are coelomoducts (Erlanger, 1891*b*, 1892), primitively paired, situated wholly within the visceral mass and opening to the innermost end of the mantle cavity, one on either side of the anus. The mode of development in several prosobranchs suggests that the terminal part is an ectodermal ingrowth from the wall of the mantle cavity. In the ancestral prosobranch (fig. 151B) it is assumed that the kidneys were simple sacs with no complex folding of the wall and were in communication with the other coelomic spaces, each being joined to the pericardium by a ciliated renopericardial duct which, on the right side, received the duct from the single gonad. This arrangement is retained in the diotocardians, though with modifications which concern differences in the development and histology of the two kidneys, the loss of the renopericardial duct and the point of opening of the gonadial duct (p. 321). In no living gastropod do the two kidneys retain their primitive symmetry. In some diotocardians the left is much reduced in size as in *Diodora* (fig. 151D) and the Patellacea, in which both kidneys may lie on the right of the pericardium (fig. 151C), or, as in *Emarginula*, where it may be represented by a patch of cells on the anterior wall of the pericardium with no communication with the exterior or with the coelom. In another series of diotocardians the wall of this kidney is papillated, with numerous papillae projecting far into the lumen and practically obliterating it. This type of sac is found in the zeugobranchs *Haliotis* and *Scissurella*, in the various members of the Trochidae (fig. 151E) and in the Turbinidae.

In addition to the cells which form the epithelium lining the kidney sacs of prosobranchs, other cells are involved in excretory activity. These are partly blood cells, partly cells like those found in the blood but actually stationary in a few restricted sites of the body, and partly cells in the epithelium of the digestive gland. The cells in the blood are phagocytic and pick up material of excretory significance which is travelling in the bloodstream. Some are situated in the connective tissue of the kidney lamellae, and they also occur in the gills (Bernard, 1890; Dakin, 1912; Cuénot, 1914) and in the auricles of *Viviparus* (Cuénot, 1914), and possibly of other animals as well. Presumably, once they are laden with material, these cells migrate out of the body of the animal and so evacuate the excretory substance.

The right kidney of the diotocardian is unexpectedly large and often conspicuous owing to its pigmentation which, for example, is brown to black in *Haliotis* and *Patella*, and rose pink in *Calliostoma*. In *Patella* (rk, figs. 261, 268) it spreads around the visceral mass immediately beneath the mantle, encircling the inner surface of the shell muscle, and a smaller limb stretches across to the left behind the pericardium and rectum; from the right side the kidney expands ventrally to cover the right half of the under surface of the visceral hump. The cavity is the largest continuous internal one of the limpet's body though its lumen is locally obstructed by infoldings of the renal epithelium. In mature animals the right kidney is displaced somewhat by the development of the gonad

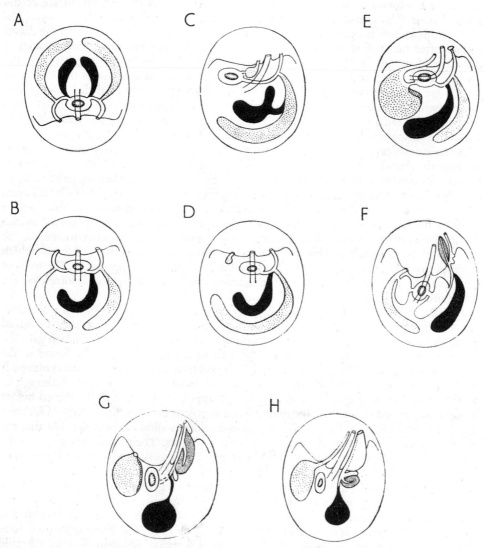

Fig. 151.—Diagrams to show the inter-relationships of rectum, gonad, pericardial cavity, kidneys and
mantle cavity in a series of molluscs. The primitive median position of the rectum and pericardial
cavity is more or less retained. The left kidney is always shown to the left of these structures, the
right kidney and its connexions to the right, so that the disposition of the parts does not necessarily
correspond to their anatomical arrangement. A, ancestral mollusc, pretorsional, with the mantle
cavity directed posteriorly; B, ancestral prosobranch, post-torsional, with the mantle cavity facing
forwards; C, Patellacea; D, *Diodora*; E, Trochacea; F, *Theodoxus* ♀; G, monotocardian ♀; H,
*Viviparus*. In these diagrams the pericardial cavity and the ducts from it to the mantle cavity are
unshaded, the kidney is lightly stippled, the gonad is black; glandular enlargements on the urinogenital
or genital ducts are heavily stippled and the ventricle is represented in the pericardial cavity. Note
the occurrence of a nephridial gland on the pericardial wall of the left kidney in Trochacea (E) and
Monotocardia (G), the occasional persistence of a gonopericardial duct in Monotocardia (G) and the
enlargement of the renopericardial canals in *Theodoxus* (F) (and other Neritacea) to produce a coelomic
body cavity.

which pushes forwards and to the right from the left side of the ventral surface of the visceral mass. The gonad opens to this kidney to discharge the sex cells (fig. 151C). In *Haliotis* this kidney is equally extensive though only a small portion is seen on the dorsal surface after the shell is removed, for it is covered by the more superficial gonad and digestive gland. As in *Patella*, the renal sac is lobed, the lobes extending between the viscera. Their extremities are thin areas of glandular tissue, in contrast to the main part of the sac which is very spongy owing to the infoldings of the epithelial lining. The vast network of vessels of the renal portal system penetrates the folds and bulges into the sac. The renal cavity narrows anteriorly to a pouch with simple walls which is ventral to the pericardium and close against the wall of the left kidney; it communicates with the mantle cavity by a slit-like opening. The gonad discharges by a wide permanent slit into the dorsal wall of the kidney, which in this vicinity is very thin. Crofts (1929) found no connexion between this kidney and the pericardial coelom in either sex, so that this direct route by which fluid from the pericardial coelom might reach its lumen is closed. In trochids, the right kidney (rk, figs. 53, 145, 157) is more compact and is divisible into a large posterior lobe and a small anterior one which passes forwards into the thickness of the mantle skirt, narrows as it approaches the opening to the mantle cavity and is thin-walled. This anterior part receives the renopericardial canal which conveys the genital cells to the renal coelom for their discharge (fig. 151E). The walls of the posterior part of the kidney are thickened considerably by the foldings of the epithelium.

That the renal cells of the right kidney have an excretory activity is shown after intravenous injection of dilute acid dyes such as trypan blue, when the dye can soon be traced in the vacuoles of their cytoplasm. The cytoplasm also contains granules which give the organ its colour and, together with the contents of the vacuoles, may be found in the lumen of the kidney. The colour of the granules corresponds in some archaeogastropods to colours in the shell, and like these, may be of dietary origin (p. 135). Although in higher prosobranchs pigments of dietary origin appear to be chemically altered before being incorporated in the shell, the resemblance in colour between the kidney of *Littorina* and *Natica* and the right kidney of some diotocardians would support the idea that the pigments come, directly or indirectly, from plant sources. Their small quantity and the brevity of their sojourn in the digestive gland may be the reason why they fail to colour it perceptibly, whereas their accumulation in the kidney results in a conspicuous pigmentation. Granules in the digestive gland of trochids give a positive test for chlorophyll and so do the granules in the right kidney (Deshpande, 1957). This kidney alone appears to have a depurative function and Crofts (1929) has shown that in *Haliotis* it is capable of eliminating acid substances in colloidal solution. The renal cells vary considerably in appearance according to their state of activity. Sometimes short vibratile cilia can be seen on the living cells and these probably pass waste to the renal opening; at other times they seem to be lost.

The left kidney of *Diodora* (lk, fig. 257) and of the Patellacea (lk, fig. 266) is so reduced as to suggest that its function is negligible. In *Diodora* it is a simple sac lined by ciliated epithelium which is not folded. In *Patella* the wall against the pericardium is thickened by connective tissue with a few muscle fibres and blood lacunae, suggestive of a nephridial gland. The papillary sac (lk, figs. 53, 145, 157), the left kidney of other diotocardians, is of considerable size and has a compact and rather solid construction, for stout papillae project inwards from all the walls. In trochids and turbinids it lies in the mantle skirt. It typically retains the connexion with the pericardium and its creamy white colour and translucent papillae contrast sharply with the colour of the right kidney. Each papilla consists of a tall epithelium, usually ciliated, surrounding a core of spongy connective tissue in which there may be yellowish spherules or crystals in the form of rods or lamellae (Cuénot, 1914). According to Perrier (1889) the crystals form a reserve of protein which is later passed into the blood. The connective tissue is penetrated by blood spaces with numerous amoebocytes and there are a few muscle fibres. Cuénot (1914) regarded this tissue as the basal syncytial part of the epithelial cells which, he believed, have distinct boundaries only in their distal parts where the nuclei are placed. Examination of fresh epithelial cells shows that they contain numbers of small pale yellow or colourless granules, and very often larger colourless inclusions. These contents differ in all respects from those of the cells of the right kidney. The amoebocytes associated with the papillary sac have often dense granular cytoplasm and they penetrate between the epithelial cells and pass almost to the surface of the papillae. Any substance injected intravenously passes very rapidly into the blood lacunae of the kidney, but is not excreted by the epithelium, though the phagocytes are capable of selecting basic particles such as ammoniacal carmine from the blood (Crofts, 1929; Deshpande, 1957), and it is probable that some of these pass through the epithelium and fall into the cavity of the kidney. It is of interest to note that in *Patella*, which has no papillary sac, particles injected into the blood stream are localized in the pallial gills where there is a large number of phagocytes (Cuénot, 1914).

Pelseneer (1896) and Cuénot (1899) regarded the special phagocytic function of the papillary sac as being of greater importance than has been revealed by the work of later investigators. However, this kidney has undoubtedly an additional phagocytic activity. Spillmann (1905) considered that the minute granules which it often contains originate in the pericardial wall, and enter by way of the renopericardial canal, and that urates and uric acid are passed into the sac from the blood; these substances, if present at all, are in very small quantities. So far experiments have failed to attribute any precise function to this sac. Undoubtedly it is excretory, for globules with colourless inclusions are discharged from the epithelium, though the rate of excretion from the left kidney is much slower than from the right. It may be that the papillary sac is also concerned with the uptake of ions from the blood in the maintenance of the correct internal environment: this would account for the numbers of amoebocytes in its tissues since in the monotocardian *Calyptraea chinensis* (Fretter, 1953a) these wandering cells seem to be concerned with just such a regulatory function.

On the left wall of the papillary sac towards the pericardium there is, in trochids, a special thickening of tissue which is called the nephridial gland. It consists of a pad of connective tissue which is penetrated by tubular extensions of the lumen of the sac, and also by blood lacunae and muscle fibres. The blood lacunae connect with a single blood vessel which passes directly to the left auricle (fig. 16). The epithelial cells of the tubules are full of granules and are ciliated, and in the underlying tissue there are numerous amoebocytes; indeed it is here that Frank (1914) claimed to have observed all stages in the formation of blood corpuscles. Perhaps it is on this account that the name 'blood gland' has occasionally been used for the more superficial region alongside the pericardial cavity and further away from the main part of the kidney sac. Other workers have failed to verify Frank's observations although amoebocytes undoubtedly abound. In species with a well developed nephridial gland the so-called blood gland is so clearly just a part of the whole glandular mass that it seems unnecessary to separate it as an independent unit of the renal complex. This kind of tissue is also found as a part of the nephridial gland of the single kidney of many monotocardians. In both the gland offers a large surface in contact with blood on one side and urine on the other, the very circumstances in which regulation of the water and ionic content, or reabsorption of other substances from the blood, may be easily achieved (p. 294).

It may be that some diotocardians divide their excretory activities between the two kidneys, the right one being concerned with nitrogenous waste and the left with the regulation of water and ionic concentration. The monotocardians live more frequently in the upper littoral zone and brackish water than the diotocardians, and are also abundantly represented in the freshwater fauna. They are, therefore, faced to an even greater extent with the problems of osmoregulation and ionic control. It is tempting to think that they have retained the left kidney of the diotocardian as much for the power which it already possessed of carrying out these functions, as for its dissociation from the reproductive system, and have added to it the metabolic excretion which was previously handled by the right kidney. That has been retained to some extent because of its traditional connexion with the gonad but in no living monotocardian does it fulfil any excretory function. The homology of the sole kidney of the monotocardian and the left kidney of the diotocardians is also borne out by the similarity of their vascular arrangements (p. 278).

Thus in the Monotocardia the sole kidney is the left (figs. 151G, 1, 2, 148A), a capacious sac communicating with the pericardial cavity by a ciliated canal (rpc, figs. 16, 152) and opening to the deeper parts of the mantle cavity (mc) by a slit-like aperture (ko) provided with a sphincter muscle (rsp). This lies on the right of the pericardium on the middle of the anterior wall of the sac, which is otherwise undifferentiated and is partly covered by a low, ciliated epithelium perhaps devoid of any excretory activity. This is typically concentrated on the epithelium overlying the folds on the posterior and dorsal walls of the kidney sac (kf, abk), and in the nephridial gland (ng), lying on the left side and in some species spreading anteriorly. The lamellae vary in complexity from animal to animal, being elaborately branched in the more advanced monotocardians (fig. 153). Each contains muscles and a central blood space running through connective tissue, and is covered by a characteristic epithelium (fig. 154B) of low columnar cells which have a large nucleus, a vacuolated cytoplasm, and, frequently, granules of varying size.

The volume of the kidney fluctuates from species to species as also do its colour and the extent to which the lamellae are developed. In *Balcis alba* it is surprisingly large, with the lumen finely subdivided by numbers of trabeculae; in *Lamellaria* it is small though the nephridial gland is well developed. Sometimes the kidney is divisible externally into 2 sections on account of differences in colour. Thus in *Natica* the right section (abk, fig. 152) is red, brown or yellow and bigger than the left (kf), which is white like the nephridial gland beside it, and these 2 regions have histological and perhaps physiological differences. The left one (fig. 154) has crystalloid contents (Cuénot, 1914) whilst the right, which has deep folds related to the blood vessels (arv, fig. 152), has epithelial cells with dense contents (fig. 154C). In *Trivia* and *Simnia* there is a similar subdivision of the kidney. In the Rachiglossa (fig. 153) the kidney is more elaborate, with 2 systems of lamellae, primary (pkf) and secondary (skf), and according to Cuénot the two have different blood supplies but these are merely dorsal (darv) and ventral (varv) branches of the same afferent renal vein which, as in mesogastropods, is formed by the fusion of blood streams from the head–foot and the visceral mass. The renal epithelium has 2 types of cells, one which is vacuolated and has a striated border, and the second, far less numerous, is ciliated. In the primary folds the connective tissue is well developed and is a spongy network with blood spaces and phagocytic cells. This tissue, which is negligible in the Taenioglossa, appears to act as a trap for unwanted particles which may be circulating in the blood; in this respect it is similar to a papillary sac and, moreover, in some species is filled with irregular discs of a protein material, which recall the crystalloid proteins in the kidney of naticids, as well as those in the papillary sac of trochids.

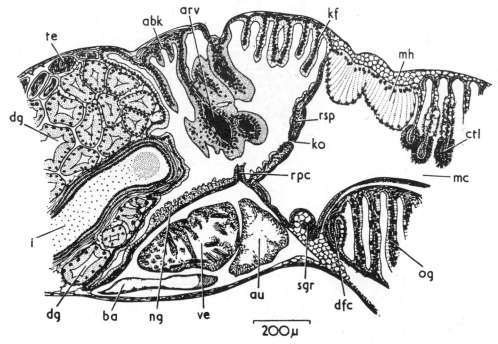

FIG. 152.—*Natica alderi:* longitudinal section through upper end of mantle cavity and base of visceral hump to show the kidney sac in relation to surrounding organs.

abk, absorbing part of kidney; arv, afferent renal vessel; au, auricle; ba, bulb of aorta; ctl, ctenidial leaflet; dfc, dorsal food channel of oesophagus; dg, digestive gland; i, intestine; kf, folded surface of kidney; ko, kidney opening; mc, mantle cavity; mh, mucous cells of hypobranchial gland; ng, nephridial gland; og, oesophageal gland; rpc, renopericardial canal; rsp, renal sphincter muscle; sgr, seminal groove; te, testis; ve, ventricle.

In the minute gastropods *Omalogyra atomus* (k, fig. 184A), *Rissoella diaphana* and *R. opalina*, and in the pyramidellids, the kidney is a small vesicle with unfolded walls which spreads forwards in the mantle skirt and is not contained in the visceral mass, nor is there a nephridial gland developed. These prosobranchs have lost the gill so that the forward position of the kidney may be valuable for the sake of the capillary bed which migrates with it. Perhaps it is for the same reason that the kidney occupies a corresponding position in the 2 British terrestrial prosobranchs *Pomatias elegans* and *Acicula fusca*.

The aberrant aspidobranch *Theodoxus fluviatilis* has only a single kidney (k, fig. 52) which, as in the Monotocardia, is on the right of the pericardium. It opens (ko) at the base of the mantle cavity near the vestigial right gill (ho) ('organe creux' of Lenssen, 1899). It is divisible into a thin–walled sac, opening to the mantle cavity and extending

posteriorly for some distance, and an overlying limb in which the cavity is traversed by
deep infoldings of the wall. The greater part of the thin-walled sac has a low epithelium
with no cilia except in the duct leading to the uropore, whilst all the dorsal part is
glandular and is divisible histologically (and perhaps functionally) into 2 regions. Bourne
(1908) described this kidney as a tubular structure bent on itself and so resembling a

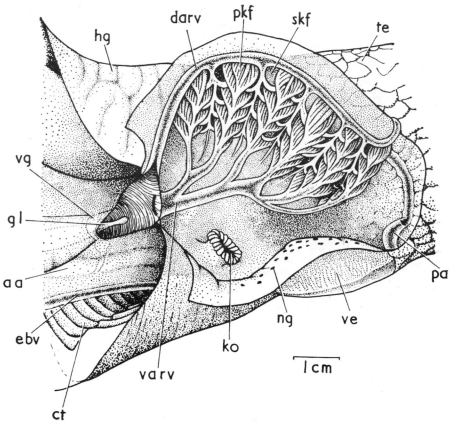

FIG. 153.—*Nucella lapillus:* kidney sac opened to show double series of folds on the wall.
    aa, anterior aorta; ct, ctenidium; darv, dorsal branch of afferent renal vein; ebv, efferent branchial
vessel; gl, posterior tip of gland of Leiblein; hg, hypobranchial gland; ko, kidney aperture; ng,
nephridial gland; pa, posterior aorta; pkf, primary kidney folds; skf, secondary kidney folds; te,
testis; varv, ventral branch of afferent renal vein; ve, ventricle; vg, visceral ganglion.

lamellibranch coelomoduct. The anterior end of the glandular part opens into the
extensive pericardial coelom by way of the nephridial canal: indeed, it may be the enlargement of this and, to an even greater extent, of the gonopericardial canal which has
caused the expansion of the coelom in the Neritacea. In freshwater pectinibranchs the
kidney shows a similar modification, suggesting that the development of an extensible
thin-walled region is associated with some physiological requirement. In *Ampullarius*
Sachwatkin (1920) has shown that the anterior lobe opens to the mantle cavity and the
posterior lobe to the pericardial cavity. On the basis of his description it would appear

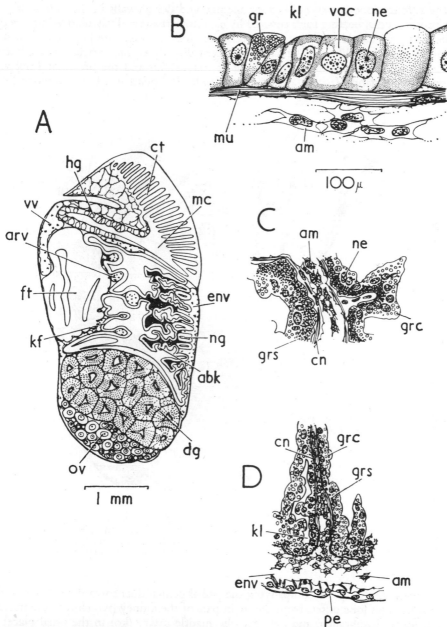

Fig. 154.—*Natica alderi:* histology of the kidney. A, plan of transverse section at level of inner end of mantle cavity, showing sites of cells drawn in B, C and D; B, cells from unfolded part of kidney sac and folds on left dorsal wall (kf); C, cells from folds on right dorsal wall (abk); D, cells of nephridial gland and blood gland (ng).

abk, absorbing part of kidney; am, blood cell; arv, branch of afferent renal vein; cn, connective tissue with few intermingled muscle fibres; ct, ctenidium; dg, digestive gland; env, efferent vessel from nephridial gland; ft, female genital tract; gr, granules of excretion; grc, colourless granules of excretory material in superficial parts of cells; grs, darkly stained granules of excretory material in deep parts of cells; hg, hypobranchial gland; kf, folded surface of kidney; kl, lumen of kidney sac and its extension into tubules of nephridial gland; mc, mantle cavity; mu, muscle cell; ne, nucleus of epithelial cell; ng, nephridial gland, including so-called 'blood gland'; ov, ovary; pe, outer pallial epithelium; vac, vacuole; vv, visceral vein.

II

that the anterior lobe corresponds to the median and dorsal walls of the kidney sac of other prosobranchs, bearing folds covered by excretory tissue and vascularized by vessels connected to the ctenidium whereas the posterior lobe contains the homologue of the nephridial gland and, like that structure, is linked directly to the auricle by its efferent vessel. The homology of the anterior lobe of *Ampullarius* and the ureter of *Viviparus* suggested by Fernando (1931*b*) appears improbable. *Bithynia* has a broad anterior lobe

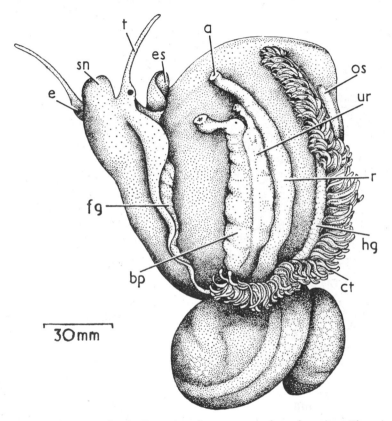

FIG. 155.—*Viviparus viviparus:* female dissected to show contents of mantle cavity. The animal has been removed from the shell and the mantle skirt cut along the left and turned to the right.
a, anus; bp, brood pouch; ct, ctenidium; e, eye; es, exhalant siphon; fg, food groove; hg, hypobranchial gland; os, osphradium; r, rectum; sn, snout; t, tentacle; ur, ureter.

of the kidney (ak, fig. 55) accompanying the pallial genital duct towards the edge of the mantle skirt. This lobe differs from the main part of the kidney (which is in the normal position for a prosobranch, and opens to the mantle cavity (ko) in the usual place) in that its lumen is not subdivided by septa. In *Viviparus*, however, the pallial region of the kidney (ur, fig. 155) brings the opening to the edge of the mantle skirt; it is analogous to the pallial genital duct (Johansson, 1950), being developed from a longitudinal pallial fold (p. 331), and is not an outgrowth from the kidney lined by renal epithelium as it would appear to be in *Bithynia*. *Valvata* is often mentioned as the only other prosobranch besides *Viviparus* which possesses a ureter opening far forwards. In this genus the kidney (pk, fig. 156) extends through the mantle skirt to the base of the bipectinate ctenidium (ct) which is more anterior and also shorter than in other prosobranchs, for it lies along the anterior third of the mantle skirt with the tip projecting from the shelter of the

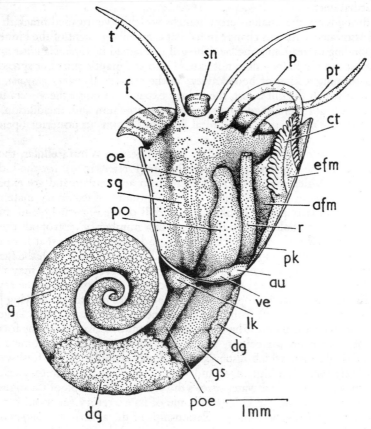

FIG. 156.—*Valvata piscinalis*: animal removed from shell, mantle cavity opened along the left side and mantle skirt folded to the right. Some organs are seen by transparency.

afm, afferent membrane of gill; au, auricle; ct, ctenidium; dg, digestive gland; efm, efferent membrane of gill; f, foot; g, gonad; gs, gastric shield; lk, left kidney; oe, oesophagus; p, penis; pk, pallial extension of kidney; po, pallial oviduct; poe, posterior oesophagus; pt, pallial tentacle; r, rectum; sg, salivary gland; sn, snout; t, tentacle; ve, ventricle.

cavity. The opening of the kidney, unlike that of *Viviparus*, is concealed when the mantle cavity is opened, for it is in a small cul-de-sac at the base of the ctenidium posterior to the last filament. This pallial region of the kidney is lined by the same excretory cells as the main part which is posterior to the mantle cavity, and its walls are folded to give a number of trabeculae which more or less repeat the pattern of branching of the renal portal blood vessel. The true ureter is a short narrow duct lined by columnar epithelium and ciliated at the opening. In *Valvata* it is the visceral part of the kidney which has smooth unfolded walls, although there is a simple fold dorsally which deepens and passes into the pallial region. When the mantle cavity is opened it is seen that there has been a forward shifting of the organs of the pallial complex affecting the gill, the kidney and the heart (au, ve) though leaving behind most of the thin-walled part of the kidney sac (lk) which is of considerable size. At the anterior end of this visceral region arises the renopericardial duct.

The hydrobiids are the smallest prosobranchs which have invaded brackish and fresh-water and associated with this change in habitat is an enlargement of the kidney sac with no corresponding increase in lamellae. The gill is retained in *Hydrobia ulvae* and *Potamopyrgus jenkinsi* and the kidney does not extend into the mantle skirt but spreads between the viscera forming a kind of body cavity; in the related *Assiminea grayana*, a brackish water form in which the gill is lost, the kidney expands amongst the viscera in the same way, though it is not there lined by an excretory epithelium and, in addition, it extends forwards alongside the rectum and genital duct, but retains its posterior opening to the mantle cavity.

In prosobranch molluscs in which all or some digestion is intracellular, the functions of the kidney and the digestive gland interdigitate (Fretter, 1939), for the kidney is not only an organ in which the products of catabolism accumulate and are expelled from the body, but an organ through which a certain amount of excretory matter from the digestive gland similarly passes. In like manner cells of the digestive gland may take up waste products of metabolism from the blood. In a number of gastropods the gland has special cells in which this waste is accumulated and elaborated, so that it can be stored for some time without leaving the body. Eventually it is excreted with the faeces as part of the liver string (lrs, figs. 127B, C, F) though in short-lived species it may never leave the body. Such cells (ex, fig. 123A) frequently occur in small groups in the crypts of the tubules of the digestive gland, projecting for some distance into the underlying haemocoel (hc) and almost constricted off from the rest of the epithelium, so that a large surface is in close contact with the blood. The waste within their cytoplasm is in the form of small spherules, often of a brown colour, which fuse to form large conglomerations, and, perhaps, one single mass which distends the cell considerably. In the freshwater proso-branchs *Bithynia tentaculata* (fig. 123A) and *Valvata piscinalis* the excretory cells are very obvious. It may be that in freshwater species this accessory function of the digestive gland is of importance in freeing the kidney of some of its excretory function, for in these it is largely concerned with the osmotic relationships of the animal. In *Viviparus viviparus*, for example, the digestive gland contains more uric acid than the kidney in summer and not much less in winter when metabolism is at a reduced level of activity (Spitzer, 1937).

Prosobranch gastropods are primarily marine and it is assumed that their blood is generally in osmotic equilibrium with sea water. However, the few investigations which have been made on molluscs as a whole suggest that they may all actively maintain some degree of difference in ionic concentration across their external surfaces as well as across the walls of the kidney. Ionic regulation, consisting of the maintenance of increased potassium and calcium in the blood plasma, has been shown for *Neptunea antiqua* and *Buccinum undatum* (Robertson, 1949), whilst in the latter (Duval, 1924) and *Patella vulgata* (Krogh, 1939) the Cl' concentration of the blood is lower than that in the sea water with which they are in equilibrium (blood Cl'/water Cl' = 0·96).

It is assumed that such differences in concentration are maintained by a filtration of fluid from the blood into the kidney, and a differential reabsorption or selection of ions and organic and inorganic compounds by the renal tissue. The renal cells may also have an

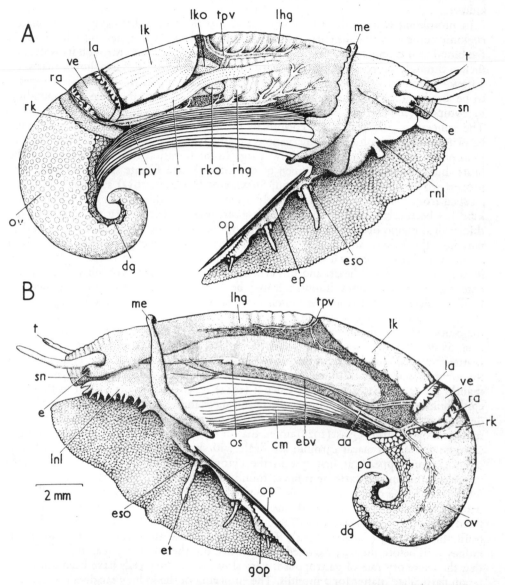

Fig. 157.—*Monodonta lineata:* animal removed from shell and seen A, from the right; B, from the left.
aa, anterior aorta; cm, columellar muscle; dg, digestive gland; e, eye; ebv, efferent branchial
vessel; ep, epipodium; eso, epipodial sense organ; et, epipodial tentacle; gop, glandular area below
operculum; la, left auricle; lhg, left hypobranchial gland; lk, left kidney (papillary sac); lko, left
kidney opening; lnl, left neck lobe; me, mantle edge; op, operculum; os, osphradium; ov, ovary;
pa, posterior aorta; r, rectum; ra, right auricle; rhg, right hypobranchial gland; rk, right kidney;
rko, opening of right kidney (urinogenital); rnl, right neck lobe; rpv, right pallial vein; sn, snout;
t, tentacle; tpv, transverse pallial vein; ve, ventricle around rectum.

excretory function and actively transport material from the blood to the lumen of the kidney.

In prosobranchs the kidney typically opens into the pericardial cavity by a ciliated coelomostome in which the cilia beat towards the renal sac. When the ventricle contracts the blood in it is under considerable pressure and filtration of fluid through its wall and, thence through the coelomostome, is very probable. Picken (1937) has shown that such a flow of fluid into the pericardial coelom in the swan mussel *Anodonta cygnea* appears to be an ultrafiltrate of the blood, nearly free of protein, but otherwise corresponding in composition. The site of filtration is the ventricle (Florkin & Duchateau, 1949). The concern of the pericardial coelom in the initial stages of urine formation may be primitive for the phylum. Observations on an advanced gastropod, the giant African pulmonate *Achatina fulica*, fail to show a significant filtration through the wall of the heart, but the presence (in the lumen of the kidney) of a filtrate similar to what that process would have produced (Martin, Stewart & Harrison, 1954) suggests that it has escaped from the blood vessels intimately associated with this organ. No work of this kind has been carried out on prosobranch gastropods, but it is very probable that the thin-walled region of the kidney in contact with haemocoelic spaces may allow fluid to pass into the kidney and be added to that derived from the pericardial cavity. In a monotocardian prosobranch practically all the blood is filtered through the kidney on its way to the gill and heart, and this arrangement suggests the possibility of fluid also entering the kidney from this source. It may be, however, that there is no force adequate to drive blood plasma from the vessels into the kidney sac, and the sole effect of the arrangement is to bring about the absorption of waste material by the kidney cells from the blood. These cells accumulate ammoniacal carmine, indigocarmine and saccharated iron oxide after injection, from which it appears that they abstract dissolved waste matter from the blood, store it in their cytoplasm, either in the vacuolar contents or in the granules, and ultimately shed it to the lumen of the kidney sac for emptying to the mantle cavity. In the Stenoglossa, Cuénot (1914) described 2 types of cell in the renal epithelium, one, unciliated, which collects and sheds indigocarmine, the second, ciliated, dealing with ammoniacal carmine. This double excretory pathway also appears in some mesogastropods: thus Quast (1928) noted that in *Cyclostoma* (= *Pomatias*) *elegans* indigo-carmine and ammoniacal carmine are dealt with by separate cells, and that whereas indigocarmine appears at first free in the cytoplasm and is only later collected into vacuoles, ammoniacal carmine is never found except in vacuoles. In the Stenoglossa, in which cells in the connective tissue of the renal sac have an important role in collecting particulate waste from the blood, the nephridial gland does not contain numbers of fixed phagocytes, whereas in the Taenioglossa phagocytic cells in the nephridial gland fulfil this function (Cuénot, 1914). The length of time such particles remain in the kidney cells before they are excreted is unknown, but there is every reason for believing that the excretory rate of gastropods is very slow; the kidney cells have been known to retain particulate matter for 2 months. The emptying of the kidney sac does not occur in any particular rhythm.

Strunk (1935) has shown that in whelks (*Buccinum undatum*) injected with eriocyanin in sea water the dye is taken up by the kidney and never by the nephridial gland. About twice the normal amount of urine is formed, though the process is slow and it takes about 72 hrs for the animal to get rid of 0·5 ml 1% eriocyanin. The nephridial gland shows the presence of sugar and protein in its cells, though Strunk (1935) failed to find them in the kidney or blood vessels immediately associated with it. He concluded that the gland absorbs substances from the urine, and suggested that it is divorced from strictly excretory activity since it contains none of the uric acid traceable in the adjacent kidney. On the other hand it was found that the rest of the kidney has no such resorptive powers and is excretory only. If reabsorption (perhaps of salt and water) from the renal filtrate does occur through the walls of the fine ciliated tubules of the nephridial gland then the cilia on the renal epithelium may assist in the circulation of fluid whilst the sphincter at the external opening of the kidney is contracted to prevent the escape of the urine. In the pelagic heteropods the kidney sac is periodically flushed out by water sucked in through the external opening, and then expelled again (Strohl, 1914). In these forms a valve in the renopericardial duct can close the passage to the pericardium.

More precise work on the absorption of osmotically active substances from the urine has been done with pulmonate gastropods. Florkin (1935) found that in *Lymnaea stagnalis* samples of urine taken close to the pericardium have the same molar concentration as the blood, though it is lower in the final urine. Freezing point determinations show the urine of *Achatina fulica* to be hypotonic to the blood, the freezing point of the blood being −0·462° and that of the urine −0·285°C. There is evidence that glucose is reabsorbed from the filtrate in the kidney and that the mechanism by which this is done is thrown out of action by phlorizin (Martin, Stewart & Harrison, 1954).

All animals which have penetrated brackish water from the sea appear to have a salt concentration lower than that of sea water. Some become isotonic with the medium in which they live, which means that their tissues tolerate a lower salt concentration and they reduce the energy required for osmotic regulation, whilst others, failing to acquire this tolerance, are now hypertonic to the surrounding water. The initial reduction of the blood salt concentration may have taken place in brackish water while the animal was still poikilosmotic, but life in freshwater would be possible only when the animal was able to maintain an osmotic gradient and have the power of absorbing all the common salts against it. Such a dynamic balance can only be maintained by a continuous expenditure of energy. Since most marine animals are capable of concentrating some ions this may have been one of the simpler requirements for the conquest of the new habitat. No brackish water gastropod has been investigated from this point of view, and only *Mytilus edulis* amongst the bivalves (Potts, 1954a). In *Mytilus* there appears to be no ability to maintain hypertonicity by regulating salt loss in dilute sea water, and the ionic regulation is only slight. However, it maintains somewhat higher internal concentrations of K, Ca and total $CO_2$. Potts (1954b) has calculated that the lowering of the salt concentration of the blood in animals living in brackish water is the most important means of reducing the strain on osmoregulatory mechanisms, and that the production of a hypotonic urine gives little advantage until the salinity of the external medium is well below half that of sea water. On the other hand, in freshwater animals the production of urine which is isotonic with the medium can reduce osmotic work by as much as 90%. The bounding membrane of these animals is much less permeable to salts and not very permeable even to water except on the respiratory surfaces, where permeability to dissolved gases is inseparable from an appreciable permeability to water. The possession of a gill by all British prosobranchs which are found in freshwater shows that they entered this habitat by way of brackish water, and in *Potamopyrgus jenkinsi* this change of habitat took place as recently as the latter part of the last century. This is the only freshwater hydrobiid, though other species live in brackish water: *Hydrobia ulvae* is found in estuaries and muddy flats and can withstand salinities ≮1·0‰ (Johansen, 1918), whilst *H. ventrosa* lives on mud in quiet brackish water, and is not normally found in pure sea water or freshwater. Both of these species must be able to maintain an osmotic gradient, though there may be some other factor, perhaps concerned with reproduction, which prevents their final entry to freshwater.

It has been shown (Krogh, 1939) that *Viviparus viviparus* has considerable powers of active uptake of chloride ions in spite of the very low concentrations normally found in freshwater, and is able to reduce the concentration of chloride ions in water from 1·14 to 0·10 mM. This ability to make good salts lost from the body may be a function of the gut epithelium, as well as of the outer skin, for it is well known that ions will pass freely through the lining of the gut, and consequently salts contained in the food become available. However, the food itself can only be a subsidiary source of salts, for freshwater gastropods are able to withstand starvation for many days, though for shorter periods than related marine forms. The extent to which the intake of fluid by the gut contributes to the salt and water balance is unknown for any mollusc, but presumably the outer surface of the body and the gut work in conjunction with one another in maintaining hypertonicity of the blood, and regulate their respective activities according to changes in the external medium and the quantity and nature of the food.

It is tempting to think of the structural peculiarities of the kidney of *Theodoxus*, *Viviparus*, *Potamopyrgus*, *Hydrobia*, *Bithynia*, *Assiminea* and *Valvata* as being associated with the reabsorption of ions by the renal epithelium, for it is only in these genera that there is a pronounced enlargement of the thin-walled part. This gives a vesicle of considerable size in which the urine may be retained whilst water and salts, which have filtered through the renal epithelium or passed through by diffusion or active transport, may be reclaimed. The histochemistry of the renal epithelium is unknown in freshwater and marine prosobranchs.

Waste nitrogen from protein catabolism is excreted from the body of the mollusc in various forms and, as in other invertebrates, unchanged amino-acids, which are nevertheless potential metabolites, are lost in the excreta. Each day in *Viviparus*, 27·3–29·1% of the non-protein nitrogen is excreted as amino-acids (Spitzer, 1937), suggesting inefficiency in the metabolic processes, or of the excretory filter. In the majority of the aquatic invertebrates which have been investigated the greater part of the nitrogen is excreted in the form of ammonia and this amounts to 50% in *Littorina* (Spitzer, 1937). Some of the remainder, up to 29% in *Littorina*, will be purine nitrogen derived from the metabolism of nucleoprotein. Ammonia is very toxic to the tissues, though it is a relatively diffusible substance. For animals living in water and having a relatively vast volume into which this poison can be discharged and dispersed as soon as it is formed, it is an easy and satisfactory way of disposing of nitrogenous waste. In various groups of the animal kingdom ammonia may be converted into the secondary products urea and uric acid, both of which are less toxic and therefore require less water for their excretion because they can be tolerated in greater concentration. The possession of the enzymes necessary for the conversion of ammonia into these compounds is then a pre-adaptation to a habitat in which the water supply is more limited. Gastropods are unlikely to be able to produce urea by the ornithine cycle (Baldwin, 1957) and that which they do excrete is probably derived entirely from the arginine of their diet. Hence their only possible metabolic pathways are the de-amination of amino-acids, with the consequent production of ammonia, or a completely different treatment of the amino-acid molecule. Strohl (1914) was the first to point out that whereas uric acid is found in the kidney of gastropods, in lamellibranchs its place is taken by urea. In all likelihood uric acid and other purines are treated in the same way by the animal, and on this basis Spitzer (1937) found that in *Littorina* they comprise 29·5% of the total non-protein nitrogen excreted in the summer and 17·0% of that in winter. Though Spitzer suggested that they are only an intermediate step in metabolism, the corresponding figures for *Viviparus* are 36·1 and 41·6% respectively, and these higher percentages are in agreement with the results of Needham (1935). *Viviparus* excretes much less ammonia than *Littorina*, and this may be associated with the fact that the snail lives in freshwater, that the osmoregulatory function of the kidney necessitates the retention of the urine for some time, and that it is ovoviviparous.

Comparison of kidney function based on quantitative analyses of its contents is of little value in prosobranchs because of a number of factors. These include such things as the unknown but irregular rate of elimination of urine and the intricate and intimate intermingling of kidney tissue with surrounding organs. In small animals this means that surgical removal of the kidney almost certainly leads to partial loss of its tissue and contents and the inclusion of foreign tissue, or both. If estimations of the non–protein nitrogen be made on the whole animal then these must include the digestive gland, and it is known that, at least in some gastropods, this gland transforms the nucleoprotein of the food into purine bases which may be excreted with the faeces (Fretter, 1939). Such difficulties as these, however, do not arise in the case of land snails like *Helix pomatia*, and quantitative estimations of uric acid give figures of up to 810 mg/g dry weight for the kidney of this species (Needham, 1938); this may be three-quarters of the dry weight of the organ. This uricotelic metabolism of the terrestrial pulmonates is not only an advantage during embryonic life, but is one of the factors permitting hibernation and aestivation, periods during which the kidney stores this relatively innocuous product in large quantities.

Bearing in mind the difficulties in carrying out comparative experimental work on nitrogen excretion in prosobranchs we can now proceed to examine the findings of Needham (1935, 1938). This writer investigated the excretory nitrogen content of the whole body and kidneys of a variety of gastropods, seeking to correlate the type of nitrogen compound excreted with the habitat and reproductive methods as he had so brilliantly done for the vertebrates. Some of the figures which he obtained are given in Table 11 and these do seem to indicate a broad similarity between gastropods and other kinds of animals in this respect, the terrestrial forms being more apt to produce uric acid. Gastropods are not, however, convenient experimental animals, some of Needham's ways of obtaining his nitrogen figures were not good (e.g. the dissection of a kidney which has many ramifications, as in *Patella vulgata*); moreover figures which he quoted (1935) as *calculations* have become apparently definite findings in such compilations as that of Prosser *et al.* (1950). For these reasons it is not advisable to place too much importance on Needham's figures for prosobranchs; there are, however, some special cases in this group which may now be considered. These include forms which live in the more unusual habitats. *Littorina neritoides* occurs in the splash zone of some rocky shores, uncovered by water except at spring tides, where the ability to synthetize waste nitrogen into a non-toxic product is invaluable. This must be purely an adaptation for the adult mode of life, for the eggs are broadcast and produce free-swimming veliger larvae. In another member of the Littorinacea, *Pomatias elegans*, the retention of uric acid is found to be 80 mg/g dry weight of the whole body, which is extremely high and exceeds that of pulmonates. In this terrestrial prosobranch there is a special gland, the concretion gland, which appears as white bands near the kidney and intestine and contains glycogen, pigment and urates (Kilian, 1951). Although ductless, it has a rich blood

TABLE II

(After Needham, 1935; 1938)

| Environment | | Uric acid (mg/g dry weight) | |
|---|---|---|---|
| | | Kidney | Whole body |
| Marine . . . | *Patella vulgata* | 0·49 | — |
| | *Gibbula umbilicalis* | 2·4 | — |
| | *Monodonta lineata* | 1·65 | — |
| | *Littorina littorea* | 1·5 | 0·1 |
| | *Littorina littoralis* | 5·0* | 0·35 |
| | *Littorina saxatilis* | — | 1·1 |
| | *Littorina neritoides* | — | 2·4 |
| | *Turritella communis* | 6·0 | — |
| | *Nucella lapillus* | 4·5 | — |
| | *Nassarius reticulatus* | 2·9 | — |
| | *Buccinum undatum* | 4·0 | — |
| Freshwater . . | *Viviparus contectus* | 35 | 2–5 |
| | *Potamopyrgus jenkinsi* | — | 0·0 |
| | *Bithynia tentaculata* | — | 5·0 |
| | *Lymnaea stagnalis* | — | 3·5 |
| Terrestrial . . | *Pomatias elegans* | — | 80·0 |
| | *Helix pomatia* | 700 | — |

* Presumably wrongly quoted by Needham for *L. rudis* (= *saxatilis*) in table 2 (1935) and fig. 3 (1938).

supply by which materials may reach or leave it: together with the kidney it is the site of an accumulation of nitrogenous waste which Kilian (1951) concluded can be used in times of reduced protein metabolism. For this species there is little doubt that uricotelic metabolism is associated with terrestrial life and its accompanying periods of water shortage, inactivity due to low temperature and the development of the embryo in a capsule deposited in the soil. In *Pomatias* there is no ureter and the excretion from the kidney which passes into the posterior end of the mantle cavity moistens the respiratory surface of the mantle skirt and may be almost pure water. *Bithynia tentaculata* is also of some interest, for although it is a freshwater prosobranch, it contains amounts of uric acid corresponding to some of the pulmonates and exceeding that of *Viviparus contectus*. This may be associated with the osmoregulatory mechanism which necessitates the emptying of the large kidney sac at only infrequent intervals. Moreover, *Bithynia* can survive some weeks on damp grass out of water (Lilly, 1953).

From these considerations it would seem that, amongst other things, a tendency towards uricotelic metabolism in the more primitive marine gastropods enabled more advanced forms to exploit freshwater and even to leave the aquatic environment and adopt a terrestrial mode of life. For this the excretion of uric acid and the consequent conservation of water are salient adaptations.

# CHAPTER 13

# THE NERVOUS SYSTEM AND SENSE ORGANS

THE molluscan nervous system consists essentially of a circum-oesophageal ring from which two longitudinal nerve cords pass posteriorly on each side. One of these pairs is ventral and lies embedded in the foot; the other is dorsal and is related to the visceral hump and mantle cavity. The former pair constitutes the pedal cords, the latter the pleural or pallial nerve cords. In the most primitive of the molluscs, the chitons, it is not possible to distinguish ganglia on the nerve cords: nerve cells are, in fact, generally distributed along them, forming a peripheral zone, whilst the central area constitutes a neuropile, composed of fibres only. The pedal cords are connected to one another across the mid-line of the body by numerous transverse nerves so that this part of the nervous system resembles a ladder in appearance. It therefore bears a superficial resemblance to the ventral nerve cords of many arthropods and annelids—apart from the absence of ganglia—and it has been assumed by some workers that this indicates affinity with these groups. In many species of chitons the pedal and pallial cords of the same side are also frequently connected by anastomoses, but the right and left pallial cords are not directly connected to one another except at the extreme posterior end of the animal, where they unite dorsal to the rectum.

The circum-oesophageal ring at the anterior end of the body of a chiton is connected to the pedal and pallial cords laterally, is completed dorsally by a cord running over the initial part of the gut and by a similar but more slender connexion ventrally. The dorsal part of this ring is known as the cerebral commissure, the ventral part as the labial commissure.

In gastropods the nervous system is constructed on the same general plan but is complicated by the effects of the torsion which these molluscs undergo. The parts of the system which lie in the head and foot of the animal are not involved in this process, so that the relationship of the pedal cords and cephalic sections is not affected, but the pallial cords, which run from the head into the visceral hump, and are known, in the gastropods, as the visceral loop, are. The process of torsion (as explained on p. 11) involves the rotation in an anticlockwise direction of the visceral hump on the head-foot through 180°. This has the effect of twisting the visceral loop into the shape of a figure-of-eight and of entangling it with the alimentary canal in such a way that one half now crosses from the right anteriorly to the left posteriorly dorsal to the oesophagus, and the other half crosses from the left anteriorly to the right posteriorly ventral to the oesophagus. The two parts unite posteriorly dorsal to the posterior oesophagus, but as this has turned over during the process of torsion, this topographically dorsal position indicates that the posterior end of the visceral loop is morphologically ventral to the alimentary canal. In this respect the gastropods agree with the other molluscs, and it is the chitons which are anomalous in having the orientation of these parts reversed.

In addition to showing the effects of torsion, the gastropods differ from chitons in that an aggregation of nerve cells to form ganglia has occurred, although the rate at which this takes place varies within the group and from place to place within the nervous system. In all, however, 7 pairs of principal ganglia appear at various situations on the nerve cords of a gastropod, and various other ganglia may also be encountered in particular prosobranchs. These are usually developed in proximity to one of the major sense organs.

The evolution of the nervous system within the prosobranchs is most easily followed by examination of a series of examples. Of these the most primitive is *Haliotis* (fig. 158), the nervous system of which has been described by de Lacaze-Duthiers (1859), Haller (1884, 1886), Bouvier (1887) and Crofts (1929).

It is one of the characteristic features of the lower prosobranchs that the haemocoelic cavity separating the body wall of the head from the buccal mass is extremely narrow, a fact which makes the dissection of the nervous system in that area difficult, for it is precisely there that the cerebral ganglia (cg) lie and the commissure (ccm) which links them one with the other. The ganglia lie laterally and merge without obvious boundary into the commissure; all are pressed against the buccal musculature so as to be concave on the inner side. Ventrally and anteriorly each ganglion is extended into a nerve trunk (lgn) running underneath the extreme anterior end of the oral tube, the 2 trunks linking up with each other in the mid-ventral line to complete a circum-oesophageal nerve ring. The ventral half of this constitutes the labial commissure and it contains numerous nerve cells, although these are not aggregated into visibly differentiated labial ganglia. The connexion between these ganglionic areas and the cerebral ganglia is known as the labial connective. From its cerebral end a further connective arises, which passes between different layers of buccal muscles to the cleft between the origin of the radular sac below and that of the anterior oesophagus above: here each swells into a small buccal ganglion (bg), the right and left ganglia being connected by a buccal commissure. The terms stomatogastric ganglion and commissure may also be applied to these structures.

Postero-ventrally, on each side, the cerebral ganglion is extended into 2 trunks which run backwards and ventrally out of the head into the anterior parts of the foot, where they connect with a very large mass of nervous material which proves to contain 4 ganglionic centres. Two of these lie more ventrally and take the form of elongated strands, running one on either side of the mid-line, throughout the greater length of the foot: these are the pedal ganglion cords (pdc). The two are connected to one another by 15–36 transverse commissures (pcm) at more or less regular intervals along their entire length, though the commissure at the anterior end is considerably larger than any of the others. At this level two other ganglia lie dorsal to the pedal ganglia: these are the pleural ganglia, sometimes known as the pallial ganglia. On each side the nerves from the cerebral ganglion connect, one with the pleural ganglion, one with the pedal ganglion of the same side. The former trunk is called the cerebropleural connective (cpc), the latter the cerebropedal connective (cpdc).

The main part of the nervous system of *Haliotis*—what may be regarded as its central rather than peripheral nervous system—is completed by nerve trunks leading to ganglia which are related to the pleural ganglia and which constitute the visceral loop. From the right pleural ganglion arises a trunk (the supra-oesophageal connective (suv)) which runs dorsally over the mid-oesophagus to the animal's left side, where it connects with a ganglion placed near the end of the efferent membrane of the left gill. This is the left branchial ganglion (lg). A similar trunk passes to a right branchial ganglion (rg) from the left pleural ganglion with the difference that this time the trunk passes ventral to the mid-oesophagus and is, for that reason, known as the sub-oesophageal connective (sbv). The visceral loop is completed by nerve trunks which run posteriorly from close to the

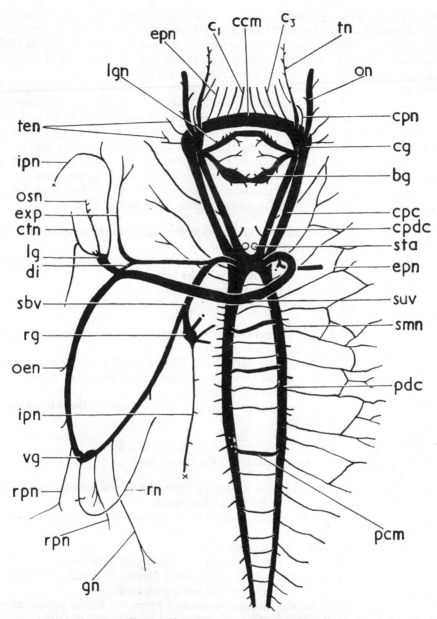

FIG. 158.—*Haliotis tuberculata:* diagram of the nervous system.    Based on Crofts.

bg, buccal ganglion; $c_1$, $c_3$, cerebral nerves; ccm, cerebral commissure; cg, cerebral ganglion; cpc, cerebropleural connective; cpdc, cerebropedal connective; cpn, cephalic pleat nerve; ctn, ctenidial nerve; di, dialyneury; epn, epipodial nerve; exp, external pallial nerve; gn, gonadial nerve; ipn, internal pallial nerve; lg, left branchial ganglion; lgn, labial commissure; oen, oesophageal nerve; on, optic nerve; osn, osphradial nerve; pcm, pedal commissure; pdc, pedal cord; rg, right branchial ganglion; rn, rectal nerve; rpn, renopericardial nerve; sbv, sub-oesophageal part of visceral loop; smn, nerve to shell muscle; sta, statocyst; suv, supra-oesophageal part of visceral loop; ten, tegumentary nerve; tn, tentacular nerve; vg, visceral ganglion.    The points where a right dialyneury has been cut are marked . . ;    those where a circumpallial nerve has been cut are marked x x.

branchial ganglia to unite, dorsal to the posterior oesophagus, at a point nearly level with the posterior end of the mantle cavity: at this point lies (somewhat asymmetrically) a single ganglion. This is known as the visceral or abdominal ganglion (vg). In *Haliotis* it is diffuse, somewhat irregular, and might be thought of as formed by the union or partial separation of right and left concentrations of nerve cells.

There are, therefore, in *Haliotis*, 6 pairs of ganglia with a seventh median ganglion which may have a double structure. These are connected by transverse connexions which link ganglia carrying the same name, e.g. buccal and buccal, pedal and pedal. Such connexions are known as commissures. The only ganglia not linked by commissures are the pleural and branchial. The ganglia are also linked longitudinally and in these cases the links have ganglia carrying different names at their ends, e.g. cerebral and pleural, pleural and visceral. This type of nerve trunk is known as a connective.

Each ganglion innervates a special area of the animal's body. This may be most conveniently indicated by listing the nerves arising from each.

Cerebral ganglion and commissure
(1) Tentacular nerve (tn) to sense organs in the tentacle. It is often ganglionated at its base.
(2) Optic nerve (on) to eye and also to skin and muscles of eye stalk. Small ganglia may lie on its branches.
(3) Statocyst nerve to statocyst (sta).
(4) A group of nerves ($c_1$, $c_3$), 6–8 in number, to the dorsal and lateral lips.
(5) Epipodial nerve (epn) to anterior part of epipodium on head between tentacle and snout.
(6) Cephalic pleat nerve (cpn) (Crofts, 1929) to the cephalic pleat or lappet, a transverse fold of skin across the dorsal surface of the head between the tentacles.
(7) Tegumentary nerves (ten), 2 on each side, to the skin on the side of the head.

Labial ganglion
(1) Nerves, 4 on each side, to the ventral lips.
(2) Nerves to muscles of the buccal mass.

Buccal ganglion
(1) (Arising more accurately from the buccal commissure.) Nerve pair to muscles of radular sheath.
(2) (Arising also from the buccal commissure.) Nerve pair to radular membrane.
(3) Nerve to oesophageal valve.
(4) Nerve to radular sheath and oesophageal pouches.
(5) (From the buccal connective.) Nerve to dorsal wall of buccal cavity, where right and left nerves anastomose.
(6) (From the buccal connective.) Nerve to buccal pouch, salivary gland, wall of buccal cavity and oesophageal gland.

Pleural ganglion
(1) The external pallial nerve (exp) from each ganglion runs laterally and dorsally to enter the corresponding mantle lobe, running forwards to its anterior end, innervating its edge. Each nerve forms an anastomosis (di) with the corresponding branchial ganglion, a condition known as a dialyneury.

Pedal ganglion (1) Epipodial nerves (epn), 2 from the cerebropedal connective and many from the pedal ganglion to innervate the epipodial tentacles.
(2) Nerves, numerous, to shell muscles (smn).
(3) Anterior pedal nerve to anterior part of foot ventrally.
(4) Posterior pedal nerves, numerous, to central and posterior parts of foot, ventrally.

Branchial ganglion (1) Osphradial nerve (osn) to osphradium.
(2) Ctenidial nerve (ctn) to gill.
(3) Internal pallial nerve (ipn) to corresponding half of mantle skirt.
(4) Tegumentary nerve to body wall nearby.
(5) (From left part of visceral loop.) Oesophageal nerve (oen).
(6) (From each side of visceral loop.) Reno-pericardial nerve (rpn).
(7) (From right part of visceral loop.) Gonadial nerve (gn).

Visceral ganglion (1) Rectal nerve (rn).

The nervous system of *Haliotis* is like that of most of the more primitive prosobranchs. The points which emphasize its primitiveness are: (1) the slight degree of separation of ganglia from nerve trunks; (2) the elongation and forward position of the cerebral ganglia; (3) the length of the commissure between the cerebral ganglia; (4) the presence of labial ganglia and of a labial commissure; (5) the indirect connexion of buccal ganglia to cerebral ganglia by way of the labial commissure; (6) the origin of the statocyst nerves directly from the cerebral ganglia; (7) the ventral position of the pleural ganglia, which appear almost as if they were dorsal lobes of the pedal ganglia; (8) the extreme elongation of the pedal ganglion cords; (9) the numerous pedal commissures giving a ladder-like nervous system in the foot, reminiscent of the double ventral nerve cord with transverse connexions of annelids and arthropods; (10) the absence of ganglia on the visceral loop apart from the abdominal; (11) the origin of many nerves from the visceral loop; (12) the fact that the only connexions between the branchial ganglia and the pleural ganglia of the same topographical side occur indirectly, as anastomoses between the peripheral ends of nerves arising from these centres, i.e. are of the type known as a dialyneury.

Though these are primitive features in the organization of the nervous system of prosobranchs, several point to an advance over the condition found in chitons, yet indicating a distinct relationship with that group; others, like the dialyneury, are novelties probably due to the imposition of torsion. A dialyneury, for example, allows—at least in theory—a better co-ordination of pallial control in that there is no longer any necessity for messages from one part of the pallial edge to be relayed to the left pleural—left cerebral—right cerebral—right pleural—supra-oesophageal ganglia in order to reach a contiguous part of mantle innervated from the last of these nerve centres. To what extent the connexions which occur in *Haliotis* in fact permit this to occur is not known, but this union is the beginning of one evolutionary trend which persists throughout the prosobranchs and leads to a general concentration and closer union of nerve centres. A special aspect of this main change affects the pedal and pleural ganglia, the former of which become gradually shorter and concentrated anteriorly, whilst the pleural, which in *Haliotis* appear almost as appendages of the pedal ganglia, migrate away from these in a dorsal direction until they lie alongside the cerebral ganglia. The type of nervous system which has pleural and pedal ganglia contiguous, ventral to the gut and both linked by long connectives to the cerebral ganglia, is known as hypoathroid (fig. 161A);

it is characteristic of the Archaeogastropoda but is also to be found in some of the lower mesogastropods, mainly Architaenioglossa.

The nervous system of *Patella vulgata* (fig. 159) has been described by Bouvier (1887), Gibson (1887), Pelseneer (1898–99) and Davis & Fleure (1903). It shows the continuation of a number of trends incipiently visible in *Haliotis* or other rhipidoglossans. The cerebral ganglia (cg) are moderately expanded swellings lying well forward in the head and

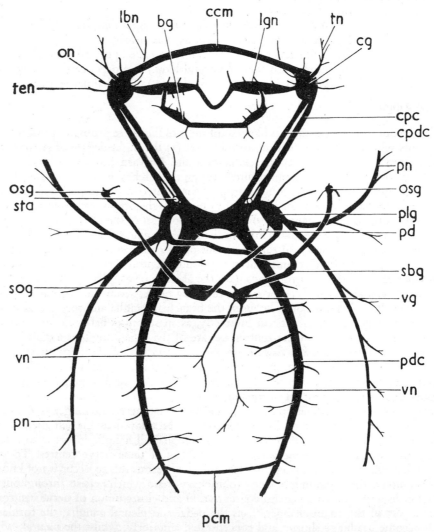

Fig. 159.—*Patella vulgata:* diagram of the nervous system. Based on Davis & Fleure and Pelseneer. bg, buccal ganglion; ccm, cerebral commissure; cg, cerebral ganglion; cpc, cerebropleural connective; cpdc, cerebropedal connective; lbn, labial nerve; lgn, labial ganglion; on, optic nerve; osg, osphradial ganglion; pcm, pedal commissure; pd, pedal ganglion; pdc, pedal cord; plg, pleural ganglion; pn, pallial nerve; sbg, sub-oesophageal ganglion; sog, supra-oesophageal ganglion; sta, statocyst; ten, tegumentary nerve; tn, tentacular nerve; vg, visceral ganglion; vn, visceral nerve.

connected to one another by a long commissure (ccm) dorsal to the gut. From their posteroventral ends 2 connectives (cpc, cpdc) run ventrally and back to the pedal (pd) and pleural (plg) ganglia which lie, one alongside the other on each side, underneath the buccal mass in the haemocoel of the anterior part of the foot. The 2 pedal ganglia lie near the mid-line, the 2 pleurals are more laterally placed, and there is a short but distinct pleuropedal connective uniting the two. The pedal ganglia are drawn out into cords (pdc) running back along the foot, but there are only a few commissures (pcm) linking these, one at the extreme anterior end, the others at irregular intervals along their length.

The cerebral ganglia are also related to the labial (lgn) and buccal ganglia (bg). The former lie close under the skin, in the walls of the oral tube, ventrolaterally, and united across the mid-line by a labial commissure. The buccal (or stomatogastric) commissure lies in the usual place, dorsal to the radular sac but ventral to the anterior oesophagus, and carries, right and left of the mid-line, slight swellings which are the buccal ganglia: these connect to the labial ganglia.

The visceral loop of *Patella* is not a very conspicuous part of the nervous system, perhaps because of the general reduction in importance of the mantle cavity and its contents in the life of the animal. As a result of the shortening of that part of the body, the visceral ganglion (vg) is placed nearly in the same transverse plane as the pleurals, with the result that the figure-of-eight of the visceral loop lies almost vertically. Because of the brevity of the visceral loop no nerves leave it: all come instead from the associated ganglia, of which *Patella* possesses three. A supra-oesophageal ganglion (sog) of moderate size lies on the visceral loop at the point where the nerve to the left osphradium leaves, a much smaller sub-oesophageal ganglion (sbg) (hardly, indeed, deserving the name) lies at the corresponding point on the right, and there is a single visceral ganglion (vg) related to the rectum. These supra- and sub-oesophageal ganglia co-exist with the homologues of the branchial (now called osphradial) ganglia of *Haliotis* so that they are real evolutionary novelties: they may be referred to collectively as parietal ganglia.

According to Thiem (1917b) the peripheral nerves conform to a more or less standard pattern in the Docoglossa (=Patellacea). Six nerves leave each cerebral ganglion in addition to the commissure and connectives, innervating the tentacle (tn), the eye (on), and the dorsal and lateral walls of the snout (lbn). The labial ganglia give nerves to the inner lips. The buccal ganglia similarly give nerves to muscles of the odontophore and the dorsal folds of the oesophagus. From the pleural ganglion on each side originates a variable number of pallial nerves (pn). The supply of nerves to the viscera is achieved on a pattern rather different from what has been described for *Haliotis*: the supra- and sub-oesophageal ganglia give off only one nerve, which runs to the corresponding osphradial (or branchial) ganglion (osg). Although the osphradium itself is of considerably less importance than in most prosobranchs, its ganglion is relatively more important since from the left osphradial ganglion come off nerves to the osphradium, the gill (if present), pericardium and left kidney, whilst from the right osphradial ganglion arise nerves going to the right kidney and the salivary glands. The visceral ganglion (vg) is the starting point of 4 nerves (vn) going to the rectum, the right renal papilla, the left renal papilla, and the remaining viscera respectively.

In *Acmaea* (fig. 160) the tendency towards a lessening of the visceral loop is carried to greater lengths than in the Patellidae (Willcox, 1898), and it is no longer twisted into a figure-of-eight, except in rare specimens. Instead, it is a slightly asymmetrical nerve trunk (vco) running from one pleural ganglion to the other. There are no visible ganglia on it, though cells present in it may represent the visceral ganglion. It gives rise to 2 nerves, one going to each osphradial ganglion, that on the left being much the larger and innervating the ctenidium (ctn).

The Trochacea exhibit a condition in the nervous system very like the zeugobranchs, the main difference being the development of a supra-oesophageal ganglion on the

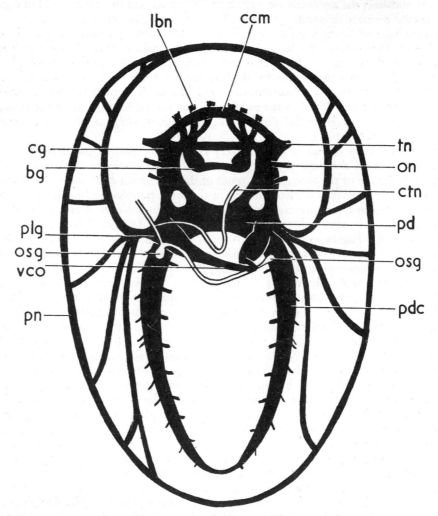

FIG. 160.—*Acmaea fragilis:* diagram of the nervous system. Based on Willcox.
bg, buccal ganglion; ccm, cerebral commissure; cg, cerebral ganglion; ctn, ctenidial nerve; lbn, labial nerve; on, optic nerve; osg, osphradial ganglion; pd, pedal ganglion; pdc, pedal cord; plg, pleural ganglion; pn, pallial nerve (circumpallial); tn, tentacular nerve; vco, visceral loop.

course of the visceral loop (sog, fig. 53); a corresponding sub-oesophageal ganglion is less frequently developed (sbg, fig. 145), probably because of the loss of the right gill. A left osphradial ganglion (osg) also occurs from which the osphradium and ctenidium are innervated.

The remaining group of the Archaeogastropoda with which we are here concerned, the Neritacea, departs markedly from the others in respect of the state of its nervous system and shows in this, as in nearly all other features of its organization, a more advanced state. This is particularly true of the visceral loop where, in *Theodoxus*, the part which runs from the right pleural ganglion to the supra-oesophageal is so thin as to suggest that it is all but functionless, a theory borne out by its absence in some members of the group. With the disappearance of the supra-oesophageal connective from the visceral loop the supra-oesophageal ganglion and the closely associated left osphradial ganglion would be isolated from the rest of the anterior nervous system if a new connexion had not been established with the left pleural ganglion. Such a direct link between a parietal and a pleural ganglion is known as a zygoneury, and it clearly confers the same functional advantage as a dialyneury but in a more effective manner. Because of the disappearance of the gill and osphradium on the right, the sub-oesophageal ganglion is not tied to a particular level in the body as is the supra-oesophageal and it is therefore free to migrate forwards until it comes close to the left pleural ganglion, to which it is attached by the sub-oesophageal connective. At the same time a zygoneury develops to connect to the right pleural ganglion and its final position is between the 2 pleurals. In other respects the central nervous system of a neritid is less modified, the pleural ganglia still lying alongside the pedals, which are long swollen cords with numerous commissures, the whole effect being ladder-like. The cerebral ganglia are fusiform, with a long commissure, and a labial commissure is present to which the buccal ganglia connect. The cerebropleural and cerebropedal connectives join so as to appear as a double nerve trunk. Two visceral ganglia lie at the posterior end of the visceral loop.

In the distribution of the peripheral nerves two points are deserving of mention. Of these one is the aberrant innervation of the osphradium and ctenidium, which is by way of a nerve which leaves the left pleural ganglion rather than from the supra-oesophageal. This arrangement might appear to indicate that the osphradium and ctenidium of the Neritacea were new structures and not homologous with similar formations in other prosobranchs, as has, indeed, been held by Thiele (1929–35). This, however, seems to be a rather extravagant conclusion to reach in view of the similarities in location and structure which exist between neritacean and other prosobranch gills and osphradia, and a much simpler explanation would be that the point of separation of the branchial and osphradial nerve has migrated from the supra-oesophageal ganglion along the zygoneury which connects it with the left pleural ganglion so that it now appears to originate in that centre. (This might also involve a transfer of control from right to left pleural ganglion.) The branchial and osphradial nerve connects with nerves from the supra-oesophageal ganglion so that a dialyneury occurs in addition to the zygoneury already described.

In most mesogastropods a number of changes occurs in the nervous system so that it shows a more advanced state than that of archaeogastropods. These are not very evident in the lowest group of the Mesogastropoda, the Architaenioglossa, in some of which an almost unmodified hypoathroid arrangement persists. Most mesogastropods, however, show a tendency for the following changes: (1) the cerebral ganglia move dorsally and lie closer together; (2) for this reason the cerebral commissure becomes shorter; (3) the cerebral ganglia tend to migrate posteriorly to the level of the anterior end of the mid-oesophagus, and so behind the buccal mass: this allows greater concentration; (4) the labial commissure tends to disappear; (5) the labial ganglia disappear; (6) as a consequence of this the buccal ganglia are the only ones in relation to the anterior end of the gut connected to the cerebrals; because of their original link with the labial ganglia, the cerebrobuccal connective traces a circuitous route from the one ganglion to the other, and, though appearing as a single nerve, must be regarded as morphologically made up partly of a cerebrolabial connective and partly of a labiobuccal one; (7) the pleural ganglia become wholly separated from the pedals and tend to migrate dorsally towards the cerebrals; (8) the pleuropedal connective therefore elongates; (9) the pedal ganglia tend to become concentrated anteriorly; (10) the pedal commissures become reduced, most mesogastropods having only one, though a second, much more slender one, often occurs behind this; (11) the posterior pedal nerves elongate as the pedal ganglia concentrate anteriorly; (12) the statocyst nerve runs from the cerebral ganglion through the cerebropedal connective and therefore appears to originate from the pedal ganglion.

Of these changes the most important are those affecting the three major ganglia, cerebral, pleural and pedal. They have the general effect of bringing them all into proximity in the neighbourhood of the point where anterior and mid-oesophagus join behind the buccal mass; this forms a nerve ring at a point where the gut is often narrow enough to ensure close contact between the ganglia and so allow a real nerve centre to arise. Although no gastropod appears to have made much of the chance of mental evolution which this situation offers, it is precisely the same situation which the cephalopods have exploited with conspicuous success.

Two main stages may be recognized in the evolutionary trend which has just been outlined. One is that in which the pleural ganglia have become well separated from the pedals with which they had been previously associated, but have not yet migrated to the proximity of the cerebrals: they still lie ventral to the gut. This is a condition known as dystenoid (fig. 161B) and it is exhibited by *Viviparus*, for example. In most mesogastropods, however, cerebral and pleural ganglia lie alongside one another—in some cases contiguous, in others even fused—dorsal to the gut and connected to the pedal ganglia, which always retain their primitive ventral situation, by connectives of equal length. This is known as an epiathroid nervous system (fig. 162A).

The nervous system of *Viviparus* has been described by Bouvier (1887). The cerebral ganglia lie in juxtaposition above the oesophagus and behind the buccal mass, embedded to a certain extent in the salivary glands. From them nerves pass to the usual destinations —eye, tentacle (which on the right side in males is modified to act as a penis), dorsal and lateral skin of the snout and the dorsal and lateral lips. Most nerves of the last group emerge from a particularly prominent anteroventral prolongation of the ganglion, which is known as the labial lobe. That this is in fact a labial ganglion conjoined with the cerebral is suggested by the fact that one of the nerves originating from it is the labial commissure, which still persists in *Viviparus*. The buccal ganglia are also related to these lobes. The pleural ganglia lie ventral to the cerebrals, but quite apart from the pedals, on which 2 connectives converge on each side, one cerebropedal, the other pleuropedal. These are sufficiently apart dorsally, nevertheless, for one of the extrinsic muscles of the buccal mass to pass between them. The pedal ganglia are still primitive and have the form of elongate cords with 3 commissures linking right to left along the length of the foot.

So far as the rest of the nervous system is concerned there is little call for comment. As in many of the lower gastropods a sub-oesophageal ganglion is absent, though a supra-oesophageal one is present giving off a nerve to the osphradium. The visceral loop near the supra-oesophageal ganglion is the origin of the branchial nerve, and pallial nerves leave from the region on the right where a sub-oesophageal ganglion might

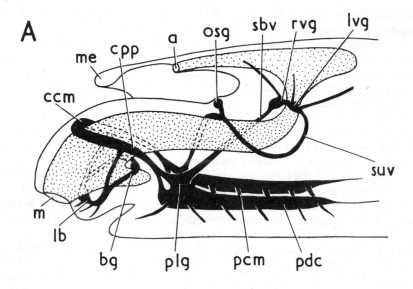

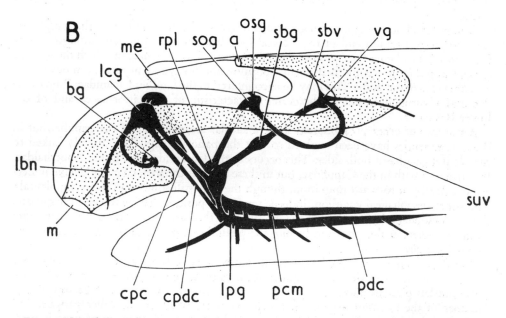

FIG. 161.—Lateral views of the anterior end of a prosobranch to show A, diagram of hypoathroid nervous system (e.g. rhipidoglossan); B, diagram of dystenoid nervous system (e.g. *Viviparus*).

a, anus; bg, buccal ganglion; ccm, cerebral commissure; cpc, cerebropleural connective; cpdc, cerebropedal connective; cpp, cerebropleuropedal connective; lb, labial ganglion; lbn, labial nerve; lcg, left cerebral ganglion; lpg, left pedal ganglion; lvg, left (or left part of) visceral ganglion; m, mouth; me, mantle edge; osg, osphradial ganglion; pcm, pedal commissure; pdc, pedal cord; plg, pleural ganglion; rpl, right pleural ganglion; rvg, right (or right part of) visceral ganglion; sbg, sub-oesophageal ganglion; sbv, sub-oesophageal part of visceral loop; sog, supra-oesophageal ganglion; suv, supra-oesophageal part of visceral loop; vg, visceral ganglion.

have occurred. On both sides of the body these anastomose with pallial nerves from the corresponding pleural ganglia so that right and left dialyneuries exist.

A further advance still is found in *Littorina*, the nervous system of which has already been described in detail (p. 37). In this animal both cerebral and pleural ganglia lie dorsal to the gut behind the buccal mass, although the pedals are still placed in the haemocoel of the foot and are connected to the others by long connectives (figs. 14, 20). They are now ovoid nervous masses, no trace of the long pedal cords remaining, except for lobed outgrowths of the main ganglia from which the nerves arise. Of the original multiple commissures only two remain, one thick and prominent, the other a very tenuous connexion linking the lobes from which the posterior pedal nerves spring, and possibly of little functional importance (pcm, ppd, fig. 22).

The labial ganglia and the labial commissure have been lost: only the buccal ganglia survive in the innervation of the anterior gut walls (bg, fig. 14). The ventral lips, originally innervated from the labial ganglia, now receive their nerve supply from the cerebral ganglia which also innervate the rest of the snout, the tentacle, the eye and, by fibres running in the cerebropedal connective, the statocyst.

The visceral loop carries supra-oesophageal, sub-oesophageal and a bilobed visceral ganglion. The first of these innervates the osphradium and gill, the sub-oesophageal supplies the right half of the mantle and on both sides dialyneuries unite these nerves and others originating in pleural and pedal ganglia (di, fig. 20). No zygoneury has been formed.

A number of stages representing various degrees of concentration of the ganglia of the oesophageal region and of the visceral loop may be distinguished amongst prosobranchs, the first being the condition already described for *Littorina*, in which the ganglia of the visceral loop occupy their normal position and no zygoneury has been developed on either side of the body. This may be encountered in the families Lacunidae, Pomatiasidae and Hydrobiidae, and is, therefore, characteristic of the Littorinacea and of the lower Rissoacea.

A number of other prosobranchs show a similar arrangement of the ganglia, but in them zygoneuries have been evolved so that the parietal ganglia are directly linked to the pleural ganglia of both sides. This occurs in the Ianthinidae and in the Aporrhaidae. It is also met with in the Capulidae, but in these animals the parietal ganglia have undergone a degree of forward migration, though they are still some way from the pleurals. The supra-oesophageal ganglion, indeed, retains its position left of the oesophagus and the sub-oesophageal ganglion lies on the right of that structure. The Ianthinidae differ from the others in this group in having the pleural ganglia fused to the corresponding cerebral ganglia.

The third stage which may be discriminated is derived directly from the second by a forward movement of the sub-oesophageal ganglion so that it comes to lie between the right and left pleurals underneath the gut. In this position it has in fact become a new member of the circum-oesophageal nerve ring established by the other ganglia. The supra-oesophageal ganglion maintains its typical situation. This group of prosobranchs contains the genera *Bittium, Clathrus, Natica, Trichotropis* and *Turritella*.

In a fourth group (fig. 162B) the forward migration of the sub-oesophageal ganglion (sbg) has also involved the supra-oesophageal ganglion (sog) so that both these structures come to lie alongside the corresponding pleural ganglion (lpl, rpl) and the visceral loop appears to pass from supra-oesophageal ganglion on the right to sub-oesophageal ganglion on the left with only the visceral ganglion (or, more usually, ganglia) (vg)

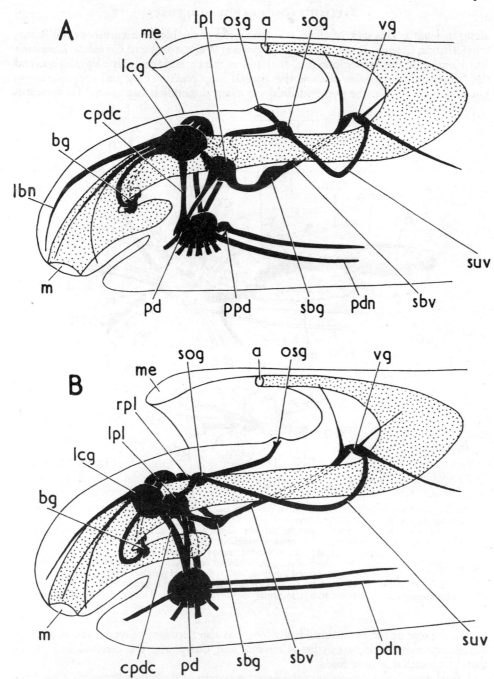

FIG. 162.—Lateral views of the anterior end of a prosobranch to show A, diagram of epiathroid nervous system (e.g. most monotocardians); B, diagram of concentrated nervous system (e.g. higher monotocardians).

a, anus; bg, buccal ganglion; cpdc, cerebropedal connective; lcg, left cerebral ganglion; lbn, labial nerve; lpl, left pleural ganglion; m, mouth; me, mantle edge; osg, osphradial ganglion; pd, pedal ganglion; pdn, pedal nerve; ppd, postpedal commissure; rpl, right pleural ganglion; sbg, sub-oesophageal ganglion; sbv, sub-oesophageal part of visceral loop; sog, supra-oesophageal ganglion; suv, supra-oesophageal part of visceral loop; vg, visceral ganglion.

along its length. This state of affairs is encountered in the higher members of the Rissoacea (*Alvania*, *Cingula*, *Rissoa*, *Tornus*), *Calyptraea* (Weise, 1924) and *Crepidula*, *Lamellaria* and *Velutina*, in the Stenoglossa (fig. 163) and in the parasitic animals *Balcis*, *Eulima* and the pyramidellids. In most of these the visceral loop remains long and streptoneurous, but in some (*Cingula*, the pyramidellids) the visceral ganglion has moved far forwards

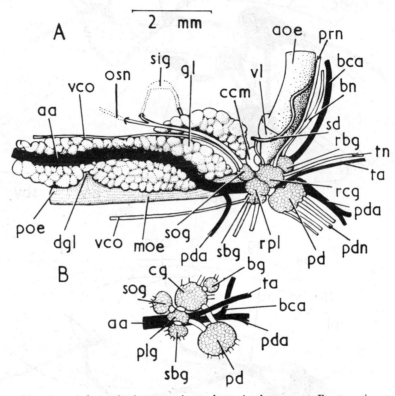

Fig. 163.—*Nassarius reticulatus:* A, the nerve ring and associated structures; B, nerve ring stretched to show the course of related blood vessels.

    aa, anterior aorta; aoe, anterior oesophagus; bca, buccal artery; bg, buccal ganglion; bn, buccal nerve; ccm, cerebral commissure; cg, cerebral ganglion; dgl, duct of gland of Leiblein; gl, gland of Leiblein; moe, mid-oesophagus; osn, osphradial nerve; pd, pedal ganglion; pda, pedal artery; pdn, pedal nerve; plg, pleural ganglion; poe, posterior oesophagus; prn, proboscis nerve; rbg, right buccal ganglion; rcg, right cerebral ganglion; rpl, right pleural ganglion; sbg, sub-oesophageal ganglion; sd, salivary duct, the salivary gland removed; sig, siphonal ganglion; sog, supra-oesophageal ganglion; ta, tentacular artery; tn, tentacular nerve; vco, visceral loop; vl, valve of Leiblein.

and in the case of the pyramidellids the loop has also become euthyneurous. In some of the genera mentioned in this list (*Crepidula* and *Calyptraea*) the cerebral and pleural ganglia on each side have fused.

    A final stage in the evolution of the nervous system of the mesogastropods is exemplified by a number of animals in which some fusion of ganglia on nerve ring and visceral loop has occurred. This may also be accompanied by fusion of cerebrals and pleurals so that, on occasion, complex nervous masses of multiple origin may arise. The animals which are known to possess nervous systems of this sort are *Valvata*, *Assiminea*, *Paludinella*, *Omalogyra*, *Skeneopsis* and some species of *Eulima*. As these are all small, or extremely small, it appears likely that the fusion of the ganglia is as much an adaptation to this as an attempt to produce a more highly co-ordinated nervous system.

In *Valvata* (Bouvier, 1887; Bernard, 1888) the cerebral and pleural ganglia on each side are fused, and the 2 pedals are closely approximated, although they still lie ventrally in the foot. In the visceral loop the supra-oesophageal ganglion has moved forward and fused with the right pleural and the sub-oesophageal has migrated until it lies alongside the left pleural. The single visceral ganglion has retained its posterior position on the visceral loop and there is one other ganglion placed near the point where a connexion is established between a pallial nerve originating in the supra-oesophageal ganglion and another coming from the left pleural ganglion: this is probably an osphradial ganglion. A similar dialyneury, but no ganglion, occurs on the animal's right.

In *Assiminea* and *Paludinella* (Thiele, 1929–35) a similar fusion between the right cerebral, right pleural and supra-oesophageal ganglia has taken place but the left has retained a greater degree of separation, the left pleural and the sub-oesophageal ganglion lying between the cerebral above and the pedal ganglion below. In *Omalogyra atomus* (fig. 184A) the nervous system retains its primitive disposition except that on each side the cerebral and pleural ganglia have fused. No visceral ganglion can be made out in the nervous system of this minute animal, but it is probable that this is a consequence of the difficulty of working with such a small creature and it may well be present. A similar nervous system occurs in *Skeneopsis planorbis*, but in the species of *Rissoella*, *opalina* and *diaphana*, a greater degree of fusion of ganglia has taken place and the visceral loop seems to have been drawn forward and probably untwisted in the process. Two large ganglia lie above the buccal region and 2 below, whilst buccal ganglia lie alongside the root of the radular sac. The 2 ventral ganglia have the statocysts lying beside them and are clearly pedal; the dorsal ones, however, have been formed by the fusion of ganglia and their morphological value remains uncertain.

The sensory equipment of the prosobranchs cannot be compared in its acuity with that of the cephalopod molluscs or with that of many other types of animal. Their bodies, however, are well supplied with sense organs of various sorts, of which eyes, osphradia, tentacles and statocysts are the most important distance receptors and numerous other organs set in various parts of the body the major local ones. The whole surface of the body is naturally sensitive to contact and chemical stimulation, but the tentacles and lips of the head, the sides of the foot and the mantle edge, including the siphon where one is developed, appear to be more sensitive than the surface in general.

The tentacles are obviously the seat of a well developed tactile sense and are used by the animal as a main guide to its movements throughout the environment in which it lives. They are kept in continuous movement, the main direction being up and down, and their motion is timed with the locomotor waves which are moving along the foot. In view of the probability that the cephalic tentacles are simply the most anterior of a series set along head and foot this is not surprising. In many prosobranchs the sensitivity of the tentacles is increased by the presence of innumerable immobile cilia set over their surface: these are particularly obvious in the trochids, rissoids and pyramidellids, in the last group of which they have been shown to be compound cirri (Fretter & Graham, 1949). The cilia are connected to sensory cells which in turn are related to the terminations of branches of the tentacular nerve. In the trochids they have been examined by Burdon-Jones & Desai (*in lit.*) who refer to them as brush organs. They are composed of a group of 3–5 bipolar neurones, the T-shaped outer ends of which underlie a ring of immobile cilia. Burdon-Jones & Desai regard them as touch-taste receptors. They are particularly common on the cephalic and epipodial tentacles, on the papillae at the base of the latter, on the epipodial ridge and on the fringed edge of the left neck lobe. In these situations they appear to be of importance in testing the nature of the substratum and the turbidity of the water entering the mantle cavity. The poor visual equipment of the ordinary prosobranch (Willem, 1892c) makes the tactile sensitivity of these structures important, and probably similar but less well developed sensory structures are located at all other parts of the body. In the archaeogastropods, for example, special sensory organs of unknown significance are placed at the base of the epipodial tentacles (eso, fig. 80); these may be compared to those on the mantle edge of *Acmaea* (ms, fig. 73).

The tentacles, however, are also supposed to be the seat of an olfactory sense. This is additionally ascribed to another sense organ, the osphradium or Spengel's organ as it was originally called, located in the mantle cavity. Ankel (1936a), for example, has shown how specimens of *Nassarius* are able to find their way to food when only the siphon projects out of the sand in which they are buried, so that the siphon and the mantle cavity are the only parts of the body exposed to stimulation. This mechanism and the differentiation between smell and taste has been studied by Henschel (1932).

The osphradium is an organ located in the mantle cavity either on or near the ctenidium. Like that structure, it is double in the diotocardians, single in the monotocardians, and it tends to be lost when the ctenidium is lost. The basommatophoran pulmonates are notable examples of a group in which the ctenidium has gone but the osphradium persists, but there are some examples of the same thing in prosobranchs, e.g. *Pomatias* (Garnault, 1887) and *Assiminea grayana*. In the nuchal cavity of *Patella* there are 2 orange papillae which are normally called osphradia, and there is certainly a nerve centre associated with each. In addition to this, however, Spengel (1881) found blood spaces, and for this reason regarded the structure as the remains of the whole osphradium-ctenidium complex. Bernard (1890), re-investigating its structure, confirmed Spengel's description without, however, committing himself to Spengel's homologies.

Bernard (1890) has given a good survey of the gross morphology of the osphradium throughout the prosobranch series and this has been supplemented by Yonge (1947). In the diotocardians the usual appearance of the osphradium is a ridge placed on the ctenidial axis, in *Emarginula* and *Diodora* lying both dorsally and ventrally. In the trochids, on the other hand, the osphradium forms a kidney-shaped elevation at the place where the free portion of the ctenidial axis joins the mantle skirt, on the anterior border of the efferent membrane (osg, fig. 145), and it occupies a similar position in *Haliotis*. In the other diotocardians the osphradium is not closely related to the ctenidium but lies near it on the roof or floor of the mantle cavity, as in the Neritacea where it is formed by a ridge on the mantle skirt. In the docoglossans some uncertainty surrounds the organ, especially in view of the loss of gills which these animals often exhibit. Thus in *Acmaea* Bernard (1890) described as osphradia a pair of tubercles lying, the left by the base of the ctenidium, the right by the reproductive aperture, but was unable to find sensory epithelium on their surface. Willcox (1898), on the other hand, thought that she had found sensory cells. Thiem (1917a, b) described osphradia in several acmaeids but again failed to find either sense cells or nerves from the underlying ganglia: he also failed to find the tubercles in *A. virginea*. He regarded these structures as partially ctenidial in origin like those of *Patella*. Yonge (1947) believed that neither of these tubercles is an osphradium at all and located this structure on the left side in a patch of sensory cells anterior to the tubercle: no corresponding structure, however, lies in front of the right tubercle. The osphradia of *Patella* have already been mentioned and similar structures—except for the lack of vascular spaces (Bernard, 1890)—occur in *Patina*.

In the majority of the mesogastropods the osphradium has the form of a linear ridge lying parallel to the ctenidial axis and to its left. This is to be found, for example, in *Littorina* spp. (figs. 7, 8), in *Bithynia tentaculata* (fig. 55), in the rissoids, in *Pomatias elegans* (fig. 313), in *Bittium reticulatum* (fig. 190B), in *Aporrhais pespelicani* (fig. 179), in *Crepidula fornicata*; in *Trivia* (fig. 172) and in *Natica catena* (fig. 180A) the osphradium enlarges somewhat to occupy a triangular area in the former genus. There is an indication of a considerable increase in the size of the organ in the Stenoglossa, where the ridge has developed a double series of lateral foldings, giving the whole organ something of the appearance of a bipectinate ctenidium (fig. 275). For this reason the osphradium has sometimes been known as the 'fausse branchie'.

The osphradium consists of an epithelium of sensory cells mixed with pigment cells overlying a ganglion. The ganglion is related to the branchial nerve and the supra-oesophageal and right pleural ganglia. The precise relationships of the nerve vary within the prosobranchs and three different arrangements may be distinguished. In the majority of rhipidoglossans a nerve runs from the supra-oesophageal part of the visceral loop and expands into a branchial ganglion. This sends nerves to the gill, the osphradium and to local parts of the mantle skirt. In the Docoglossa and the remaining rhipidoglossans (Neritacea) there is no branchial ganglion and the osphradium receives its nerve directly from the supra-oesophageal ganglion, from the same nerve, indeed, as goes to the ctenidium. In the monotocardians, also, there is no branchial ganglion and the osphradial branch of the branchial nerve gradually assumes so much more importance than that to the gill that it is better designated the osphradial nerve.

Although the function of the osphradium has usually been regarded as olfactory, or gustatory, and the organ the seat of a chemical sense since it is placed across or along the stream of water entering the mantle cavity (fig. 276), it is worthwhile noting that it is also sited at a place where it would be affected by the amount of particulate matter in the incoming water. For this reason Hulbert & Yonge (1937) have held that it is used by the animal as an indicator of the amount of suspended matter rather than as an organ of more strictly chemical sense.

The second organ of sense which acts as a distance receptor is the eye, found in almost all gastropods, the only exceptions being a few blind ones which come from habitats to which light does not penetrate in sufficient quantities to make the possession of a photo-sensitive organ useful and in a few other cases (e.g. *Ianthina*) where this explanation does not hold, and where, indeed, a plausible reason for its absence or ineffectiveness is hard to find. The gastropod eye must be regarded mainly as an organ acting as a simple detector of light and the direction from which it comes, since its image-forming powers seem to be extremely poor (Willem, 1892a, b, c). The eye is normally situated on an eye stalk which lies on the side of the head immediately posterior to the cephalic tentacle. Although originally separate from this (e.g. *Haliotis*)—and still partially so in the Trochacea (figs. 53, 69, 91)—the 2 structures become so closely fused in most proso-branchs that the eye usually appears to be placed on a small bulge at the base of the tentacle (figs. 7, 57). In a small number of animals the eyes have migrated to a deeper situation and in the pyramidellids they have also migrated towards the mid-line, so that they now lie between the 2 tentacles (figs. 134, 135, 298).

In the lower families of the diotocardian prosobranchs (Haliotidae, Fissurellidae, Patellidae) the eye is an open vesicle with a moderately wide mouth (e.g. *Patella*, fig. 164A); in the Trochacea whilst still open, the vesicle has a constricted aperture (fig. 164B). In the Neritacea and all other prosobranchs (e.g. *Trichotropis*, fig. 164C) the vesicle has

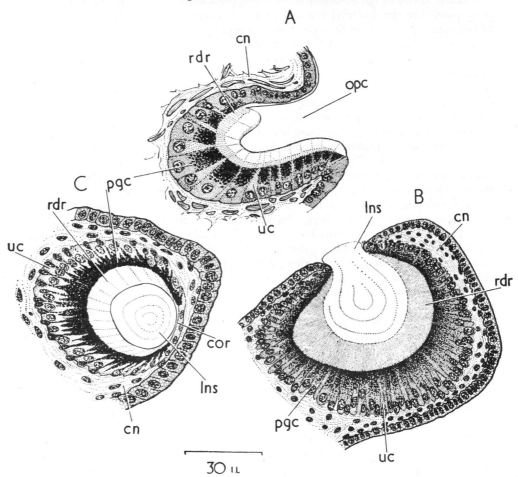

FIG. 164.—Eyes in vertical section. A, *Patella vulgata*; B, *Cantharidus clelandi*; C, *Trichotropis borealis*. cn, connective tissue; cor, cornea; lns, lens; opc, opening of optic cup; pgc, pigmented cell of retina; rdr, rod of retinal cell; uc, unpigmented cell of retina.

closed off from the surface of the skin and has no connexion with the outside environment. In the case of the open eye of the typical diotocardian the cavity is filled, wholly or partly, with a secreted mass of material acting, perhaps, as a lens or refracting medium (lns, fig. 164B). Its detailed structure is a matter of debate: according to Hilger (1885) and most other writers on the subject the cavity of the eye is filled with a homogeneous mass of emplema (to give it Grenacher's name), whereas Patten (1886b) found it divisible into a hard, outer, biconvex lens and an inner vitreous in *Haliotis*, which was the only gastropod with which he worked. In the Patellacea, however, the cavity of the eye (opc) is usually thought to be filled with sea water. In this case the eye might be regarded as either a more primitive stage from which the eye of the other diotocardians with its emplema might be derived, or a degeneration from this by loss of emplema. Hilger (1885), however, thought that he had some evidence suggesting the presence of a cuticle over the open mouth of the optic vesicle, which would bring the patellacean eye more into line with that of the other diotocardians: no other worker has suggested the occurrence of this.

In the prosobranchs with closed eyes the homogeneous vitreous appears to be limited to the Neritacea, and the great majority have a spherical lens lying under the outermost part of the optic vesicle (lns, fig. 164C) and separated by a small quantity of vitreous from the retina: it has, however, been suggested that this gap between lens and retina is an artefact and that no vitreous is naturally present.

Although there is this considerable degree of variation in the general structure of the eye within the prosobranchs, the histology of the wall of the optic vesicle appears, on the other hand, to be relatively uniform throughout the class. The bulk of the epithelium lining the vesicle makes up the light-percipient layer or retina, a small part underneath the skin in closed eyes forming a cornea (cor, fig. 164C) made of thin, unpigmented and translucent cells like those of the overlying epidermis. Little progress was at first made in understanding the histological nature of the retina because—inevitably—it was originally attempted to explain it on the same basis as that of the vertebrate eye, and it was only when Hensen (1865) showed that its development was wholly different that some success in understanding it was reached. The most important investigators of its structure have been Fraisse (1881), Hilger (1885), Grenacher (1886), Patten (1886b), Carrière (1889), Hesse (1900) and Bäcker (1903), and their findings as to retinal structure are almost identical. All are agreed that in the retina there occur two types of cell, one containing pigment (pgc), the other without (uc), but they differ amongst themselves as to the function that the two types subserve in the actual sensory act. The pigmented cells and unpigmented cells alike are supposed to be sensitive to light in the more primitive forms although the latter are usually held to be the more important; in higher prosobranchs the unpigmented cells come to be the only sensory ones and the pigmented cells have no direct visual importance, though they are presumably useful accessory structures. This conclusion is reached mainly because it is only the unpigmented cells which bear rods distally and are connected by neurofibrillae to the underlying nerve fibres. The pigmented cells, which may share in sensitivity in lower forms, become, in the more specialized eyes, only supporting cells for the unpigmented, though they may share in the production of the cuticular material of the lens and even of the rods. Bäcker (1903), for example, has shown that each rod consists of a stainable axis embedded in cuticle: he regarded the axis as being essentially a surface prolongation of the unpigmented cell and the cuticular material in which it is embedded as a supporting and perhaps also an optical device secreted by the pigmented cells.

The heteropods are free-swimming active predators that catch their prey by sight, and this is possible because of the important development which their eyes have undergone. These have been carefully investigated by Hesse (1900) in *Carinaria mediterranea*. The eyes are large—3·8 mm in an animal 15 cm in length—and are shaped like a tapered cylinder (figs. 165A, B) with its long axis parallel to the long axis of the body and its narrower end directed forwards. This end bulges somewhat because of the presence of a spherical lens (lns). The cylinder is circular in cross-section in its anterior half but is flattened dorsoventrally in its posterior part. The optic nerve (on) runs from its base to the cerebral ganglion.

The wall of this eye is lined by an epithelium composed mainly of pigmented cells. These are absent over the lens, where a clear transparent cornea (cor) occurs and also over the greater part of the dorsal surface. A few small unpigmented spots (us) are also present in the ventral wall. Since the heteropods normally swim upside down this means that the window in the pigmented layer is pointing down into the depths of the water.

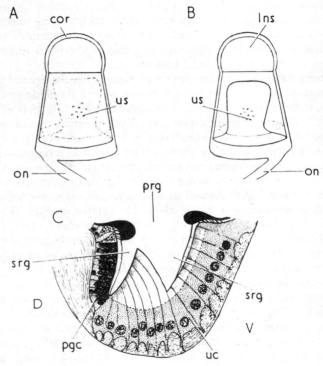

FIG. 165.—Heteropod eye: A, in ventral view; B, in dorsal view; C, vertical section of retina. After Hesse.

cor, cornea; D, dorsal; lns, lens; on, optic nerve; pgc, pigment cell; prg, primary retinal groove; srg, secondary retinal groove; uc, unpigmented retinal cell; us, unpigmented spot in pigmented wall of eye; V, ventral.

The retina (fig. 165C) is a narrow band of cells, running across the base of the eye from right to left. It lies at the base of a groove (prg) and is itself scored by 2 deep grooves (srg). The dorsal wall of the groove is made of pigment cells (pgc) extending from the main cavity of the eye, its ventral wall by retinal cells (uc). The dorsal half of the retina is composed of cells of varying height, the ventral ones being tallest, the dorsal ones smallest. As a result the surface of these cells, like that of the ventral ones, looks across the retinal groove towards the pigment cells and is therefore parallel to the long axis of the eye. The images of the objects being viewed fall along these surfaces and the retina is therefore provided with two surfaces which give the animal information about the distance of the object which is being viewed. No accommodation is required—no mechanism to achieve it exists—since the arrangement of the sensitive retinal surfaces gives this information directly. This retina gives the animal a view of what lies ahead, and the mollusc arranges to sight potential prey in this way before making its final pounce upon it, an action for which the accurate judgement of distance is necessary. An accessory source of visual information, however, is provided by other sensitive cells placed further forwards in the eye: these are, in fact, the cause of the unpigmented spots on the ventral wall of the eye opposite the window in the dorsal wall. These record movement in the water below and the objects to which they react might then be inspected in more detail if the heteropod turned and looked straight at them through the front of the eye and the main part of the retina.

In prosobranchs, as in other molluscs, there also occurs the type of sense organ known as a statocyst. This name and the idea underlying it—that the organ is one for equilibration—were first published by Delage (1887) in relation to what had previously been called an auditory capsule or otocyst (Lacaze-Duthiers, 1872). The experimental work of Tschachotin (1908) gave firm support to the idea that these structures were indeed organs of balance rather than of hearing.

The statocysts arise as ectodermal invaginations which sink inwards and close off, though occasional hollows in the statocyst nerve may perhaps be vestiges of the original invagination (Buddenbrock, 1915). They form vesicles which in most prosobranchs lie in the proximity of the pedal ganglia, though the precise situation is somewhat variable. They were originally thought to be innervated by nerves from the pedal ganglia, but Lacaze-Duthiers (1872) showed that the fibres really arose in the cerebral ganglia and ran thence, sometimes direct to the statocyst (*Pomatias elegans, Capulus ungaricus, Viviparus viviparus, Theodoxus fluviatilis*), sometimes branching off to the statocyst from the cerebro-pedal connective (*Patella vulgata, Natica catena*) but in most species run through the pedal ganglia and so mimic pedal nerves in appearance. The statocyst nerve arises from the posterior part of the corresponding cerebral ganglion alongside the area from which the optic nerve springs.

As in the case of the eyes much attention has been paid to the statocysts of heteropods, where they are large and accessible, but the organs appear to be very uniform throughout the prosobranchs. The following account is based on Ilyin (1900), Tschachotin (1908) and Pfeil (1922). Each statocyst is a spherical cavity about 0·25 mm in diameter lined by an epithelium containing 2 types of cell, giant and syncytial. The giant cells are few in number and vary a little (11–13 in *Helix pomatia*) but whatever number occurs in the right statocyst will also occur in the left. They consist of a central area which contains the nucleus and which occupies the whole depth of the epithelium; from this pseudopodia-like extensions reach out in all directions over the inner surface of the statocyst. These meet, tip to tip, similar extensions from other giant cells. The greater part of the inner surface of the statocyst is lined by the giant cells. The second type, the syncytial cell, forms the rest of the wall; it therefore underlies the arms radiating from the bodies of the giant cells and fills up the whole thickness of the epithelium in the lacunae between them.

The whole inner surface, whatever type of cell it may be formed from, is ciliated, and the wall rests on an outer layer of connective tissue. Beyond the fact that the statocyst is undoubtedly an organ of equilibration, which was convincingly shown by Tschachotin (1908), the functioning of the statocyst is not known. Pfeil (1922), however, believed that it is the giant cells which are the essential sensory cells and that the syncytial base on which they rest is merely for their support. The cilia are very short and do not seem to have sense hairs of different length mixed up with them.

The cavity of the statocyst is filled with fluid, secreted from the cells which line it, and in this float calcareous particles, either one statolith or several smaller statoconia. Though statoconia appear on the whole to be characteristic of the more primitive prosobranchs and the single statolith of the more advanced types there is no very clear systematic base to this difference. Statoconia occur in all the Archaeogastropoda and in the Viviparidae, Valvatidae and some other families of mesogastropods, mostly with a distribution in freshwater. The other mesogastropod families and the Stenoglossa have a single statolith in each statocyst.

The nervous system of many animals, in addition to its more ordinary role of rapid correlation of sensory and motor activity, undertakes in addition the long term control of many processes by means of the secretion of hormones or neurohormones. In vertebrates and insects this is a well known phenomenon, but, though less spectacular, it also occurs in molluscs and in particular in the gastropods. The first record of a hormone-like substance secreted in a mollusc was made in *Aplysia* and *Pleurobranchaea* by Scharrer (1935) who observed droplets or granules in cells of most of the ganglia which also entered the nerves. The number of animals in which this was found to occur grew rapidly, mainly by the work of Gabe (1953*a*, *b*), until Gersch (1959) was able to state that the total number of gastropod species known to elaborate neurohormones was 71, of which 23 were prosobranchs, 46 opisthobranchs and 2 pulmonates. These last are *Ferrissia* (Lever, 1957) and *Helix* (unpublished work by Jungstand quoted by Gersch). As in many other groups of animals the neurosecretory cells are likely to have an annual cycle of activity though this has so far only been exposed for those found in *Viviparus* (unpublished work by Gorff quoted by Gersch), where granules can be found in some ganglion cells and traced from there into certain nerves where they lie amongst the nerve fibres. They abound in summer and have a minimum in winter.

The precise physiological role played by neurosecretory substances in gastropods is not clear, although some physiological effects brought about by them are quite obvious. Their occurrence has mainly been tested for by measuring their effects on the heart of *Aplysia* or *Helix* or, more recently, *Venus*, or on the crop of *Aplysia*, all of which organs are commonly stimulated to increased amplitude and rate of contraction by extracts of ganglia or nerves (Scharrer, 1937; Gabe, 1954; Welsh, 1953, 1957). Analysis by paper chromatography showed that the substance responsible for this was not adrenaline, noradrenaline nor 5-hydroxytryptamine, and might perhaps be a mixture of substances. In *Helix*, Meng (1958) has shown that there are 2 neurohormones, one causing an acceleration and the other a retardation of the heart beat: the former he showed to be 5-hydroxytryptamine, the latter acetylcholine.

# CHAPTER 14

# THE REPRODUCTIVE SYSTEM — 1

THE coelom of present day molluscs is divided into three cavities, pericardial, renal and gonadial. It is assumed that in the ancestral mollusc (fig. 151A) the last two were paired and that all the cavities were in communication with one another by narrow ducts. The protogastropod probably had a similar arrangement of the coelom. It opened to the mantle cavity by two ducts, one on either side of the anus, which were, most probably, urinogenital in function, for it is assumed that as in living diotocardians the gonad had no separate opening to the outside of the body, but discharged its products by way of the kidney. In modern gastropods (fig. 151B) there is a single gonad, presumably the (post-torsional) right, which in the most primitive, the diotocardians, discharges into the right kidney: in *Diodora*, *Puncturella* and the trochids (figs. 151D and E) the connexion is with the right renopericardial duct; in the Patellacea (Goodrich, 1895) and in *Pleurotomaria* (Woodward, 1901a) it is with the kidney (fig. 151C). The connexion with the kidney may be by a simple longitudinal slit as in *Patella*, or it may be by several openings as Thiem (1917b) described for monobranchs (e.g. *Acmaea*), which break through only when the gonad is ripe. There is some doubt as to the precise state of affairs in *Haliotis* since according to Haller (1894), Fleure (1903), Totzauer (1902) and Meyer (1913) there is a right renopericardial duct into which the gonad opens, but according to Perrier (1889), Erlanger (1892) and Crofts (1929) this duct is absent in the adult and the gonad discharges directly to the right kidney. It may be possible to reconcile these contradictory statements on the assumption that a renopericardial duct does in fact form at an early stage as found in the early post-veliger by Crofts (1937) in *Haliotis* and receives the gonadial duct, and that in a certain number of individuals the pericardial end persists, but in another series it aborts, leaving the gonad and kidney in apparently direct connexion. In all these prosobranchs the course taken by the genital products in passing from gonad to mantle cavity is through a composite duct the proximal part of which is derived from the gonad and the distal from the kidney.

The position of the gonad varies. In diotocardians with a helicoid spiral shell (trochids (ov, fig. 157), *Pleurotomaria* and *Scissurella* (te, fig. 255)) it occupies a position similar to that in the monotocardians and, with the digestive gland, comprises the visceral coils, lying mainly on the columellar side. The spire is reduced to one coil in *Haliotis* and the gonad is in a corresponding position. In patelliform genera (*Acmaea*, *Lepeta*, *Patella*, *Patina*, *Puncturella*, *Propilidium*) it lies between the visceral mass and foot (ov, fig. 261) except anteriorly, and when ripe spreads around the periphery of the visceral mass sometimes more particularly on the right side (g, figs. 257, 266).

Most diotocardians are littoral. The sexes are separate and there is no copulation; the eggs are fertilized after they leave the female. In *Patina pellucida*, *Patella caerulea* (Ankel, 1936a), *P. lusitanica* (von Medem, 1945) and *Gibbula tumida* (Gersch, 1936) the male and female are close together during the emission of the gametes, and this is probably true for other species. The gonad is relatively much greater in volume than in species which copulate. In female *Patella vulgata* the ovary is 1 : 3·75 the body weight, whereas in the monotocardian *Lamellaria perspicua* it is only 1 : 21·6. *Haliotis tuberculata* will shed about 20,000 eggs at one spawning, emitting them through all the pores of the shell, the greatest quantity passing through the second and third oldest, and sperm from the male may make the water turbid for a distance of 3 ft (Crofts, 1929). The males are the first to spawn thus stimulating the females to shed their eggs (Boutan, 1892). This phenomenon of a ripe male inducing females to spawn is of widespread occurrence in marine invertebrates, and trochids have been observed to behave likewise (Robert, 1902), but Gersch (1936) denied it for *Gibbula cineraria*, though he admitted that spawning, once started, spreads rapidly through a whole population.

In some invertebrates the fusion of egg and sperm is brought about by substances secreted by each of these cells which help to overcome the hazards of external fertilization. Both gametes have been shown to secrete 2 types of fertilization substances, or gamones. Gynogamone I, secreted by the eggs, accelerates the movements of the sperm so that they reach the egg more rapidly. Once the sperm has reached the egg it is agglutinated by gynogamone II, which has little or no effect on sperm of other species. The sperm produce androgamone I which slows down their movement before they are liberated. After liberation they are stimulated by gynogamone I and may move up a gradient of this gamone to the egg. Later androgamone I cancels the effect of gynogamone I and so prevents the sperm being attracted to a fertilized egg. The sperm also produce androgamone II which causes local solution of the egg jelly and membrane and so facilitates penetration. These 4 gamones have been reported in *Haliotis*, *Diodora* and *Patella* (von Medem, 1945) and even egg cases have been found to be as effective as the whole egg in attracting spermatozoa, probably due to contamination with gynogamone substance.

Although some diotocardians shed their eggs singly to become planktonic, others embed them in a gelatinous secretion forming fixed egg masses. In the former case they develop to free trochophore or veliger larvae, but those in protective coverings are not freed until they have developed to the crawling stage. The eggs have investments which are produced by the ovary. In *Patella* and *Patina* the egg membrane is surrounded only by a gelatinous covering which swells when the eggs are discharged into the water. According to Lebour (1937) the eggs of *Gibbula cineraria*, *G. umbilicalis*, *Monodonta* and *Tricolia* have an albuminous layer within the gelatinous sheath, though we are unable to identify this and believe that the apparent double covering is merely a line of contact between denser inner jelly and a thinner more superficial layer, all of which is secreted by the egg within the ovary (jo, fig. 166A). All these forms lay their eggs singly. In the top shells of the genera *Monodonta* (fig. 53) and *Gibbula* the urinogenital aperture of the female (rko) is, unlike that of the left kidney (lko), provided with glandular rosette-shaped lips which are yellow or bright orange in the living animal. They are not developed in the male. In *Tricolia* (rko, fig. 77) such lips are present in both sexes, but are larger in females. The secretion from the lips is wholly mucus and may augment secretion from the hypobranchial gland in entangling the egg stream within the mantle cavity. According to Gersch (1936) the hypobranchial gland secretes most actively during the breeding season, and he concluded that it provides the embedding medium for the egg masses in *Gibbula tumida*.

Within the family Acmaeidae there is surprising variation in the method of spawning. *Acmaea virginea* sheds the sex cells (fig. 167A) singly into the plankton, but Willcox (1905a) recorded that in *A. tessulata* the eggs are embedded in very thin mucus in which they lie one cell deep and at regular intervals apart; the mucus is secreted by the sole

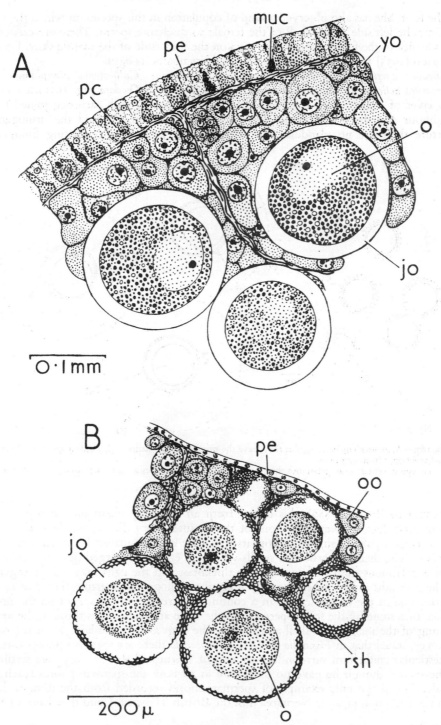

Fig. 166.—Transverse section through superficial part of upper visceral hump showing outer pallial epithelium and adjacent ovary: A, *Monodonta lineata*; B, *Diodora apertura*.
    jo, jelly round egg; muc, mucous cell; o, ovum; oo, oocyte; pc, protein secreting cell; pe, pallial epithelium; rsh, reticulated shell; yo, young oocyte.

of the foot. She has also observed a kind of copulation in this species, in which the male mounts the left side of the shell of the female to discharge sperm. These are carried to the vicinity of the female opening by cilia on the underside of the mantle skirt. Finally, Thorson (1935) has shown that *Acmaea rubella* incubates its eggs.

*Diodora apertura, Cantharidus exasperatus, C. striatus, Calliostoma zizyphinum* and *Margarites helicinus* produce spawn of differing shapes. In *Diodora* (fig. 167B) it consists of a layer of eggs one cell thick and several inches across, with each egg joined to its neighbour and the whole firmly fixed to the substratum. Around the urinogenital aperture there are no glandular lips which might produce a cementing fluid, and,

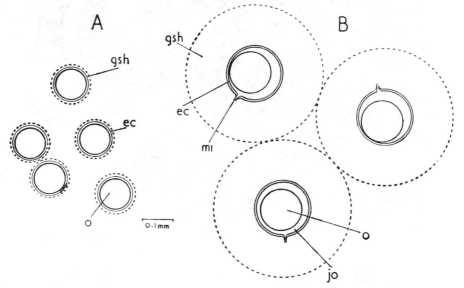

FIG. 167.—A, *Acmaea virginea*: eggs as they leave the urinogenital aperture.   B, *Diodora apertura*: three adjacent eggs from egg mass.
ec, egg covering; gsh, gelatinous sheath of egg; jo, jelly round egg; mi, micropyle; o, ovum.

according to Boutan (1886), this comes from an accessory gland on the wall of the urinogenital duct. However, sections of the mature ovary (fig. 166B) show that each ovum secretes a shell (rsh) which appears reticulate in fixed material, and an inner jelly coat (jo). The shell, in particular, swells when the egg is discharged (gsh, fig. 167B) to form a gelatinous sheath of considerable thickness, and the eggs may adhere together by these sheaths alone. When the eggs leave the urinogenital aperture they pass to the anterior end of the mantle cavity in a continuous stream and are spread on the under surface of a stone by the foot. Sperm from the male are said to pass through the apical opening of the mantle and shell and fertilize the eggs as they are laid. Medem (1945), however, stated that in *Fissurella* (=*Diodora*) *nubecula* there are spermatophores formed by testicular epithelium surrounding packets of sperm and that the eggs are fertilized in the ovary, though he gave no indication as to how the spermatophores reach the female. This is the only example of spermatophores recorded from the diotocardians with the exception of some Neritacea (not the British *Theodoxus*), and they have a penis.

Spawn masses of *Margarites helicinus* (Fretter, 1955b) (fig. 168A) are irregular clumps of 100 or more eggs deposited on seaweed and on the undersides of stones. Each clump adheres by the outer envelope which is moulded by the foot of the female and produced into anchoring threads. The eggs have gelatinous coats (jo, figs. 168A, c) developed in the ovary and the outer secretion in which each spawn mass is embedded (j, fig. 168A) comes from a gland associated with the urinogenital papilla (ugp, figs. 168C, 169). This, in the female, projects freely into the mantle cavity, with no attachment to the mantle

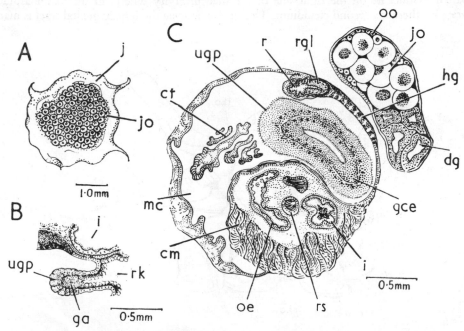

FIG. 168.—*Margarites helicinus:* A, single spawn mass; B, longitudinal section through the urinogenital papilla of a male animal; C, transverse section through a female at the level of the inner part of the mantle cavity; the section also cuts one turn of the visceral hump.

cm, columellar muscle; ct, ctenidium; dg, digestive gland; ga, urinogenital duct; gce, glandular and ciliated epithelium; hg, hypobranchial gland; i, intestine; j, jelly of egg mass; jo, jelly round egg; mc, mantle cavity; oe, oesophagus; oo, oocyte; r, rectum; rgl, rectal gland; rk, right kidney; rs, radular sac; ugp, urinogenital papilla, projecting into mantle cavity.

skirt or body wall and the epithelium of tall gland cells which lines it also covers its outer surfaces. In males the papilla (ugp, fig. 168B) is very much smaller.

*Calliostoma zizyphinum* produces an egg ribbon many times longer than broad, attached at one end. It contains several hundred eggs each about 0·28 mm in diameter, which is about twice the diameter of the eggs of *Gibbula cineraria* and *G. umbilicalis*. This species also shows sexual dimorphism. In the male the left and right kidney apertures lie level with one another at the posterior end of the mantle cavity, but in the female the right one (rko, fig. 170) is considerably further forwards since a glandular section is added which, unlike that of *Margarites*, is in the thickness of the mantle skirt and is assumedly derived from a closed off portion of the mantle. It appears to replace, or even be derived from the posterior part of the right hypobranchial gland; this is reduced in female *Calliostoma* though not in males, and is fully developed in female *Margarites*. The glandular section of the duct in *Calliostoma* (ugp) is built on the same plan as the pallial oviduct of the monotocardians—lined by columnar ciliated epithelium, the lateral walls deep and thickened by tightly packed bundles of subepithelial glands, the dorsal and ventral walls narrow and comparatively thin. The secretion from the duct is mucus and as the eggs pass to the urinogenital aperture, each covered by a gelatinous sheath, a further fluid is poured over them and binds them into an egg ribbon. Both rectum and pallial oviduct lie on the right side of the mantle cavity where, in the lower aspido-branchs, there is a second ctenidium. Thus in *Calliostoma* the female genital tract is made

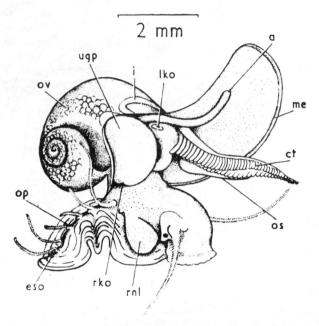

FIG. 169.—*Margarites helicinus:* female, dissected to show contents of the mantle cavity from the right. a, anus; ct, bipectinate ctenidium; eso, epipodial sense organ; i, intestine; lko, opening of left kidney; me, mantle edge; op, operculum; os, osphradium; ov, ovary; rko, opening of right kidney; rnl, right neck lobe; ugp, urinogenital papilla.

up of (a) the ovarian duct which discharges the eggs into the kidney, (b) part of the right kidney and its duct, and (c) a glandular duct—urinogenital in function—derived from the mantle. This triple origin of the genital duct is the general plan on which that of higher gastropods, both male and female, is built.

The eggs of monotocardians have more elaborate investments from the pallial oviduct which in these prosobranchs traverses the whole length of the mantle cavity on the right side, running parallel with the rectum (fig. 171A). The proximal glandular area (ag) provides the albumen in which the eggs are embedded, and the shell which may surround this. From the more anterior parts (rlc, llg) are secreted the protective outer coverings of the egg mass, which vary in thickness and consistency. Within these coverings the egg develops to the veliger or crawling stage; in no species is there a free

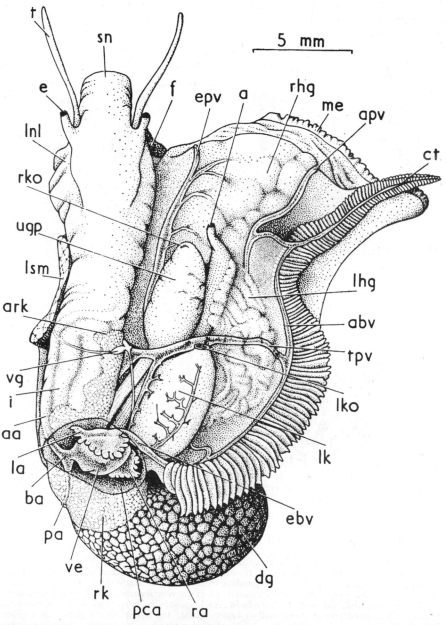

FIG. 170.—*Calliostoma zizyphinum:* female dissected to show the vascular system in the mantle skirt and the contents of the mantle cavity. Some other organs are seen by transparency.

a, anus; aa, anterior aorta; abv, afferent branchial vein; apv, anterior pallial vein; ark, anterior lobe of right kidney; ba, bulbus aortae; ct, ctenidium; dg, digestive gland; e, eye; ebv, efferent branchial vein; epv, efferent pallial vein; f, foot; i, intestine; la, left auricle; lhg, left hypobranchial gland; lk, left kidney (=papillary sac); lko, opening of left kidney; lnl, left neck lobe; lsm, left shell muscle; me, mantle edge; pa, posterior aorta; pca, pericardial cavity opened; ra, right auricle; rhg, right hypobranchial gland; rk, right kidney; rko, opening of right kidney (urinogenital); sn, snout; t, tentacle; tpv, transverse pallial vein; ugp, urinogenital papilla; ve, ventricle; vg, visceral ganglion.

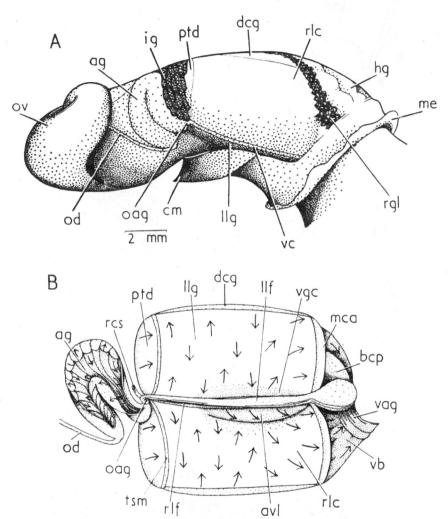

FIG. 171.—*Nucella lapillus:* A, visceral hump seen from right side after removal of the shell; B, female genital duct. The muscular vestibule and the capsule gland have been opened by a dorsal longitudinal incision, and the albumen gland by a longitudinal incision along the right side. Arrows show ciliary currents. The bursa copulatrix and the anterior end of the ventral channel are distended with sperm.

ag, albumen gland; avl, anteroventral lobe of capsule gland; bcp, bursa copulatrix; cm, columellar muscle; dcg, gland cells of dorsal wall of capsule gland; hg, hypobranchial gland; ig, ingesting gland; llf, left longitudinal fold; llg, left lobe of capsule gland; mca, mucous cells of the anterior border of capsule gland; me, mantle edge; oag, opening of albumen gland to capsule gland; od, ovarian duct; ov, ovary; ptd, posterior tip of capsule gland; rcs, receptaculum seminis, into which the ingesting gland opens; rgl, rectal gland; rlc, right lobe of capsule gland; rlf, right longitudinal fold; tsm, transverse muscular strip; vag, vagina; vb, vestibule; vc, ventral channel of capsule gland; vgc, anteroventral gland cells of capsule gland.

trochophore as in the more primitive diotocardians. The pallial oviduct is also elaborated for the reception and storage of sperm since the eggs are fertilized in its upper part; there may be a bursa copulatrix (bcp, fig. 171B) into which the seminal fluid is deposited, and a receptaculum seminis in which the sperm are stored. The complexity of the male genital duct is associated with the habit of internal fertilization (fig. 172). In most species sperm are transferred to the oviduct by a penis (p), which, save in a few, is pedal in origin and situated behind the right cephalic tentacle, and the vas deferens (vd) opens at or near its tip. The pallial section of the vas deferens may be enlarged and glandular forming a prostate (pr).

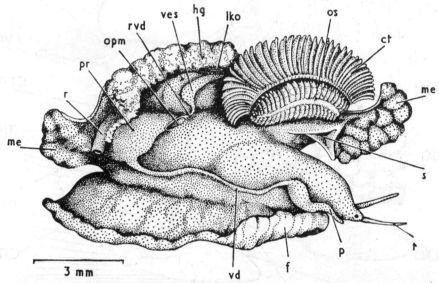

FIG. 172.—*Trivia monacha:* male, dissected to show contents of mantle cavity from the right.
ct, ctenidium; f, foot; hg, hypobranchial gland; lko, opening of left kidney; me, mantle edge; opm, opening of prostate to mantle cavity; os, osphradium; p, penis; pr, prostate; r, rectum; rvd, renal vas deferens; s, siphon; t, tentacle; vd, vas deferens; ves, vesicula seminalis.

The posterior region of the genital duct of monotocardians runs along the columellar side of the visceral hump (od, fig. 171A) and connects the gonad with the pallial duct. It is thin-walled and comparatively narrow. In females of some species, the distal part of this section is in communication with the pericardium by a gonopericardial duct (gpd, fig. 173); in males there may be a vestige of this. The position and structure of this duct and our knowledge of its development in *Viviparus* confirm its homology with the post-torsional right renopericardial duct of Diotocardia. The region of the gonoduct with which it connects is, therefore, derived from the right kidney or its duct, and will be referred to as the renal genital duct (rvo). In female *Littorina* (Linke, 1933) and in the stenoglossans (Fretter, 1941) this region is histologically similar to the gonopericardial duct and is quite short: both have a ciliated epithelium in which the cells are densely packed, and a subepithelial muscular coat. The gonopericardial duct opens into the pericardium by a ciliated funnel around which the musculature is pronounced, and the

funnel may be closed off from the pericardial cavity. The initial part of the genital duct
which leads from the gonad to the renal section is comparatively long and shows evidence
of a gonadial origin, since Linke (1933) has shown that in *Littorina* its epithelium is similar
to the undifferentiated cells of the gonad. For this reason it will be referred to as the

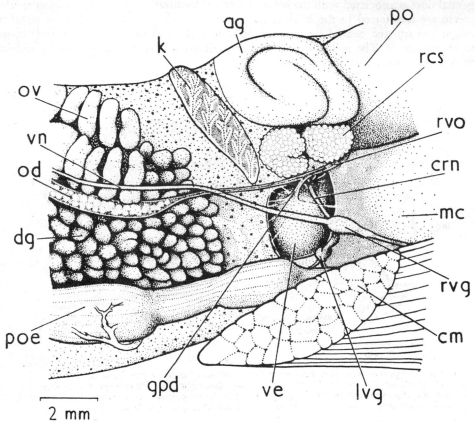

FIG. 173.—*Nucella lapillus:* female, part of base of visceral hump from the right side dissected to expose
the pericardial cavity, which has not, however, been opened, the ovarian and gonopericardial ducts.
   ag, albumen gland displaced to expose receptaculum seminis; cm, columellar muscle; crn, nerve
to heart and kidney; dg, digestive gland; gpd, gonopericardial duct; k, kidney; lvg, left visceral
ganglion; mc, mantle cavity seen through mantle skirt; od, ovarian duct; ov, ovary; po, pallial
oviduct; poe, posterior oesophagus; rcs, receptaculum seminis; rvg, right visceral ganglion; rvo,
renal section of oviduct; ve, ventricle; vn, visceral nerve.

gonadial duct. In males its lower part stores ripe sperm (ves, fig. 172; td, fig. 174). In
the Neritacea there is some modification of the connexion between the genital and pericardial coeloms. The coelom in this aberrant group is more extensive than in other
gastropods and more spacious than the haemocoelic spaces, which tend to be filled by
an abundant development of connective tissue. A large coelomic cavity, the true pericardium, surrounds the heart and is continued into a wide passage which receives the
renopericardial canal, and a further large expansion, the gonadial coelom, communicates
with the oviduct by a conspicuous oviduco-coelomic funnel. This connexion has not

been traced in the male. Bourne (1908) stated that there can be no doubt that the gonad has been derived from the wall of the right part of the gonadial coelom.

The origin of the various parts of the reproductive system can be followed in the embryology of one of the most highly organized taenioglossans, which retains in its development an unexpectedly primitive condition of the coelom. The classical work of Erlanger (1891b; 1894) on *Paludina* (=*Viviparus*) *vivipara* showed that there are 3 evaginations from the primary coelomic sac, which itself will form the pericardial cavity. Two of these are the rudiments of the right and left kidneys, each becoming gradually constricted from the pericardium, though retaining a connexion by way of the reno-pericardial canal. They lie against the ectoderm, which very soon forms duct-like pro-longations of the mantle cavity one towards each: the right one coalesces with the original right kidney (which will become the single kidney of the adult) and forms its duct, whilst the left is arrested in its growth and the corresponding kidney disappears. Both kidney rudiments and their pallial apertures are involved in 180° torsion. The third outgrowth of the pericardium forms later close to the origin of the original left kidney; it is nipped off from the pericardial epithelium and forms a vesicle which is the rudiment of the gonad. At the same time an ingrowth from the mantle cavity, the arrested duct of the kidney which has disappeared, grows towards the gonad and finally fuses with it to form its duct.

A further study of the development of *Viviparus viviparus* was made by Drummond (1903) who agreed with Erlanger's account with one significant exception. She found that both the original left kidney and its duct, which is formed from the mantle, are present at the time when the gonad is formed and from that time decrease in importance. The gonad is at first solid and connected to the kidney by a thickening of the pericardial wall. At a later stage it becomes hollow and its lumen communicates with that of the original left kidney in the region of the thickening, close to the renopericardial aperture. The genital products must therefore pass through the post-torsional right kidney and its duct—though these are relatively insignificant in size as compared with the gonadial and pallial sections of the mature oviduct.

This account of the development of the urinogenital system of *Viviparus* dismisses previous speculations as to possible relationships between the two renal organs of Dioto-cardia and the single one of Monotocardia. Perrier (1889) stated that the single kidney of the Monotocardia is homologous with the post-torsional right one of Diotocardia, that the left forms the nephridial gland—which appears as part of the single kidney—and that the duct of the right kidney is concerned in the formation of the genital duct, the connexion of the functional kidney to the mantle cavity being a new structure. He based his conclusions on the anatomy of modern Diotocardia in which the actual right kidney is always the larger and the only one to show extensive renal epithelium. However, these present day animals must be regarded as too advanced to form the basis of such an argument.

The ducts of the right and left kidneys as shown in the embryology of *Viviparus* are extremely short invaginations from the innermost end of the mantle cavity, yet in the adult the genital aperture and the opening of the ureter are at its mouth. Johansson (1950) has studied a later stage in the development of the genital and renal ducts and has shown that the two invaginations arise from the inner end of a longitudinal groove in the mantle skirt. He thinks that the pallial ureter has originated in close association with the pallial genital duct in one of two ways: either the posterior end of the pallial genital groove enclosed the opening of the left invagination of the mantle cavity as well as the right and then closed and divided to form pallial genital duct and ureter, or the ureter has arisen from an external groove along the pallial genital duct. This groove would widen posteriorly to embrace the opening of the invagination forming the initial part of the ureter and then close to form the long pallial ureter of the adult. However, our present interest is in the pallial genital duct, which first appears as a longitudinal groove in the mantle skirt, later closing so that no indication of the open condition remains. Such a change from an open channel to a closed duct probably occurred in the course of evolution of the genital system of the monotocardians. It occurs in the life history of each individual of the protandrous hermaphrodites *Calyptraea*, *Crepidula* and *Capulus*. In the male phase the vas deferens is a narrow, ciliated groove traversing the length of the mantle cavity and passing anteriorly to the penis (sgr, fig. 185A), whilst in the transition to the female phase the pallial part of the groove alone persists; it closes and the walls hypertrophy to form the albumen and capsule glands which bulge into the mantle cavity (po, fig. 198).

The question as to the ultimate fate of the right kidney (apart from its duct) still remains unanswered. Both are arrested in their development, no renal epithelium is differentiated and they form only a very small part of the whole genital tract. Linke (1933) suggested that the receptaculum seminis of Monotocardia, which in many species is placed at the inner end of the pallial duct, may be derived from the duct of the kidney, and although Thiele (1929–35) would agree with this for the *Littorina* spp. (rcs, fig. 23) he suggested that in many other prosobranchs its position is incompatible with this.

The structure of the genital system and the formation and deposition of egg capsules are as well known for *Nucella lapillus* as for any prosobranch, and, since the dog whelk is a very familiar intertidal species passing its whole life history on the shore, its genital system (except the gonad) will be described in some detail. It selects a moist and shady surface of rock for a spawning ground and some 30 or more individuals may congregate there, not feeding for the time. In such a group uncovered by the tide some individuals may be seen copulating whilst others are depositing egg capsules. Experiments show that copulation is repeated at intervals between which a few capsules are laid.

There are no easily visible sexual characters by which the sexes of *Nucella* are distinguishable externally except the penis, which lies behind the right tentacle, though this is difficult to see as it is concealed in the mantle cavity. Pelseneer (1926a) recognized a size difference and stated that in general the broadest specimens are females. If the shell be removed from a mature male (fig. 174) the testis (te) is seen in the upper coils of the visceral mass as numerous tubules lying over and between the lobes of the digestive gland (dg). The tubules join one another and form a common duct, the testicular duct (td), which passes forward along the columellar side in a superficial position. This duct acts as a vesicula seminalis and during breeding its epithelium will ingest and digest the effete, or perhaps superfluous, spermatozoa. At the anterior end of the vesicula seminalis a sphincter closes the entrance to a short, straight, ciliated duct running beneath the intestine and pericardium to the prostate (pr) at the posterior end of the mantle cavity. The duct is surrounded by a layer of circular muscles. It is the renal vas deferens. There is no vestige of a gonopericardial canal as in the closely related *Ocenebra erinacea* in which the renal vas deferens gives off towards the pericardium a short diverticulum, the blind end of which is connected with a slight prominence on the pericardial wall by a band of dense connective tissue and muscle fibres.

The renal vas deferens leads through an entrance guarded by a sphincter to the narrow ventral wall of the prostate, which runs parallel with the rectum (r) to the edge of the mantle skirt. Its lateral walls are thickened by the profuse development of glands which are grouped in clusters beneath the ciliated epithelium, so that in transverse section the lumen appears as a vertical slit. The prostate is closed off from the mantle cavity (mc) except at the posterior extremity near the renal vas deferens, where there is a minute aperture between two flaps of tissue, which are ventral extensions of the epithelium lining the gland and are continuous with the inner epithelium of the mantle skirt. In front of the opening these flaps fuse with one another, but the line of fusion remains

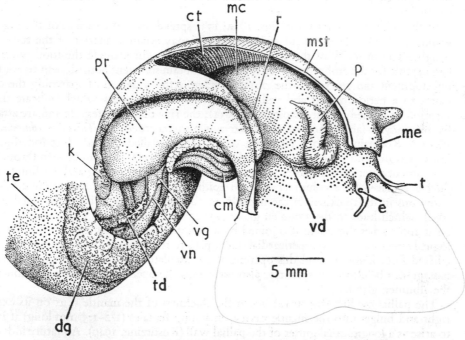

FIG. 174.—*Nucella lapillus:* male, removed from shell and partly dissected to show genital duct.
cm, columellar muscle; ct, ctenidium; dg, digestive gland; e, eye; k, kidney; mc, mantle cavity opened; me, mantle edge; mst, cut edge of mantle skirt; p, penis; pr, prostate gland; r, rectum; t, tentacle; td, testis duct acting as vesicula seminalis; te, testis; vd, vas deferens leading from prostate to penis; vg, visceral ganglion; vn, visceral nerve.

distinct as two opposing strips of epithelial cells. From the anterior end of the gland a narrow duct (vd) passes along the right side of the head to the penis (p) which lies behind the right cephalic tentacle. Along the whole length of the duct can be seen the two strips of epithelium which fused to close it, evidence of its derivation from an open seminal groove such as is found in *Littorina* (sgr, fig. 9). Only one type of secreting cell occurs in the prostate gland, opening to the lumen between the ciliated cells and providing a fluid in which the sperm are discharged. The cilia cause an anteriorly directed current, which probably has little effect on the forward passage of seminal fluid, which is more forcibly moved by the peristalsis of the anterior section of the duct leading to the penis. This duct is narrow and runs in the body wall along a slight ridge; it is lined by columnar ciliated cells and surrounded by a thick layer of circular muscles.

The penis (p, fig. 174) is flattened, and its duct is not centrally placed but lies towards the posterior edge. The histological structure of the epithelium is similar to that of the preceding section of the vas deferens. At its tip the two layers of fused epithelium which close the duct separate to form the penial aperture. A layer of circular muscles lies beneath the epithelium of the duct and extends beneath the fused strips of epithelium. Throughout the thickness of the penis vascular spaces are numerous, and between them run muscle fibres which are in association with a thick coat of muscles beneath the outer epithelium; the penial nerve, which arises from the right pedal ganglion, is centrally situated.

In the female the ovary (ov, figs. 171A, 173) spreads over the surface of the digestive gland in the visceral mass and when mature it may attain a quarter of the total body weight. The majority of the eggs which it produces will provide the food within the egg capsule for the embryos, which in this way obtain sufficient nourishment to complete development and emerge in the crawling stage. After a period of spawning the ovary passes to a period of rest and yellow-brown inclusions appear which indicate the re-sorption of unused oocytes (Kostitzine, 1934); the ripe ones disintegrate and are attacked by phagocytes (absorption of unused ova is also recorded for *Turritella communis* by Pérez & Kostitzine (1930)). From the ovary a thin-walled ovarian duct (od, fig. 173) leads forwards and ventrally on the right side of the viscera, and can be seen through the integument anteriorly. It passes beneath the kidney (k) where the glandular lining of the duct is replaced by a columnar, ciliated epithelium thrown into longitudinal folds by variations in the thickness of the underlying connective tissue. This is the renal section (rvo), which leads to the albumen gland (ag) at the posterior end of the mantle cavity. As it approaches this gland it is joined by a gonopericardial duct (gpd) of similar histo-logical structure. The gonopericardial duct opens to the pericardium by an inconspicuous ciliated funnel, and around this opening the musculature is well developed so that the passage can be closed. A sphincter also surrounds the opening of the renal oviduct into the albumen gland.

The pallial oviduct (fig. 171A) lies in the thickness of the mantle skirt on its extreme right and bulges into the mantle cavity; in young females (1·2–1·5 mm long) it is seen to arise as a longitudinal gutter of the pallial wall (Kostitzine, 1949). A mature individual removed from its shell and viewed from the right side shows the albumen gland (ag) as a U-shaped loop at the posterior end of the duct, with the concavity of the gland directed ventrally, and the distal limb opening to the much larger capsule gland. Between the two glands is a mass of deep brown tubules which will be referred to as the ingesting gland (ig), and its duct as the receptaculum seminis. The capsule gland leads forward to the anterior end of the mantle cavity and, on dissection, it can be seen as an opaque white or yellowish mass divided into right and left lobes (rlc, llg). These are joined dorsally and ventrally by a comparatively thin and narrow wall forming dorsal and ventral sutures (vc), so that in transverse section the lumen of the gland has the appearance of a dorsoventral slit. From the narrow ventral wall, where gland cells are absent, arise two longitudinal folds of tissue which form a channel between them. This can be shut from the lumen of the capsule gland so that it becomes a functionally closed duct. It leads posteriorly to the duct of the ingesting gland, the receptaculum seminis (rcs, fig. 171B), and anteriorly to a bursa copulatrix (bcp). The bursa is a pouch into which the penis discharges sperm and prostatic fluid, and the receptaculum seminis an area near the site of fertilization where the sperm may be stored for a longer period, orientated and nourished by the female. The albumen gland (ag) opens into the posterior ventral wall of the capsule gland on the right side of the ventral channel (oag). Anteriorly the capsule gland leads to a muscular vestibule (vb) through which the ventral channel passes to the bursa copulatrix. When filled with sperm the bursa bulges into the vestibule. The short vagina (vag), into which the penis is inserted to deposit sperm into the bursa, and from which the fully formed egg capsules pass from the vestibule to the exterior, opens on the right anterior extremity of the mantle cavity, ventral to the anus; the opening is surrounded by a sphincter.

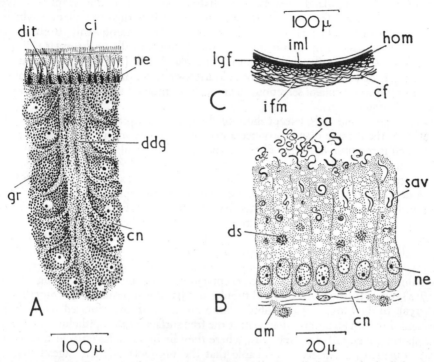

FIG. 175.—*Nucella lapillus:* parts of transverse sections through A, the wall of the capsule gland, showing single cluster of gland cells; B, the ingesting gland; C, the wall of an egg capsule.

am, amoebocyte; cf, circular fibres; ci, cilia; cn, connective tissue; ddg, duct of deep gland cell; dit, distal tip of duct of subepithelial gland cell filled with mucoid protoplasm; ds, sperm undergoing digestion; gr, granular protein secretion; hom, homogeneous layer; ifm, interfibrillar mucoid matrix; iml, inner mucous layer of capsule; lgf, longitudinal fibres; ne, nucleus of ciliated cell; sa, spermatozoa; sav, spermatozoon in vacuole of cytoplasm.

The pallial oviduct has a ciliated epithelium (ci, fig. 175A), except in the ventral channel in which the epithelium is columnar and unciliated. In the albumen and capsule glands the walls are thickened by subepithelial gland cells grouped in clusters, the ducts from each cluster running parallel with each other to open between the ciliated cells. In the albumen gland there are 3 kinds of secreting cells and their secretions combine to form the albuminous fluid in which the eggs are embedded.

If the capsule gland is cut open mid-dorsally (fig. 171B) it will be seen that the right lateral wall has a ventral longitudinal cleft separating an anteroventral lobe (avl) from the rest of this glandular area. This lobe, together with two adjacent longitudinal strips of tissue (vgc), is more translucent than the surrounding area and of a slightly yellowish hue. The subepithelial gland cells are all similar and produce 2 different secretions which occur in the cells as 2 different types of spherules, one protein and the other muco-protein. An area along the dorsal wall (dcg) of the capsule gland has a similar appearance in the living state, and the gland cells here also produce 2 secretions. Near the posterior end of the capsule gland 2 narrow strips of tissue (tsm), one on either side and arising near the opening of the albumen gland, separate right and left posterior tips (ptd) from the main mass of the gland. Beneath the ciliated epithelium of the strips is a layer of circular muscles and a few muscles radiate outwards: it is this musculature which distinguishes the strips and constricts them from the surrounding wall. Both the strips and the posterior tips of the gland are made up of mucous cells, and similar cells border the anterior extremity of each lobe (mca). The gland cells (fig. 175A) constituting the main mass of the capsule gland contain colourless granules of an irregularly oval shape, and again produce 2 types of secretion, an amorphous mucoid secretion (dit) and a protein secretion in granules (gr).

Hence all the gland cells, except those of the posterior tip and the anterior border of each lobe of the capsule gland, produce a double secretion and it is the intertwining of these which is responsible for the fibrous structure of the wall of the egg capsule.

The vestibule, vagina and bursa copulatrix are clothed by a columnar, ciliated epithelium and are extremely distensible. The walls of the bursa are thrown into folds of various depths and sperm are everywhere attached to the epithelium, while more may fill the lumen; they have been deposited here by the penis. Excess sperm may be found in the ventral channel closely packed together, with their heads embedded in the distal cytoplasm of the epithelium, and their tails projecting into the lumen. Somehow or other they reach the receptaculum seminis (rcs, fig. 171B), the walls of which are surrounded by a very thick coat of circular muscles and have masses of sperm invariably attached to their columnar epithelial lining. The receptaculum leads into the ingesting gland (ig, fig. 171A) which is composed of blind tubules and has the appearance of a digestive gland (fig. 175B). In the lumina of the tubules large numbers of unorientated sperm (sa) may be present, but some lie motionless against the free surface of the epithelium as if trapped. These sperm are engulfed by the cells, where they lie in vacuoles (sav) in the cytoplasm and are digested (ds): it seems probable that the products of their digestion give the gland its brown colour. Blood spaces with amoebocytes (am) surround the gland, from which the amoebocytes appear to carry waste. This gland may serve as a mechanism for ridding the animal of unwanted sperm and, perhaps, of deriving nourishment from them.

The method of functioning of the pallial oviduct may best be considered after a brief description of the egg capsule. This is a vase-shaped structure about 8 mm high (fig. 242A). It is circular in transverse section and broadest in the middle where its diameter is about 2 mm. At one end the capsule tapers to a short stalk and then expands into a basal disc (b) which is firmly anchored by cement to the substratum. At the opposite end there is a circular aperture which is filled with a plug of mucus (pl). Two longitudinal lines of thickening (su) can be traced over the smooth surface, and these are placed so as to divide the wall into two approximately equal lobes. Distally the suture of one side meets that of the other through the plug which is thus subdivided. The wall consists of 3 layers (Ankel, 1937b) in addition to a thin mucous sheet (iml, fig. 175C) which covers it internally, separating it from the albumen and eggs. The three comprise an inner layer of a homogeneous transparent substance (hom), probably conchiolin, and middle and outer layers of fibres orientated in definite ways and separated by distinct spaces. The inner fibres appear to run in a longitudinal direction (lgf) and the outer ones in a circular direction (cf). Sections of newly formed capsules show the interfibrillar spaces filled with a mucous or mucoid substance (ifm), but when the capsule has weathered for some time this tends to contract leaving the spaces between the fibres observed by Ankel (1937b). In the stem and basal disc the fibres are more irregularly arranged. The capsule contains several hundred eggs embedded in an albuminous fluid: only about 15–30 hatch, the remainder being devoured by their fellows (Lebour, 1937).

If an egg capsule is found within the capsule gland the plug is seen to be at the upper end, near the posterior mucous tips, and the base anterior. From this it can be deduced that the plug is secreted by the posterior mucous tips and the capsule wall by the rest of the gland. The method of formation of the capsule would appear to be as follows. Several hundred eggs pass down the gonadial duct and distend the albumen gland, where they are embedded in albuminous fluid. The exact site of fertilization is unknown: if sperm from the receptaculum and the ventral channel are passed into the albumen gland on the relaxation of the sphincter muscle which guards its opening, then fertilization will occur in the lumen. Otherwise spermatozoa may be poured on to the eggs as they enter the capsule gland. Meanwhile the cavity of the capsule gland becomes filled with a mass of secretion. Its cells produce first the protein matter and then, in increasing quantities, the mucoid substance, and the result is that the lumen is filled with fluid which is almost pure protein in the centre, but consists, in its outer layers, of an emulsion in which the mucoid material is dispersed in a continuous phase of protein. Because of the steadily increasing quantities of mucus and of the accompanying decrease in the production of protein, the size of the mucoid droplets steadily increases from the centre to the periphery of the mass, and the strands of protein which separate the drops gradually decrease in size. The predominantly transverse ciliary currents on the walls of the gland rotate the mass and draw out the drops of mucoid material into streaks parallel to the transverse axis of the gland, and the protein material separating them is drawn out into strands elongated in the same direction. When the duct between the albumen gland and capsule gland is opened, the albumen and the eggs are forcibly passed into the central portion of the secretion lying in the latter, so as to invaginate this into a vase-shaped structure with a round hole at the inner end into which the plug will later be fitted. This process of invagination deposits the eggs and their accompanying albumen in the centre of the mass of secretion occupying the capsule gland, which is composed of unmixed protein material, and from this is formed the innermost layer of the capsule. It has also the effect of drawing the outer emulsion of protein and mucoid secretion into sheets around the inner homogeneous layer in which the direction of elongation of the mucoid droplets now lies parallel to the direction of movement of the eggs, that is, parallel to the long axis of the gland: from this results the longitudinal direction of the strands of the inner part of the fibrous coat. The outer part of this layer, being still exposed to the ciliary currents on the wall of the gland, retains the original alignment of the drops and so gives rise to the outer part of the fibrous coat in which the fibres are circular in direction, except for material which gives rise to the basal disc. This is accumulated at the anterior end of the capsule gland where the direction of the ciliary beat is mainly anterior. With the disappearance, on exposure, of the mucous dispersed phase the space occupied by it is left as a series of lacunae separating what now appear as strands of fibrous material. The mucus which lines the wall internally is secretion from the posterior tips, and was dragged along with the mass of eggs when it passed into the capsule gland. These tips continue to pour out secretion while the wall of the capsule is being elaborated by the more anterior parts of the genital duct. The mucus forms an accumulation which is fitted into the hole in the upper part of the capsule apparently by the muscular action of the transverse strips which border the mucous tips anteriorly. These press the upper edge of the wall of the capsule on to the mass of mucus so that the cavity within is securely closed. The suture which divides the plug into 2 equal halves demarcates the limit of the secretion produced by each posterior tip.

The egg capsule is passed from the oviduct along a temporary groove of the foot to the sole and is inserted in the ventral pedal gland which lies immediately behind the accessory boring organ. It is held in an approximately vertical position with the plug innermost and the gland embraces the capsule tightly so that only the base protrudes from its opening. Whilst held in this position the wall of the capsule is compressed and moulded to the final, smooth, vase-shaped outline. The stalk is constricted from the basal region and the latter finally pressed out to form a disc and fixed to the substratum by the sole of the foot. Mucus is secreted by the subepithelial cells of the gland to act as a lubricant during the fashioning process. Finally the foot is lifted off the capsule and the wall of conchiolin hardens still further in contact with sea water.

Variation in the structure of the reproductive ducts within the monotocardians is chiefly concerned with the degree of closure of the pallial section and differences in its glandular equipment, the structure of the penis, and, in the female, the number and position of the sperm pouches. Owing to its comparative simplicity in structure the male system exhibits fewer differences from species to species than does the female and will be considered first.

In some Monotocardia the testis produces more than one type of sperm which develop in the same tubules: eupyrene sperm (fig. 176) which fertilize the eggs, and have nuclei containing the haploid number of chromosomes, and others which are atypical and may be hyperpyrene (with more than the haploid number), dyspyrene or oligopyrene (with only part of the haploid set), or apyrene (enucleate). In the diotocardian gastropods with external fertilization the eupyrene sperm (fig. 176) are similar in structure to those of the more primitive Metazoa (Franzén, 1956). Each consists of a short head (hd) containing the nucleus, which is typically oval in outline, a middle piece of 4 or 5 mitochondrial spheres (msa) usually lying transversely across the base of the head and embedded in an insignificant mass of protoplasm, and a tail composed of a long filament. Except for a terminal region the tail filament is covered by a thin layer of undifferentiated cytoplasm. In the Monotocardia the eupyrene sperm differ from this. In them the mitochondria collect around the base of the nucleus in 4 large spheres as in the Diotocardia, but later they disperse to form a cylindrical covering over a part of the axial filament, and a more or less elongated middle piece is formed (mp). The electron microscope has revealed that in *Viviparus viviparus* the cylindrical covering comprises 4 tape-like fibres, spirally wound, and that the axis of both middle piece and tail is composed of about 7 fibres (Hanson, Randall & Bayley, 1952). A variable amount of change also occurs in the nucleus: in some species (*Bittium reticulatum*, fig. 176, 3) it remains relatively short, forming about 1/20 of the total length of the sperm (Franzén, 1955), whereas in others it lengthens so that both head and middle piece are filiform, and in *Cingula semistriata* (fig. 176, 2) the nucleus comprises about half the length of the sperm. The length of the tail varies considerably: it may be longer than the middle piece, as in *Clathrus clathrus* and *Crepidula fornicata*, or shorter as in *Viviparus viviparus*. These modifications of the eupyrene sperm of the Monotocardia would appear to be associated with internal fertilization, for they are found alike in species in which copulation occurs, in which spermato-zeugmata occur (*Clathrus clathrus*, *Ianthina* sp. (Ankel, 1926)) and species with neither penis nor spermatozeugmata (*Turritella communis* (Bataillon, 1921), *Bittium reticulatum* (Franzén, 1955)), the only common feature being internal fertilization. Within the female the sperm are stored in a limited area. They are packed parallel with one another with no apparent space between, their heads embedded in the epithelium of the storage area.

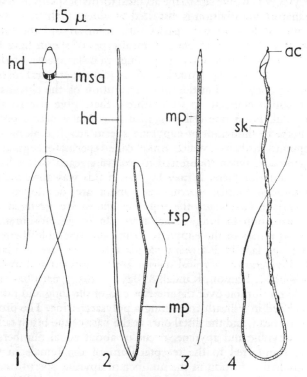

FIG. 176.—Eupyrene sperm: 1, *Gibbula cineraria*; 2, *Cingula semistriata*; 3, *Bittium reticulatum*; 4, a pyramidellid. After Franzén.
ac, acrosome; hd, head of sperm; mp, middle piece of sperm; msa, mitochondrial sphere in middle piece of sperm; sk, spiral keel on sperm; tsp, tail of sperm.

From this epithelium they may derive nourishment. Undoubtedly the shape of the monotocardian spermatozoon facilitates close packing, and other differences from the sperm of Diotocardia may also be associated with this period of suspended activity within the female duct. In the receptaculum seminis of *Theodoxus fluviatilis* the orientation of the sperm is unusual for it is the tails and not the heads which are embedded in the epithelium.

In opisthobranchs and pulmonates the structure of the mature spermatozoon is still further modified. The boundary between middle piece and tail is indistinct for these two regions consist of a central axis around which a thin membrane of cytoplasm is coiled in a spiral, and there is usually a spiral ridge on the surface of the nucleus. The pyramidellids (fig. 176, 4) have this type of sperm with a spiral keel (sk), giving further evidence of their opisthobranch affinity (see p. 639). Also in their sperm the nucleus is short as it is in a number of primitive opisthobranchs, including *Acteon tornatilis*, whereas in other opisthobranchs the nucleus is elongated, though short heads also occur in some nudibranch sperm (Franzén, 1955). The primitive features of the diotocardian spermatozoon cannot be traced in the stages of spermatogenesis of euthyneurous gastropods and pulmonates.

The spermatocytes which give rise to the atypical forms of spermatozoa show abnormal growth and the maturation division is distorted or absent (Schitz, 1920*a*, *b*); sooner or later the chromatin, at least in part, passes into solution and the centrioles undergo multiple division. In *Bithynia tentaculata* 2 atypical types of sperm have been recognized (Ankel, 1924, 1933), hyperpyrene and oligopyrene; in other species of *Bithynia* only one has been described. In the Scalidae (Ankel, 1926, 1930*a*) the atypical spermatocyte grows to resemble a young oocyte and at the time of solution of the chromatin about 2,000 centrioles appear which elongate to form fibres; these give rise to a plate extended posteriorly into a tail. From one cell 50 $\mu$ in diameter a structure 900 $\mu$ is developed which acts as a nurse to thousands of eupyrene sperm attached along the tail in spiral rows. Such compound structures, which Ankel called spermatozeugmata, may be found in the vesicula seminalis; when transferred to sea water each swims by the undulating movements of the anterior plate. It may be that in this way the functional sperm can travel longer distances. Similar spermatozeugmata are developed in *Ianthina* and *Cerithiopsis* (fig. 177). In *Cerithiopsis* the eupyrene sperm are arranged along the tail of the atypical spermatozoon in longitudinal rows. In other prosobranchs the atypical sperm do not act as nurses to the eupyrene forms and resemble them more closely in structure and size—in fact in *Bithynia tentaculata* the two are similar in appearance (Ankel, 1933). In *Viviparus* the atypical sperms are vermiform and motile, having 8–16 tails apiece (Meves, 1903; Hanson, Randall & Bayley, 1952); each has one chromosome, and the head lies like a thimble over the anterior end of the long and rather thick middle piece which is enclosed in a sheath containing a polysaccharide. The proximal centrioles lie in the apex of the head, and the distal ones at the base of the brush tail. The two types of spermatozoa, eupyrene and apyrene, occur in about equal numbers in the vesicula seminalis and are transferred to the receptaculum of the female in this proportion. There is then a gradual reduction in the number of apyrene sperm since they have the shorter life (Ankel, 1925). In *Nassarius* and *Fusus* (Pelseneer, 1935) the oligopyrene sperm are fusiform with little power of movement. In *Nucella lapillus* the two types are identical to look at when ripe though they have undergone different maturation processes (Portmann, 1931*b*) so that the atypical form has an abnormal chromatin content.

Sperm dimorphism occurs in a number of families (Viviparidae, Hydrobiidae (Bithyniinae), Turritellidae, Aporrhaidae, Cerithiidae, Scalidae, Calyptraeidae, Capulidae, Lamellariidae, Eratoidae, Muricidae, Buccinidae, Nassariidae and Fasciolariidae) yet its significance remains obscure. It has been suggested that the atypical sperm of *Viviparus* provide nourishment for the functional ones (Hanson, Randall & Bayley, 1952) since the sheath of the middle piece disintegrates in the female duct liberating the polysaccharide. However, in other species their food reserves may be required for more important activity than this, for it is tempting to think that spermatozeugmata fulfil the function of a penis where that is absent (Cerithiopsidae, Scalidae, Ianthinidae). In *Ianthina janthina* there is neither penis in the male nor bursa copulatrix and receptaculum seminis in the female, and degenerating spermatozeugmata liberating clouds of eupyrene sperm have been seen in all parts of the female duct from the mucous gland to the ovary

(Graham, 1954*b*). This pelagic prosobranch may be a protandrous hermaphrodite which passes through more than one breeding cycle in its life history and until our knowledge is more complete the possibility of self-fertilization cannot be overlooked. As it has neither active locomotion nor penis cross-fertilization is difficult, but the gregarious habit, keeping the animals in close contact, and the powerfully swimming spermato-

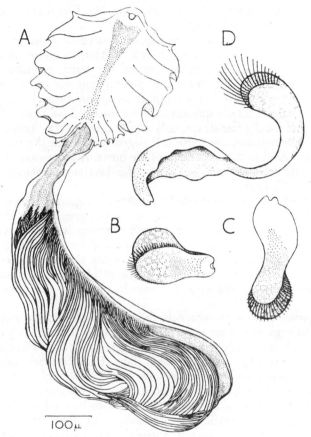

Fig. 177.—*Cerithiopsis tubercularis:* A, spermatozeugma with longitudinal rows of eupyrene spermatozoa on its tail; B, C, D, developing spermatozeugmata.

zeugmata probably permit it to occur. Moreover Wilson & Wilson (1956) described the liberation of aggregates of spermatozeugmata from a single animal in captivity which supports the suggestion that the eupyrene sperm are transported from a male to a female individual. As yet no spermatozeugma has been found in the female reproductive ducts of *Cerithiopsis* or the protandrous hermaphrodite *Clathrus*; in contrast to *Ianthina* the pallial oviduct is open and has a receptaculum seminis.

There is a record of apyrene sperm in the cytoplasm of eggs of *Aporrhais pespelicani* 20 minutes after the egg had been fertilized by normal spermatozoa, though they were then ejected (Kuschakewitsch, 1910). In his experiments on artificial fertilization of this prosobranch Kuschakewitsch found that only the eupyrene sperm orientated themselves with respect to the egg; the entrance of an atypical spermatozoon seems fortuitous.

It is of interest to note that in the Turbellaria there is more than one type of spermatozoon, all functional, though a given species has only one kind. In some species each has a filamentous head and 2 flagella (*Dendrocoelum lacteum*), in others each sperm has 2 projecting bristles, one on each side (*Macrostomum*), whilst in the alloiocoel genus *Plagiostomum* the spermatozoon is broad with wing-like lateral extensions reminiscent of the atypical sperm of prosobranchs.

The origin of apyrene spermatozoa and spermatozeugmata may perhaps be traced to the nurse cells which were described by Ankel (1930c) in species of *Littorina*. These cells, derived from the germinal epithelium of the testis, measure about 10 $\mu$ in diameter, are loaded with yolk granules and the eupyrene sperm bore into them with their heads. Sometimes the whole body moves by co-ordinated beating of the sperm tails, but usually they are totally quiescent. In the ducts of the male this is the way in which the sperm are usually found: it is only after transfer to the bursa copulatrix of the female that the two separate, the nurse cell degenerating and the sperm re-attaching themselves by their head to the epithelium of the bursa. A somewhat similar association between sperm and nutritive cells occurs in the bivalves *Montacuta ferruginosa* and *M. substriata* (Oldfield, 1959).

The epithelium of the vesicula seminalis in *Littorina* ingests a certain number of the sperm and nurse cells, and digests them. Ingestion continues during the whole period of sexual activity, suggesting that the production of sperm is in excess of requirements. Perhaps only senile sperm are removed in this way, and by such a selective mechanism an effective stock is maintained within the duct; or the absorption may be haphazard, and merely a means of safeguarding the duct against blockage. A similar ingestion of sperm by the epithelium of the vesicula seminalis occurs in the Stenoglossa (Fretter, 1941).

In the egg capsules of some prosobranchs there may be found abortive ova known as nurse cells or food eggs, which are eaten by the normal embryos. They are ova arrested in development and commonly unfertilized (Staiger, 1951) as in *Pisania maculosa* (fam. Buccinidae), *Fasciolaria tulipa* and *F. lignaria* (fam. Fasciolariidae), or fertilized as in *Nucella lapillus*, *Buccinum undatum* and *Murex trunculus*, though with no subsequent syngamy of the male and female pronuclei. In both *F. lignaria* and *M. trunculus* these ova undergo cleavage resulting in groups of cells with haploid nuclei, and Portmann (1925) described their segmentation in *N. lapillus*. All these rachiglossans have two types of sperm, and it has been suggested that the cause of sterility of the nurse cells is their atypical fertilization by oligopyrene sperm (Portmann, 1927, 1931a). In a study of *F. tulipa* Hyman (1923) (not realizing that the majority of the food eggs in this species are unfertilized) supported this theory on the grounds that the proportion of eggs to nurse cells (1 : 59) is remarkably close to that of eupyrene to oligopyrene sperm (1 : 50). However, this cannot be the only cause of the origin of sterile ova, for in *Natica catena* only one type of spermatozoon has been traced yet numbers of food eggs are found in the egg capsule (Ankel, 1930b). This theory fails to take into account possible differential survival of sperm types within the female. To what extent atypical sperm survive there is not known; in *Crepidula onyx* they do not enter the receptaculum seminis (Coe, 1942), but disintegrate in the cavity of the pallial oviduct. A second suggestion as to the origin of food eggs we owe to Glaser (1906) who drew a parallel, later emphasized by Burger & Thornton (1935), between the production of two types of ova and the two types of sperm

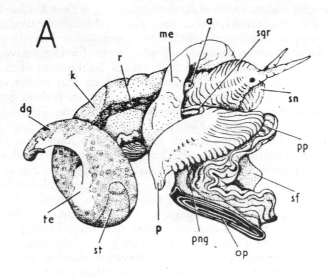

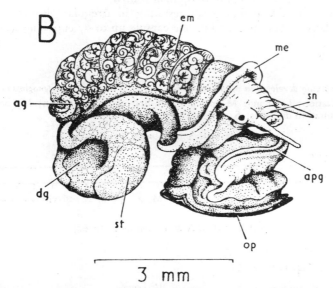

3 mm

FIG. 178.—*Littorina saxatilis:* A, male removed from shell, seen from right side; B, female, with young in brood pouch, removed from shell and seen from right side.

a, anus; ag, albumen gland; apg, opening of anterior pedal gland; dg, digestive gland; em, embryos in brood pouch which is subdivided into compartments by septa; k, kidney; me, mantle edge; op, operculum; p, penis; png, penial glands; pp, propodium; r, rectum with faecal pellets; sf, sole of foot; sgr, seminal groove; sn, snout; st stomach; te, testis.

and considered that the cause of sterility was inherent in the behaviour of the ova. This view has been upheld by Staiger (1950c). He has shown that in *Pisania maculosa* only 2% of the eggs undergo normal development; 90% are not fertilized (even though they must pass the site of fertilization on their passage through the oviduct), suggesting that the mechanism by which germ cells are brought together does not operate in their case. The remainder which are fertilized and will become food eggs have their development arrested at 4 different stages along the course of development of the normal eggs; in one of these polyspermy occurs. These facts indicate that within one species the sterile ova do not form a homogeneous population. They are perhaps genetically determined and their sterility due to a heterozygotic factor system. This suggestion is supported by the constant proportion of all types of eggs in capsules of any individual and in broader limits within any one species. For instance in *Murex trunculus* all ova are fertilized by eupyrene sperm and only 4% develop normally. Of the others 6% undergo no cleavage and the others divide whilst the male pronucleus remains in the vegetative area; it never reaches the animal pole and the parthenogenetical development is soon arrested. In *Buccinum undatum* it is seldom that an egg is unfertilized and no atypical sperm are involved. Abnormalities in eggs appear after fertilization so that the suggestion that there may be two types of eupyrene sperm only one of which would stimulate the female nucleus, is still a plausible one. About 75% of the eggs in a capsule stop development at the metaphase of the first maturation division and then degenerate according to Staiger (1951); the remaining 25% complete maturation but only in 1% does syngamy occur and normal development follow.

Polyspermy is usually pathological, resulting in irregular cleavage. In *Fasciolaria lignaria* it is relatively common and in one capsule up to 77 eupyrene sperm have been

TABLE 12

*To show the varying development of the commonest type of food egg in the Stenoglossa (after Staiger).*

F, fertilization; L, laying; M, metaphase of first cleavage division; $M_1$, $M_2$, first and second maturation divisions; S, union of pronuclei.

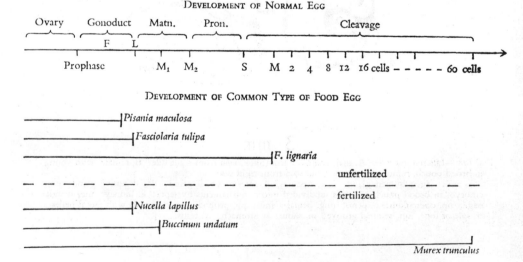

DEVELOPMENT OF NORMAL EGG

found in a single egg whilst the majority of the food eggs were unfertilized (Staiger, 1950c). Eggs entered by two sperm are known, however, to undergo normal development since in *Murex trunculus* (Staiger, 1951) one spermatozoon may remain in the yolk, paralleling the behaviour of that entering a food egg, and the other fertilize the ovum.

In a number of mesogastropods the vas deferens anterior to the renal section is an open groove throughout its length to the tip of the penis (figs. 181B, C); the species in which this occurs are not necessarily related. An open duct is found in *Littorina littorea* (sgr, figs. 9, 10), *L. littoralis* and *L. saxatilis* (sgr, fig. 178) (Linke, 1933), yet in the closely related *Cremnoconchus syhadrensis* (Linke, 1935b), a freshwater Indian form, and the terrestrial *Pomatias elegans*, the duct is closed. It is open in the advanced genera *Aporrhais* (sgr, fig. 179), *Balcis* and *Natica* (sgr, fig. 180) and in the male phase of the protandrous hermaphrodites *Calyptraea*, *Crepidula* and *Capulus*. The groove is characteristically ciliated throughout its length. The pallial section may be narrow (*Calyptraea* (pvd, fig. 181B), *Crepidula*, *Capulus*, *Balcis*) or it may be bordered by a glandular prostate of considerable size (*Littorina* (pr, fig. 181C), *Aporrhais* (pr, fig. 179A), *Natica*). Other genera in which an open duct occurs lack a penis and the vas deferens ends at the mouth of the mantle cavity: in all these there is a large prostate gland. *Cerithiopsis tubercularis*, *Bittium reticulatum* and *Clathrus clathrus* have an open prostate and no copulatory organ. In *Cerithiopsis* and *Clathrus* spermatozeugmata occur: it may be that the oligopyrene sperm obviate the possession of a penis by carrying the eupyrene sperm to the female.

In the evolution of the male genital duct an open pallial groove for the passage of sperm through the mantle cavity may have been the first part to appear: the sperm would enter the female by way of the inhalant respiratory current. However, the living gastropods in which this condition obtains are in other respects advanced, so that the simplicity of their genital system is likely to be secondary and may be correlated with the shape of the shell (p. 359). Small size may also affect the reproductive ducts and may be associated with the lack of a penis in *Cingulopsis*, its very large size in *Skeneopsis* and its unusual position and structure in *Omalogyra* and the pyramidellids.

In the majority of monotocardians the vas deferens is closed and there is a penis. The pallial region of the duct may have an outlet to the inner end of the mantle cavity (dm, opm, figs. 180B; 181D, F, I) which is slit-like or at the end of a short muscular duct, and, perhaps, represents the incomplete closure of an originally open groove (*Lacuna vincta*, *Cingula cingillus*, *C. semicostata*, *C. semistriata*, *Rissoa inconspicua*, *R. parva*, *R. lilacina*, *Alvania punctura*, *Barleeia rubra*, *Circulus striatus*, *Erato voluta*, *Trivia monacha* (opm, fig. 172), *T. arctica*, *Lamellaria perspicua*, *Nucella lapillus*, *Ocenebra erinacea*, *Buccinum undatum*, *Nassarius reticulatus*). In the rachiglossans *Ocenebra erinacea* and *Nucella lapillus* the longitudinal line of closure may be traced throughout the length of the male duct to the penial aperture, and the opening of the prostate to the posterior end of the mantle cavity is seen as a region in which these epithelia have not fused. In some species of rissoids (*Cingula semicostata*, *C. semistriata*, fig. 181D) only the regions of the duct anterior to the prostate show evidence of having been derived from an open groove.

There is typically a prostate along the pallial region of the male duct. It may form a wide sac-like portion and have subepithelial glands thickening the deep lateral walls (*Hydrobia ulvae*, *Erato voluta*, *Trivia monacha*, *T. arctica*, *Nucella lapillus*, *Ocenebra erinacea* (pr, fig. 181J)) or the gland cells may lie in the epithelium only as in the small rissoids (*Cingula semicostata*, *C. semistriata*, *Alvania punctura*, *Rissoa inconspicua*) and in *Barleeia rubra*, *Assiminea grayana*, *Cingulopsis fulgida* and *Pomatias elegans*. In *Pomatias* and *Hydrobia*

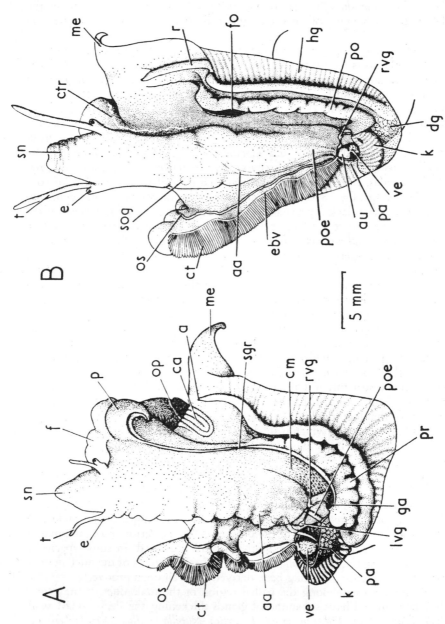

FIG. 179.—*Aporrhais pespelicani:* A, male, removed from shell, with the mantle cavity and pericardial cavity opened to display the contents; B, female, similarly dissected.

a, anus; aa, anterior aorta; au, auricle; ca, ciliated area; cm, columellar muscle; ct, ctenidium; ctr, exhalant tract; dg, digestive gland; e, eye; ebv, efferent branchial vein; f, foot; fo, female opening; ga, genital aperture, opening of renal vas deferens to prostate; hg, hypobranchial gland; k, kidney; lvg, left visceral ganglion; me, mantle edge; op, operculum; os, osphradium; p, penis; pa, posterior aorta; po, pallial oviduct; poe, posterior oesophagus; pr, prostate gland; r, rectum; rvg, right visceral ganglion; sgr, seminal groove; sn, snout; sog, supra-oesophageal ganglion, seen by transparency; t, tentacle; ve, ventricle.

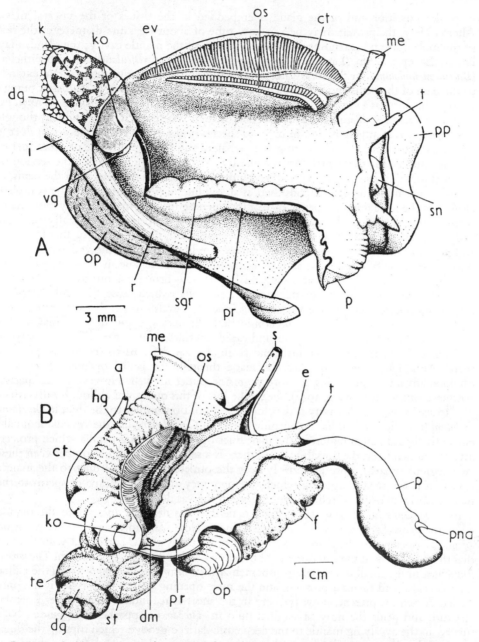

FIG. 180.—A, *Natica catena:* male, removed from shell, with the mantle cavity opened to show its contents; viewed dorsally. B, *Buccinum undatum:* male, similarly dissected, but seen somewhat from the right side.

a, anus; ct, ctenidium; dg, digestive gland; dm, diverticulum of male duct opening to mantle cavity; e, eye; ev, efferent branchial vessel; f, foot; hg, hypobranchial gland; i, intestine; k, kidney; ko, kidney opening; me, mantle edge; op, operculum; os, osphradium; p, penis; pna, penial aperture; pp, propodium; pr, prostate gland; r, rectum; s, siphon; sgr, seminal groove; sn, snout; st, stomach; t, tentacle; te, testis; vg, visceral ganglion.

*ulvae* the posterior end of the gland is embedded in the tissues of the visceral mass. Alternatively, the prostate may be a narrow tube of about the same diameter as the rest of the male duct and extending beyond the mouth of the mantle cavity; the glands may be in the epithelium (*Lamellaria perspicua* and *Nassarius reticulatus*) or subepithelial (*Buccinum undatum*). In the freshwater architaenioglossan *Viviparus* the prostate extends to the base of the penis and is conspicuous in its anterior part owing to its bright orange colour; the duct has a very thick layer of muscles throughout its length. In *Cingula cingillus*, *Rissoa parva* and *R. lilacina* the pallial section of the vas deferens is not glandular, though in *Cingula* it is relatively broad. In the two species of the genus *Rissoa* the penial duct is broad and has gland cells alternating with ciliated cells like the prostate of other forms. This is unusual, for the penial duct is typically narrow and muscular like the section of the duct which runs in the body wall and links the pallial vas deferens with the penis.

Although in the mesogastropods there is an evolutionary trend towards the complete closure of the male duct, the persistence of the opening into the mantle cavity in so many forms suggests that it plays some important role. The opening is typically into the posterior end of the cavity, though in *Hydrobia ulvae* (dm, fig. 181E) it is further forwards and near the anterior part of the gland. Sperm are liberated from the vesicula seminalis only at the time of copulation and are transferred to the female in prostatic secretion. The flow of seminal fluid towards the penial aperture is brought about by the relaxation of muscles at the distal end of the vesicula seminalis, which cease their sphincter-like action and release sperm to the vas deferens where peristalsis forces them anteriorly; the pressure set up in the duct must be considerable. If during copulation the male is disturbed, the withdrawal of the penis and rapid contraction into the shell may only be possible with an escape of seminal fluid from the vas deferens to relieve the pressure there. Although some escape may be made through the penial opening there is an obvious advantage in having a more posterior outlet as well. However, one species, *Neptunea antiqua* (Johansson, 1942), shows the loss of this outlet, for although a diverticulum towards the mantle cavity is developed in a position similar to the duct in *Buccinum undatum* (dm, fig. 180), it has no opening there. In *Cingula cingillus* the vesicula seminalis enters the broad pallial region of the male duct by way of a long papilla which projects into the lumen from the dorsal wall and there is a second communication between these two regions situated more posteriorly near the outlet of the pallial duct to the mantle cavity. It is this second opening which in emergency allows the escape of sperm to the mantle cavity in order to relieve the pressure in the vas deferens.

In *Cingulopsis fulgida* (fig. 181G) there is neither vas deferens anterior to the mantle edge nor penis (Fretter, 1953b). The pallial duct is closed and forms a prostate: it has no accessory opening to the mantle cavity, and presumably this is correlated with the fact that the duct opens at the anterior end of the cavity and ends there. Similarly in *Theodoxus fluviatilis*, in the small terrestrial prosobranch *Acicula fusca* and in *Simnia patula* the pallial duct is closed and forms a prostate, and the male opening at its anterior end is the only outlet. A penis is present, however, and in the short space intervening between genital aperture and penis the flow of seminal fluid in *Theodoxus* appears to be guided by a furrow in the overlying mantle to the deep cuticularized groove which runs up the outer edge of the dorsoventrally flattened penis to its tip; in *Acicula* and *Simnia* there is a ciliated groove along the right side of the head which unites the opening of the prostate with the penial groove.

Some species show an advance in the organization of the male duct in having the prostate separate from the duct along which the sperm pass, and a hypertrophy of this

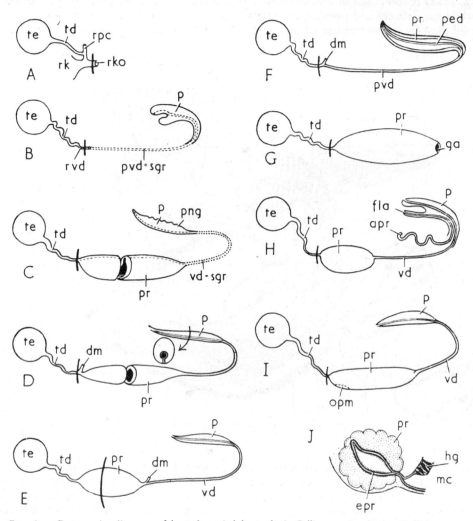

FIG. 181.—Comparative diagrams of the male genital ducts of: A, *Calliostoma zizyphinum*; B, *Calyptraea chinensis*; C, *Littorina littorea*; D, *Cingula semistriata* (with transverse section of penis to show closure of duct by fusion of epithelia); E, *Hydrobia ulvae*; F, *Rissoa parva*; G, *Cingulopsis fulgida*; H, *Bithynia tentaculata*; I, *Ocenebra erinacea*; J, *Ocenebra erinacea*: diagrammatic transverse section of prostate to show closure of gland by fusion of epithelia. The limit of the mantle cavity is indicated by a thick line.

apr, accessory prostate gland; dm, diverticulum of male duct opening to mantle cavity; epr, epithelium through which prostatic glands open; fla, flagellum; ga, genital aperture; hg, hypobranchial gland; mc, mantle cavity; opm, opening of prostate to mantle cavity; p, penis; ped, penial duct; png, penial glands; pr, prostate gland; pvd, pallial vas deferens; rk, right kidney; rko, right kidney opening; rpc, renopericardial canal; rvd, renal vas deferens; sgr, seminal groove; td, testis duct; te, testis; vd, vas deferens.

gland is a characteristic of some freshwater species. In *Bithynia tentaculata* the gland (pr, fig. 182A) is composed of numerous tubules clustered around the posterior part of the pallial vas deferens and opening at intervals into it; they are joined into a more or less solid mass by connective tissue (Lilly, 1953). In the hermaphrodite *Valvata piscinalis*, the

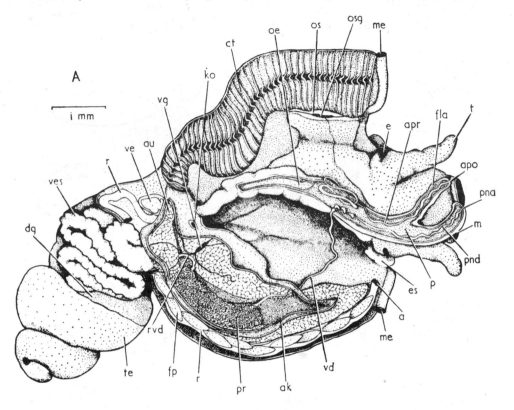

prostate (pr, fig. 187B) is the largest accessory gland of the reproductive system (Cleland, 1954): it spreads into the visceral coils posterior to the mantle cavity and its anterior parts penetrate the haemocoel alongside the muscles of the foot. The gland consists of small tubules which join one another to form a broad duct and near the opening of the duct the vas deferens has a similar glandular lining. *Velutina velutina* (fig. 194C), also herma-phrodite, has 3 large accessory glands separated from the main course of the genital duct and one of these (pr) is associated with the vas deferens.

Copulation occurs in the majority of monotocardians. The penis is typically of pedal origin, innervated by the right pedal ganglion and situated on the head behind the right tentacle; this is also true for *Pomatias elegans* (Creek, 1951) despite statements to the contrary. There are, however, exceptions to this, for in *Bithynia tentaculata* it appears to be pallial, being innervated from the sub-oesophageal ganglion, and in the Viviparidae (fig. 183) it seems to be cephalic since the vas deferens runs through the right tentacle to a finger-like process which normally lies folded back in a pouch (ops) on the right side and opens at its tip (ga). This is in agreement with other peculiarities met in the Architaenioglossa and perhaps suggests that they have evolved from a different stock from the other monotocardians. In *Omalogyra* and *Odostomia* (figs. 187C, D) the copulatory organ is a muscular invaginable tube, so different from the common pattern that it will be dealt with independently. Apart from these animals the penis is not invaginable: when at rest

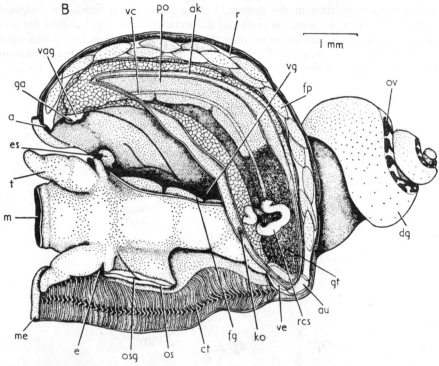

FIG. 182.—*Bithynia tentaculata:* A, male, dissected to show reproductive organs. The mantle cavity has been opened dorsally and the kidney overlying the vas deferens divided longitudinally and its halves pulled apart to expose that structure; the penis and its flagellum dissected to show the penial duct and accessory prostate gland. B, female, with the mantle cavity and anterior part of the kidney opened dorsally, as in the male. After Lilly.

a, anus; ak, lumen of anterior extension of kidney; apo, opening of accessory prostate gland; apr, accessory prostate gland; au, auricle; ct, ctenidium; dg, digestive gland; e, eye; es, exhalant siphon; fg, food groove; fla, flagellum of penis; fp, faecal pellet in rectum; ga, genital aperture; gt, glandular tubules of pallial oviduct; ko, kidney aperture; m, mouth; me, mantle edge; oe, oesophagus; os, osphradium; osg, osphradial ganglion; ov, ovary; p, penis; pna, penial aperture; pnd, penial duct; po, pallial oviduct; pr, prostate gland; r, rectum; rcs, receptaculum seminis; rvd, renal vas deferens; t, tentacle; te, testis; vag, vagina; vc, ventral channel of pallial oviduct; vd, vas deferens leading from prostate to penis; ve, ventricle; ves, vesicula seminalis; vg, visceral ganglion.

it is hidden in the mantle cavity. It is essentially a muscular and vascular process: muscles lie round the seminal duct or groove and make up most of the surrounding tissue, and between them run abundant blood spaces. When the penis is erected blood engorges these spaces and may enlarge it to twice its normal size, or more. The shape of the penis varies. It may be conical, broad at the base and tapering to a pointed tip (*Capulus* and *Trivia* (p, fig. 172)) and there may be glands around the base and tip secreting to the surface (*Crepidula*). Or the penis may be laterally compressed as in *Buccinum* (p, fig. 180B), or relatively larger and thinner as in the minute forms *Skeneopsis* (fig. 184B) and the rissoids (fig. 67) in which it extends to the posterior end of the mantle cavity of the male when folded back at rest, and at copulation approaches the posterior end of the mantle cavity of the female. It must pass through the length of the pallial oviduct to reach the bursa copulatrix in the rissoids, but in *Skeneopsis* it follows a longitudinal groove (ch, fig. 194B) between the shell and the mantle on the right side of the female, to a sperm pouch (rcs) which has its opening there (mrs). In *Buccinum* the external opening of the vas deferens is at the apex of a short papilla (pna, fig. 180B) situated subterminally on the anterior edge of the penis: at copulation the penis is not inserted far into the

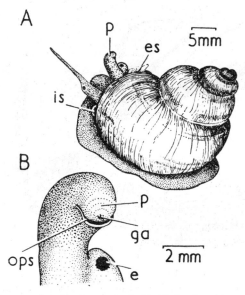

FIG. 183.—*Viviparus viviparus*, male: A, whole animal; B, details of penis.
     e, eye; es, exhalant siphon; ga, genital aperture; is, inhalant siphon; ops, opening of penis sheath; p, penis.

female duct for the seminal fluid is deposited in a bursa copulatrix near the genital aperture (Fretter, 1941).

Other devices for filling sperm pouches at the upper end of the pallial oviduct are associated with some modification of penial structure. In *Lamellaria perspicua* (p, fig. 94) the penis has a stout basal region, which is laterally compressed, and a slender apical region which is set at right angles to the base and arises from it subterminally, the origin being set in a groove. At copulation the basal part lies in the pallial oviduct, which it equals in length, and the slender part extends to the receptacular ducts (dr, rcs, fig. 193C). The free edges of the penial groove may embrace the base of the slender part and steady it. In *Calyptraea chinensis* (Giese, 1915) there is a different modification: the penis (p, fig. 181B), which may measure two-thirds the body length, has a distal lobe which is distended at copulation to grip the wall of the upper end of the pallial oviduct, and the vas deferens, an open groove, broadens beyond the origin of the lobe to a cup-shaped depression which is directed towards the group of openings of the receptaculum seminis (rcs, fig. 198).

The outer epithelium of the penis is frequently glandular, producing secretions which may help to lubricate its movement in the female and secure its position during copulation. The glands may lie in the epithelium and be very abundant, as in *Barleeia rubra*, which has, perhaps, an unusual method of copulation (p. 364), or some may be grouped in large subepithelial bundles which project from the surface as prominent papillae in *Caecum glabrum* (Götze, 1938). In this minute form (fig. 38B) there is one large adhesive gland on the underside of the penis and a number of smaller ones elsewhere; in each the secreting cells open separately to the outside, though the openings are clustered together. *Littorina littorea* (Linke, 1933) has longitudinal rows of compound glands along the anteroventral wall of the broad, flat penis (png, figs. 9, 10), which appear as mammilliform projections. The deep seminal groove runs along the opposite wall. At copulation only the tip of the penis enters the uterus and the broad middle region lies in the mantle cavity of the female, secured, apparently, by secretion from these glands. Mucus from cells in the penial epithelium may help to lubricate the passage of the organ. Compound adhesive glands are also developed in the penis of *L. littoralis* and *L. saxatilis* (png, fig. 178A). Each opens to the surface by a ciliated duct leading from a reservoir which is lined by gland cells and ciliated cells. The wall of the reservoir has a coat of circular muscles penetrated by the ducts of 10-25 tubular glands which are grouped around it. The extremely long penis of *Assiminea grayana* has a longitudinal row of about 8 muscular projections along its anteroventral wall. They are not associated with glands, but may serve the same purpose of securing a hold on the female during copulation; the pallial oviduct has no vaginal channel.

There is some question as to the function of the penial gland of *Bithynia tentaculata* (apr, figs. 181H, 182A). The penis (p) is bifid, with a median flagellum (fla). An accessory gland opens at the tip of the flagellum (apo, fig. 182A): it consists of a single tubule coiling in the tissues of the penis and extending posteriorly into the haemocoel. When the penis is erected the flagellum diverges from it so that it is doubtful whether at copulation its gland discharges into the female duct; the secretion may be poured on to the wall of the mantle cavity and hold the penis in position. This may also be true for the pelagic prosobranch *Carinaria* which has a penial appendage bearing the opening of a gland (fig. 301B) and in which copulation may be difficult owing to its mode of life.

In a number of opisthobranchs, especially the Ascoglossa, the penis is armed with spines or hooks which are cuticular secretions used to stimulate the partner. Only in one prosobranch, the ectoparasite *Pelseneeria stylifera* (Ankel, 1936a) are such spines known to occur.

One of the outstanding characteristics of the hermaphrodite reproductive system of the pyramidellids (Fretter & Graham, 1949) is the position of the penis and its associated structures which lie in the haemocoel, apart from the rest of the genital system; the penis is contained in a sheath which opens beneath the mentum and passes back through the nerve ring (ops, figs. 187D, 134). Normally in a gastropod the passage through the nerve ring is traversed only by the digestive tube and its associated glands, muscles and blood vessels. Perhaps the penis was carried into this position by the development of the long, acrembolic proboscis which characterizes the pyramidellids. The opening of the penial sheath is connected with the opening of the pallial genital duct by a ciliated tract which runs back along the right side of the head, ventral to the base of the tentacle, on to the floor of the mantle cavity to end at the genital aperture (sgr). The sheath lies dorsal to

13

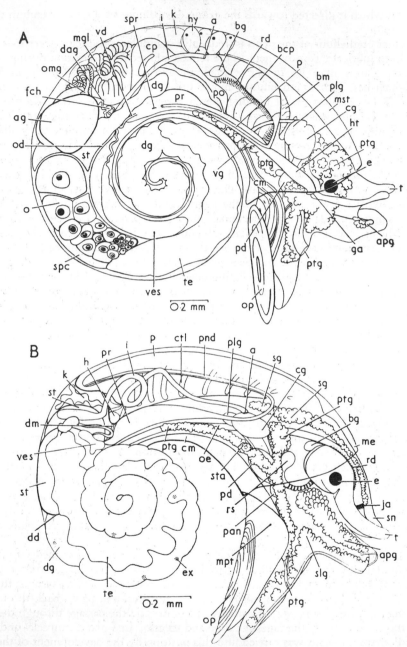

FIG. 184.—A, *Omalogyra atomus*; B, *Skeneopsis planorbis*. The animals are seen as transparent objects. a, anus; ag, albumen gland; apg, anterior pedal gland; bcp, bursa copulatrix; bg, buccal ganglion; bm, buccal mass; cg, cerebral ganglion; cm, columellar muscle; cp, capsule gland; ctl, ctenidial leaflet; dag, duct of albumen gland; dd, opening of duct of digestive gland to stomach; dg, digestive gland; dm, diverticulum of male duct opening to mantle cavity; e, eye; ex, excretory cell in digestive gland; fch, fertilization chamber; ga, genital aperture; h, heart; ht, hermaphrodite duct; hy, hypertrophied glands opening to mantle cavity near anus; i, intestine; ja, jaw; k, kidney; me, mantle edge; mgl, mucous gland; mpt, metapodium; mst, mantle skirt; o, ovum in ovary; od, ovarian duct; oe, oesophagus; omg, opening of albumen gland to mucous gland; op, operculum; p, penis; pan, parapedal ganglion; pd, pedal ganglion; plg, pleural ganglion; pnd, penial duct; po,

(facing p. 354)

the gut and may be flung into one or two broad loops when the animal is withdrawn into its shell. It is broad posteriorly and narrows to its opening, and on the dorsal wall, in front of the tip of the retracted penis, opens the short duct of a large muscular sac, the sperm sac (spc). A duct, the vas deferens (vd), arises near the opening of the sac and runs posteriorly in the thickness of the dorsal wall of the sheath towards the base of the penis. In *Odostomia* and *Chrysallida* the vas deferens, a closed duct, passes through the penis to its tip, and in the surrounding tissues are large blood spaces: when the penis is erected it appears as a long whip-like structure, turgid with blood and tapering to a fine point. During copulation the individual which acts as male creeps on to the surface of the shell of its partner, everts the penis and bends it ventrally so that it passes into the mantle cavity and through the genital aperture of the female. The withdrawal of the penis is brought about by the contraction of its longitudinal muscles and those of the sheath, and the consequent expulsion of blood into the general haemocoel. The fibrillae of these muscles are striated. The sperm sac must be filled prior to copulation, for it is difficult to see how sperm could reach it once the penis is protruded. The common genital aperture (ga) lies on the floor of the mantle cavity to the right, and about one-third of the total depth of the cavity inwards from its mouth. The path of the spermatozoa can be followed from this opening along the ciliated tract (sgr) to the opening of the penial sheath, and through the anterior ciliated part of the sheath into the sperm sac. During copulation contraction of the walls of the sac will force its contents along the vas deferens to the penis. In *Turbonilla elegantissima* (Fretter, 1951c) the opening of the hermaphrodite duct is on the propodium in front of the right tentacle and to the right of the mentum; in fact it is anterior to the opening of the penial sheath. The penis has no duct and either no blood spaces or only insignificant ones. In the retracted state (p, fig. 187E) it has the appearance of a long muscular scoop attached posteriorly to the wall of the sheath. The vas deferens (vd) arises from the mouth of the sperm sac (spc) as a groove which is morphologically open, though physiologically closed by apposition of the lips. It runs along the penial sheath to the posterior end of the penis, then opens to the concave surface of this scoop-shaped organ. Seminal fluid is propelled through vas deferens and penis by local muscular contractions.

*Omalogyra atomus* (fig. 184A) is one of the most minute of British molluscs and its reproductive system is specialized. It is hermaphrodite (Fretter, 1948) and during the summer months, when the *Ulva* on which it feeds is abundant, one generation follows another very rapidly. An individual collected at this time of the year has no structure which could act as a copulatory organ, and it is probable that self-fertilization is then practised. Only immature forms tide over the winter and these come to maturity in the spring. They differ from the summer forms in certain structural details. In the reproductive system the male organs are the first to mature. Through the lumen of the vas deferens runs a muscular tube (p, figs. 184A, 187C), open and directed inwardly, its anterior end arising from a large sac (bcp) connected to the anterior hermaphrodite portion of the pallial duct; the sac may be homologous with the bursa copulatrix of other forms. It is assumed that this tube is the copulatory organ: sperm liberated from the vesicula seminalis (ves, td) and prostatic secretion from the wall of the posterior half of the vas deferens (pr) could be sucked through the penial tube into the muscular

pallial oviduct; pr, prostate gland; ptg, posterior pedal gland (the labels placed on the mouth of the gland and on its anterior and posterior lobes); rd, radula; rs, radular sac; sg, salivary gland; slg, sole gland; sn, snout; spc, sperm sac; spr, opening of sperm sac into prostate gland; st, stomach; sta, statocyst; t, tentacle; te, testis; vd, pallial vas deferens; ves, seminal vesicle; vg, visceral ganglion.

sac (bcp); the direction of the tube could then be reversed so that it protrudes through the genital aperture and into the hermaphrodite duct of the copulating partner. The muscular wall of the sac would contract and so transfer the seminal fluid. This suggested method of copulation is unusual and may be correlated with the small size of the mollusc as well as the isostrophic shell. There is a second muscular sac (spc) which is connected to the posterior end of the prostate by a narrow, ciliated duct; it is only present in animals collected during the spring months. The sac frequently contains sperm and prostatic secretion in large quantities, and the sperm appear as though they are disintegrating. Perhaps its function is to clear the pallial vas deferens of sperm and prostatic fluid which have failed to enter the copulatory organ. A similar method of clearing the genital duct of unwanted material is found in the hermaphrodite opisthobranchs, in which the bursa frequently fulfils this purpose.

Woodward (1899) has described the reproductive system of the rare monotocardian *Adeorbis* (= *Tornus*) *subcarinatus* and stated that the male has neither penis nor accessory gland and that the vas deferens opens 'high up and close to the external opening of the kidney'. The oviduct, however, has a pallial section. Unless *Adeorbis* is an exception to all other monotocardians which have been studied, internal fertilization occurs; yet we have no suggestion as to the way in which it is brought about.

There would appear to exist a connexion between the state of development of the gonad and the state of development of the secondary sexual organs in at least some prosobranch molluscs. This is particularly well seen in *Littorina*. *L. littorea* breeds at Plymouth from November to May, chiefly in February and March, and during these months when the gonad is ripe the penis, prostate and pallial oviduct are at a maximal size. The reduction of the gonad during late spring and early summer is, however, concurrent with a reduction in size of these organs. During July and August no male has a functional penis: it is of insignificant size, the glands are reduced to only the pits of the chief follicles, the muscles are thin and short—in fact the tissues assume an embryonic appearance which is retained until the gonad enlarges and matures in the autumn. Linke (1934*b*) has shown that at the end of the breeding season material from the destruction of the genital system is stored in connective tissue cells (fig. 124). A permanent reduction in the size of the gonad may be brought about by trematode infection, and as the gonad is destroyed the secondary sexual structures are reduced to vestiges. This also holds for *L. saxatilis*. In this viviparous species the annual rhythm of sexual activity appears less marked, since the breeding seasons of the varieties (see p. 537), each with its own resting period, tend to overlap (James, personal communication).

A similar correlation between the condition of the gonad, penis and pallial genital duct occurs in the protandrous hermaphrodites *Calyptraea*, *Crepidula* (fig. 185) and *Capulus*. At the transition from male to female stage the reduction of the penis (p) is synchronized with the reduction of the testis, and as the ovary develops the walls of the pallial duct, which is formed from the closure of the narrow seminal groove, hypertrophy to form the albumen and capsule glands. Such events suggest a hormonal control, though this has been little investigated. Rohlack (1959) has, indeed, found an oestrogen (not identical with that of vertebrates) in the ovary of *Littorina littorea*, though not in any other part of the body. Despite this she suggested that the sex cycle is probably controlled by temperature: perhaps both factors interact. Like Linke (1934*a*) she was unable to carry out successful injections since experimental animals invariably died. No androgens were found in males.

# CHAPTER 15

# THE REPRODUCTIVE SYSTEM—2

IN the more primitive oviparous British monotocardian gastropods (Lacunidae, Hydrobiidae, Rissoidae) the oviduct is closed throughout its length and the genital aperture is near the mouth of the mantle cavity alongside the anus (fig. 186). There is no evidence in the adults of these, or of more advanced groups, that the pallial region has been formed by the fusion of the lips of a longitudinal groove on the mantle skirt as has been described for the prostate of *Ocenebra* (fig. 181J) and *Nucella*. However, sections of *Calyptraea chinensis* show that on the ventral wall of the pallial oviduct there is a narrow longitudinal strip of cubical cells which are neither ciliated, nor like the epithelium elsewhere, nor underlain by glands. This is the line of closure in the transformation of the male stage with an open seminal groove to the female with a closed duct. In the majority of the mesogastropods this ventral wall is relatively thin and its musculature well developed: in some animals the penis slides along it in passing from the genital aperture to the inner end of the pallial duct (rissoids, *Capulus*, *Calyptraea*, *Crepidula*, *Lamellaria*), and in others this ventral path is followed by the sperm which, deposited in the lower regions of the duct, are making their way to the receptaculum seminis. When used as a path for sperm the ventral channel may be elaborated. In *Littorina* spp. and in the Rachiglossa the bursa copulatrix and receptaculum seminis are at opposite ends of the channel which is arched over on either side by a longitudinal fold so that the sperm travel in a physiologically closed duct, separated from the reproductive glands.

Johansson (1948a) has shown that in the development of *Hydrobia ulvae* the closure of the pallial duct is delayed and in young forms it opens widely to the mantle cavity by a ventral slit. At the free edge of the median lip of this opening there is a ciliated groove or gutter which extends beyond the slit anteriorly, and runs posteriorly along the internal line of closure of the duct to form the vaginal channel. It leads to the bursa copulatrix at the inner end of the pallial duct. The receptaculum seminis is immediately beyond the bursa and the channel can be traced beyond its opening as far as the gonopericardial duct. From this Johansson concluded that the gonopericardial duct in this, and in other species in which it occurs (Johansson, 1956a), marks the division between the mesodermal and ectodermal parts of the genital duct; a similar conclusion was reached by Krull (1935). The renal oviduct will, theoretically, include a section of each part, the mesodermal region being derived from the rudiment of the right kidney, and the ectodermal from an invagination of the mantle cavity which forms its duct. With the ontogenetic and phylogenetic modifications of the genital duct the exact boundaries of this section in the various species of monotocardians are no longer traceable with certainty in the adult, nor are they of any real significance.

In some genera a gonopericardial duct occurs in the female, while in the male there may be a vestige in the form of a dense strand of connective tissue passing from the vas deferens to the pericardium (*Littorina* spp., *Ocenebra erinacea*, *Nassarius reticulatus*). In the

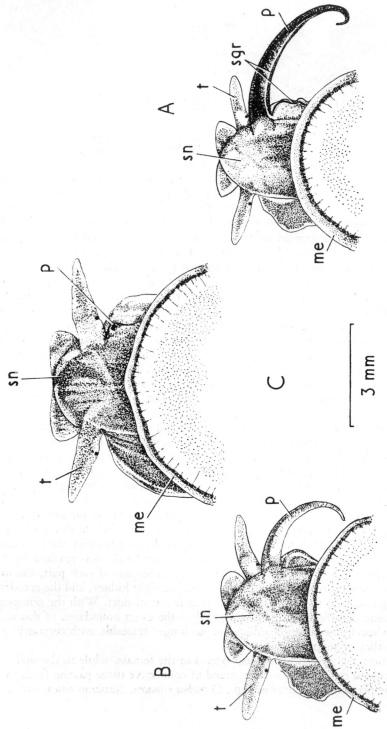

Fig. 185.—*Crepidula fornicata*: dorsal view of anterior halves of 3 animals to show changes in penis with change in sex.   A, functional male;   B, transitional stage;   C, functional female.
me, mantle edge;  p, penis;  sgr, seminal groove;  sn, snout;  t, tentacle.

protandrous hermaphrodites *Calyptraea* and *Crepidula* the duct first makes its appearance as a strand of connective tissue as the female organs develop (Giese, 1915) and later it cavitates. The occurrence of a gonopericardial duct cannot be regarded as giving any indication of phylogenetic relationship since it is found in the Stenoglossa (gpd, fig. 173), which are specialized in other respects, and is lost in many of the more primitive meso-gastropods: in *Bithynia tentaculata* its presence has been mentioned by some workers (Krull, 1935) and denied by others (Lilly, 1953), suggesting that it is not always developed. The persistence of the duct in females shows that at least it is no handicap in the function-ing of the genital system, and its formation at the transition from male to female stage of *Calyptraea* and *Crepidula* suggests that it may serve some essential role. There is an unusual condition in *Circulus striatus* where the kidney (k, fig. 188A) extends between the pericardium and the genital duct (ag), and this duct opens into the kidney and not into the pericardium (gk). A similar link between the female genital duct and the kidney occurs in *Truncatella subcylindrica* (fig. 314C). The opisthobranchs have no vestige of the primitive connexion between gonoduct and any other derivative of the coelom.

Johansson (1948a) stated that the ciliated groove, which in *Hydrobia* is incorporated in the ventral wall of the pallial duct to form the ventral channel, is not completely enclosed by the duct in *Rissoa violacea* (=*R. lilacina*) and *R. membranacea*: it is present in immature and mature individuals as an outer ventral gutter against the median wall of the capsule gland, and, as a consequence, this gland has no clearly defined ventral channel. However, the gutter must be enclosed posteriorly as Johansson regarded the bursa copulatrix as an outgrowth from it, and similarly he regarded the vagina as an enclosed anterior part. Moreover in *Cingula cingillus*, *C. semicostata*, *C. semistriata*, *Rissoa parva*, *R. lilacina*, *Alvania beani*, *A. abyssicola*, *A. punctura* a thin-walled vaginal channel is well defined along the capsule gland but there is no longitudinal fold of tissue which separates it, even incompletely, from the lumen of the gland as in *Hydrobia ulvae* and *Potamopyrgus jenkinsi*.

Most species in which the prostate gland is open throughout its length and no penis is developed, have an open pallial duct in the female (*Turritella* (figs. 186, 189), *Bittium* (fig. 190), *Cerithiopsis*, *Clathrus*). It is in the form of a glandular groove with deep lateral walls, joined by a narrow dorsal wall and open ventrally. It may be physiologically closed with an anterior aperture, and along the ventral free edge of the median wall there may be a ciliated groove (thought to be homologous with that described for *Hydrobia*) which in *Bittium reticulatum* is most pronounced and leads to the bursa (bcp, rcs, fig. 190) and the receptaculum. Johansson (1947) referred to this groove as a sperm collecting gutter. This open condition of the genital ducts and the lack of a penis, is presumably an advantage; in other respects the species which have it are advanced. In some genera it appears to be correlated with a long, narrow mantle cavity containing a relatively large ctenidium. In *Turritella*, *Bittium*, *Cerithiopsis* and *Clathrus* the shell is a close spiral with a small apical angle and small mouth; the mantle cavity is deep, following the course of the tight spiral of the shell, and it may have reached a minimal breadth for maintaining proper ventilation. Should it be still further restricted by the presence of a penis in the male, its breadth might be brought below the limit for efficiency; in support of this it is to be noted that the female glands swell relatively less than in species in which the duct is closed. Perhaps it is for this reason that the sperm are transferred to the female by a method involving an open pallial duct. Moreover, in such tightly coiled spirals there will be a greater degree of shortening of the right side of the body and so less space for the right half of the pallial complex, which is, in the monotocardian, the genital duct and rectum. *Turritella communis* is a ciliary feeder living in muddy situations and is

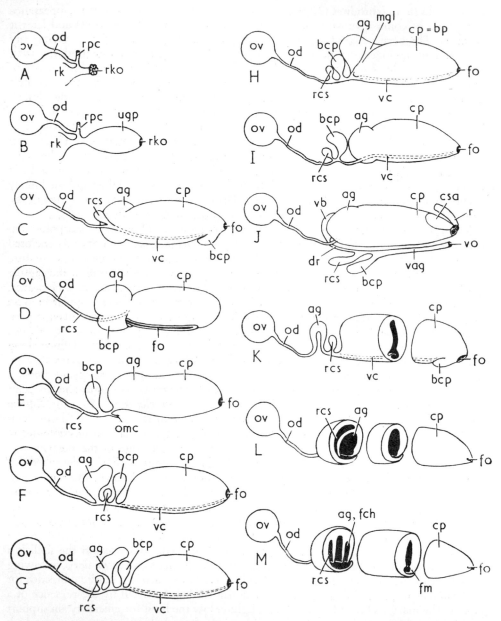

Fig. 186.—Comparative diagrams of the female genital ducts of: A, *Gibbula* and *Monodonta*; B, *Calliostoma*; C, *Littorina littorea*; D, *Pomatias elegans*; E, *Acicula fusca*; F, *Cingula semicostata*, C. *semistriata, Rissoa parva*; G, *Cingula cingillus*; H, *Potamopyrgus jenkinsi*; I, *Hydrobia ulvae*; J, *Theodoxus fluviatilis*; K, *Nucella lapillus*; L, *Clathrus clathrus*; M, *Turritella communis*.

ag, albumen gland; bcp, bursa copulatrix; bp, brood pouch; cp, capsule gland; csa, crystal sac; dr, duct of receptaculum; fch, fertilization chamber; fm, flange bordering edge of left wall of pallial oviduct; fo, female opening; mgl, mucous gland; od, oviduct; omc, opening to mantle cavity; ov, ovary; r, rectum; rcs, receptaculum seminis; rk, right kidney; rko, right kidney opening surrounded by a glandular lip in A; rpc, renopericardial canal; ugp, urinogenital papilla; vag, vagina; vb, vestibule; vc, ventral channel; vo, vaginal opening.

specialized in accordance with this. The mantle cavity is isolated from the environment by a curtain of tentacles which hangs from the mantle skirt across the pallial opening (pt, fig. 64) and so prevents silting of the cavity: should copulation occur, the introduction of the penis into the female aperture would impair this isolation. With an open pallial duct exposing the receptaculum seminis at its upper end the sperm may be transferred to the female by the inhalant water current. The animals are gregarious and spawning of large numbers probably occurs simultaneously.

There are other advanced mesogastropods with a more spacious mantle cavity in which there is no penis and the pallial genital ducts are open (e.g. *Fagotia esperi* (Soós, 1936)). The presence of this apparently primitive condition in these species may be correlated with some unknown factor in their mode of life, or perhaps an alteration in shell shape is recent and the structure of the genital duct not yet changed to conform to the new type of shell.

The British eratoids, *Erato voluta* (fig. 32), *Trivia monacha* and *T. arctica* (figs. 193A, B), and the terrestrial prosobranch *Pomatias elegans* (fig. 186D) have a comparatively short and deep pallial section to the oviduct, with the capsule gland opening ventrally to the mantle cavity along the greater part of its length. In the male there is a penis and the vas deferens is closed except, perhaps, for a small outlet to the mantle cavity posteriorly. The egg capsules are large and spherical (figs. 205, 214) and embedded in some kind of substratum when they are laid. The ventral opening of the capsule gland may be correlated with the size and shape of the capsules, and the mantle cavity is broad so that it would not be incommoded by their passing through it. A similar ventral aperture occurs in the hermaphrodite *Velutina velutina* (fig. 194C) which also has large egg capsules and a broad mantle cavity; these capsules are embedded in the tissues of the compound ascidian *Styela coriacea* according to Diehl (1956).

Two kinds of sperm pouch are developed on the female duct (fig. 186) communicating (with few exceptions) with the ventral channel and apparently developed as outgrowths from it: the bursa copulatrix (bcp) which receives sperm and prostatic fluid, and the receptaculum seminis (rcs) to which the sperm pass from the bursa. In the receptaculum the sperm are normally orientated, lying closely packed, each with the tip of its head embedded in the cytoplasm of an epithelial cell and its tail directed into the lumen, and here they have a longer stay than in the bursa, only leaving the pouch at the time of fertilization. Occasionally, but not usually (Stenoglossa (Fretter, 1941)), sperm are also orientated in the bursa. The position of the sperm pouches varies and also their number. The receptacular pouch is typically at the inner end of the pallial duct, not far from the site of fertilization: it may lie between the albumen and capsule glands (figs. 186F, K), or posterior to both (fig. 186G), or, more unusually, it may arise from the albumen gland (*Trivia monacha*, *T. arctica*, *Lamellaria perspicua* (rcs, figs. 193A, B, C)). Although in some species the bursa copulatrix is immediately anterior to the receptaculum, in others it is at the opposite end of the ventral channel and near the genital aperture (*Littorina* (fig. 186C); Stenoglossa (fig. 186K)). Johansson (1953) considered the proximal position of the bursa to be the more primitive and associated originally with an open pallial groove which received sperm by way of the inhalant stream of water, the distal pouch having arisen after the closure of the pallial duct and the development of a penis. In the 2 sperm pouches of *Bithynia tentaculata*, one at each end of the pallial duct, spermatozoa mingled with prostatic fluid have been identified (Krull, 1935; Lilly, 1953) suggesting that each acts as a bursa and that the depth to which the penis discharges its contents may vary. An even more unusual condition is found in *Aporrhais pespelicani* which has 3 bursae in

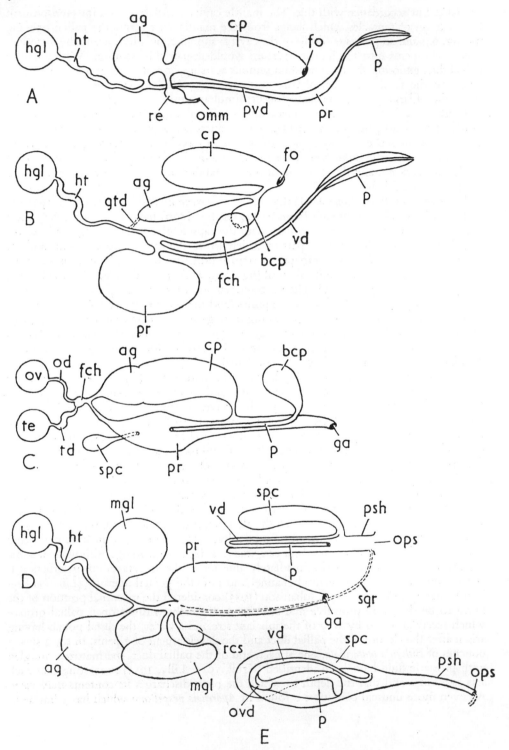

the anterior half of the pallial duct. They are embedded in the thickness of the lateral walls and open near the slit-like genital aperture (Johansson, 1948b); ingoing ciliary currents mark the entrance to each. There is still another pouch which opens mid-ventrally not far from the posterior lip of the genital opening with which it is connected by a groove. The effective beat of the cilia along this groove is away from the pouch, which, Johansson suggested, is a receptaculum seminis.

In some species sperm are stored in a region of the gonoduct which is proximal to the pallial glands, in which case the receptacular pouch may be reduced, as in *Alvania subsoluta* (Johansson, 1956a), or lost, as in the Indian pond snail *Cremnoconchus*, the terrestrial *Pomatias elegans* and *Lacuna pallidula* (Gallien & Larambergue, 1938). In *Pomatias* sperm are orientated over the entire surface of this region of the oviduct (rcs, fig. 186D), whereas in *Cremnoconchus* and *Lacuna* its wall is constricted longitudinally to form one channel for the eggs and another for the orientated sperm. The small terrestrial prosobranch *Acicula fusca* has a single pouch at the inner end of the pallial duct (bcp, fig. 186E) where orientated sperm are always present in large numbers, sometimes with prostatic fluid. It has been termed the bursa copulatrix (Creek, 1953) though its functions would appear to be combined with those of a receptaculum. A certain number of sperm also accumulate in the region of the oviduct immediately posterior to the pouch. Here the epithelial cells are large except in two or three places where they form longitudinal grooves in which sperm are orientated. The large cells lining the duct between the rows of sperm are either mucous glands or ingesting cells which take up sperm and apparently digest them in the cytoplasm. Creek suggested that the sperm accumulated in the duct may be the excess of those which left the sperm pouch at the time ripe eggs were liberated from the ovary, and, trapped in the duct, they orientate themselves and remain healthy for some days. This appears to be the course of events in *Trivia monacha* in which sperm with a similar history are accumulated in a bunch of branching diverticula of the renal oviduct (br, fig. 193A); they are orientated in the lower parts, whilst at the blind ends of the tubules they lose their orientation, their heads shorten and they are ultimately devoured and digested by amoebocytes. In *Bithynia tentaculata* (Lilly, 1953) orientated sperm are frequently found in the glandular tubules of the posterior part of the pallial glands (gt, fig. 182B), as well as in the coiled muscular part of the gonoduct (rcs) which precedes both these glands and the proximal bursa. This coiled region resembles the receptacular part of the duct of *Alvania abyssicola* and is presumably of ectodermal origin, representing an invagination of the mantle cavity (Johansson, 1956a).

In a few species the vaginal channel is separated anteriorly from the pallial oviduct so that the female genital system has two openings to the mantle cavity. In *Theodoxus fluviatilis* (figs. 186J, 195) these openings are alongside one another, and from the vaginal duct (vag) arise the bursa copulatrix (bcp), which receives the penis, sperm and prostatic

FIG. 187.—Comparative diagrams of the hermaphrodite genital ducts of: A, *Rissoella diaphana*; B, *Valvata piscinalis*; C, *Omalogyra atomus*; D, *Odostomia* spp.; E, penis and related structures of *Turbonilla elegantissima*.

ag, albumen gland; bcp, bursa copulatrix; cp, capsule gland; fch, fertilization chamber; fo, female opening; ga, genital aperture; gtd, position of Garnault's duct; hgl, hermaphrodite gland; ht, hermaphrodite duct acting as vesicula seminalis; mgl, mucous gland; od, ovarian duct; omu, opening of muscular sac to mantle cavity; ops, opening of penial sheath; ov, ovary; ovd, opening of vas deferens to base of spoon-shaped penis; p, penis; pr, prostate; psh, penial sheath; pvd, pallial vas deferens; rcs, receptaculum seminis; re, muscular pouch, probably homologous with receptaculum seminis; sgr, seminal groove; spc, sperm sac; td, testis duct acting as vesicula seminalis; te, testis; vd, vas deferens.

secretion, and the receptaculum seminis (rcs), in which the sperm are orientated with their tails attached to the epithelium. A narrow, coiled duct leaves the stalk of the receptaculum and passes to a fertilization chamber at the upper end of the pallial duct; it is the only connexion between the vaginal channel and the oviduct. In *Cingulopsis fulgida* (fig. 191) the separated channel forms a narrow muscular duct (mdt) which is shorter than the oviduct so that it opens well within the mantle cavity. It leads to the upper end of the pallial duct where there is a single receptacular pouch with orientated sperm (rcs) and a muscular sac which, during the breeding season, has been found to contain a fluid with staining properties similar to those of prostatic secretion (as, sas)—it is probably a bursa copulatrix. There is no penis in the male and the method by which sperm reach the female can only be surmised: seminal fluid directed to the mantle cavity with the inhalant flow of water may be drawn up the accessory duct, and at some point on its course the sperm are separated from the prostatic secretion. This may occur in the muscular sac, though no sperm have been found with its contents.

In *Acicula fusca* (fig. 186E) the pallial oviduct has no thin-walled vaginal channel, but anterior to the origin of the sperm pouch the oviduct opens to the mantle cavity by a very short duct (omc), which may represent a much reduced vaginal channel separate from the duct. Creek (1953) suggested, however, that it is too short to be used by the penis since the mantle cavity is deep and the penis small; but she has not observed the method of copulation. Nor has it been observed in *Barleeia rubra* in which a diverticulum of the mantle cavity opens into the upper end of the pallial oviduct, near the double receptaculum seminis. In this species there is no vaginal channel and it is thought that during copulation the penis passes through the mantle cavity to the upper end of the pallial duct to deposit seminal fluid; this might account for the unusual abundance of gland cells in the epithelium covering the penis.

Johansson (1953) regarded the posterior opening of the oviduct to the mantle cavity as a primitive character. It may be assumed that in the gastropods the pallial ducts in both sexes were originally open grooves and internal fertilization may have been practised before the penis evolved. When during the course of evolution the oviducal groove closed, a proximal opening for the entry of sperm may have been retained at least until the penis developed. This condition is fulfilled in *Triphora perversa* (Johansson, 1953) in which the male has an open pallial duct and no penis, and the female a closed duct except for a posterior opening leading to the bursa copulatrix.

Other species in which no copulation takes place have an open pallial oviduct and the sperm pouches are typically in the thickness of the lateral walls and open ventrally to the mantle cavity. There may be both bursa and receptaculum, or receptaculum only. At the inner end of the pallial duct of *Turritella communis* (figs. 186M, 189) are 2 pouches, one on either side of the longitudinal glandular tract. The pouch lying against the right wall, near the columellar muscle, is the smaller and acts as a receptaculum seminis (rcs). Ciliated ridges pass from its opening to the mantle cavity and the effective beat of the cilia is away from the pouch, so that the sperm must swim against the ciliary current to enter it. The left pouch (af) is embedded in the thickness of the left wall and has a fairly extensive opening along the ventral edge; anteriorly the lips of this opening fuse and are continuous with the flange bordering the free edge of the wall. The lips are very mobile and can envelop the openings of the renal oviduct and receptaculum seminis. This second pouch is glandular and the eggs may be fertilized here and surrounded by albumen, though Johansson (1946) regarded it as a bursa copulatrix and the flange bordering the free edge of the wall as a sperm-collecting gutter (as in *Bittium reticulatum*). Each capsule

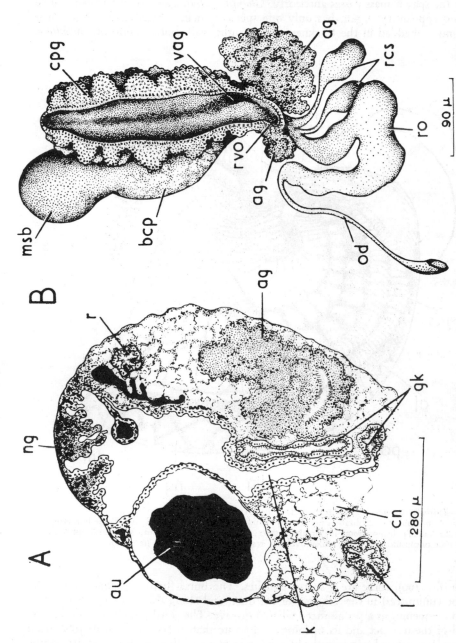

FIG. 188.—*Circulus striatus*: A, transverse section of female showing the connexion between the genital duct and the kidney; B, dissection of the female reproductive system. The capsule gland has been opened by a longitudinal cut, the ovarian duct transected near the ovary, and some of the albumen gland removed.

ag, albumen gland; au, auricle; bcp, bursa copulatrix; cn, connective tissue; cpg, capsule gland; gk, renal oviduct and its opening into kidney; k, kidney; l, intestine; msb, muscular sac at end of bursa copulatrix; ng, nephridial gland; od, ovarian duct; r, rectum; rcs, receptaculum seminis; ro, renal oviduct; rvo, opening of renal oviduct; vag, vagina.

consists of a group of eggs embedded in albumen and surrounded by a wall which is
secreted as the spawn mass passes anteriorly. *Clathrus clathrus*, also with an open pallial
duct and no copulatory organ, has only one sperm pouch, a receptaculum, which is
posterior and embedded in the thickness of the right wall, but in contrast, in *Bittium*

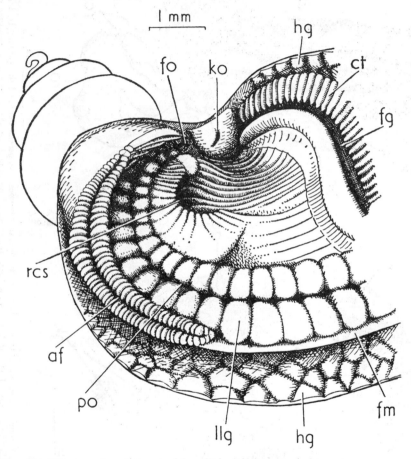

FIG. 189.—*Turritella communis:* upper part of the pallial oviduct.
af, albumen gland and fertilization pouch; ct, ctenidium; fg, food groove; fm, flange bordering
edge of left wall of pallial oviduct; fo, female aperture; hg, hypobranchial gland; ko, kidney opening;
llg, left lobe of capsule gland; po, pallial oviduct; rcs, receptaculum seminis (see text).

reticulatum (fig. 190), there are 3 sperm pouches. The bursa (bcp) in *Bittium* is anterior
to a receptaculum (rcs) in the left wall of the duct, and along the free edge of the wall
leading to its opening is a pronounced ciliated groove. The third pouch is alongside the
right wall of the oviduct and its opening is opposite that of the bursa (rcs); Johannson
(1956b) found orientated sperm in the lumen, and suggested that this pouch is the homologue of the receptaculum of *Turritella* and that it is being functionally replaced by a
new receptaculum in the opposite wall of the duct.

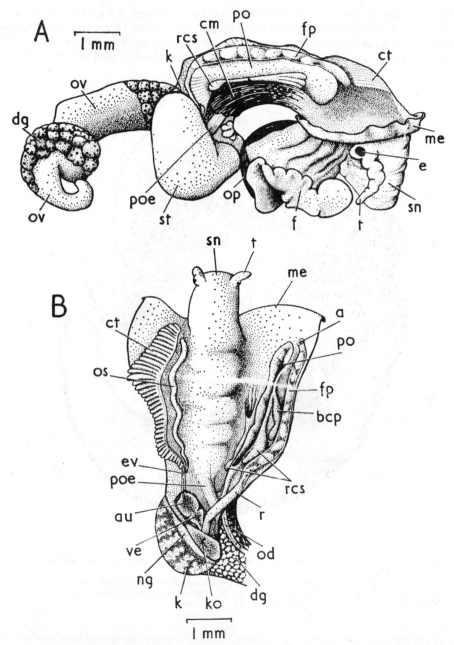

FIG. 190.—*Bittium reticulatum:* A, female removed from shell and seen from the right; B, female removed from shell and mantle cavity opened to show its contents.

a, anus; au, auricle; bcp, bursa copulatrix; cm, columellar muscle; ct, ctenidium; dg, digestive gland; e, eye; ev, efferent branchial vein; f, foot; fp, faecal pellet in rectum; k, kidney; ko, kidney opening; me, mantle edge; ng, nephridial gland; od, ovarian duct; op, operculum; os, osphradium; ov, ovary; po, pallial oviduct; poe, posterior oesophagus; r, rectum; rcs, receptaculum seminis (see text); sn, snout; st, stomach; t, tentacle; ve, ventricle.

*Balcis alba* has an open pallial oviduct (po, fig. 140) and there is a penis in the male. At the inner end of the mantle cavity the glandular oviduct is closed for a very short distance before it narrows and receives the muscular duct of a receptaculum seminis. The mantle cavity of *Balcis* is comparatively deep and curved, and it is doubtful whether the penis

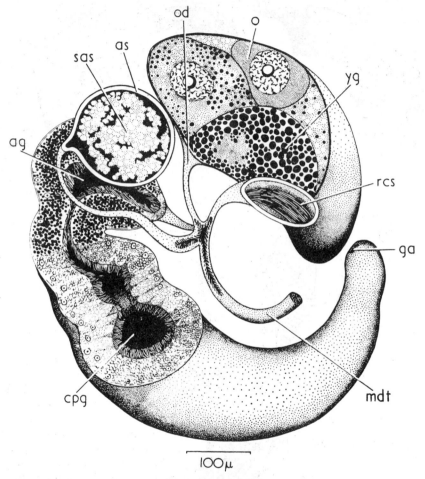

FIG. 191.—*Cingulopsis fulgida:* semi-diagrammatic representation of the female reproductive system, with some parts opened.

ag, albumen gland; as, accessory sac, perhaps homologous with bursa copulatrix; cpg, capsule gland; ga, genital aperture; mdt, muscular duct; o, ovum in ovary; od, ovarian duct; rcs, receptaculum seminis; sas, secretion in accessory sac; yg, yolk granule.

can reach the remote receptaculum, though it may deposit the sperm near its duct. The pallial oviduct is also open in *B. devians*; in this species, however, no males have been described (Fretter, 1955a).

Only a single sperm pouch, a receptaculum seminis with orientated sperm, is present in a number of monotocardians with closed oviducts; it is a dorsal outgrowth of the initial part of the pallial duct with no direct connexion with the ventral channel. As far as is known this pouch receives the sperm directly from the penis, which penetrates far into the oviduct. It may be a simple sac as in *Capulus* (Giese, 1915), *Erato voluta* and *Trivia monacha* (rcs, fig. 193A), or subdivided into diverticula, 6 in *Calyptraea* (Giese, 1915) (fig. 198), *Lamellaria* (fig. 193C) and *Trivia arctica* (fig. 193B), 3 in *Crepidula* (Giese, 1915) and *Trichotropis* (Graham, 1954a). The duct of each diverticulum is muscular and may help the uptake of sperm during copulation and their later ejection for fertilization. There is no bursa in the toxoglossan *Mangelia* (Robinson, 1955) and the penis is extremely long and probably penetrates along the ventral channel to the proximal end of the capsule gland, where there is a receptaculum seminis and sperm-ingesting gland.

Internal fertilization and the manufacture of egg capsules in the closed pallial duct may lead to an accumulation of waste, and in some species there are means of ridding the duct of this. Mention has already been made of ingestion of spermatozoa in the female duct of *Acicula*, *Trivia monacha*, *Nucella* and *Mangelia*. In *Nucella* copulation and capsule formation may continue for some months, necessitating the maintenance of an efficient stock of sperm, and in accordance with this the ingesting gland is large. It is similarly developed in the other Stenoglossa as an outgrowth from the receptaculum seminis, though it may be smaller in those with a more restricted breeding period. The receptaculum (the duct of the ingesting gland (ig, rcs, fig. 171)) may be surprisingly short and surrounded by a thick muscular coat. In *Ocenebra* and *Buccinum* yolk granules have been found in the lumen of the gland and in the resorptive cells. The waste yolk, which is considerable in *Buccinum*, must originate from eggs which, for some reason, have not been included in a capsule. Sometimes amoebocytes may be seen in the bursa copulatrix of this whelk ingesting prostatic secretion which has been left there after the sperm have passed to the receptaculum. *Cerithiopsis tubercularis* has a sperm-ingesting gland associated with the receptaculum seminis (fig. 192). At the extreme posterior end of the open pallial oviduct is a small cul-de-sac which receives ventrally the renal oviduct and dorsally accommodates spermatozoa which have entered the duct by way of the inhalant water current. The sperm are orientated in a shallow pouch lined by ciliated cells and a duct leads dorsally from the pouch and bifurcates distally. Each bifurcation (dr) opens to a receptaculum which is lined by relatively enormous cells, except around the entrance where there is a patch of low columnar epithelium with orientated sperm (sa). In the cytoplasm of the epithelium elsewhere there are tangled balls of sperm which are undergoing digestion (ds): the length of time these have been in the female is unknown. In some prosobranchs the sperm in the receptaculum appear to remain healthy for several weeks. In *Viviparus*, Ankel (1925) found sperm in the pouch 5 months after copulation; some, though only a few, were oligopyrene sperm which have about half the length of life of the eupyrene sperm. Sperm which make their way to the albumen gland in *Viviparus* live even longer—11 months has been estimated for the eupyrene and 7 for the oligopyrene—and Ankel (1925) suggested that the longer life is due to the fact that they are less crowded there than in the receptaculum.

The minute hermaphrodite *Rissoella diaphana* (fig. 194A) has another method by which waste material is cleared from the genital duct. There is a muscular sac (re) which communicates with the ventral wall of the posterior end of the capsule gland by a short duct, and has an outlet to the mantle cavity by way of a longer duct (omm). After an egg capsule has been laid the pouch may be enlarged by enormous quantities of unwanted secretions and spermatozoa; at other times it is empty and quite minute. Presumably the contents are emptied to the mantle cavity, for there is no indication that the mollusc puts them to any profitable use. The relationship of this pouch to the other parts of the genital duct suggests that it is homologous with a receptaculum seminis. The oviduct has no pouch in which orientated sperm are stored.

The glandular equipment of the pallial duct of the monotocardian gastropod provides the nutritive and protective coverings for the eggs. The inner surface of the duct is lined by a ciliated epithelium and the secreting cells may be glands placed in the epithelial layer only (fig. 194A), or (frequently) grouped in clusters concentrated beneath the deep lateral walls (fig. 175A). The cilia can do little more than distribute the secretion over the

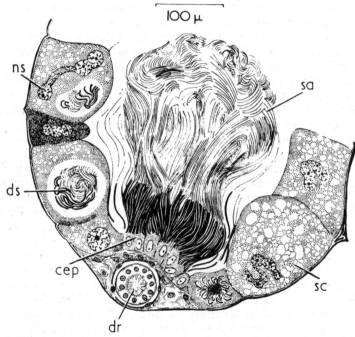

FIG. 192.—*Cerithiopsis tubercularis:* part of transverse section through receptaculum seminis, showing absorption of sperm.
    cep, ciliated epithelium; dr, duct of receptaculum seminis; ds, sperm undergoing digestion; ns, nucleus of secreting cell; sa, orientated spermatozoa; sc, secreting cell.

surface of the duct, and the movement of the egg mass is brought about by muscles in the connective tissue surrounding the duct. Glands of the posterior part of the pallial duct secrete the albumen, whilst anteriorly the secreting cells form a capsule gland. In some species each egg with its supply of albumen is surrounded by a shell which is secreted by a special area of the wall of the duct near the anterior end of the albumen gland.

The simplest arrangement of glands is in the open pallial oviduct, which has an uninterrupted development of secreting cells from the inner end of the mantle cavity to its anterior limit, and the sperm pouches are placed typically against the lateral walls or in their thickness. In the closed duct, however, the outgrowth of sperm pouches from the ventral channel may separate a proximal from a distal glandular area, as in some rissoids and the Rachiglossa (figs. 186F, G, K). Moreover there is a tendency for the

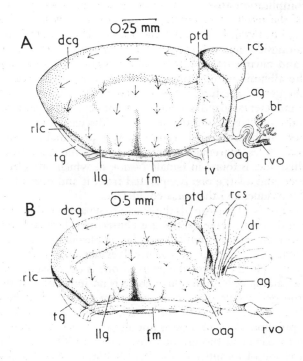

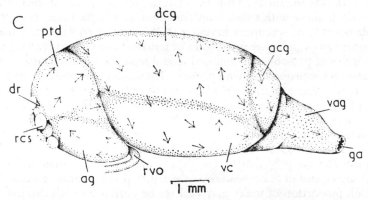

FIG. 193.—Renal and pallial oviducts, seen from the right, of A, *Trivia monacha*; B, *T. arctica*; C, *Lamellaria perspicua*.

acg, anterior lobe of capsule gland; ag, albumen gland; br, branching diverticula on renal oviduct; dcg, dorsal lobe of capsule gland; dr, duct of receptaculum seminis; fm, flange of tissue forming part of mouth of genital duct; ga, genital opening; llg, left lobe of capsule gland; oag, opening of albumen gland to capsule gland; ptd, posterior tip of capsule gland; rcs, receptaculum seminis; rlc, right lobe of capsule gland; rvo, renal oviduct; tg, thin anterior wall of capsule gland; tv, thin ventral wall of capsule gland; vag, vagina; vc, ventral channel.

proximal glandular development to project posteriorly into the visceral mass. In some species a further complication arises when some of the accessory glands separate from the main course of the oviduct; in hermaphrodite forms this may also apply to the prostate (*Valvata* (pr, fig. 187B), *Velutina* (pr, fig. 194C)). The minute *Caecum glabrum* has separate sexes and alongside the oviduct are 2 glands, one on either side. They have been termed the uterus and nidamental glands by Götze (1938), and it is suggested that the former provides the albuminous covering for the eggs. It has no connexion with the oviduct except at the genital aperture, which consequently appears as a double opening. The opening of the nidamental gland is alongside but independent, and this gland, which probably produces the outer covering of the capsule, discharges not to the oviduct but to the mantle cavity. Such an unusual arrangement is presumably associated with the small size of the snail. A less extreme example illustrating the separation of the various elements of the pallial duct is found in female *Natica*, in which one gland lies along the course of the oviduct, and a large one is separated from it and opens to the base of the vagina alongside the oviduct and the bursa copulatrix.

Although in the majority of gastropods the sexes are separate and unchanged throughout the life of the individual, some species are consecutive hermaphrodites, first male and then female, and others are simultaneous hermaphrodites. The approach of the female phase in protandrous hermaphrodites involves not only a change in the gonad, but, in the monotocardians, the loss of the penis (if one is developed) and modifications of the pallial duct so that in older individuals there is no indication of the previous sex. When limpets of the genus *Patella* are examined they are found to be either male or female, yet there is evidence that in *P. vulgata* sex change occurs (Orton, 1920) in at least 90% of the population. Perhaps most if not all individuals are male when they first mature and change to female at the age of 1 year or more (Orton, 1928a). A study of this species from a range of localities in the British Isles (Orton, Southward & Dodd, 1956) has shown that the smaller limpets, between 16 and 25 mm in shell length, are at least 90% male. In those with a shell length of about 40 mm the sexes are approximately equal, while 60–70% of specimens having a shell length of 60 mm are female; in still larger specimens an even higher proportion of females occurs. Sex reversal (which takes place in a number of prosobranch molluscs) would seem the most reasonable explanation for this change in sex proportion with growth. There are no secondary sexual characters to involve considerable anatomical changes and since between periods of spawning the gonad has a long resting phase when sex is not determinable, a change occurring then would pass unnoticed. The Mediterranean limpet, *P. caerulea*, is also a protandrous hermaphrodite and the change from male to female gonad occurs during the resting period (Bacci, 1947; Pellegrini, 1948). In British patellids other than *P. vulgata* sex change is far less probable: 30–40% females are already present in the smallest size groups of maturing *P. aspera*, and in *P. intermedia* every size group with mature gonads shows 70% males—a high proportion of males may perhaps be correlated with external fertitilization in a sedentary animal.

Occasionally limpets with a hermaphrodite gonad are found. Dodd (1956) examined 43,257 individuals of *P. vulgata* and 5 were hermaphrodite, a percentage of 0·012; a similar percentage was obtained for *P. intermedia* and 10 times more for *P. aspera*. He concluded that such hermaphroditism is accidental and has no connexion with change of sex.

The other diotocardians in which hermaphrodites have been reported are *Acmaea fragilis* (Willcox, 1898), and *A. rubella* (Thorson, 1935), which are not British, and

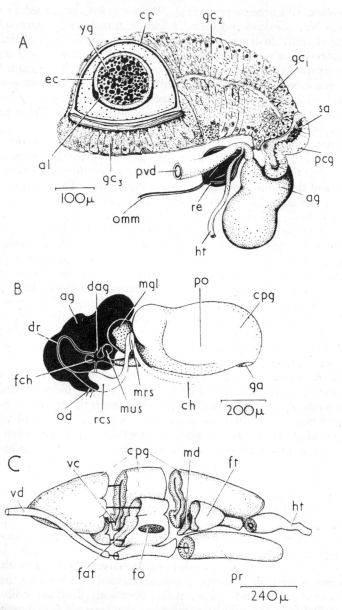

FIG. 194.—Genital system of A, *Rissoella diaphana*; B, *Skeneopsis planorbis*; C, *Velutina velutina*: the first includes a section across an egg capsule within the capsule gland.

ag, albumen gland; al, albumen; ch, channel along inner surface of mantle; cp, egg capsule; cpg, capsule gland; dag, duct of albumen gland; dr, duct of receptaculum seminis; ec, egg covering; fat, female atrium; fch, fertilization chamber; fo, female opening; ft, female duct; ga, genital opening; $gc_1$, gland cells secreting albumen-like substance; $gc_2$, gland cells secreting mucin-conchiolin; $gc_3$, gland cells which thicken base of egg capsule; ht, hermaphrodite duct; md, male duct; mgl, mucous gland; mrs, mouth of receptaculum seminis; mus, muscular pouch; od, ovarian duct; omm, opening of muscular sac to mantle cavity; pcg, posterior lobe of capsule gland; po, pallial oviduct; pr, prostate gland; pvd, pallial vas deferens; rcs, receptaculum seminis; re, muscular sac, probably homologue of receptaculum seminis; sa, spermatozoa; vc, ventral channel; vd, vas deferens; yg, yolk granules in egg.

*Puncturella noachina* (Rammelmeyer, 1925). Willcox (1898) examined 13 specimens of *A. fragilis* from New Zealand and found 5 female, 6 male and 2 hermaphrodites. She concluded that all individuals are at first male and then pass through a brief hermaphrodite phase before changing to females. Thiem (1917b), however, held that all monobranchs have separate sexes and that the sex of an individual is constant. In *Puncturella noachina* Rammelmeyer (1925) found spermatogenesis occurring in the gonad (of about 20 individuals) which had ripe eggs and assumed that the species is hermaphrodite, though presumably differing from *Patella vulgata* and *Acmaea fragilis* in being a simultaneous hermaphrodite.

In the monotocardians consecutive hermaphroditism occurs in the Scalidae, the Ianthinidae (Ankel, 1926), the Capulidae and the Calyptraeidae. It has been studied particularly well in *Crepidula* perhaps because of the economic importance of this genus, its abundance and the unique association of the individuals. These limpets form groups of up to 12 animals each clinging to the shell of the one beneath in such a way that the right lips of the shells, and therefore the genital apertures, approximate and the whole chain bends to the right (fig. 197). The groups continue from year to year, newly arrived young attaching themselves to the tip of the group as the old individuals die at the bottom. On an average one individual is added to the chain each year (Walne, 1956). The whole chain may be fixed to the substratum by its oldest member or the oldest shell may be empty and the chain unattached. These chains have usually been regarded as an association for breeding but recent work by Wilczynski (1955) has suggested that they may be more important in creating a strong feeding current from which all members will benefit. The limpets take 4–5 years to reach full size and most individuals live for 8–9 years (Walne, 1956). Only the youngest are able to move freely, for after about 2 years the power of locomotion is gradually lost.

Conklin (1897) was the first to show that *Crepidula fornicata* is a protandrous hermaphrodite and this was later verified by Orton (1909). The oldest animals are females, the youngest males. At the time when an individual settles the gonad has both spermatogonia and oogonia, but in the male phase the oocytes remain small with the nuclei apparently devoid of chromatin. The penis becomes functional only when the gonad has produced enough sperm to fill the vesicula seminalis (Coe, 1948). The gonadial duct at this stage acts as a vesicula seminalis and at copulation the sperm are freed to the renal vas deferens and so to the posterior end of the mantle cavity. From here a ciliated groove passes forwards to the outer edge of the food groove, along which it runs anteriorly, and then crosses to approach the base of the penis. The penis is long and tapering with glands around the base and at the tip; when in use it is passed into the mantle cavity of the underlying female and inserted into the pallial oviduct. Association of young *Crepidula* with the female prolongs the male phase and stimulates spermatogenesis (Coe, 1944). In the older members of the chain, the females, the genital duct differs from that of the male in having a gonopericardial duct between the renal oviduct and the pericardial cavity, and a closed pallial duct with glandular walls. At the upper end of the pallial duct are tubules comprising the receptaculum seminis into which sperm are deposited by the penis. There is no bursa copulatrix. Sperm in the tubules of the receptaculum remain functional for more than a year (Coe, 1942) and in a single female of the species *onyx* the tubules store sufficient sperm to fertilize the 50,000–200,000 eggs produced within that time. The penis in the female phase is reduced to a vestige and is lost completely in older females (fig. 185). The early stages in its reduction can be followed in one or two individuals in the middle of a chain which are undergoing sex inversion (fig. 197): regression of the penis begins as spermatogenesis stops and continues as sperm in the gonad degenerate, and as follicle cells appear and multiply and eggs develop. Before the female becomes functional all sperm are cytolyzed, but the

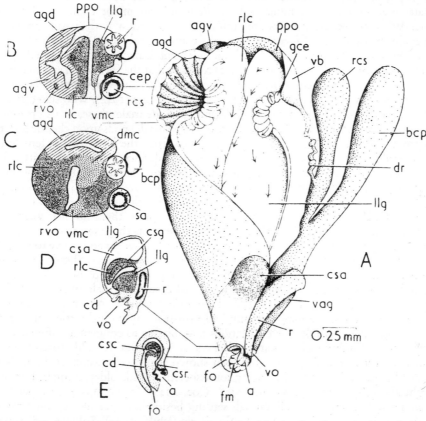

FIG. 195.—*Theodoxus fluviatilis:* A, pallial oviduct, seen from the dorsal surface, posterior end above. The bursa copulatrix and the receptaculum seminis have been dissected to one side and parts of the albumen and capsule glands opened. Arrows show the course of ciliary currents. B, C, D, E, transverse sections across the duct at the levels marked; in these the bursa and receptaculum are shown in their natural positions.

a, anus; agd, dorsal lobe of albumen gland; agv, ventral lobe of albumen gland; bcp, bursa copulatrix; cd, duct of capsule gland; cep, strip of tall columnar ciliated cells; csa, crystal sac; csc, opening of crystal sac to duct of capsule gland; csg, glandular ventral wall of crystal sac; csr, opening of crystal sac to rectum; dmc, dorsal strip of mucoid gland cells; dr, duct of receptaculum seminis; fm, fold acting as valve; fo, opening of pallial oviduct; gce, glandular and ciliated strip spreading ventrally from albumen gland; llg, left lobe of capsule gland; ppo, posterior wall of pallial oviduct; r, rectum; rcs, receptaculum seminis; rlc, right lobe of capsule gland; rvo, renal oviduct; sa, orientated spermatozoa; vag, vagina; vb, vestibule; vmc, ventral strip of mucoid gland cells; vo, opening of vagina.

reduced penis may sometimes be seen in an animal incubating a spawn mass (fig. 212A). The pallial oviduct is formed during the transitional period by the closing of that part of the sperm groove which runs through the mantle cavity and by the hypertrophy of its walls. The isolation of a male during the breeding season will lead to the onset of the female phase (Coe, 1944), though usually the first female stage is reached in the third summer (Cole, 1956).

The work of Gould (1919, 1947) and Coe (1938a, b, 1944, 1948) suggests that the transition from male to female occurs at different times in different individuals and indicates that sex change is influenced by other animals in the chain and by external factors. When immature limpets are cultured in association with mature females, the great majority assume the functional male phase and Gould (1919) held that the intimate association of the young individual with an older one is necessary for the male phase to develop. He presented evidence (1919, 1952) to show that the formation and maintenance of the male phase is influenced by a substance or substances secreted into the water by mature females, and this view was at first rejected by Coe (1944), who stated that there is no direct evidence that either the development of the male phase, or its prolongation by association with the female in any species of *Crepidula* depends upon chemical secretion or hormone which might pass through the water from the body of the female to the male. Coe also suggested (1938b) that a male individual, during association with a female, receives stimuli through the sense organs which influence its male characters, presumably by hormones secreted by its own body. However, in a later paper (1953) he supported Gould's conclusion that a female liberates a substance influencing the sexual activity of young individuals and this, he considered, immobilizes them in her vicinity; this influence is strictly specific. Not all young males react in the same way to the mating stimulus, for some leave their mating positions after a few weeks and move to neighbouring objects where they begin transformation to the female phase. Should an immature individual settle on a rock instead of joining a colony, the male phase may be relatively brief and followed rapidly by the transitional and then the female phase, or the animal may pass directly from the non-sexual to the female condition. Alternatively the solitary limpet may remain in the male state until an immature individual settles on it and then its sex changes (Coe, 1948). These variations may be due to congenital differences in the the tendency of individuals towards maleness or femaleness (Gould, 1952; Coe, 1953; Montalenti, 1960). For *C. plana* it has been shown that the omission of the male phase may not be due to lack of opportunity for association with older animals, but may be brought about by starvation (Gould, 1947; Coe, 1948). In the Japanese slipper limpets, *C. aculeata* and *C. walshi*, small animals settling beside large females become male at a size about half that at which isolated animals do (Ishiki, 1936). Solitary males become hermaphrodite but those associated with females remain male and may grow as large as the female. When several small limpets of *C. walshi* settle together one rapidly becomes female, the others male.

Should individuals comprising a chain be separated the oldest are unable to attach themselves again to any object, perhaps because the mouth of the shell has grown to fit over another *Crepidula* shell or a specific rock surface and is useless in fitting against a surface of different shape. Those individuals die of starvation or through attack by enemies. The younger members of the chain, however, tend to collect in new groups with females at the bottom and young males at the top (Coe, 1938b). If this is achieved without attempted copulation or during periods when the animals are not sexually active then it would seem to imply that these limpets display a recognition of sex which in other prosobranchs is pronounced only during periods of copulation, but this is perhaps not surprising in animals which are permanently associated.

The sex cycle of *Calyptraea chinensis* differs from that of *Crepidula* in several respects. In *Calyptraea* sex change always occurs at a particular stage in the life cycle (Pellegrini,

1949) and not, as in *Crepidula*, at different times in different animals (fig. 199); moreover, each individual passes through a functional male phase. There appears to be no self-fertilization (Wyatt, 1957). Males and females are associated only during the breeding season when the smaller male is carried by the female; at other times they are isolated. Bacci (1951) working on *Calyptraea chinensis* at Naples, where breeding occurs between December and May, showed that in the developing gonad of a young individual and in the youngest functional male which has recently paired, oocytes are absent. In larger specimens up to 6 mm in length, which may be isolated or in copulation, oocytes are developing, for during the functional male phase the gonad becomes hermaphrodite. During its first breeding period each individual is a functional male only. This may last 3–4 months and then, as the gonad changes, the excess sperm are resorbed and the penis is reduced and finally lost. The individual may have a second and third season as a female, and meanwhile growth continues and it may attain 17 mm in shell length. The changes in sex appear to be unaffected by external stimuli. In the male phase the pallial genital tract is similar to that of *Crepidula* in that there is an open seminal groove, which runs from the inner end of the mantle cavity to near the tip of the penis. With the loss of the penis that part of the seminal groove which extends beyond the opening of the mantle cavity is lost, too, whereas that part within the cavity closes to form the pallial oviduct, and narrow tubules, usually 6, grow out from the dorsal wall at the upper end of the duct; their openings lie close together and can be closed by muscles in their walls, and the blind end of each swells to form a vesicle for sperm (rcs, fig. 198). These structures constitute the receptaculum seminis. In the female phase a gonopericardial duct is present.

The sex cycle of *Capulus ungaricus* and *Trichotropis borealis* (Graham, 1954a) resembles that of *Calyptraea chinensis*, though there are differences in the structure of the genital duct (Giese, 1915). In the functional male of *Capulus* the renal vas deferens opens anteriorly to a small pouch from which the seminal groove passes to the mouth of the mantle cavity, and then along the right side of the head and along the penis to its tip. The pouch was regarded by Giese as the initial part of the uterus and even in the male phase a single dorsal vesicle opens from it, the future receptaculum seminis. The penis has no glands and tapers to a pointed tip. Very young males were not examined by Giese to see whether the upper part of the uterus and the receptaculum were already developed. In the male phase of *Trichotropis* there are rudiments of the female accessory glands which may, perhaps, have some prostatic function (Graham, 1954a). In neither species has a gonopericardial duct been found.

Much less is known about the change in sex in the various members of the Scalidae and Ianthinidae. Ankel (1936a) stated that in *Scala* (=*Clathrus*) *clathrus* in the Gulf of Naples each breeding season brings a sex reversal, the female phase of the gonad overlapping with the male so that oogenesis begins in the superficial ends of tubules in which spermatogenesis can still be followed in the lumina and ducts. Laursen (1953) suggested that in *Ianthina* there is a similar sex change repeated several times throughout the life history, not perhaps in each breeding season, though this is not confirmed by Ankel (1926, 1930a) for *I. pallida* (=*I. bicolor* of Ankel; see Laursen, 1953), nor by Graham (1954b) for *I. janthina*. These workers found that the smaller animals are males and the larger females and concluded that sex change occurs only once in the life of the individual. In both genera the change in the genital duct between male and female phase is relatively slight. There is neither penis in the male, nor bursa copulatrix in the female, nor a receptaculum in *Ianthina*. In *Clathrus* the pallial duct is open in both sexes and the female differs from the male in having a receptacular pouch at its inner end. In *Ianthina janthina*

(Graham, 1954b) the genital duct is closed throughout its length. The pallial section in the male (fig. 196A) consists of a caecal posterior part with numerous tubular glands which are not mucous (pgl), and an anterior prostatic part in which the walls are covered with an epithelium mainly of mucous cells and are flung into irregular foldings (fpr). All parts of the male duct contain spermatozeugmata and the glands may provide them with nutrient material. However, Graham suggested that some part of this glandular equipment foreshadows the female condition (fig. 196B) in which the caecal posterior section of the duct is enlarged to form the albumen gland (ag) and there is hypertrophy of the anterior section (mgl) so that the walls, almost entirely covered by large mucus-secreting cells, are irregularly folded to form 3 pouches on the right side. This species is viviparous and free-swimming veligers are liberated (Wilson & Wilson, 1956). Spermatozeugmata liberating eupyrene sperm may be seen in all parts of the female duct. Fertilization appears to take place in the ovary, which is filled with developing eggs and young, and spermatozeugmata in all stages of degeneration. The genital duct contains older embryos and the mucous glands produce a histotrophe for their nourishment. The site of fertilization is unusual, though Ankel (1930a) had already suggested that in I. pallida fertilization probably occurs as soon as the eggs have escaped from the germinal epithelium and in the very tubules in which they have matured. Two British species of Ianthina, I. exigua Lamarck and I. pallida Thompson are oviparous, and according to Laursen embryos of oviparous species are nourished by mucus from the egg capsule, so that in all species mucus of oviducal origin is the pabulum on which the embryos are reared.

There are 4 British prosobranchs which are viviparous—Littorina saxatilis (fig. 178B), Potamopyrgus jenkinsi (fig. 309), Viviparus viviparus (fig. 223) and V. contectus—and the pallial duct is modified to form a brood pouch in which the embryos are retained until their development is complete, although Smidt (1944) stated that the young of P. jenkinsi may hatch with a very small velum and have a brief pelagic stage. Both albumen and shell glands are developed in the pallial oviduct of the viviparous species, but the capsule gland is replaced by a thin-walled brood pouch; before the embryos enter it each is provided with albumen and a shell. Along the ventral wall of the pouch in Littorina and Viviparus (Ankel, 1936a) are 2 longitudinal folds limiting a sperm channel which leads to the receptaculum, and a similar channel is developed in Potamopyrgus. The brood pouch is more complex in L. saxatilis and may accommodate up to 900 eggs according to Linke (1933), though in winkles from the Channel Pelseneer (1911) found only two-thirds this number, and at Whitstable the larger individuals have only about one-third (Berry, 1956) at the height of their breeding season; very young individuals may have less than 40 eggs. What varieties of the species were examined by these workers is not known, nor is it known whether the varieties differ from one another in this respect. Thorson (1946) suggested that one factor affecting productivity is the salinity of the water in which the animals are living. Transverse folds arise from the longitudinal folds and subdivide the lumen of the pallial oviduct of L. saxatilis into smaller pouches in which the embryos are grouped. Groups of about 20 are at the same stage of development with the youngest ones nearest the upper end; the embryos move forward as their development proceeds. The wall of the pouch is vascular and its epithelium is ciliated and has mucous and protein-secreting cells. These glands produce a fluid which surrounds the embryos and is kept in circulation by the ciliary currents. There is no evidence that the embryos obtain nourishment from the fluid or directly from the maternal tissues; if they are removed from the brood pouch they will develop in sea water; moreover, the shell is impermeable to proteins (Linke, 1933). The albumen, however, supplements the yolk provided in the egg. It becomes less viscous during development and the veliger rotates in its albuminous covering and gradually devours it (fig. 222). The pronounced vascularization of the brood pouch is presumably correlated with the respiratory requirements of the brood. A holotrichous ciliate *Protophrya* is frequent in the mantle cavity of *L.*

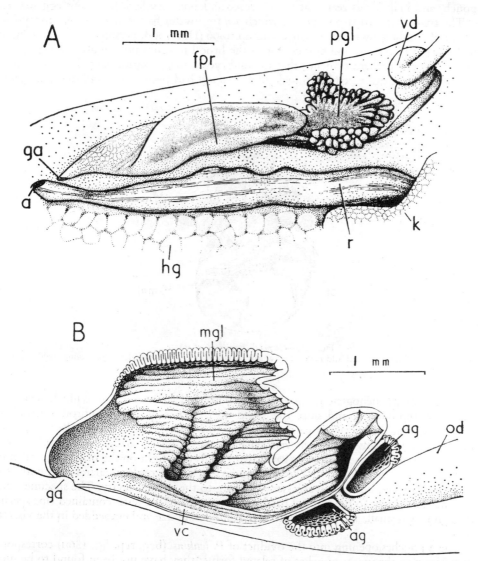

FIG. 196.—*Ianthina janthina:* A, dissection to show genital duct of animal in male stage, seen in ventral view from the mantle cavity; B, dissection of genital duct of animal in female stage.

a, anus; ag, albumen gland; fpr, fold within prostate gland alongside ventral channel; ga, genital aperture; hg, hypobranchial gland; k, kidney; mgl, mucous gland; od, ovarian duct; pgl, pigmented gland on male duct; r, rectum; vc, ventral channel; vd, vas deferens.

*saxatilis* and enters the pallial oviduct where it may be seen creeping over the surface of the egg shells.

At Cullercoats, on the Northumberland coast, Seshappa (1947) found specimens of a thin-shelled variety of *L. saxatilis* otherwise agreeing with the variety *patula* of Jeffreys (1865). The reproductive system is unusual in that a capsule gland replaces the brood pouch, and individuals reared at the Cullercoats laboratory laid gelatinous egg masses.

The two other viviparous species, which are freshwater forms, have fewer embryos—35–40 in a fully grown *Potamopyrgus* and up to 96 (Heywood, personal communication) in *Viviparus viviparus*—and in these forms the brood pouch is not subdivided into compartments nor is there evidence that the embryos obtain nourishment other than yolk and albumen. Until recently no male of *P. jenkinsi* had been found and the species was

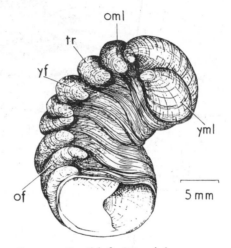

Fig. 197.—*Crepidula fornicata:* chain.
of, old female; oml, old male; tr, transitional form; yf, young female; yml, young male.

known to be parthenogenetic. Boycott (1919) isolated very young individuals which, at maturity, reproduced, and since there was no evidence of a hermaphrodite gland he concluded that the species is parthenogenetic, the only parthenogenetic British prosobranch. These results have been verified by others (Quick, 1920). The discovery of a single male of the variety *carinata* (Patil, 1958) sheds new light on the origin of parthenogenesis in the species (p. 587). The reproductive system agrees in general plan with that of *Hydrobia ulvae*, but has no accessory opening to the mantle cavity. The specimen was of a size equivalent to the normal parthenogenetic form, the testis contained ripe sperm, though it was small, and the prostate was of moderate size and embedded in the visceral mass.

The 2 pouches opening into the oviduct of *P. jenkinsi* (bcp, rcp, fig. 186H) correspond in position to the sperm pouches of related forms; they have not been found to be used as such, though at least one of them has some functional importance. This is the pouch corresponding to the bursa copulatrix. It is relatively enormous in size and in all specimens with embryos in the brood pouch is filled with secretion. This secretion has staining properties which suggest that it is albuminous, and there is also a mucous component which must be derived from a gland adjacent to the albumen gland. Each egg in the brood pouch is surrounded by albumen and externally by a thin mucous coat which forms the shell. It receives both secretions from glands at the posterior end of the brood pouch (ag, mgl); the mucous gland surrounds the posterior wall of the pouch (bp). It is assumed that secretions not used in the formation of the egg capsules are sucked into the bursa copulatrix which thus acts as a waste dump. This may be a subsidiary function of the bursa in related species, though they produce egg capsules, and unwanted secretions from the duct may be extruded when the capsules are spawned. The ultimate fate of the waste in *P. jenkinsi* is unknown: it may be voided to the mantle cavity by way of the ventral channel which is partially separated from the brood pouch by an epithelial fold.

The species of monotocardians which are simultaneous hermaphrodites are *Valvata piscinalis* (fig. 187B), *Rissoella diaphana* (figs. 187A, 194A), *R. opalina*, *Pelseneeria stylifera*, *Velutina velutina* (fig. 194C) and perhaps *Omalogyra atomus* (figs. 184A, 187C). Sperm and ova are either produced in the same acini of the gonad (*Rissoella* spp.), or in different acini (*Valvata*, *Velutina*), or the gonad is bilobed with an ovary and a testis (*Omalogyra*). The lay-out of the hermaphrodite ducts varies considerably from species to species, suggesting that hermaphroditism has arisen independently in the different groups to which these animals belong. It is simplest in *Rissoella*. The hermaphrodite duct, on reaching the posterior end of the body whorl, divides into 2 branches which diverge, and one leads to the pallial vas deferens (pvd, fig. 187A) and the other to the pallial oviduct (ag). The plan of each of the 2 pallial ducts resembles that of small monotocardians in which the sexes are separate: the vas deferens runs forwards beneath the pallial oviduct, becomes glandular, forming a prostate, towards the mouth of the mantle cavity and passes up the right side of the head and through the penis to its tip; no glands occur in the penial duct. The pallial oviduct comprises an albumen gland and a capsule gland, and the duct of a muscular sac opens ventrally to the wall which separates them. The female aperture is at the mouth of the mantle cavity. Excess secretion and sperm from the pallial oviduct collect in the muscular sac and are discharged to the mantle cavity by way of a short duct (omm). The hermaphrodite duct of *Velutina* is, in plan, a modification of the genital duct of *Trivia*. In both sexes in *Trivia* (figs. 193A, B) the pallial region forms a pouch of considerable size which is glandular, with a pronounced development of muscles, and opens by a ventral longitudinal slit to the mantle cavity. The corresponding pallial region in *Velutina* (fig. 194C) is a similar pouch, and its opening is the female aperture (fo), but the glandular elements are stripped from the walls leaving a columnar ciliated epithelium rich in mucous cells, and a thick muscle coat. There is a tubular gland opening into the posterior wall, ventral to the opening of the hermaphrodite duct, and a large composite gland running parallel with the pouch and extending beyond it both anteriorly and posteriorly. This gland has a ventral channel, with secreting cells unlike those elsewhere, and with an independent opening to the anterior wall of the pouch, adjoining the opening from the dorsal part of the same gland. The posterior tubular gland is probably a prostate (pr) since from its opening a short, deep, ciliated groove, into which is directed a groove from the hermaphrodite duct, passes anteriorly to the opening of the vas deferens. The narrow vas deferens (vd) runs up the right side of the head and through the penis to its tip. The egg capsule in *Trivia* is moulded by the ventral pedal gland of the female. This gland is not developed in *Velutina*, and in this species the capsule may be fashioned by the muscular pouch of the hermaphrodite duct. In *Mangelia* and perhaps other toxoglossans the outer wall of the capsule is shaped by a terminal section of the oviduct and not by a ventral pedal gland. Despite this all capsules have the same accuracy of form.

The genital system of *Valvata piscinalis* and *Omalogyra atomus* is more complex. In *Valvata* (fig. 187B) there are 2 genital openings—the male at the tip of the penis and the female near the mouth of the mantle cavity. As in *Rissoella*, the hermaphrodite duct (ht), which acts as a vesicula seminalis, bifurcates anteriorly to give oviduct and vas deferens. The latter has a straight course to the tip of the penis, and, not far from its

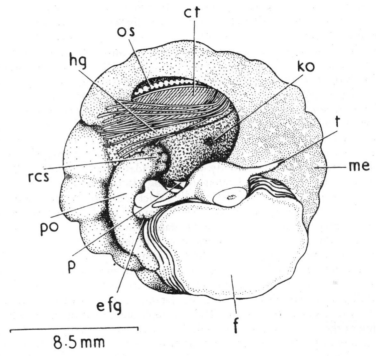

8.5 mm

FIG. 198.—*Calyptraea chinensis:* female, in ventral view, dissected to show receptaculum seminis.
ct, ctenidium; efg, expanded anterior end of food groove; f, foot; hg, hypobranchial gland; ko, kidney opening; me, mantle edge; os, osphradium; p, remains of penis; po, pallial oviduct; rcs, receptaculum seminis; t, tentacle.

origin, receives the opening of an enormous prostate gland (pr) which is separated from the duct and spreads in the haemocoel. The arrangement of the oviduct and its glands is not so simple. The initial part of the duct is narrow, and it then swells rather abruptly into a large pouch (fch), the fertilization chamber (Cleland, 1954), constricts again, and enlarges into a second pouch (bcp), the bursa copulatrix. It passes from the bursa as a narrow channel which, after receiving the duct from the albumen gland (ag), opens into the anterior end of the capsule gland (cp), not far from the genital aperture (fo). It has been suggested by Johansson (1955) that this course, along which the eggs travel to the capsule gland, represents the vaginal channel of less specialized monotocardians, which has separated from the accessory female glands. He described a narrow connexion (gtd) between the albumen gland and the hermaphrodite duct (it was previously found by

Garnault) and suggested that the separation of the channel starts from that point. The connexion is apparently inessential since it is not always present.

*Omalogyra atomus* (figs. 184A, 187C) stands apart from the other hermaphrodite forms in having the gonad divided into ovary (ov) and testis (te) and only one genital opening near the mouth of the mantle cavity on the right side. The only structure which could act as a copulatory organ is a whip-like muscular tube (p) (not present in summer individuals, p. 355) which may be protruded through the genital opening. From the genital aperture (ga) the hermaphrodite duct passes back for a short distance and bifurcates into vas deferens and oviduct which are both glandular, forming the prostate gland (pr), and the capsule and albumen glands (cp, ag) respectively. Posteriorly each duct narrows before opening to the fertilization chamber (fch), which also receives the testicular (td) and ovarian (od) ducts. Immature individuals tide over the winter, and animals collected in spring show the vas deferens as the principal genital duct. At this stage the opening of the pallial oviduct into the hermaphrodite duct is far too small to allow the passage of an egg capsule—in other words the animal is purely male. It is assumed that later the reproductive system undergoes the necessary changes associated with the adoption of the female phase. This is found in all summer individuals. The capsule gland is then voluminous and lies on the right side of the vas deferens and not above it as in spring forms, and it is broadly open to the hermaphrodite duct anteriorly; the opening of the vas deferens into this duct is minute and surrounded by a sphincter; there is no sperm sac or penial tube and the bursa has a long muscular duct, but has itself an insignificant musculature. The histology of the bursa in the female phase resembles that of the sperm sac (spc) in the male phase (p. 356), and the function of these 2 structures appears to be similar, for in the bursa waste secretion from the genital ducts may accumulate and later be disposed of; the accumulation is greatest after an egg capsule has been deposited. This anatomical femaleness does not prevent the formation of apparently ripe spermatozoa in the testis, and their passage into such parts of the male system as are present, and although the lack of a penis and associated structures would appear inevitably to preclude copulation and cross-fertilization, it may not be incompatible with successful self-fertilization.

The pyramidellids, which are superficially prosobranch in appearance, show evidence of their opisthobranch affinity in the structure of the reproductive organs (fig. 187D). The gonad is hermaphrodite (hgl) and sperm and ova are produced in the same tubules. There is a single genital duct (ht) which extends from the gonad to the genital aperture (ga). This is at the anterior end of the mantle cavity in *Odostomia* and *Chrysallida* and on the propodium in *Turbonilla elegantissima*. The duct is divided into an upper thin-walled region and a broader pallial part which is glandular and ciliated in its proximal half, and ciliated and muscular distally. The gland cells of the pallial duct are epithelial in position, and they appear to be functional only during early sexual maturity when the male system, but not the female, is mature; they presumably produce a prostatic secretion. Running along the median wall of the pallial duct as far as its inner end is a ciliated gutter which communicates with a single sperm pouch (rcs). After copulation spermatozoa fill this pouch, surround its opening to the pallial duct and are concentrated along the ventral gutter. Secretions concerned with the formation of egg capsules come from glands which are separated from the hermaphrodite duct and open into its upper thin-walled part (ag, mgl). As in opisthobranchs the ova receive their albuminous covering as they pass along the spermoviduct and do not enter the albumen gland, and large mucous glands provide a jelly in which the eggs are embedded. Other opisthobranch characters are evident in the open seminal groove (sgr) leading from the common genital aperture to the penis, which is invaginable, and the sperm sac, which is attached to the penial sheath and is filled with spermatozoa before copulation (p. 355). This general plan resembles the arrangement of the male organs in the opisthobranch *Philine aperta*, though the position of the penis in the pyramidellid is unique (perhaps associated with the evolution of the long acrembolic proboscis), and the structure of this organ resembles more closely that of *Omalogyra atomus*.

Within the prosobranch gastropods all types of sexuality occur. The majority are separately sexed. Of the hermaphrodites some are simultaneous hermaphrodites, others consecutive hermaphrodites and in one species, *Clathrus clathrus*, sex reversal appears to take place at each breeding season. Hermaphroditism prevails in the other two orders of the class, the Opisthobranchia and Pulmonata, so that of more than 20,000 species of living gastropods only about half are unisexual. It is partly on this account that there

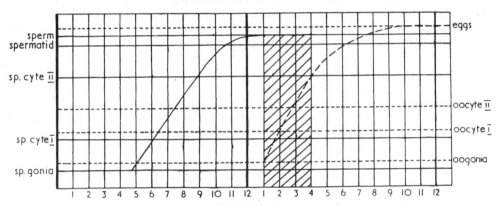

Fig. 199.—Graph showing the reproductive cycle of *Calyptraea chinensis*. Figures on the abscissa represent months of the year; on the ordinate the solid line represents the development of spermatozoa, the pecked line, of eggs. The hatched area represents the transition from male to female. After Pellegrini.

have been varied speculations as to the sex of the archimollusc and archigastropod. Simroth (1896–1907) suggested that the archigastropod was hermaphrodite and, as in Turbellaria, the gonad was comprised of male and female follicles. The Diotocardia with protandrous species support this idea of a hermaphrodite ancestor, but Simroth regarded the lack of copulation and accessory glands in this group as secondary and not primary, as is more commonly believed. On the contrary, Pelseneer (1895) held that the archimollusc was not hermaphrodite, and he thought of the most archaic forms of the different groups of molluscs as unisexual, with hermaphroditism as a sign of advancement. Giese (1915) agreed with him. A study of the reproductive ducts of the hydrobiids influenced Krull (1935) in supporting Simroth's view. The subdivision of the pallial oviduct into the main glandular egg-conducting area and the ventral ciliated groove he likened to the bipartite division of the spermoviduct of monaulic pulmonates. He regarded the pulmonates as the most primitive and suggested that the Monotocardia and the Neritidae evolved from them on the one hand and the opisthobranchs on the other, with the more archaic gastropods, the Diotocardia, branching from the stem arising from the hermaphrodite Urgastropod before the pulmonates evolved. These rather unorthodox ideas are open to much criticism; as Hubendick (1945) has pointed out, too much importance is attached to a single character—the spermoviduct—in assessing the affinity between such major groups of the Mollusca. However, in view of the fact that

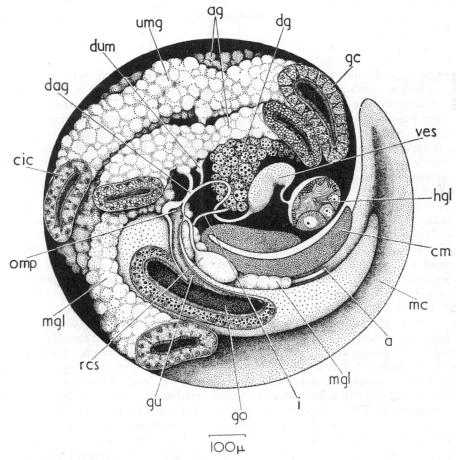

FIG. 200.—*Odostomia lukisi:* the visceral hump has been cut across at the level of the reproductive ducts and the cut surface is viewed from above; the haemocoel is black.

a, anus; ag, albumen gland; cic, ciliated cell; cm, columellar muscle; dag, duct of albumen gland; dg, digestive gland; dum, duct of upper mucous gland; gc, gland cell; go, glandular part of pallial hermaphrodite duct; gu, gutter along glandular part of pallial hermaphrodite duct; hgl, hermaphrodite gland; i, intestine; mc, mantle cavity; mgl, lower mucous gland; omp, opening of lower mucous gland into glandular part of pallial hermaphrodite duct; rcs, receptaculum seminis; umg, upper mucous gland; ves, seminal vesicle.

hermaphroditism occurs in all classes of the phylum with the exception of the most highly specialized, the cephalopods, it is tempting to believe that the ancestral mollusc was hermaphrodite, and although this condition may not have persisted into most modern diotocardians, the tendency to produce a hermaphrodite condition is undoubtedly present.

14

# CHAPTER 16

# SPAWN

THE eggs of diotocardians are each surrounded by a vitelline membrane and a sphere of albumen, both produced by the ovum, and in species which form spawn masses they are bound together in a gelatinous secretion. This is produced either by the ovum (*Diodora*) (gsh, fig. 167B), or by the enlarged urinogenital papilla (*Margarites*; ugp, fig. 169), or by a short pallial duct (*Cantharidus, Calliostoma*; ugp, fig. 170). It appears to form no barrier to external fertilization but this must occur close to the time of spawning, for the secretion hardens considerably when exposed to sea water. The egg mass is manipulated by the foot which fastens it to the substratum. No monotocardian is known in which the ovum produces all the investments which surround it— in fact there is no suggestion except in the family Lacunidae (Hertling, 1928) that it produces anything but the vitelline membrane. Their eggs have more elaborate coverings derived from the pallial oviduct, which extends through the length of the mantle cavity; these last longer and the eggs are slower to develop than those of diotocardians. They are provided with albumen which is used as food for the developing embryos and which in *Viviparus* contains mineral salts but neither carbohydrates nor fat (Charin, 1926). The albumen is not homogeneous; the part immediately surrounding the embryo is typically semifluid and clear, the remainder more viscous and usually granular, changing in consistency as development proceeds. In the land snail *Succinea putris* (George & Jura, 1958) there is an outer insoluble skin of albumen which gives positive tests for arginine, tyrosine, -SS- groups and polysaccharides, and which presumably constitutes the last food of the embryo before it escapes. The inner albumen comprises polysaccharides and simple proteins soluble in water. These snails have no free larva and need a considerable supply of food. All but a few species of monotocardians produce egg capsules with a resistant wall which may allow passage of salts and water. This is unlikely to be true of freshwater forms which must maintain osmotic independence, except *Viviparus*, where the capsules remain in the oviduct and have been shown by Charin (1926) to be permeable to water and salts, and perhaps in the parthenogenetic *Potamopyrgus jenkinsi*, which is also viviparous. The wall frequently shows a fibrillar appearance due to conchiolin, and a suture separating it into 2 equal halves, which reflect the bilobed structure of the oviduct. The manufacture of a capsule, which occurs after the eggs have been fertilized, may take some hours. Their shape and size vary from species to species, though the differences are often trivial, and may be due to the varying methods by which they are manipulated after leaving the oviduct. Usually they are secured to a holdfast. Only in 2 British species (*Littorina littorea, L. neritoides*) is the capsule liberated to the plankton, and in these it is passed to an ovipositor (opr, fig. 289A) where it is moulded to its definite shape and freed to the sea. In some species a fixed gelatinous spawn mass is produced in which the eggs, each in an albuminous covering, are isolated from one another.

The diversity in the type of spawn produced by species of one genus may be as great as that of species from unrelated families. The 4 species of *Littorina* commonly found on rocky shores may be cited as an example. They have contrasting spawn and breeding habits which are associated with the differing provision made for the young and the suppression of the larval phase in the life history (Tattersall, 1920). Two have planktonic capsules and veliger larvae, a third fastens its gelatinous spawn on the fronds of the fucoids amongst which it lives and the young emerge in the crawling stage, and the fourth is viviparous. Their zonation is especially interesting. *Littorina neritoides* is the highest of them all, living in crevices of exposed rocks often above levels ever reached by the sea, for which reason it was thought for some time to be viviparous. However, its method of reproduction by planktonic capsules was discovered almost simultaneously by Linke (1935*a*) and Lebour (1935*c*). The capsule (figs. 201D, E) has the shape of a biconvex disc measuring about 0·18 mm in diameter and with a height of about half this. It contains a single egg (de) surrounded by albumen (al) and then an egg covering (ec). Lysaght (1941) has shown that in the Plymouth area *Littorina neritoides* spawns only when it is submerged. She suggested that the snails living well above the tide do not migrate downwards, so that except in severe storms spawning can only take place at the fortnightly spring tides. However their spawning period is during the winter and spring (September–April) when the level of the tide may be increased by rough weather. Observations made by us on the Gower peninsula, S Wales, seem to indicate a genuine downward movement of about 8 ft in March at spring-tide time carried out by very ripe animals, though no opportunity of checking the occurrence of planktonic capsules at the same time was available. Egg capsules may frequently be taken from the pallial oviduct, fully formed though softer than capsules in the plankton, suggesting that they are ready to be released when conditions are appropriate. It is of interest to find that the fortnightly spawning rhythm is also evident in individuals which live in high rock pools and are always submerged. After a planktonic life the metamorphosing larvae may be cast up with the tide, or settle lower on the shore and migrate to some extent to dry rocks, but the way in which the young reach the habitat of the adult is unknown. Lysaght (1941) has suggested that the larvae are able to settle only on exposed rock faces devoid of fucoids.

The common periwinkle, *Littorina littorea*, also has pelagic capsules, different in shape, though similar in construction (Caullery & Pelseneer, 1910). The adult of this species is the largest of the 4 and inhabits the lower half of the shore. It breeds chiefly in the spring, though at Plymouth capsules may be found in the plankton during any month (Lebour, 1947). The capsule (figs. 201C, F) resembles in shape a British soldier's steel helmet. It measures about 1 mm across and contains 1–5 eggs (de) which are pink in colour; up to 9 eggs have been recorded from a single capsule by Linke (1933), though so large a number is rare. The shape is moulded by the ovipositor which, according to Linke (1933), produces the tough external membrane with the circular brim (om). A gelatinous fluid (gf) fills the space between this membrane and the egg covering (ec). The supply of albumen around each egg (al) is small and unimportant as food. The capsules are liberated an hour or two after copulation and then intermittently for a month or more, the single copulation sufficing (Tattersall, 1920). Hatching, which may occur on the sixth day in normal sea water (Tattersall, 1920), is due to increased osmotic pressure within the capsule causing a rupture in the wall (Linke, 1933). The eggs develop in water of salinity 20‰ or over, though the lower salinities slow down development (Hayes, 1927*b*).

The viviparous periwinkle, *Littorina saxatilis*, breeds throughout the year at Plymouth (Lebour, 1937), though at Whitstable there is a decline in activity (p. 356) from June to

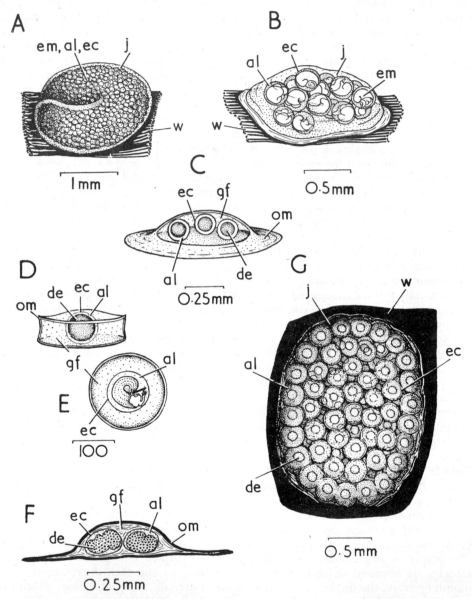

FIG. 201.—Spawn. A, *Lacuna vincta*; B, *Lacuna pallidula* to show embryos nearly hatching; C, *Littorina littorea*; D, *Littorina neritoides*, from the side; E, the same from above; F, *Littorina littorea*, in vertical section; G, *Lacuna pallidula* newly laid, from above.

al, albumen; de, developing egg; ec, egg covering; em, embryo; gf, gelatinous fluid; j, jelly of egg mass; om, outer membrane; w, weed.

mid-August, when the ovary is reduced (Berry, 1956). This species extends several feet above HWM, though not so high as *Littorina neritoides*, and is also found as low as half-tide level. The eggs (fig. 222A), which are retained in the brood pouch during development, are each surrounded by a larger supply of albumen (fa, va) than in the preceding species, and then an egg covering (ec). The albumen is eaten as food and in the early stages of development is fluid only in the vicinity of the embryo. Its jelly-like consistency at the periphery changes as development proceeds. The veliger (fig. 222B) rotates in the

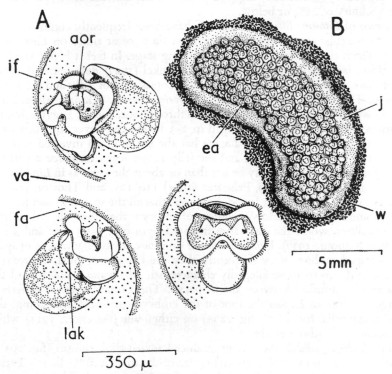

FIG. 202.—*Littorina littoralis*: A, developing embryos; B, spawn on weed.
aor, alleged apical organ; ea, egg with albumen and egg covering; fa, fluid albumen; if, interface between fluid and viscous albumen; j, jelly of egg mass; lak, larval kidney; va, viscous albumen; w, weed.

fluid and at a later stage (figs. 222C, D) when the albumen has gone, the embryo creeps around the egg covering. Finally it rasps the wall of its cell with the radula and makes a hole through which it escapes (Linke, 1933). Freed individuals move rapidly amongst the embryos in the lower part of the oviduct; they escape through the genital aperture and live in the same rock crevices as the adults.

The flat periwinkle, *Littorina littoralis*, lives only where large algae are growing, especially *Ascophyllum*, *Fucus vesiculosus* and *F. serratus*, and deposits its gelatinous egg mass (fig. 202B) on damp, unexposed fronds, especially of *Fucus*. It usually spawns at night, a few hours after copulation. The spawn is flat and may be kidney-shaped in outline, measuring 7 × 3 mm (Linke, 1933; Lebour, 1937), or it may be oval or circular. It contains 90–150 eggs, each with albumen and egg covering as in the other species, arranged regularly in 2–3 layers one above the other and embedded in a jelly (j) which is hard throughout. The jelly prevents the spawn from drying and protects the embryos from infection; only if the spawn mass is in the later stages of development and unhealthy does it allow entry to ciliates and nematode worms. The young take 2–3 weeks to hatch, passing through the veliger stage (fig. 202A) within the egg covering and biting their way out with the radula. By this time the surrounding jelly has swollen with the uptake of water and the young can make their escape. The adults can live in water of low salinity (10–15‰) but Hertling (1928) has shown that the development of the egg ceases at a salinity of 25‰ or below.

The spawn of *Littorina littoralis* appears to have been frequently confused with that of *Lacuna pallidula* (fig. 201G) which is also laid on *Fucus* or at times on *Laminaria* fronds, and from which the young hatch in the crawling stage. In fact it is not at all clear that the confusion has been dispelled. Hertling & Ankel (1927) differentiated between the spawn of the 2 species on the grounds of shape, consistency of jelly and the arrangement of the eggs. They stated that the spawn of *Littorina littoralis* is kidney-shaped in outline, the jelly in which the eggs are embedded hard throughout, and the eggs (each surrounded by albumen and egg covering) arranged in 2–3 layers and never squashed against one another, whereas the egg mass of *Lacuna* has the shape of an inverted watch glass, is approximately circular in outline, and the jelly rather soft except for a stiff rind. The number of eggs in each mass may be less than or about the same as in *Littorina*: Hertling & Ankel (1927) quoted 60–140, Pelseneer (1911) 110–125, and Thorson (1946) gave a number as low as 13. Thorson found, however, that all the spawn masses in The Sound are smaller and have a much lower content of embryos than those described from more Atlantic localities, where the size varies from a length of 3·9–5·3 mm and a breadth of 3·3–4·5 mm (Lebour, 1937). *Littorina littoralis* does not always lay masses of spawn with a kidney-shaped outline. Very frequently they are circular or oval, approximating in both shape and size to those allegedly characteristic of *Lacuna pallidula*, and this is the main cause of confusion between the 2 species. The 2 may be easily differentiated in later stages because in *Lacuna* the foot of the embryo, just before hatching, shows the enlarged metapodial lobes (mt, fig. 286A) on either side (Pelseneer, 1911) which allow it to be identified without doubt.

In adult *Lacuna pallidula* there is pronounced sexual dimorphism (fig. 203) and the female (fl) may attain more than twice the size of the male (ml). Gallien & Larambergue (1938), working at Wimereux, found that the females attain a shell length of 12 mm and the males 5·8 mm; the weight of the female may be 10 times that of the male (Thorson, 1946). The species is an annual though the females live longer than the males which disappear after copulation. The breeding period is late winter and spring and may extend into the summer. At this time the animals move from deeper water to the inter-tidal zone and they may be seen in pairs, the male attached to the shell of the female towards the opening of the mantle cavity on the right side; this appears to be the position for copulation, as in many other species.

The spawn of only one other British species of *Lacuna* has been described, that of *L. vincta*. It forms the familiar yellowish rings (fig. 201A) which may be found from January to early summer on various weeds, green, brown and red; Lebour (1937) stated that other egg masses of similar shape which are pink or green almost certainly belong to another species. The rings are slightly spiral and each is made of a gelatinous substance with 1,000–1,200 eggs embedded in it. These eggs are only half the size of those of *L. pallidula*, or less than half, the diameter ranging from 103–128 $\mu$. Each is surrounded by a small sphere of albumen and then an egg covering. Hertling (1928) held that the albumen is not used as food, but to raise the osmotic pressure, and that it brings about the swelling of the egg covering which doubles in diameter during development and finally bursts to liberate the embryos. The young hatch as veligers after a development lasting 2–3 weeks, the rate of development being influenced by the temperature (Hertling, 1931). The jelly in which the eggs are embedded is no barrier to the entry of salts and the egg covering allows the escape of $CO_2$ and the passage of water and salts in both directions (Hertling, 1928). To begin with the jelly is viscous, but gradually it swells with the uptake of water and allows the veligers to leave. Hertling (1928) has distinguished a very fine inner membrane close to the egg of *L. vincta* which, he suggested, is secreted by the egg itself. It is visible up to the veliger stage, separating the fluid albumen surrounding the embryo from the outer albumen which is more viscous. The presence of such a membrane in *L. pallidula* is uncertain, though an interface between thick and

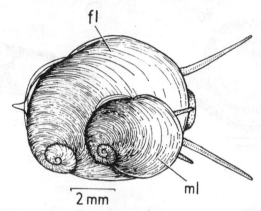

FIG. 203.—*Lacuna pallidula:* male and female in pairing position, from above. fl, female; ml, male.

thin albumen simulating a membrane can be identified in *Littorina littoralis* (if, fig. 202A). If Hertling's suggestion is correct, it would mean that at least in some members of the Lacunidae the ovum, as in the archaeogastropods, secretes coverings other than the vitelline membrane.

There is only one other species of British prosobranch, *Bittium reticulatum*, which produces a coiled, gelatinous egg mass (fig. 204C). As in *Lacuna vincta* it contains several hundred eggs each with a supply of albumen and an egg covering separating it from its neighbours. However the eggs of *Bittium* are much smaller (about 60 $\mu$ diameter) and the supply of albumen correspondingly reduced. There is little possibility of confusing the spawn of the 2 species since in *Bittium* it is a narrow cord coiled in an anticlockwise direction to form a tight spiral which is fixed to rock, stone or weed, and it measures only about half the diameter of the spawn of *L. vincta*. The young escape as veligers with horn-coloured shells.

The importance of albumen as a supply of food for the developing embryo is emphasized in the terrestrial prosobranch, *Pomatias elegans*, which occurs in large numbers in parts of southern England where a thin layer of comparatively alkaline soil (pH 7·5–7·9) covers calcareous rocks. *Pomatias* is a member of the Stirps Littorinacea (Thiele, 1929–35)

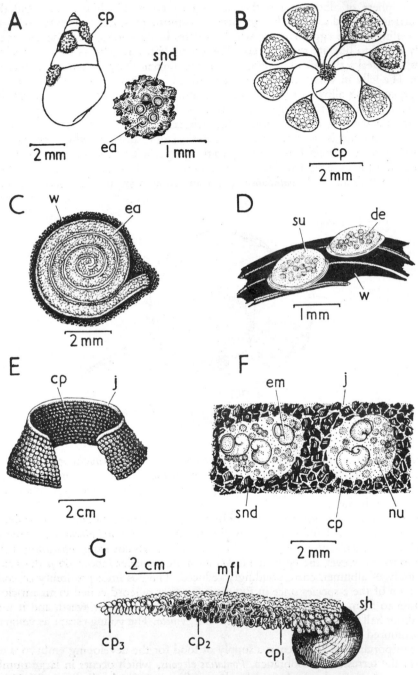

FIG. 204.—Spawn. A, *Hydrobia ulvae*, spawn attached to shell on left, and one spawn mass on right; B, *Turritella communis*; C, *Bittium reticulatum*; D, *Rissoa parva*; E, *Natica catena*; F, *Natica catena*, section showing 2 egg cases and surrounding jelly; G, *Ianthina exigua*.

cp, egg capsule; $cp_1$, youngest capsules; $cp_2$ capsules containing shelled embryos; $cp_3$, empty capsules; de, developing egg; ea, developing egg with albumen and egg covering; em, embryo; j, jelly of egg mass; mfl, mucous float; nu, nurse cell; sh, shell; snd, sand grains; su, suture of egg capsule; w, weed.

and may be regarded as a culmination of the trend towards a terrestrial habit which is displayed by the littorinids. The spherical egg capsules (fig. 205), which measure about 2 mm in diameter, are deposited just beneath the surface of the soil on warm humid days between March and September, the largest number being laid in May and June. The female covers each with a layer of soil particles (snd) about 0·5 mm thick as soon as it is laid, so that they are well camouflaged (Creek, 1951). The capsule contains a single egg (de) measuring about 0·14 mm in diameter. This is similar to the diameter of the eggs of *Littorina littorea* (0·13 mm, Linke, 1933) which, in contrast, has a pelagic stage in its development. The egg of *Pomatias* contains little yolk, but a large supply of albumen (al) which is used as food, and the cephalic vesicle (p. 446) provides the embryo with a special means of absorbing this. Between the albumen and the covering of earth, and of about the same thickness as the latter, is a transparent coat made up of an inner mucoid layer (iml) and an outer layer of concentrically arranged fibres of conchiolin (olc) embedded in a mucoid matrix; this construction is similar to that of the resistant walls

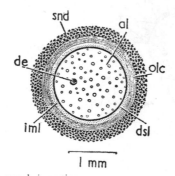

FIG. 205.—*Pomatias elegans:* egg capsule in section.
   al, albumen; de, developing egg; dsl, deeply staining layer round albumen; iml, inner mucous layer of capsule; olc, outer fibrous layer of capsule; snd, soil particles.

of egg capsules of some Stenoglossa (*Ocenebra, Nucella, Buccinum*) (fig. 175C). In the Stenoglossa there is a special gland in the foot of the female which finally shapes and deposits the capsule. In *Pomatias* this is done by the surface of the sole which rolls the capsule in the soil. Creek (1951) suggested that the mucus which holds together the soil particles comes from the anterior pedal mucous gland. The embryo takes long to develop, about 3 months, and when it hatches its supply of albumen is exhausted and its volume, as compared with that of the first cleavage stage, has increased fifteen-fold. However the albumen and yolk do not together supply the full requirements for development since the embryo absorbs water and salts from the soil; moreover Creek (1951) has shown that there is some factor in the natural soil water which is necessary. This is in contrast to the terrestrial snail *Helix* for there is no evidence that its egg absorbs water or anything else from the environment but oxygen; the egg coverings are not impermeable, but water in excess of the animal's requirements is provided (Needham, 1938).
   The spawn of the only other British terrestrial prosobranch, *Acicula fusca*, is unknown.
   Amongst the smallest egg capsules of marine prosobranchs, yet by far the most abundant on many coasts, are those of the various species of rissoaceans (Table 13). They are usually lens-shaped (fig. 204D), circular in outline, with a flattened area attached to the substratum and the free surface convex. Occasionally they are ovoid (*Cingula semi-*

*costata*) or are nearly spherical (*Barleeia rubra*) and with only a small area of attachment. The capsule contains 1, 2 or several eggs (up to 100 have been recorded in *Rissoa guerini*) which all float together in an albuminous fluid. The limiting wall is fairly thick and tough, and usually so transparent that the contents of the capsule can be seen through it; frequently it shows a fibrillar structure. When only 1 or 2 eggs occur together, the young emerge in the crawling stage (*Cingulopsis fulgida*, *Cingula semicostata*, *C. cingillus*, *Barleeia rubra*), but with larger numbers of smaller eggs the embryos are freed as veligers. The veligers may have a long planktotrophic life, and because of their immense numbers form an important constituent of inshore plankton. Moreover, since their breeding times vary, young and old stages of different species may be seen in the plankton at all times of the year (Table 13). Many rissoids inhabit regions between tide marks and may be found in every type of habitat on rocky shores, extending seawards from about mid-tide

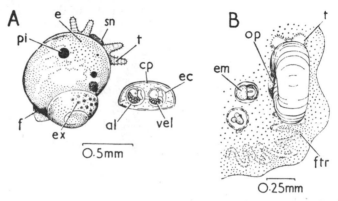

Fig. 206.—A, *Rissoella opalina*, whole animal seen from above, with one egg capsule alongside; B, *Omalogyra atomus*, whole animal on weed, seen from above, with 2 egg capsules.

al, albumen; cp, egg capsule; e, eye; ec, egg covering; em, embryo; ex, pigmented spherules in excretory cells of digestive gland; f, foot; ftr, feeding track; op, operculum; pi, group of pigmented cells at anus; sn, snout; t, tentacle; vel, veliger.

level. On some shores, especially in the SW, *Rissoa parva* is the most numerous species. Its capsules are laid on weed, often in rock pools on the lower part of the beach. Each contains 6–50 eggs which hatch in about 10 days as veliger larvae. At the time of hatching a suture, which appears as a distinct fine line over the convex surface of the wall, ruptures and forms the escape hole. The wall of the capsules of *R. guerini* and *Barleeia rubra* breaks in a similar way, but in *Cingula semicostata* the wall has concentric striae radiating from a centre near the surface of attachment and this is the site of emergence of the young (Rasmussen, 1951), and the lens-shaped capsule of *R. membranacea* has an oval hole in the centre of the convex surface covered by a membrane which ruptures when the larvae are ready to escape (Smidt, 1938).

There are a few minute mesogastropods classified near the rissoids, inhabitants of rock pools, which have egg capsules similar to the rissoid type. They breed during the late spring and summer months. In *Skeneopsis planorbis* and *Omalogyra atomus* (Fretter, 1948) the capsules (fig. 206B) are spherical or ovoid, slightly flattened along the surface of attachment to an algal frond or filament. The outer wall is relatively thick and made of conchiolin threads embedded in a mucoid matrix. Through it can be seen the single egg

TABLE 13

*Egg Capsules and Seasonal Breeding of some Marine Rissoaceans (partly based on Lebour, 1934a)*

| Species | Months during which breeding has been recorded at Plymouth<br>J F M A Ma Ju Jl Au S O N D | Egg capsules |
|---|---|---|
| Cingulopsis fulgida | | Capsule attached to weed, often coral-lines, lens-shaped (0·32 mm across), contains one egg, no free larvae. |
| Cingula semicostata | | Capsules in muddy gravel under stones, ovoid (0·48–0·64 × 0·32–0·48 mm), very tough, thick wall, small area of attachment, contains one egg, no free larvae. |
| C. semistriata | | Capsule attached to weed or other substratum, lens-shaped (0·56–0·64 mm across and 0·24 mm high), contains 12–22 eggs, free veliger larvae. |
| C. cingillus | | Capsule laid in narrow crack or crevice of rock, attached, lens-shaped (0·64–0·72 mm across), contains one and sometimes up to four eggs, no free larvae. |
| Alvania punctura | | Sublittoral, capsule laid in captivity on shell or weed, lens-shaped (0·32–0·48 mm across), contains 12–14 eggs, free veliger larvae. |
| Rissoa sarsi | | Capsule lens-shaped, attached (0·48 mm across), contains 10–14 eggs, free veliger larvae. |
| R. inconspicua | | Sublittoral. Capsule laid in captivity on weed, debris or shell of another, lens-shaped (0·48–0·64 mm across), contains 6–9 eggs, free veliger larvae. |
| R. parva | | Capsule attached to weed, lens-shaped (0·64 mm across), contains 6–50 eggs, free veliger larvae. |
| R. guerini | | Capsule attached to weed, lens-shaped (0·96–1·4 mm across), contains 80–100 eggs, free veliger larvae. |
| R. membranacea | | Capsules attached to Zostera, lens-shaped (1·4–1·6 mm across), contains 40–60 eggs, free veliger larvae. With loss of Zostera through disease this rissoid has disappeared. |
| Barleeia rubra | | Capsules attached to weed, spherical, small area of attachment, contains one egg, no free veligers. |

(sometimes 2 in *Skeneopsis*) embedded in albumen. The eggs are heavily yolked and the young pass through the veliger stage within the capsule. In *Skeneopsis* the diameter of the capsule is about 0·4 mm. In *Omalogyra* it is half this, though the development of the egg is more rapid and may be completed in 10 days, whereas in *Skeneopsis* it may take twice as long. The 2 species of *Rissoella* are found in the same rock pools. They both

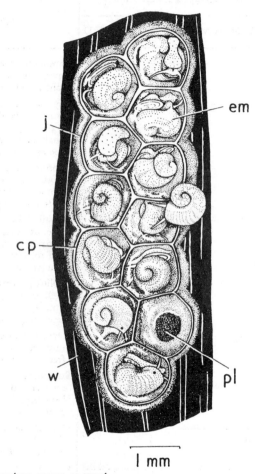

I mm

FIG. 207.—*Bithynia tentaculata:* spawn on weed.
cp, wall of egg capsule; em, embryo in capsule; j, jelly of egg mass; pl, plug hole through which embryo has just escaped; w, weed.

have hemispherical capsules attached along the flattened base to weed. The capsule of *R. diaphana* (fig. 194A) has 1 or 2 eggs and that of *R. opalina* (fig. 206A), which is larger (breadth 0·65–0·4 mm, height 0·5 mm), 2 or rarely 3. Unlike the rissoids each egg has a supply of albumen and its own covering (ec) and they float in a fluid which fills the capsule. There is an intracapsular veliger stage (vel) and development is completed in about a fortnight.

The British prosobranchs which inhabit freshwater are members of Thiele's (1929–35) Stirps Rissoacea or are more primitive forms. They comprise *Viviparus, Bithynia, Valvata* and *Bythinella scholtzi*, which are found exclusively in freshwater, and *Theodoxus* and *Potamopyrgus jenkinsi* which live also in brackish water. *Viviparus* and *P. jenkinsi* are viviparous and the others lay egg capsules and there is no planktonic larval phase. The capsules of *Bithynia* (fig. 207) and *Valvata* (fig. 208) are both laid on weed during the late spring and summer months. Those of *Bithynia* are usually attached to the under surface of leaves and are unmistakable, for a number of approximately hemispherical capsules are accurately arranged side by side in 2–3 parallel rows, those of one row alternating and interlocking with those of the other. The capsules adhere to the weed (w) by the outer coat and are moulded and pressed into place by the sole of the foot; there is no

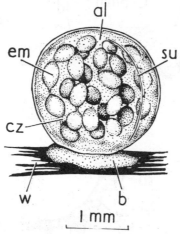

FIG. 208.—*Valvata piscinalis:* egg capsule on weed.
   al, outer albuminous fluid; b, base of capsule; cz, chalaza; em, outer mucoid coat surrounding albumen in which embryo is embedded; su, suture; w. weed.

special pedal gland for this purpose. Each is filled with albumen and contains a single egg, orange in colour, which can be seen through the transparent wall. The wall is composed of threads of a protein, probably conchiolin, intermingled with a mucoid secretion, except for the centre of the convex surface where there is a disc-shaped, mucoid plug. The plug separates from the capsule when the snail is ready to hatch (pl). The number of capsules in a single spawn mass varies considerably: occasionally there may be as few as 4 in each row, though Moquin-Tandon (1855) gave a maximum of 70 capsules and Nekrassow (1928) found 98. However, such large numbers are infrequent. The young escape after an embryonic period of about 2–3 weeks, depending on temperature. The egg mass of *Valvata* is of a very different form. The capsule of *V. piscinalis* is spherical, approximately 1 mm in diameter, and is attached to weed by a cement (b). Around part of the wall opposite to the point of attachment is a suture (su) (Cleland, 1954) along which the capsule bursts when the young hatch. There are several eggs in each capsule: 9–19 appears to be a common number, though Germain (1930) mentioned 10–60. Each egg embedded in albumen forms an ellipsoidal mass enclosed within a very thin mucoid covering (em). The case around an egg is at first continuous with that of the next and is constricted to a thread (cz) between the two. In this way all eggs within a capsule may be joined into a continuous string which is coiled in an outer fluid (al), though the connexions soon break. A single snail may lay about 10 capsules with a total of about 150 eggs (Frömming, 1956). The embryonic period lasts 15–30 days. During this time the mucoid covering around each egg is ruptured and it would appear that the swelling of the contents of the capsule eventually bursts the wall and liberates the young (Heywood, personal communication). The capsules of *V. cristata* described by Nekrassow (1928) differ in shape and in the number of eggs each contains. There may be up to 4 eggs enclosed in a sac-shaped capsule attached at the base and according to Frömming the embryonic period lasts 30–40 days.

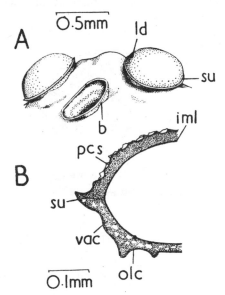

FIG. 209.—*Theodoxus fluviatilis:* A, egg capsules on a stone; the young animal has escaped from one and the base remains; B, vertical section of part of wall of egg capsule.

b, base of capsule; iml, inner mucous layer of capsule; ld, lid of capsule; olc, viscous outer layer of capsule; pcs, particles from crystal sac; su, suture; vac, vacuoles filled with mucus.

*Theodoxus fluviatilis* lives on stones, sunken wood and aquatic plants in canals, rivers, lakes and also in brackish water. The spawn (fig. 209), fixed to the substratum or to the shell of another snail of the same species, is a flattened sphere made up of approximately equal halves sutured together (su) around the equator (Andrews, 1935b). The lid (ld) breaks off when the young escape. The walls are of tough conchiolin, white to straw colour, lined internally by a homogeneous membrane enclosing an albuminous fluid in which the eggs float. The upper half, or lid, is strengthened by a surface layer of sand grains and diatom cases (pcs), which are poured on to it and adhere to its outer sticky covering as the capsule passes from the capsule gland to the genital aperture. These particles come from the crystal sac which lies against the terminal part of the pallial oviduct (csa, fig. 52). The sac collects them from the rectum for storage and later they pass to the terminal region of the oviduct with which the sac communicates (Fretter, 1946b). Bondeson (1940) has shown that capsules laid by individuals living in freshwater are larger and contain more eggs than those laid in brackish water. Thus a capsule from brackish water may have a diameter of 800 $\mu$ and contain 50–60 eggs, whereas one from freshwater may have a diameter of 1,000–1,200 $\mu$ and contain 140–150 eggs. In each capsule one egg cleaves more readily than its neighbours and this precocious embryo uses the others as food and develops to the creeping stage before it hatches. Embryos developing in freshwater and with a larger supply of food attain a larger size (751–910 $\mu$) than those developing in brackish water (650–775 $\mu$). This is the only prosobranch known in which the number of nurse cells and the size of the egg vary with the habitat of the adult. But an interesting correlation between ecological conditions, egg size and life history occurs in another brackish water gastropod, *Odostomia scalaris*, a pyramidellid, which is also marine. It is an ectoparasite of *Mytilus* and is found with its host in habitats of varying salinities. The egg masses (figs. 210C, D, E) are fixed to the shell of the bivalve or other substratum. Each consists of an irregularly shaped mass of jelly which may measure 2–4 mm across and about 2 mm high and contain 40 or more eggs, their size varying with the number. Each egg (de) lies at the centre of an oval mass of transparent albumen (al) which is covered by a thin, though tough, egg covering (ec), and the eggs are linked together by a continuation of the covering from one to the next (cz). Thus the covering may be considered as a long tube coiled irregularly in the jelly, expanded at regular intervals by the eggs and contracted between them to a fine strand. (The spawn of some specimens of *Odostomia eulimoides* (figs. 210A, B) and of the primitive opistho-branch *Onchidella celtica* is similar, though another pyramidellid, *Eulimella nitidissima*, lays ovoid gelatinous egg masses with only about 6–7 eggs in each, and they are not linked together by a covering (Rasmussen, 1944).) Pelseneer (1914) was the first to study the development of *Odostomia scalaris* and he described the egg mass as containing an average of 50 oval eggs, each about 0·38 mm in the longest diameter, which develop in 25 days to miniatures of the adult. He gives no mention of the locality from which the specimens came. Later Rasmussen (1944) described the egg masses and embryonic development of specimens from the innermost part of the Isefjord, Denmark, where the salinity is 20‰. The eggs, however, are smaller (0·18–0·20 mm diameter) than those described by Pelseneer and about 500 occur in one mass. The young are freed as larvae after a develop-ment of 6·5 days at 19°C. The length of the free-swimming stage is unknown, but the small velum indicates that it is short. At Frederikssund in the Roskildefjord, where the salinity is lower (16·1‰), Rasmussen (1951) found the individual eggs to be even larger than those described by Pelseneer and in their development the planktonic phase omitted. It seems probable that Pelseneer's specimens were also from a more brackish water, and under these conditions the pelagic phase in development is omitted.

*Hydrobia ulvae* is another species which inhabits brackish water and is capable of withstanding wide fluctuations in salinity (p. 579); in favourable habitats such as mud flats and salt marshes it is present in myriads. Spawning is spread over several months. On some parts of the Tamar estuary, Plymouth, the main period is autumn and on others, such as St John's Lake, it extends to February and March (Rothschild, 1941a). For the Swansea area Quick (1920) mentioned May–August, but suggested that it extends to other months. The capsules are fastened to shells of other individuals of the same species, male and female, perhaps for lack of other firm substrata in the habitat. As many as 22 have been recorded on one shell (Linke, 1939), though this is exceptional and the average is 4 even where the population is dense. Each (cp, fig. 204A) has the shape of a typical rissoid capsule, fastened by the flattened base and with the free surface convex. This surface is covered with sand grains (snd). The capsule contains a number of eggs

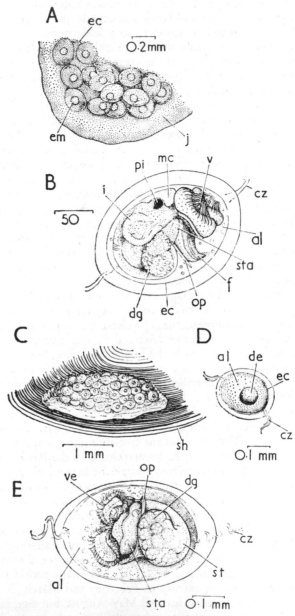

FIG. 210.—*Odostomia eulimoides:* A, part of egg mass showing eggs in an irregular string embedded in clear jelly; B, part of egg string to show veliger larva just before hatching.

   *O. scalaris:* C, egg mass on shell of *Mytilus;* D, a single egg at early stage of development; E, part of egg string to show veliger larva just before hatching.

   al, albumen; cz, chalaza; de, developing egg; dg, digestive gland; ec, egg covering; em, embryo; f, foot; i, intestine; j, jelly of egg mass; mc, mantle cavity; op, operculum; pi, pigment patch; sh, shell of *Mytilus;* st, stomach; sta, statocyst; v, ve ,velum.

floating in an albuminous fluid (ea): Lebour (1937) gave the number as 3–7, Smidt (1951) 4–16, and Quick (1920) as many as 25. Smidt (1944) held that the pelagic larval stage is suppressed, on the grounds that although the adults are very abundant in Copenhagen harbour he did not find the larval stage there, though he admitted that there is a brief distributive phase before settlement. Other workers, however (Henking, 1894; Quick, 1920; Lebour, 1937; Linke, 1939; Thorson, 1946), have described a free veliger, although Lebour (1937) suggested that its planktonic life is short. Thorson (1946), obviously surprised at the apparent lack of knowledge of the life history of this common species, studied hauls from the Southern Harbour, Copenhagen, and found numbers of larvae which he identified without doubt (comparing them with veligers hatched in captivity) as belonging to *H. ulvae*. All had a small and scarcely bilobed velum and the organs of the body relatively advanced, indicating a short pelagic phase. However, the numbers he obtained were nothing to what might have been expected, for in certain areas of the bottom more than 1,000 adults/m sq may be found, all with egg capsules on their shells in summer months. Perhaps there is more to be discovered about the life history of this animal and the possibility still exists that the larval stage may be free-swimming or suppressed according to circumstances (assuming that it has been correctly identified in the first place). Even if set free, larvae may avoid capture by staying near the bottom, and all evidence seems to point to the conclusion that the planktonic phase is at most a brief, and probably a non-feeding stage of the life history.

It is well known that in the related species *Hydrobia ventrosa*, which lives amongst algae and on mud in brackish water, the larval stage is suppressed. The globular capsules, covered with grains of sand, are fixed to stones; each contains a single egg which hatches as a young snail. These capsules are similar to those of *Assiminea grayana* which are passed from the oviduct as the snail creeps over the mud on which it lives. They, however, are unattached, but, owing to the sticky consistency of their walls, may become grouped in clumps and be camouflaged by adhering particles. It might be expected that the veliger stage of this species (which inhabits brackish water) would not be free: a free larva, however, has been described from capsules kept in an aquarium (Sander, 1950). Development has not been studied in natural conditions.

When the egg capsule of the mesogastropod leaves the genital duct it is, in most species, manipulated by the foot which may give it a final moulding while the wall is still pliable. The wall hardens in contact with the water and it may be that the foot applies secretion to hasten this. In certain species the wall is reinforced by particulate matter which is pressed into it while soft. In *Theodoxus* this is done before the capsule leaves the duct; in *Hydrobia ulvae* and *H. ventrosa* it is after this and presumably occurs when the foot fixes the capsule. The minute egg cases of the marine prosobranch *Aporrhais pespelicani* are deposited singly, or 2 or 3 together, in the muddy sand in which the adults live and they are obscured by the particles which accidently adhere to the thick outer wall. The capsules are spherical, about 0·24 mm in diameter, and each contains only 1 egg.

Two genera the members of which live on sandy shores and produce large egg masses, strengthened and camouflaged by the sand or mud, are *Clathrus* and *Natica*. Vestergaard (1935) was the first to give an account of the spawn of *Clathrus* (fig. 211). The adults of *Clathrus clathrus* spawned in an aquarium which had sand in the bottom, and she described a winding string of triangular capsules 3 cm long and each capsule 2 mm high. The larvae hatched 9 days later through an aperture at the apical end of the capsule. Spawn from the Salstone in the Salcombe estuary, Devon, which is described by Lebour (1937), differs from this, for the capsules are covered with fine mud instead of sand. They are polygonal and very irregular, only occasionally being triangular. Moreover, each string measured 5–6 cm and the individual capsules 2–4 mm across at the widest part. Lebour stated that several such spawn masses were found lying on mud near green weed and that one adult was found beneath the surface of the mud with the egg string attached to it by the slimy thread which links the capsules together. It may be that spawning takes place beneath the surface as in *Natica*. On some occasions *Clathrus* has been seen on the surface of sand trailing its egg string along. One string obtained by Prof. L. A. Harvey in the Scilly Isles (fig. 211) exceeded 23 cm in length and was made up

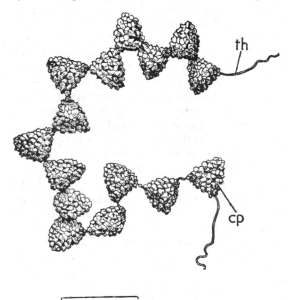

4 mm

FIG. 211.—*Clathrus clathrus:* spawn.
cp, egg capsule;  th, thread linking capsules.

of 170 capsules closely packed, each pyramidal in shape and about 1·5 mm across the base. The walls of the capsules (cp) were covered with sand grains securely cemented together and the thread of secretion (th), probably conchiolin, which held them was naked for a short distance at either end. It seems, therefore, that *Clathrus* will use either mud or sand particles in the manufacture of the spawn and that the size of the capsules, and more especially their number, may vary from one string to another. Thorson (1946) figured part of an egg mass of *Clathrus turtonis* with capsules of about the same size and shape as those of *C. clathrus*, covered with accurately arranged particles of fine sand.

*Natica* is popularly known as the necklace snail owing to the shape of its egg mass which has the appearance of a collar stiffened with sand (fig. 204E). Projections from the surface indicate egg cases arranged in horizontal rows, usually one above the other. The collars, which have the shape of the old-fashioned Eton style, may be rigid or flexible. They are less than 3 mm thick and of varying height and length. When newly formed each has a smooth, viscid texture due to a thin surface layer of mucus, which, however, is lost after a day or so. Beneath is clear jelly (j, fig. 204F) in which the egg cases (cp) are embedded and throughout the thickness of the jelly are particles of sand, fine or coarse, and sometimes bits of shell (snd). The nature of these particles depends upon the substratum in which the collar is formed. The size of the egg cases varies according to the species; when large they form prominent bulges from the surface of the collar, while with the smaller cases its walls are smooth. Each has a thin limiting membrane which surrounds the albuminous fluid containing the eggs. In *N. pallida* the individual cases are large, measuring 2·5–3·0 mm across and there are only 40–50 of them in an egg mass (Thorson, 1935). They each contain a single egg and the embryo hatches in the creeping stage. In contrast *N. poliana* (Lebour, 1937) produces egg cases which are only 0·24 mm across and not visible to the naked eye, and the egg collar has smooth and flexible walls; it measures about 25 mm long and 7·8 mm high—half the size of the collar of *N. pallida*. The single egg in each case develops in 3 weeks to the veliger stage and is then freed. The spawn of *N. catena* is the best known and was first described by Jeffreys (1867) who stated that the embryonic stage lasts at least 2 months. The largest collar recorded is 45 mm high with a basal length of 160 mm (Lebour, 1936); others may be half this size. The egg cases are large (1·425 by 1·925 mm), arranged in rows one above the other and bulge prominently from the rigid walls. Each contains 2–4 eggs and numerous nurse cells (nu); Ankel (1930b) mentioned 50 nurse cells and Thorson (1946) an average of 62. The nurse cells are eggs which cleave in an atypical way and serve as food for the developing embryos (Ankel, 1930b); this is the only known naticid which has them. In other prosobranchs in which the embryos are similarly fed there is typically no pelagic phase in development, and Thorson (1946) described the suppression of this phase in *N. catena* from Danish waters. He suggested that the larva dredged from sandy bottoms near Plymouth and provisionally assigned to this species by Lebour (1936), belongs to *N. montagui*, though no undoubted adult of this species has been identified there recently. However, he did not exclude the possibility of *N. catena* having a pelagic phase in the warmer waters of the English Channel (Thorson, 1950).

The only detailed description of the formation of the egg collar of a naticid was given by Giglioli (1955) whose observations were made on the intertidal species *Polinices triseriata* and *P. heros*. Their distribution extends from the Gulf of St Lawrence to N Carolina. There is no reason to believe that the formation of the collar in other naticids differs from this, except perhaps in unimportant details. The initial phase of collar formation begins on the surface of the sand when the tide is nearing low water. The snail lies on its side with the foot fully extended longitudinally and folded to make a median longitudinal furrow. From the anterior end of the furrow pours mucus, which is dispersed into long festoons by the water movements (Wheatley, 1947); it is produced by gland cells on the foot, mainly the goblet cells of the propodium (Giglioli, 1955). With the beginning of the flood tide the snail burrows into the sand to a depth of 5–10 cm leaving the gelatinous festoons on the surface. It rests on its side with the apex of the shell directed obliquely upwards, and then begins to move slowly in a clockwise direction along a circular route, forcing its way through the sand. The large propodium (pp, fig. 304D) is characteristically folded back over the shell covering the head, and between propodium and shell (sh) the egg ribbon emerges (er), pressed between the two. As the ribbon loses contact with the foot the pressure between shell and sand continues to mould it, determining its breadth and distributing the egg cases evenly. At the same time, sand particles are rolled into the intercapsular jelly. In some naticids the upper and lower margins of the collar are free from capsules, which are pressed away from these borders by the moulding action of the foot. When all the eggs have been spawned the snail moves spirally around the collar smoothing the foot over the outer and inner walls and progressing in a clockwise direction. At the same time a thin pellicle of mucus is added which binds the collar until the matrix jelly has hardened. Each time the snail moves under the collar when it is travelling along its spiral course, the spawn is lifted and tilted towards the surface. As soon as it reaches the surface it is left. Giglioli (1955) was of the opinion that a certain amount of the intercapsular jelly comes from the propodium, but he also expressed the view that it may come from the expanded glandular chamber of the lower oviduct. He has found that in *P. triseriata* the capsular membrane and the albumen appear to control the ionic balance between the pregastrular embryo and the sea water, with which the early embryo is not isotonic (Giglioli, 1949). Later changes in the capsular jelly, conditioned by the developing embryo, progressively diminish the ability of the collar to withstand desiccation. It becomes brittle and crumbles under the flood tide releasing the larvae. The embryos of deep sea naticids hatch by boring through the capsular walls (Thorson, 1935).

In one family of prosobranchs the female guards the egg capsules until the young escape. This is the Calyptraeidae, and the reproductive behaviour of its genera is associated with their sedentary mode of life. The egg capsules, characteristically thin-walled, are concealed beneath the anterior part of the shell, so that they lie along the course of the inhalant flow of water which, in these sedentary, ciliary-feeding prosobranchs, is strong. In *Capulus ungaricus* a single spawn mass in the shape of a thin-walled, somewhat sausage-shaped sac, is held in a fold of the propodium (Ankel, 1936a). It contains several hundred eggs. A single mass figured by Thorson (1946) has at least 5,000 eggs. The young escape as echinospira larvae through a fissure along the under surface of the cocoon and the parent then discards the embryonic membranes. Should the egg mass be abandoned earlier the larvae do not live long. The eggs of a single spawning of *Calyptraea chinensis* are contained in a number of capsules which are attached to the substratum, usually a stone. They are covered by the part of the body in front of the foot (Lebour, 1937). Each is a very soft-walled bag, triangular in outline and measuring about 3 mm in length, and all are fixed in a bunch by their narrow ends. A capsule contains only 12–24 eggs, concentrated towards the broad end, and the young escape as miniatures of the adult with an embryonic shell of $1\frac{1}{2}$ whorls. This shell usually shows clearly in the young adult (fig. 40D). Egg capsules of *Crepidula fornicata* are similar (fig. 212), though somewhat more balloon-shaped and stalked and are united by their stalks to form a bunch of up to 70 or more. The bunch is fastened to the substratum on which the parent lives, either a stone or the shell of the underlying limpet (fig. 212B), and is hidden from view. If a chain of individuals be separated during the breeding season it is not unusual to find a female holding the stalks of a number of capsules by the anterior tip of the foot (fig. 212A). It may be that the foot collects them as they leave the oviduct and later fixes the whole bunch. A single capsule measures 2–4 mm across at the broad end and contains 250–300 eggs which float in the common mass of albumen. The young escape as veligers and remain some time in the plankton. Coe (1942) found that in capsules of *C. onyx* half the embryos frequently disintegrated and were used as food by the survivors and Thorson (1940a) stated that in some capsules of *C. walshi* from the Persian Gulf there was a suggestion that embryonic cannibalism had occurred, for some embryos were much larger than others and these appeared to be disintegrating. This is not a normal occurrence in the genus *Crepidula* and can only have been accidental. In capsules in which embryos are not separated from one another but share a supply of albumen it seems likely that a healthy individual will automatically devour disintegrating tissues with the albumen which is used as food. Lebour (1934*a*) similarly found that from egg capsules of *Rissoa membranacea* which have 40–60 eggs apiece, a smaller number of embryos developed and suggested that the others were used as nurse eggs. This may have been an abnormality due to the fact that the eggs were laid in captivity.

The egg masses of *Turritella communis* (fig. 204B) are not unlike those of *Crepidula* in that each is a cluster of spherical or ovoid capsules held together by the intertwining of their stalks. However, in *Turritella* some hundreds of capsules form a single cluster

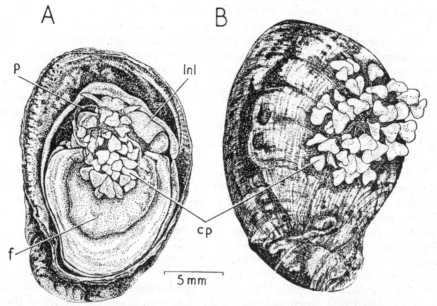

Fig. 212.—*Crepidula fornicata*: A, female, from below, with egg capsules held under the foot; B, empty shell, from above, with attached egg capsules.
cp, egg capsule; f, foot; lnl, left neck lobe; p, vestigial penis, unusually large for a female.

(Lebour, 1933*c*). A capsule measures at first about 1 mm across, but stretches as the eggs develop so that its walls become thinner. It contains 6–20 eggs which develop to the veliger stage in a week or 10 days and hatch.

Some carnivorous prosobranchs and some ectoparasites secure their egg capsules to the animals on which they live. The spawn of *Odostomia scalaris* (fig. 210C), which is attached to the shell of *Mytilus*, has already been described, and *O. eulimoides*, an ectoparasite of *Chlamys opercularis* and *Pecten maximus*, deposits a similar type of spawn on the ears or valves of these lamellibranchs (fig. 210A). *Pelseneeria stylifera* lives on the surface of sea-urchins and its egg capsules may also be found there. They are not unlike those of the calyptraeids in that each is cushion-shaped, approximately triangular in outline, colourless and transparent and with a short stalk for attachment. However, they are deposited singly and not grouped together in bunches. Each measures about 1·2 × 1·1 mm and contains 60–400 eggs. The capsules are usually fixed around the bases of the spines, which afford protection, and they are apparently untouched by pedicellariae. *Pelseneeria* is recorded from Plymouth on *Psammechinus miliaris* and *Echinus esculentus*, and Lebour (1932*b*) described the capsules on *Psammechinus*. Ten to a dozen were found on one individual, all on the aboral surface. The young escape as veligers which probably remain long in the plankton.

Other prosobranchs which browse on the soft tissues of colonial animals spread their egg masses on the surface of these or bite holes from the tissues and sink them within. The only British species which feeds on alcyonarians is the poached egg shell, *Simnia patula* (fig. 296), and its spawn is laid as a continuous layer on *Alcyonium digitatum*. A collection of capsules appears as a circular mass an inch or more in diameter. The capsules are pressed against one another so that the outline of each is polygonal rather than circular. A single one measures about 3·5 mm across and contains several hundred eggs all of which appear to develop and the young escape as veliger larvae (Lebour, 1932*a*). These remain long in the plankton and only gradually assume their diagnostic features—the velum of 4 long narrow lobes and the reticulate markings of the shell (fig. 249). The 2 species of *Cerithiopsis* which live on sponges produce lens-shaped capsules like those of rissoids and place them singly in holes made in the sponge. The capsules of *C. tubercularis* are laid in *Hymeniacidon* and each contains a large number of minute eggs which measure only 0·06 mm in diameter (Lebour, 1933*b*). *C. barleei*, living on *Suberites domuncula*, embeds its nests of eggs in this sponge so that the top of each is hardly visible from the surface. One specimen kept in captivity (Lebour, 1933*b*) laid 20 capsules which were distributed at intervals of 5 mm or more apart and each contained about 200 eggs. In both species the young escape as veligers which remain in the plankton for some time.

The test of compound ascidians is used as the spawning ground of *Velutina velutina*, *Lamellaria perspicua* and *Trivia monacha*. These species sink their capsules into holes. Those of *L. perspicua* (fig. 213) are laid in the tissues of *Leptoclinum*, *Polyclinum* and probably other ascidians. Each is pot-shaped, with a rounded base and tapers slightly towards the circular opening which is filled with a plug. It measures 2–3 mm high. Only the plug surrounded by a low rim of capsule wall (cr) is exposed at the surface of the ascidian. The wall of the capsule is thin and is divided into approximately equal halves by a suture which runs down its length and can be seen across the surface of the plug (sup); it reflects the bilobed structure of the pallial oviduct (Fretter, 1946*b*). Externally the wall has a fibrillar appearance, the fibrillae running in a circular direction. There is also a thin inner layer to the wall (ilc) which completely surrounds the albumen (al), and so is continuous beneath the substance of the plug. The plug is composed of two different layers both of which are distinct from the wall of the capsule. The outer opercular layer (olp) is the harder and its surface markings suggest that it is made up of concentric layers of material; the concentric markings are bisected by the suture. The thickness of the inner layer (ilp) varies considerably from capsule to capsule. It forms a cementing substance which appears to diminish as the capsule ages and at the same time there is some reduction in the diameter of the overlying operculum. Both these events seem to be preparatory to the opening of the capsule by the loss of the plug. Through the transparent plug can be seen the contents of the capsule—many unshelled eggs (em) in an albuminous fluid. According to Ankel (1935) the number of eggs varies from 1,000–3,000 and they are arranged in a continuous layer, one egg thick, around the wall. Giard (1875) and Pelseneer (1911) believed that some of these are nurse eggs devoured by the developing embryos, but Ankel (1935) could find no evidence of this. The plug is freed from the opening of the capsule when the echinospira larvae are ready to escape.

*Lamellaria*, unlike *Trivia*, possesses no ventral pedal gland for the final moulding and deposition of the egg case. With the aid of the radula it bites small round holes in the compound ascidian and the foot apparently receives the capsules from the oviduct and embeds each vertically in a hole so that they are scattered only a few millimetres apart.

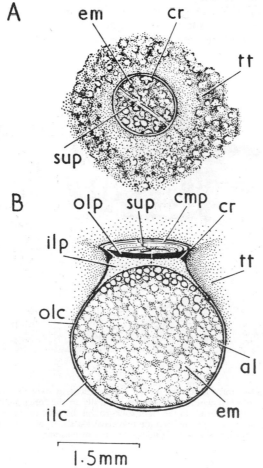

FIG. 213.—*Lamellaria perspicua*: A, surface view of egg capsule buried in tunicate test; B, vertical section of tunicate colony showing embedded capsule.

al, albumen; cmp, concentric markings on plug; cr, rim of egg capsule; em, embryo; ilc, inner layer of capsule wall; ilp, inner layer of plug; olc, outer layer of capsule wall; olp, outer layer of plug; sup, suture on plug; tt, test of tunicate.

The test of the ascidian thickens around the capsule and secures it more firmly and may form a protecting rim around the plug. *Velutina velutina* lays similar capsules in the test of *Styela* (Diehl, 1956) and only the transparent plug is visible on the surface; the young escape as echinospira larvae.

The egg capsules of *Trivia monacha* (fig. 214) may be found in the tissues of *Polyclinum*, *Diplosoma* and *Botryllus*. Each projects as a funnel from the surface of the test. The capsule is an erect vase-shaped structure, circular in transverse section, rounded at the base and, above, the constricted neck broadens to a tall funnel. The plug (pl) at the base of the funnel blocks the entrance and closes off the sac in which the eggs float in an albuminous fluid (eec). The capsule is about 5 mm high, the funnel making up about half of this, and the diameter in the broadest region of the egg sac is about 2·5 mm. The wall has a fibrillar texture and shows 2 longitudinal lines of thickening which divide the capsule into two equal halves, and a suture can be traced across the plug. Female individuals have a ventral pedal gland (fig. 68) which appears as a pit in the mid-ventral region of

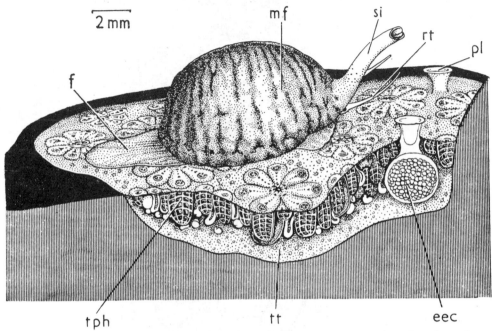

FIG. 214.—*Trivia monacha*: this figure represents a cowrie crawling over the surface of a colony of the tunicate *Botryllus schlosseri* which has been cut vertically in the foreground to show the zooids and an egg capsule embedded in it. In the right background the neck of a second capsule is visible.
eec, eggs in egg capsule; f, foot; mf, mantle fold covering shell; pl, plug; rt, right tentacle; si, inhalant siphon; tph, pharynx of zooid of tunicate; tt, test of tunicate.

the sole (p. 118). In anaesthetized animals a small papilla (vp) surrounded by a deep groove is protruded from the pit and the size and shape of the papilla suggest that it is concerned with the moulding of the funnel of the egg capsule. After the capsule has been placed in the hole bitten from the test of the ascidian the gland drives it into position, at the same time gripping the pliable portion of the capsule wall and fashioning it into its final form. Its action is lubricated by secretion from glands in the epithelium and in the connective tissue below (gvp).

Three species of *Ianthina* are stranded from time to time along the W and SW coasts of the British Isles, carried northwards by winds and currents. These prosobranchs are holopelagic and usually occur in shoals in warmer waters. One species, *I. janthina* (fig. 299), is viviparous and retains the eggs in the oviduct where they develop to veligers which are liberated. The others, *I. exigua* (fig. 204G) and *I. pallida*, produce egg capsules which, however, are not freed to the plankton, but are grouped along the under surface of the float which is made of air bubbles coated with mucus, and is attached to the propodium. The float is present in all individuals, males and females. According to Simroth (1895) the veliger larvae also have a long mucous strand attached to the foot, with a small swelling at the end which contains air bubbles; this is the first flotation device the animal possesses. Laursen (1953) stated that in the oviparous species the mesopodium, which is short and broad, has 2 funnel-shaped depressions lying side by side into which glands open. The mucus for the formation of the float comes from the right

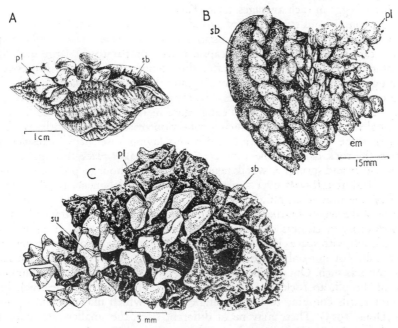

FIG. 215.—Egg capsules of stenoglossans. A, *Urosalpinx cinerea* on shell of same species; B, *Nassarius reticulatus* on *Ensis* shell; C, *Ocenebra erinacea* on stone.
em, embryo; pl, plug; sb, substratum; su, suture.

funnel, and from the left pass the egg capsules, which are then attached to the float. He found that the oviduct does not open into the mantle cavity (from whence according to Simroth (1895) the eggs pass to an ovipositor for deposition), but penetrates the mantle and passes obliquely down into the left side of the foot to this funnel, where it opens. Thiele (1897) also described the sole of the foot as grooved and glandular, providing the mucus for the float and helping in the manufacture of the capsules. However, he mentioned no opening of the oviduct on the sole, where, indeed, its position is highly peculiar (p. 563).

The egg capsules of *Ianthina* (fig. 204G) are pear-shaped with a stalk-like projection at one end for attachment to the float; this end is the first to emerge from the foot according to Laursen (1953). At the opposite end small spines project from the surface, scattered or in rows. In *I. exigua* they extend over two-thirds the length of the capsule and in *I. pallida* they are scattered over half the length; the longest are distally placed. In any one egg-raft capsules of all ages may be found, with embryos in stages of development up to the veliger, and finally empty capsules. The number of eggs in a capsule and the number of capsules attached to the float vary with the size of the individual and with the species. In *I. exigua* the capsules, each about 2 mm long, are arranged in rows and number about 250 in a float 5 cm long. The average number of eggs per capsule is 175, and none of these appears to be a nurse cell. The embryos feed on the albuminous fluid which surrounds them. *I. pallida* has a longer float, about 7 cm, and larger capsules which range from 4–7 mm in length. They are more closely packed along the float and the number of eggs in each averages 5,500 (Laursen, 1953).

The most conspicuous egg masses of prosobranchs and the most familiar to the older naturalists are those of certain rachiglossans such as *Buccinum undatum* whose spawn is frequently cast upon the shore. The capsules are comparatively large and the walls tough, taking long to weather away after the young have escaped. Moreover, some species are gregarious at the time of spawning and the spawn of several females unites to give rise to a massive array of capsules which can hardly pass unnoticed. At spawning time male and female *Nucella lapillus* congregate in rock crevices in the lower half of the intertidal zone. The animals in such a collection cease feeding for the while and, of the females, some will be copulating and others laying vase-shaped capsules, securely fastened to the rock close to one another. Spawning takes place throughout the year, chiefly in winter and spring. A whelk takes more than an hour to produce 1 capsule and 10 may be laid at intervals over a period of 24 hours (Pelseneer, 1935). The number laid by any one individual ranges from 6–31, the average being 15 (Pelseneer, 1935). The spawn of the whelk *Buccinum undatum* has a very different appearance for it is in the form of ball-shaped clusters of several hundreds of capsules piled irregularly on one another, though with spaces between (fig. 216). The masses are sometimes referred to as 'sea wash balls' for not only have they the appearance of a sponge, but are said to be used by sailors as such. One whelk may produce up to 2,000 capsules, fastening those at the base of the pile to rock or a shell (though they frequently come free), but often several individuals combine to form a single cluster which may contain up to 15,000 capsules (Dons, 1913). These may be of different sizes, the smaller ones coming from smaller whelks. A capsule has the shape of a concavo-convex lens with a diameter of about 12 mm, and is fastened to its neighbours by peripheral projections from the wall. The convex surface faces away from the centre of the cluster, and the plug, which closes the capsule until the young escape, is located near the margin of the concave face, away from the points of attachment. The young have escaped from most of the clusters cast up by the tide, but sometimes younger capsules containing embryos are attached to the emptied ones. A newly laid capsule contains several hundred eggs: Portmann (1925) stated 50–2,000 or more, and 3,200 have been obtained from the largest capsule collected around Plymouth. From such capsules only 10–30 young emerge, for the rest of the eggs fail to develop. They retain their original shape whilst the successful embryos develop and then these eat the uncleaved eggs, swallowing them whole. Each embryo devours a 100 or so nurse eggs, and when these are finished it may turn cannibal and eat unhealthy individuals. The embryonic phase lasts about 2 months and when the young creep away they measure about 1 mm in length. The spawn of the closely related *Neptunea antiqua* is similar, though the capsules are in smaller clusters of about a dozen to a 100, and from each only 2–4 embryos hatch (Jeffreys, 1867). They are large, with a length of 6–8 mm, and it is estimated that each has devoured 2,500 eggs. Even this number is small as compared with the supply of food eggs in the northern whelk *Volutopsius norwegicus*. It lays solitary capsules which are about 2·5 mm in diameter, subhemispherical and attached by the flattened base. Thorson (1940*b*) has estimated that each of the 2–4 embryos which hatch as miniatures of the adult had 20–40 times as many nurse eggs as an embryo of

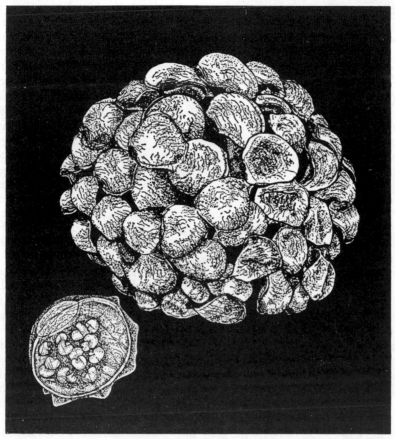

FIG. 216.—*Buccinum undatum*: egg capsules agglomerated into spawn mass, with left, below, a single capsule containing young whelks. In the single capsule note (above) the plug crossed by a suture joining right and left halves; note also (round its lower edge) the peripheral flange by which it is attached to neighbouring capsules.

*Neptunea*, that is 50,000–100,000. There is thus considerable intra- and inter-specific variation in the amount of food available for a single embryo in the family Buccinidae, which affects the length of time the embryos stay in the capsule and their size and stage of development when they emerge. This is particularly well seen in *Colus islandicus* where the size of the embryo varies from 3·5–8·5 mm in length according to the number developing in the capsule.

There is doubt as to whether all the eggs in the capsule of the dog whelk *Nucella lapillus* undergo early cleavage stages, Portmann (1925) alleging that division stops in the food eggs after a small sphere of cells has been formed and Staiger (1951) stating that they stop development before cleavage begins. These eggs form a central mass of yolk on which the embryos feed. A capsule may have several hundred eggs, even up to a thousand, and about 15–30 undergo normal development, occasionally fewer. At an early veliger stage (p. 459) these attach themselves by the sucking lips to the column of food (fig. 242A), and in contrast to the embryos of *Buccinum* development is arrested until the food is eaten. At a later stage unhealthy embryos may also be devoured. The size of the embryos varies: Risbec (1937) observed one capsule 5 mm tall with only 2 embryos one of which attained 2·5 mm. The vase-shaped capsule (p. 337) is fitted with an apical plug of mucus which is loosened and lost at the time the embryos hatch. Ankel (1937*b*) has shown that the plugs of fresh capsules are softened to a pulp by a mixture of embryo dog whelks in sea water, though not by crushed salivary glands of the adult, and concluded that they are normally dissolved by an enzyme liberated by the embryos. In a related purpurid of the Persian Gulf, *Thais hippocastanea*, the egg capsules have a similar appearance except that the top is covered by a thin, transparent membrane through which the contents can be seen (Thorson, 1940*a*). The nurse eggs seem to be eaten whole by the 4 or 5 embryos which develop, and it would appear that these escape from the capsule by rasping a single large hole in its wall. In emptied capsules the apical membrane is intact and the wall perforated; Thorson (1940*a*) has suggested that the embryos are too large to pass through the apex. This unusual means of escape has been recorded by Pope (1910–1911) for the oyster drill *Urosalpinx cinerea*. He watched young drills cut small circular holes in the egg case and then push their way through. However, he believed that this method of escape occurs only when embryos near the apex of the capsule are not developed sufficiently to emerge and they obstruct the normal passage.

The capsules of *Urosalpinx* (fig. 215A) and of the tingle *Ocenebra erinacea* (fig. 215C) are constructed in a similar way to that of *Nucella*, and are of about the same size, though details in the shape vary. Each is vase-shaped with a narrow stalk which expands to a broad basal attachment to the substratum, and distally a circular opening which is filled with a plug (pl). Unlike the capsule of *Nucella* the walls are flattened or concave on one side and convex on the other. The curvature is more pronounced in *Ocenebra* in which the middle of the convex surface may be produced into a slight keel so that in transverse section the capsule is approximately triangular. There are 2 longitudinal sutures visible on the surface of the smooth yellow walls running up the centre of the concave and convex faces and continuous over the plug. In *Urosalpinx* the exposed surface of the plug is flat and flush with the rim of the capsule. It shows concentric markings which are bisected by the suture so that it is similar to the plug which closes the capsule of *Lamellaria perspicua*. Moreover, as in *Lamellaria*, there is a second inner layer to the plug forming a complete seal over the opening and actually separating the outer horny layer from the rim of the capsule (Hancock, 1956). In *Ocenebra* the plug projects beyond the rim of the capsule to a conspicuous keel along the line of the suture and it is composed of only one type of secretion which is mucoid. The detailed structure of the wall shows all the characteristics which have been described for the capsule of *Nucella*: an outer fibrous layer, with circular fibres externally and longitudinal ones internally, overlying a homogeneous semitransparent layer, which is thicker in *Urosalpinx* than *Ocenebra*, and then a thin inner skin which surrounds the contents of the capsule. The fibrous part of the wall and the underlying homogeneous layer are protein, probably conchiolin, and between the fibres is a mucoid substance. Each of these 2 secretions forms a layer of the plug of *Urosalpinx*, the outer layer being similar to the homogeneous skin of the capsule wall.

A capsule of *Urosalpinx* contains up to 35 eggs which float in an albuminous fluid, though occasional capsules contain much larger numbers (Hancock, 1957). An average-sized capsule of *Ocenebra* also contains about 35 eggs. Lebour (1937) who quoted the number as 12–20 was probably dealing with the smaller capsules, whereas in large ones, 9–13 mm high, Hancock (1957) found a range of 52–167 eggs, and Lamy (1928) up to 196. These larger numbers are exceptional. During the breeding season a female *Ocenebra* deposits 30–40 capsules. In any one a few eggs may be very small, and give rise to retarded veligers (Risbec, 1937) which are devoured by the normal embryos. However, there is no regular practice of embryonic cannibalism either in *Urosalpinx* or *Ocenebra*. Risbec (1937) stated that there are often clumps of ciliated cells in the capsules of *Ocenebra*, and suggested that they are fragments of the velum which have been cast off and not absorbed as in *Nucella*. The embryos of *Urosalpinx* develop to the crawling stage in about 2 months at 15·9°C and those of *Ocenebra* in about 3 months at 10–19°C (Hancock, 1957); they escape through the apical opening of the capsule. During their embryonic development the plug which closes the capsule gradually loosens and is lost by the time the young are ready to emerge. Hancock (1956) suggested that in *Urosalpinx* the embryos liberate a substance, probably an enzyme, which is responsible for this.

The spawn of *Nassarius reticulatus* (fig. 215B) consists of capsules which are slightly convex on one surface, flattened on the other and are fastened to any hard object in the vicinity; some have been found attached to an egg collar of *Natica*. The capsules are frequently laid evenly spaced in rows and as in *Urosalpinx* and *Ocenebra* several individuals may lay alongside one another. Each is about 5 mm high and 4 mm across at the broadest point; distally it tapers to a very small round opening closed by a plug, and proximally it has rather a broad basal attachment to the substratum. The walls have a fibrillar structure, but are thinner and more transparent than in the capsules of other rachiglossans. The lateral margins of the flattened sides extend to form a flange and this is continuous over the distal end, forming a rim to the plug on one side. A capsule contains from 50–2,000 eggs which after about a month are liberated as veligers; Ankel (1929) suggested that they secrete a substance which dissolves the plug. The egg capsules of *N. incrassatus* and *N. pygmaeus* are similar, though smaller and with fewer eggs.

The differences in shape of the egg capsules of the various species of Rachiglossa are not due to any fundamental dissimilarities in the structure of the female genital ducts, but to specific differences in the shape of the ventral pedal gland which moulds the capsules passed to it in an unfinished state from the oviduct. The capsule is passed along a temporary groove on the foot to the pedal gland which grips it so that the plug is directed to the inner end. A limited amount of secretion from the gland acts as a lubricant and a hardening mixture, but it has never been suggested that this adds to the substance of the capsule. When the capsule of *Nassarius reticulatus* leaves the genital duct it is biconvex, with 2 longitudinal lines of thickening extending from the plug to the thick basal plate; its walls are flexible. Within the pedal gland the flanges are shaped from the longitudinal thickenings and the basal disc is constricted from the capsule, which now assumes its final flattened shape in accordance with that of the gland. The capsule is retained for some minutes whilst it is kneaded by the pedal musculature, the walls smoothed and hardened and the disc pressed against the substratum, to which it adheres. In *Buccinum undatum* the convex face of each egg case is, at this stage, stamped with a reticulate pattern. The fashioning by the pedal gland takes 15–20 min in *Thais haemastoma* (Franc, 1941*b*) and then the whelk lifts the mesopodium and leaves the capsule firmly attached.

In *Ocenebra* the 2 longitudinal sutures, which result from the bilobed structure of the genital duct, are accurately placed one in the middle of the concave surface and the other in the middle of the convex, and in every capsule this is the same. The orientation of the capsules in the ventral pedal gland of individuals of any one species must always be remarkably similar.

A second type of egg case is found in the Stenoglossa (fig. 217). It is lens-shaped with a flattened base circular or oval in outline, by which it is attached, and a convex upper surface. The periphery is edged with a narrow brim and in the middle of the convex face is the round or oval exit hole, covered by a membrane and surrounded by a thick edge from which 2 sutures diverge. These run to the base of the capsule and divide the wall into 2 equal halves. The wall is semitransparent so that the contents are visible.

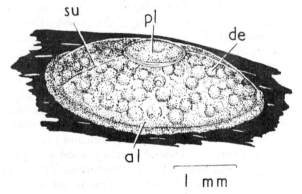

Fig. 217.—*Philbertia gracilis:* egg capsule on stone. The surface bears reticular markings not shown in the figure.

al, albumen; de, developing egg; pl, plug; su, suture.

Such capsules are laid by *Trophon* spp. (Lebour, 1936; Thorson, 1946) and contain less than a dozen rather large eggs which hatch as miniatures of the adult. They also occur in all the British turrids of which the spawn has been described, but contain a large number of smaller eggs all of which develop to free veliger larvae. According to Lebour (1934*b*) the size of the capsules of the turrids in the vicinity of Plymouth varies from a diameter of about 1·6 mm in *Mangelia nebula*, in which there are about 60 eggs per capsule, to 3·4 mm in diameter in *Philbertia gracilis* (fig. 217) which has 40–80 eggs (Lebour, 1933*d*). However, there is probably considerable variation within any one species for Jeffreys (1867) gave the diameter of the capsule of *P. linearis* as 5 mm and its contents as 200–300 eggs, whereas Lebour (1934*b*) gave the corresponding measurement as ranging from 1·5–2·0 mm and the number of eggs as 60–80. *P. purpurea* lays an even larger number of eggs, 350–400, in a single capsule (Franc, 1950).

Like other rachiglossans, *Trophon* has a ventral pedal gland in females only, which presumably moulds the egg capsules. Of the turrids, however, *Mangelia brachystoma* (Robinson, 1955) is reported to have no such gland, although the remarks of Ankel (1936*a*) would lead one to suppose that one is present in *Philbertia gracilis*. The exposed surface of the capsule of *P. gracilis* has a coarse reticulate marking, presumably due to the moulding action of the foot, and this may vary slightly from one group of capsules to another showing characteristics of the individual which produced them (Ankel, 1936a).

There is only one British member of the family Fasciolariidae, *Troschelia berniciensis*, and this is rare. Thorson (1940b) has described the egg capsules as ovate, with a greater diameter of 16 mm and a lesser of 11 mm; a longitudinal ridge around the wall gives it a walnut shape. It contains only one embryo, which is presumably nourished by nurse eggs like the embryos of other species of this family (Hyman, 1923).

# CHAPTER 17

# DEVELOPMENT

THE molluscs along with the platyhelminths and annelids have eggs which cleave spirally. Conklin's work (1897) on the development of the egg of the prosobranch *Crepidula* may be regarded as the foundation of our knowledge of spiral cleavage in molluscs. The size of the egg in prosobranchs varies considerably, for in some species there is little yolk and in others much. In *Viviparus* the diameter of the egg is only about 18 $\mu$, in *Littorina littorea* 130 $\mu$, and this is far exceeded in the Stenoglossa, for the corresponding measurement of the egg of *Trophon muricatus* is 480 $\mu$. The quantity of yolk affects the difference in size between megameres and micromeres, which is very marked in the Stenoglossa. Typically the third cleavage is dexiotropic, the fourth laeotropic and subsequent cleavage planes alternate. This results in the formation of a dextral snail. Occasionally sinistral individuals or races occur, and there are some species (e.g. *Triphora perversa*) which are consistently sinistral. Sinistrality may be the result of the reversal of the third and subsequent cleavages, for such a change in cleavage pattern (Crampton, 1894) is known to give the sinistral individuals of certain pulmonates (*Ancylus, Physa, Planorbis*).

Cell lineage has been studied for a number of molluscs. Besides *Crepidula* these include the prosobranchs *Patella caerulea* (Patten, 1886a; Wilson, 1904), *Theodoxus fluviatilis* (Blochmann, 1882), *Trochus* (= *Gibbula*) *magus* (Robert, 1902) and *Littorina littoralis* (Delsman, 1914). The results show general agreement as to the origin of the germ layers. The first three quartettes of micromeres give rise to all the ectoderm: the first forms the pretrochal ectoderm which will be the ectoderm of the head, the second and third the rest. These micromeres may also form ectomesoderm. It is from 2$d$ that much of the dorsal and ventral ectoderm of the body is derived, including the shell gland and the ectoderm of the foot. Endoderm arises from 4$A$, 4$B$, 4$C$ and also the fourth quartette of micromeres 4$a$, 4$b$, 4$c$. Erlanger (1892), Conklin (1897), Robert (1902) and Wilson (1904), working with *Bithynia, Crepidula, Gibbula magus* and *Patella caerulea* respectively, described the division of the megamere of quadrant $D$ as giving 4$D$, which also forms endoderm, and 4$d$ which is exclusively responsible for the teloblastic mesoderm as it is in annelids. However, Wilson (1904) expressed some doubt as to the identification of 4$D$ and 4$d$ in the embryos of *Patella*. The time of origin of 4$d$ in molluscs varies. In *Gibbula* it is at the 64-cell stage, in agreement with annelids, whilst in *Crepidula* (and also the nudibranch *Fiona* (Casteel, 1904)) it appears immediately after a short rest period which follows the 24-cell stage. Heath (1899) has accurately traced the origin of the mesoblast in *Ischnochiton* at the 72-cell stage. He was unable to decide whether any of the descendants of 4$d$ form endoderm, nor could Robert (1902) determine this for *Gibbula*, but this occurs in other prosobranchs and supports the endodermal nature of the teloblastic mesoderm, which is shown by the destiny of the sister cell 4$D$ (see Table 14). Three divisions of the endomesoderm cell are concerned with the formation of endoderm in *Crepidula* and *Fiona*. Smith (1935), Crofts (1937) and Creek (1951) suggested that in *Patella vulgata, Haliotis* and *Pomatias* the megamere of the quadrant $D$

TABLE 14

The origin of endomesoderm in:

A. *Patella coerulea*, after Patten (1886a);

B. *P. coerulea*, after Wilson (1904). This diagram shows only the probable state, for Wilson (p. 206) expresses some doubt as to the identification of 4D and **4d**;

C. *Crepidula*, after Conklin (1897);

D. *P. vulgata*, after Smith (1935); *Haliotis*, after Crofts (1937); *Pomatias elegans*, after Creek (1951).

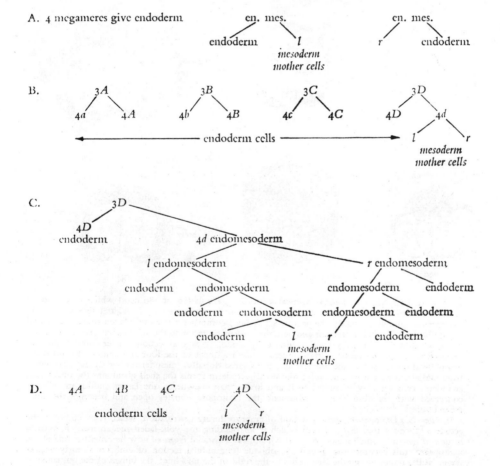

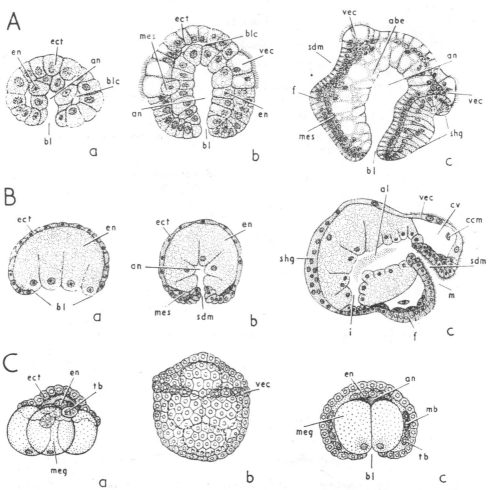

FIG. 218.—A, *Viviparus viviparus:* *a*, vertical section of gastrula (about 180 cells) which is formed by invagination of the endomeres. The gastrula is radially symmetrical. *b*, sagittal section of early trochophore (about 400 cells); the prototroch (velum) comprises 2 rows of ciliated cells; the ventral surface of the embryo is to the left and here the *ectoderm* posterior to the velum gives rise to the mesoderm, which is thus formed some time after gastrulation. *c*, sagittal section of later embryo similarly orientated. From the ventral surface protrudes the rudiment of the foot and anterior to this is the oesophageal invagination; the prevelar area is displaced dorsally; mesoderm now separates ectoderm from endoderm except mid-dorsally; the dorsal ectoderm forms the shell gland and the underlying endoderm cells are closely applied to it and lower than elsewhere; the larger endoderm cells are concerned with the absorption of albumen; the blastopore remains open and becomes the anus. After Dautert.

B, *Crepidula fornicata:* *a*, vertical section of embryo during gastrulation, which is by epiboly; the ectoderm forms a thin layer of cells which is surrounding the yolk-laden megameres. *b*, vertical section of gastrula; small mesoderm cells which have separated from 4*d* now lie on either side of the blastopore; this becomes the mouth. *c*, oblique longitudinal section of embryo at early veliger stage; at the posterior end the section lies to the right of the mid-line; the lumen of the gut contains ingested albumen; the ciliated cells of the velar area rotate the embryo in the albuminous fluid; with the growth of the foot, the expansion of the shell gland and the enlargement of the whole region produces mesoderm and that all the endoderm is derived from the other three megameres, though these authors have not followed the full details of cell lineage.

The type of blastula varies with the size of egg. In species with little yolk there is a moderate (*Patella caerulea, Pomatias*) or even wide cleavage cavity (*Littorina littoralis, Viviparus, Bithynia*), but before gastrulation begins, or at its onset, the animal and vegetative poles may flatten, narrowing the blastocoel. The flattening is pronounced in *Littorina, Pomatias* and *Bithynia*, and also occurs in *Viviparus* (Dautert, 1929) where, however, the blastocoel remains wider. In eggs with considerable yolk and consequently large megameres the resulting blastula is a more or less solid sphere (*Crepidula, Nassarius, Fusus, Ocenebra, Urosalpinx, Nucella*). A large quantity of the yolk is held by 4D, and in *Nucella* and *Nassarius* 4D has a volume as large, or even larger, than the combined volume of the other megameres.

The gastrula is formed in different ways according to the size of the megameres. In *Viviparus* all blastomeres are of nearly equal size (fig. 218A), the micromeres being as big as the megameres, which invaginate into the segmentation cavity so that a wide archenteron (an) is formed. The blastopore (bl) remains as an inlet for the albumen, which is absorbed by cells of the endoderm at an early stage (abe) and compensates for lack of yolk. At the time the gastrula is formed no mesoderm has developed. In species with a small to moderate amount of yolk gastrulation is brought about by epibolic growth of the micromeres over the megameres, together with some movement of these larger cells into the segmentation cavity; in contrast to *Viviparus* the primordial mesoderm cells appear during this process. Epiboly and invagination are of equal importance in the production of the gastrula of *Pomatias* and *Littorina*, but in the slightly more yolky eggs of *Patella vulgata, Haliotis* and *Gibbula magus* gastrulation is effected mainly by epibolic growth. In *Pomatias* the flattening of the gastrula at the 64-cell stage brings the 4 megameres to the region of the vegetative pole, and at the same time one of the megameres moves into the blastocoel, which is being gradually obliterated. This is presumably 4D behaving differently from the other 3 megameres; Creek (1951) concluded that it gives rise to mesoderm only. Gastrulation is continued by the invagination of the megameres into the concavity formed by the epibolic downgrowth of the micromeres. These border a wide circular opening to the archenteron, the blastopore. In *Haliotis* and *Patella* no flattening of the blastula occurs and gastrulation begins by the inward growth of the megameres 4A, 4B, 4C, 4D which reduce the segmentation cavity and for a short time remain in connexion with the surface by long necks. At the same time the ectodermal cap of micromeres extends over them, spreading downwards to reach the

posterior to the velum, the mouth comes to lie further and further forward and the stomodaeum now runs posteriorly from the mouth to the mesenteron.   After Conklin.

C, *Theodoxus fluviatilis*: *a*, early gastrula from the left; the ectoderm of this side has been removed to reveal the small endoderm cells budded from the megameres and one of the 2 teloblastic mesoderm cells; gastrulation is by epiboly. *b*, gastrula seen from above with the future anterior end towards the top; the 4 megameres are seen by transparency. *c*, vertical section of gastrula passing through the blastopore; the small endoderm cells have shifted beneath the ectoderm of the animal pole to form a continuous layer which, with the megameres, encloses the archenteron; the megameres form the rudiment of the digestive gland; the 2 teloblastic mesoderm cells have given rise to the mesodermal bands, laterally placed.   After Blochmann.

abe, absorbing cell of endoderm; al, albumen in mesenteron; an, archenteron; bl, blastopore; blc, blastocoel; ccm, cerebral commissure; cv, cephalic vesicle; ect, ectoderm; en, endoderm; f, foot; i, intestine; m, mouth; mb, mesodermal band; meg, megamere; mes, mesoderm; sdm, stomodaeal invagination; shg, shell gland; tb, teloblastic mesoderm cell; vec, velar cells.

vegetative pole. The region where the megameres are exposed is the blastopore, and the archenteron appears only after division of the invaginated cells. Of the megameres, that of quadrant *D* is the first to divide. According to Smith (1935) and Crofts (1937) it gives, during the gastrulation of the embryo of *Patella vulgata* and *Haliotis*, two equal-sized

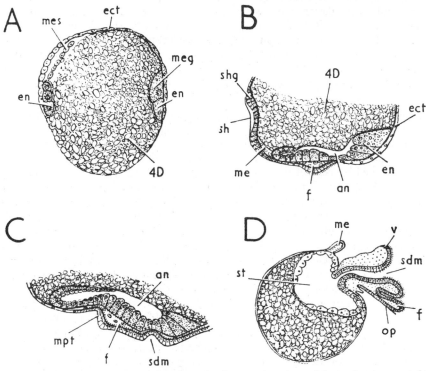

FIG. 219.—*Nassa mutabilis:* A, vertical section of early gastrula; most of the section is occupied by megamere 4*D*; the micromeres are spreading over the megameres and at the same time endoderm cells are dividing from 4*A*, 4*B*, 4*C*, 4*a*, 4*b* and 4*c*; the mesoderm is derived from 4*d*.

B, the vegetative part of a section through an embryo in which the micromeres cover the vegetative pole; the small endoderm cells have also shifted to this region and, with the large megameres, line a cavity, the archenteron; 4*D* forms a central core of yolk; rudiments of the foot and shell have appeared.

C, part of a section through an embryo to show the stomodaeal invagination.

D, longitudinal section through a much later embryo to show the relationship between the gut and the yolk. After Bobretzky.

an, archenteron; ect, ectoderm; en, endoderm; f, foot; me, mantle edge; meg, megameres; mes, mesoderm; mpt, metapodium; op, operculum; sdm, stomodaeum; sh, shell; shg, shell gland; st, stomach; v, velum.

cells which are spherical or sub-ovoid in shape. They are considered to be the teloblastic mesoderm cells situated near the blastopore (pm, fig. 224) and they contrast with the elongated appearance of the other 3 undivided megameres (en).

In *Crepidula* (fig. 218B) and the Stenoglossa (fig. 219) gastrulation is by epiboly and after the formation of the fourth quartette there is an interval before the yolk-laden megameres divide. Meanwhile the micromeres multiply and spread over them as a thin layer (ect). In *Crepidula* the nuclei of the megameres (en) become very large and lie in the protoplasmic portion of the cell, away from the mass of yolk and near the surface just in advance of the edge of the micromeres, and in this position they move towards the vegetative pole. In both *Crepidula* and *Fusus* (Bobretzky, 1877) small cells are divided from the megameres chiefly in the region of the blastopore, and they form the ventral

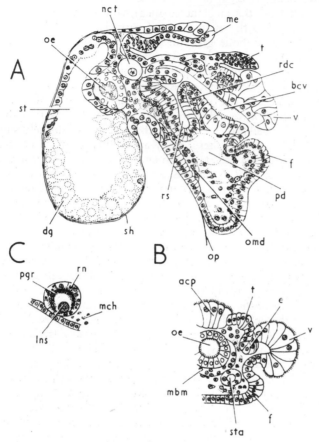

FIG. 220.—*Littorina littoralis:* A, longitudinal section of embryo after torsion; B, transverse section through head-foot of younger embryo; C, section of developing eye, showing closed vesicle. After Delsman.

acp, apical cell plate; bcv, buccal cavity; dg, digestive gland; e, eye; f, foot; lns, lens; mbm, muscles of buccal mass; mch, mesenchyme; me, mantle edge; nct, nephrocyst; oe, oesophagus; omd, developing opercular branch of columellar muscle; op, operculum; pd, projection of developing pedal ganglia on to sagittal plane; pgr, pigment granule; rdc, radular cartilage; rn, retinal cell; rs, radular sac; sh, shell; st, stomach; sta, statocyst; t, tentacle; v, velum.

wall of the archenteron which is clothed dorsally by the megameres. The distribution of the yolk in the embryos of *Nassarius*, *Urosalpinx* and *Nucella* is such that one megamere is far larger than the other three. As the micromeres grow over the megameres to approach the vegetative pole the 3 smaller megameres divide, and the resulting endoderm cells shift around the large yolky cell towards this pole to line the greater part of the archenteron (fig. 219). This, however, is a relatively inconspicuous cavity and, with the teloblastic mesoderm cells formed during gastrulation, forms part of a germ disc which lies over the surface of the megameres.

The movement of endoderm cells during the development of the archenteron in *Theodoxus* (Blochmann, 1882) is in the reverse direction (fig. 218C). Small endoderm cells (en) are cut off from the megameres (meg), which are small compared with those of the Stenoglossa, during the early stages of gastrulation, whilst the micromeres (ect) are enclosing them by epibolic growth. These endoderm cells migrate through the blastocoel towards the animal pole to form a continuous layer beneath the ectoderm and so become the dorsal wall of the primitive gut.

The primary or teloblastic mesoderm is at first represented by two cells, the teloblasts, lying in the blastocoel near the blastopore, one on either side of the archenteron, and these divide to give off new cells anteriorly. In typical cases two short mesodermal bands, bilaterally arranged, are formed by the activity of the teloblasts and the sub-division of the cells formed by them. They are at first dorsal in position. In *Crepidula* they are formed after the 65-cell stage and eventually each band comprises only 8 or 9 cells (fig. 221A, mb). In *Haliotis* there is a total of 10 mesoderm cells at the time the trochophore larva is freed (fig. 225A) and more are formed later (rmc, fig. 225C). During the pretorsional larval stage of *Haliotis* and *Patella* the anterior ends of the bands are broken up into irregular, spindle-shaped cells which will develop into muscle cells of the head and foot, and also into vascular tissue in *Haliotis*. Others surround the dorsal and lateral parts of the ectodermal foregut. The remainder of the bands will give rise to the velar retractor muscle (developed from the right one alone and responsible for the first or rapid stage of torsion), the columellar muscle (developed from the left band alone), and the coelomic walls of the kidney and pericardium from which the gonad will later arise. These are the only coelomic cavities to be formed. In *Crepidula* torsion is complete before the veliger is freed and it is differential growth which leads to the mesenteron being looped into a figure-of-eight. No larval retractor muscle was found by Conklin (1897) and he stated that all signs of teloblasts and mesodermal bands have disappeared as such before the beginning of the torsion of the gut, and before the early differentiation of the nervous system. However, when the veliger larva hatches there is a well developed larval retractor muscle of unknown origin (lr, fig. 236A) which in this prosobranch is apparently late to develop and is not concerned with torsion. Unfortunately we have no knowledge of the development of tissues from the teloblastic mesoderm in *Crepidula*, for details of the internal development of later embryos have not been worked out. In fact later developmental stages have been followed in adequate detail only in *Viviparus* (Erlanger, 1891*b*; Tönniges, 1896; Drummond, 1903; Andersen, 1924*a*, 1924*b*), *Patella* (Patten, 1886*a*; Smith, 1935; Crofts, 1955), *Pomatias* (Creek, 1951) and *Haliotis* (Crofts, 1937, 1955).

The terrestrial prosobranch *Pomatias elegans* completes development to the crawling stage within the egg capsule. The egg (fig. 205) which measures 0·14 mm in diameter, has little yolk and at an early stage the embryo absorbs albumen through special ectoderm cells in the swollen cephalic region (cv, fig. 232A). The embryo is characterized by the early development of abundant teloblastic mesoderm which, by the gastrular stage, forms a compact layer between ectoderm and endoderm, and is thickest on the right and left sides. By the early veliger stage these lateral thickenings, corresponding to the mesodermal bands of other species, are no longer distinguishable owing to the increase of mesoderm dorsally and ventrally. A considerable quantity has also developed in the foot and visceral mass. However, none of the cells shows specific differentiation—in fact the differentiation of muscle is delayed until torsion is complete. With the loss of the free larval stage both contractile tissue and blood are late to develop.

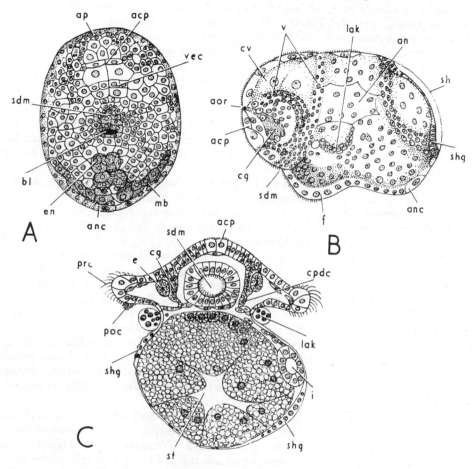

FIG. 221.—*Crepidula fornicata:* A, embryo showing closure of the blastopore; B, side view of older embryo; C, horizontal section of still older embryo at a ventral level. After Conklin.

acp, apical cell plate—the end of the guide line lies at the centre of a group of 7 cells which will give rise to this structure; an, archenteron; anc, anal cells; aor, apical organ; ap, animal pole now migrated so as to be visible in ventral view; bl, blastopore; cg, cerebral ganglion; cpdc, cerebropedal connective; cv, cephalic vesicle; e, eye; en, enteroblasts; f, foot; i, intestine; lak, larval kidney; mb, left mesodermal band; poc, postoral cilia of velum; prc, preoral cilia of velum; sdm, stomodaeal depression beginning, in C, stomodaeum; sh, shell; shg, shell gland; st, stomach; v, velum; vec, velar cells, arranged in 2 transverse rows.

In addition to the mesoderm which is bilateral and teloblastic in origin, cells may pass into the blastocoel from the ectoderm after the appearance of the teloblasts. In *Crepidula* their origin has been traced to the descendants of the second quartette of ectomeres, 2a, 2b, 2c. They are scattered cells, chiefly concerned in the formation of muscle fibres in the foot, and also in the head vesicle and velum, which are embryonic or larval organs.

This ectomesoderm is often referred to as larval mesoderm or mesenchyme, though adult tissues are allegedly derived from it. However, it appears to be neither constant in origin nor has it been found in all the embryos of prosobranchs which have been studied. In *Patella caerulea* (Patten, 1886a), *P. vulgata* (Smith, 1935), *Haliotis* (Crofts, 1937), *Pomatias* (Creek, 1951) and *Theodoxus* (Blochmann, 1882) all mesoderm appears to come from the mesodermal bands, and Robert (1902) stated that if ectomesoderm is formed in trochids its development must be very late for he was unable to trace it. However, it is developed in *Littorina littoralis* and originates from the cells $3a^{2111}$, $3a^{2211}$ and $3b^{2111}$, $3b^{2211}$ (as in *Fiona*, *Physa* and *Planorbis*), and Delsman (1914) observed the ectomesoderm joining with the cells of the endomesoderm so closely that in this species the two cannot be differentiated later. Indeed he found it impossible to decide whether the heart and kidney arise from ectomesoderm or endomesoderm, or a combination of both. In the trochophore stage of polychaetes larval mesenchyme is maximal in species which have little yolk and minimal in larvae with a rich food supply (Meyer, 1901), but no such correlation can be made in prosobranchs.

The aberrant freshwater prosobranch *Viviparus*, in which the young complete development in the oviduct, appears to stand apart from all other molluscs in the mode of origin of the mesoderm. The small yolkless eggs develop rapidly to a trochophore stage so that the archenteron can take up the albuminous fluid (c, fig. 218A). Only at this stage does mesoderm formation begin. Erlanger (1891a and b; 1894) was the first to study the embryology and he stated that a median bilobed pouch which pushes into the blastocoel from the ventral surface of the intestine is the origin of the mesoderm. The pouch separates from the gut, loses its cavity, and gives rise to two irregular mesodermal bands which extend forwards at the sides of the gut. Anterior cells of each band form a larval kidney, a compact posterior mass cavitates to form a coelomic vesicle which will become part of the pericardial sac, and the cells of the mid-region scatter in the blastocoel. Such enterocoelic mesoderm formation has not been described for any other mollusc and seems an incongruity in an embryo developing from an egg which cleaves spirally. However, it could be regarded as a modification of the teloblastic method, brought about by the delay of separation of the teloblasts and their derivatives from the enteroblast 4D.

Erlanger's results were soon challenged by Tönniges (1896) who stated that all adult mesoderm in *Viviparus* arises as an ectodermal proliferation; later, he repeated this investigation and obtained the same result (Otto & Tönniges, 1906). Dautert (1929) agreed that only ectomesoderm is developed and traced its origin to cells of the second and third quartettes. He found that it appears at the ventral surface of the embryo (c, mes, fig. 218A), beginning in the region of the prototroch and spreading to the blastopore. The mesoderm spreads laterally between ectoderm and endoderm, but not mid-dorsally, where the two layers remain in contact. No coelomic cavity is formed and the mesoderm gradually disperses. However, a slightly later and less detailed investigation by Fernando (1931a) supported the enterocoelic method of mesoderm formation. In interpreting his results Dautert (1929) suggested that endomesoderm is normally formed in gastropods during the early stages of development, and that these are telescoped in *Viviparus* so that its development is suppressed. Consequently only ectomesoderm, which is of later appearance, is found in this genus. The only other account claiming that all mesoderm is derived from the ectoderm is given by Sarasin (1882) for *Bithynia*, but this was conclusively disproved by Erlanger (1892), who described a teloblastic origin.

The spiral cleavage of the eggs of platyhelminths, annelids and molluscs typically results in the production of ectomesoderm from the second and third quartettes of micromeres, and its failure to develop in certain prosobranchs and some other gastropods (*Aplysia*, *Siphonaria*, *Limax*) is undoubtedly secondary. This mesoderm seems to

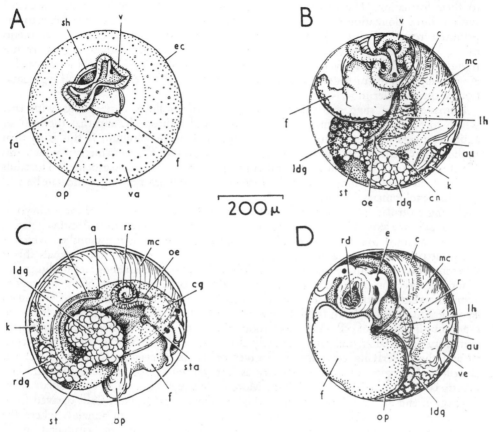

Fig. 222.—*Littorina saxatilis:* embryos from brood pouch. A, veliger stage; B, late veliger; C, just before hatching; D, hatching by rasping through egg membrane.

a, anus; au, auricle; c, cilia on mantle skirt; cg, cerebral ganglion; cn, connective tissue loaded with calcareous granules; e, eye; ec, egg covering; f, foot; fa, fluid albumen; k, kidney; ldg, left lobe of digestive gland; lh, larval heart; mc, mantle cavity; oe, oesophagus; op, operculum; r, rectum; rd, radula; rdg, right lobe of digestive gland; rs, radular sac; sh, shell; st, stomach; sta, statocyst; v, velum with slight ciliation; va, viscous albumen; ve, ventricle.

have appeared first in evolution and is present in the Radiata; in the Deuterostomia it does not develop. Its loss in prosobranchs seems to have no evolutionary significance since it apparently fails to develop in some archaeogastropods with a primitive life history and yet is present in mesogastropods in which the larval stages are abbreviated or suppressed. Conklin (1897) emphasized the radial origin of the total mesoderm in *Crepidula*, for ectomesoderm arises in the three quadrants *A*, *B* and *C*, and endomesoderm in quadrant *D*. He suggested that this radial origin may be a primitive character which is lost in other gastropods.

With the possible exception of *Viviparus* it is from endomesoderm derived from teloblasts in the vicinity of the blastopore that the adult musculature, the renopericardial complex and haemal tissue are produced, though some ectomesoderm may contribute to their formation. The paired mesoderm bands which are developed are associated with a slight elongation of the embryo. In *Patella* and *Haliotis* they unite beneath the primitive rectum (fig. 225C), where, during the early part of torsion, solid rudiments of the kidneys and pericardium appear. The coelomic cavities of these organs are not represented until the late veliger stage when torsion is complete. No coelomic pouches are developed in the mesodermal bands, as in annelids, nor is there any sign of segmentation of the mesoderm.

Remane (1950) suggested that the mesoderm of molluscs corresponds with that which forms the larval segments of polychaetes and arthropods, and that the later or adult segments of these groups are not represented in the phylum. If this is so then molluscs have either lost, during the course of evolution, the metamerism which this larval mesoderm displays, or the mesoderm was never at any time segmented. The adult anatomy of *Neopilina* may suggest the former view, though nothing more can be said until its development is known.

During gastrulation the blastopore is formed at the vegetative pole of the embryo so that the primary axis of the ovum—a straight line passing through animal and vegetative poles—is retained. As the trochopore stage develops a new axis is established which is the principal one of the larva and adult: in all bilaterally symmetrical animals this is different from the primary one. In the typical trochophore of annelids and molluscs this change in direction of the axis is indicated by the apparent migration of the blastopore along the ventral surface towards the prototroch; the movement may be accompanied by its gradual closure from behind forwards. In both phyla the displacement is due to rapid multiplication of cells in the posterodorsal region, which will become the posterior extremity of the larva, and can be directly attributed to the activity of the derivatives of 2*d* and the underlying cells, the derivatives of 4*d*. In *Crepidula*, Conklin (1897) has described the region of greatest activity as just ventral to the future shell gland and superficial to the mesoblastic teloblasts. More or less regular rows of cells radiate from this region and are particularly well marked on the ventral surface. Cells derived from 2*d* and 4*d* are also associated with the formation of the trunk in annelids where the continued elongation of this region is accompanied by metameric segmentation. In gastropods, however, this growth results in a ventral curvature of the trunk, so that mouth and anus remain at no great distance from one another. It is also associated with the formation of the shell on the posterodorsal surface, and the growth of the foot ventral to the stomodaeum.

The flow of ectoderm cells from the area of rapid multiplication results in the bending of the egg axis. In the trochopore larva of *Polygordius* it is the vegetative pole, marked by the blastopore, which appears to move forward along the ventral surface, and Smith (1935) has described a similar reorientation of the axis in the trochophore of *Patella vulgata*. After the formation of the blastopore in *Patella* two cells dorsal to it form the anal tuft or telotroch, and a flattening and division of cells on the dorsal surface, between this region and the prototroch, drives the blastopore ventrally and then forwards. The cells between the anal tuft and blastopore also multiply and spread anteriorly, continuing the forward thrust. Such a change in position of the blastopore is brought about in a

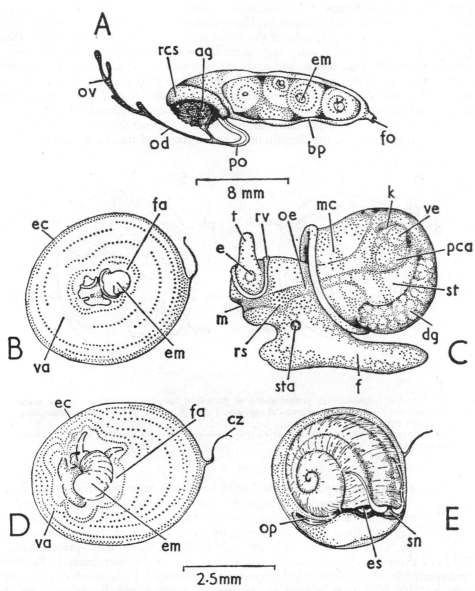

FIG. 223.—*Viviparus viviparus:* A, diagram of female reproductive system with the brood pouch opened; B, C, D and E, 4 developmental stages, B a young veliger, E just before hatching. In C the embryo has been dissected out of its coverings.

ag, albumen gland; bp, brood pouch; cz, chalaza; dg, digestive gland; e, eye; ec, egg covering; em, embryo; es, exhalant siphon; f, foot; fa, fluid albumen; fo, female opening; k, kidney; m, mouth; mc, mantle cavity; od, ovarian duct; oe, oesophagus; op, operculum; ov, ovary; pca, pericardial cavity; po, pallial oviduct; rcs, receptaculum seminis; rs, radular sac; rv, remains of velum; sn, snout; st, stomach; sta, statocyst; t, tentacle; va, viscous albumen; ve, ventricle.

similar way in *Haliotis* (Crofts, 1937) and *Gibbula magus* (Robert, 1902), and in these three diotocardians there is at the same time a reorientation of the endoderm cells and the formation of teloblastic mesoderm. There is probably some shifting forward of the animal pole with the hypertrophy of the dorsal area, but it can only be slight in these species for they hatch at an early stage as trochophore larvae; these show no forward movement of the apical region, and retain throughout the cell migrations the circumapical symmetry of the prototroch which is essential to their movements through the water. There are other gastropods in which the main direction of movement of the proliferated cells in the dorsal region is anterior and displaces the animal pole. These have no free trochophore stage and their embryos have a considerable amount of yolk. In them, the vegetative pole may remain more or less fixed and the change of axis be due

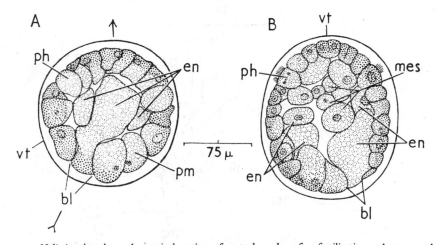

FIG. 224.—*Haliotis tuberculata*: A, vertical section of gastrula, 7 hrs after fertilization. Arrow marks embryonic axis passing through animal and vegetative poles. B, vertical section of early trochophore, 11 hrs after fertilization. After Crofts.

bl, blastopore region; en, endoderm cells; mes, mesoderm cells; ph, prototroch; pm, primitive mesoderm cells; vt, vitelline membrane.

to a shifting of the animal pole. Thus in *Crepidula* the uppermost part of the vertical axis of the gastrula is bent forwards at an angle of 90° and the position of the blastopore itself is hardly changed, nor are the endoderm cells influenced by the shifting of the ectoderm.

The end result of these cell movements is the same and the blastopore comes to lie mid-ventrally, immediately beneath the cells of the prototroch or preoral velum. With one exception the mouth is formed in the region of the blastopore. In *Viviparus* the hypertrophy of the dorsal ectoderm causes some forward displacement of the animal pole, but the blastopore remains in its original position and finally becomes the anus.

Only a few gastropods have a trochophore larva and these include the diotocardians *Haliotis*, *Patella*, *Patina*, *Acmaea*, *Gibbula*, *Monodonta* and *Tricolia*. In other prosobranchs a corresponding embryonic stage can be recognized. The larva is top-shaped with the prototroch at its greatest diameter. This consists of one row of cells in *Haliotis* (fig. 225A), *Acmaea*, *Gibbula* and *Monodonta*, two in *Patella* (fig. 234A), and in the corresponding embryonic stage it consists of two rows of cells in *Viviparus*, three in *Bithynia* and even more in *Crepidula* (fig. 221C). In the centre of the pretrochal area a tuft of apical cilia may develop from an ectodermal thickening, the apical plate cells. Unlike the cilia of the prototroch they are not motile; it has been suggested that they have a sensory function and may help to preserve equilibrium in the actively moving larva. (In a later stage in the development of *Crepidula* an apical sense organ arises (p. 457) and becomes connected with the cerebral ganglia, but it is not associated with a bunch of large cilia, for over the apical and many surrounding cells the cilia are short and fine.) From the pretrochal ectoderm on either side of the apical plate cells a sense plate (cephalic plate) develops (acp, figs. 220B, 221). These later give rise to the cerebral ganglia by a proliferation of cells inwards from the surface, the eyes, which are formed in connexion with the ganglia as separate involutions, and the tentacles.

The blastopore may close for a brief period after its anterior migration. Before its closure it is sunk into a depression, the stomodaeal invagination, in *Crepidula*, though the depression is formed after closure in *Haliotis* and the trochids. In *Patella* and *Littorina littoralis* (Delsman, 1914) the blastopore remains open and is carried inwards to communicate with the larval stomach. The narrowest part of the stomodaeal invagination will later give rise to the oesophagus, which is therefore ectodermal in origin. However, in the development of *Crepidula adunca*, Moritz (1939) stated that it is the anterior end of the oesophagus which marks the junction of ectoderm and endoderm. In the late trochophore stage there may be a thickening in the posterior wall of the buccal region of the stomodaeum which foreshadows the radular sac. In contrast to the trochophore of annelids the archenteron is a blind sac with, perhaps, an oral opening, though when the trochophore of *Haliotis* is freed even this is not formed: ano-pedal flexure has begun before the proctodaeum is developed and is complete before the stomodaeum opens to the gut. The position of the future anus may be marked externally by anal cells. This is a single large ectodermal cell near the telotroch in *Patella vulgata*, but in some other genera a number of anal cells (anc, fig. 221) appear in or near a position once occupied by the posterior margin of the blastopore (*Haliotis, Littorina, Crepidula, Calyptraea, Nassarius, Nucella*). Finally the hind gut connects with the ectoderm between the anlage of the shell gland and foot and here the ectoderm forms a shallow proctodaeal invagination. The anal opening may be late to form and in the embryo of *Crepidula* this is after torsion has occurred.

In the trochophore of annelids paired larval or head kidneys are formed. These are protonephridia with solenocytes. In prosobranch gastropods no free trochophore or veliger has been found to possess a larval kidney though such structures do occur in the embryonic veliger stage. Only in two genera, *Viviparus* and *Bithynia*, do these resemble the protonephridia of the annelid trochophore (p. 457).

The development of *Haliotis tuberculata* (though not the cell lineage) has been carefully studied by Crofts (1937, 1955) and as she is the first author to describe the details of torsion her account will be followed here. The main events may be summarized thus:

1. Pelagic phase:
   Trochophore freed from egg membranes: 8–13 hrs after fertilization (fig. 225A).
   Early veliger larva prior to torsion: 9–27 hrs after fertilization (figs. 225B, c).
   First 90° torsion of veliger: begins 29–35 hrs after fertilization and takes 3–6 hrs (fig. 227C).

2. Transition from pelagic to benthic life: not less than 3 days after fertilization.

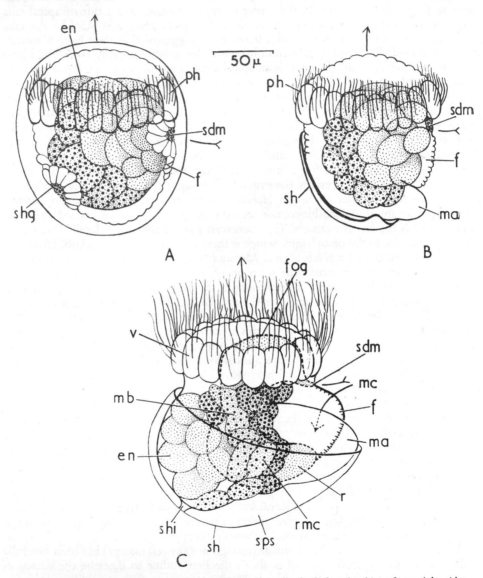

FIG. 225.—*Haliotis tuberculata*: A, trochophore larva immediately before hatching, from right side; B, early veliger, 16 hrs after fertilization, from right side; C, early veliger, 19 hrs after fertilization, from right side. Endoderm shaded with small dots, mesoderm with large and small dots. Arrows mark embryonic axis passing through original position of animal and vegetative pole. After Crofts.

en, endoderm; f, foot; fog, fore gut; ma, mantle skirt; mb, mesodermal band; mc, mantle cavity; ph, prototroch; r, rectum; rmc, rudiment of muscle cell of right mesodermal band; sdm, stomodaeal invagination in region of closed blastopore; sh, shell; shg, shell gland; shi, attachment of shell to integument; sps, space between visceral mass and shell; v, velum.

3. Benthic phase:

Benthic veliger stage established: not less than 3 days after fertilization (fig. 228A).

Second 90° torsion of veliger: begins about 5 and ends about 12 days after fertilization; velum disappears during this phase (figs. 228B, 229A).

Final phase of metamorphosis: begins 12 days after fertilization and ends about 2 months after fertilization (fig. 229B).

The first two divisions of the fertilized egg give four blastomeres which then divide by a process of spiral cleavage similar to that found in platyhelminths and annelids. The third cleavage, which is spiral, gives four large megameres with much yolk, and four micromeres. The megameres bud off successive quartettes of micromeres towards the animal pole and a spherical blastula is formed with a very reduced blastocoel. Gastrulation is by epiboly, and the megameres $4A$, $4B$, $4C$ and $4D$ are pressed into the segmentation cavity and obliterate it. $4A$, $4B$ and $4C$ are irregular in shape and elongated in the polar direction, whilst $4D$, which is nearer the blastopore, divides equally to form two almost spherical cells (pm, fig. 224A). Crofts suggested that, as in *Patella vulgata* (Smith, 1935), these two cells give rise to mesoderm, whereas the endoderm is derived from the other three megameres (en). The invaginated cells are so large that there is no archenteric cavity in the early gastrula, and this appears only later when these cells have divided. During gastrulation the embryo elongates in the direction of the axis through the apical plate, and the prototroch (ph, figs. 224A, B) forms as a ring of ciliated cells encircling the apical area. The cilia rotate the embryo within the vitelline membrane from about 8 hours after fertilization. The blastopore (bl), at first posterior and centred on the axis of the apical field, moves towards the prototroch along the ventral surface, leaving a temporary groove along this path. The migration of the blastopore appears to be due to a multiplication of mesoderm cells, which have now become dorsolaterally placed, and, at the same time, an increase in ectoderm cells along the dorsal surface, and is accompanied by the gradual shifting of the axis of the endoderm and mesoderm.

The trochophore larva (fig. 225A) is freed from the vitelline membrane 8–13 hrs from the time of fertilization. It is then about 0·13 mm long and differs superficially from the trochophore of *Patella* (fig. 234A) in the absence of apical cilia and telotroch, and in the fact that the prototroch comprises a single and not a double row of ciliated cells. The rudiments of the molluscan characters have scarcely begun to appear at this stage, although a shallow depression on the dorsal surface of the body, slightly towards the right, indicates the developing shell gland (shg, fig. 225A), and immediately posterior to the ventral lip of the blastopore is a median swelling, the rudiment of the foot (f). At about this stage the blastopore is closed and the stomodaeal pit (sdm) formed near its point of closure. The mesoderm now comprises 10 cells which are orientated in the posttrochal region. The trochophore is positively phototactic and swims near the surface of the water with the prototroch directed upwards, the lashing of the cilia causing a rotatory movement. This larval stage is of short duration.

The transition to the veliger is accompanied by little modification of the swimming organ, for the velum retains the simple character of the preoral ciliated prototroch—a circle of ciliated cells constricted from the rest of the body, and comprising at first 16 cells, with an increase in the older veliger to 24. As the larva grows the cilia become more numerous and longer. The whole pretrochal area is involved in the formation of the velum.

The early veliger, the larval stage preceding torsion, is characterized externally by the development of the shell (sh, figs. 225B, C) and mantle (ma) and an increase in the size of the foot (f). The cells of the shell gland, which in the trochophore line a shallow depression, multiply rapidly, and this, together with the enlargement of the primitive mid-gut and mesodermal bands, causes the eversion of the gland at about 14 hrs after fertilization. A delicate shell of watch-glass shape is secreted; it is of transparent conchiolin and without calcareous spicules. At about 18 hrs the shell gland has spread over most of the dorsal region of the body and the shell has increased around its margin to form a deep saucer. Its expansion is most rapid over the posterior end of the body, where it begins to spread on to the ventral surface. The shell is attached to the body at its periphery, and rapid multiplication of cells near its right ventral edge produces a thickening which is the mantle fold or skirt (ma). The fold increases in size and spreads over the foot (f), and the cavity which it encloses is the mantle cavity (mc). In *Haliotis*

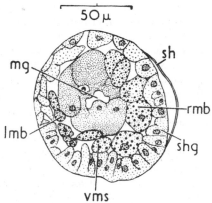

Fig. 226.—*Haliotis tuberculata*: transverse section of early veliger (17 hrs) to show the larger mesodermal band on the right side; the section has passed through the shell gland and shell on this side. After Crofts.

    lmb, left mesodermal band; mg, cavity of mid-gut; rmb, right mesodermal band; sh, shell; shg, shell gland; vms, ventral union of right and left mesodermal bands.

this cavity is not at first in the mid-ventral line as in *Patella* (Smith, 1935) and *Trochus* (Robert, 1902), for the mantle skirt is developed on the right side of the body and then spreads to the left over the pedal rudiment. However, by 29 hrs—just before torsion begins—the deepest part of the cavity is mid-ventral. The development of the mantle skirt is accompanied by corresponding changes in the shell (sh) which, early on the second day, has a wide ventral opening and is constricted dorsally between the enlarging visceral mass and the velum. At this stage the veliger presents an all but symmetrical external appearance and has a nautiloid exogastric shell. The opening of the mantle cavity is a broad transverse slit curving under the foot, with the mouth directly anterior to it. The visceral mass contracts away from the inner surface of the shell (sps, fig. 225C), giving a space which may contain gas; in other veligers, this has been thought to have a hydrostatic function.

    Before torsion begins, the digestive tube, as in all gastropod larvae, is curved into a U-shape, so that the rectum (r), instead of being directed posteriorly as in chitons, is directed ventrally and anteriorly. It is separated from the stomodaeum by the foot (f). This dorsoventral flexure (= ano-pedal flexure) is, like the shape of the shell, another consequence of the differential growth of the visceral hump. In *Haliotis* the flexure begins at about 19 hrs after fertilization, that is before the proctodaeum has been formed, and is completed before the stomodaeal invagination has established connexion with the endoderm cells. At 27 hrs these cells have formed the rudiments of the larval stomach, the digestive gland and intestine. The digestive gland occupies the whole of the left and most of the dorsal part of the visceral dome and has a single opening into the left wall of the stomach. The small larval stomach is lined by cubical cells which have extended anteriorly to meet the stomodaeum. The rudiment of the radular sac does not appear until after the first phase of torsion.

During dorsoventral flexure of the digestive tube the mesoderm cells give rise to a right and a left mesodermal band (mb). At 17 hrs after fertilization the right band is distinctly the larger. Five large mesoderm cells on the right side elongate at about 22 hrs after fertilization to form spindle-shaped muscle cells (rmc), and as these grow the visceral hump is gradually displaced to the left so that even before torsion the veliger is asymmetrical. Posteriorly the muscle cells converge and are attached to a projection of the mantle which is joined to the apex of the shell on the right side (lra, fig. 227). There is a similar attachment of mantle and shell though, as yet, with no related muscle on the left side. Anteriorly the muscle cells diverge: three pass forwards along the right side of the larva and have attachments to the mantle (1, 2), the velum (2, 3) and the stomodaeum (3); the remaining two twist dorsally over the gut to the left side of the foot (5, 6), velum (4, 5, 6) and stomodaeum (4), and one of these (4, 5) divides after the first half of torsion, thus giving three muscle cells related to each side of the anterior region of the body. This asymmetrically placed larval retractor muscle of the head and left side of the foot is the cause of the beginning of torsion ontogenetically.

As expressed by Garstang (1928), the posteroventral position of the mantle cavity and the exogastric shell of the early veliger are disadvantageous since the larva cannot withdraw wholly into the shell. When torsion is complete the mantle cavity lies over the head with the opening directed anteriorly: it has been displaced 180° relative to the head and foot. In such a position the head and then the foot can be withdrawn to its shelter, and in the majority of prosobranchs an operculum on the metapodium closes the cavity. In *Haliotis* an operculum is secreted by unicellular glands of the ectoderm of the metapodium just before torsion begins, and it is still present in the post-larva of 44 days old; it is never calcified and later disappears.

At the stage which precedes torsion the body consists essentially of two halves, an anterior cephalopedal mass and a posterior visceral hump, the two connected by a narrower 'neck'. As the process of torsion, which is about to be described, involves the relative movement of these two halves of the body on each other it is necessary to explain that in dealing with the changes which are involved all references will be made in relation to the dorsal and ventral sides of the adult body. These adult axes coincide with the larval axes so far as the cephalopedal mass is concerned, but the larval axes of the visceral hump, though coincident with these before torsion, are altered by that process. It may be, as Crofts' (1955) description of *Haliotis* suggests, that the first part of the actual rotatory movement appears to be one of the head-foot on the visceral hump, but as the twisting takes place when the larva is planktonic, and not related to any substratum, and as the orientation of the cephalopedal mass is that on which adult anatomy is based, we have chosen to use that orientation as the standard to which the changes in development will be related.

Torsion takes place in two phases. The first 90° of rotation occurs as soon as the larval

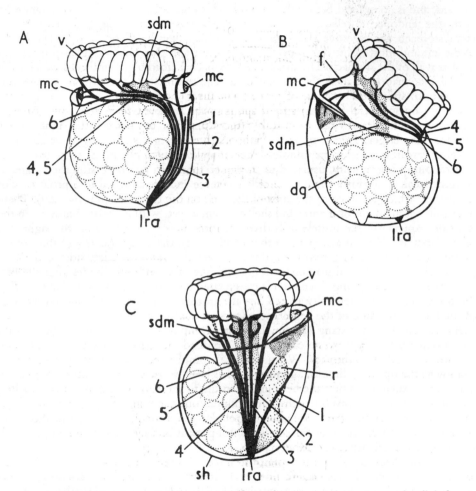

FIG. 227.—*Haliotis tuberculata:* veliger larva to show the course of the larval retractor muscle cells before torsion, A and B, and after 90° torsion, C.    A, dorsal view;  B, from the left;  C, dorsal view with respect to foot (see text).    After Crofts.

dg, digestive gland;  f, foot;  lra, attachment of larval retractor muscle to shell;  mc, mantle cavity (stippled);  r, rectum;  sdm, stomodaeum;  sh, shell;  v, velum.

1–6 cells of larval retractor muscle;  cells 4 and 5 are incompletely separated before torsion.  **The** muscle cells originate on the shell and are inserted:

1. to outer region of mantle on right side.
2. one process to mantle near deepest part of mantle cavity, and a second under ventral right side of velum.
3. one process to epithelial cells under velum on dorsal right side and a second to right side of stomodaeum.
4. one process to epithelial cells under velum on dorsal left side, and a second to left side of stomodaeum.  The proximal part of this muscle cell is incompletely divided from 5 before torsion.
5. one process to left side of velum and a second to left posterior region of foot.
6. one process to left side of velum and two processes to left region of foot.

muscle cells have any contractile power, 29–35 hrs after fertilization, and is completed
within 3–6 hrs. To understand this phase it is necessary to consider the relationships
of the right larval retractor muscle. This runs from an attachment on the right side of
the shell (lra, fig. 227A) forwards along the right side of the visceral hump to the head
and foot. Most of the fibres curve dorsally and some pass across to the left side of the
body so that the muscle forms a fan of fibres originating on the shell and inserted on head
and foot. As soon as these fibres are sufficiently differentiated their contraction will tend
to straighten this curve. When this happens the visceral hump and head-foot will be
twisted one on the other in such a way that the head-foot is turned through 90° so that
its ventral side faces the left side of the visceral hump, that is, it moves to the left. As a
result, the mantle cavity lies on the right side of the cephalopedal axis (mc, fig. 227C)
and it is possible for the velum and foot to retract partly within the endogastric shell.
The asymmetrical right larval retractor muscle is now straightened and lies dorsal to the
primitive gut.

The second phase of torsion takes place slowly during the transition from planktonic
to benthic life. When the larva is about 40 hrs old it rests on the bottom between
intervals of swimming; the intervals shorten and after the third day it becomes entirely
benthic. The larva attempts to creep, though with little success at first, for the foot is
unable to get a suitable hold owing to the difficulty of balancing the weighty visceral
hump and to the small size of the plantar surface. Between attempts the larva will lie
with the left side of the shell, on which the margin is shorter, on the ground. By the
time the musculature and the sole of the foot are well developed, and the creeping habit
established, the larva is about 6 days old (fig. 228B) and the second 90° of torsion has
begun. It is not completed until about a week later when the early post-veliger stage is
reached (fig. 229A). This second phase of torsion is brought about by differential growth,
for which the development and migration of the columellar muscle are mainly
responsible.

The origin of the larval retractor muscle migrates gradually from its posterodorsal
attachment towards the anterior left side, and so comes progressively nearer the left
margin of the shell (lr, fig. 228A). After the creeping stage has been reached additional
muscle fibres extend into the foot, and it becomes mainly a left pedal retractor by the
time the velum is lost (lsm, fig. 229A). Until then (about 9–10 days after fertilization) it
is also the sole head retractor. A small retractor of the post-torsional right side of the foot
develops from the pretorsional left mesodermal band and becomes obvious during the
third day of development, though it is not functional until the fifth day. This muscle
will become the columellar or right shell muscle of the adult. When it is first developed
it runs from the rudiment of the columella to the foot, and retracts the cephalopedal
mass and operculum into the shell (rsm, fig. 228B). It has, at this time, the same arrangement as the columellar muscle of gastropods with typical dextrally coiled shells. During
the later veliger stages of *Haliotis*, however, the columella fails to develop further and
the shell attachment of the muscle migrates anteriorly towards the centre of the last
whorl (rsm, figs. 229A, B). As it does so it gains in size and functional significance and
the pallial cavity expands over the dorsal aspect of the head-foot from the right side.
By the time the velum is lost—by the cells being gradually nipped off—the topographical
left larval retractor and the right retractor or columellar muscle are about equal in
size (fig. 229A). Torsion is now complete and the shell is fully endogastric, but the anus
(a) is still on the right side of the mid-dorsal pallial cavity. From the external viewpoint
the larva at this stage presents a comparatively symmetrical appearance. The essential

difference in organization from the moment at which torsion began is the altered
disposition of the head-foot and visceral mass which is the consequence of that
process.

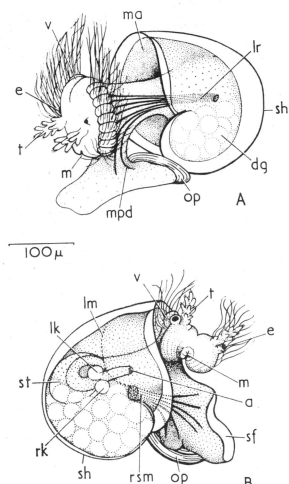

FIG. 228.—*Haliotis tuberculata:* A, benthic larva 4½ days old. The first phase of torsion is complete
and the mantle cavity is on the right side of the cephalopedal mass. B, benthic larva, 6 days old, at
the beginning of the second phase of torsion. After Crofts.

a, anus; dg, digestive gland; e, eye; lk, left (dorsal) kidney; lm, posterior limit of mantle cavity;
lr, larval retractor muscle; m, mouth; ma, mantle; mpd, fibres of larval retractor extending into
foot; op, operculum; rk, right (ventral) kidney; rsm, right shell muscle; sf, sole of foot; sh, shell;
st, stomach; t, tentacle; v, velum which is lost mid-dorsally and mid-ventrally.

The later asymmetry of the body which gives the characteristics peculiar to the adult,
is brought about by the hypertrophy of the columellar muscle displacing the mantle
cavity to the left. The muscle becomes a stout central pillar (rsm, fig. 229B) which with
the pedal muscles can contract the whole body against the rock surface. In doing this

it may help in producing the flattened shell into which the animal can no longer retract completely.

The dextral coiling of the shell can be followed from the third day of development, when the pallial fold is on the right side of the body and before the second phase of torsion has begun. A more rapid growth of the shell on the right side causes the creeping larva to bear towards the left, and the tilting of the shell is emphasized by the unequal distribution of weight in the visceral mass due to the presence of the digestive gland and velar retractor muscle on the left with little but the mantle cavity to counterbalance

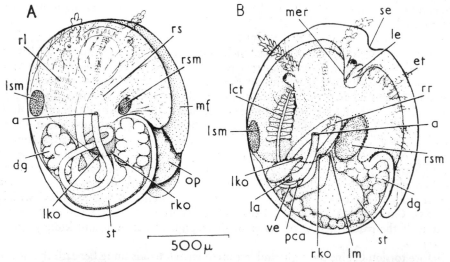

Fig. 229.—*Haliotis tuberculata:* A, post-larva 12 days old. The velum has been recently lost. Note the extensive mantle fold on the right side and the dextral coiling of the shell. B, post-larva 44 days old. The pallial cavity is already displaced somewhat to the left by hypertrophy of the right shell muscle. After Crofts.

a, anus; dg, digestive gland; et, epipodial tentacle; la, left auricle; lct, left ctenidium; le, larval process of epipodium; lko, left kidney opening; lm, posterior limit of mantle cavity; lsm, left shell muscle developed from larval retractor muscle; mer, mantle emargination; mf, mantle fold; op, operculum; pca, pericardium; rko, right kidney opening; rl, rudiment of left ctenidium; rr, rudiment of right ctenidium; rs, radular sac; rsm, right shell muscle; se, shell emargination; st, stomach; ve, ventricle.

them on the right. During the end of the second and throughout the third week of development (after torsion is complete) the right mantle fold secretes shell so rapidly as to roll the left margin inwards. The expanded right side of the shell now becomes attached to and wraps itself around the apex (fig. 229B) so as to produce the exaggerated development of the right side which is characteristic of the adult (fig. 85).

In the larva which is undergoing the second phase of torsion the left ctenidium and osphradium are represented by a longitudinal ridge of thickened, ciliated epithelium on the mantle skirt, separated from the rectum by epithelium which in the late veliger stage will form the left hypobranchial gland. These rudiments of the pallial complex are distinguishable only during the last quarter of the 180° torsion (rl, fig. 229A). Along the small part of the ridge which will become the osphradium the cilia are short, but the branchial part is more thickly covered with longer cilia, and in specimens 23 days old the rudiments of the first gill lamellae are formed.

There is only room enough on the right side of the rectum for the right renal opening until the post-veliger is about a month old (rko, fig. 229A). At 6 weeks, however, the mantle cavity between the columellar muscle and the rectum has expanded and the rudiment of the right ctenidium and osphradium is present (rr, fig. 229B); gill lamellae develop about a fortnight later. This ctenidium and the right hypobranchial gland are always the smaller. This postponement of the development of the organs of the post-torsional right side of the mantle cavity to the period of metamorphosis foreshadows the conditions in the more advanced Diotocardia and the Monotocardia in which these organs are lost.

It is assumed (Crofts, 1937) that until the right ctenidium is developed the flow of water through the pallial cavity of the metamorphosing *Haliotis* is similar to that of the gastropod with a single ctenidium, that is, it enters by the left side of the cavity and leaves above the anus on the right. At the time the right ctenidium is developing the first shell hole is formed. A small slit appears in the mantle margin (mer, fig. 229B) and in the overlying shell (se) on the right side of the head, and later the edges of the slit fuse. Peripheral shell growth completes the first shell hole when the ormer is about 2 months old and both gills are present. The pallial flow of water now assumes the adult condition, entering on both right and left sides and passing vertically to leave the mantle cavity through the hole. As the ormer grows and the pallial cavity moves forwards there is an alternate splitting and closing of the margin of the mantle to form a series of holes, one in front of the other; those formed first and no longer of use are filled with shell (fig. 85). Garstang (1928) suggested that the holes are formed as a consequence of the fouling of the pallial stream of water in the region of the anus and kidney apertures (p. 91).

Before torsion begins the right and left mesodermal bands unite beneath the primitive rectum and it is the cells of this region which later form the kidneys and the pericardium. However, at this stage in the development of *Haliotis* and in the development of *Patella* (Smith, 1935), only the solid renal rudiments can be recognized, and during the first phase of torsion they comprise, together with the proctodaeum, the only indications of the pallial complex. In veligers showing 90° torsion the presumptive kidneys, still solid masses of cells, lie dorsal and ventral to the rectum (drk, vrk, fig. 230C), on either side of which they are linked by mesoderm which will form the pericardium (rp). It will be understood that at this stage the gut has also undergone 90° torsion and that its topographically dorsal side is morphologically right and its topographically ventral side is morphologically left (p. 435). When torsion is complete the kidneys are in their definitive position, right and left of the rectum, but it is not until the late veliger, when the reduction of the velum begins, that a cavity appears in each. The two kidneys are then almost equal in size and are lined by cubical cells which are ciliated. The presumptive pericardial cells now form a delicate wall surrounding the rectum and enclosing the pericardial cavity (pca, fig. 229B). This communicates with each kidney by a renopericardial canal. Ingrowing cells of the pericardial wall become arranged around the rectum to form the ventricle (ve) and from this rudiment of the heart cells arise to form the left auricle (la). Later a smaller right auricle is similarly developed. In the early post-veliger the heart begins to pulsate.

The openings of the kidneys to the mantle cavity are not established until 12 days after fertilization (lko, rko, fig. 229A), although on the third day simple ectodermal invaginations from which they will arise are formed in the deepest part of the cavity, the post-torsional left one dorsal and the post-torsional right one ventral to the anus. The openings are not ciliated.

In specimens 3½ weeks old the right kidney is the larger and its epithelium is thrown into a few folds which foreshadow the complex folding of the adult. In the adult this

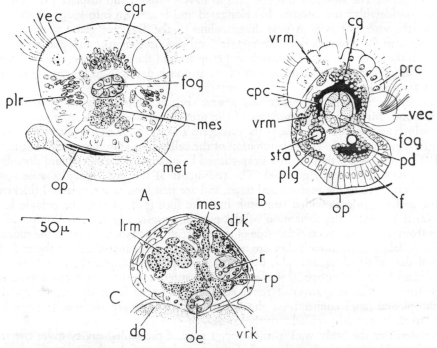

FIG. 230.—*Haliotis tuberculata*: A, transverse section through cephalopedal mass of veliger immediately before torsion begins; B, transverse section through cephalopedal mass of veliger after the first phase of torsion; C, transverse section of veliger after first phase of torsion to show renopericardial rudiments. After Crofts.

cg, cerebral ganglion; cgr, rudiment of cerebral ganglion; cpc, cerebropleural connective; dg, digestive gland; drk, dorsal rudiment of kidney; f, foot; fog, fore gut; lrm, larval retractor muscle; mef, mantle fold; mes, mesenchyme cells; oe, oesophagus; op, operculum; pd, pedal ganglion; plg, pleural ganglion; plr, rudiment of pleural ganglion; prc, prevelar cell; r, rectum; rp, rudiment of pericardium; sta, statocyst; vec, cells of velum; vrk, ventral rudiment of kidney; vrm, velar retractor muscle.

kidney, by far the larger of the two, communicates with the gonad, and its duct is a urinogenital duct.

At the end of the pelagic phase of torsion the stomodaeal invagination has developed into the foregut which communicates with the oesophagus. This contrasts with the development of *Littorina littoralis* (Delsman, 1914) in which the blastopore does not close, the stomodaeal invagination extends to the stomach and the oesophagus is ectodermal. The digestive gland now opens into the stomach by a single left duct. The anterior diverticula of this gland are ventral so that there is room in the dorsal region of the shell for the retracted head. The larva does not feed until early benthic life and then it is a filter feeder: until the velum disappears particles in suspension are collected from a current which is maintained by the velar cilia and those surrounding the mouth. At the end of the second week there has developed a cylindrical snout with jaws and the radular ribbon supported by two cartilages. The larva now collects loose fragments such as diatoms and Foraminifera from the stones on which it creeps. The gut is ciliated throughout its course. The stomach and oesophagus have enlarged and displaced the digestive gland considerably; the intestine has elongated and is thrown into loops on the dorsal part of the visceral hump. A new diverticulum of the digestive gland with a separate opening into the stomach does not appear until the close of metamorphosis; it comes to lie on the right side of the stomach and crop and, in the adult, curves around the left of the columellar muscle. The caecum of the stomach develops in the young ormer of about 2·5 mm long.

The differentiation of the nervous system begins before torsion, 27–36 hrs after fertilization. Mitosis in the ectoderm of the prevelar area gives rise to rounded nerve cells which aggregate at the base of the ectoderm and form the rudiments of the cerebral ganglia (cgr, fig. 230A). The delamination of the cells is not complete until after the first half of torsion, when they form a strap-shaped band around the dorsal and dorsolateral part of the foregut (cg, fig. 230B). The rudiments of the pedal ganglia arise slightly later, though still in the pretorsional stage, and are first seen as anterolateral thickenings of the pedal ectoderm which later sink into the foot (pd). Before the pelagic half of torsion is complete the formation of the pleural ganglia begins: a collection of cells sinks from the ectoderm on either side of the head (plr, fig. 230A), dorsal to the rudiments of the pedal ganglia, though they are not completely delaminated before the end of the second day of development (plg, fig. 230B). The pleural ganglia then lie close to the pedals and form a pleuropedal nerve mass. The anterior nerve ring is completed at the same time by the migration of nerve cells and fibres to form the cerebropedal and cerebropleural (cpc) connectives; the limits of the ganglia are not precise since (as in chitons) the nerve cells spread into the cords.

Ectoderm of the body wall in the deepest part of the pallial cavity gives rise to the pleurovisceral nerve cords at the end of the second day of development. They are delaminated from the ectoderm of the twisted 'neck' region soon after it has been involved in the first half of torsion. These cords have the appearance of short outgrowths from the pleural ganglia. The one associated with the right ganglion is short and on the right side of the oesophagus; it will form the supra-oesophageal connective. The other, associated with the left pleural ganglion, is longer, ventral to the oesophagus and pointing to the right. This sub-oesophageal connective is the only part of the nervous system to show the influence of the 90° torsion: the ectoderm from which it is formed was on the left side of the body before torsion began, but at the time of delamination it is ventral in position. In older veligers the visceral processes consist of nerve cells surrounding nerve fibres.

In the early post-veliger the supra-oesophageal pleurovisceral cord is displaced somewhat to the left by the enlarging columellar muscle. It passes dorsal to the gut to join the single branchial ganglion which is formed from nerve cells in the mantle skirt on the seventh or eighth day of development. This ganglion innervates the left ctenidial and osphradial rudiment. The pallial cavity has now completed 180° torsion and the proximal halves of the pleurovisceral cords show the streptoneurous condition; the visceral ganglion develops later when the typical figure-of-eight of the visceral loop is completed. The branchial ganglion of the post-torsional right side is not obvious until 44 days after fertilization and it does not join the sub-oesophageal connective until the ormer is 2 months old (rg, fig. 231). At this time the pleurovisceral cords have posterior prolongations beneath the epithelium of the floor of the pallial cavity and these unite to complete the visceral loop and form the single visceral ganglion (vg). This posterior part of the visceral loop is dorsal to the oesophagus. Dialyneury (p. 39) on both right and left is established later. The branchial ganglia of the adult are on short off-shoots of the visceral loop and not, like true parietal ganglia, on its course.

The buccal ganglia (bg) can be seen between the oesophagus and the radular sac before the velum disappears. They arise as outgrowths of the labial processes of the cerebral ganglia; in this they agree with *Acanthochitona* (Hammersten & Runnström, 1926) and

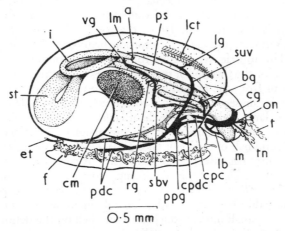

Fig. 231.—*Haliotis tuberculata:* diagram to show the nervous system in a post-veliger 2 months old, after metamorphosis is complete. Mantle cavity stippled. After Crofts.

a, anus; bg, buccal ganglion; cg, cerebral ganglion; cm, right shell muscle; cpc, cerebropleural connective; cpdc, cerebropedal connective; et, epipodial tentacle; f, foot; i, intestine; lm, posterior limit of mantle cavity; lb, labial commissure; lct, left ctenidium; lg, left branchial ganglion; m, mouth; on, optic nerve; pdc, pedal cord; ppg, pleuropedal ganglion mass; ps, pallial slit; rg, right branchial ganglion adjacent to rudiment of right ctenidium; sbv, sub-oesophageal pleurovisceral connective; st, stomach; suv, supra-oesophageal pleurovisceral connective; t, tentacle; tn, tentacular nerve; vg, visceral ganglion.

differ from *Patella* (Smith, 1935). In the adult the buccal ganglia are hardly distinguishable from their commissure and connectives since all have a peripheral layer of nerve cells.

The sense organs of the veliger comprise the tentacles, eyes and statocysts and in the early post-veliger the first epipodial tentacle appears. In larvae which have undergone 90° torsion a pair of invaginations of the ectoderm near the junction of the laterodorsal part of the foot and the head are the developing statocysts. The two cup-shaped depressions close off from the surface and sink into the foot by the third day (sta, fig. 230B). The statocysts then lie close to the pleuropedal ganglia though they are innervated by nerves from the cerebral ganglia. The tentacles arise from the lateral part of the prevelar area and can be recognized in larvae two and a half days old. They soon elongate and point ventrally, and papillae develop over the surface, the longer ones having tufts of immobile cilia which are sensory. An eye develops at the base of each tentacle on the outer side. It first appears as a group of pigmented epithelial cells which become raised on a small projection, the optic tubercle. The pigment cells sink and form a shallow retinal cup. The retinal cells secrete cuticular outgrowths to initiate the rods and the crystalline lens, and by the end of the second week the lens blocks the opening to the cup and projects from the tip of the optic stalk. The cup is never closed. Both eyes and tentacles are innervated by the cerebral ganglia by nerves bearing small ganglia (on, tn, fig. 231).

The first epipodial tentacle arises on the right side of the foot on a process which supports the operculum. Additional tentacles (et) appear during the third week of development on dorsal enlargements on both sides of the foot. They develop papillae with sensory processes similar to those of the cephalic tentacles.

Crofts (1955) has shown that the mechanism of torsion in the other primitive gastropods *Patella vulgata*, *Patina pellucida* and *Calliostoma zizyphinum* (the *Trochus conuloides* of Robert (1902)) is essentially similar to that of *Haliotis tuberculata*. Mesoderm cells give only a right retractor muscle before torsion begins, so that the pretorsional veliger is asymmetrical. This muscle, which goes to the velum, stomodaeum and left side of the foot, is responsible for the first 90° of torsion. The extrinsic musculature of the right side of the foot develops from the pretorsional left mesodermal band after the first phase of torsion and assists in the second phase; it contributes to the single columellar muscle of *Calliostoma* and the large right shell muscle of *Haliotis*. In *Haliotis*, *Calliostoma* and *Patella* the position of the shell attachment of the pretorsional right larval retractor muscle alters while the second half of torsion is taking place: it migrates to the left and forwards. By the time the velum has disappeared and torsion is complete it is equal in size to the definitive right shell muscle and the two occupy corresponding positions left and right of the main axis. In *Calliostoma* the larval retractor is reduced in the post-larval stage and then lost, as presumably happens in other prosobranchs with a single shell muscle. In *Haliotis* it persists as a small muscle attached to the shell on the definitive left side, and it occurs in a similar way in many diotocardians and in some monotocardians with broad limpet-like shells (p. 140). In *Patella* and *Patina* both left and right shell muscles probably unite to form the horseshoe-shaped shell muscle of the adult. The specialized characteristics of the four genera investigated by Crofts (1955) develop after torsion is complete and the velum has been lost for some days.

There are differences in the early development of these genera which may be correlated with the amount of yolk in the egg, and the stage at which the embryos are freed from their membranes. In *Patella* the eggs are somewhat smaller than in *Haliotis*, having less yolk, and development has gone on for about 60 hrs before torsion begins; that is about twice as long as in *Haliotis*. The pretorsional larva is therefore further advanced: statocysts have developed and the rudiments of the pedal and cerebral ganglia are already delaminated. The pelagic phase of torsion takes 10–15 hrs and is brought about by the contraction of the 6 cells of the larval retractor muscle which have a distribution similar to those in *Haliotis*. These cells, however, differ in being remarkably slender and without yolk. The second phase of torsion, which is due to differential growth, is rapid and takes about 30 hrs. The greater speed may be attributed to the fact that the larvae are older and their tissues further differentiated than in *Haliotis*.

The eggs of *Calliostoma* are heavily yolked, and in contrast to the other two genera the veliger stage is completed before hatching, and the young emerge from the spawn in the crawling stage, when the velum is lost and cephalic tentacles with eyes and epipodial tentacles are developed. In the pretorsional veliger the 6 cells comprising the larval retractor muscle are shorter and stouter and their attachment to the shell is in the

middle region of the right side instead of at the posterior end—a displacement due to
the larger amount of yolk in the visceral mass. The first phase of torsion involves a
rotation of rather more than 90° owing to this position and takes about 4 hrs. From the
onset of torsion development is speeded up as compared with *Haliotis* and the second
phase is completed in about 30 hrs.

   Crofts' admirable account (1955) of the mechanism of torsion in the diotocardians
enables us to assess the importance of some of the hypotheses which have been for-
mulated concerning this process. Torsion occurs in the development of all prosobranchs
either in the pelagic larvae or in the embryo, and Garstang (1928) believed that it arose
as a larval mutation which persisted owing to its survival value. It seems of immediate
advantage to the larva since the rotation of the mantle cavity to an anterior position
enables the head and foot to be withdrawn into it for protection. In fossils there are no
animals showing an intermediate stage of the 180° rotation: Garstang (1928) envisaged
its rapid completion, and up to the time when his theory was made known this appeared
probable, for Boutan (1899) had claimed that it occurred in a few minutes in both
*Haliotis* and *Acmaea* and Robert (1902) had given the time as 6–8 hrs in different
trochids. Boutan (1886, 1919) suggested that torsion was due to antagonism between
the growth of the foot and the shell during development: if both were equally well developed at the same time they interfered with one another and the pressure of the one
against the other brought about the rotation of the head-foot on the visceral mass. He
assumed no results of torsion beneficial either to the larva or to the adult; moreover he
denied the occurrence of detorsion in the development of euthyneurous gastropods and so
suggested that the nudibranchs were more primitive than the prosobranchs. Adult anatomy
and more recent embryological studies give no support to these ideas. Boutan (1886,
1919), Naef (1913, 1926) and Garstang (1928) all suggested that torsion involves a certain
amount of twisting by muscular contraction. Garstang (1928) was the first to suggest
that two muscles were concerned and that the origin of torsion is based on a mutation
which affected their symmetry and produced a cephalic retractor with a posterior attachment and a left pedal retractor with a more anterior attachment, the two functioning
more or less at right angles to one another. However, Smith's account (1935) of the
development of *Patella vulgata*, Crofts' (1937) of *Haliotis tuberculata* and Ramamoorthi's
(1955) of *Melania crenulata* show that at the time of the onset of torsion there is only one
retractor muscle which is asymmetrically placed with its posterior attachment on the
right side of the shell apex (lra, fig. 227). It runs forwards to the right and left sides of
the head and the left side of the foot (Crofts, 1955). It is this muscle which is the main
mechanical cause for the beginning of torsion. Crofts' studies on *Patella* (1955) do not
support Smith's view that the muscle was originally an unpaired dorsal one, nor that the
complete 180° rotation occurs in the pelagic phase of the larva. The components of the
larval retractor relate to the velum and the left side of the pedal rudiment and so function
as Garstang suggested for the two separate retractors, at right angles to one another.
Pelseneer (1911), Naef (1913, 1926) and Smith (1935) suggested that the columellar
muscle of the adult is derived from the velar retractor. This is now disproved (at least
for certain diotocardians) since the velar retractor, if it persists, lies on the post-torsional
left side. In the development of the Diotocardia there is a pair of retractor muscles and
because of the asymmetry of the primitive digestive gland (which is directed towards
the pretorsional left side of the visceral mass) the retractor of that side, the future columellar muscle, is delayed in development until the first half of torsion is complete and creeping begins. Garstang's hypothesis may therefore be modified in the light of Crofts'

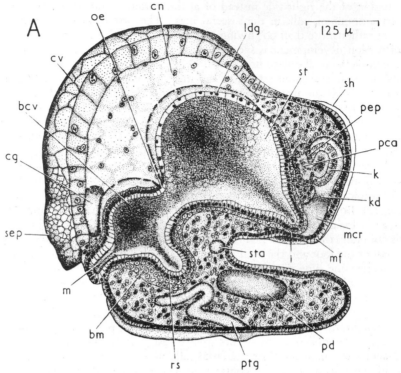

FIG. 232.—*Pomatias elegans:* A, reconstruction of right half of embryo at the mid-veliger stage, before torsion; B, reconstruction of right half of embryo at the late veliger stage, torsion almost complete. After Creek.

a, anus; apg, anterior pedal gland; bcv, buccal cavity; bg, buccal ganglion; bm, buccal mass; ccm, cerebral commissure; cg, cerebral ganglion; cm, columellar muscle; cn, connective tissue; cv, cephalic vesicle; dfc, dorsal food channel of oesophagus; f, foot; h, heart; i, intestine; k, kidney; kd, kidney duct; ko, kidney opening; ldg, left lobe of digestive gland; m, mouth; mc, mantle cavity; mcr, right invagination of mantle cavity; mf, mantle fold; oe, oesophagus; oea, oesophageal opening; op, operculum; pca, pericardial cavity; pcm, pedal commissure; pd, pedal ganglion; pep, pericardial epithelium; plg, pleural ganglion; ptg, posterior pedal gland; rdg, right lobe of digestive gland; rs, radular sac; sbg, sub-oesophageal ganglion; scm, spiral caecum of stomach; sep, sense plate; sg, salivary gland; sh, shell; sog, supra-oesophageal ganglion; st, stomach; sta, statocyst.

investigations to suggest that the postulated mutation caused a separation in the time of development of the right and left larval retractor muscles rather than a differentiation in the strength each exerts.

The first and rapid phase of torsion occurs when the body is of small size and the muscle is just beginning to differentiate, so that the reorientation of the larval tissues is easily accomplished by its contraction because of the undeveloped histological state of the rest of the body of the larva, and because it is pelagic and the rotation is unhampered by drag on a substratum. The benthic phase of torsion is slow and brought about by differential growth. It occurs during the early stages of organogeny when the pedal sole is developing and the larva or embryo creeps about its environment. Naef (1913) concluded from the results of the investigations on *Acmaea* (Boutan, 1899) and *Viviparus*

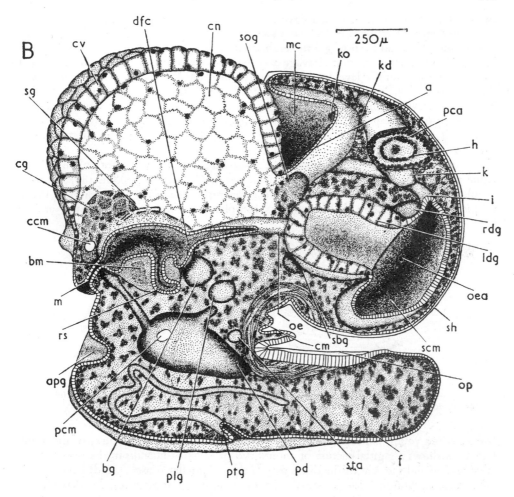

(Drummond, 1903; Erlanger, 1891b) that torsion brought about by differential growth must be a secondary modification found only in the less primitive gastropods. He stands alone in considering the ancestral gastropod as a free-swimming nautiloid form with the head-foot connected to the visceral mass by a narrow waist, the flexibility of which permitted an easy twist to bring the mantle cavity to an anterior position when the gastropod became benthic. He assumed that torsion occurred rapidly in post-larval life to meet the needs of the benthic adult. Neither palaeontology nor phylogeny supports these views. Naef would regard the veliger larva as a phylogenetic reminiscence of the ancestral free-swimming gastropod and not a simple modification of the trochophore larva in which the prototroch is elaborated to meet the demands of a longer pelagic period.

In some specialized monotocardians no larval muscles are developed before torsion is accomplished and the whole is brought about slowly by differential growth. Perhaps the most outstanding example of this is *Pomatias elegans* (Creek, 1951), a terrestrial member of the Littorinacea, in which development takes about 3 months. A free larva is suppressed and the embryonic velum is swollen into a cephalic mass which retains the cilia in some areas and can rotate the embryo in its ample supply of albumen. Torsion begins 3½ weeks after the first cleavage and proceeds by differential growth taking 31½ days. No musculature is developed in the body until later than this and none ever enters the transformed velum. Fig. 232A shows that in the mid-veliger stage before torsion begins the nervous, alimentary and renopericardial systems are further developed than in the pretorsional stages of *Haliotis*, yet the mesoderm which will give rise to the musculature is undifferentiated, and not until torsion is almost complete do the first pedal muscles appear.

The other prosobranchs in which torsion is known to be brought about only by differential growth are *Littorina littoralis* (Delsman, 1914), *Crepidula* (Conklin, 1897; Moritz, 1939), *Ocenebra aciculata* (Franc, 1940) and *Viviparus* (= *Paludina*) (Drummond, 1903). In *Littorina* and *Ocenebra* development is completed within the egg capsule, and in

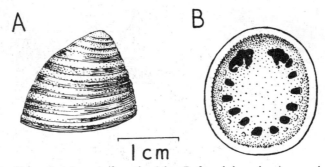

FIG. 233.—*Archaeophiala antiquissima:* A, from the right; B, from below, showing muscle scars (black) and shadow scars. After Knight.

*Viviparus* the young are retained in the oviduct until they are miniatures of the adult. Fig. 220A shows a sagittal section of an embryo of *Littorina littoralis* in the veliger stage after torsion and the cells of the distal part of the columellar muscle (omd) have not yet differentiated, though in the proximal region (not shown in the figure), they have begun to elongate.

Throughout the rocks of the Cambrian age there are fossils of the most primitive of all molluscs, the Monoplacophora, with low, cup-like shells and 5–8 pairs of adductor muscle scars symmetrically arranged (fig. 233). Nowhere is there space between the scars for a pallial cavity of the gastropod type, so presumably they had a pallial groove as in *Neopilina* (Lemche, 1957). These fossils, which are closely related to the gastropods (Knight & Yochelson, 1958), suggest that the soft parts were bilaterally arranged and that the animal had not undergone torsion. Knight, the distinguished palaeontologist, has said (1952) that a prerequisite for the initiation of torsion would be the reduction in the number of these shell muscles to a single pair. This might occur with the development of a high, narrow shell which would cause the pairs of muscles to be crowded together, and as a consequence, perhaps, the elimination of all but a single pair, though Knight & Yochelson (1958) no longer find support for this in the fossil record. Or it might be brought about by the crowding together of the muscles on each side as suggested by the Devonian genus *Cyrtonella* (Knight, 1947). In the Lower Cambrian genus

*Helcionella* are species with a low cup-shaped shell and, concurrent with these, others with high narrow shells; within this range this kind of modification of the muscles might be expected, but unfortunately the muscle scars of this genus are unknown and the effects of the decreased breadth of shell cannot therefore be checked. These animals are now classified as gastropods (Rasetti, 1957; Knight & Yochelson, 1958). Knight, agreeing with Garstang (1928), suggested that torsion may be due to a mutation. He and Yochelson (1958) believed that torsion occurred just as suddenly phylogenetically as it does today in the development of some modern gastropods and that this spectacular rotation of the visceral hump on the head-foot was initiated somewhere before the bellerophonts. He regarded the bellerophonts as diotocardians with a high degree of bilateral symmetry. The shell is typically coiled in a close spiral, the coiling being plane rather than helicoid, but the most important characteristic for the present consideration is that these animals possessed two symmetrical retractor muscles inserted one at each end of the columella, which in them runs transversely from right to left. In this position they would serve as retractors of the head and foot. The shell also has an emargination, as in the later fossil pleurotomarians. In the Recent genus *Pleurotomaria*, as described by Bouvier & Fischer (1902) there is, however, only a single columellar muscle.

The bellerophonts are contemporary with the earliest known pleurotomarians which date back to the Cambrian over 400 million years ago and were the most numerous, varied and abundant of all gastropods throughout succeeding Palaeozoic time. The two were obviously related and Knight suggested that the bellerophonts had paired ctenidia, osphradia, hypobranchial glands, auricles and kidneys, as do the Recent members of the families Pleurotomariidae, Haliotidae and Scissurellidae, which are included by him in the superfamily Pleurotomariacea (= those families of Thiele's Zeugobranchia with spirally coiled shells in the adult). The bellerophonts differ from the Pleurotomariacea in being symmetrical prosobranchs.

If we can assume that the production of torsion in a bellerophont was by means of a development similar to that exhibited by *Haliotis* then it involved the asymmetrical development of the larval musculature. Once torsion had occurred, however, a re-modelling of the animal's structure produced an adult with a bilaterally symmetrical body. There is therefore no connexion between larval asymmetry (the cause of torsion) and the adult asymmetry and loss of organs characteristic of so many prosobranchs. Adult asymmetry is a separate phenomenon to be associated with the adoption of the helicoid rather than the plane coiling of the visceral hump: wherever that occurs, asymmetry to a greater or less degree is found; whenever it is absent, either primitively as in Bellerophontacea, or secondarily as in Fissurellidae and Patellacea, bilateral symmetry is characteristic.

From the preceding account it will be seen that torsion is not a phenomenon which lends itself to a gradual step-by-step development, and yet the oldest theories concerning its origin assume that it came about by stages in the adult. These ideas often originated from the fact that early workers failed to regard torsion and the lateral asymmetry of the gastropod body as two distinct phenomena brought about by different causes. Lang (1891) held that the twisting of the visceral mass on the head-foot was stimulated by the top-heavy, conical shell carried by the adult, and Plate (1895) attempted to explain both torsion and the asymmetrical coiling of the shell as due to asymmetry of the lobes of the digestive gland. However, such theories are only of historical interest.

# CHAPTER 18

# LARVAL FORMS

THE British prosobranch gastropods exhibit great variety in the spawn masses they produce and in the provision made for their embryos, and in many species this is related to the state of development of the young at the time of hatching. Within their investments the eggs may complete their development to the crawling stage, although in the majority of species the young hatch as pelagic larvae, and, after a period of time varying with the species, become benthic and attain the habitat of the adult. Only in certain diotocardians are the eggs freed singly to the plankton, unprovided with membranes except those secreted by the ovum itself (*Haliotis tuberculata, Patella* spp., *Patina pellucida, Acmaea virginea, Gibbula magus, G. cineraria, G. umbilicalis, Monodonta lineata, Tricolia pullus*). These species have a free-swimming trochophore, whereas in all other gastropods the embryo becomes a larva when the trochophore stage has been passed through and the coiled shell is formed. The free trochophore stage (fig. 234A) is brief and the larva soon develops (a) a shell, which comes to occupy the entire dorsal surface behind the prototroch, (b) an enlargement of the prototrochal girdle which forms the velum, and (c) ventrally, behind the mouth, a protuberance which is the developing foot (fig. 234B). These are the principal external changes in the transformation to the veliger, the characteristic larva of the Mollusca. The velum is the feeding and swimming organ of the larva, fulfilling only larval needs, and in the diotocardians it remains comparatively inconspicuous (fig. 225C), unlobed and projecting only slightly from the preoral surface, whereas in the monotocardians, with typically a longer pelagic life, it is enlarged to form lateral lobes which are beset around the edge with a thick covering of cilia (fig. 235). By the time the velum of the mesogastropod has grown to any size torsion has taken place and it can be withdrawn and folded into the anterior mantle cavity, the opening to which is then closed by the operculum (op) of the retracted foot. It is not until the end of larval life that the velum gradually disappears and is finally lost. As in other groups with pelagic larvae the final settlement is probably susceptible of a certain amount of control by the larva which allows it to select an appropriate substratum, but little work on factors affecting larval settlement has been done with molluscs. It is known, however, that the settling of larvae of those species of *Odostomia* which parasitize the polychaet *Pomatoceros* is accelerated by the presence of the worms and delayed by their absence.

In *Patella* the gelatinous layer which surrounds the egg when it is spawned soon disappears, although in top shells which shed their eggs singly (*Gibbula, Monodonta*) it protects them during their embryonic stage and the trochophore larva can be seen revolving within the covering. The embryo of *Patella* hatches 24 hrs after fertilization and the trochophore, measuring 0·18 mm across, has a tuft of apical cilia (at, fig. 234A), and a prototroch (apt, ppt) of 2 rows of ciliated cells surrounds the larva at its greatest diameter. The prototrochal cilia beat in a clockwise direction and rotate the top-shaped larva through the water. Short cilia cover the area between the prototroch and apical tuft. On either side of the apical plate there is a prominent patch of stiff cilia which have undoubtedly (Smith, 1935) some sensory function (similar tufts are also present in the larva of *Acmaea* (Boutan, 1899)) and 2 cells bearing similar cilia form the telotroch (tl). Two days after fertilization changes have been effected by which the larva is transformed

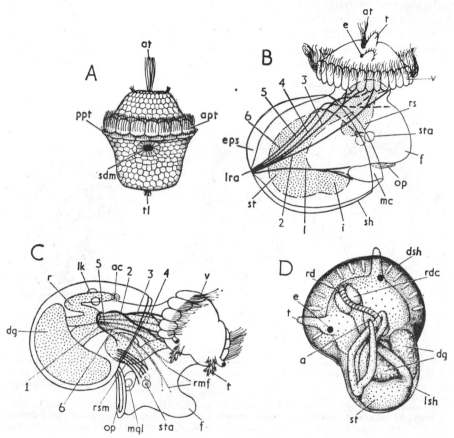

FIG. 234.—*Patella vulgata:* A, early trochophore, after Smith; B, pretorsional veliger (about 70 hrs after fertilization), after Crofts, showing the asymmetrical larval retractor muscle responsible for the first 90° of torsion. C, post-torsional veliger (about 96 hrs after fertilization), after Crofts, showing dorsal position of rectum and larval retractor muscle, and right shell muscle (=columellar muscle). D, dorsal view of larva during metamorphosis, after Smith, showing the definitive shell appearing as an outgrowth from the mouth of the larval shell. The latter will ultimately be lost.

a, anus; ac, anal cell; apt, anterior cilia of prototroch; at, apical tuft; dg, digestive gland; dsh, adult shell; e, eye; eps, extra-pallial space; f, foot; i, intestine; lk, rudiment of left kidney; lra, attachment of larval retractor muscle to shell; lsh, larval shell; mc, mantle cavity; mgl, mucous gland; op, operculum; ppt, posterior cilia of prototroch; r, rectum; rd, radula; rdc, radular cartilage; rmf, pedal retractors; rs, radular sac; rsm, right shell muscle; sdm, stomodaeum; sh, shell; st, stomach; sta, statocyst; t, tentacle; tl, telotroch; v, velum; 1–6, cells of larval retractor muscle.

into a pretorsional veliger: the shell and foot (sh, f, fig. 234B) are present and the anterior row of ciliated cells of the prototroch (v) has developed longer and more numerous cilia, whilst the posterior row has been lost. Torsion begins while the larva is free-swimming. The first 90°, brought about by contraction of the 6 cells of the larval retractor muscle,

16

is accomplished in 10–15 hrs, and the second phase, due to differential growth, takes about 30 hrs (Crofts, 1955). The larva both swims and crawls during the second phase and, although the velum is retained, there is a break in the girdle of ciliated cells mid-dorsally and mid-ventrally (v, fig. 234C). Larvae in which torsion is complete are 3½–4 days old and their pelagic life has ended. The velum does not finally disappear until the third week when the snails are actively crawling (Smith, 1935), and at about the same time the operculum is lost. The shell of the veliger is coiled dextrally, though with hardly more than one whorl, and at the time of metamorphosis, when in the crawling stage, a

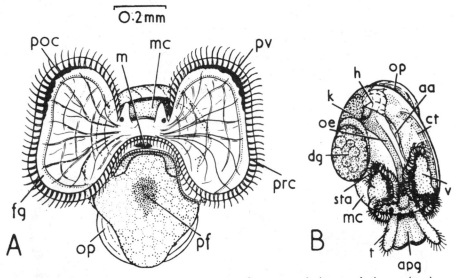

Fig. 235.—*Littorina littorea:* veligers at swimming-crawling stage. A, in ventral view, swimming; B, in dorsal view, crawling. The anterior border of the velum bears a characteristic band of dark pigment visible through the colourless shell when the animal crawls. Older larvae have also pigment on the sole of the foot. The digestive gland is yellow-green.

aa, anterior aorta; apg, anterior pedal gland; ct, ctenidium; dg, digestive gland; fg, food groove; h, heart; k, kidney; m, mouth; mc, mantle cavity; oe, oesophagus; op, operculum; pf, pigment on foot; poc, postoral cilia of velum; prc, preoral cilia of velum; pv, pigment on velum; sta, statocyst; t, tentacle; v, velum.

secondary symmetry is developed in both shell and animal (lsh, dsh, fig. 234D). The new shell which is added at the peristome of the larval one is on a new axis inclined down-wards and to the left of the original larval axis. At the end of metamorphosis a shell plate is secreted across the base of the larval shell which is then lost (pch, fig. 268).

The embryos of diotocardians which develop from eggs laid in gelatinous masses or ribbons (*Diodora apertura, Margarites helicinus, Gibbula tumida, Calliostoma zizyphinum, C. papillosum, Cantharidus striatus, C. exasperatus, Skenea serpuloides*) pass through both trochophore and veliger stage, and the young creep from the gelatinous coverings as miniatures of the adult, with sometimes a vestige of the velum. In *Calliostoma zizyphinum* the veliger rotates in its albuminous covering (which was secreted by the egg whilst still in the ovary) and gradually devours it, and as the muscles of the foot develop it creeps around the wall of its spherical cell. Torsion is complete by the end of 3½–4 days of development, rotation through 180° taking a total of about 36 hrs, which is slightly more rapid than in *Patella* and considerably more rapid than in *Haliotis* (Crofts, 1955). From the very onset of torsion development is speeded up in *Calliostoma* as compared with these two zeugobranchs. This is partly owing to the larger amount of yolk, which displaces the larval retractor muscle and so causes rather more than 90° rotation during the first phase of torsion, and also because of the retention of the larva within the egg membranes. By the fifth day of development (when the embryo may hatch) the first epipodial tentacles are present, whereas in *Haliotis* they appear on the tenth day. In *Cantharidus striatus* Robert (1902) stated that the larvae have epipodial tentacles at 124 hrs and are hatched in the crawling stage at this time, but the free larvae of *Gibbula magus* reach the same stage of development at 150 hrs. It would thus appear that the rate of development in those members of the Diotocardia in which there is no free larval stage is more rapid.

No diotocardian is known in which the young hatch as veligers, yet all monotocardians with an indirect development emerge from the egg mass in this form, and when torsion is complete. The pelagic larval phase of the monotocardian is considerably longer than that of the diotocardian and may extend to 2 months, as in the British species of *Nassarius*, *N. reticulatus* and *N. incrassatus*, for many species have exploited this period of their life history, so that it becomes of greater importance in distribution. About a third of the British mesogastropods hatch in the crawling stage and these emerge from egg masses which are usually deposited in the vicinity of the adults. They include the minute specialized prosobranchs of rock pools—*Rissoella diaphana*, *R. opalina*, *Omalogyra*, *Skeneopsis*, *Cingulopsis*; some small rissoaceans—*Cingula cingillus*, *C. semicostata*, *Barleeia rubra*; the ovigerous species of *Ianthina* and also *Calyptraea chinensis*, *Littorina littoralis* and *Lacuna pallidula*. Amongst the Stenoglossa only 8 species out of 20 have a larval stage— *Nassarius reticulatus*, *N. incrassatus*, *N. pygmaeus*, *Lora turricula*, *Mangelia nebula*, *Philbertia gracilis*, *P. leufroyi*, *P. linearis*.

Each lobe of the velum of the monotocardian gastropod (fig. 235A) consists of an upper and lower epithelium with an underlying nerve net, muscle fibres which are components of the larval retractor muscle, and, in certain species, pigment cells (pv), which may be a mark of identification of the species. In the thickness of the lobe are large blood spaces. The ciliation is confined to a marginal zone (fig. 236). The edge is thickened and bears long cilia on the upper surface (prc) which are set in transverse rows, and on the under surface there is a sulcus covered by short cilia (fg), with its inner border formed by a somewhat prominent ridge with cilia of intermediate length (poc). Owing to the transparency of the tissues this inner ciliated band is always visible on the upper surface of the velum (fig. 235A); ventrally it becomes postoral and forms the posterior lip of the mouth (m), whilst the upper ciliated band is preoral. The two are homologous with the prototroch and metatroch of a trochophore. When the velum is expanded the cilia are constantly beating and a current in the sulcus wafts food—nannoplankton—into the mouth. Along the outer (preoral) ciliated band, which, with the muscles, makes the velum a powerful swimming organ, the metachronal waves of the cilia travel in a clockwise direction (fig. 237A) with their effective beat passing at right angles to this, that is into the food groove (Knight-Jones, 1954). The cilia are long and the metachronal waves particularly conspicuous. Within the sulcus the metachronal waves, at least in some genera (*Nassarius*), move in the opposite direction to the effective beat of the cilia. The natural position of the larva when swimming in the plankton is with the shell below and the foot and velum above, but the velum, especially when long lobes are present, may alter its position in many ways, the lobes flapping slowly, incompletely covering the shell or remaining outspread. The withdrawal of the velum into the mantle cavity is rapid and accompanied by a slowing down and cessation of ciliary beat. With this the larva sinks slowly through the water. Food particles collected by the velum are transferred to the stomach by the ciliated lining of the oesophagus and in the stomach they are kept in a rotary movement, presumably by ciliary action. From time to time contractions of the wall of the stomach may be seen, but no particulate material appears to pass to the

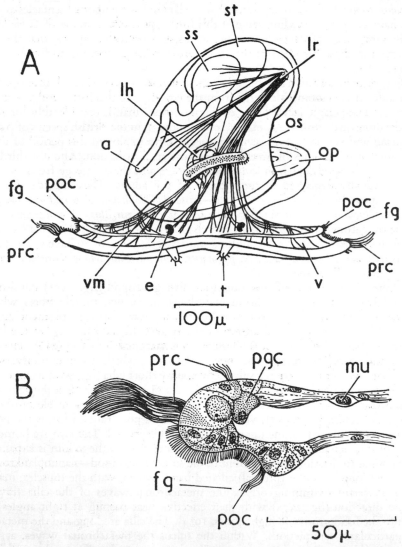

FIG. 236.—*Crepidula fornicata:* A, free-swimming veliger seen from above; B, T.S. edge of velum, after Werner.

a, anus; e, eye; fg, food groove; lh, larval heart; lr, larval retractor muscle; mu, muscle cell; op, operculum; os, osphradium; pgc, pigment cell; poc, postoral cilia of velum; prc, preoral cilia of velum; ss, style sac region of stomach; st, stomach; t, tentacle; v, velum; vm, velar muscle.

ducts of the digestive gland. In the embryo this gland plays an important part in the uptake and digestion of the albumen, which can be seen in large vacuoles distending its cells.

Associated with the hypertrophy of the velum and its important vascular supply is the development of a larval heart which is formed and starts to function before hatching (lh, figs. 241, 245). It arises as a vesicular differentiation of the ectoderm. Franc (1943) has shown that in *Pisania maculosa* (fam. Buccinidae) it first appears between the anus and

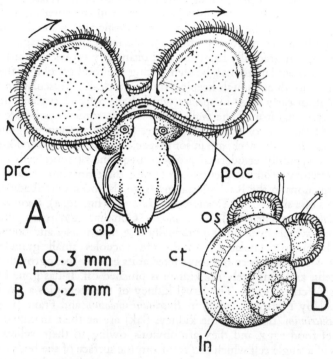

FIG. 237.—*Rissoa parva*: A, veliger, ventral view, swimming.  Arrows indicate direction of movement of metachronal waves of velar cilia.  B, veliger, dorsal view, creeping.

ct, ctenidium;  ln, line along periphery of shell characteristic of late larvae of this species;  op, operculum;  os, osphradium;  poc, postoral cilia of velum;  prc, preoral cilia of velum.

the right wall of the developing foot. When torsion occurs it is brought forwards to a dorsal position on the floor of the mantle cavity and appears as a blood sinus with contractile walls which lies obliquely above the oesophagus (oe) at the base of the velum (v), and the network of powerful muscle fibres in its walls can be seen through the overlying tissues. These muscles are usually held to be of mesenchymal origin, though Franc (1943) preferred to interpret them as differentiations of the original ectodermal layer. The heart has an anterior opening connected with blood spaces in the velum and foot, and a posterior opening to blood spaces in the visceral sac, and Werner (1955) has shown that in *Crepidula* there is an anterior and posterior valve. The fluid passes through it in an anteroposterior direction, and then from the visceral mass the flow is anterior to the foot and velum. The blood spaces in the velum make it an important respiratory organ and its continuous movement assists circulation. Before the larva hatches the rate of beat of the larval heart is comparatively low: in *Crepidula fornicata* it is about 24-35/ min (Werner, 1955) though about twice as fast after hatching; when the velum is withdrawn, however, the beat is reduced or even stopped. The larval heart is present in species with no free larval stage and Franc (1940) has shown that in the embryo of the stenoglossan *Ocenebra aciculata* its rate of beat is similar to that of *Crepidula* before hatching. In all species which have been observed the heart persists for some time after the true heart has been formed, though there seems to be no relationship between the beat of the two, and it finally becomes incorporated in the anterior aorta.

The foot (fig. 238) in the early veligers of gastropods is a small ventral projection behind the mouth, which narrows posteriorly, and from an early stage is provided with an operculum (op). It gradually lengthens and ultimately grows forwards into a flexible process which in older larvae may be seen licking the food groove of the velum in the vicinity of the mouth as though keeping the tract clear. Musculature in the foot is differentiated at an early stage in species which have a free larva and the late embryo may be seen creeping around the wall of the capsule some days before it escapes as a young snail. At the base of the foot are large, paired statocysts (sta) and dorsal to its origin, on each side of the neck, are in some species the so-called larval kidneys (lak, fig. 241). These are typically ectodermal projections of one or more cells in which, it has been held, excretory products accumulate during the embryonic phase. They are particularly conspicuous in the Rachiglossa and have also been described (Pelseneer, 1911) in the embryos of a number of Taenioglossa (*Littorina* (fig. 202A), *Lacuna*, *Rissoa*, *Natica*, *Lamellaria*, *Calyptraea*, *Crepidula*). In *Crepidula* (Conklin, 1897) each consists of several ectodermal cells which swell up and gradually lose their nuclei and boundaries, and the protoplasm becomes vacuolated. Within the vacuoles small granules accumulate. Gradually the whole mass becomes constricted at its base by the ingrowth of surrounding ectodermal cells, and ultimately the kidney is pinched off. It has gone by the time the larva hatches (Werner, 1955). The larval kidney of the Stenoglossa has been described in some detail by Portmann (1930) in *Buccinum undatum* and Franc (1940) in *Ocenebra aciculata*. In *Buccinum* (fig. 243B) the kidneys (lak) are at their maximal size when the larva is full of food eggs, and they are obvious owing to their yellow-green colour. Each consists of a single cell which projects from the surface of the body and also spreads far beneath the ectoderm, and into which pass two types of amoebocyte concerned with excretion. One type, filled with crystals of waste, is shed from the larval kidney, the other disintegrates within the renal cell and the waste which it contains is either emitted from the surface of the kidney or passes into the amoebocytes and leaves with them. In this way unwanted material is shed into the egg capsules in *Buccinum*, and the larval kidney is not, as suggested by Pelseneer (1911) for this and other species, an organ of accumulation which entraps the toxic waste during the long intracapsular life. However, in *Ocenebra*, Franc (1940) had no evidence that amoebocytes are concerned and described

---

Fig. 238.—*Nassarius*: veliger larvae. A, B, C, *N. reticulatus*: A, just after hatching; B, its shell; C, about 40 days old.  D, E, F, G, *N. incrassatus*: D, 2 weeks; E, 3 weeks; F, about 13 weeks after hatching; G, swimming-crawling stage.  The 2 species differ in the longer velar lobes, each with 2 black apical pigment patches, of *N. incrassatus* contrasted with the shorter lobes, each with continuous, reddish-brown, marginal pigment band of *N. reticulatus*.

bk, beak of shell; f, foot; lpv, lower pigment patch of velum; op, operculum; poc, postoral cilia of velum; prc, preoral cilia of velum; ps, pigment on sole of foot; pv, pigment on velum; sit, siphonal tube; sta, statocyst; upv, upper pigment patch of velum.

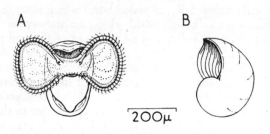

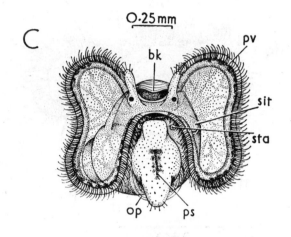

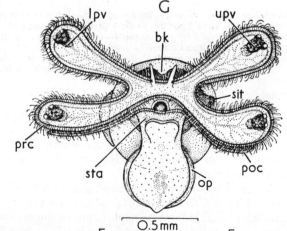

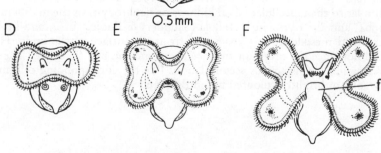

each kidney as a single cell (with a stalk cell added later) which is stuffed full of granules of many sizes, and often with yolk, and which elongates transversely so that the two kidneys form an almost complete collar around the head of the embryo. When other larval organs diminish the kidneys are reduced in size. They become detached later and may be found in the capsule after the larva has left. Franc suggested that the yolk granules are digested in the renal cell, which would account for its regression in size. He also found (1941a) yolk granules in the larval kidneys of *Thais haemastoma*, and these facts, together with the observations that the larval kidneys get smaller in the late embryo of this and other species, led him to the conclusion that the so-called excretory bodies may

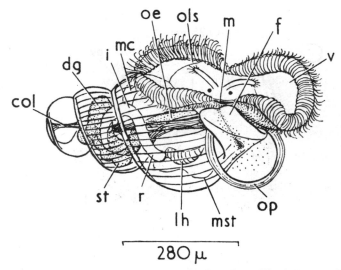

FIG. 239.—*Aclis minor:* free-swwiming veliger. Note that the coiling of the shell is so tight as to bring the dorsal surface of the body, where the larval heart lies, to the underside of the body whorl as seen in the figure. The larval shell is characterized by ribs on the younger whorls and by the colour: initial whorl brown, subsequent whorls bluish and columella violet.

col, columella; dg, digestive gland; f, foot; i, intestine; lh, larval heart; m, mouth; mc, mantle cavity; mst, mantle skirt; oe, oesophagus; ols, outer lip of shell; op, operculum; r, rectum; st, stomach; v, velum.

be deposits of nutritive materials. Moreover, he found that in *Pisania maculosa*, a rachiglossan of warmer seas which absorbs numbers of food eggs in the embryonic stage, the larval kidneys are not loaded with obvious excreta. Waste leaves the body by cells which escape from the posterior part of the sole of the foot, the free edge of the mantle and the intertentacular zone of the velar area.

Unicellular structures, one on either side of the oesophagus in the veliger stage of *Littorina littoralis*, were referred to by Delsman (1914) as nephrocysts (nct, fig. 220). They are similar to the unicellular larval kidneys or nephrocysts of the nudibranch *Fiona* (Casteel, 1904) and the tectibranch *Aplysia* (Saunders & Poole, 1910), and lie between the ectoderm and mesoderm, not projecting from the surface of the body. However, Delsman did not trace the origin of these cells in *Littorina*, nor their fate. They do not apparently amass any conspicuous accumulations like the corresponding cells in *Aplysia* which may contain brightly coloured lipoid droplets.

In the freshwater pectinibranch *Viviparus viviparus* there are undoubted larval kidneys in approximately the same position. They are apparently mesodermal in origin, and according to Erlanger (1894) are developed from the anterior end of the mesodermal band on each side. Each is a V-shaped tube with the apex directed forwards; the internal or upper limb is a solenocyte and opens to the lower limb which leads to the exterior. A second freshwater form, *Bithynia*, is the only other pectinibranch known to have similar kidneys in embryonic development, though they occur in pulmonate gastropods, and in *Physa* (Wierzejski, 1905) their origin is similar to that in *Viviparus*. It is tempting to homologize this type of kidney with the protonephridium of a trocho-

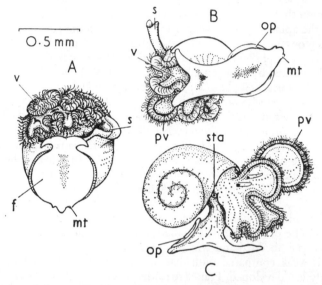

FIG. 240.—*Nassarius reticulatus:* veliger larvae at swimming-crawling stage, about seven weeks after hatching. The foot is acquiring the characteristic shape of the adult.

f, foot; mt, metapodial tentacle; op, operculum; pv, pigment on velum; s, siphon; sta, statocyst; v, velum.

phore, but that is an ectomesodermal organ (Meyer, 1901). Its occurrence in freshwater species may mean that it is concerned with osmoregulation.

In the early development of the embryonic veligers of some prosobranchs an apical sense organ has been described. Patten (1886a), Wilson (1904) and Smith (1935) figured a prominent one in *Patella* (at, fig. 234A) and Crofts (1937) mentioned the occurrence of a group of small cilia on 2–3 cells of the apical plate of *Haliotis*, which soon disappear. It was first mentioned in some detail by Conklin (1897) in *Crepidula* (aor, fig. 221), and consists of 4 apical cells, initially slightly indented on their outer surface, with a few cells which they have proliferated inwards towards the cavity of the head vesicle (acp), and these meet a strand of tissue growing out from each cerebral ganglion (cg). The organ is therefore V-shaped with the apex of 4 cells on the surface covered by fine cilia; there is no bunch of long cilia as in many trochophore larvae. The organ arises from the point at which the polar bodies were extruded. Later the outgrowths from the cerebral ganglia meet one another and form the cerebral commissure, and the connexion with the apical organ and the organ itself is lost. In the newly hatched veliger of *Crepidula* Werner (1955) described the remains of the organ as consisting of large, subepidermal, vacuolated cells between the bases of the tentacles, and the epidermis which covers them has short cilia, though no cilia occur elsewhere on the head except those associated with the velum. In *Trochus* Robert (1902) has described an apical invagination of cells ($1q^{111}$ and $1q^{112}$) which is developed at the 97-cell stage and has disappeared about the 145-cell stage. It may represent a transitory sense organ. However, the invaginated area is not ciliated, though Robert stated that sometimes in older embryos, especially of *Trochus striatus* (= *Cantharidus striatus*), there are some very short cilia in this position. A similar apical invagination was described by Blochmann (1882) for *Neritina*, but Conklin (1897) was of the opinion that the embryos in which it was described were abnormal. Pelseneer (1911) figured the apical organ in veliger embryos of *Lacuna pallidula*, *Littorina saxatilis* and *L. littoralis* (aor, fig. 202A) as a protuberance and did not mention the histological structure. However in *Littorina littoralis* Delsman (1914) described a group of large vacuolated cells covered by short cilia between the bases of the developing tentacles and referred to it as the apical cell plate (acp, fig. 220B). A tentacle, eye and cerebral ganglion arise from cells on either side between this plate and the velum, though there appears to be no connexion between apical cells and cerebral ganglia as in *Crepidula*. Pelseneer (1911) stated that in the rachiglossans *Nassarius*, *Nucella* and *Buccinum* there is a sense organ at the junction of the right and left halves of the cerebral commissure, which forms a projection from the surface of the head, and he figured it in older embryos of *Buccinum* as a swelling on the commissure well away from the surface tissues. The function of this organ is obscure, and old authors, like McMurrich (1886), regarded it as a rudimentary structure.

The velum in embryos which are never freed is typically bilobed, and the lobes are small (fig. 241). The preoral girdle of cilia (prc) rotates the embryo in the albuminous fluid in which it is embedded and which is used as food, though the locomotory power of the velum is weak compared with that of free larvae, and its cilia and musculature correspondingly less developed. Franc (1940) has suggested that in *Ocenebra aciculata* the movement of the veliger mixes enzymes which the embryo produces with the surrounding albumen, so that it becomes less viscous and is conveyed more easily by cilia to the mouth. In this species development is completed in 46 days, but it is not until the 45th day that the velum is completely absorbed and all trace has gone. In *Fusus*, Portmann (1955) stated that the fluid is ingested by swallowing movements of the stomodaeum. A thickening is developed in the dorsal wall of the stomodaeum by means of which a rhythmical closure is effected. It disappears when the albumen is exhausted and only then does further differentiation of the stomodaeum occur and the radular sac appear. The albumen is taken up by the epithelial cells of the albumen sac, a development of the midgut in the region from which the stomach will later differentiate: it is a large and conspicuous part of the gut, for the differentiation of the stomach and digestive gland is delayed. This larval structure eventually becomes reduced in size and disappears, though even when the young escape from the capsule it occupies the apical region of the shell. In yet another respect the embryonic development of this stenoglossan is specialized, for the 4 megameres, filled with yolk granules, persist to a late stage. After giving rise to the endoderm they help to line the mesenteron until, with the extension of the true lining of the gut, they are gradually excluded from the lumen and degenerate.

The development of the veliger embryos of the dog whelk (*Nucella lapillus*) is unusual since it is arrested at an early stage, during the period of uptake of all the available food eggs in the capsule. At this time (fig. 242) the cephalic region, foot and visceral mass are differentiated and the secretion of the shell (sh) has begun. The cephalic region is composed of large cells and has no rudiment of eye or tentacle; it is reminiscent of the cephalic mass of the veliger stage of *Pomatias elegans*, though much smaller. It is bordered by ciliated cells (prc) which represent the preoral band of the velum, though the cilia are

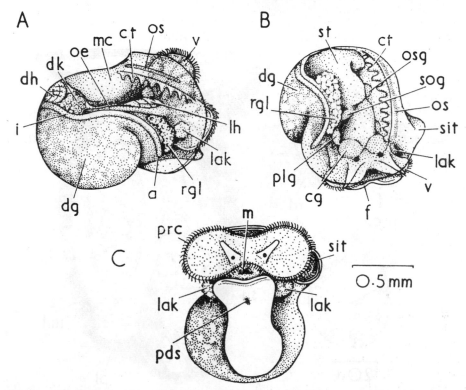

FIG. 241.—*Nucella lapillus*: late embryos from egg capsule; A, in lateral, B, in dorsal and C, in ventral view. Note special larval heart and kidneys, reduced velum and large rectal gland. The digestive gland is swollen with ingested food.

a, anus; cg, cerebral ganglion; ct, ctenidium; dg, digestive gland; dh, developing heart; dk, developing kidney; f, foot; i, intestine; lak, larval kidney; lh, larval heart; m, mouth; mc, mantle cavity; oe, oesophagus; os, osphradium; osg, osphradial ganglion; pds, accessory boring organ; plg, pleural ganglion; prc, preoral cilia of velum; rgl, rectal gland; sit, siphonal tube; sog, supra-oesophageal ganglion; st, stomach; v, velum.

not thickly set, and its tissues are transparent like those of the foot, so that the course of the gut and the statocysts are visible. The velum (v) has neither food-collecting groove nor postoral band of cilia, for the food eggs are sucked into the gut and the embryos remain attached to the food, which forms a central core in the egg capsule (fe), until all has gone. The lips of the large circular mouth of the embryo, surrounded dorsally by long cilia, are applied to the food, and the stomodaeum, also strongly ciliated (sdm), pumps it into the stomach where it is stored. If the embryos are detached they rotate slowly through the albuminous fluid, but soon attach themselves again. In the second phase of development (fig. 241) the embryonic or larval heart (lh) and kidneys (lak) are formed, and later the true kidney and heart (dk, dh). The differentiation of the liver (dg) is delayed and occurs only when the first coil of the shell is complete and some larval characters are disappearing. As the tentacles and eyes develop the velar lobes become more pronounced and are constricted from the head, though compared with those of

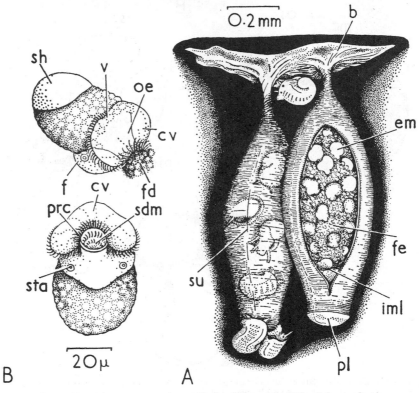

Fig. 242.—*Nucella lapillus:* A, 2 egg capsules attached to substratum. The right one has been opened to show young embryos (em) ingesting food eggs (fe); the left one contains a few larvae ready to hatch, and two others are emerging after loss of the plug (pl). B, young embryos in lateral and ventral view showing gut gorged with food eggs and poor development of other structures. The upper embryo is sucking food.

b, base of capsule; cv, cephalic vesicle; em, embryo within capsule; f, foot; fd, food; fe, food eggs within capsule; iml, inner mucous layer of capsule; oe, oesophagus; pl, plug; prc, preoral cilia of velum; sdm, stomodaeum; sh, shell; sta, statocyst; su, suture; v, velum.

related Stenoglossa, such as *Nassarius*, they are inconspicuous in size and ciliation. The embryos of *Buccinum undatum* (fig. 243) also depend on food eggs for their nourishment: these are stored in the mid-gut, which is greatly distended, and digested and absorbed by a special vesicular enlargement of the intestine which later disappears. These eggs retain their original spherical shape and no cleavage occurs, and development proceeds while the embryo feeds, though the development of the digestive gland is delayed (Portmann, 1925).

In the terrestrial snail, *Pomatias elegans* (Creek, 1951), the egg is small and surrounded by a large amount of albumen which is used by the embryo as food. Intracapsular development continues until the animal is a miniature adult and this takes about 3 months. The embryonic veliger stage has the cephalic region highly modified into a swollen area (cv, fig. 232) which has some short cilia (not shown in fig.), and rotates the embryo in the albumen. No velum is developed. In the early veliger stage, 15 days after the first cleavage, the cephalic region covers three-quarters of the external surface.

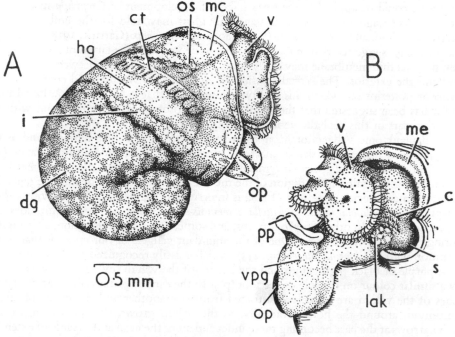

FIG. 243.—*Buccinum undatum:* embryos from egg capsule. A, from right; B, details of head and foot from left. Note the conspicuous patch of cilia (c) on the left side of the head. In other respects these larvae resemble those of *Nucella lapillus*.

c, cilia; ct, ctenidium; dg, digestive gland; hg, hypobranchial gland; i, intestine; lak, larval kidney; mc, mantle cavity; me, mantle edge; op, operculum; os, osphradium; pp, propodium; s, siphon; v, velum; vpg, ventral pedal gland.

It has undoubtedly an absorptive function, and its precocity in development is shared with the digestive gland, which assumes quite early its role as a storage organ, accumulating albuminous fluid. The cephalic mass is at its maximal development during the mid and late veliger stages, and is then steadily reduced and disappears by the time of hatching, when the supply of albumen is exhausted and the volume of the embryo, as compared with the first cleavage stage, has increased fifteen-fold. Embryos of *Pomatias* have neither larval heart nor larval kidneys.

Cephalic vesicles which are smaller though superficially similar to the cephalic mass of *Pomatias*, are developed not only in the early veliger stage of *Nucella* (cv, fig. 242), *Fusus* and *Buccinum*, but also in some *Crepidula* spp. (Conklin, 1897). In these genera the vesicle is reduced and lost as the velum develops, and there is no evidence that it has an absorptive role. However, in *Crepidula adunca* of the N Californian coast, there is no free larval stage and the head vesicle is larger and the velum much smaller than in species with an indirect development. Delsman (1914) suggested that hypertrophy of the cephalic region is an adaptation to provide a greater surface area for the absorption of oxygen, and that it is absent in *Littorina littoralis*, the embryology of which he studied, because it develops in the littoral surf zone where the water is supersaturated with oxygen and supplementary respiratory organs are not required. It is doubtful whether this argument could be applied to the early stages of development of *Crepidula* species with a free veliger stage and the stenoglossans, though it may hold for the embryos of the terrestrial pulmonates *Helix pomatia* (Fol, 1880) and *Agriolimax* (Carrick, 1938). However, Moritz (1939) suggested that in *Crepidula adunca* the vesicle is the larval organ of respiration since its thin membrane may easily allow the exchange of gases between the haemocoel and the exterior. The cephalic vesicle of *Agriolimax* is vascular and contractile like a similar posterior sac which this embryo possesses, so that it functions as a larval heart and it has been suggested that the larval heart of prosobranchs is homologous with the posterior part of this cephalic vesicle (Simroth, 1896–1907).

In all planktonic veligers of Monotocardia the velum is at first bilobed, and as the larva grows it increases in size to meet the increased needs of food and buoyancy (fig. 238). In the majority of species it remains as a single lobe on either side of the head, the two meeting ventrally in the region of the mouth and mid-dorsally behind the tentacles, where in most species the girdle of cilia is interrupted (fig. 235). In larvae with a short pelagic life—*Hydrobia ulvae*, *Turritella communis*—the shape of the velum does not appear to change. In others its proportions, and sometimes its pigmentation, alter rapidly during the early pelagic phase. One of the abundant veligers of our coasts is that of the common winkle, *Littorina littorea* (fig. 235), which is easily recognized by the conspicuous dark purple or black pigment around the border of the velum (pv) and, in older larvae, by a similar colour on the sole of the foot (pf). In the earliest planktonic stage the lateral lobes of the velum are scarcely constricted from one another and the girdle of cilia is continuous around the head. Gradually, as the velum grows, the lobes elongate and each narrows at the base becoming more independent of the head and capable of extensive swimming movements, and, at the same time, the bands of cilia are interrupted mid-dorsally. In this species the planktonic life may be little more than a fortnight, though Thorson (1946) stated that in The Sound the larvae may not settle for a month or more. In the three genera *Bittium*, *Cerithiopsis* and *Triphora* (fig. 244C) the velar lobes (v), as they enlarge and are constricted at the base, retain the rounded shape, but grow unequally. The inequality of the lobes is least pronounced in *Bittium reticulatum* in which the right, when fully grown, is somewhat larger than the left; the right is distinctly larger in *Cerithiopsis*, whereas in *Triphora perversa*, in accordance with the reversal of the arrangement of organs in the mantle cavity, the left is the larger.

Larvae which remain long in the plankton and are of considerable size before they settle have the most elaborate vela. In the turrid *Mangelia nebula* (fig. 244D), in which the shell attains a length of 1 mm and has $3\frac{1}{2}$ whorls before metamorphosis, the velar lobes are broad and elongated. Each has a slight mid-lateral constriction tending to divide it into dorsal and ventral parts and the breadth at the constriction, the narrowest part, far exceeds the height of the shell. The swimming of the larva is by the undulating movements of the velum and the metachronal beating of the cilia, though the cilia are not particularly long and seem of less importance. In the later stages of development the velum is held over the shell so that the animal is covered and swims completely hidden by it. The velum is conspicuous not only for its size but also for its ornamentation of brilliant orange spots (pv) which vary in number and arrangement and increase with age, tending to form a border as well as being scattered irregularly over the surface. In the

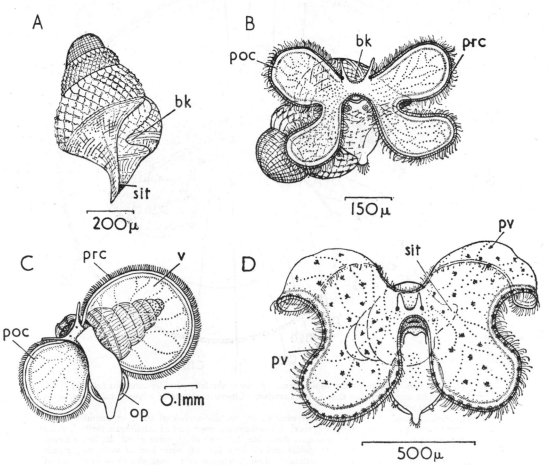

FIG. 244.—A and B, *Philbertia linearis*, shell and veliger in ventral view; C, *Triphora perversa*, veliger in ventral view; D, *Mangelia nebula*, veliger in ventral view.

bk, beak; op, operculum; poc, postoral cilia of velum; prc, preoral cilia of velum; pv, pigment of velum; sit, siphonal tube; v, velum.

related turrid *Philbertia linearis* (figs. 244A, B), also with a long larval life, the shell has 4½ whorls at metamorphosis and a length of about 1 mm. The velum is colourless, at first bilobed, then longer and slightly indented at the sides to form 4 blunt lobes. These elongate whilst the breadth of the velum increases only slightly, and eventually the lobes when deflected posteriorly may project some way beyond the apex of the shell. The velum has thus an extensive margin for its area. The marginal cilia are long and, perhaps more than the muscles of the velum, are responsible for swimming. *Aporrhais pespelicani*

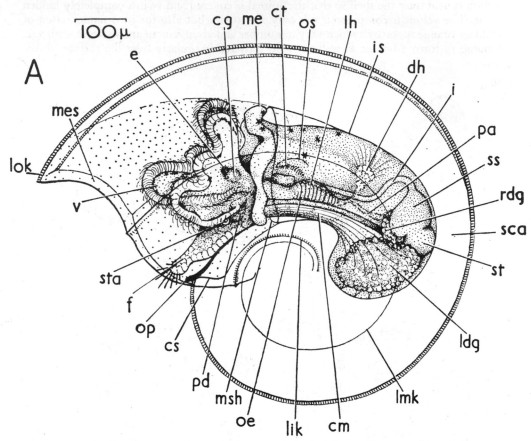

Fig. 245.—*Lamellaria perspicua*: echinospira larva.  A, from the left, partially retracted into shell; B, from the right, somewhat less than fully expanded.  Chromatophores of a tawny colour occur on the mantle and velum.

cg, cerebral ganglion; cm, columellar muscle; cs, chiselled surface of shell; ct, ctenidium; dh, definitive heart developing; e, eye; f, foot; i, intestine; is, inner part of echinospira shell; l, point where lip rests on main part of echinospira shell; ldg, left lobe of digestive gland; lh, larval heart; lik, left inner keel of shell; lmk, left middle keel of shell; lok, left outer keel of shell; me, mantle edge; mes, mouth of outer part of echinospira shell or scaphoconch; msh, mouth of inner part of echinospira shell; oe, oesophagus; op, operculum; os, osphradium; pa, posterior aorta; pd, pedal ganglion; rdg, right lobe of digestive gland; rik, right inner keel of shell; rmk, right middle keel of shell; sca, space between scaphoconch and inner part of shell; ss, style sac region of stomach; st, stomach; sta, statocyst; v, velum.

reaches a larger size (1·25 mm) before metamorphosis and its velum, at first bilobed, soon changes to 4 and then 6 lobes which are deep.

The dissimilar appearance of the larva of the two turrids shows that the form of the fully developed velum in larvae with a long pelagic phase is of no taxonomic value. This is also illustrated by the larvae of the two British species of *Nassarius* which occur in the lower parts of the intertidal zone, *N. reticulatus* extending to a depth of a few fathoms, and *N. incrassatus* to about 46 fathoms. In the adult the latter is about half the

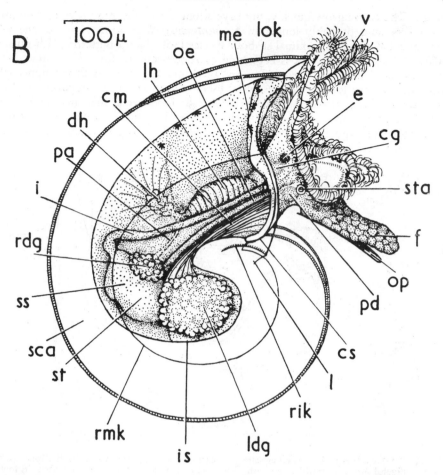

size of the former and the newly hatched larva is also considerably smaller. The following measurements are given by Lebour (1931a) for the early larval stages of these species:

| | | | | | |
|---|---|---|---|---|---|
| *N. reticulatus* | Breadth of body whorl of shell | . | . | . | 0·28–0·30 mm |
| (figs. 238A, | Breadth of velum | . . . | . | . | 0·29–0·32 mm |
| B, C; 240) | | | | | |
| *N. incrassatus* | Breadth of body whorl of shell | . | . | . | 0·18–0·20 mm |
| (figs. 238D, | Breadth of velum | . . . | . | . | 0·20–0·24 mm |
| E, F, G) | | | | | |

Both larvae are at first similar in appearance except that in *N. reticulatus* the velum has a continuous reddish brown border just inside the margin, whereas in *N. incrassatus* there is no pigmentation for the first few days. The shell is smooth, unsculptured, very transparent and consists of one whorl. The outer lip is drawn out slightly at the centre to form an incipient tooth (bk), and the hollow on either side supports a lobe of the velum. As the tooth grows it is bent inwards and the hollows deepen as the velum

enlarges. The larvae grow quickly, but have a long free-swimming period, 2 months in
*N. reticulatus* and probably longer in *N. incrassatus*. After about 3 weeks the velum
becomes 4-lobed and the animal in both species looks like a butterfly with outspread
wings. By this time pigment is beginning to concentrate to form large spots in each
corner of the velum of *N. incrassatus* (lpv, upv), one associated with the upper ciliary
band, one with the lower, and these velar lobes now grow out to an enormous length.
When the shell is approximately 0·8 mm long the lobes are at their maximal development and each is twice as long as the shell and often longer. The velum of *N. reticulatus*
is never so large and remains only slightly 4-lobed. This species attains only about

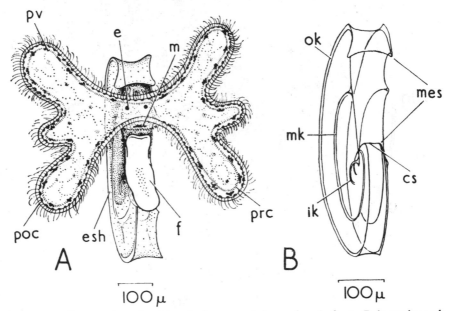

FIG. 246.—*Lamellaria perspicua*: A, echinospira larva extended, seen from in front; B, its scaphoconch.
cs, chiselled surface of shell; e, eye; esh, outer part of echinospira shell or scaphoconch; f, foot;
ik, inner keel; m, mouth; mes, mouth of outer part of echinospira shell or scaphoconch; mk, middle
keel; ok, outer keel; poc, postoral cilia of velum; prc, preoral cilia of velum; pv, pigment on velum.

two-thirds the size of *N. incrassatus* at metamorphosis, although the adult and the first
larval stage are much larger. The long velar lobes of *N. incrassatus* are sometimes outspread with little motion except the metachronal beating of the cilia, and the shell hangs
downwards from them; at other times they move like the wings of a pteropod and
propel the animal along. Towards the end of larval life the larvae can both crawl and
swim (fig. 240); this stage immediately preceding metamorphosis has been called the
veliconcha by Werner (1939). The shell mouth has no longer the projecting tooth, but
the margin is simple with a slightly crenated edge, and the siphonal tube of the shell is
fully formed and contains the mantle siphon (s). The shell of *N. reticulatus* then measures
about 0·8 mm long and that of *N. incrassatus* 1·2 mm.

The larvae of some mesogastropods have a comparatively long life in the surface
waters and, as well as a large velum, an elaborate shell, which helps to keep them afloat.

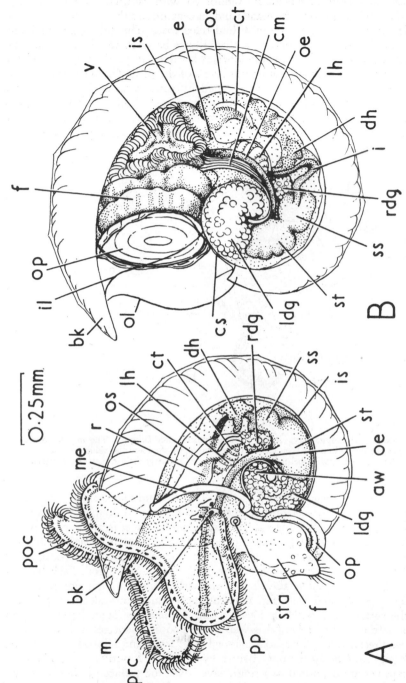

FIG. 247.—*Trivia monacha*: echinospira larva from the left. A, extended; B, fully retracted. Note the spiral coiling of the scaphoconch, its beak and the crumpling of the opercular edge on retraction. The larva is more heavily pigmented than that of *Lamellaria*, with brownish black gut and brown spots on velar edge only.

aw, apical whorl of shell; bk, beak; cm, columellar muscle; cs, chiselled surface of shell; ct, ctenidium; dh, definitive heart; e, eye; f, foot; i, intestine; il, inner lip of scaphoconch; is, inner part of echinospira shell; ldg, left lobe of digestive gland; lh, larval heart; m, mouth; me, mantle edge; oe, oesophagus; ol, outer lip of scaphoconch; op, operculum; os, osphradium; poc, postoral cilia of velum; pp, propodium; prc, preoral cilia of velum; r, rectum; rdg, right lobe of digestive gland; ss, style sac region of stomach; st, stomach; sta, statocyst; v, velum.

It consists of an inner layer of conchiolin reinforced with calcareous matter (is, figs. 245A, B) which is closely applied to the mantle and, except around the mouth, is separated from a much larger layer of conchiolin by a fluid-filled space. The fluid appears initially to be extra-pallial like that which occurs in all molluscs between the living tissues and shell, and which at the edge of the mantle lobes of bivalves, in particular, also fills the space between the periostracum and calcareous layers of the shell. The outer layer of the shell of these specialized larvae has been regarded hitherto as an accessory shell, the scaphoconch, and the inner layer as the true shell. The name echinospira has been given to them and they are found in 7 British prosobranchs (Lebour, 1935a, 1937): 3 in the family Lamellariidae—*Velutina velutina, Lamellaria perspicua* (figs. 245, 246) and *L. latens*; 3

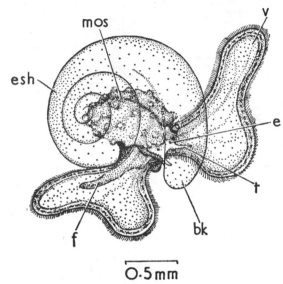

FIG. 248.—*Erato voluta*: echinospira larva during metamorphosis, after Lebour. The mantle covers the true shell and the operculum has been lost, but the echinospira shell and the velum persist.
bk, beak; e, eye; esh, echinospira shell; f, foot; mos, mantle fused over shell; t, tentacle; v, velum.

in the family Eratoidae—*Trivia monacha* (fig. 247), *T. arctica* and *Erato voluta*—and one in the family Capulidae—*Capulus ungaricus*. The shell has the typical double appearance in the embryo and it grows rapidly during larval life. The outer layer (sca, fig. 245), which is thin, colourless and glass-like in transparency, coils in one plane in *Lamellaria* and has the sides flat with 2 peripheral keels (ok, fig. 246); the inner calcareous layer (is, fig. 245) grows less rapidly and, in contrast to the outer, forms a helicoid spiral. Each has not more than 1½ whorls. In *Velutina* the shell is similarly coiled though not carinated, whereas in *Trivia* (fig. 247) and *Erato* (fig. 248) both periostracal and calcareous parts are helicoid, and the surface is smooth. In *Velutina* and *Capulus* the outer layer is almost gelatinous in its softness. The velum (v) is well developed in all species: it is bilobed in *Capulus, Velutina, Erato* and *Trivia monacha*, 4-lobed in *T. arctica* and 6-lobed in *Lamellaria*.

*Simnia patula* (fig. 249), being the only British cypraeacean, is without an echinospira larva. Its egg capsules are deposited in a single layer over the surface of *Alcyonium* and each contains numerous eggs. These are pink at first, but as development proceeds become brown owing to the development of the shell. In the newly hatched larva the shell has 1½ whorls and is sculptured with irregular granules. At the outer lip a reticulate marking appears and a characteristic tooth and as the shell increases the reticulate pattern persists (fig. 249). The larva is supported in the surface waters by the conspicuous velum of 4 long, narrow lobes and when the shell is about 0.6 mm long, from apex to shell siphon, the velum measures 3·0 mm across. Larval life is probably long (Lebour, 1932a).

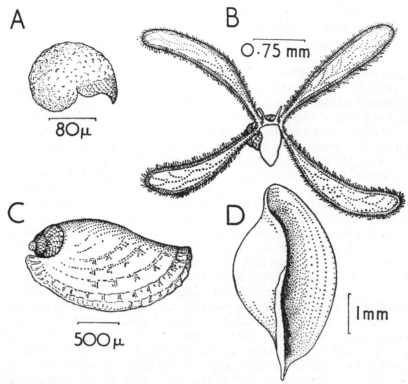

Fig. 249.—*Simnia patula:* **A,** shell of larva 3 days old. The granular surface of the protoconch contrasts with the reticulate pattern appearing on the outer lip. **B,** larva with 4-lobed velum which is colourless. **C,** shell of crawling stage (veliconcha) from shelly gravel, showing granular surface of protoconch, reticulate pattern of larval whorls and beginning of adult shell with ribs. **D,** shell showing adult characters. After Lebour.

At the early crawling stage the velum is lost and the mantle begins to grow over the shell; the tooth of the shell disappears and the reticulate marking is replaced by straight ribs. The adult shell gradually envelops the larval one.

The earliest observations on echinospira larvae concern *Lamellaria*. Giard (1875) studied the embryology of *Lamellaria perspicua* and noticed two apparent shells, and his work was confirmed and elaborated by Pelseneer (1911). Simroth (1895) gave a summary, with illustrations, of the echinospira larvae from the Plankton Expedition, and later (1911) described the northern forms including *Lamellaria*. None of these workers, however, observed the later larval stages, and it was not until Lebour (1935a) successfully reared the larvae that the external development from the egg to metamorphosis was observed. Likewise she extended the preliminary observations of Pelseneer (1926*b*) on the larva of *Trivia* (Lebour, 1931*b*), and also gave an account of other British echinospira larvae (Lebour, 1937). Her observations on *Lamellaria perspicua* inspired Garstang (1951), and his amplification of her work is incorporated in his poem 'Echinospira's Double Shell'. This gives a most accurate account of the larva, though it still holds that there are 2 shells, the entrance to which cannot be closed by the operculum.

The idea that the echinospira larva has 2 shells, the relationship between which has always been problematic, seems a much more artificial explanation than the suggestion that the 2 shells are merely the periostracal and calcareous parts of the gastropod shell separated from one another to a greater extent than usual. Although *Simnia* has no echinospira shell a pointer to its nature is perhaps given in the revealing statement by Lebour (1932*a*): 'It was interesting to find that when these embryos were fixed in Bouin-Duboscq a film separated off from the shell, presumably the periostracum, forming a covering of exactly the shape of the accessory shell of *Trivia*.' In the growth of the shell of any gastropod the formation of a layer of conchiolin, which is known as the periostracum, precedes the formation of a layer of conchiolin impregnated with calcareous salts. The areas which produce them at the mantle edge form two concentric circles separated by an indifferent epithelium. In the embryo the shell gland first appears as a pit which everts and spreads over the visceral mass. It secretes a layer of conchiolin which represents the outer layer of the echinospira shell and, as the visceral mass grows, the gland cells which produce this come to form a ring at the mantle edge. The second ring of gland cells of the adult, more posteriorly placed and secreting calcareous salts in addition to conchiolin, is also derived from the shell gland, and, in the echinospira, its cells produce the inner calcified layer of the shell after the outer layer has grown away from the visceral mass as noted by Pelseneer (1911) in the embryos of *Lamellaria perspicua*. In veligers in which the protoconch is not calcified the activity of these cells is delayed. As the shell of the echinospira larva grows they add to the lip of the inner layer which embraces the visceral hump, and the outer ring of glands, which, from the start, is considerably more active, adds to the larger outer layer. The echinospira veliger differs from all others in that the growing edges of the 2 layers of the shell diverge markedly as the larva grows; this divergence exaggerates the degree of separation of the periostracal and the inner layer of the shell so that their union to form a single shell, as in other gastropods, never can occur. The distance between the growing edges represents the indifferent mantle epithelium which separates the secreting areas. The mantle edge of all echinospira larvae (me, figs. 245A, B; 247) is thickened and very mobile. When the larva is extended to swim and feed it surrounds the opening of the periostracal part of the shell and adds secretion to it; the radiating striae mark these periods of secretory activity. When the veliger withdraws, the mantle edge is folded back on itself (fig. 247B), the velar lobes fold dorsally over the head, and the operculum (op) (absent in the adult) closes the shell, fitting against the opening of the inner layer, which is small as compared with the mouth formed by the periostracum. The larva, as it grows, is hampered by the restricted space into which it must withdraw, and from the moment that the mouth of the shell starts to overgrow the first whorl—which would then project into it and constrict it still further—the larva sets about enlarging the space by chiselling away the periostracal layer of this whorl (cs, figs. 245, 246B, 247B) with the ventral edge of the operculum. This has the effect of opening the space between the 2 layers of shell to the external medium so that it becomes filled with sea water, and of giving the larva slight freedom of movement within this space. The operculum of *Trivia* (op, fig. 247) becomes considerably larger than the opening which it closes, so that as the larva withdraws into the shell the rim of the operculum is bent forwards to fit the opening, and, ventrally, folds into a pointed V-shaped gouge. When the larva emerges this gouge comes against the periostracum and slices it away horizontally (cs, fig. 247B); the chiselled surface is then smoothed by mucus from the mantle (Garstang, 1951).

All this happens some time before the larva settles, but is a preliminary to the loss of the periostracal layer. *Lamellaria perspicua* metamorphoses when the echinospira shell is about 2·25 mm across; at this time the mantle is no longer extended to the edge of the larval shell, but has gradually inserted itself between the periostracal and calcareous layers. These separate from one another. The outer layer is cast off, the operculum lost and the mantle spreads over the inner layer of the shell. From this moment onwards the further secretion of the periostracal layer will be associated directly with the calcareous material as it is in the adult prosobranch. The outer shell of echinospira larvae is therefore seen as a larval development of periostracum, a larval organ facilitating pelagic life and shed at metamorphosis. During the metamorphosis of *Velutina* the outer layer of the shell is similarly cast off (Lebour, 1935a), and for *Trivia* Lebour (personal communication) tells us that 'further investigation has shown that my statement concerning the absorption of the echinospira shell by the mantle is wrong, for although the covering is extremely fragile it can be shed whole by the late larva as a very thin helicoid shell'. *Erato voluta* (fig. 248) differs in that the mantle (mos) envelops the true shell while the echinospira shell (esh) still covers it and this is not cast off for some time; moreover the velum (v) persists even longer than the shell.

In all other embryos of monotocardians the shell, or protoconch, is a layer of conchiolin which is closely applied to the mantle and, at some time, may be calcified. It first appears as a shallow cap which deepens as the shell gland spreads over the visceral mass, and in species with free larvae it is already spirally twisted with about $1\frac{1}{2}$ whorls at the time of hatching. Its surface may be smooth or ornamented with spiral striae, pits or tubercles. The shell which is added to the protoconch during larval life may be similar, though frequently the sculpture is more complex, foreshadowing the patterning of the adult, and the changes in the shell are synchronous with the change in mode of life. During adult life the soft underlying tissues move forward from the embryonic and larval coils of the shell, which may then be lost. In species in which the adult shell is a tall spire and there is a fairly long pelagic stage, the shell of the larva at metamorphosis may have several whorls, up to 8 or 9 in *Triphora perversa* according to Fischer (1887), $5\frac{1}{2}$ in *Philbertia teres* (Lebour, 1934b), 5 in *Balcis alba* (Lebour, 1935b), $4\frac{1}{2}$ in *Cerithiopsis tubercularis*, *C. barleei* and *Philbertia gracilis* (Lebour, 1933b, 1933d, 1934b), $3\frac{1}{2}$ in *Mangelia nebula* (Lebour, 1934b). In all these the surface has features of the adult shell. In *Balcis alba* it is smooth and colourless and the protoconch grades into the teleoconch without abrupt change; in the adult the tip of the spire (the embryonic and larval whorls) is nearly always broken off, and is filled with calcareous secretion from the underlying mantle. In specimens of *Triphora perversa*, which have 6 whorls at metamorphosis, the embryonic shell is tuberculate (fig. 244C), the following whorls are sculptured with longitudinal striae and are keeled, whilst the sixth is tuberculated as in the adult. The embryonic shell of *Philbertia gracilis* is sculptured with irregular dots and flecks and the following whorls are keeled and have oblique striations. This shell is unlike that of related species, for the remaining turrids may be divided into 2 groups, those with smooth apices representing the embryonic shell (*Haedropleura*, *Lora*, *Mangelia*) and those with reticulate or elaborately sculptured apices (*Philbertia*, fig. 244A). The embryonic and larval whorls of turrids show plainly in the adult though the sculpture may be worn. All these are shells of planktotrophic larvae and prosobranchs of this habit agree in having a protoconch which is smaller, usually shows some sculpture and is narrowly twisted. By contrast, the protoconch of prosobranchs without a larval stage is larger, smoother and inflated to an almost spherical shape. The pelagic larva experiences a relatively abrupt change of life at metamorphosis; the non-pelagic does not. This is normally reflected in an abrupt change from protoconch to teleoconch in the one case and by a gradual transition in the other. Inspection of the apical region of a shell therefore permits one to say whether a pelagic or non-pelagic development has occurred. This is the shell apex theory first suggested by the work of Dall (1924).

There is one feature developed in larval shells of unrelated species: a large outgrowth from the upper lip which is bent over the mouth of the shell so that a velar lobe is supported in the concavity on either side (bk, figs. 238, 244B, 247, 248). A similar curved beak has already been described in *Nassarius* and is pronounced in the larval shells of *Bittium*, *Triphora*, *Cerithiopsis* and all turrids (fig. 244); it disappears at the end of larval life, and has not been described (or does not occur) in species in which the veliger stage is passed through in the egg capsule. The siphonal canal (sit), characteristic of the shell of a number of monotocardians, is developed in the shell of the veliger, either free or embryonic (fig. 241).

In species with a short pelagic phase the shell is less developed. In *Turritella communis*, which has a tall spire in the adult, there are only 2½ whorls at metamorphosis, the last developing the adult pattern of spiral ribbing. *Rissoa membranacea* has only 2 whorls as compared with 4 in *R. parva* and 3½ in *R. sarsi*, both with a longer pelagic phase. When the free-swimming stage is suppressed the crawling stage may start with only 1½–2 whorls as in *Barleeia rubra*, *Cingula cingillus* and *Colus islandicus* (Lebour, 1937), and they are heavy-looking as compared with the coils formed during a free veliger stage. In *Colus* the embryos are nourished by nurse eggs and the size of the crawling stage varies with the nourishment available in the capsule. Thorson (1935) described one capsule from which only one embryo emerged and it was 8·5 mm long, with a shell of 3½ whorls, a little more than half a whorl being spirally sculptured as in the adult. The embryos of other Stenoglossa (*Ocenebra* and *Nucella*) which are similarly nourished emerge from the capsule with up to 2½ coils to the shell.

In some shells the protoconch and teleoconch are remarkably dissimilar owing to a change in the direction of coiling, or to the fact that whereas the initial coils are contiguous the later ones unroll more or less completely and continue their course in a much looser spiral (*Vermetus*) or in a nearly straight line (*Caecum*, fig. 38B); or the adult shell expands to a patelliform shape (fig. 234D). The planktonic larvae of a number of animals traditionally regarded as monotocardians have a sinistral shell though the adult is dextral. They belong to the Pyramidellidae, and the sinistrality of the larval shell is one of their opisthobranch characters. This shell is colourless and smooth. The adult shell is dextrally coiled and carries the minute protoconch (figs. 250A, B) horizontally across its apex (*Odostomia plicata*, *O. turrita*, *O. unidentata*, *O. acuta*, *O. conoidea*, *Turbonilla crenata*, *T. elegantissima*, *Eulimella macandrei*, *E. laevis*, *E. nitidissima*). There are other members of the pyramidellids in which all the shell whorls have a normal dextral appearance and there is no indication of any aberrant larval coiling either externally (Thorson, 1946), or when the apex of the shell is broken and examined internally (*Chrysallida decussata*, *C. indistincta*, *C. obtusa*, *C. spiralis*, *Menestho divisa*, *M. obliqua*, *M. clavula*, *Odostomia scalaris* and *O. eulimoides* (fig. 250C)). It seems probable that in these species the pelagic phase is greatly reduced or absent. The adult shell of *Caecum imperforatum* (fig. 38B) is a slightly arched tube with a round mouth at the broader end and a rounded septum posteriorly, and there is no trace of coiling. The larva, however, has a spiral planorbiform shell of about 2½ whorls which in the adult is separated by a calcareous septum and cast away. The Chinaman's hat shell (*Calyptraea chinensis*) is of contrasting shape: it is patelliform and retains at the apex the embryonic shell of 1½ whorls (fig. 40D). There is no free larva in this species.

Veligers of a few species are easily recognizable in the plankton not only on account of specific characteristics of the velum or the coiling and sculpture of the shell, but more particularly by its colour. The larval shell with the most distinctive colour is that of *Aclis minor* (fig. 239), which is a purplish blue with a purplish red umbilicus and columella. Closer examination shows that the first whorl is colourless and undecorated, the others tinted and with several fine longitudinal ribs like the adult shell. Horn colour is a more usual tint for the larval shell, as in *Alvania punctura*, *Cerithiopsis* and *Triphora*, and the

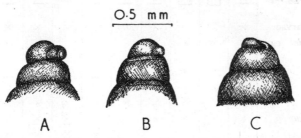

FIG. 250—Shell apices of pyramidellids: A, *Odostomia unidentata*; B, *O. plicata*; C, *O. eulimoides*. A and B show heterostrophy.

larvae of *Philbertia gracilis* are easily identified since the heavily sculptured shell is a dark brown.

These various characteristics of the larval shell of gastropods have been used for taxonomic purposes—in fact Iredale (1911) suggested that no genus should be permitted to contain species with more than one type of apex. Clearly this produces an impossible situation, for within a single genus like *Cingula* or *Natica*, some species have no pelagic phase whilst others have, and this fact alone may give rise to differences in the shell apex. However, with a certain caution, the larval shell may be used in the identification of adult specimens, though diagnostic markings are often worn or obliterated. Its greatest value is undoubtedly in the recognition of the planktonic larva.

Our knowledge of the molluscan larvae of the English Channel comes from the work of Lebour. This mainly concerns the larvae of gastropods, for they are the most easily recognizable in the plankton, whereas the larvae of many species of bivalves are so much alike that it is difficult or impossible to determine the individual species. During the period 1940–45 records were kept of the larval forms in the inshore plankton of Plymouth (Lebour, 1947) and the results for the prosobranch gastropods which were identified are shown in Table 15; unidentified gastropod larvae were present in every month. The rissoids are amongst the commonest, occurring throughout the year, often in large numbers (the actual species of these larvae were not recorded). Their abundance may be partly explicable in the light of the observations made by Smidt (1938) that in *Rissoa membranacea* at least one-eighth of the eggs laid complete their development, a much greater proportion than in other prosobranch species; this rissoid, however, has a short pelagic stage.

TABLE 15

*Occurrence of Prosobranch Larvae in Inshore Plankton at Plymouth, 1940–45 (after Lebour, 1947)*

| Species | Jan. | Feb. | Mar. | Apr. | May | Jun. | Jul. | Aug. | Sep. | Oct. | Nov. | Dec. |
|---|---|---|---|---|---|---|---|---|---|---|---|---|
| *Patella vulgata* | ⊠ | x̲ | × | × | | | | | × | × | x̲ | ⊠ |
| *Patina pellucida* | | × | | | | | | × | × | | × | × |
| *Littorina littorea* egg capsules | x̲ | ⊠ | ⊠ | x̲ | x̲ | x̲ | × | x̲ | x̲ | x̲ | x̲ | x̲ |
| *Littorina littorea* larvae | × | × | | × | × | × | × | × | × | × | × | × |
| *Littorina neritoides* egg capsules | × | × | × | × | | | | | × | | | × |
| Rissoid larvae | × | × | × | x̲ | x̲ | x̲ | x̲ | x̲ | x̲ | x̲ | x̲ | x̲ |
| *Trivia arctica* | × | × | × | × | × | | | | | | | |
| *Trivia monacha* | | | | × | × | × | × | × | × | | | |
| *Lamellaria perspicua* | × | × | × | × | × | × | x̲ | x̲ | × | × | × | × |
| *Simnia patula* | | | | | | × | × | × | x̲ | | | |
| *Natica catena* | | | × | × | × | x̲ | x̲ | × | × | × | | |
| ?*Bittium reticulatum* | | | | | | | × | × | | | | |
| *Triphora perversa* | | | | | | | × | × | × | × | | |
| *Cerithiopsis tubercularis* | × | | | | | × | × | × | × | × | | |
| *Cerithiopsis barleei* | | | | | | | | | × | | | |
| *Balcis* sp. | | | | | | | | | × | | | |
| *Caecum* sp. | × | | | | | | × | × | × | × | x̲ | × |
| *Nassarius reticulatus* | | x̲ | | x̲ | x̲ | x̲ | × | × | × | × | | |
| *Nassarius incrassatus* | | | | × | x̲ | x̲ | x̲ | x̲ | × | × | | |
| ?*Haedropleura septangularis* | | | | | × | × | x̲ | × | × | | | |
| *Mangelia nebula* | | | | | | | × | × | × | × | × | |
| *Philbertia gracilis* | | | | | × | × | x̲ | x̲ | × | | | |
| *Philbertia linearis* | | | | | | x̲ | ⊠ | x̲ | x̲ | x̲ | | |

×   Recorded.
x̲   Common.
⊠   Abundant.

Lebour's studies of the eggs and larvae of the prosobranchs of Bermuda (Lebour, 1945) show that the majority of molluscs in these warmer seas have free-swimming larvae, and Thorson (1950), using her investigations, has calculated that it concerns 85% of the

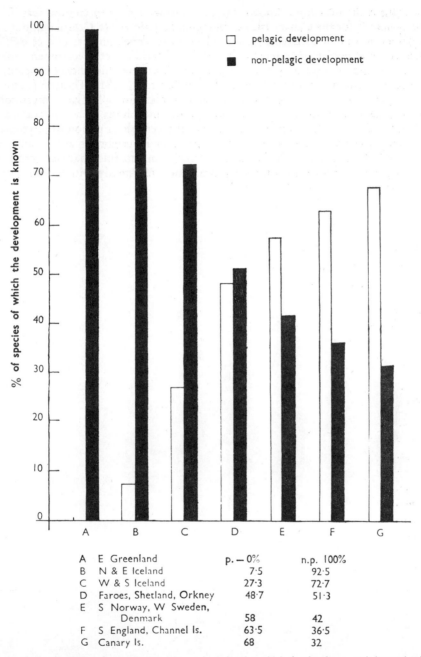

| | | p. — 0% | n.p. 100% |
| A | E Greenland | | |
| B | N & E Iceland | 7·5 | 92·5 |
| C | W & S Iceland | 27·3 | 72·7 |
| D | Faroes, Shetland, Orkney | 48·7 | 51·3 |
| E | S Norway, W Sweden, Denmark | 58 | 42 |
| F | S England, Channel Is. | 63·5 | 36·5 |
| G | Canary Is. | 68 | 32 |

FIG. 251.—Graphs giving the percentage of prosobranchs (for which the development is known) with free-swimming larvae (white columns), and those in which the larval stage is suppressed (black columns). A, E Greenland; B, N and E Iceland; C, W and S Iceland; D, Faroes, Shetland, Orkney; E, S Norway, W Sweden, Denmark; F, S England, Channel Is.; G, Canary Is.; n.p., non-pelagic larval development; p., pelagic larval development. After Thorson.

species; this is the maximum known for any marine area, even tropical seas. Thorson (1950) gave 68% for the Canary Islands. In the high arctic seas (E Greenland) not a single prosobranch is known to have a pelagic phase in its development; in fact 95% of all marine species of bottom invertebrates living there have a direct development; there are, however, pelagic larvae of polychaetes, echinoderms and lamellibranchs (Thorson, 1936). The antarctic plankton has no molluscan larvae (Simroth, 1911). Thorson (1950) stated that in order to survive in the high arctic areas a planktotrophic larva must complete its development, from the time of hatching to metamorphosis, at a temperature below 4·5°C and within $1-1\frac{1}{2}$ months, which includes the very short period of phytoplankton production. The prosobranchs more than any other invertebrates are sensitive to environmental changes, and it is therefore not surprising to find that the percentage of species in the N Atlantic with a pelagic phase varies consistently with latitude (fig. 251).

# CHAPTER 19

# THE ROCKY SHORE: LIMPETS

THE sublittoral part of the rocky shore is thought to have been the ancestral home of the prosobranch molluscs, and the most primitive prosobranchs living today, the zeugobranchs, retain a similar habitat. They are rock clingers living near ELWST, or deeper, and avoiding well lit areas; gathering their food from the surface of the substratum in the vicinity of their home; spawning into the sea, and after a planktonic larval period settling on the rocks to take up their final niche. The evolution of the ability to endure variations in temperature, light, humidity and salinity allowed the prosobranchs to escape from the sublittoral areas and colonize the beach. Here their distribution is governed by the extent to which their emancipation has proceeded. Food preferences and the ability to endure periods of restricted feeding, together with their response to gravity, are other factors governing their distribution on the shore, which, for some species, lies between very narrow limits. Certain pre-adaptations, anatomical and behavioural, must have speeded this evolution. These concern especially the shell, into which the snail retreats and virtually shuts itself off from the external environment, and the foot, which maintains balance as the animal creeps, though if waves are strong the foot will hold the animal motionless against the rocks. Prosobranchs colonizing the upper parts of the shore near high tide level are still dependent on the tide, for in no littoral species can reproduction be fulfilled without the snails being able to discharge eggs or young to the sea, or the fixed spawn being immersed periodically. Even in the viviparous *Littorina saxatilis* the eggs do not develop normally, and the young do not apparently leave the brood pouch, unless the female is at times covered with water. The young snails are more sensitive to the changing conditions than the adults: they more or less avoid them, and are found either at lower levels on the beach or they hide.

The intertidal level at which a species lives is no true indication of its tolerance of exposure, for on an irregular shore the S and SW faces of the rocks will receive maximal illumination and heat, whereas adjacent N and NW faces and overhangs, sheltered from the sun, provide shade and lower temperature. A few species of prosobranchs can withstand the force of the summer sun on dry exposed rocks, and even during abnormally hot periods this does not appear to be a lethal factor. Indeed *Monodonta* and *Littorina littorea* are recorded as living on boulders where the temperature may be 40°C which is exceptionally high for the British Isles. The temperature of their body tissues during the period of exposure may remain a degree or so lower than that of the air (Deshpande, 1957), due to the fact that water in the pallial cavity is slow to heat and loss by evaporation through the shell mouth, though slight, will tend to lower the temperature. However, contrary results have been obtained by Southward (1958) who has shown that the body temperature of limpets exposed to air under varied weather conditions is higher than might be expected from the sea and air temperatures. Up to 20°C there is accurate correspondence between the temperature of the limpet and that of an inanimate object; between 20° and 30°, however, the animal remains a little cooler than its surroundings. Results of a similar experiment with 'a top shell' showed the animal tissue had a higher temperature over the range 16·3–30·0°, which was covered in 90 min. The rising tide brings a sudden fall in temperature and this may help to stimulate the animals to activity. Evans (1948) studied the effect of temperature, apart from desiccation, on 11 common species of British littoral molluscs during the summer—*Patella vulgata*, *P. intermedia*, *P. aspera*, *Gibbula cineraria*, *G. umbilicalis*, *Monodonta lineata*, *Littorina littorea*, *L. saxatilis*, *L. neritoides*, *L. littoralis*, *Nucella lapillus*. The animals were immersed in sea water with a temperature increment of 1°C/5 min. At 30° most species showed some signs of distress and active movement usually ceased. The temperature of heat coma of each species was registered and the thermal death point. *G. cineraria*, which occurs at very low levels,

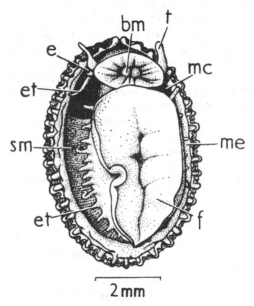

Fig. 252.—*Emarginula conica:* animal in ventral view.
bm, buccal mass; e, eye; et, epipodial tentacle; f, foot; mc, nuchal cavity; me, mantle edge; sm, shell muscle; t, tentacle.

has the lowest thermal death point at 36·2°C and irritability is no longer recorded at 34–35°C (heat coma). In *L. neritoides*, which lives well above HWST, death occurs at 46·3° and heat coma at 38°; this littorinid, most tolerant of heat, has the most southerly distribution, extending into the Black Sea and N Africa. The degree of heat tolerance of each species appears to be related to the temperature range which it experiences in the precise niche of the shore which it inhabits. *N. lapillus* has a rather similar vertical range to *L. littorea*, but is more restricted to shade near its upper limit and correlated with this is its much lower lethal temperature of 40° as compared with 46° for *L. littorea*. The thermal death points of the 11 species which were studied are high in comparison with the normal temperatures of the environment, and it can only be concluded that temperature alone can have no direct limiting effect on their vertical distribution. For instance, in its natural environment, *Nucella* rarely needs to withstand air temperatures

above 25°. Gowanloch & Hayes (1926) working at Halifax, Nova Scotia, found that
*L. littorea* and *L. saxatilis* from different levels on the shore have correspondingly different
death temperatures, but Evans recorded no significant differences with animals from
Cardigan Bay. Both these winkles and also *L. littoralis* occur in N Russia and workers
there have found *L. saxatilis* the most tolerant of low temperatures surviving more than
27 hrs in air at −9·4° (Gurjanova, Sachs & Uschakov, 1930).

When conditions are adverse snails tend to remain inert, and consequently the activity
of species which inhabit the shore varies with the tide, which imposes a rhythm on behaviour. Activity is influenced also by the alternation of day and night. As the tide
retreats the prosobranchs on rocks become inert before the surface dries, many having
returned to a home or protective crevice where the period of ebb tide will be spent.
However, during darkness, if the air be still and the habitat moist, there is considerable
activity. Many individuals in rock pools, both those which are more or less permanent
inhabitants and the casual winkle or topshell, will continue to move about and feed
at LW even in bright sunlight, and carnivores such as the dog whelk may continue to
suck the flesh of their prey in some sheltered gully. However, for the majority, especially
the herbivores and scavengers, there is a rhythm of locomotory activity and feeding.
It has been suggested that this may be an endogenous rhythm rather than a direct in-
duction by environmental factors (Brown, Fingerman, Sandeen & Webb, 1953) and it
may persist when external conditions remain constant. Bohn (1904) described a fortnightly rhythm of activity in *L. saxatilis*, coinciding with the spring tides, and stated
that when snails are brought into uniform conditions in the laboratory they become
active at 15-day intervals corresponding with the spring tides. Stephens, Sandeen &
Webb (1953) have shown that only about 2% of a population of the mud snail *Nassa
obsoleta* may be active at LW as against 54% at HW, and individuals collected from
localities with different tidal times—not only from between tide-marks, but also from
below—show activity patterns correlated with their local conditions. The expression
of the tidal pattern of activity of these animals persisted in the laboratory for approximately 36 hrs at 22° and for considerably longer at 12°, and it appeared to be revived
by 24–48 hrs stay at 12° after the animals had become apparently arhythmic at the
higher temperature.

Rhythmical activity will be reflected in oxygen consumption. Gompel (1937) found
that oxygen consumption in *Patella vulgata* is maximal at high tide and minimal at low,
and Sandeen, Stephens & Brown (1954) described a persistent diurnal and tidal rhythm
of consumption in *Littorina littorea* and *Urosalpinx cinerea*. The diurnal rhythm in
*Urosalpinx* is one with maximum oxygen consumption between 04.30 and 06.30 hrs
and between 19.30 and 21.30 hrs with a lesser maximum at 14.30, and minimal consumption between 00.30 and 01.30, between 11.30 and 13.30 and at 16.30 hrs. The
persistent tidal rhythm involves minimal rates of oxygen consumption about 5 hrs
after low tide and maximal rates 2–3 hrs before low tide. Two such rhythms of different
frequencies have been demonstrated in other invertebrates including the lamellibranchs
*Crassostrea virginica* (Brown, 1954) and *Venus mercenaria* (Bennett, 1954). The resultant
pattern of such rhythms is of semilunar frequency and shows peaks coincident with
spring tides; these may be part of the mechanism regulating spawning. When *Littorina
irrorata* is exposed after a long period of submergence oxygen consumption increases
(Newcombe, Miller & Chappel, 1936) and is recorded as 0·31 ml/gm/hr at 32°C. Subsequent submergence at the same temperature brings about a reduction to 0·179 ml/gm/hr.
These results partly reflect differences in the availability of oxygen in air as compared

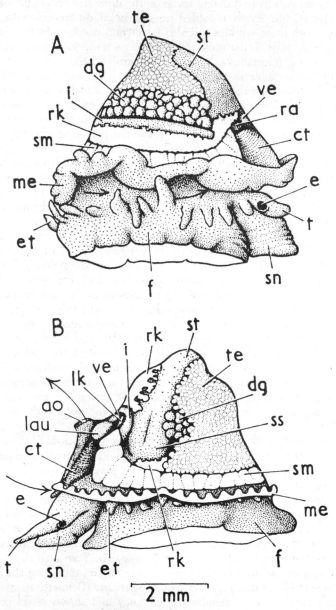

FIG. 253.—*Emarginula conica:* animal removed from shell and seen A, from the right; B, from the left side. Arrows indicate ciliary and water currents.

ao, apical opening of mantle cavity; ct, ctenidium; dg, digestive gland; e, eye; et, epipodial tentacle; f, foot; i, intestine; lau, left auricle; lk, left kidney; me, mantle edge; ra, right auricle; rk, right kidney; sm, shell muscle; sn, snout; ss, style sac region of stomach; st, stomach; t, tentacle; te, testis; ve, ventricle.

with water. The consumption varies with the temperature; it is maximal for *L. irrorata* at 35° and decreases rapidly at lower temperatures, and below 10° it is difficult to obtain reliable results.

For easy discussion the prosobranchs which live on rocky shores have been dealt with here under the three general headings 'limpets', 'whelks and tingles' and 'other prosobranchs'. These will be found immediately below and in Chapters 20 and 21 respectively.

Like the word 'worm' the word 'limpet' is not an accurate zoological term, but is merely the name of a shape, the shape of the simple, conical shell which is found in those gastropods that live habitually in one place, clinging to the substratum and often withstanding the wash of waves or the current of a torrential stream. It is often assumed that the ancestral gastropod had a simple cap-shaped shell like that shown by recent limpets, but in no living limpet is the shape of the shell primary: in every instance it has been secondarily derived from a helicoid spiral shell which may still be seen in the young stages (fig. 234D). As the animals grow, however, the body whorl of the shell grows disproportionately large and provides accommodation for all the soft parts, whilst the original spire is usually wholly worn away. The mouth of the shell becomes round or oval and the sole of the foot acquires more or less the same shape. The operculum is lost, because the animal never normally lets go of the substratum to which it clings, and the columellar muscle usually becomes horseshoe-shaped (fig. 39B), probably formed by the union of originally separate right and left shell muscles.

Limpets may be found in all groups of gastropods. *Ancylus*, the freshwater limpet, and *Siphonaria*, found on tropical beaches, are both pulmonates, but most limpets are prosobranchs and, in particular, belong amongst the more lowly members of that group such as the Zeugobranchia and Patellacea (=Docoglossa). A few monotocardians have also adopted this rock-clinging mode of life like the Chinaman's hat shell (*Calyptraea chinensis*) and the Hungarian cap shell (*Capulus ungaricus*).

The Zeugobranchia are perhaps the least successful of these three groups of prosobranch limpets. They are an archaic group dating back to late Cambrian, differing from other prosobranchs in a number of important ways. The two other groups are much younger, the Patellacea dating certainly from the Trias (Wenz, 1938) and perhaps from the Silurian (Knight, 1952) and the Calyptraeacea from the lower Cretaceous. In both these groups, too, the calculations of Schilder (1947) suggest that a flowering into many species has occurred only within geologically very recent times.

Of these animals the calyptraeaceans are protandrous hermaphrodites and some approach to this condition is exhibited by the docoglossan limpets. With a few exceptions these are the only undoubted prosobranchs which show this—the other hermaphrodites being perhaps more truly opisthobranchs or having opisthobranch affinities—and the association of the hermaphrodite condition with the limpet mode of life may be significant.

The Zeugobranchia are a small group of prosobranchs which are not richly represented in British waters since these lie in too cold an area of the world. Most zeugobranchs prefer warmer conditions, although the restriction of the family Scissurellidae to cold water areas shows that it is not beyond their power to adapt themselves in this way. Of 18 genera listed in Thiele's *Handbook* (1929–35) only 5 are to be found in British seas, even when this phrase is interpreted in the broadest sense to include the Channel Islands. These animals are the ormer, *Haliotis tuberculata* L., which is exclusively Sarnian, three species of the genus *Emarginula*, the slit limpets *E. reticulata* Sowerby,

17

*E. conica* Lamarck, and *E. crassa* Sowerby, the keyhole limpet *Diodora apertura* (Montagu), *Puncturella noachina* (L.), and *Scissurella crispata* Fleming.

With the exception of *Haliotis* and *Scissurella* these animals appear to lead essentially the same kind of life—that of the rock-clinger spending long periods in one and the

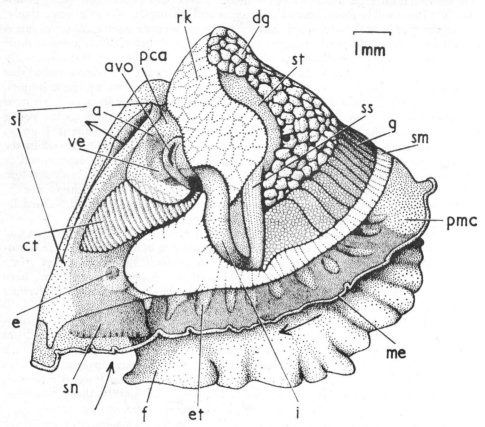

FIG. 254.—*Puncturella noachina:* animal removed from shell and seen from the left.   Arrows indicate ciliary and water currents.

a, anus, seen through mantle skirt; avo, auriculo-ventricular opening; ct, ctenidium, seen through mantle skirt; dg, digestive gland; e, eye, seen through mantle skirt; et, epipodial tentacle, seen through mantle skirt; f, foot; g, gonad; i, intestine; me, mantle edge; pca, pericardial cavity; pmc, posterior part of mantle cavity; rk, right kidney; sl, extent of slit in mantle skirt; sm, shell muscle; sn, snout, seen through mantle skirt; ss, style sac region of stomach; st, stomach; ve, ventricle.

same spot from which it makes periodic excursions for feeding. This may be verified by direct observation of *Emarginula reticulata* and *Diodora apertura*, which live between tidemarks, but is only an inference in the case of those other members of the group which live in deeper waters. For this type of life they are adapted by the limpet-like shape, the conical shell and the foot which gives them considerable powers of adhesion, though never equal to those of the docoglossan limpets. As in these the shell muscle has a horseshoe-shaped attachment to the shell and is cup-shaped, broken

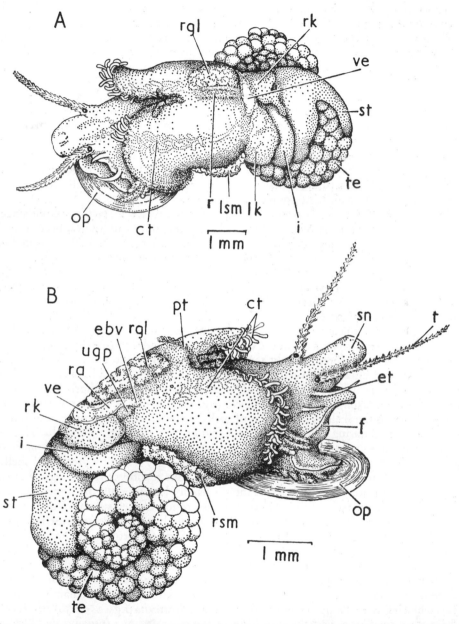

FIG. 255.—*Scissurella crispata:* animal removed from shell and seen A, from the dorsal side; B, from the right.

ct, ctenidium with filiform filaments; ebv, efferent branchial vessel; et, epipodial tentacle; f, foot; i, intestine; lk, left kidney (papillary sac); lsm, left shell muscle; op, operculum; pt, pallial tentacle; r, rectum, seen through mantle skirt; ra, right auricle; rgl, rectal gland; rk, right kidney; rsm, right shell muscle; sn, snout; st, stomach; t, tentacle; te, testis; ugp, opening of right kidney (urinogenital papilla); ve, ventricle.

anteriorly, roofed over by the shell and fringed sideways by the mantle, with the head occupying the gap in the horseshoe at the front. In *Haliotis* and *Scissurella* there are two shell muscles right and left, and the hypertrophy of the right one in *Haliotis* gives it a median attachment to the shell (rsm, fig. 85) and displaces the mantle cavity to the left. In many limpet-like animals the mantle carries sensory processes, but in the zeugo-branchs this tendency is exaggerated and the edge of the mantle skirt thickened and made warty with processes of sensory importance. These papillae are least numerous in *Puncturella*. Augmenting this sensory equipment is the epipodium, which varies in nature from genus to genus. It is at its most elaborate in *Haliotis*, where it forms a collar which projects rather high up the side of the foot and is beset with numerous sensory bosses, small tentacles and, especially dorsally, long tentacles. In *Diodora*, *Emarginula* (figs. 252, 253) and *Puncturella* (fig. 254) the epipodium is less developed and takes the form of a circlet of separate tentacles running round the sides of the foot, and in *Scissurella* (figs. 255, 256) these are reduced in number.

Each epipodial tentacle is, presumably, generally sensitive to tactile stimuli since it contains a prominent nerve related to the pedal ganglia, but in addition it bears a special group of sensory cells lying at its base on the ventral side (eso, fig. 80). The precise func-tion of these organs is not known, but they must add considerably to the total sensitivity of the margin of the body of the limpets. An epipodial tentacle lies behind the right tentacle in *Emarginula*, *Diodora* and *Puncturella*, where it is bifid. This has, because of its position, been assumed to act as a penis (Odhner, 1932) but is almost certainly not so since it occurs in both sexes.

During early life the anterior edge of the mantle skirt in all the Zeugobranchia shows a cleft which is repeated as a slit in the overlying shell. Under this lie the anus, excretory and reproductive apertures. The slit remains as such in the pleurotomariids, scissurellids (sls, fig. 256) and Emarginulinae (fig. 30), its inner end being closed by secretion of shell material as the animal grows and leaving a track over the older whorls known as the slit band (slb, fig. 256A). In the genus *Haliotis* (fig. 85) the slit is at regular intervals closed near the edge of the shell by deposition of shelly material, so that its upper end remains open for a period during which further marginal growth may form a new slit. This may be repeated a few times so that the slit is represented by a series of holes (hs) under one of which the anus is placed. Eventually the older holes get closed by growth of shell. In *Puncturella* and in *Diodora* the young animal has a slit mantle skirt and shell, but as it gets older the mantle edges fuse across the slit basally leaving only the upper part as an opening. Where the pallial fusion has occurred secretion of shell substance goes on with the result that the slit becomes converted into a hole lying on the anterior face of the shell. It remains thus in *Puncturella* (fig. 254) but differential growth in *Diodora* converts it into an apical aperture (fig. 30).

Whatever its final form, this hole first appears as a bay at the edge of the mantle skirt and exhibits the same general features as that part of the body does elsewhere. The edge of the skirt often protrudes through a slit or hole as a kind of short exhalant siphon, and bears tentacles, as in *Puncturella*, where there are six, *Scissurella* (figs. 255, 256) and *Haliotis*, where three small ones pass through three of the separate holes (usually the oldest and two others according to Crofts (1929), though they may vary their position).

The head, foot, mantle and mantle cavity of some of the Zeugobranchia are bilaterally symmetrical (*Emarginula*, *Diodora* (fig. 257), *Puncturella*). Even where this is not true (*Haliotis* (fig. 229B) and less so, *Scissurella*), a double set of pallial organs occurs, with those on the left larger than those on the right. The gills (fig. 257) are bipectinate and are slung over the greater part of their length by efferent membranes (efm) passing from the floor of the mantle cavity to the ctenidial axis and by afferent membranes connected to the roof. The anus (a) lies in the central compartment of the mantle cavity flanked by two apertures, an excretory one on the left, a urinogenital one on the right (rko). The roof of the cavity between these and the gill axis forms right and left hypobranchial glands, so that at first sight these limpets look very much as one supposes the original symmetrical gastropod may have looked. They may be used to suggest this type of animal indeed, but it must be realized that they are far from being primitive and are highly specialized for their rock-clinging mode of life. So far as their external features

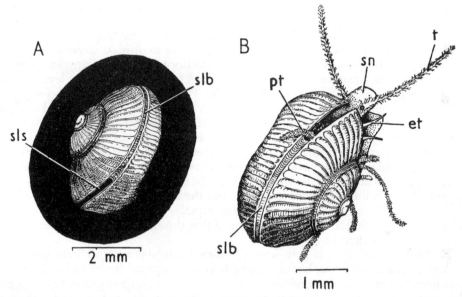

FIG. 256.—*Scissurella crispata:* A, shell; B, animal, alive, in dorsal view.
et, epipodial tentacle; pt, pallial tentacle; slb, slit band; sls, slit in shell; sn, snout; t, tentacle.

are concerned this is reflected in the slit or apical hole which they possess in the mantle: this permits water to enter the mantle cavity anterolaterally, to wash over the ctenidial leaflets and to escape from the mantle cavity dorsally, where the out-thrust mantle edge acts as a siphon and directs the water current away from the animal's head.

This is the solution to the sanitary problems of the gastropod mantle cavity found by the zeugobranchs, but, whilst it is good in its way, the animal probably loses as much as it has gained by its adoption. The introduction of an apical hole into the shell of a keyhole limpet certainly allows the escape of the exhalant water current from the mantle cavity, but also means that the shell is no longer a waterproof cover, and this may seriously affect the mollusc's ability to live in an intertidal habitat. It certainly seems to imply that it is impossible for any zeugobranch limpet to live in the same kind of exposed situation as would be occupied by the common limpet, and all zeugobranchs are to be found at low water level or below—that is, in situations where the tendency to desiccation is least.

In correlation with the presence of slit or apical hole the intestine is short and not concerned with the elaboration of faecal pellets (p. 230); the stomach has lost its caecum and sorting areas (p. 223). A siphon runs along the intestine (p. 233), which passes through the ventricle. The left kidney is minute, if not functionless, and has no renopericardial connexion (Ziegenhorn & Thiem, 1926) though Crofts (1929) recorded one in *Haliotis*. The right is responsible for all the excretory activity and also acts as a conduit for the genital products. In *Diodora nubecula* von Medem (1945) stated that the spermatozoa are shed in packets surrounded by testicular epithelium and that these enter the female gonad in which the eggs are fertilized: this is certainly not true of other zeugobranchs in which sperm are emitted in the usual way and fertilization is external. Apart from these features the general organization is what would be expected in a primitive proso-branch.

The mode of life of *Haliotis tuberculata* has been described by Stephenson (1924) and Crofts (1929). The animals live on rocky shores, for the most part, where there is little sand or other sediment which might clog the respiratory apparatus. They usually live at LWST though they may be found to a depth of 5–6 fathoms, or at higher levels in tidal pools of such size as not to heat up too rapidly. They avoid light and therefore spend daylight hours hidden under a rock or in a crevice, attached by their powerful foot and coming out only at nightfall. They tend to hide in any appropriate situation rather than have a definite 'home'. The shell, the epipodium and the sides of the foot (which cannot be drawn under its shelter) are protectively coloured with blotches and streaks of brown, green or red, and mimic the normal encrusting growth of the rocks to which the animal clings. Their attachment to the rock is extremely tenacious and the pull on the shell effected by the shell muscles will tear that from the body rather than detach the body from the rock. When they do move they move rapidly, Stephenson recording a speed of 5–6 yards per minute, though Crofts cautioned that this distance would not be actually traversed in such a short time.

The food of *Haliotis* is largely seaweed, particularly the more delicate red weeds like *Delesseria* and *Griffithsia*, but the animal is in part a detrital feeder and in the course of its browsing takes detritus and pieces of almost all encrusting organisms into its gut. The animals appear to be susceptible to lack of oxygen, to brackishness and stillness of the water and, except when minute, are difficult to keep in aquaria for these reasons. They seem to have a rather extended breeding season. Fertilization is external and a free-swimming veliger is produced.

Of the three species of *Emarginula* occurring in this country only *E. reticulata* is at all likely to be found by the ordinary shore collector, *E. crassa* and *E. conica*, which can occur occasionally in that habitat on W British coasts, being usually dredged. *E. reticulata* may be collected from the underside of stones not normally higher than LWST and extending thence downwards to considerable depths. All species are particularly fond of stones with rough pitted surfaces into the crannies of which they withdraw and out of which it is often difficult to prise them. Unlike *Haliotis* they do not object to sediment and are often found on stones covered with a thin deposit of fine mud. This is stirred up as the limpet creeps and particles caught between foot and mantle edge are carried for-ward to the mantle cavity and leave by the pallial siphon (ao, fig. 253B). Similar rejection currents along the side of the foot occur in *Puncturella*. Their mode of life appears to be much more like that of a patellid than that of *Haliotis* and they seem to make excursions for feeding purposes and return to a 'home'. Their food is sometimes said to be algae (Eigenbrodt, 1941), though they are often to be found in positions where the search for

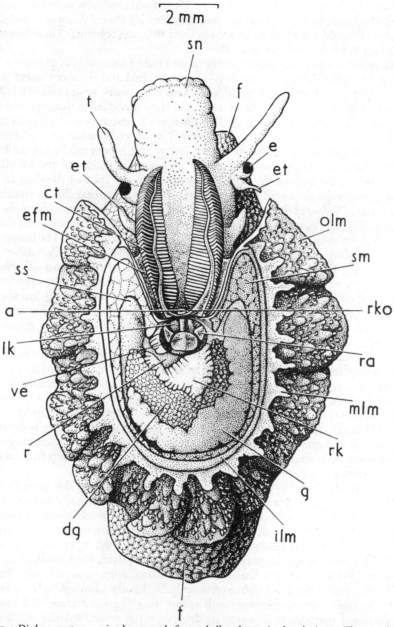

FIG. 257.—*Diodora apertura:* animal removed from shell and seen in dorsal view. The mantle skirt over the main pallial cavity bearing the hypobranchial glands has been removed and the pericardial cavity opened.

a, anus; ct, ctenidium; dg, digestive gland; e, eye; efm, efferent membrane of ctenidium; et, epipodial tentacle; f, foot; g, gonad; ilm, inner lobe of mantle edge; lk, left kidney; mlm, median lobe of mantle edge; olm, outer lobe of mantle edge; r, rectum; ra, right auricle; rk, right kidney; rko, opening of right kidney (urinogenital papilla); sm, shell muscle; sn, snout; ss, style sac region of stomach; t, tentacle; ve, ventricle.

these would involve them in lengthy forays. Their food certainly includes considerable quantities of sponge, but it is likely that they ingest much mixed detrital material as they feed: diatom frustules are often to be seen in their stomach contents. Their reproduction is not known but is likely to be as in *Diodora*.

*Diodora apertura* is not uncommon in the same kind of situations as provide a suitable habitat for *Emarginula reticulata*, but it is more restricted and does not occur on the E coasts of England or Scotland. Littoral specimens are usually found only at LWST on pitted rocks with a covering of slimy mud and they are smaller than specimens from deeper waters. The animal is sluggish, like *Emarginula*, and appears to live in the same way and feed on similar food. It is characterized by an elaboration of the mantle edge (figs. 80, 257) which is exposed as the limpet creeps, but is covered by the shell when it is gripping the rock, though not completely so, for the tentacles of the middle pallial layer (mlm) lie at the ends of the ridges radiating from the apex of the shell and so can never be completely protected (me, fig. 40A). These zeugobranchs are intolerant of brackish water, *Diodora apertura* dying out in the estuary of the Rance when the salinity falls to 21‰ (Fischer, 1931) and this seems to be a general characteristic of all the zeugo-branchs. Fischer also noted that it can withstand prolonged starvation. The limpet appears to have a breeding season extending over a considerable period, December to May (Pelseneer, 1935), the eggs (140 $\mu$ diameter) being yellow in colour and adhering to the substratum after extrusion from the mantle cavity. They hatch in the crawling stage, possessing a shell with $1\frac{1}{2}$ whorls and neither hole nor slit, and having lost the velum. Later a slit appears at the edge and is converted to a hole which gradually moves to an apical position. The mouth of the shell expands and the spire becomes minute and in older stages is worn off so as to leave a conical shell with an apical hole.

*Puncturella noachina* is not a littoral animal but may be dredged on rocky or clay bottoms particularly off the northern parts of Britain. It is, like *Scissurella*, a cold water animal and occurs widespread in the Arctic, Antarctic and cold temperate Atlantic and Pacific Oceans. In lower latitudes it finds the coldness it appreciates at greater depths and whereas it may be found at a depth of 20 m off E Greenland it occurs at 1100 m off Portugal (Thorson, 1944). Little is known about its biology, but there is no reason to suppose that it is significantly different in its way of life from other zeugobranchs. Specimens have been seen to eat diatoms and detritus which they rasp from the surface of stones as they creep.

*Scissurella crispata* (figs. 255, 256) is the least well known of this group of British prosobranchs, being recorded only off the Shetland Islands, on shelly and stony ground off the Orkneys, NW Scotland, Antrim and W Ireland, though it occurs widely over arctic seas and at a greater depth further south. One living specimen—the animal drawn in figs. 255 and 256—was dredged in 105–110 f at 47° 35′ N, 7° 13′ W in shell gravel, and in this locality the species may be moderately abundant, for a small sample of the dredging yielded three empty shells and two others with dead animals. The living specimen was found by Dr Daphne Atkins who kindly allowed us to examine it. It was remarkably active, creeping with speed over the substratum and rasping the surface for food particles as it went. In this respect it resembled the related *Incisura* (*Scissurella*) *lytteltonensis* described by Bourne (1910) from seaweed in rock pools at Lyttelton Harbour, New Zealand, one specimen of which was observed to crawl for a distance of nearly half an inch in the space of a quarter of an hour. The animal has a shell coiled in a spiral like that of a pleurotomariid with a prominent slit and slit band. The snout (sn) is large and through the outer tissues can be seen the stout jaws and posteriorly the salivary glands. The body tissues appear a greyish white against the pearl-white shell which is semitransparent and of a delicate texture. When the animal is active a number of tentacles, pallial and pedal (et, pt), are extended, and the longer ones are waved slowly through the water. Two or more pallial tentacles project from the

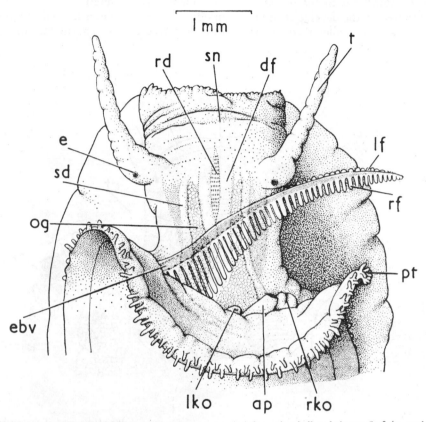

FIG. 258.—*Acmaea tessulata:* the animal has been removed from the shell and the roof of the nuchal cavity folded back to show the contents; in dorsal view.

ap, anal papilla; df, dorsal fold of oesophagus, seen by transparency; e, eye; ebv, efferent branchial vessel; lf, ctenidial leaflet on left side of axis; lko, opening of left kidney; og, anterior end of oesophageal gland, seen by transparency; pt, pallial tentacle; rd, radula, seen by transparency; rf, ctenidial leaflet on right side of axis; rko, opening of right kidney; sd, left salivary duct, seen by transparency; sn, snout; t, tentacle.

slit of the shell. They, and also shorter ones, arise from the edge of the mantle skirt and their surface is tuberculate, as is also this edge. The epipodial tentacles may be similar, though two conspicuous ones behind each eye are short and stout, pointed and with the edge entire. The specimen, which was sectioned, was a male with no accessory genital structures. The reproductive habits of *Scissurella* are unknown and likely to remain so until more extensive local collecting can be undertaken.

The limpets which are classified in the Patellacea comprise one of the most successful groups of gastropods. Some species colonize the most exposed parts of the seashore with a degree of freedom not reached by any other mollusc. They include *Patella*, *Patina*, *Acmaea* and also *Lepeta* and *Propilidium*, the least abundant in our seas. In these genera the overgrowth of the mantle edge (which is concurrent with the development of the cap-shaped shell of the limpet) encloses a pallial groove which encircles the foot and is continuous with the pallial cavity, or nuchal cavity, anteriorly. The groove is not restricted by the development of an epipodium as in zeugobranchs, and the anterior mantle cavity is smaller than in those more primitive forms. The mantle margin is

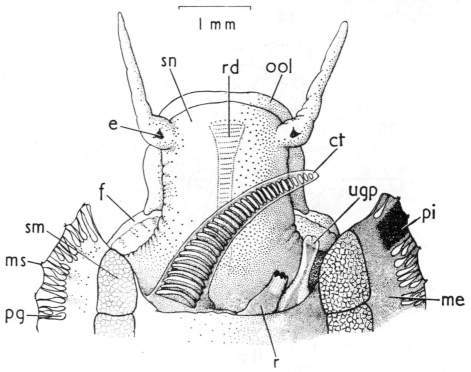

FIG. 259.—*Acmaea virginea:* the animal has been removed from the shell and the roof of the nuchal cavity cut away to show the contents; in dorsal view.

ct, ctenidium; e, eye; f, foot; me, mantle edge; ms, sensory organ on mantle edge; ool, outer lobe of outer lip; pg, repugnatorial pallial gland; pi, pigment patch in edge of mantle skirt; r, rectum; rd, radula, seen by transparency; sm, shell muscle; sn, snout; ugp, urinogenital papilla (opening of right kidney).

typically fringed with tentacles which may compensate for the lack of epipodial tentacles. The direction of the water current through the nuchal cavity and pallial grooves differs from genus to genus. Only *Acmaea* (figs. 258, 259, 260) has a ctenidium. It is a left one (ct), which is elongated and held horizontally across the nuchal cavity, so that the tip can sometimes be seen projecting from the right anterior margin of the shell as the animal creeps. When the limpet comes to rest the muscles of the ctenidial axis contract and withdraw the gill into the cavity; it may be reduced to about half of its original length. The respiratory current is drawn into the nuchal cavity on the left side and passes between the ctenidial filaments towards the right and posteriorly, and the cilia of the epithelium lining the floor of the cavity lead particulate matter in the same direction. Along each pallial groove is a powerful ciliary current beating posteriorly (instead of anteriorly as in *Emarginula* and *Puncturella*) which carries material from the nuchal groove to the mid-line posteriorly where the two currents meet (fig. 73). All sediment, faeces, renal and perhaps reproductive products, leave the limpet by this route and are expelled from under the posterior edge of the shell.

The genera *Patella* and *Patina* have pallial gills (pag, figs. 50, 261, 266, 267B) set on the outer edge of the pallial groove. They hang down from its roof and encircle the head-foot in *Patella*, but in *Patina* the ring is incomplete anteriorly. In *Patina* the exhalant current from the mantle cavity conveying away all material leaves the body from the

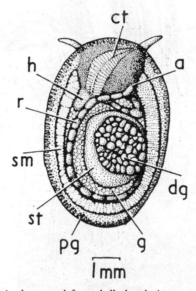

FIG. 260.—*Acmaea virginea:* animal removed from shell, dorsal view.

a, anus, seen through mantle skirt; ct, ctenidium, seen through mantle skirt; dg, digestive gland; g, gonad; h, heart in pericardial cavity; pg, repugnatorial pallial glands; r, rectum, with faecal pellets; sm, shell muscle; st, stomach.

right side of the nuchal cavity. The inhalant current is drawn into the pallial groove in all regions where gills occur, by the cilia on the gills. Sediment entering with the current is entrapped in mucus from a glandular region around the foot, and passes anteriorly along the pallial groove with the water flow, and through the nuchal cavity to leave on the right. *Patella*, with a complete circlet of pallial gills, has yet another arrangement of currents in the mantle cavity and of disposal of material from the body (figs. 48C, 267B). A gentle inhalant current is drawn in all around the margin of the mantle by the cilia on the gills, and a weak current leaves the mantle cavity ventral to this inhalant flow. Particulate material is directed from the body by cilia on the sides of the foot and on the roof of the nuchal cavity, which conduct it to a position midway along the right pallial groove. Here it accumulates and is expelled from time to time, not by ciliary action, but by sharp contractions of the shell muscle. Limpets removed from rocks often leave an accumulation of faecal pellets in this situation which have been collected

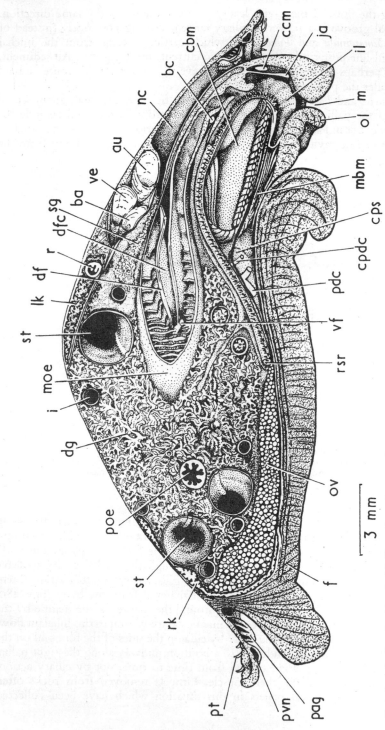

FIG. 261.—*Patella vulgata*: sagittal half seen from the cut surface.
au, auricle; ba, bulb of aorta; bc, buccal commissure; cbm, cartilage of buccal mass; ccm, cerebral commissure; cpdc, cerebropedal connective; cps, cephalopedal blood sinus; df, dorsal fold of oesophagus; dfc, dorsal food channel; dg, digestive gland; f, foot; i, intestine, which is cut (but not labelled) 7 other times; il, inner lip; ja, jaw; lk, left kidney; m, mouth; mbm, muscles of buccal mass; moe, mid-oesophagus; nc, nuchal cavity; ol, outer lip; ov, ovary; pag, pallial gill; pdc, pedal cord; poe, posterior oesophagus; pt, pallial tentacle; pvn, pallial vein; r, rectum; rk, right kidney; rsr, radular sac in radular sinus; sg, salivary gland; st, stomach also cut (but unlabelled) once more; ve, ventricle; vf, ventral fold of oesophagus.

from the nuchal cavity and await expulsion. The forceful expulsive movement compensates for the lack of a glandular streak around the foot of *Patella* except in young individuals, and may be a decisive factor in enabling this limpet to live in situations where there is considerable sediment. The ciliary currents in this process are strongly developed only in limpets less than 10 mm in length, in which the transverse, left to right current through the nuchal cavity is marked. *Lepeta* and *Propilidium* (fig. 262) have no gills. A flow of water enters the nuchal cavity and is directed posteriorly by cilia on the walls of the pallial groove to leave the body posteriorly.

Limpets of the genus *Patella* are amongst the most ubiquitous animals on the rocky shore and the most abundant representative of the Patellacea in the British Isles. The stout, conical shell, concealing the soft tissues of the body and ribbed from apex to margin,

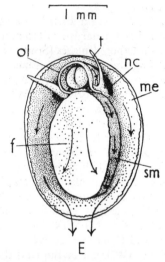

Fig. 262.—*Propilidium exiguum:* animal in ventral view.   Arrows show direction of water currents.
   E, exhalant current; f, foot; me, mantle edge; nc, nuchal cavity; ol, outer lip; sm, shell muscle;
   t, tentacle.

is a familiar sight on rocks and boulders to which the limpet clings with proverbial strength (see p. 142). Its grip is increased by nearby vibrations or when it is touched. Otherwise, when water covers the animal, whether it be stationary or on the move, the edge of the shell is raised slightly and there is a gentle, respiratory flow of water to the circlet of gills (fig. 48c). Empty shells of limpets are common amongst the jetsam on the beach, on cliff ledges where gulls have been feeding, and in the kitchen middens of olden times when, more than now, this prosobranch was used as food. The commonest species is *Patella vulgata*. It may be found on both rough and smooth rock as well as on pebbles which are not subjected to too much movement, and it is frequent on all angles of slope. It occurs in conditions ranging from considerable exposure to those offering most shelter from the surf, and extends from high on the beach to MLWS, where the population density falls off rapidly. The limpet does not particularly favour sheltered regions with a thick growth of fucoids, and in areas covered with a felt of smaller weeds, such as *Enteromorpha, Porphyra* and *Bangia*, it clusters in clearings amongst the algae. The level which these limpets reach on the upper shore is dependent upon the exposure and aspect of the locality: in an extremely well splashed, shaded situation Evans (1947) found them to a height of 8 ft above EHWS. The presence of algal food does not in itself lead to the colonization of the higher levels (Lewis, 1954a), though this is the factor emphasized by Das & Seshappa (1947). In particular situations the seasonal variation in sunshine causes a downward migration of limpets in spring and summer and a return upward movement in autumn and winter, though the upward movement is not confined to individuals which originally occupied the high levels (Lewis, 1954a). *P. vulgata* invades estuaries where there is sufficient rock or stone on which it may live, and in such muddy habitats, with abundant silt and detritus, the growth rate is rapid (Fischer-Piette, 1948). Pollution also increases the size of the shell and the rate of growth. The limpet can endure low salinities: in the Rance, Fischer (1931) found that it dies out only when the salinity is reduced to 3–1‰.

There are two other species of *Patella* on British shores, *P. intermedia* and *P. aspera* (for synonyms see pp. 679, 680). The former is less tolerant of sheltered conditions than *P. vulgata* and is usually found in exposed places (Southward & Orton, 1954) and only along the S and SW shores of England. It may be mixed with *P. vulgata* on bare rock, but does not follow it into sheltered or polluted waters, nor on to boulders or shingle. Its lower limit is vague: it is not found below MLWS and in most places dies out between MLWN and MLWS. It extends up the shore to MHWN (Evans, 1947), and this upper limit may be raised by splash to EHWS, or at this level it may be found in *Lithothamnion*-encrusted pools. *P. aspera* is characteristic of exposed reefs on the lower part of the shore where fucoids are poor or absent and *Corallina* is the chief alga (Eslick, 1940; Evans, 1947); here it particularly favours shallow pools or runnels of water, and it also frequents overhanging rocks and the banks of gullies. This species is common down to the lowest level of the intertidal area and appears to extend into the sublittoral. On very exposed, wave-beaten surfaces it may extend up the shore to MTL, though on more sheltered reefs it is found only to MLWN. In the *Lithothamnion* pools it is often more abundant than *P. vulgata* and *P. intermedia*, even above high water.

Along some parts of the S and SW coast of England the three species of *Patella* can be found in quantity within an area of a few square metres, and with a little experience they can be readily identified in the field (Table 16). If they are removed from the rock and viewed ventrally for comparison it will be seen that the colour of the foot is greyish-green in *P. vulgata* and *P. intermedia*, though it is darker in the latter species; in *P. aspera* it is light in colour, orange to creamy pink or cream. The marginal tentacles of the mantle also differ. They are transparent in *P. vulgata* and coloured like the background, a feature by which this species is readily distinguished; a cream colour in *P. aspera*, and are most conspicuous in *P. intermedia* in which they are opaque cream or white like the tentacles of a *Sagartia*. If the limpets are removed from their shells certain differences in the inner surface of the shell (including the head scar) are noticeable. In *P. vulgata* there is a nacreous lining which may show a green or blue iridescence, and in older shells a yellowish cast; around the margin of young shells there may be red, orange, yellow, brown or perhaps green rays. The head scar, of variable size, may be a silvery nacreous area, or an opaque white or grey. In *P. aspera* the inner surface of the shell has a porcellanous appearance and may be white, and the head scar, in contrast, orange or creamy yellow; marginal rays are never conspicuous. These rays, however, are a distinctive feature of *P. intermedia* since they are dark in colour. The whole inside of the shell is usually dark in this species and the head scar is dusky cream with perhaps an orange tinge. The species may also be separated on their breeding season which has been re-corded by Pelseneer (1911), Orton (1946) and Fischer-Piette (1946) (see Table 16).

Over a hundred years ago it was realized that the British species of *Patella* could be distinguished by the characteristics of the radula (Woodward, 1851–56; Cooke,

TABLE 16

| Feature | *Patella vulgata* | *Patella intermedia* | *Patella aspera* |
|---|---|---|---|
| Colour of foot . . | Grey-green | Dark grey-green | Cream to orange |
| Marginal tentacles . | Transparent, no white | Opaque cream or white | Cream |
| Inner surface of shell . | Green or blue nacre, yellower in old shells | Dark | Porcellanous, white |
| Marginal rays . . | Red-brown at margin only | Dark, conspicuous | Not conspicuous |
| Head scar . . . | Silvery, opaque white | Dusky cream | Cream to orange |
| $\dfrac{\text{Length of radula}}{\text{Length of shell}}$ . | Range of means $1\cdot51$–$1\cdot75$ | $1\cdot60$–$2\cdot10$ | $1\cdot05$–$1\cdot15$ |
| $\dfrac{\text{Length of radula}}{\sqrt[3]{\text{Shell volume}}}$ . | $3\cdot2$–$4\cdot8$ Mean $3\cdot90$ | $4\cdot1$–$5\cdot7$ Mean $4\cdot71$ | $2\cdot5$–$3\cdot5$ Mean $2\cdot90$ |
| Pluricuspid tooth . | See | fig. 263, | p. 496 |
| Microstructure of shell fibres | Stout and thick | Intermediate | Long and narrow |
| Relation to weed (see p. 498) | On *Fucus* | On *Himanthalia* | On *Himanthalia* |
| *Urceolaria* (see p. 498) . | Without zooxanthellae | With zooxanthellae | With zooxanthellae |
| Breeding period . | Winter; max. Oct.–Dec. Rests spring, early summer | Summer Rests Jan. (perhaps) | Summer Rests Jan. |

1917). If the radulae are removed and the length of each measured against that of the shell, the range of the means of the ratio (length of radula/length of shell) sepa-rates *P. aspera* ($1\cdot05$–$1\cdot15$) from the other two species ($1\cdot51$–$2\cdot10$) (p. 172), and this difference is supported by differences in the pluricuspid teeth of the radula (fig. 263). These teeth have each three cusps with characteristic size and shape associated with the species, and there is an incipient fourth cusp in *P. vulgata* and *P. aspera*. The appearance of the three cusps in *P. aspera* is distinct from that of the other two species, which are much more closely related in this character, and are also more variable (Evans, 1953). In *P. aspera* the innermost cusp is the smallest, and if the other two are of unequal size it is the outer which is larger. In *P. vulgata* and *P. intermedia* the three cusps are typically unequal, the innermost is the smallest and the median the largest, though there are variants in each species in which the middle and outer cusps approach one another in size. In both species the median cusp has unequal sides, the inner being shorter than the outer. In *P. vulgata* the cusps are sharply pointed, whereas in *P. intermedia* they taper to blunt tips. The shape of the pluricuspid is so variable that on this basis Evans (1953), dealing mainly with the limpets along the S coast, subdivided each species into groups. However, these will not be dealt with here and only the most frequent types of pluricuspid are shown in fig. 263.

Some authors describe differences in the shape and sculpturing of the outer surface of the shell of the three species. Jeffreys (1865) stated that in *P. aspera* the shell is depressed, with fine sharp ribs and the apex near the anterior end, and that in *P. intermedia* it is

FIG. 263.—Outlines of the pluricuspid radular teeth of limpets, after Evans. A, *Patella vulgata*; B, *Patella intermedia*; C, *Patella aspera*.

smaller, flatter and more oval than in *P. vulgata*, and has fewer ribs. However, Fischer-Piette (1935b) and later workers noted the inconstancy of these characters, which appear to give little reliable help in the separation of the species. Some variations are undoubtedly phenotypic. Thus specimens of *P. vulgata* living in estuaries and under thick growths of weed have a thinner, more regular shell with finer external markings than individuals in exposed positions. Undoubtedly there are fundamental differences in the shell of the different species, but only the most experienced worker can separate these from the abundant variations presumably of environmental origin.

The microstructure of the shell of the limpet shows a fibrous texture in sections viewed under low magnification. The fibres run through the thickness of the shell, perpendicular to the internal and external surfaces. They are stout and thick in *P. vulgata*, long and narrow in *P. aspera* and intermediate in *P. intermedia* (Lhoste, 1944, 1946).

These three species of *Patella* also occur on the coast of Brittany where they are easily distinguishable (Fischer-Piette, 1935b), but further S, along the Basque coast, a number of intermediate types are found, making identification more difficult, and here some features of the Mediterranean species *P. caerulea* are also displayed. Fischer-Piette (1948) held that *P. vulgata* and *P. aspera* maintain their identity in this area as they do in Brittany, and that all transitional types are forms of *P. intermedia*. From his survey he concluded that the limpets may have arisen from a polymorphic species, 'Patella depressa-caerulea' which gave rise to *vulgata* and *aspera*, and from which *intermedia* emerges as a distinct species to the N and *caerulea* to the S. He made a far less thorough investigation of the limpets along part of our Channel coast, and found the three species unmistakable in the W, but their distinction obscured on travelling E. On the Isle of Wight he found the characteristics of the limpets approaching those of the Basque coast, even to the occasional appearance of features of the Mediterranean form, *caerulea*. A more detailed investigation of the region was made by Evans (1953) who confirmed that transitional types of shell and pluricuspid tooth do occur with increasing frequency from the W to the Isle of Wight. E of this island neither *intermedia* nor *aspera* is found, which agrees with their distribution on the channel coast of France (Fischer-Piette, 1941b). However, Evans (1953) found *vulgata* at least as variable as *intermedia* on the S coast of England and suggested that *aspera*, *intermedia* and also *caerulea* are more closely related to *vulgata* than to each other. Indeed he found that the *caerulea* facies is not displayed by *intermedia* but by *vulgata*. So he discarded Fischer-Piette's hypothesis of a depressa-caerulea root-stock and tentatively substituted a *vulgata*-like type. From this he envisaged the following stages in the emergence of the species: at Bognor reef, E of the Isle of Wight, the *vulgata* population on wave-beaten rocks, but not on the sheltered pier, shows some characters of *aspera* and *intermedia*, though neither of these is present as distinct species. The population on the Isle of Wight shows, according to Evans (1953), a further stage in evolution since *aspera* is isolating itself as a true species; it is only much further W (beyond Torquay) that undoubted *intermedia* form a significant fraction of the limpets; *caerulea* has never separated as a species in the British Isles although some of its features are indicated in the *vulgata* stock.

Thus in W Europe the genus *Patella* is divided into distinct species which show a certain degree of ecological divergence, and at least in two areas the characters of these species intergrade. Both Fischer-Piette and Evans regarded the Basque coast and the vicinity of the Isle of Wight, where intergrading types are most pronounced, as areas of emergence of species from a more primitive stock. However, the fact that they may be centres of hybridization cannot be overlooked, for the breeding periods overlap to some extent and on the Isle of Wight all three species have full gonads in late summer. This idea has been considered by these workers. Orton (1946) reported that artificial fertilization between the British species was carried out in the field, but the conditions for this were not satisfactory. The work was done in N Cornwall and if hybrids do arise in this area, and in other regions of the western coast, few can survive—in fact the existence of true hybrids, here or elsewhere, has yet to be proved. Moreover, Evans (1953) considered that if cross breeding between the species of *Patella* occurs it is of no importance in the production of the intermediate types.

The population centred around the Isle of Wight and of the Basque coast could be regarded from a different aspect, for it may be that in regions where the species of *Patella* intergrade we have the natural selective factors which keep them apart elsewhere failing to operate. Indeed these populations may be considered as ones from which stable gene complexes have failed to emerge rather than ones in which they are in the process of emergence.

Limpets are undoubtedly very variable, for along the eastern part of the S coast where only *P. vulgata* persists this species shows variations which are different from those on the Isle of Wight, and not in the direction of *aspera*, *intermedia* or *caerulea* (Evans, 1953). The occurrence of only *vulgata* in this area is curious. Presumably ecological conditions favour only this species in both the adult and larval stage, and they may also be responsible for the variations which are different from those further W. On the Dutch coast *P. vulgata* is again the only species (Lucas, 1954), though all three species occurring in the Channel are occasionally cast up on weeds. Limpets on *Fucus* are invariably *P. vulgata*, all those adhering to *Himanthalia* are either *P. intermedia* or *P. aspera*, neither of which persist. Despite these observations no correlation between weed and any stage in the life history of the limpet has been recorded on the Channel coasts from which these presumably came.

Parasites and symbionts often show specific preferences, and it is interesting to find two physiological races of the peritrich protozoon, *Urceolaria patellae* (Brouardel, 1948) related to the species of *Patella*. These ciliates are epizoic and may even be ectoparasites (Hyman, 1940). Two strains occur, one with zooxanthellae. The strain without the symbiotic cells settles for preference on the gills of *P. vulgata*: the other avoids this species and prefers *P. aspera* and *P. intermedia*. The differentiation of this species suggests that speciation of *Patella* is no recent event. It would be interesting to see how *Urceolaria patellae* behaves in regions like the Isle of Wight and Basque coast.

Limpets move about when the tide is in and the sea not too rough, and browse on detritus and algal growth; under thick fucoid covering, and in other sheltered localities when the weather is damp individuals may be found on the move during the day, after the tide has fallen. Numbers browse over damp rocks at night. It is generally accepted that each medium or large individual returns after feeding to a so-called home, that is, a definite position on the rock where it remains stationary. The broad flat foot fixes the animal to its home and the elliptical edges of the conical shell fit the particular patch of rock so accurately that each ridge is covered by an exactly fitting indentation of the shell. This means that every time the limpet settles its orientation is the same and its shell, as it grows at the edge, fits into the irregularities of the home. Consequently when the shell is pulled on to the exposed rock at the ebb tide on a sunny day, little or no evaporation can take place under its edge and the soft tissues are sealed off from the external environment. The limpet remains motionless, the head raised from the rock and withdrawn into the nuchal cavity, the tentacles relaxed and the foot spread over the substratum, though not to grip it tightly. At any near vibration the shell muscles contract vigorously, clamping the animal to the rock. The full strength of pull of the pedal muscles has been estimated as $3 \cdot 5$ kg/cm$^2$ (Fischer, 1948): it is their force (together with the fact that the conical shell offers little resistance) which secures the animal against the action of the waves in the most exposed situations. On soft rock the surface of the home is worn away by the limpet and a scar is made. These scars are often abandoned by the individuals which formed them, for there is usually some movement of limpets from one place to another; this is more frequent on smooth rock, especially if damp (Orton, 1929b), than on uneven surfaces and on rocks thickly covered with *Balanus* where the number of homing places is limited. Sometimes, on smooth rocks, limpets will return to rest anywhere within a specific area of a few square inches. Jones (1948) observed the movements of a number of limpets (*P. vulgata*) on smooth, flat, limestone rock which was bare of fucoids and *Balanus* and dry at low tide: many of them had home scars suggesting that they had been there for some time. He found that each week some of the 182 individuals had moved to a new site, and after 6 months only 9 were occupying their original area. There was no obvious common direction of migration and the distance moved was usually only a few yards, though one individual moved 30 yards down the shore.

Although homing is usually regarded as part of normal limpet behaviour it appears to be absent in some species of *Acmaea* (Villee & Groody, 1940) though Hewatt (1940) recorded examples of it in a species in which Villee & Groody failed to substantiate its occurrence. The mechanism by which homing occurs is unknown. The capacity to home seems to vary with the circumstances in which the limpets live—nature of rock surface, vegetation and the like—and with age, young limpets being more given to vagrancy than adults. This perhaps explains the difference between the results of Villee & Groody and those of Hewatt. Morgan (1894) showed that the percentage of limpets successfully returning to their home fell off greatly when the distance over which they were experimentally moved exceeded their normal feeding range. This and other experiments suggest that the animals rely either on the trails which they leave as they go out from their home (Piéron, 1909; Hewatt, 1940), or on a knowledge and memory of their territory. The sense-data which the animals use are probably olfactory and are appreciated predominantly by the marginal pallial tentacles (Davis, 1895). Similar statements may be made about *Acmaea*, *Diodora* and the pulmonate limpet *Siphonaria* (Willcox, 1905*b*).

When *Patella* feeds it moves systematically around its home rasping with the radula anything which it happens to meet. Consequently there is considerable variation in diet. The head and tentacles protrude from the margin of the shell and the anterior part of the body swings slowly from side to side in a pendulum action, directing the radular teeth across the substratum. Where the surface permits, as on rocks with a layer of sediment, these feeding tracks are often obvious and it can be seen that the limpet frequently follows the outward track back home again, or it may return by a different route. The whole journey will cover two feet or so, sometimes following a zigzag path. Small limpets occasionally home on the shells of older ones and, if removed and placed a short distance away, will return. Individuals removed several feet from their scars do not appear to make their way home again. Individuals living in the *Balanus* zone collect diatoms, silt and debris, others living amongst *Enteromorpha*, *Ascophyllum* and *Fucus* fill the gut with algae. The larger algae can be utilized as food since the limpet has enzymes capable of digesting laminarin (Dr V. C. Barry, quoted by Jones, 1948), and fucoidin and of de-esterifying their carbohydrate sulphates (Dodgson & Spencer, 1954). Fischer–Piette (1948) found that specimens of *P. vulgata* living under the cover of fucoids in sheltered localities at St Malo, Dinard, have a more rapid growth rate, a higher ratio between the volume of the animal and that of the shell, and attain a larger size and earlier sexual maturity than individuals on exposed rocks with barnacles. He did not believe that the quieter waters can be the factor which is directly responsible for these differences, since waves and currents aid growth (Hatton, 1938; Fischer–Piette, 1948), and although pollution and silting are favourable for nutrition, they do not affect the onset of sexual maturity. He regarded *Fucus* as the important factor, especially as a food rather than a shelter. He recognized the fucoid mantle as a mechanical barrier to the settlement of the larvae on the underlying rocks, thus accounting for the difference in the density of adults under *Fucus* and on bare rock with *Balanus*. Large concentrations of limpets were found in some localities between belts of *Fucus* and bare rocks with barnacles, the size of the individuals being intermediate between those of these two zones. Fischer-Piette likened these concentrations to those of *Nucella* which may be found bordering a mussel bed, and stated that where the limpets are most abundant the *Fucus* is destroyed by their attack.

Jones (1948), who studied the limpet population in localities at Port St Mary, Isle of Man, found that individuals living on rock which is bare of both fucoids and

*Balanus* are still larger than those amongst *Fucus*. The population density is highest on rocks with barnacles, where it may attain 240/sq m, and lowest on bare rock: high density is correlated with low mean size and low density with high mean size. Samples from under beds of thick fucoids have a low density and a medium average size, whilst those among thin *Fucus serratus* have a fairly high density and a fairly high mean size, resembling the population described by Fischer-Piette. Jones concluded that although the presence of fucoids favours the growth of *Patella*, the determining factor is the amount of feeding space over which the limpet can browse without competing with others. This space is perhaps restricted by the stems of algae in thick fucoid zones where the limpets do not seem to make the best use of the available food (Jones, 1948), and on rocks covered with barnacles it is limited by interspecific competition (Hatton, 1938; Evans, 1947). There must, of course, be a critical size at which population density begins to affect growth rate, though nothing is known of this. Das & Seshappa (1947) found that on the rocky shore at Cullercoats, Northumberland, the population density decreases slowly from LWNT to HWST, and that generally the larger limpets predominate at higher levels, even though they are covered by the tide for a shorter time and so their feeding time is less. Again, this may suggest that differences in the mean size between limpets from the lower and upper shore can be explained by the feeding space available, though the possibility of an upshore migration of the larger limpets to areas where competition is less cannot be neglected. Orton (1929b) held that in some high-water situations adults occur where younger and smaller individuals, less than 25 mm, could not exist.

If a limpet (*Patella vulgata*), motionless on dry rock, be splashed with sea water, the front edge of the shell is lifted and the head and tentacles extended (Arnold, 1957). With repetition of this treatment it moves away. However, if freshwater trickles down the shell and comes in contact with the mantle edge and pallial tentacles, the limpet withdraws and clamps the shell on to the substratum. These responses are effected without the entry of water to the mantle cavity where the osphradia are situated: the perception of salinity is by receptors in the mantle fringe and cephalic tentacles. Arnold has shown that where limpets are similarly stimulated by sea water of reduced salinity the magnitude of the response is approximately correlated with the salinity. This is especially obvious in limpets living high on the shore which are much less sensitive to reduced salinity than those from low tidal level. They are stimulated to creep by half-normal sea water or less whereas the others fail to creep when the salinity is 80% normal or less. Similarly, limpets from a high level are more readily stimulated by the splash of normal sea water than those from a low level. There appears, indeed, to be an increasing tolerance of low salinities from the lower to the upper limit of distribution of the species on the shore, and also a more immediate and larger response to splash by the high tide individuals which are exposed for longer periods. It may be that the degree of sensitivity to salinity limits the position of the individual limpet on the shore; or the same potentialities may be possessed by all individuals but they become acclimatized to a particular level on the beach.

It has been estimated that during the first year of life an area of about 75 sq cm/cc of limpet is required to provide sufficient food for the maintenance of an individual. Moore (1938c) calculated this from regions in a thick felt composed of *Enteromorpha* sp., *Porphyra umbilicalis* and other algae, kept clear of new growth by browsing limpets which homed there. Limpets devour the spores of algae as they settle on the rock and before they have a chance of establishing themselves as sporelings, and will destroy, though slowly, a matting of fine weeds such as *Enteromorpha*. These green algae (which often appear first on a cleared area) prevent the settling of barnacles, and may provide protection for the fucoids to grow until they are relatively immune from the attack of limpets. The established plants seem to withstand the depredations of the limpets for some time, and Jones (1948) held that the regression of a belt of fucoids is slow, for the mollusc does not make a determined attack on it, but browses along the edge and eats the alga when it comes against it. However, he did not encounter anything approaching the population density described by Fischer-Piette in the immediate proximity of belts of fucoids.

The population of *Patella vulgata* on the shore is apparently recruited from spat settling with maximal abundance on rocks near LWNT (Jones, 1948), and in pools and moist crevices at higher levels (Orton, 1929b). The planktonic larva settles when it is not more than 0·2 mm long (Smith, 1935). The mortality of such minute forms is likely to be higher on bare rock which dries as the tide ebbs than on rock covered with *Balanus* and, more especially, with scattered plants of *Fucus*, which remain comparatively moist. Jones (1948) found the highest density of settlement in shallow pools, where it may reach a number of 150–250/sq m, and from the pools the spat moves out, at a size of 3 mm or more, to populate surrounding areas. These observations are contrary to those of Hatton (1938) who held that the newly settled spat will not remain in pools, and described a denser settling on exposed surfaces than on sheltered ones. From experiments he deduced that the alternation of immersion and exposure seems to be necessary for the very young individuals. The rate of growth of the young limpet varies considerably. Russell (1909) estimated that limpets in certain established populations in Scotland attain a length of about 29 mm in the first year, during which time they reach sexual maturity, and probable sizes at the end of the second and subsequent years are 38 mm, 44 mm, 48 mm, 53 mm. Shells over 50 mm may be considered more than 5 years old. This growth rate is slow as compared with that of the first limpets which settled on concrete piles of a new wharf at Plymouth during very favourable weather (Orton, 1928b). They measured 26–35 mm in length at the end of the first year and 53 mm at the end of the second; this second measurement approaches that given by Fischer-Piette for the largest individuals at Dinard. He found that longevity is greatest where growth is slowest and *vice versa*: limpets living in the most normal habitat, on rock with cirripedes, though not under the influence of strong currents, lived up to 15 years, and those under *Fucus* only about 3 years (1941a).

The shells of limpets which live at a high level on the shore are, at the adult stage, higher than those of individuals near low water level or in rock pools (Russell, 1907). Russell suggested that the difference is due to exposure. Orton (1929b; 1932) correlated these differences with differences in the degree of exposure to desiccation. The limpets near low water remain fairly damp during the short time they are left by the tide, whereas those at high water are uncovered for the greater part of the day and their surroundings will dry up seriously, especially on a south-facing slope, unless the rock is covered by weed. Orton suggested that the tall spire with a relatively narrow base is produced by the limpet which holds close to the rock to prevent the desiccation of its tissues: the continued downpull of the muscles during the hours of exposure pulls in the mantle skirt which is responsible for new growth at the margin of the shell. Consequently a smaller peripheral increment of growth will be made by these individuals than by others living lower on the shore, or in rock pools, in which the shell muscles are relaxed. Some limpets living at high levels show a more gradual steepening of the shell than others, and this may indicate that they started life lower on the shore and ascended to the higher and more exposed levels as the thickening shell made it possible (Moore,

1934). Very occasionally a shell is encircled by a ledge at a certain distance from the apex (fig. 267A), which is due to an abrupt alteration in the angle of growth and indicates a sudden change from a dry to a damp habitat (Moore, 1934). Flat shells are comparatively thin, but very tall ones are thick especially in the region of the apex where they may attain a thickness of about 1 cm. This thickening gives protection against exposure.

In the Pacific our common limpet, *Patella*, is not represented and its position on the shore is occupied by species of the related genus *Acmaea*. These limpets occur in great numbers in a variety of situations, approaching the size of *Patella* and clinging to the rock with no less tenacity. They are less specialized in structure in that they retain a single bipectinate gill. *Acmaea scutum* and *A. cassis* (=*pelta*) occur throughout the intertidal range on the Oregon coast (Shotwell, 1950) and, contrary to *Patella*, the larger individuals by volume are more abundant on the lower parts of the shore, and no relationship between height of shell and position on the shore can be established. Shotwell, using the findings of Abé (1931), suggested that the smaller limpets have a relatively greater mantle cavity, and therefore retain a larger amount of water when uncovered by the tide and that this protection against desiccation enables them to survive high on the beach. Another species, *A. limatula*, also with a wide vertical distribution along the coast of Southern California has no correlated difference in size. However, individuals at higher levels have thicker and heavier shells and a relatively larger extra-pallial space separating the shell from the body tissues than those on the lower part of the shore. This space is filled with fluid which may act as a reservoir against water loss by evaporation during the hours of exposure (Segal, 1956).

On British shores the genus *Acmaea* is represented by two species; neither is abundant and both occur only from near low water to a depth of a few fathoms. The two differ anatomically in several points though these do not appear to be correlated with differences in habitat. *A. virginea*, the pink-rayed limpet, is to be found on all rocky coasts, while *A. tessulata*, the tortoiseshell limpet, has a more restricted range which is N of the Humber and N Wales, also in N Ireland. This species also occurs on the Atlantic Coast of America and ranges from the Arctic Seas to Long Island Sound, New York. It is the larger and may attain more than an inch in length, though this is rare. Both feed on diatoms and encrusting algal growth, and spend long periods on the same position on the rock, leaving it only for feeding excursions. They move slowly, Willcox (1905a) recording a maximal speed of 3 in/min for *A. tessulata*. She also stated that in autumn it retires below the low water mark. Lilly *et al.* (1953) have shown that *A. virginea*, whilst not much affected by current strength, has a preference for the tops of boulders, probably to avoid silt.

The blue-rayed limpet, *Patina pellucida*, sometimes known as peacock's feathers, is associated with species of *Laminaria* and other brown weeds near low water; the younger stages may also be found on rocks and stones favouring situations where the movement of the water is neither too great nor too little (Ebling *et al.*, 1948). It is much smaller in size than the common limpet and the approximately conical shell, which is horn coloured or brown, has conspicuous blue rays radiating backwards from the summit; in certain lights these are an iridescent green. There are two ecotypes of the species each with characteristics of habitat and structure, the latter affecting mainly the shell (figs. 30, 264). One variety, *pellucida*, which lives on the fronds of *Laminaria* has a smooth, elongated oval and low shell, with the summit placed near the anterior end. It is normally devoid of either epiphytic or epizoic growth, so that the rays, 2–8 in number, are not concealed. The shell is translucent and the soft underlying tissues of the body are pigmented and visible by transparency. The second variety, *laevis*, lives in caves in the holdfasts of *Laminaria* and, in contrast, has a rough and usually high shell which is approximately circular in outline with a central summit, though the proportions are more variable than in the variety *pellucida*. The shell is pale brown or greenish brown in colour and opaque, with 2–46 blue rays, and there are also red-brown rays which alternate with them; the whole surface, however, may be concealed with growths of various kinds. The soft tissues of the body of this variety are not pigmented. For many years these two ecotypes were considered to be different species, but a study of the life history proved otherwise (Graham & Fretter, 1947). The limpets breed maximally in winter and spring, and numbers of planktonic larvae are settling in May as spat about 2 mm long; they are all alike with the characteristics of *pellucida*. These characters persist into the adult stage in all individuals except those which migrate into the holdfasts of

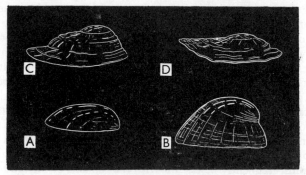

FIG. 264.—*Patina pellucida:* profiles of 4 types of shell, × about 3. A, young *pellucida* from frond of *Laminaria*; B, old *pellucida* from frond of *Laminaria*; C, D, 2 shapes of *laevis* from *Laminaria* holdfast.

*Laminaria.* The limpets on the fronds feed on the substance of the weed or on diatoms and similar minute material which settles there. As they grow they retain the thin shell characteristic of the newly metamorphosed animal. Because of exposure to light the soft tissues become pigmented and with exposure to wave action the shell develops into a rather low structure which reduces the risk of it being swept away. *Patina* which are carried by water currents or migrate into the space inside the holdfast of *Laminaria* excavate caves directly under the stipe or sometimes on the outside of the lowest part of the stipe. They grow a thick stony, calcareous shell which fits into the more limited space available and is high because it is sheltered from the waves. The prominent red lines which develop may be due to the difference in diet. The number of limpets which ultimately end in the holdfasts is greater than the number which fell there by chance as spat and those that migrate to this habitat show an abrupt change in shell structure which marks the time of their migration. The oldest part of the shell has the proportions, colouring and texture of the thin variety *pellucida*, the more recently formed part the characteristics of the variety *laevis*. So far as the soft parts of the animals are concerned there are only trifling differences between the two. For instance, in both, the general plan of the gut coils is the same though their exact disposition varies so as to give in the one a lay-out elongated in one direction and in the other in a direction at right angles to that.

The radula has apparently the same arrangement in both thick- and thin-shelled varieties and bears a close similarity to that of *Patella* but there is a greater degree of wear in those animals in the holdfast. They feed on the tissues of the stipe which they undercut so that their diet is mainly undiluted *Laminaria*.

The young which settle as spat in May grow to a length of about 5 mm in the following autumn and about 10 mm after a year of sedentary life, becoming sexually mature at 5 mm length. The majority die after a settled life of 12 months and nearly all those that live longer belong to the variety *laevis*, and have the more sheltered life. These figures concerning length of life are comparable with those for *Patella vulgata* (Fischer-Piette, 1948) growing at a maximal rate, e.g. under *Fucus*.

The movements of the blue-rayed limpet on the fronds of *Laminaria* are associated with the life cycle of the weed. *Laminaria digitata* has a long fruiting season, with maxima in spring and autumn. After the autumn fruiting the distal half of the frond gradually disintegrates and breaks away, and a certain amount of breakdown occurs after the spring fruiting. During the autumn there is a movement of limpets down the frond giving a concentration on its basal half. The migration takes place about the time when the animals are becoming sexually mature and is of very great importance as a means of securing a base on which they may survive the winter. The stimulus for migration may be chemical changes in the plant tissues, for these are eaten by the limpet. In spring it seems that a certain amount of the spat-fall will be cast away with the disintegrating frond, though a much greater amount will be lost from the settlement on rocks and other unsuitable substrata where prolonged life is not possible. *Laminaria cloustoni* fruits during winter and the old growth is carried up on the new frond which grows at its base until the spring, when it is cast off as 'Mayweed'. The limpets migrate down the frond in late autumn but movement seems to stop when the animals reach the basal part of the old frond. Limpets must frequently be cast off with the remains of the old frond though this will not happen until their breeding period is over and they are then probably exhausted and moribund.

The mesogastropods which have adopted a limpet-like form are members of the Calyptraeacea—*Capulus*, *Calyptraea* and *Crepidula*. They have a cap- or slipper-shaped shell and only in the adult stage of *Calyptraea* is there no suggestion of a dextral coil. In *Capulus* (fig. 24) the shell is not unlike a jester's cap in shape and internally can be seen the scar of attachment of the horseshoe-shaped shell muscle. In the other two genera this muscle is attached to a shelf-like projection, which in the low conical shell of *Calyptraea* projects obliquely across the posterior wall, near the apex, and in *Crepidula* forms a transverse partition (sl, fig. 39A) across the posterior half of the base, set only a short distance in from the edge. Thus when the shell of *Crepidula* is turned over it has the appearance of a rounded slipper with the shelf forming the toe-cap. These 2 genera of limpets have complete or effective loss of movement. They are found in comparatively clear water or in silty habitats, though since they are fixed to stones, rock or shells, they live above the bottom deposits. They filter the sea water for their food and, as in lamellibranchs, the necessity for providing feeding currents and extensive food-collecting surfaces has been met by a modification of the gill. The mantle cavity is long and deep and with a breadth anteriorly corresponding to that of the shell, and the monopectinate gill with elongated filaments hangs diagonally from its roof and is many times longer than that of the more typical snail (fig. 58). It maintains the strong flow of water which traverses the cavity from left to right. The radula is no longer used for rasping as in the diotocardian limpets. It draws into the gut the mucous masses laden with the particles which have been collected without selection save for size (p. 98). These limpets lay egg capsules which are incubated by the female (p. 404). They are retained beneath the anterior part of the shell, either held by the propodium or fixed to the substratum, and so lie in the course of the current of water maintained by the ctenidium. Observations in Essex (Chipperfield, 1952) suggest that these limpets usually spawn twice a year, some time between April and October, and that there may be a period of concerted spawning at, or immediately after, neap tides.

The protandrous hermaphrodite *Calyptraea chinensis* is dredged on stony ground in shallow water around the SW coast, and in the sheltered and perhaps silty lower reaches of rivers. It occurs with less frequency intertidally, where it may be collected from the

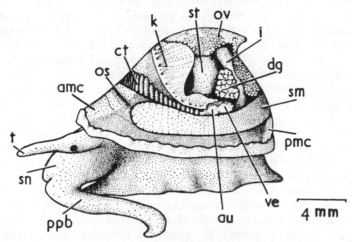

FIG. 265.—*Capulus ungaricus:* animal removed from shell, from the left.
amc, anterior part of mantle cavity; au, auricle; ct, ctenidium seen through mantle skirt; dg, digestive gland; i, intestine; k, kidney; os, osphradium; ov, ovary; ppb, proboscis; pmc, posterior mantle cavity; sm, shell muscle; sn, snout; st, stomach; t, tentacle; ve, ventricle.

undersides of stones or shells. It grips these objects with the broad sucker-like foot and remains in the same position for long periods of time, though it will move about over limited distances, especially during the breeding season when pairs come together. At Plymouth copulation occurs all the year, chiefly October to April, and the females deposit egg capsules between April and September (Wyatt, 1957). The habits of *Crepidula* are better known, for this genus has the peculiar habit of living in chains of up to a dozen or more, each clinging to the shell of the one beneath, and the sex and age of the individuals vary with their position in the chain (fig. 197). The sexual biology of the species is discussed on p. 374. Only males, the last to settle, may leave the chain and move elsewhere. In older individuals the foot is used only to keep the limpet fixed and loses its power of creeping so that a chain once dislodged will be cast about by the sea. *Crepidula fornicata* was introduced to the British Isles from the Atlantic coast of America and the earliest record of its occurrence is at Liverpool in 1872 (McMillan, 1938-39) where it may have been introduced with American clams, *Venus mercenaria*, which were laid down in the neighbourhood. More specimens were brought to the same locality with American oysters about 1880. *Crepidula* and the oyster compete in the same habitat and the shell of living oysters is frequently selected by young slipper limpets as a surface for attachment; indeed, the limpet thrives and breeds most effectively on grounds which produce oysters of the finest quality, though it is more resistant to extreme cold and low salinities. Consequently its rapid spread along the coasts of Britain has been a matter both of general zoological interest and of practical concern to those whose oyster beds are threatened. Consignments of American oysters to the Essex coast at Brightlingsea in 1890 introduced the limpet to these areas, where now it forms masses inches deep over the bottom of sheltered creeks in which oysters were once abundant. The combined strengths of the feeding current set up by thousands of individuals on the shore and the accumulation of faeces and pseudofaeces cause the deposition of mud on the oyster beds so that oyster spat will not settle. To reclaim grounds thus lost to cultivation necessitates the removal of up to 20 tons of *Crepidula* per acre, or even more (Cole & Hancock, 1956). Once such ground is cleared of the largest colonies it is not less than 10 years before a climax density is again reached. The species has died out in the Liverpool area, but from Essex it has spread N to the Scottish border and along the S coast as far as Land's End (Cole, 1952). It has also been found in Milford Haven, Pembrokeshire (Cole & Baird, 1953). The rate of spread along the Cornish coast is comparatively slow: perhaps conditions are not so favourable for it there. However, the dread that it might become common can be deduced from the fact that in the late forties when it first appeared in the Helford River five shillings was paid for each *Crepidula* collected, though later the rate was reduced to a penny (Cole & Hancock, 1956). Between the years 1949 and 1953 the number of limpets taken on the Helford River oyster grounds increased about eighty-fold. The spread of *Crepidula* from place to place is speeded by its rapid rate of increase, for under favourable conditions three broods of larvae are produced each year, and especially by its easy transport on vessels, floating wreckage and seaweed: it is supposed that in this way it crossed the North Sea about 20 years ago and subsequently spread along the shores of Holland, Germany and Denmark. In 1949 a small number was found in two places on the French coast which may have been conveyed there with installations for the Normandy invasion.

Occasionally fixed solitary female limpets are found, with no indication that they have ever formed the lower member of a chain, and sometimes these individuals are guarding embryos. Orton (1950a) suggested that they may be self-fertilizing and that sperm retained from the male phase is carried over to the female phase. If this does occur it will be of extreme importance in the distribution of the species.

*Capulus ungaricus* (figs. 265, 60) has limited powers of movement and is often found attached to the shells of lamellibranchs which are dredged from comparatively shallow water. It also occurs on gravel ground attached to stones, rock or valves of shells, and very occasionally frequents the lower parts of the littoral zone. In this limpet the lower lip is prolonged to form a proboscis (ppb) which has a dorsal groove leading posteriorly to the mouth. The proboscis rests on the flat upper surface of the anterior prolongation of the foot, and food particles from the mantle cavity are led there and then licked up by the proboscis and conveyed to the mouth. The proboscis is capable of considerable extension and individuals which live on shells of living lamellibranchs may use it to reach the food in the food grooves of the gill lamellae, or on the recurrent ciliated path along the edge of the mantle of the host. The relationship with lamellibranchs is facultative, for when removed from the shell the limpet will settle elsewhere and collect adequate food by its own ciliary feeding mechanism. *Capulus* has been found associated with *Pecten*, *Chlamys*, *Modiolus*, *Monia* and *Astarte* and probably occurs on other bivalves.

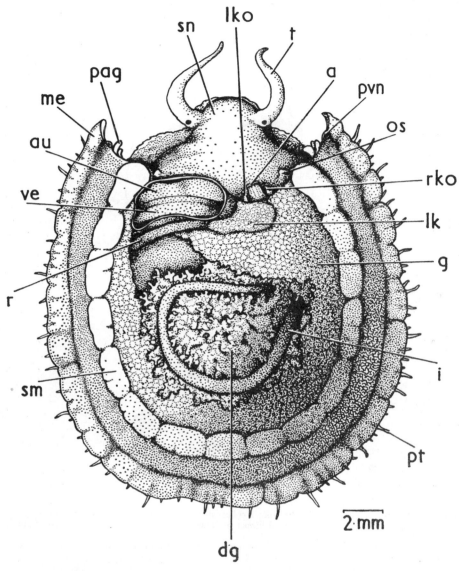

FIG. 266.—*Patella vulgata:* the animal has been removed from the shell and the roof of the nuchal and pericardial cavities cut away to show the contents; dorsal view.

a, anus; au, auricle; dg, digestive gland; g, gonad; i, intestine; lk, left kidney; lko, left kidney opening; me, mantle edge; os, osphradium; pag, pallial gill; pt, pallial tentacle; pvn, pallial vein; r, rectum; rko, right kidney opening (urinogenital); sm, shell muscle; sn, snout; t, tentacle; ve, ventricle.

It has also been collected from the ciliary feeding gastropod *Turritella communis*. It occupies a characteristic position at the edge of a valve of the lamellibranch or the mouth of the gastropod shell, away from the exhalant current. The anterior margin of its shell

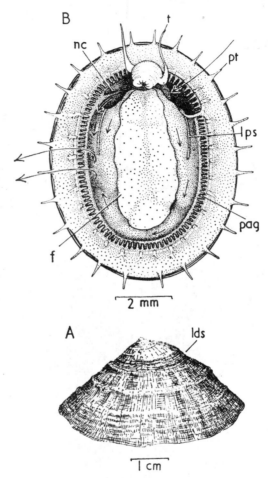

FIG. 267.—*Patella vulgata:* A, shell of animal collected in cave at high water mark, Langland Bay, Glamorgan, to show ledging; B, small limpet in ventral view. Arrows show direction of ciliary and water currents.

f, foot; lds, ledge on shell; lps, lateral pallial streak; nc, nuchal cavity; pag, pallial gill; pt, pallial tentacle; t, tentacle.

overlaps the valve edge which at this point may have a semilunar gap where growth has been delayed owing to the presence of the limpet. There is a possibility that it may rasp this edge with its radula (Sharman, 1956). Limpets in captivity have remained in this settled position up to three months (Sharman, 1956), but still retain the ability to creep elsewhere. The point on the shell where the limpet was sitting is marked by a scar, which may be just a cleaner patch, or a circular area within which the sculpture has gone. More than one individual may be attached to a shell or stone, and sometimes the limpets are associated in pairs, a smaller one resting on a larger. The smaller individual is orientated in the same direction as the larger, and is usually about midway between the apex and the anterior edge. *Capulus* is a protandrous hermaphrodite (p. 377) and this associa-

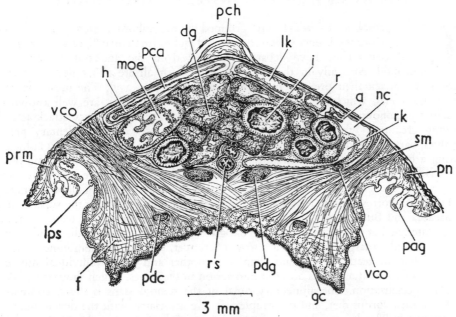

FIG. 268.—*Patella vulgata:* transverse section of young animal.
      a, anus; dg, digestive gland; f, foot; gc, gland cells of sole gland; h, heart; i, intestine; lk, left kidney; lps, lateral pallial streak; moe, mid-oesophagus; nc, nuchal cavity; pag, pallial gill; pca, pericardial cavity; pch, protoconch; pdc, pedal ganglion cord; pdg, pedal ganglion; pn, pallial nerve; prm, retractor muscle of mantle edge; r, rectum; rk, right kidney; rs, radular sac in radular sinus; sm, shell muscle; vco, visceral connective.

tion may occur only during the breeding season. There is no evidence that solitary individuals are self-fertilizing.
      Sometimes *Crepidula* settles on the edge of a scallop shell, and although it has no proboscis to tap the food collected by the bivalve it may benefit from the feeding current. This trend towards the establishment of an association with other animals is followed further by *Thyca*, a capulid of warmer seas, which is completely dependent on echinoderms. It is attached throughout life to its host and, by means of a long proboscis, penetrates the tissues and sucks the coelomic fluid (Koehler & Vaney, 1912).

# CHAPTER 20

## THE ROCKY SHORE: WHELKS AND TINGLES

**T**HOSE prosobranchs which are grouped in the suborder Stenoglossa did not appear before the Upper Cretaceous period and more than 40% of known species are Recent. They have departed furthest from the ancestral, rock-clinging gastropod, especially in their feeding habits, for all are either flesh or carrion feeders and attack their prey by means of a proboscis (fig. 277). The most advanced forms, the cones, which are not represented in the British fauna, are well known for inflicting poisonous wounds by which they immobilize their prey. They attack actively moving creatures, whereas the more primitive carnivores choose sedentary prey—bivalves, barnacles and tube worms—and may get at the flesh by the laborious fashion of boring a hole in the shell to make an entrance for the proboscis. As the name of the suborder indicates, the radula is no longer a broad ribbon with a large number of teeth in each row. Indeed it shows the greatest reduction in tooth number of all prosobranchs, and there is a corresponding reduction in the size of the buccal mass. In the superfamilies Muricacea and Buccinacea (fig. 105E) each radular row has typically 3 teeth, a median and 2 laterals, but in the majority of Toxoglossa (fig. 105F) both median and laterals are absent and 2 marginals represent a row. Moreover, the radular membrane is usually lost, so that the teeth are separate from one another and under individual muscular control; only one at a time is brought into action in the cones, which show the peak of radular specialization. The alimentary canal of the stenoglossans is short, compatible with the carnivorous diet, and its complexities are associated with the development of the proboscis. This has involved the forward migration of the oesophagus through the nerve ring, which comes to occupy a more posterior position than in other prosobranchs, and the salivary ducts no longer pass through it. The glandular tissue, which has been stripped from the mid-oesophagus so that it is a simple tube, forms the gland of Leiblein in the Rachiglossa and perhaps the poison gland of toxoglossans. It is essentially such specializations of the gut that separate these higher prosobranchs from the mesogastropods (figs. 113, 116); the rest of their anatomy calls for little comment. The plan of the reproductive ducts in species which have been investigated resembles that of *Littorina*, though the histology, especially in the female, is more elaborate. This elaboration (fig. 171) is associated with the complexity of the wall of the egg capsules which the duct secretes, and with the development of a special sperm-absorbing gland (ig) from part of the receptaculum seminis (rcs).

The Stenoglossa are almost all marine and avoid brackish water, though *Nucella*, *Buccinum*, *Urosalpinx* and *Nassarius reticulatus* can tolerate a moderate amount. The shell, which is always external, is siphonate and the pallial siphon (in some species very long) can be used as a distance receptor. Working in conjunction with the osphradium (os, fig. 276) it may test the environment into which the animal moves, and can be seen examining the substratum and possible food at some distance from the body. By means of the siphon a flow of clean water is passed through the mantle cavity while the mollusc is feeding on putrefying flesh or is all but buried in mud or sand.

The most primitive stenoglossans, the muricid whelks, are small and on the whole slow-moving. They are predatory and bore the shells of other molluscs to get at their flesh, and all have an accessory boring organ (= pedal sucker of Fretter (1946a) and accessory proboscis of Carriker (1943)) which helps in boring (Carriker, 1959; and see p. 244). All, except species of *Trophon*, are intertidal, so that their habits are, on the whole, well known, more especially as some species ravage young oysters and have been the concern of oyster farmers for many years. Even before this muricids were familiar shells, for the Tyrian purple of the ancients (secretion from the hypobranchial gland) was obtained from certain species of *Murex* and *Thais*. These species are believed to be *Murex brandaris*, *M. trunculus* and *Thais haemastoma*—none of them British—

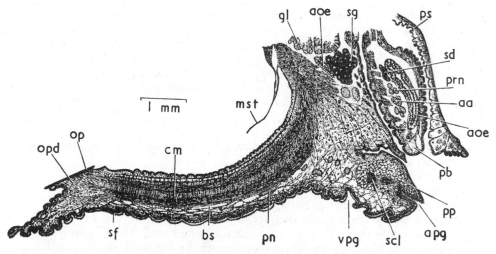

Fig. 269.—*Nassarius reticulatus:* sagittal section of head and foot of a young female.

aa, anterior aorta in proboscis; aoe, anterior oesophagus cut twice, once in proboscis, once in body; apg, opening of duct of anterior pedal gland; bs, blood space in foot; cm, columellar muscle, which is highly organized in this genus; gl, gland of Leiblein; mst, posterior part of mantle skirt; op, operculum; opd, operculigerous disc; pb, proboscis; pn, pedal nerve; pp, propodium; prn, proboscis nerve; ps, proboscis sheath; scl, sagittal canal of anterior pedal gland; sd, salivary duct; sf, sole of foot; sg, salivary gland; vpg, opening of ventral pedal gland.

though British species of related genera secrete the fluid to some extent. There is no free larval stage in the life history so that dispersal is essentially limited to the snail's ability to crawl about.

*Nucella lapillus* (fig. 35) is the common carnivorous prosobranch of most rocky shores, occurring in large numbers within the balanoid zone. The upper limit of the species at most places is between EHWN and MHWN, but it may be found in sheltered crevices up to MHWS. It is not tolerant of heavy surf unless shelter is available and is not normally found under a thick covering of weed, perhaps because of the lack of the barnacles which it eats, though it may seek shelter under weed which is near its feeding grounds. The lower level of abundance lies between MLWN and MLWS where food and sheltered crevices are available, and it occurs in the sublittoral zone down to a depth of 10 fathoms (Moore, 1936). The whelks are frequently found clustering in rock crevices in the intertidal area either for shelter or for breeding. Fischer-Piette (1935a) suggested that they are driven to shelter by extreme cold or the risk of drying up, and it is known that in the Gullmar Fjord, Sweden, they go below low water for the winter, presumably to avoid the ice (Gislén, 1930). The northern limit of distribution of the species is near the 0°C winter isotherm of oceanic water (Moore, 1936) which suggests the presence of ice as a limiting factor. The southern limit is close along the 19°C summer isotherm of oceanic water, though the intertidal temperatures would be considerably higher; the upper lethal temperature has been estimated as about 35°C (Gowanloch, 1927). Butler (1954) stated that in the related American species *Thais f. floridana* spawning is initiated at a water temperature of 20°C and ceases at temperatures exceeding 30°C.

There is some doubt as to the tolerance of low salinities, for whereas Agersborg (1929) recorded *N. lapillus* in freshwater pools along the edge of high water in N Norway and suggested that there it remains out of sea water most of the time, Pelseneer (1935, p. 323) stated that it can survive 9·5 days in freshwater, and Fischer (1931) found that it dies out only at the low salinity of 10‰ in the Rance, though the eggs are killed at low salinities tolerated by the adults. Other records suggest far less tolerance. It does not penetrate beyond the extreme mouths of the Tamar and Yealm estuaries at Plymouth (Moore, 1938b), nor beyond the mouth of the Tees, which is highly polluted (Alexander, Southgate & Bassindale, 1935): earlier records (Fischer, 1928) show it in the estuary of the Rance only down to a salinity of 22·8‰, and around the island of Tromö, S Norway (Ökland, 1933), it does not occur when the summer salinities fall below 20–25‰ even though *Mytilus* and *Balanus* are in abundance. It seems that its distribution must be regulated by a number of factors and not by salinity alone.

The diet which the adult seems to prefer is barnacles, *Balanus balanoides* or *Chthamalus stellatus*, and it eats various kinds of molluscs, the favourite being *Mytilus edulis*. The whelks are commonly found on mussel beds, sometimes trapped in byssus threads which are anchored around them whilst they are inactive during an interval between periods of feeding, or whilst the shell of another mussel is being bored. This process is slow and may take 2 days. Although the whelk characteristically bores the shells of molluscs to get at the soft parts (p. 245), it opens barnacles by forcing the valves apart and Dubois (1909) claimed that hypobranchial secretion anaesthetizes the prey (p. 121). Fischer-Piette (1935a) has shown that the rate of destruction by the dog whelk may be sufficient to change the balance of life on a stretch of shore. He studied an area covered by barnacles with *Nucella* feeding on them, and on which *Mytilus* settled as the barnacles were cleared. When all available barnacles had been destroyed the prosobranch started on the mussels, though its efforts to eat them seemed clumsy at first, and empty shells were sometimes bored from either inside or out. Later, with greater efficiency, the whelk forced the shells of the smaller mussels apart without boring them. So many mussels were killed that barnacles were able to recolonize the rocks and the *Nucella* returned to their original diet, though the barnacles were not attacked until they were about 6 months old and had attained a fair size. The dog whelk may also destroy oyster spat. In the up-river nursery grounds of oysters in Essex giant *Nucella* of about twice the normal height may be collected (Cole, 1956). The young whelks may have a different diet. They emerge from capsules laid in the vicinity of the adults and Colton (1916) suggested that they feed on young *Mytilus* which are presumably near the empty capsules. However, Moore (1938b) held that their feeding grounds are lower on the shore. Here he has found numbers of young *Nucella*—perhaps carried by wave action—living on the underside of stones among the tubicolous polychaete *Spirorbis borealis*. The young whelks which he kept in captivity ate these worms and not small barnacles, although they tended to change to this diet when they had attained a height of about 8–10 mm. Perhaps at this size they normally migrate to the barnacle zone where they are frequent in sheltered crevices. Adults and young may frequently be found, nevertheless, on shores devoid of *Spirorbis* e.g. Rhossili Bay, S Wales; perhaps in these circumstances other worms are eaten since at Rhossili vast colonies of *Sabellaria* occur.

Mature (fig. 35) and immature (fig. 270) shells of *N. lapillus* differ considerably. The shell which is still growing, is characterized by the outer lip being thin and sharp. At the onset of maturity growth of the lip ceases and this region of the shell thickens, sometimes up to 5 mm. The outer lip becomes rounded and develops a series of teeth along its inner edge which restrict the opening. Sometimes another tooth develops on the inner lip. Thickened shells of sexually mature individuals have been recorded as small

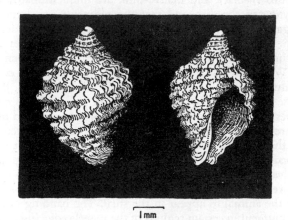

1 mm

FIG. 270.—*Nucella lapillus:* shells of young dog whelks, the right one in apertural view, the left in abapertural view.

as 13 mm high (Moore, 1936) though 45 mm is the size of a large specimen from the shore. However, a thin type as large as 63 mm in height and others approximating to this size have been found in deeper water: it is suggested that in the sublittoral habitat growth is not inhibited at sexual maturity, though an examination of the sex organs of these individuals has not been made. In a study of the growth rate of animals from the littoral zone Moore (1938a) found that in the first year the shells attained 10–15 mm in height, grew another 11 mm in the second year and less in the third when the whelks attained sexual maturity. He found no differences in the rate for the two sexes. The shell of this whelk is initially imbricated (Labbé, 1926) and in the intertidal zone small individuals in their first year are often found with the longitudinal striae forming a flounce-like ornamentation (fig. 270). In larger snails subjected to wave action this characteristic is lost. However, animals in deeper water (which have been regarded as the variety *imbricata*) sometimes retain it in the adult, and Colton (1922) found this type of shell characteristic of sheltered mud flats in Mount Desert Island, Maine.

The colour of the shell of *Nucella* is extremely variable. It may be a uniform white, or yellow which may shade into orange, and some shells are banded with yellow on white or on black or brown. Other shells may be brown shading into black and this is the colour which shows the strongest tendency to banding. Finally shells may be mauve,

18

grading occasionally into pink, and the mauve may be overlaid with bands of black or brown. The breadth of the bands varies from individual to individual but they are constant in position throughout the life of the animal. *Thais lamellosa* fills a similar ecological niche on the Pacific coasts of North American and is even more variable in colour and form than *Nucella*. Colton (1916) stated that in the Mount Desert region the abundance of coloured *Nucella* is greater with increasing wave exposure, and also shows a slight increase in places of extreme shelter. He found more white shells in the *Balanus* zone than in the *Mytilus* zone. However, Colton (1922) concluded that variation in colour and shell sculpture is due to hereditary factors, and that the proportion of any one colour variety found in a single station is determined by natural selection, more light snails being found on light environments than on dark ones. Moore (1936) has held that the colour types brown-black and mauve-pink are unquestionably dependent on the abundance of *Mytilus* in the diet, and that the pigments are derived from the prey. Moreover he suggested that this diet delays sexual maturity and so decreases the proportion of mature shells in the population and consequently increases the shell height at which sexual maturity sets in; it produces a fatter shell, a more open spiral and hence a wider aperture. White shells are associated with a *Balanus*-fed community. Moore transferred individuals with coloured shells to a diet of *Chthamalus*, *Balanus* and *Mytilus* respectively. Those on mussels showed no change in pigmentation either in the brown or the mauve types, whereas the new shell growth which appeared on the barnacle-fed individuals had a reduced pigmentation, though the speed of the reduction varied considerably. When these animals were returned to their normal diet of *Mytilus* the pigmentation reappeared. However, shells from a *Balanus*-fed population showed no pigmentation in their newly formed shell after a period of 6 months on a diet of *Mytilus*, suggesting that it requires long periods of feeding on mussels before sufficient pigment is accumulated in the animal to appear in the shell. The banding of a shell is produced by localization of pigment in certain regions of the mantle edge (fig. 35), and occasionally these bands are very narrow. Moore suggested that in extreme cases the pigment-susceptible areas in the mantle edge may be narrowed to extinction, resulting in an animal which, though feeding on *Mytilus*, has a white shell. He considered the relationship of yellow shells to environmental factors as more doubtful (Moore, 1936), though he found this type most abundant on coasts with a moderate degree of wave exposure and practically absent in extreme shelter and extreme exposure. In some localities the true pigmentation of the shell is masked by boring filamentous algae which give it a greenish brown colour.

Agersborg (1929) basing his conclusions on a study of *Nucella lapillus* in N Norway suggested that variations in the shell of this species, concerning size, thickness, spire and surface texture, were due to an interaction of environmental and genetic factors, and more recently Staiger (1950a, b, 1954, 1955) has followed up this problem. He showed that at Roscoff there exist two races of *N. lapillus*, one with 18 pairs of chromosomes, the other with 13. Because of the chromosome numbers found in other stenoglossan species it seems reasonable to suggest that the race with 13 pairs is an evolutionary novelty which would require a certain degree of isolation to arise. The two races cross and segregation gives animals with all possible numbers of chromosomes from 13-18 pairs. Investigation shows that the 13 race predominates in exposed areas, the 18 race in sheltered habitats and intermediates occur in places with moderate exposure. The thickness and length of the shell are also related to the chromosomal composition of the individual: the thickness is greater in a mixed population than in a pure one (13 or 18 chromosome pairs). Heterogeneity, however, increases the versatility of the population in tolerating a variety of ecological conditions and for this reason it is not possible to explain the successful occupation of a micro-ecological niche in terms of one factor alone. For example, the mean body-size of a heterogeneous population increases with exposure: this is due to a balance between the increased vigour of the mixed stock and its lesser adaptation to exposure and the lesser vigour of the 13-chromosome race coupled with its greater adaptation to exposure. No correlation between chromosome number and colour of shell has yet been made.

Some egg capsules of *Nucella* (fig. 242A) are mauve or brownish in colour instead of the usual yellow, and Moore (1936) also attributed this colouring to the pigment derived

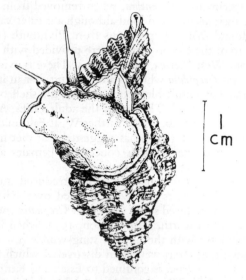

FIG. 271.—*Ocenebra erinacea:* the rough whelk-tingle seen from below as it creeps on a glass plate. The apex of the shell is below and its siphonal canal points upwards. The siphon projects from its tip. The animal is a female and on the sole of the foot may be seen 2 apertures: the anterior is that of the pit in which the accessory boring organ lies, the posterior is that of the ventral pedal gland.

from a diet of *Mytilus*. However, the pigment may come from secretion of the hypobranchial gland (p. 126) which can easily contaminate the capsules as they are laid, and, in extreme cases, even affect the colour of the yolk. The odour of this same secretion has been claimed to be the cause of sexual aggregation (p. 121).

*Ocenebra erinacea*, the European sting winkle (fig. 271), may be found with *Nucella* near low water on some rocky shores. It is, however, predominantly a sublittoral form occurring down to about 50 fathoms, and its invasion of the littoral zone is dependent upon temperature: in some parts of the SW, where recently its numbers have increased, it may be found at mid-tide in sheltered crannies especially in the warmer months, though not in exposed places like *Nucella*. It is now distributed along the W and SW coasts and is scarce in the SE where, previously, it occurred in greater abundance. During the unusually cold winter of 1928–29 *Ocenebra* suffered virtual extinction in the region of the River Blackwater, Essex, whereas the closely related American oyster drill *Urosalpinx* increased in abundance (Orton & Lewis, 1931). *Ocenebra* is now reappearing in the area

(Mistakidis & Hancock, 1955). The food selected is commonly lamellibranchs, *Tapes*, *Cardium*, *Venus*, which are associated with more sheltered habitats than the prey of the dog whelk, for in its sublittoral habitats *Ocenebra* frequents silty grounds with rock, stones and perhaps clinker. On the shore the animal may be found eating barnacles, small tubicolous worms, mussels and anomiid bivalves and is frequently associated with oyster beds, especially when other food is less abundant. In the Helford Estuary (Cornwall) it is a significant predator on the beds of cultivated oysters and here the American drill *Urosalpinx*, a more destructive oyster pest which is common on the Essex coast, does not occur. Both eat oyster spat as well as boring the adults, and in the months of May and June which are their breeding time, they are hand picked from the oyster beds. It would appear that specimens of *Ocenebra*, when removed from their natural habitat, retain a preference for their accustomed food although a greater variety may be offered. Thus Orton (1929a) found that 264 specimens from Plymouth (where no oysters are found) attacked only 10 of the oysters which were provided with other food, while 30 smaller individuals from West Mersea, Essex, ate 45. There is evidence that the winkle sometimes attempts to eat *Crepidula* which is a recent intruder in its habitat, though the shells are often perforated at unsuitable points such as the shelf or the edge overlying the mantle and foot (Orton, 1950b). The size of the adult varies. At Plymouth it ranges from less than 20 to 40 mm in length, whilst further W, at Falmouth, there is an increase of about a third of this. Hancock (1957) has suggested that diet may influence the size though probably more than one factor is concerned. Females are larger than males and may be at least twice as numerous on the shore.

Both prosobranch gastropods which have been introduced into this country from America are important oyster pests and were shipped over with oysters. *Urosalpinx cinerea* seems to have been introduced some years after *Crepidula* and was first recognized here in 1928 (Orton & Winckworth, 1928; Orton, 1930) when it was realized that it had been confused previously with the English sting-winkle (for it resembles *Ocenebra* in size, shape and habits); specimens were then discovered which had been collected in 1920. So far as is known, *Urosalpinx* is confined to Essex and Kent, where it has shown itself to be a danger to the shell-fish industry. Indeed, less than 10 years after it was first recognized there its numbers had so increased that one shilling per 1,000 drills was paid to dredgermen on the River Roach, Essex (Cole, 1942). In 1936–37 the sum paid out amounted to £9 5s., representing a total of 185,000 drills. In the River Crouch, Essex, the drill is now present on grounds up to 14 miles from the mouth and concentrations of up to 10,000 per acre have been recorded. Here its density has increased considerably during the past 15 years (Mistakidis, 1951; Hancock, 1959). It feeds in the same way as *Ocenebra* by drilling an entrance through the shells of other molluscs to reach the flesh, which is devoured. It chooses a variety of hosts including *Ostrea edulis* and its spat, *Mytilus edulis*, *Cardium*, *Paphia*, *Crepidula*; it also relishes barnacles, and frequently cannibalism has been observed. Observations on the Essex oyster beds show that the drills feed preferentially on oyster spat, and each destroys about 40 spat during the feeding season. Oysters larger than spat are not seriously damaged when spat is available.

Unlike *Crepidula*, this pest has not spread rapidly from the two centres where it was introduced, which are believed to be Brightlingsea and West Mersea, Essex (Cole, 1942), and there are no records of it in the oyster beds of Holland, Belgium and France (Carriker, 1955). This may be due to the fact that *Urosalpinx* lacks a free-swimming larval stage and its distribution depends entirely on its slow rate of creeping and on possible transportation by human or other agencies. Moreover it lacks the gripping power which in the limpet has accounted for successful transference over long distances on floating wood and weed. In the United States of America the drill is present from Maine to Florida on the E coast and in Washington and California on the W, and the steady decline in oyster production from 231 million pounds in 1910 to 77 million pounds in 1950 has been attributed to it (Glancy, 1953). It reaches a greater size in England than in its natural habitat on the Atlantic Coast of the States and appears to be more prolific on the British oyster beds (Cole, 1942).

The occurrence of *Urosalpinx* in the intertidal region of the shore in SE England varies with the season. Although an area between LWST and 12 m or more below is perhaps the most frequented zone, large numbers of the mollusc migrate on shore during spring and early summer, travelling over fairly firm mud where there are shells, living mussels, *Littorina* and oysters, and avoiding soft ground devoid of hard objects. Many migrate to near mid-tide level. A single individual can move 2 m a day, and although there may be a certain amount of horizontal migration the main one is vertical (Hancock, 1959) and is associated with spawning. Some egg capsules are deposited on the shore, fixed to stones, oysters and other objects, but most are deposited just below LWST. Little food is taken while the drills breed in May and June, but as the peak of the spawning period passes feeding begins and continues until the end of October. Feeding is also dependent on temperature: Hanks (1957) has shown that it does not occur below 5°C, is intermittent below 10°, rises steadily to a maximum at 25° and ceases again at 30°.

The young begin to emerge from the capsules early in July after an incubation period of about 8 weeks. Since each female may deposit 25 capsules in a single laying (Cole, 1942) and about a dozen young emerge from each, there is a considerable annual increase in numbers. Moreover, both males and females may live to an age of 13–14 years. The young drills attack oyster spat which has recently settled and do considerable damage. In autumn there is a reverse migration of both young and old followed by winter hibernation beneath the surface of the mud. Hibernation generally occurs when the temperature falls below 7°C and the drills remain quiescent until the temperature again reaches 9°–10°C when the snails become active and feeding begins, together with the spawning migration (Hancock, 1959).

Several methods have been tried to control the pest: the most successful in the United States is claimed to be the trapping of the drills during the breeding season. A wire bag about 12 × 15 in in size is partly filled with small bait oysters and shell to give added weight and a holdfast for the victims. The bags are attached to lines about 8 ft apart on ground infested with drills and at regular intervals of time the mollusc and its spawn are cleared away and the bait renewed. In Britain this method appears to have little success and a more effective control has been repeated dredging for adults and spawn during the spring and summer, and also hand picking them from the shore (Cole, 1956), though a cheaper and simpler method is the use of curved roofing tiles which have been exposed on the shore over a winter to remove newness, and are then placed in rows near LWST. The drills congregate on the curved under-surface and are destroyed about once a fortnight (Hancock, 1959).

The largest of the British prosobranch gastropods are some of the whelks which fall into the family Buccinidae. Occasional specimens of *Neptunea antiqua* attain a shell height of 8 in. Their size and palatable flesh have made this group of molluscs well known, and also the fact that the shell is stout and slow to disintegrate after the whelk is dead. Only one species, *Buccinum undatum* (fig. 272), the common whelk, is found in all parts of the British seas and on every kind of ground from near low water to the greatest depth. Its local abundance has made it in times past an important item of food. In the Whitstable area in the middle of the last century the whelk fishery yielded £12,000 a year, for those days a considerable sum. Important areas for the fishery now lie between Grimsby and Southampton, though this is probably on account of the large markets in SE England. The mollusc was once regarded as a greater delicacy than now. In Roman

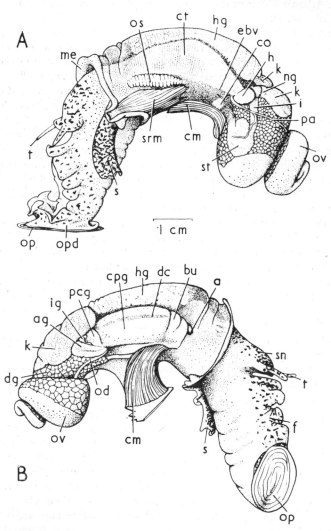

FIG. 272.—*Buccinum undatum*: the animal has been removed from the shell and is seen A, from the left; B, from the right.

a, anus; ag, albumen gland; bu, bursa copulatrix; cm, columellar muscle; co, oesophageal caecum, seen by transparency; cpg, capsule gland; ct, ctenidium; dc, dorsal channel along capsule gland; dg, digestive gland; ebv, efferent branchial vessel; f, foot; h, heart; hg, hypobranchial gland; i, intestine; ig, ingesting gland; k, kidney; me, mantle edge; ng, nephridial gland; od, ovarian duct; op, operculum; opd, operculigerous disc; os, osphradium; ov, ovary; pa, posterior aorta; pcg, posterior lobe of capsule gland; s, siphon; sn, snout; srm, siphonal retractor muscle; st, stomach; t, tentacle.

kitchen middens in this country whelk shells have been found mixed with oyster shells. and Jeffreys (1867) recorded that in 1504 the enthronement feast of the Archbishop of Canterbury, William Wareham, included 8,000 whelks costing 5 shillings per 1,000. *Neptunea antiqua*, the red whelk, is also marketable and may be included in catches with the common whelk. It is a sublittoral form found in shallow waters, but does not occur in S and SW England nor S Wales. Whelks which are marketed from the Northumbrian and Scottish coasts may also include *Colus gracilis* though this is accidental as, for some reason, *Colus* is not used as food. Murray & Hjort (1912) stated that *Neptunea antiqua* and *Colus gracilis* occur in the North Sea everywhere from Denmark to the Scottish coast, sometimes in great numbers, and in one haul from a depth of 96 m 130 *Neptunea* and 375 *Colus* were taken. *Buccinum* is also found here down to 100 m, though never in such abundance. Little is known of other species of *Buccinum*, except for their rather occasional occurrence in dredgings. On the whole they are characteristic of soft substrata, and they can plough through the surface layers of sand or mud and retain a clean current of water through the mantle cavity since the pallial siphon is long and kept clear of the bottom (si, fig. 276). At the breeding period the females seek some hard object on which to deposit the egg capsules. They are hemispherical or semi-ovoid, attached by the broad base and only in *Buccinum undatum* and *Neptunea antiqua* are they heaped on one another to form an agglomerate mass (fig. 216). Those of other whelks are conspicuous owing to their size: a capsule of *Volutopsius norwegicus* measures 3 cm across the base. As far as is known no species has a free larval stage.

*Buccinum* may be left uncovered by the tide and on rocky shores it will then retreat into its shell and behave like other univalves, clinging to the rock until the tide returns. Sometimes on muddy and sandy shores a low spring tide leaves numbers of large whelks exposed. This may be seen where the tidal range is great, as at Oxwich Bay, S Wales, and more dramatically in the Bay of Fundy on the N Atlantic coast of Canada. In these circumstances, instead of withdrawing into the shelter of the shell and sealing it with the operculum, or seeking some nearby stone on which to cling, the whelks continue to creep about, sometimes moving on to drier ground further from the sea. Eventually, as a result of enfeeblement due to desiccation, many lie senseless on the shore, and some are eaten. Gowanloch (1927) concluded that the deep sea population of *Buccinum* forms a reserve from which a small temporary intertidal one is drawn. These molluscs fail to become successful shore-living forms because they lack the protective behaviour which ensures survival. Unlike *Littorina littorea* they show no tendency to migrate to their normal level on the shore when displaced to a position above their usual habitat, and they may die from desiccation within a metre of shelter. There is some evidence that the whelk moves from deeper to shallower water at spawning time, which is winter in most localities, and many females may come to the same place to spawn, forming separate smaller or combining to form larger heaps of eggs.

The common whelk, and probably other members of the Buccinacea, are carnivores with a tendency to scavenging and will attack animals which are moribund, and fresh corpses. It is uncertain whether they eat putrefying flesh. The living animals which are attacked are sedentary or trapped forms. *Buccinum* is known to eat a variety of bivalves and reach the flesh not by the slow boring of the shell, but by taking advantage of its greater size and strength. It will open the shells of living cockles and scallops by settling on or near the upper valve and then, with a sudden quick movement, insert the edge of its own shell between the open valves, preventing their closure. The proboscis is inserted and the soft tissues attacked. Dakin (1912) found that the proboscis first destroyed the adductor muscle of a *Pecten maximus* and so disabled the closing mechanism of the valves. *Mytilus*, *Ostrea* and *Mya* are also eaten; the last is an easy prey since its soft tissues are never totally concealed by the shell. Although the whelk occurs on oyster beds Hancock (1957) found that in the laboratory oysters are only occasionally eaten and cockles are preferred. The maximum feeding rate was recorded in April when 2 cockles a week sufficed: the opening and eating of each may take less than an hour. Although on the shore more food may be required, the actual time spent in feeding must be remarkably little. Unlike *Ocenebra* and *Urosalpinx* the common whelk continues to feed all the winter in the laboratory, provided that the water temperature does not fall below 5°C.

The whelk's habit of eating moribund animals, or those entrapped, and of sensing them from a distance, is better known, and is exploited by the fisherman. Whelk pots, made of withy and twine woven on an iron frame, are baited with freshly dead crabs or fish, and crabs strung in a bunch and sunk in the sublittoral zone will also attract whelks from a considerable radius. The whelk will penetrate the carapace of the crab with its radula. On one occasion (fig. 277) a moribund holothurian was seen to be attacked from the other side of a partition, the proboscis of the whelk being directed through a crevice on to the prey. It then reached a length of 18 cm, just over twice the length of the shell. It is stated that in Denmark the whelk may be a menace to the plaice fisheries (Petersen, 1911) for it attacks fish entangled in nets, bores through the skin and devours the tissues. A dozen or more whelks may be attached to the same fish. The animals occur in such numbers that in one area 3,845½ bushels of *Buccinum* mixed with *Nassarius reticulatus* were trapped between 5 April and 8 November. *Buccinum*, in its turn, is preyed on by fish, and is used as bait in fishing. Jeffreys (1867) found 30 to 40 shells in the stomach of a single cod and occasional ones may be found in the stomach of rays and dogfish.

The empty shells of whelks, as well as those which are inhabited, are favourite homes of other animals. Murray & Hjort (1912) found that every one of the 375 *Colus gracilis* in a haul from the North Sea had the sea anemone *Hormathia digitata* on its shell, and several *Neptunea antiqua*, the larger whelk, had two large actinians of a different species, *Tealia felina* and *Metridium senile*. The anemones are thus carried on to feeding grounds which may provide no holdfast for them. Other anemones, *Calliactis parasitica* and *Adamsia palliata*, live only on shells inhabited by hermit crabs. The older stages of *Eupagurus bernhardus* and *E. prideauxi* leave the shells of trochids, periwinkles and dog whelks, which they inhabit when young, and are dependent on whelk shells when fully grown. The shell then becomes the home of the numerous commensals associated with the pagurids and is protected.

There is considerable variation in the shell of *Buccinum undatum* and *Neptunea antiqua*: Jeffreys (1867) listed 6 varieties of the former each associated with a different type of habitat. They are marked by differences in the size of the whole shell, in the body whorl and the spire, and in the thickness and ribbing. Small forms deprived of decoration, which are found in brackish water, constitute one of the 6, and the unusually large specimens of the Dogger Bank which have thin shells with long spires are another. Besides these variations monstrosities are sometimes found: the shell may be sinistral; the whorls keeled; the spire may be extended to a considerable length and the whorls flattened; the body whorl may be compressed and elongated to give the shape of a *Voluta*; the operculum may be patelliform or there may be two or three.

Perhaps the most agile of all British prosobranchs are the species of *Nassarius*. Two of these, *N. reticulatus* (figs. 273, 35) and *N. incrassatus*, are common and may be collected near low water: the former also lives in brackish water, when the shell grows thicker

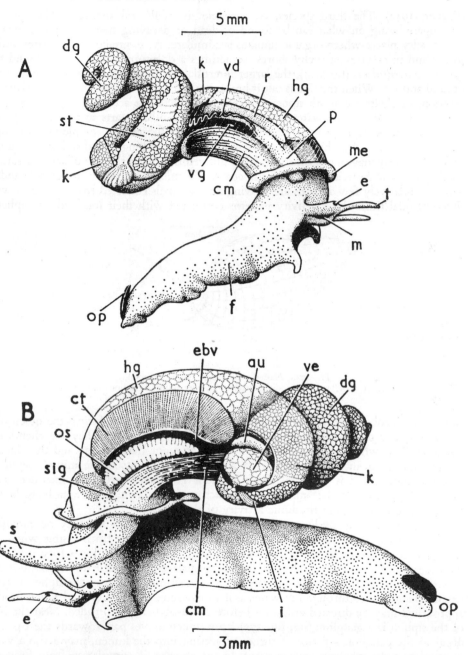

FIG. 273.—*Nassarius reticulatus:* the animal has been removed from the shell and is seen A, from the right; B, from the left.

au, auricle; cm, columellar muscle; ct, ctenidium; dg, digestive gland; e, eye; ebv, efferent branchial vessel; f, foot; hg, hypobranchial gland; i, intestine; k, kidney; m, mouth (opening of proboscis pouch); me, mantle edge; op, operculum; os, osphradium; p, penis within mantle cavity; r, rectum; s, siphon; sig, siphonal ganglion; st, stomach; t, tentacle; vd, vas deferens; ve, ventricle; vg, visceral ganglion.

(Berner, 1942). The third species, *N. pygmaeus*, is sublittoral and rare. They are all scavengers living on what can be found of dead or decaying flesh, and consequently favour silty places where organic remains accumulate. *N. incrassatus* congregates under stones and in crevices of rocky shores; sometimes a dozen or more may be found together. *N. reticulatus* (fig. 274), the larger intertidal form, favours a greater abundance of sand and silt. When the tide is out it buries itself just beneath the surface in a slanting position, or shelters beneath stones and few individuals are active, though some may continue to feed. As the water covers it again the mollusc starts to move and glides with remarkable rapidity over the surface of the soft substratum, or ploughs through the surface layers, often hidden from view except for the long pallial siphon (fig. 274). A study of the behaviour of other species in this genus shows a rhythm of activity caused by the tide. The American species *Nassa obsoleta* has maximal activity at high tide and at low tide relatively few animals are moving about. Snails collected from localities with different tidal times show activity patterns correlated with their local tides (Stephens,

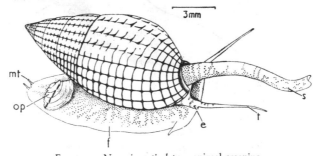

FIG. 274.—*Nassarius reticulatus:* animal creeping.
e, eye; f, foot; mt, metapodial tentacle; op, operculum; s, siphon; t, tentacle.

Sandeen & Webb, 1953). Ohba (1952) has shown that in *Nassarius festivus* the quiescence during low tide may be broken by the presence of food, to which they are chemically attracted. This whelk is, as a rule, more active at night than by day and this diurnal rhythm appears to mask the tidal activity at night. The activity of the animals begins to increase at dusk and is maximal about an hour later (Ohba, 1954); it then decreases, though about 40% of the animals remain active until dawn. Light appears to be the factor which regulates the rhythmic activity of this species.

The siphon is relatively longer than that of other Stenoglossa and may be extended to a length exceeding that of the shell; sometimes only the tip is visible when the animal is scavenging deeper in the mud or sand. The mollusc moves forwards with the tube directed backwards, clearing the dorsal surface of the shell, and through it can be seen to pass the strong inhalant water flow. Sometimes, however, the siphon is fully extended and waved through the water as if to examine the vicinity, and when food is approached may be directed around it before the proboscis is protruded. Near the base of the siphon is a ganglion (sig, fig. 275) from which nerves pass towards the tip, and distal to the ganglion a flange of tissue, projecting into the lumen, may act as a valve in regulating the inhalant water current. In the absence of stimulation from food the animals are not affected by water currents, but when stimulated they exhibit a positive rheotaxy and move upstream to the food, which is found over the last 21 cms by a phobic mechanism (Henschel, 1932). They react positively to a great variety of chemical substances e.g. 1% glucose, 0·5% sucrose, 0·1–1·0% starch, 0·1% glycocol, 0·025% glycogen, and to skatol; a mixture of these reinforces the stimulating effect.

The foot of *Nassarius* is large, broad in front and with angulated corners which are recurved, deeply grooved and richly innervated; it narrows posteriorly and has a median notch, on either side of which is a short metapodial tentacle. It is exceedingly mobile not only in swift gliding movements over rock and as a ploughshare through the sand, but also in manipulating fragments of food, pushing them towards the surface and often wrapping itself around whatever is eaten. The mouth (fig. 133) is at the end of the long eversible introvert which can be extended to a length over half as long again as the shell. The end of the proboscis has a sucker action so that the whelk can cling to the food while the radula rasps it, and, in this way, food at some distance may be eaten. Both *N. incrassatus* and *N. reticulatus* are found in lobster pots and whelk pots, attracted by the carrion there, for scent undoubtedly plays a great part in directing them to food. A dead fish or bivalve which they relish will bring whelks from some distance, as will fish caught in nets. They differ from *Buccinum* in devouring putrefying flesh with avidity. According to Starmuhlner (1956) *N. incrassatus* eats mainly decaying sponges.

*Nassarius reticulatus* is preyed upon by starfish, though sometimes it does not fall an easy catch, for it responds to their attack with a quick evading reaction. If the posterior end of the foot is touched there is a rapid response. The shell is moved forwards to the right or left and twisted on the head-foot so that the apex is directed anteriorly and the mouth faces upwards. Then, without pause and with equal speed, the shell is flung across the head-foot as the columellar muscle gives a sudden contraction, raises the foot off the ground and swings the body in the opposite direction to that of the shell. The whelk thus scampers to and fro, for the leaping movement may be repeated several times in an attempt to evade the predator. The ability to do this is undoubtedly related to the organization of the dorsal pedal musculature (fig. 269) which is similarly elaborate in *N. incrassatus*. Hoffmann (1930) suggested that when the starfish touches the mollusc the stimulus is received by special cells on the dorsal surface of the foot, not, perhaps, in the metapodial tentacles, for the removal of these is without effect. The stimulant may be a protein secreted by special glands in the skin of the starfish, though the same reaction may be induced by a great variety of stimuli.

*Nassarius* is less timid than most prosobranchs and so its activities can be observed more easily—even when depositing spawn the female is not easily distracted by intruders. The spawning behaviour is probably similar to that of other stenoglossans. The siphon is first directed over the hard surface, shell, stone or rock, on which the egg cases will be deposited, as though examining it, and the surface may then be cleaned by the radula. Soon the whelk settles with the right side of the foot raised from the ground so as to form a groove which links the genital aperture with the ventral pedal gland. When an egg capsule passes from the oviduct it is manipulated along the groove by the musculature of the foot and directed into the gland, where it may remain for about 5 min. The sole of the foot is then pressed against the substratum while the capsule is moulded and the visceral mass may be rocked from side to side whilst the base of the egg case is secured. Eventually the anterior part of the foot is drawn up and back, as the muscles of the pedal gland relax, and the capsule is left. The next one is deposited in a similar way nearby, so that several come to be arranged in equidistant rows (fig. 215B). Frequently, as in other Stenoglossa, more than one female will use the same spawning ground. The eggs hatch as veligers which have a rather long pelagic life, whereas in the larger whelks of the superfamily Buccinacea the larval stage is suppressed.

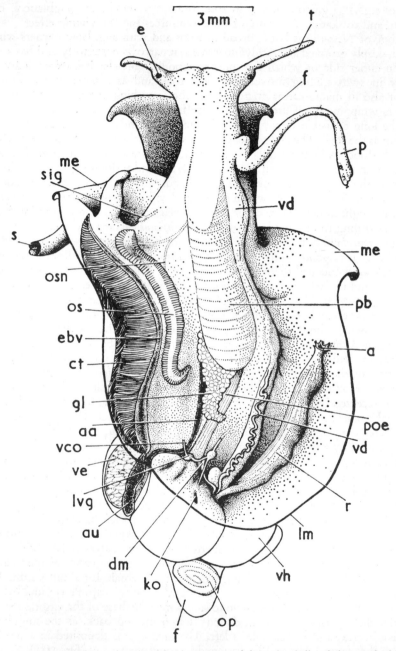

FIG. 275.—*Nassarius reticulatus:* the animal has been removed from the shell and the mantle skirt cut longitudinally along the mid-dorsal line. In addition to the contents of the mantle cavity some structures are seen by transparency.

a, anus; aa, anterior aorta; au, auricle; ct, ctenidium; dm, diverticulum of male duct opening to mantle cavity; e, eye; ebv, efferent branchial vessel; f, foot; gl, gland of Leiblein; ko, opening of kidney to mantle cavity; lm, cut edge of mantle skirt; lvg, left visceral ganglion; me, mantle edge; op, operculum; os, osphradium; osn, osphradial nerve; p, penis; pb, proboscis; poe, posterior oesphagus; r, rectum; s, siphon; sig, siphonal ganglion; t, tentacle; vco, left part of visceral loop; vd, vas deferens; ve, ventricle; vh, visceral hump.

A general obscurity surrounds the British members of the Toxoglossa. Eighteen species are listed, but all except two species of *Mangelia* are said to be scarce or rare. The majority are dredged and only isolated specimens are found. The food is not known for any species. However, the structure of the gut of *Mangelia* (Robinson, 1955) shows that the animals are undoubtedly predacious carnivores of a highly specialized kind (fig. 104). Consequently their distribution will be restricted to the vicinity of their prey, and when this is known for each species these molluscs may be secured in greater abundance. The

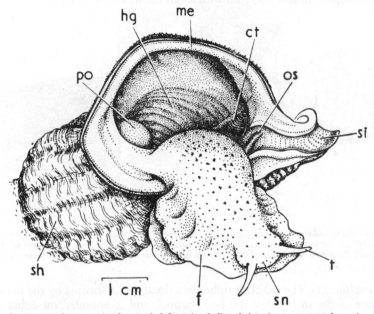

FIG. 276.—*Buccinum undatum:* animal extended from its shell and showing contents of mantle cavity.
ct, ctenidium; f, foot; hg, hypobranchial gland; me, mantle edge; os, osphradium set across base of siphon; po, pallial oviduct; sh, shell; si, siphon; sn, snout; t, tentacle.

prey is undoubtedly a soft-bodied creature which will be pierced suddenly by the point of the radular tooth and injected with secretion from the poison gland. The secretion would be directed into the buccal cavity with some force by the contraction of the huge muscular bulb at the blind end of the gland, and would be directed along the shallow trough of the tooth. This is similar to the attacking action of some cones (p. 205), but in *Mangelia* the tip of the proboscis, the true mouth, is surrounded by a sucker reminiscent of that of the pyramidellids. The sucker is probably used only to secure the necessary contact on the body of the prey while the tooth is brought into action. There is no evidence that it is used to suck the body fluids, and if it does so this can be only a minor role, for the stomach of the toxoglossans and the histology of the digestive gland have not the characteristics of those of a fluid feeder. Presumably the prey is manipulated by the proboscis and swallowed whole.

Most of the British toxoglossans are found on soft ground, mud or sand with perhaps some gravel, though some species of *Philbertia* favour stony bottoms. In these situations there also occur errant annelids which may be their prey, and may be hunted by the mollusc burrowing through the surface layers of the substratum. These toxoglossans show adaptations for this. The shell (fig. 26B) is the shape of an elongated spindle offering little resistance if dragged through the soil. The head-foot is separated from the visceral mass by a moderately long neck, which allows considerable play of the visceral mass as the animal creeps forwards and encounters obstacles. The mantle cavity, which is wide and depressed, may be closed to the exterior by the thickened edge of the mantle which forms a collar leaving only the inhalant and exhalant passageways exposed. There is an extensible inhalant siphon in *Mangelia* with a valve at its base which regulates the inhalant

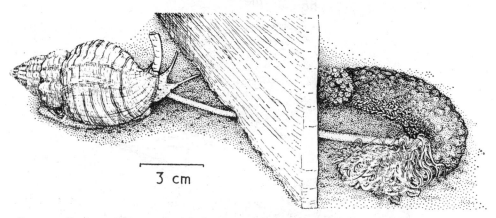

3 cm

FIG. 277.—*Buccinum undatum:* animal feeding on moribund holothurian. The predator and its prey are separated by the wooden partition between 2 aquarium tanks. The prey must have been sensed by smell and the whelk has extended its proboscis underneath the partition in order to reach its food.

water current (fig. 31). The exhalant siphon is a small gutter formed by the mantle where the free edge of the shell meets the body whorl, and is bounded on either side by a prominent ridge of ciliated epithelium. Specimens of *Mangelia powisiana* collected from the muddy sand at White Patch, Plymouth, where it occurs with large numbers of the annelids *Lumbriconereis latreilli* and *Melinna palmata*, on which it perhaps feeds, have been seen to burrow with astounding rapidity, and Jeffreys (1867) stated that he observed *M. nebula* burrowing in the sand at Oxwich, near Swansea, where tubicolous polychaetes also abound, at the retreat of the tide. It is probably for this reason that specimens of our toxoglossans are so rarely seen. The egg capsules of a number of species have been described, for they are fixed on stones or shells, and also some of the veliger larvae. As far as is known all species have free veligers.

# CHAPTER 21

# THE ROCKY SHORE: OTHER PROSOBRANCHS

THE family Trochidae includes the animals popularly known as top shells which favour shores with broken reefs and undisturbed boulder beaches and are intolerant of excessive exposure, since they have little power of adhesion. *Gibbula cineraria*, *G. umbilicalis* and *Monodonta lineata* are common intertidal trochids and a fourth, *Calliostoma zizyphinum*, occurs at MLWS and below. *G. cineraria* (figs. 279, 280) is the only one which is found on all coasts of the British Isles, and *Monodonta* has the most restricted occurrence (McMillan, 1944). It may be found in the S and W between Poole in Dorset and the Mersey, and in the S and W of Ireland (Southward & Crisp, 1954). Even within these areas its distribution is patchy. On sheltered coasts it is typical of the region between high and low neap tide, though there are areas (e.g. R. Yealm at Noss, S Devon) where it occurs abundantly to a higher level and in reduced salinity. Outside this range it cannot survive, but the reason is unknown. *Monodonta* is conspicuous owing to the large size of its robust shell, the exposed mother-of-pearl on the apex, the tooth (tcl, fig. 281) on the columella (from which it is named) and its occurrence on bare rocks and stones which are sheltered from the sea though subjected to the full force of the sun. Only when winter temperatures are very low does it move away from exposed surfaces. Smaller individuals are not readily visible, for they tend to live apart, hidden in pits and crevices of the rock. They settle from the plankton at lower levels on the beach and need the protection of crevices as they migrate upwards to the adult position.

*Gibbula umbilicalis* is a more familiar species for it is widespread and rather more tolerant of wave action than *Monodonta* (Southward & Orton, 1954); otherwise it favours similar grounds and, with *G. cineraria*, is often associated with fucoids and, in exposed regions, may be restricted to pools and the undersides of stones and boulders which may be bare of weed. It is absent from the E coast of Scotland and England, and in the NW is less abundant than *G. cineraria* and somewhat patchy in its distribution. Its upper limit on the shore is slightly lower than that of *Monodonta* and lies between EHWN and MHWN, though this may be raised by splash. Its numbers begin to dwindle below MLWN, which is about the upper limit of *G. cineraria*, and below MLWS the species may be absent; in contrast to *Monodonta* it is sometimes dredged. Young animals of the two species of *Gibbula* are often difficult to find for they are concealed in damp crevices, under stones and in rock pools along the lower part of the beach.

The shells of *G. umbilicalis* and *G. cineraria* are found together and on occasions seem difficult to distinguish (fig. 282). The shell of *G. umbilicalis* may be more depressed and never pyramidal in form as is sometimes that of *G. cineraria*. Moreover the spiral ridges on the whorls are fewer (sharper in young individuals), though this feature is not seen in worn specimens in which the mother-of-pearl at the apex is exposed. The wear here may be so great that an upper opening to the canal in the centre of the columella is produced. The longitudinal lines of colour are more conspicuous in *G. umbilicalis*: they are red or purple, broader and fewer in number, sometimes zigzag and never interrupted by the spiral ridges to give a speckled appearance. The patterning on the shell of *G.*

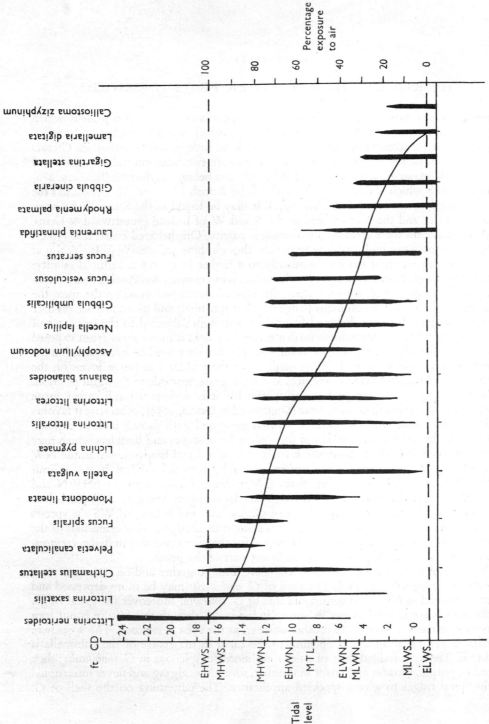

Fig. 278.—Diagram relating the vertical range of common littoral animals and plants of rocky shores to height on the shore and degree of exposure to air, based on Evans' data for Church Reef, Wembury (1947) (*Calliostoma zizyphinum* based on Colman (1933)). The distribution of each organism is given by the extent of the black line under its name. Tidal levels are given on the vertical axis at the left as are heights, in feet above chart datum. The percentage exposure to air is given along the vertical axis to the right. The superimposed curve represents the percentage exposure to air at different tidal levels.

*cineraria* is so fine that the surface has an ashy hue, and the narrow, closely set and oblique streaks of dark purple or brown may be interrupted by the spiral ridges and hardly separately distinguishable. The umbilicus of this shell is rather small, and in both species it may be obliquely funnel-shaped.

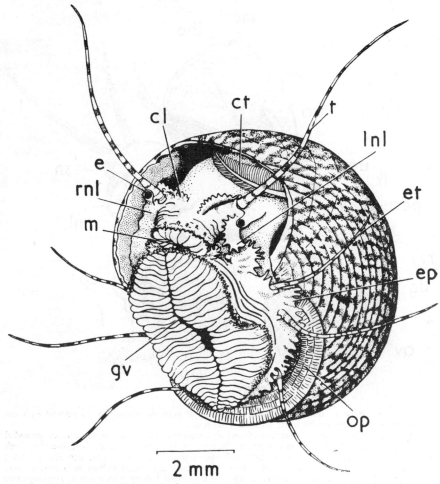

**2 mm**

Fig. 279.—*Gibbula cineraria:* living animal.
cl, cephalic lappet; ct, ctenidium; e, eye; ep, epipodium; et, epipodial tentacle; gv, groove along sole of foot; lnl, left neck lobe; m, mouth; op, operculum; rnl, right neck lobe; t, tentacle.

*Gibbula cineraria* is the abundant top shell on the E coast and extends further up the shore where there is moisture at low tide than in the W, perhaps through lack of competition from *G. umbilicalis*. It is also sublittoral, though beyond a depth of about 15 f the numbers are small. Its vertical distribution overlaps that of *Calliostoma zizyphinum*, which occurs deeper and is rarely found above MLWS, tolerating only 10% exposure in the Plymouth vicinity (Colman, 1933), whereas *G. cineraria* can tolerate up to 30%.

Both species favour a sheltered habitat and it is of interest to find that they are recorded from pools at the level of the topmost barnacles on the exposed rocky shores of Caithness (Lewis, 1954b). Ebling *et al.* (1948) showed that in situations where the current was strong specimens of *G. cineraria* were washed off weed to which they were clinging.

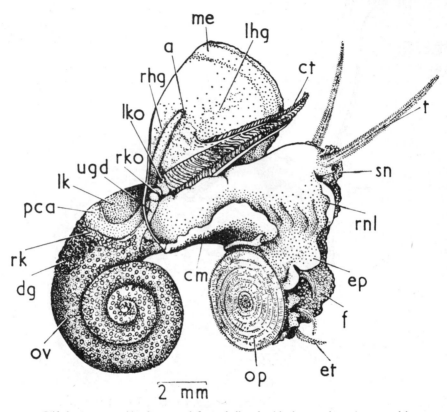

FIG. 280.—*Gibbula cineraria:* animal removed from shell and with the mantle cavity opened by a cut along the right side of the mantle skirt; seen from the right.

a, anus; cm, columellar muscle; ct, ctenidium; dg, digestive gland; ep, epipodium; et, epipodial tentacle; f, foot; lhg, left hypobranchial gland; lk, left kidney or papillary sac; lko, opening of left kidney to mantle cavity; me, mantle edge; op, operculum; ov, ovary; pca, pericardial cavity; rhg, right hypobranchial gland; rk, right kidney; rko, opening of right kidney to mantle cavity; rnl, right neck lobe; sn, snout; t, tentacle; ugd, neck of right kidney which acts as a urinogenital duct.

*Calliostoma zizyphinum* (figs. 26D, 71) is one of the most conspicuous diotocardians owing to its size and the colour of both shell and body tissues, which may be flecked with purple, crimson, reddish brown and yellow. Even the smallest individuals recently hatched from the egg ribbon are pigmented. Perhaps as in other primitive prosobranchs these pigments may be porphyrins (p. 135) of dietary origin. The glandular equipment of the foot is more pronounced than in the other trochids for besides the anterior pedal gland which discharges between propodium and mesopodium and consists of subepithelial mucous cells and PAS-negative cells, glands in and under the epithelium, with similar staining properties, open to the surface of the sole. Over the metapodium, posterior to the operculum, is a conspicuous V-shaped area grooved transversely and with abundant mucous cells, less pronounced in other genera in which the glands on the sole are well developed. Subepithelial glands diminish towards the posterior end of the sole. They are typically mucous glands and their secretion enables the snail to maintain a purchase on the rock. Ankel (1947) has observed that if *Gibbula cineraria* is disturbed when creeping the sole of the foot immediately produces a copious supply of mucus which helps the snail to increase its grip (p. 142).

Another top shell, the large species *Gibbula magus*, is occasionally collected on the shore and, indeed, is recorded as locally common on the rocks of Cardigan Bay (Flattely

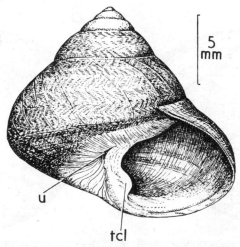

FIG. 281.—*Monodonta lineata:* shell in apertural view.
tcl, tooth on columella; u, umbilicus.

& Walton, 1922) and has been found in numbers on the coast of Connemara, Ireland, where *Lithothamnion calcareum* forms beaches between rocky headlands. Here up to 40/sq m have been seen at LWST browsing over the calcareous alga. However, its more frequent habitat is on muddy sand below LW.

In contrast to these species, both in appearance and habits, is the smallest and most primitive British trochid, *Margarites helicinus* (fig. 283). Its shell, thin and semi-transparent, is orange or reddish brown in colour and has a blue-green or purple lustre. It is primitive in that the whorls dip to the sutures and are not angulated, the umbilicus is wide and the spire low. Moreover it lacks surface ornamentation except for faint spiral striae. This species is locally abundant in areas N of the Humber on the E and the Bristol Channel on the W, and also in N Ireland, occurring gregariously amongst weed and under stones and boulders—never on exposed upper surfaces. The animal is very active and bold, and as it creeps the epipodial tentacles, of which there are 6 pairs, can be seen waving in the water (et). At its base each has a pigmented papilla with the appearance of an eye (eso). The tentacles, cephalic (t) and epipodial, are contractile, and their surface is annulated and setose. As in other trochids these epipodial outgrowths, innervated by pedal nerves, presumably increase the tactile efficiency of the foot. Although in shell form and as the possessor of 6 pairs of epipodial tentacles, *Margarites* is primitive, yet the spawn masses found with the adults are similar in their make-up to those of mesogastropods, and a free larval stage is suppressed. Evidence suggests that this prosobranch lives little more than 1 year.

As might be expected in such lowly prosobranchs as the trochids epipodial outgrowths are a conspicuous feature, 4 pairs occurring typically in *Calliostoma* and 3 in other species (et, fig. 279); in addition there is a neck lobe behind each cephalic tentacle. The margins of the lobes may be entire (rnl, lnl, fig. 283) or fringed (lnl, fig. 279). Each is ciliated dorsally and covered by a thin cuticle ventrally. On the left lobe the cilia beat in an inhalant direction and in the reverse direction on the right lobe. When the animal is

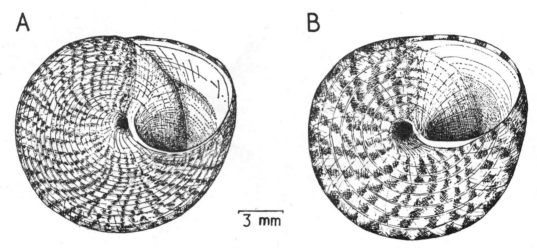

FIG. 282.—Shells of *Gibbula*: A, *G. cineraria*; B, *G. umbilicalis*.

submerged each forms a half siphon along which water passes into or out of the mantle cavity. Other lobes, innervated by nerves supplying the snout, lie one at the base of each cephalic tentacle on its median side. They are not developed in *Margarites*, are rudimentary in *Calliostoma* but large and fringed in *Monodonta* and *Gibbula* (cl). A further sensory process arises from the base of the right eye stalk in most topshells, and the sides of the foot are beset with numerous papillae covered by immobile cilia which give the surface a wrinkled appearance. These are absent in *Margarites*.

*Tricolia pullus* (fig. 284A) is the only British member of the Turbinidae, a family well represented in warmer seas and closely related to the trochids. It is small, the shell measuring up to 7 mm in height. It occurs in rock pools near LWST creeping rapidly over the weed with a shuffling motion, the snout being swung from side to side as the animal feeds; a longitudinal groove down the middle of the foot marks the division between the two halves which are advanced alternately. The red weed *Chondrus crispus* is particularly favoured, streaks on the shell and body of the snail matching its colour; these may be due to the pigment of the food as Ino (1949) has shown for *Turbo cornutus*. The red or purple streaks on the yellowish shell are frequently zigzag and contrast with the emerald green mantle and green markings on the rest of the body. This has also pink or purple lines on a background of pale yellow, whilst the head is reddish brown. The tentacles, both cephalic and epipodial, are setose and extensile and wave through the water as the animal creeps. The animals resemble trochids in general anatomy, though differing in one obvious external feature, the operculum of the shell. In a trochid the operculum is thin, horny and multispiral: in a turbinid it is calcareous and thick with a convex outer surface. Its colour in *Tricolia* is white.

Another family, the Littorinidae, includes 4 periwinkles, *Littorina neritoides*, *L. saxatilis*, *L. littoralis* and *L. littorea* which may be collected on almost any rocky or stony shore,

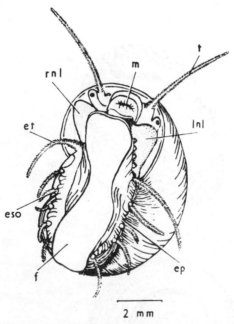

FIG. 283.—*Margarites helicinus:* living animal creeping on surface film of water, seen in ventral view.
ep, epipodium; eso, epipodial sense organ; et, epipodial tentacle; f, foot; lnl, left neck lobe; m, mouth; rnl, right neck lobe; t, tentacle.

zoned from top to bottom in that order, but overlapping considerably. *L. littoralis* may usually be separated from the three other species very readily on account of the extremely depressed spire of the shell and because of its close association with *Fucus vesiculosus* or *Ascophyllum nodosum*, but it is often a difficult matter to distinguish between specimens of the other three species, particularly when, because of age differences, they are all of similar size. For these reasons a number of critical points (mainly in their external appearance) which help in identification are summarized in Table 17.

The 2 periwinkles *Littorina neritoides* (fig. 285) and *L. saxatilis* may be collected from above EHWS especially on exposed coasts where there is considerable wave splash; the former may then be over 20 ft above the reach of the tide, and the latter about half this distance, though a height of 60 ft was recorded by Hunter (1953a) for *L. saxatilis* in the Garvelloch Islands, Argyllshire. *L. neritoides* is typically the higher, though in very sheltered places where the upper limit of both species is lowered so that they extend only as high as MHWS, the distance of a foot may separate them. *L. neritoides* favours steep, rough rocks which are very exposed, even where splash is strong, but requires cracks or crevices in which to shelter; its position on the shore is probably explicable in terms of

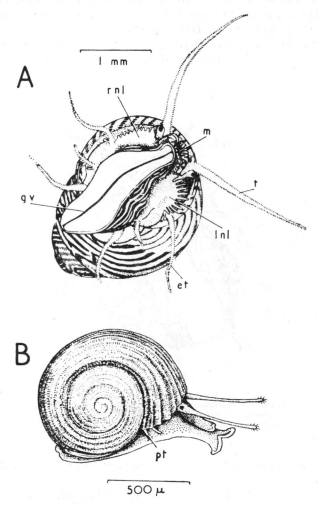

FIG. 284.—A, *Tricolia pullus*, living animal in ventral view. B, *Circulus striatus*, living animal from the right.

et, epipodial tentacle; gv, groove along mid-line of sole of foot; lnl, left neck lobe; m, mouth; pt, pallial tentacle; rnl, right neck lobe; t, tentacle.

gravity, light and the presence or absence of water (Fraenkel, 1927*a*). This species may also live submerged in high rock pools and water-filled pits in the rock. Increased wave action not only raises its upper limit of distribution, but also lowers its lower limit and may bring it below MLWN. In very sheltered places the vertical distribution is, in contrast, narrow, and the snail may not be found below MHWN. *L. saxatilis* favours a

TABLE 17

*Diagnostic Characters of* Littorina *spp. with the Most Useful Italicized*

|  | Littorina neritoides | Littorina saxatilis | Littorina littoralis | Littorina littorea |
|---|---|---|---|---|
| Spire . . . . . | High | High | *Very low* | High |
| Columella . . . . | *Dark* | Light–dark | Light–dark | *White* |
| Junction of outer lip with body whorl | Acute | *Rectangular* | Acute | Acute |
| Periostracum . . . | *Lip to aperture* | None visible | None visible | None visible |
| Black stripes on tentacles . | Longitudinal | Longitudinal | Longitudinal | *Transverse* |
| Breeding . . . . | Oviparous | *Viviparous* | Oviparous | Oviparous |

less exposed habitat and is reduced in numbers where exposure is high. It collects in crevices of irregular and broken rock, especially where there are plenty of pools and is abundant among *Pelvetia* and other weeds. Unlike *L. neritoides* it is also found on sheltered, level, rock faces. The lower limit of the species is variable: specimens may be collected at MLWS though usually the numbers dwindle at ELWN. Occasionally it is dredged for it tolerates permanent immersion. Thorson (1944) stated that living specimens are known in E Greenland from depths of 57 m and in W Greenland from 94 m. The occurrence of this species on a rocky shore in the British Isles is more regular than that of *L. neritoides* and it is plentiful on stony and silty beaches and invades estuaries where it is found with the edible winkle. At Rum Bay, Plymouth Sound, Moore (1940) found up to 3,000/sq m in a stony gully considerably overgrown with fucoids, and on the intertidal mud flats at St John's Lake, the Tamar Estuary, up to 1,100/sq m have been recorded (Spooner & Moore, 1940), the highest figures coinciding with the occurrence of *Zostera*. The snail may be found attached to weed, stone or any solid holdfast on the flats between high water and mid-tide. It often abounds in shallow brackish waters and Howes (1939) recorded it swarming on *Ruppia* in a saline Essex creek. Its rapid colonization of such habitats may be associated with its viviparity.

The high position of these 2 periwinkles on the shore indicates that they can withstand a considerable amount of exposure to air and freshwater which reaches them as rain. *Littorina neritoides* is the more resistant. It can survive absence of moisture for at least 5 months (Patanè, 1933) and regains activity within a few minutes when replaced in sea water. Colgan (1910) found that it is unharmed after exposure to dry air for 42 days, and it will survive when the water content of the body is reduced to 66% (Fischer, 1948). The gill in this species, and in *L. saxatilis*, has a reduced number of leaflets (ct, fig. 285C) as compared with the other periwinkles and the leaflets are small. Respiration is remarkably efficient as the winkles can breathe in water when its oxygen content is as low as 0·24 ml/l and they use 99·4% of the available oxygen before dying (Fischer, Duval & Raffy, 1933). The mantle cavity contains water even after long exposure to dry air, and as this moisture is reduced the operculum withdraws further into the shell. When quiescent on dry rock the metabolic rate of the winkles is low. It has been calculated that the oxygen consumption of *L. neritoides* in dry air is 5–6 times lower than in water (Fischer, Duval & Raffy, 1933). Both species can withstand immersion in freshwater for a week, and *L. neritoides* for 11 days. In light rain they are often very active and will creep about the rocks and feed. Some of the high rock pools in which they live have a high salinity, especially in summer, and Colgan (1910) found that both species survive in sea water of treble salinity for about a week. Lysaght (1941) suggested that *L. neritoides*

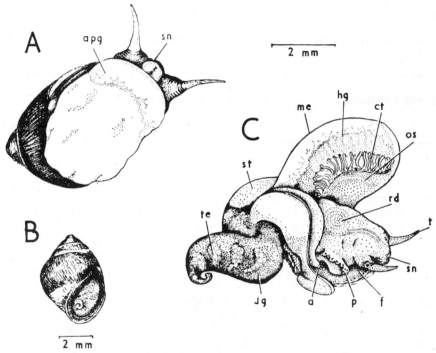

FIG. 285.—*Littorina neritoides*: A, living animal in ventral view; B, animal withdrawn into shell; C, animal removed from shell with the mantle cavity opened by a median dorsal cut, seen from the right.
a, anus; apg, anterior pedal gland seen by transparency; ct, ctenidium with reduced number of leaflets; dg, digestive gland; f, foot; hg, hypobranchial gland; me, mantle edge, cut; os, osphradium; p, penis with glands; rd, radula in radular sac seen through floor of mantle cavity; sn, snout; st, stomach; t, tentacle; te, testis.

avoids highly saline water, for when the salinity increases at low tide the snail crawls out of the pits which it inhabits on the Plymouth Breakwater, and returns when the water has been renewed by the tide.

The food of these winkles is minute algae and diatoms which are gathered from the substratum. *Littorina saxatilis* browses over *Pelvetia* and *Ascophyllum*, sometimes rasping the surface and eating decaying tissues, but usually collecting diatoms. The animals move about and feed when their habitat is moist, and if it is calm they are as active in slight rain as when covered by the tide. On warm days under heavy sea mist the majority of individuals are on the move when the tide is out, and it is at such a time that they may be seen to copulate. Hot dry weather may limit the feeding period for those living above high tide, and they appear to be able to go for weeks without food. Snails of all sizes, except the very young of *L. neritoides*, are found together in sheltered places and the smaller ones may be clustered in empty barnacle shells or rock crevices with the adults. The youngest *L. neritoides* are commonest at lower levels where the metamorphosing larvae settle on rocks devoid of fucoids, and gradually migrate to the higher and drier levels (Lysaght, 1941). These small snails are able to survive emersion for a much shorter period than the larger ones. The choice of a dry and apparently adverse habitat by the adult may be correlated with the need for shelter from the force of the waves, and, except for spawning which appears to be associated with certain spring tides (p. 387), the presence or absence of water seems to be of secondary importance since they have become better able to withstand desiccation.

Females of *Littorina saxatilis* are distinguished from males by the round aperture and the larger size of the fully grown individual. The brood pouch contains embryos in all months of the year, but the numbers may be small during the summer and are highest in spring. A fluctuation like this is pronounced only on certain shores—indeed Linke (1933) working on animals from the North Sea found the brood pouch full all the year. Berry (1956) studied a population at Whitstable, Kent, where there is a decline in reproductive activity between June and mid-August, when the penis and vesicula seminalis become reduced in the male and the ovary in the female. He found that snails living high on the beach grow faster than those at lower levels since they have a longer period of activity when uncovered by the tide: they attain a larger size and produce more eggs. The varieties described below appear to differ in breeding times.

Lysaght (1941) studied the growth rate of *Littorina neritoides* in a population on the Plymouth Breakwater where conditions for shelter and continuous feeding are very favourable and lead to the production of large individuals—one with a shell height of 10·4 mm was found. Many of the larger snails live more or less permanently in water in pits on the top of the Breakwater, and the smaller ones are most abundant on the exposed southern slopes. The growth rate appears to decrease with age and is very low in snails of 6 mm or more in height, from which it follows that the larger individuals must be many years old. There is evidence that females of *L. neritoides* grow faster than males for they are significantly more numerous amongst the larger individuals, and this difference in growth rate between the sexes appears to hold for *L. saxatilis* too (Pelseneer, 1926a). The oldest specimens of *L. saxatilis* were suggested by Thorson (1944) to have lived for at least 6 years.

The colour of the shell and of the exposed parts of the body of *Littorina saxatilis* is very variable. The former is frequently yellow, brown, orange or red and sometimes purple, black or pure white, and the body tissues various shades of white, yellow, brown or flesh-colour streaked with deep purple. It is unknown to what extent these colours are linked with food or other environmental factors and to what extent they are genetic. Varieties of the species have been based on them and on differences in shape, size and sculpture of the shell and on habitat. One, *saxatilis* of Johnston, is normally very small, with a shell height of not more than 4 mm, though it may grow larger than this in favourable circumstances. The largest specimens which we have seen were 9 mm high and were collected by Professor L. A. Harvey on wave-beaten rocks on Lundy Island; others approaching this size have been obtained by G. M. Spooner, Esq., on the Eddy-stone. This variety prefers rock crevices and empty barnacle shells throughout the barnacle zone and above, extending to a lower level on the beach than other varieties. In addition to its small size the shell is recognizable by its squat shape (due to the fact that the spire is small in relation to the body whorl), and the presence of spiral brown lines on a grey to white background. The lines vary in breadth and number, sometimes simple, parallel to and alternating with the spiral striae and usually with a broader one below the periphery, sometimes interrupted, sometimes cutting across the striae and interacting to give a reticulate pattern which appears to be associated with the most exposed habitats. The junction of outer lip and body whorl is rectangular; the spiral striae are not pronounced.

A second variety, *patula* of Jeffreys, is found high up on rocky shores at about the upper limit of barnacles, extending above and below and not avoiding a slight amount of weed cover. It is of the normal size associated with this species. Its shells vary in colour and are often black, grey, yellowish-grey or yellow, without colour patterning when adult though frequently clearer and paler in the neighbourhood of the aperture and darker on the spire. Some young ones may show occasional brown streaks. Coarse spiral striae are of regular occurrence. The variety may be further recognized by its moderately elongated shape, the sudden increase in size of the penultimate whorl and by the way in which the mouth is a little constricted by the thickening of the outer lip. The variety *tenebrosa* of Montagu has, in most cases, a smooth shell of about 6 whorls with a prominent spire. The colour is dark, usually with a brownish or orange tinge, and there is frequently a mottling of irregular, angulated streaks of light colour, though this is not as conspicuous as in *saxatilis*. The shell is thin, the outer lip never thick-edged and it meets the body whorl practically at a right angle; the outer lip is slightly dilated and there is rarely any trace of umbilicus. The largest variety, *L. saxatilis rudis* of Donovan, which may measure up to 28 mm in height and which the careless eye may easily mistake for *L. littorea*, has a very prominent spire of ventricose whorls (fig. 26A), with the apical angle less than in the other three varieties. The colour is yellow, orange or darker, or it may be white with dark spiral bands (sometimes then known as *nigrolineata*). The surface is smooth or very weakly striated below the periphery of the body whorl. The mouth is distinctly small for such a big shell and this is due almost entirely to the thickening of the peristome where inner and outer lips meet. Here, too, the mouth is turned out slightly to the left. There is almost always a dimple marking the position of the umbilicus and the parietal lip in this region is thick. The shell may be easily distinguished from that of *L. littorea* by the swollen whorls, the dark coloured columellar region and the straightness of the inner lip.

It is well to add that these varieties grade easily into one another and intermediates are to be found which cannot be satisfactorily placed in any one of them.

The edible winkle *Littorina littorea* (fig. 5), one of the most abundant of littoral gastropods, ranges from HWNT to LWEST on various types of shore. Its upper limit of distribution appears to be raised by splash (Moore, 1940; Evans, 1947), and Waterston & Taylor (1906) described it high above the sea on St Kilda. It may occur lower on stones and gullies than on a stretch of shore covered by fucoids. This is the largest of our British periwinkles and occasional specimens may attain a height of 38 mm. The shell is commonly soot-coloured, or it may be reddish orange, brown and, rarely, white. Fulvous and brown shells may be zoned with narrow rings of red or grey. The body has usually a dark hue with closely set black lines of pigment on a yellowish ground, except for the sole of the foot which is yellowish. The tentacles are annulated or streaked across with black, and appear flattened when contracted. Their pigmentation is a useful feature in distinguishing between small individuals of this species and those of the other British species of *Littorina* for in the latter there are two darker longitudinal stripes towards the tip of the tentacle, one on the upper and the other on the lower surface. On occasions the dark pigmentation of *L. littorea* is lacking. The winkle lives on rocks and amongst small stones, on gravel and on wooden structures, even on soft mud or sand (particularly if sheltered or poorly drained), but only if stones, boulders or tufts of weed occur to provide a firm base amidst these soft surroundings. It avoids a shifting substratum such as shingle, and is infrequent on chalk and limestone rock, and shores exposed to the full force of storms, for it is less tolerant of surf than *L. saxatilis* (Evans, 1947). On sheltered rocky coasts with clear water it is found at the same level as *L. littoralis*, but unlike this species, which is less resistant to drought and freshwater, away from dense algal covering. It can tolerate water of a salinity as low as 10‰ (Fischer, 1948) and often penetrates estuaries which are polluted. Indeed it can survive for some days in water without oxygen, lying meanwhile with the operculum closing the shell (Thamdrup, 1935). In the Blackwater Estuary, Essex, winkles have been dredged in considerable numbers in certain channels below low water (Wright, 1936), and there are records of specimens being dredged in other localities around our coasts to a depth of about 35 fathoms; it seems probable that some individuals may be submerged all their life. Until about 25 years ago there was an important periwinkle fishery at Maldon in the Blackwater Estuary and fisheries occurred elsewhere. The official statistics show that in 1928 22,290 cwts of periwinkles were collected in England and Wales with an average value of 11s. per cwt. Since that date the fishery has declined and is now negligible.

*Littorina littorea* tends to aggregate in damp or sheltered places at low tide and clusters may be seen resting in shallow pools and depressions in the rock, filling the angle between a vertical and horizontal slope, or heaped around stones and small clumps of algae in sandy and muddy areas. Estimations of population density around the Plymouth area show that in some localities on a rocky shore concentrations of over 950/sq m may be encountered during a low-tide period when the winkles are inactive, whereas not a single individual may occur on adjacent rocks. These clusters appear more or less permanent, for a favourable site is usually filled, many of the same animals returning repeatedly to it after feeding forays, though sometimes they join other groups. If the surface is damp the winkle clings to it with its foot, its head withdrawn into the mantle cavity. On bare rocks and boulders groups of periwinkles may appear completely dry on a hot day when the tide is out. Most individuals are then orientated with the head and the lip of the shell uppermost, and the apex directed downwards (Haseman, 1911). The mollusc is not clinging to the dry rock with the foot, but the lip of the shell is stuck to it by a film of mucus which becomes hard and brittle (Wilson, 1929). This secretion, presumably from the anterior pedal gland, is produced as the substratum dries, and as it hardens the foot is withdrawn. Its strength is sufficient to hold the snail even on a vertical surface, though on gusty days individuals may be blown off. Occasional periwinkles orientate themselves with the top of the shell upwards, but they invariably topple over. The same habit is found in *L. neritoides* and *L. saxatilis*, in the former of which it is facilitated by the presence of a pliable flap of periostracum along the outer lip of the shell (pms, fig. 289). If an individual be picked off the dry rock and the operculum touched it will withdraw further into the shell and expel water from the mantle cavity, for the winkle is not completely retracted when it lies motionless and the mantle cavity retains a supply of water. Thamdrup (1935) has calculated that the oxygen consumption of the edible winkle in air is only 26% of the consumption in water. It can live in dry air attached by its mucous support for at least 3 weeks and when splashed with water again it soon secures a holdfast with its foot and begins to creep.

The periwinkle gathers micro-organisms and detritus from the surface on which it lives, including the young sporelings of weeds and the young stages of other attached organisms, and so it must contribute to the control of settlement. It also eats decaying plant and animal tissue. As it feeds the radula erodes a soft rock surface. North (1954) studying *Littorina planaxis* in S California found that a snail feeding in a rock pool refills the gut 4–8 times daily, the food taking $2\frac{1}{2}$–6 hrs to pass through the body; the erosion of sandstone is estimated as deepening a tidal pool 1 cm every 16 years. *L. littorea* will feed at high tide on calm days, and at low tide if the substratum is not too dry and the humidity high (Thamdrup, 1935). Gowanloch & Hayes (1926) recorded the rate of creeping as 0·8–2·4 m/hr (mean 1·3 m) and from this Thamdrup (1935) calculated that during an ebb tide 4–5 m might be covered, but since the winkle often pauses to feed the longest distance travelled may be only 1·5–2·0 m. Where winkles live on a soft surface the passage of the foot makes a well defined track $\frac{3}{4}$–1 cm broad and with low edges. At Whitstable, where the winkles settle on pebbles scattered over flat sand, Newell (1958a) described U-shaped tracks radiating from the stones, each indicating a period of activity and a return to the site of rest. Those which are visible on the wet sand as the tide recedes during the day are mostly orientated with respect to the sun, indicating that the winkle first crawls towards the light and then, after a time, reverses its direction of movement (Newell, 1958b). Newell stated that on this shore the animals are active as the tide ebbs and as the incoming tide reaches them, but that they remain stationary at most other times. Owing to the turbidity of the water he was unable to follow their movements after the tide had covered them. Haseman (1911) working on a different type of shore observed that when the periwinkle is well submerged it crawls at random.

Gowanloch & Hayes (1926) carried out migration experiments with *L. littorea* in the harbour at Halifax, N.S. Their conclusions support a belief that displaced individuals migrate back to the intertidal level from which they were removed, thus presumably seeking the zone for which they are most adapted, for Hayes (1927a) has shown that winkles from different levels of the beach are characterized by different levels of photo-tactic behaviour. Gowanloch & Hayes (1926) found that in winter, when temperatures are low, the periwinkles show a decreased activity and are unable to cling to the sub-stratum, so that they get washed to lower levels where they are just covered at low tide. They stay there until the spring when, according to the authors, it is negative geotaxis, positive phototaxis and response to heat stimuli, with perhaps other factors, which cause them to regain the higher level. In extreme cold in this country one finds that winkles become inactive, are unable to cling to the shore, and are washed down by the tide.

This littorinid was introduced into the United States of America from the British Isles and was recorded on the coast of Maine in 1868. By 1880 it was one of the most abundant snails along the Massachusetts coast (Morse, 1880) and has been credited with driving the indigenous species *L. palliata* from the shores of New England. Its introduction into Canada was earlier for there are records of it in New Brunswick in 1855.

The growth rate of the edible winkle has been studied by Moore (1937a). He found that specimens from Drake's Island, Plymouth, collected from stones from MT to between MLWN and MLWS, have a shell height of about 14 mm at 6 months old; a year later when the winkle is sexually mature this is increased to 17·4 mm. At $2\frac{1}{2}$ years the average height of the shell is 22·4 mm and at $4\frac{1}{2}$ years 27·3 mm; the number of individuals exceeding this height is few, though shells 36 mm high are found in this locality. In the different habitat of Trevol (=Treval of O.S. maps), where winkles cluster on the mud flat in St John's Lake, the growth rate is similar, though it is less in the Yealm where the ground is stony and the winkles cluster on the few fucoids present. Hayes (1929) found a progressive decrease in the growth rate of the adults with increasing height above low water at St Andrews, N.B., and Moore (1940) also observed that the largest are rare or absent at the top levels, though medium-sized individuals occur throughout the local vertical range of the species. Females grow faster than males and this explains their preponderance in the larger sizes. Up to a height of 25 mm the sexes may be equal in numbers, but in taller shells the proportion of females rises rapidly to three-quarters of the population and females made up 76·9% of a sampling from Trevol with a mean shell height of 29·8 mm (Moore, 1937a). Whether they live longer than males is not known; the oldest record for an individual kept in captivity is nearly 20 years (Woodward, 1913).

In his survey of the population at Trevol Moore (1937a) sieved samples down to a depth of about 5 cm to find the smallest winkles. In this way he procured at MT individuals with a shell height of 0·5 mm which must have settled very recently. Between mid-June, when this method of sampling began, and mid-July the shell height increased to 5 mm. During the period immediately after settlement the mortality rate is undoubtedly very high, and from the size distribution curves of the Trevol population Moore (1937a) calculated that the loss of the recently settled individuals is at least 94% in July and August. For the rest of the first year the percentage mortalities are estimated at 66%, and in later years 57%. For the other two localities which were studied at the same time, Moore stated that sieving out the minute forms is difficult, as the ground is stony, and consequently the proportion of first year shells to older ones collected is too low up to a height of about 1 cm. Moore's work implies that the population of winkles on the shore is reinforced by young ones settling there. He did not study the movements of the young after settlement to find whether there was any suggestion of migration to different levels, or whether those which fortuitously settle on a favourable area merely remain there and others die.

Smith & Newell (1955) studied a population of edible winkles on a stretch of flat stony beach which covers the upper half of the middle shore at Whitstable. Here they found that adults with a shell height of 13–16 mm, which were regarded as second year individuals, make up the bulk of the population. Few winkles survive beyond this age. The specimens were hand picked and search was made for the smallest. However, only two individuals of a shell height of 2·5 mm, and nothing smaller, were seen out of several thousand collected, and the population never contained more than 4% with a shell height less than 5 mm. From this it is argued that the stock of periwinkles on the shore is renewed by the migration on to the beach of young which have been living a benthic life off-shore, or that these individuals may be cast on the shore by waves. They considered that during the first year the winkles move over the stony beach, establishing themselves in the adult zoning and thereafter their distribution pattern remains more or less constant.

*Littorina littoralis* is readily distinguished from the three other British periwinkles by the remarkably depressed spire of the shell (for which reason it is known as the flat periwinkle) and also for the variability in shell colour. This winkle, which occurs both on the E coast of N America and the W coast of Europe, is referred by Dautzenberg & Fischer (1914) to a subspecies of *Littorina obtusata*. Winckworth (1932), in his list of British marine Mollusca, followed Forbes & Hanley (1850) in giving it the status of a species and so separating it from *L. obtusata*, which has a subarctic distribution. Jeffreys (1865), unfortunately, referred to the British as distinct from the continental form as *L.*

*obtusata* and, indeed, of the two it has the more obtuse shell. In both species there are varieties in form as well as colour, though the form varieties of *L. littoralis* show many transitions and are often difficult to distinguish, particularly in the young stages. Linke (1934*a*) and Barkman (1955) have suggested that they are phenotypic variations. Form and colour vary independently. The colour is not known to be influenced by light, salinity or water movements, nor is it certain that these varieties are correlated with particular species of algae (Linke, 1934*b*); transitional forms are comparatively rare. Dautzenberg & Fischer (1914) recognized 12 colour varieties. In 5 of these the shell has a uniform colour: *citrina* (yellow), *aurantia* (red-orange), *rubens* (vermilion), *fusca* (blackish) and *olivacea* (olive green). The other 7 varieties have the body whorl either banded in a contrasting colour, marked with fine zigzag or reticulate lines, or banding and reticulate pattern may be combined: *zonata* (single band of light colour), *alternata* (2 yellow bands), *inversicolor* (shell light with 2 dark bands), *rhabdota* (shell light with numerous reddish brown bands), *ziczac* (shell light with numerous narrow dark zigzag lines), *reticulata* (shell light with a criss-cross of darker lines), *inversicolor-reticulata* (a combination of these two varieties). The shells of *citrina* are some times a bright green owing to the presence of unicellular algae, and algae may camouflage the colouring of other varieties. Milk-white shells, the variety *albescens*, also occur.

In his extensive work on this species Barkman (1955) concluded that most of the colour varieties are genetically distinct, though he suggested that *reticulata* is the juvenile form of *fusca*, and he also pointed out that young specimens of *inversicolor* have the appearance of *citrina* or *albescens*. Bakker (1959) suggested that young *olivacea* cannot be distinguished from young *citrina*. In NW Scotland Barkman found 9 of the 12 colour varieties originally described by Dautzenberg & Fischer (1914), only *rubens*, *alternata* and *inversicolor-reticulata* being absent; *fusca* is by far the most abundant. The variety *albescens* is also there.

This winkle is typically littoral and is especially associated with the fronds of the large brown algae *Fucus* and *Ascophyllum*, which offer protection against surf, desiccation and rain, as well as providing food and a spawning place. The presence of algae determines the upper limit of the species. Van Dongen (1956) has shown that the winkles are attracted by the scent of the Fucaceae from a distance of 1 m. The attraction is strongest to *F. vesiculosus* and least to *F. serratus*, and the two varieties which he worked on, *citrina* and *olivacea*, showed no marked difference in reaction. At close quarters both scent and taste play a part in the selection of weed. The snail is also found in smaller numbers on *Laminaria*, *Pelvetia*, *Chondrus* and a few other algae, though it prefers members of the Fucaceae as food; this has been confirmed by Bakker (1959). When the tide is out the winkle shelters amongst the weeds and if the humidity is high it will feed, rasping the tissues and anything which may have settled there. It favours somewhat sheltered, rocky coasts where the water is clear, avoiding turbid waters, and is intolerant of heavy surf. The lower limit of the vertical distribution of both *Littorina littoralis* and *L. littorea* is influenced by surf and shifts to higher levels on surf-beaten shores. However, 3 varieties of *L. littoralis*—*citrina*, *inversicolor* and *ziczac*—do not appear to thrive where surf is slight (Barkman, 1955).

Together with the other species of British periwinkles *Littorina littoralis* displays negative geotaxis. This is equally strong under and out of water when the humidity is high. The reaction remains constant even after long periods of immersion (370 hrs) in a confined space, and observations on the variety *olivacea* indicate no difference in this behaviour in individuals collected from different levels. This variety shows a stronger negative geotaxis than var. *citrina*, which lives at a lower level (Barkman, 1955), and its negative phototactic responses are more pronounced; it usually burrows into the tangle of algal fronds whereas the latter variety lives mainly on the surface of the weed. Reactions to gravity and light are eliminated by desiccation, which causes the snail to withdraw into its shell. Under laboratory conditions it can withstand 6 days emersion (Colgan, 1910).

Tidal movements influence the behaviour of the snail, though this has been clearly displayed only on a stretch of shore from which algal growth had been removed. Wubben observed (quoted by Barkman, 1955) that as the tide begins to rise the animals leave the water and climb the shore until desiccation stops them. As the rising tide moistens them they cling to the stones and then when covered by water climb again, but stop before the tide is full. On the falling tide they move downward, though this movement is much slower than the upward one, and they finally reach a level where the stones are dry, and come to rest. A trickle of water draining over the snails may induce them to move downwards, following the water, and it is this reaction, together with the combined influences of gravity, desiccation and light, which may account for movements synchronous with the tides.

Female individuals of *Littorina littoralis* are larger than males and slightly more numerous (Pelseneer, 1926a). Some hours after copulation, which may last 10–85 min (Linke, 1934a), spawn masses are deposited on the fronds of fucoids. Apparently no spawning takes place on other algae. The young hatch as miniatures of the adult and colonize the same habitat, though they get washed from the fucoid fronds and may be collected from more sheltered habitats nearby. Colman (1940) recorded numbers of juveniles of this species along with juveniles of *L. littorea* and *L. saxatilis* on *Lichina pygmaea*. This lichen grows as small, closely set tufts 2–3 cm in height and its finely branched fronds offer considerable protection to small littoral animals. Other young periwinkles may be found amongst the dense weed growth of rock pools. The young are less tolerant of salinity changes than the adult and, according to Hertling (1928), the eggs cease to develop below 25‰ total salinity. Adults have been recorded in water of a salinity as low as 10‰ (Fischer, 1931).

The chink shells, species of *Lacuna*, are classified with *Littorina* as the most primitive marine mesogastropods. Their popular name is derived from the shape of the prominent umbilicus, which is an elongated slit lying alongside the inner lip and continuing the spiral coiling of the columella. In their general anatomy they resemble *Littorina* (fig. 286). However, they are restricted to the lower level of the shore, occurring near low water and below, and no species can endure long periods of desiccation. They may be found in slightly brackish water: in the Baltic Jessen (1918) recorded *L. vincta* and *L. pallidula* at a salinity of 12–13‰. They are herbivorous, collecting food from the surface of weeds and from rocks and stones. *Lacuna vincta* is the most abundant species, living on brown, green and red weeds and depositing its spawn on the fronds in spring and early summer. As it creeps with an apparently unsteady and awkward gait, the 2 metapodial tentacles (mt), characteristic of the genus, can be seen projecting beyond the operculum. During this, secretion is poured out from a vast anterior pedal gland which, at least in *L. pallidula*, extends into the haemocoel below the buccal mass, and from a well developed sole gland lying in two parts, one in each lateral half of the foot. The position of the sole gland can be associated with the bipedal stepping locomotion. *L. pallidula* sometimes occurs with *Littorina littoralis* which it resembles in shell shape, for the spire is flat and the body whorl expands outwards. The spawn of these 2 species is so alike that there is often confusion over the identification (p. 390) and in both the larval stage is suppressed. This species is sexually dimorphic, and the male, 5–6 mm in shell length, may be found clinging to the shell of the female which is twice the size; they are annuals. The male

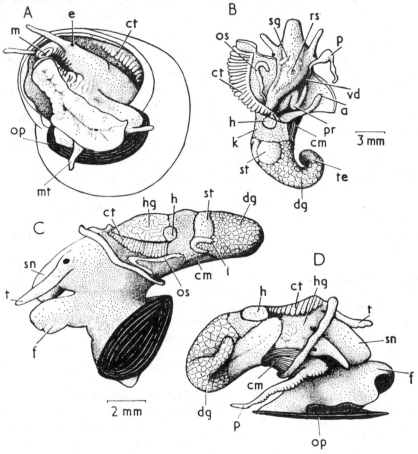

FIG. 286.—*Lacuna pallidula:* A, living animal in ventral view; B, male animal removed from shell with the mantle cavity opened by a mid-dorsal cut, in dorsal view; C, animal removed from shell, from the left; D, male animal removed from shell, from the right.

a, anus; cm, columellar muscle; ct, ctenidium; dg, digestive gland; e, eye; f, foot; h, heart in pericardial cavity; hg, hypobranchial gland; i, intestine; k, kidney; m, mouth; mt, metapodial tentacle; op, operculum; os, osphradium; p, penis; pr, prostate gland; rs, radular sac seen through dorsal wall of head; sg, salivary gland seen through dorsal wall of head; sn, snout; st, stomach; t, tentacle; te, testis; vd, vas deferens.

dies after a period of copulation and the female lives only a month or two longer (Gallien & Larambergue, 1936, 1938).

Among the most numerous prosobranchs of some rocky shores are the rissoids, though they may easily pass unnoticed because of their small size, and of the fact that they live in obscure situations. The shell, which measures only a few millimetres in height, is produced into a conical spire, and there is considerable variation in its sculpture. The surface may be smooth or ribbed (fig. 36), striated spirally or cancellated (fig. 40c). In *Alvania* and *Rissoa* there is a labial rib. There are 24 species of the family Rissoidae listed for the British Isles, all originally so classified on the bases of shell characters, radula and such soft parts as are seen when the animal creeps about. Characteristic of many members of the family are the tentacles developed from the opercular lobe of the foot (mt, figs. 287, 288), and one or two tentacles at the edge of the mantle skirt, which project over the edge of the shell when the animal is extended. There may be only one pallial tentacle (pt, fig. 67), though two, one on each side (pt, fig. 288), occur in some species of *Alvania* (*A. cancellata, A. carinata, A. abyssicola, A. punctura*). In other members

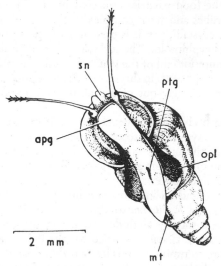

FIG. 287.—*Rissoa parva:* living animal seen from below.
apg, anterior pedal gland; mt, metapodial tentacle; opl, operculigerous lobe; ptg, opening of posterior pedal gland to sole of foot; sn, bifid snout.

of the family neither pallial nor metapodial tentacles are developed (*Cingula vitrea, C. proxima*). A silty habitat is favoured, though this may be on exposed, wave-beaten shores where there are rocks with deep sheltered crevices in which the fauna lives protected from the rapid changes of the external environment. Other species find protection among the dense tufts of smaller weeds such as *Ceramium, Gelidium, Porphyra, Nitophyllum* or the corallines of rock pools and damp crevices. The numbers are greater on such weeds as gather silt.

In all species which have been studied there is a large posterior pedal mucous gland (ptg, figs. 287, 288) as well as an anterior pedal gland, and, except in *Barleeia rubra* (fig. 289B), the secreting tissue of this gland spreads into the haemocoel of the head. In *Barleeia* it is confined to the foot, in the epithelium of which there are also numerous mucus-secreting cells. The secretion from the posterior pedal gland hardens in sea water to form tough threads which anchor the rissoid in position. Or a thread may be spun from the opening of the gland to lower the animal through the water from the surface film along which it commonly creeps or swims in an inverted position. A posterior pedal gland with similar function is developed in other small prosobranchs which are intertidal and live alongside the rissoids, and are related to them in structure and mode of life. These

19

include *Cingulopsis fulgida* (fig. 70), *Skeneopsis planorbis* (ptg, fig. 290), *Omalogyra atomus* (fig. 184A) and *Rissoella* spp. (ptg, figs. 291, 206A).

The rissoids gather diatoms, detritus and fragments of algae for their food. The snout penetrates interstices of sand or silt and explores the surface of weeds. Fragments are drawn into the gut by the radula perhaps aided by jaws. A characteristic rissoid radula is shown in fig. 292. It is typically taenioglossan, bearing many transverse rows of sharply cusped teeth, 7 to a row. The cusps of the rachidian and lateral teeth vary in number, but the marginals are almost identical in all the British species which have been studied. Secretion from a pair of salivary glands (sg, fig. 67) lubricates the action of the radula and cements together the food particles collected by it. The oesophagus and intestine are simple conducting tubes and what complexity there is in the gut is encountered in the stomach (st). Here a crystalline style is present with the accompanying gastric shield, ciliated sorting areas and typhlosoles. The style sac (ss), as described by Graham (1939) in *Rissoa parva*, lies at the anterior end of the stomach, with the intestine running along one side between it and the oesophagus; in this species the sac communicates with the intestine for about half its length. The lay-out of the alimentary canal is remarkably uniform throughout the group.

Other systems of the body show a generally uniform structure: the organs of the mantle cavity, the nervous system and, to a large extent, the reproductive system (chs. 14, 15). The arrangement of the organs in the pallial cavity is similar to that of a typical prosobranch, though the gill is short and has few filaments in some species—in *Cingula cingillus*, a species which lives high on the shore, there are as few as 6, 10–15 have been recorded in *C. semicostata* and an intermediate number in *C. semistriata*. The number increases in *Rissoa parva* and *R. lilacina* to about 20, and *Barleeia rubra* may have even more. The nervous system shows a high degree of concentration (p. 312).

Less than half the species of rissoids recorded for the British Isles occur above LWST, and of these only a few are common. Least is known about the genus *Alvania*, the members of which are typically infralittoral and live on varying types of substratum. Of the 9 species listed (p. 642), 5 are rare or even scarce, and we have no knowledge of the reproduction of 6; for the rest free veliger larvae have been described. The life history is known for a single species, *Alvania punctura* (fig. 288), which occurs amongst *Laminaria* in rather sheltered situations on all coasts, though the egg capsules may be attached to weeds higher on the shore.

Species of the genus *Rissoa* are associated with weeds near the infralittoral fringe and below, and the egg capsules are usually deposited on the fronds. The young hatch as veligers. Individuals may be seen creeping over submerged weeds which are lit by the brightest sun. Several species favour *Zostera*, especially *R. membranacea*, and the abundance of this species would appear to be correlated with the abundance of the weed. It collects its food from the surface of the plant, deposits the egg capsules there and when the young settle from the plankton they congregate on the weed. The growth rate of the recently metamorphosed individual is rapid and it may be fully grown in about a month (Smidt, 1938). The total life span is only a year or a little over. In Britain the species was abundant before *Zostera* was destroyed by disease, but from about 1938 the numbers have dwindled and now it is rare. A similar decline in population is quoted for Danish waters (Thorson, 1946). Other species of *Rissoa* with a lesser dependence on *Zostera* appear to have suffered little on account of its destruction.

A most prolific species is *Rissoa parva*, which is known not only for its abundance, variability in sculpture and colour of shell, but also for its remarkable agility and liveliness. Both the type, which has a sculptured shell with strong and slightly curved longitudinal ribs, and the variety *interrupta*, which is ribless, occur together (fig. 36). Some shells are fully ribbed, some half ribbed and some have only a trace of ribs on one or two larger whorls. Presumably there is a genetic explanation of these polymorphs, but in view of the difficulty of rearing successive generations of animals with pelagic larvae, none has yet been demonstrated. Jeffreys stated in 1867 that the variety was more common in the N; the type is now everywhere less common and in many places relatively scarce. The species is easy to recognize on account of (1) the dark purplish-brown markings at the junction of the head and body on each side; (2) a similarly coloured opercular lobe of the foot (opl, fig. 287); (3) the lateral constrictions of the foot which

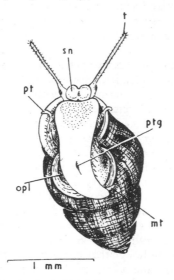

FIG. 288.—*Alvania punctura*: living animal seen from below.
mt, metapodial tentacle; opl, operculigerous lobe; pt, one of 2 pallial tentacles; ptg, opening of posterior pedal gland; sn, snout; t, tentacle.

divide it into a smaller anterior portion and a posterior one of about twice the length; and (4) the brown comma-shaped marking on the body whorl of the shell which separates this species from all other rissoids (fig. 36). Females are more numerous than males, and according to Pelseneer (1926a) comprise about 63% of the population. This is also true of *R. lilacina*.

Some counts have been made by Miss M. A. Perry to illustrate the abundance of *Rissoa parva* in the intertidal zone of Whitsand Bay, Cornwall, which is an exposed stretch of shore and we are indebted to her for permission to quote these here. In a shallow coralline pool with no depth greater than 6 in and a surface area of 3 sq ft, 3,766 individuals were collected on one occasion in September. They were mainly on the weeds, though some were in the silt at the bottom. Of this number only 13 possessed shells with ribs, the remainder being ribless. Among the smooth variety the shells of 58 were very heavily calcified, and some of these, as well as shells of other individuals, were encrusted with the stony alga *Melobesia*. In summer and early autumn large numbers of young individuals are found with the adults; although the species may breed all the year round the peak breeding time is spring and summer when individuals may hatch from the egg, pass through the pelagic larval stage and attain maturity. During the winter months many individuals are washed from the weed and perish, or migrate to join the infralittoral population. A single square foot of rock covered with weed (mainly *Chondrus* but with an admixture of coralline algae and other red weeds) was found to yield 7,114 specimens in September. In early February only 457 individuals were taken from a similar area. Of the September individuals all but 17 were the smooth variety and of the February ones all but 7. A study of similar populations at Cullercoats, Northumberland, showed a similar reduction in winter. The numbers at all times of the year were smaller than at Whitsand Bay and in the areas studied every individual had a ribless shell. A similar seasonal fluctuation in numbers has been described for *R. membranacea* and *R. inconspicua*. Petersen (1918) found that they are annuals, attaining maximal numbers during late summer in the Limfjord and he recorded 100,000 individuals/sq m with a weight of 100 gm.

*Barleeia rubra* may be found with *Rissoa parva* on weeds near low water and in rock pools along the shores of SW England and Ireland. It is not gregarious, is less active than *R. parva* and its shell and body colouring are distinctive. The shell, without sculpture and with whorls rather swollen, is remarkably strong, dark red, claret, yellowish-brown or tawny in colour. Sometimes, however, it may be lighter with a broad band of reddish-brown encircling each whorl, or this band may be divided into two (fig. 289). Another variety is white. The body is yellowish-white, usually with smoke coloured lines, but the opercular lobe of the foot is a dark purplish-brown (opl) and bears a thick, dark crimson operculum. This is one of the three British rissoids known to have no free larva. Egg capsules (which are fixed to weed) contain only one egg and a considerable supply of albumen which is used by the embryo as food.

Three of the 6 species of the genus *Cingula* are gregarious intertidal forms (fig. 293) favouring a silty habitat. The others live in deeper water and at least 2 (*proxima* and *vitrea*) on a muddy substratum, though they are rare and little is known about them. One of the most abundant species—the one which lives highest on the shore—is *C. cingillus*. It is found in silty crevices of rock, even those not covered by neap tides, and under stones where silt and diatoms collect. The solid, conical shell, which is buff and has chocolate or reddish-brown bands, makes it one of the most easily recognizable members of the crevice fauna. The animals extend down the shore to MTL and below and sometimes live in the silt at the bottom of rock pools, but always avoid strongly lit ones. On exposed rocks deep crevices, which are always moist, provide an almost constant environment and here clusters of individuals of all ages may be found together, for the egg capsules are laid in the crevices and there is no free larva. Each capsule contains a single egg. *C. semicostata* has a similar life history and may share the same habitat towards MT, though it is more frequent lower on the shore, often under stones and small boulders where, in sheltered gullies, colonies of over 50 individuals may be found closely aggregated.

Both *Cingula cingillus* and *C. semicostata* are able to live in sea water of reduced salinity. *C. semicostata* will spawn in water of a salinity of about 18‰ (Rasmussen, 1951) which is little more than half that of other waters in which it lives. Rasmussen (1951) found that given a choice of weed or empty mollusc shells, the animal chooses the latter on which to deposit the capsules, for it prefers a hard surface; spawn may be found on the stones, boulders or sides of crevices where it lives. The capsules of this species and of *C. cingillus* have a particularly thick and tough wall, and no distinct exit as in the species of *Rissoa*.

A variety of *Cingula cingillus*, var. *rupestris*, is distinguished by its cream coloured or milk-white shell, which is bandless. It is found in the deepest crevices of rock such as the Dartmouth slate reefs along the coast of Cornwall. It seems to stay in these to avoid light, perhaps because of its lack of pigment. It is gregarious but is probably never found along with the pigmented animals of the same species.

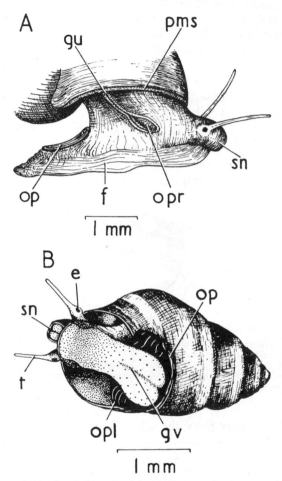

FIG. 289.—A, *Littorina neritoides*, female from the right. B, *Barleeia rubra*, living animal in ventral view. e, eye; f, foot; gu, groove from female aperture to ovipositor; gv, groove on sole of foot; op, operculum; opl, operculigerous lobe; opr, ovipositor; pms, periostracal margin of shell; sn, snout; t, tentacle.

The third intertidal species of *Cingula*, *C. semistriata*, is found under stones near those which shelter *C. semicostata*, and in crevices, but it also lives on weeds. The egg capsules are deposited on fronds, and sometimes other surfaces, and the young escape as veligers.

Classified near the Rissoidae is a number of small marine prosobranchs the systematic position of which is uncertain. They resemble rissoids in certain structural features (though in some cases the resemblances are few), live in a similar habitat and select a similar type of food. All are of small size and by comparison with the rissoids show (in some respects) a simplicity of structure and (in others) a high degree of specialization which may be associated with their habitat and their smallness. They are so different among themselves that they have been ascribed to a number of families. In the majority the shell has no resemblance to that of a rissoid, for it is roughly discoidal in shape, with an extremely short and rounded spire, and a wide umbilicus, as in *Circulus striatus* (fig. 284B), *Tornus* spp. and *Skeneopsis planorbis* (fig. 290), or it is coiled in a plane spiral with the umbilicus so widely open that the interior of the spire is exposed as in *Omalogyra atomus* (fig. 206B) and *Ammonicera rota*. This second type of shell is concave on both sides

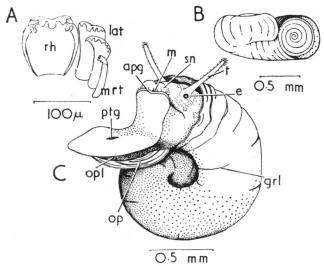

FIG. 290.—*Skeneopsis planorbis:* A, half row of radular teeth; B, shell, with operculum, in apertural view; C, living animal emerging from shell.

apg, opening of anterior pedal gland; e, eye; grl, growth line; lat, lateral tooth; m, mouth; mrt, marginal tooth; op, operculum; opl, operculigerous lobe; ptg, opening of posterior pedal gland; rh, rachidian tooth; sn, snout; t, tentacle.

and has a bilateral symmetry about the sagittal plane of the animal. A conoidal shell is characteristic only of *Cingulopsis fulgida* and *Rissoella* spp. (figs. 291, 206A).

Some of these prosobranchs are very rare. The wide distribution of *Tornus subcarinatus* given by Jeffreys is based on the occurrence of dead shells only, and since 1898, when Woodward described the anatomy of this species from 3 individuals obtained from Guernsey, no living specimens have been recorded. The only British record of *Circulus striatus* is shells from Bundoran (Jeffreys, 1865). In both these genera the detailed structure of the radular teeth is similar, and approximates most closely to that of the rissoids. The two also agree in having a pair of pallial tentacles which project from the right posterior corner of the mantle skirt (pt, fig. 284B). *Circulus* is more closely related to the rissoids than *Tornus*, especially in the structure of the alimentary canal, the kidney and the male reproductive system; the female system shows certain specializations (Fretter, 1956). In some parts of its anatomy *Tornus* is remarkably unlike any rissoid for it has oesophageal pouches and (according to Woodward (1899)) there may be a crystalline style; the male has neither penis nor accessory glands; in the nervous system there is less concentration of the ganglia.

The other genera under consideration, *Cingulopsis, Skeneopsis, Omalogyra, Ammonicera* and *Rissoella*, are associated with the finer sea weeds from MTL and lower, and they often occur in rock pools. Only *Ammonicera* is scarce. These gastropods have a large posterior pedal gland and their ability to produce vast quantities of mucus appears to be associated with their habitat. Associated with their small size is perhaps the reduction or loss of the ctenidium and the position of the kidney in the mantle skirt. *Skeneopsis* is larger than the others and has the typical arrangement of organs in the mantle cavity (fig. 184B). The number of ctenidial filaments is reduced to 9, the kidney lies near the posterior end of the cavity and the hypobranchial gland extends far back along the right side. In *Cingulopsis* the ctenidium is reduced to 3 or 4 small filaments, in *Rissoella* it is represented only by a patch of ciliated cells and in *Omalogyra* there is not even this

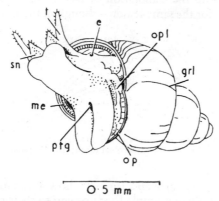

FIG. 291.—*Rissoella diaphana:* animal from below.
e, eye; grl, growth line; me, mantle edge; op, operculum; opl, operculigerous lobe; ptg, opening of posterior pedal gland; sn, snout; t, tentacle.

vestige. In these four the kidney has grown forward into the mantle skirt bringing with it a rich vascular supply and increasing the chances for the oxygenation of the blood. In the absence of a ctenidium the animals depend entirely on pallial respiration, and the stream of water through the mantle cavity is maintained by strips of ciliated epithelium which pass forward from the anus to the mantle's edge. These cause a strong exhalant stream and carry away the faecal pellets; there is a compensating inhalant flow. Associated with these ciliated strips are secreting cells which represent the hypobranchial gland. In the vicinity of the anus a group of relatively enormous gland cells opens into the mantle cavity. They can be seen through the shell and in *Rissoella* are associated with dark brown or black pigment granules: in *R. diaphana* only one such grouping of glands occurs, but in *R. opalina* (fig. 206A) there are 3, for 2 others open elsewhere into the mantle cavity.

The food of *Cingulopsis, Skeneopsis* and *Rissoella* is diatoms, algal filaments and some detritus, and since they live in damp situations they may continue to feed when the tide is out. *Omalogyra* sucks the sap from algal cells which are punctured by the stiletto–like rachidian teeth of the radula. The teeth are reduced to 3 in each row. *Ulva* is a favourite food, and as the mollusc creeps over a thallus the head moves like a pendulum leaving behind a zigzag feeding trail (fig. 206B). The stomach and cells of the digestive gland may be coloured green by the sap of the weed. In the stomach of these prosobranchs there is no style as in rissoids, though in *Cingulopsis*, *Rissoella* and *Skeneopsis* there is a gastric shield. Only in *Cingulopsis* are there oesophageal pouches. The food of *Omalogyra* needs no mechanical treatment prior to digestion and the stomach (st, fig. 184A) has a lining of digestive cells, similar to those of the digestive gland. This is reminiscent of the embryonic condition in which liver cells cover the wall of the stomach, and are constricted only later. Unlike that of some larger intertidal gastropods which are herbivores and inactive at low tide, the intestine (i) is extremely short and does not enter the coils of the visceral mass, whilst the anus (a) opens well within the mantle cavity. These differences may be correlated with the fact that these small prosobranchs live in rock pools or near low water and so are able to maintain a more or less constant flow of water through the mantle cavity to carry away the faeces; a short and histologically simple intestine suffices them for it is not concerned with the elaboration of faecal matter. A short intestine is also characteristic of rissoids—for the same reason—though in them the anus is far forward.

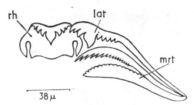

FIG. 292.—*Rissoa parva:* half radular row.
lat, lateral tooth; mrt, marginal tooth; rh, rachidian tooth.

*Cingulopsis*, *Skeneopsis*, *Omalogyra* and *Rissoella* show a maximum of numbers during the summer months when there is ample food; owing to their rapid growth and reproduction several generations of each species may co-exist. In the winter the population is at a minimum and has a high percentage of immature individuals. The rapid increase in numbers during a favourable period is reflected in the hypertrophy and complexity of the reproductive organs to provide for the protection and feeding of the embryos but in no two genera—even the hermaphrodite forms *Omalogyra* and *Rissoella*—are these alike. Relatively large egg capsules are produced, each fixed to the weed on which the animals live and containing 1–3 heavily yolked eggs, surrounded by albumen, and a thick protective wall. In contrast to the rissoids there is no free veliger larva. The young hatch from the capsule in about 2 weeks. Since they are annuals and lay large, yolky eggs, considerable expenditure of energy is involved in their reproductive activities. So long as a simple system is capable of carrying on the other activities of the animal natural selection will clearly favour lack of complexity. Some of the anatomical peculiarities of this little group of animals are due to their minuteness and are often retentions of juvenile features.

*Omalogyra atomus* (fig. 184A), one of the most minute of British molluscs, as suggested by its trivial name, has a shell which measures only about 1 mm at its broadest diameter. There are many points in its anatomy in which it differs from other prosobranchs and some of these are specializations associated with its smallness. Yet it has a remarkable array of characters in common with the most primitive opisthobranchs, the pyramidellids, which superficially resemble prosobranchs and have been classified with them until recently. These characters are in the gut, the reproductive system and the organs of the mantle cavity.

Another small prosobranch which has adopted a mode of life similar to that of some rissoids is *Bittium reticulatum*, which belongs to a group higher in the evolutionary scale, the Cerithiidae. It lives under boulders and on shelving rock faces in the lower part of the beach and below, with algae and in both sunny and shady positions, feeding on diatoms (especially *Licmophora*, *Grammatophora* and *Gomphonema* according to Starmuhlner, 1956), filamentous algae, diatoms and detritus. The fixed egg coils (fig. 204C) are unlike those of any other British operculate. Though not common in Britain it is gregarious, and several may be found under one stone. It appears to be of that numerous group of prosobranchs the numbers of which have decreased in the last century; indeed

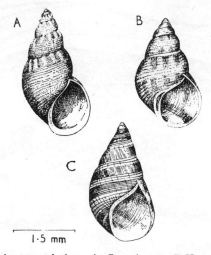

FIG. 293.—Shells of *Cingula* in apertural view: A, *C. semicostata*; B, *C. semistriata*; C, *C. cingillus*.

Marshall (1910–12) writes 'the sea shore at Falmouth consists largely of this species'. It may still be encountered in fair numbers in suitable situations in SW Ireland, e.g. Lough Ine.

A variety of carnivorous gastropods feed on semi-sedentary or sessile prey. The rocky shore with its abundance of sedentary and sessile animals is the habitat of a number of them of which the eratoids, muricaceans and pyramidellids are the best known. They attack forms which have a protective outer shell—bivalves, barnacles and other prosobranchs—and usually bore the calcareous covering to get at the soft tissues. Their feeding habits and ecology are dealt with elsewhere (p. 241). Others are ectoparasites and suck fluids. The majority of these are pyramidellids which settle near the host, accurately shoot the proboscis in the vicinity of the food, attach it by the terminal sucker and pierce the tissues with a stylet, the modified jaws; at the slightest disturbance feeding stops and the proboscis is instantly withdrawn. Each species has its food preference, which may be a particular bivalve, sedentary polychaete, echinoderm or coelenterate. These minute gastropods feed when the tide covers them, for they attack the prey when it is active. The larger animals, *Pelseneeria stylifera* and the eulimids, suck fluids and ingest loose cells of echinoderms. Their proboscis is stout and armed with neither radula nor jaws and, in contrast to the pyramidellids, it may become so firmly embedded in the host that it, rather than the foot, holds the animal attached. The third grouping of carnivorous gastropods feeds on sponges, coelenterates and ascidians. They may be seen moving over the surface of the colony, feeding as they go, and their egg capsules are attached to the surface or deposited in holes made in the tissues. Some select the deeper and softer parts of the body of the host for feeding, whilst others rasp the surface in a rather haphazard fashion.

In addition to the zeugobranchs *Diodora* and *Emarginula* which have an unspecialized method of feeding on sponges, *Cerithiopsis tubercularis*, *C. barleei*, *C. jeffreysi* and

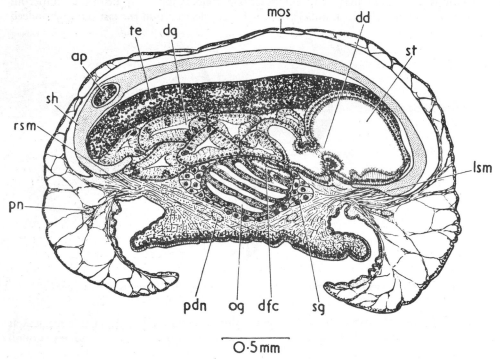

O·5mm

FIG. 294.—*Lamellaria perspicua:* transverse section through middle region of body. The spaces between shell, visceral hump and mantle are artificial.

ap, apex of visceral hump; dd, opening of duct of digestive gland; dfc, dorsal food channel in mid-oesophagus; dg, digestive gland; lsm, left shell muscle; mos, mantle lying over shell; og, oesophageal gland; pdn, pedal nerve; pn, pallial nerve; rsm, right shell muscle; sg, salivary gland; sh, shell; st, stomach; te, testis.

*Triphora perversa* have also adopted this diet, though not exclusively, for they also feed on diatoms and detritus. The larger specimens of these species attain a height of 8 mm. *Triphora* is readily distinguishable since it is sinistrally coiled, the only truly sinistral species of prosobranch in the British Isles. The organs of the mantle cavity and the nervous system are mirror images of those of the dextrally coiled *Cerithiopsis*. When these prosobranchs are examined alive it can be seen that the foot produces an abundant secretion which helps the mollusc to secure a holdfast as well as providing a viscid climbing rope by which it can lower itself through the water. The sole is truncated in front and tapers to a blunt point posteriorly, and there is frequently a transverse groove dividing it into an anterior half containing the anterior pedal gland and a triangular posterior half with the opening of the posterior pedal gland at its anterior border; this gland spreads into the haemocoel of the head. There are also glands opening to the surface of the sole lying in the epithelium and below. These carnivores have adopted a different method of feeding on sponges. They have a long acrembolic proboscis (Fretter, 1951b) which is narrow enough to pass through an osculum and reach the softer tissues, which are loosened by the jaws and raked into the buccal cavity by the numerous fine radular teeth. The spicular cortex which protects the sponge externally is avoided. *Triphora perversa* is comparatively rare intertidally. Its egg capsules have been seen by Pelseneer (1926b), fixed to a dead shell of *Glycymeris*; they have not been described from this country though they are of such a size that they could easily be overlooked. The larvae, however, are common in the Plymouth plankton, both inshore and offshore, and the adults are dredged on rock and gravel grounds. *Cerithiopsis tubercularis* is occasionally common on the SW and W coasts, clustered on the surface of *Hymeniacidon sanguinea*, in the tissue of which the egg capsules are deposited. It is also dredged, generally on sponges. Another species, *C. barleei*, is similarly associated with *Suberites domuncula*, feeding and depositing egg capsules on the sponge.

With the exception of *Velutina plicatilis*, the British members of the families Lamellariidae and Eratoidae feed on tunicates. *Velutina velutina* favours the large solitary forms *Phallusia* and *Styela* while *Lamellaria*, *Erato* and *Trivia* eat compound ascidians. In members of these families the mantle is reflected over the shell to a varying extent. In *Velutina* (fig. 128) the pallial edge is thickened by large connective tissue cells and blocks the entrance to the mantle cavity, except for the inhalant and exhalant passages, and there is only a slight reflection over the shell. In contrast, the shell of *Lamellaria* (sh, fig. 294) is permanently enclosed in the mantle (mos) from the late larval stage and the exposed pallial surface is roughened by warty tubercles in the adult and the edge thickened as in *Velutina*. In these members of the Lamellariidae there is no pallial siphon. The mantle in the eratoids and cypraeids (figs. 214, 296) spreads over the shell when the animal is active, often covering it completely, whilst it is produced into a long siphon (si) anteriorly in the eratoids.

Only *Lamellaria* and *Trivia* are intertidal and may be found with their food under boulders or on the slopes of gullies. They feed when the tide covers them. *Lamellaria* browses on *Leptoclinum* and *Polyclinum*, swallowing the test (which it cannot digest) to get at the zooids. Peach (quoted by Jeffreys, 1867) observed that *Lamellaria* migrates to shallower water to spawn, depositing the capsules in the test of the compound ascidian on which it feeds. According to Jeffreys spawning occurs from February to March. He recognized only one species of this genus, *L. perspicua*, and described it as dimorphic: the male, smaller, with the shell almost flat and the female with a convex, boat-shaped shell. Colour differences also exist between these 2 forms, which are now recognized as 2 different species (McMillan, 1939). The smaller *L. latens* has a thinner mantle and is light sandy-brown, yellowish or white and is flecked with black and sometimes yellow. *L. perspicua* is even more varied in colour and may be purplish or lilac-grey flecked with white spots, yellow mottled with red and white, or lemon with clear spots.

*Trivia* is one of the most conspicuously coloured of British prosobranchs on account of the pigmentation of its tissues, especially the mantle which covers the shell. In the young (fig. 295) the mantle is studded with conical projections, often branched, and is blotched with brown pigment; its colour is less pronounced than in the adult (Pelseneer,

1932). The adult mantle is yellow or orange-brown and the dark blotches run together to form conspicuous transverse lines (fig. 214). The foot is also pigmented with yellow and streaked with lighter or darker longitudinal lines. *Trivia* is the only British cowrie, formerly classified in the family Cypraeidae which abound in tropical seas. The warm water cowries attain a larger size and have a thicker and often deeply pigmented shell. In *Trivia* the shell is a pale flesh colour or is whitish and *T. monacha* is distinguished from *T. arctica* by 3 purplish-brown spots across the body whorl, though these are sometimes faint (Lebour, 1933*a*). The shell has no periostracum and the surface is always glossy. It is smooth in young specimens, even up to the time the adult shape has been acquired, when the body whorl hides the spire (fig. 28). In older specimens there is a sculpture of 20–25 fine thread-like ribs which cross the shell and extend to the mouth; some of these anastomose or are shorter and placed between others of full length. These ribs are added by the mantle when flexed over the shell.

When *Trivia* (fig. 214) is about to feed the siphon shows some activity and its tip sweeps over the surface of the ascidian. The animal frequently shows a preference for *Diplosoma listerianum* var. *gelatinosum*, in which the test is gelatinous and without spicules,

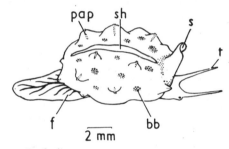

FIG. 295.—*Trivia* sp.: young animal, alive.
    bb, blotches of pigment on mantle skirt; f, foot; pap, papilla on mantle skirt; s, siphon; sh, shell; t, tentacle.

and the zooids, which are in clusters, have a meagre layer of test separating them. The tip of the proboscis is glandular and moves smoothly over the tunicate colony. The animal attacks any part of the test, biting pieces from it with the jaws to expose the zooids, which are swallowed whole (Fretter, 1951*a*). The test is not digested and can be traced into the faeces. The zooids are black and their passage one by one along the dorsal channel of the oesophagus, embraced by the longitudinal folds can be followed owing to the transparency of the tissues of the mollusc. In *Erato* (fig. 32) the inhalant siphon is used more obviously in the search for food. The animal moves slowly over the surface of *Botryllus* or *Botrylloides* lubricating its passage with secretion from the anterior and posterior pedal glands, and the long inhalant siphon is used as a sensory organ to lead the animal to a group of zooids. It will bend so that its tip momentarily covers the mouth of each zooid in turn, as though to test the inhalant water current (Fretter, 1951*a*). Chemoreceptors may also be concerned with the detection of food, though these perhaps lie in the osphradium on to which the siphon directs the water. It is the fully opened mouth of a feeding zooid which the mollusc seeks, and immediately one is selected the siphon is erected and the blunt introvert is plunged like a piston into it, its thickness stretching the opening. The mollusc settles for 20 min or more with the proboscis hidden in the zooid. It may be seen moving among the viscera, the jaws biting the tissues and the radula dragging them into the mouth. The test is avoided. Two zooids may be eaten in rapid succession. The pleurembolic proboscis is longer than that of *Trivia* and the tip is not glandular.

*Velutina velutina* may be collected from *Styela coriacea* and, like many of those proso-branchs which live on sponges and tunicates, resembles it in colour and in surface

7 mm

FIG. 296.—*Simnia patula:* 2 animals creeping over the surface of a colony of *Alcyonium digitatum*, on which they feed. The lower animal shows the blotched mantle spreading over the shell, the head and siphon (left) and the foot (right); the upper animal shows the anterior view of its foot, tentacles and siphon nearly withdrawn, head with short snout expanding distally around mouth.

texture. Secretion from anterior and posterior pedal glands and from the thickened edge of the mantle lubricates its passage over the test into which it bites holes with its jaws and then extends the proboscis to feed on the soft tissues. The epithelium of the proboscis has abundant mucous glands. A second species, *V. plicatilis*, is associated with *Tubularia* and other hydroids in the coralline zone of NE England and Scotland. It shares this liking for coelenterates with *Simnia patula*, which eats the flesh of *Alcyonium digitatum* and *Eunicella verrucosa*, and has also been found among tufts of *Tubularia indivisa*. Unlike most other carnivores *Simnia* has no introvert (fig. 296). There is a short snout which expands distally around the mouth. This expansion covers the contracted polyps, which are bitten off by a pair of strong jaws aided by the median and lateral teeth of the radula. These teeth have short blunt cusps. The marginals, 3 in number in each half row, are long and each tooth is deeply divided longitudinally into as many as 40 approximately equal parts, each shaped like a fork with 3–4 prongs. They brush up the tissues with a sweeping motion and direct them into the dorsal food channel of the buccal cavity. Thus they function like the simpler and more numerous teeth in the rhipidoglossan radula—indeed the feeding mechanism of *Simnia* is very similar to that of the sponge feeder *Diodora*.

The eulimids are ectoparasites and the least modified of a series of prosobranchs parasitic on echinoderms. They are free-living and specialized in respect of their method of feeding and the organs associated with this. Of those listed in the British fauna only 2, *Balcis alba* (fig. 140) and *B. devians* (fig. 297), are widely distributed and may be collected in numbers in their characteristic localities. *B. devians*, in which the shell measures 3 mm in length, is found in the same dredgings as *Antedon bifida* (Fretter, 1955a), roaming

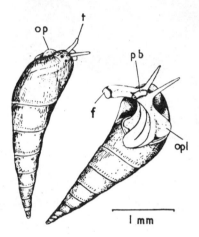

FIG. 297.—*Balcis devians:* two living animals, the right in ventral view, the left in dorsal. f, foot; op, operculum; opl, operculigerous lobe; pb, proboscis partially protruded; t, tentacle.

freely or attached to the base of a pinnule from which it sucks food (fig. 139) and one specimen has been found attached to its disc in the anterior interradius (Dimelow, 1959). It is not easy to disturb when feeding and is slow to withdraw the proboscis from the host. Its body is flecked with crimson and yellow like the tissues of the feather-star, though the colour is lost when the mollusc is starved. *B. alba*, which is often 18 mm long, is dredged in fairly shallow water and its frequent occurrence with *Spatangus purpureus* at Plymouth suggests that this echinoid may be its host, though the gastropod has never been seen feeding. It is probable that when the hosts of the various eulimids recorded in the British fauna lists are known, and their true ecological niches explored, they will appear in numbers greatly exceeding the solitary specimens which are now occasionally discovered.

*Pelseneeria stylifera*, also parasitic on echinoderms, is recorded from Plymouth on *Psammechinus miliaris* and *Echinus esculentus* and Jeffreys (1867) recorded it on *Echinus* from many other British localities at a depth ranging from 30–80 ft. Since then, however, it has become scarce. He observed the parasite creeping among the spines on the upper surface of the urchin, where he found as many as 40 clusters of spawn. Each globular egg sac is attached by a stalk to the test and contains 60–80 eggs (Lamy, 1928; Lebour, 1932*b*) which develop into typical veliger larvae. The protoconch and larval whorls persist as the characteristic styliform apex of the adult shell which has 3–4 tumid and rapidly enlarging whorls. The pseudopallium, rudimentary in the eulimids, where it lies towards the distal end of the proboscis, is larger in *Pelseneeria*, where it arises near the base of the proboscis and is reflected over the shell as the animal feeds; in more advanced parasites, which become embedded in the tissues of their host, it completely envelops the shell (*Gasterosiphon*) and even replaces it as a covering to the viscera (*Entocolax*). The proboscis of *Pelseneeria* and the method of feeding are similar to those of *Balcis*. *Pelseneeria* is said to be hermaphrodite (Koehler & Vaney, 1908), in contrast to *B. alba* in which the sexes are separate, and also, perhaps, *B. devians*, though no males of this species have been found.

Until recently surprisingly little was known about the pyramidellids and even now more than half of the 39 species mentioned by Jeffreys (1867) are described only as shells. However, the field naturalist is now alert to the possibility of finding a relationship between one of these ectoparasites and perhaps an annelid, echinoderm or molluscan host. Not only the minute size of these gastropods, but also the specialized habitat of each species, account for the obscurity which has surrounded the group. On the SW coast of England 2 species of *Odostomia* may be collected from the calcareous tubes of *Pomatoceros triqueter*, often hidden in crevices for protection. These are *O. unidentata*, the shell of which has a bluish tinge and straight-sided spire (fig. 135), and *O. lukisi* with an ivory white shell which appears very solid for its size. Sometimes *O. plicata* is in the same habitat and in contrast is yellowish in shell and soft parts. The feeding of the first 2 species is easily observed, for the animals are in no way timid (p. 252). The mollusc approaches the entrance to the calcareous tube of the host and may wait there for some time before the worm emerges to feed. It will attach its proboscis to a tentacle, pierce and then suck the worm for a minute or so at a time, unless disturbed. When feeding is over the pyramidellid may retreat to a more sheltered position and rest, with the foot and head partially withdrawn and the concavity of the tentacles directed forwards and downwards as though no longer interested in its surroundings (t, fig. 298B). *O. scalaris* settles at the edge of the shell of *Mytilus edulis* (fig. 138) and pierces the pallial tissues when the mussel is feeding, to suck blood from the pallial vein. The mussel seems undisturbed even though 2–3 parasites are feeding at one time. In rough conditions and between meals this species may be found sheltering amongst the byssus threads.

Similarly *Chrysallida spiralis* may lurk in any sheltered cranny between the irregular sandy tubes of *Sabellaria*. It feeds on this polychaete, though not by sucking the tentacles, which, unlike those of *Pomatoceros*, are moved about to pick up food particles. When the proboscis of *Chrysallida* is rolled out from the head its tip is gently directed on to the median face of a tentacle along which it slides towards the mouth and gradually disappears out of sight, hidden in the gut of the polychaete. The region which it punctures and sucks is unknown.

In contrast to these species *Turbonilla elegantissima* burrows to seek its food (fig. 137). It is found amongst silt and sand which spreads between boulders and ledges and provides suitable niches for the sedentary polychaetes *Audouinia tentaculata* and *Amphitrite gracilis*. The tentacles of these polychaetes extend between the particles for a considerable distance and are sought by the mollusc, which pierces them and sucks blood; it will also attack the gills of *Amphitrite*. The proboscis, stouter than that of *Odostomia*, is pushed through the silt to reach the worm, accurately sensing its direction. It emerges from a subterminal opening on the dorsal surface of the mentum which gives it a firm support. While the mollusc feeds buried in the silt, particles mixed with hypobranchial secretion can be seen leaving the exhalant channel of the deep and narrow mantle cavity; the wall of this channel is extended beyond the shell as a spoon-shaped siphon. At other times the parasite

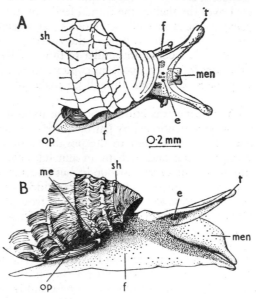

FIG. 298.—*Turbonilla fenestrata:* A, animal in dorsal view; B, seen from the right; only part of the shell is drawn.
　　e, eye; f, foot; me, mantle edge; men, mentum; op, operculum; sh, shell; t, tentacle.

will wander some distance from its host to a more superficial position on the shore, the remarkably short foot slowly dragging behind it the elongated, pointed shell, which is occasionally just raised from the ground.

One pyramidellid, *Turbonilla jeffreysi*, has been found in association with the hydroid *Halecium*, and in a short terminal region of the oesophagus every cell is filled with un-exploded nematocysts, though they have not been traced elsewhere. It seems likely that these must be voided later, for there is no indication that they are used in defence or stored.

# CHAPTER 22

# THE PROSOBRANCHS OF OTHER MARINE HABITATS

OCCASIONAL pelagic prosobranchs may be taken from the waters of our W and N coasts. They belong to two genera, *Ianthina* and *Carinaria*, and are characteristic of tropical and subtropical seas. *Ianthina* is a surface form dependent on wind rather than water movements and the mass strandings on our coasts may be correlated with prolonged periods of westerly winds. Wilson & Wilson (1956) have summarized the occurrence of *I. janthina* on the N coasts of Cornwall and Devon in August 1954 when the strandings were probably the largest for 50 years. The siphonophore *Velella* drifts with this carnivorous prosobranch and is its food, and perhaps the

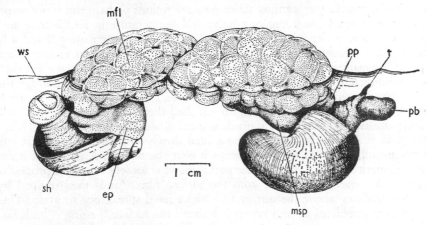

FIG. 299.—*Ianthina janthina:* animals in natural position at surface of water.
ep, epipodium; mfl, mucous float; msp, mesopodium; pb, proboscis; pp, propodium; sh, shell; t, tentacle; ws, surface of water.

source of its purple colour. Both are gregarious, drifting together apparently by chance.

*Ianthina* (fig. 299) floats at the surface with the foot (pp, msp) uppermost, by means of a bubble raft (mfl) which spreads back over the mesopodium and rests on the surface film (ws). No operculum is present in the adult. The coiled visceral mass and the mantle cavity are enclosed in a delicate violet-blue shell (sh). This is deeper in colour on the underside, which is directed uppermost in the water, and light below. The body of the animal is heavily pigmented and has a deep purple tinge, and the bifid tentacles (t) are black. The right epipodium of the foot (ep) has a more delicate appearance and expands over the shell to form a transparent membrane which, on occasions, shows rhythmical undulations. The head is large, the pretentacular region being extended to form a broad proboscis (pb) with a large terminal mouth. Behind the tentacles is the stout mobile neck which may swing the head rapidly over an arc of more than 180°. The animal has no visible eyes, so that other senses must be used to recognize the food which it hunts probably by the well developed olfactory sense in the tentacles placed lateroventrally on the head. The outer branch of the tentacle was thought by Bouvier (1886) to be an eye stalk; there is, however, no evidence for this and it appears to be part of the tentacle. Minute eyes are present (Thiele, 1928) each with a lens, lying ventral to the cerebral ganglia under the muscles of the body wall posterior to the base of the tentacle.

Mr Peter David (Hardy, 1956) has observed *Ianthina* feeding on *Velella* and gradually clearing the tentacles and blastostyles from the underside of the float until only the horny skeleton remained. The food is attacked by the radula (p. 202), which has in each row a large number of similar teeth (laterals), and jaws protect the buccal cavity of the mollusc against its own teeth (Simroth, 1895). The proboscis is moderately distensible and the radula can be protruded some distance from the mouth. The range of food is unknown, but Laursen (1953) found remains of siphonophores in the gut and also of *Halobates* and copepods. Bouvier (1886) gave *Porpita* as the food of some species and Risbec (1953b) and Laursen (1953) both have evidence that cannibalism is practised. Thus it would appear that the carnivore seizes anything that comes within its reach. Unfortunately the specimens stranded around our coasts refuse to feed even when offered *Velella*, and the gut is empty when they are found: perhaps this is not surprising in view of the altered conditions of salinity and temperature in which they are then living. The mantle cavity of *Ianthina* contains a large monopectinate gill and a hypobranchial gland which produces a purple secretion. This secretion escapes from the cavity and gradually diffuses through the water, and in some species may tint the float. It has been suggested that the fluid anaesthetizes the prey (p. 121) and although there is little evidence for this David (Hardy, 1956) has observed that *Velella* which are being attacked by the mollusc appear lifeless, do not shed their tentacles as they normally do when they die, nor contract them as much as usual when placed in formalin.

If the float of *Ianthina* be removed the animal slowly sinks and may retreat into the shell, though turbulence in the water keeps it near the surface. A new float is formed only if the anterior third of the foot (the part somewhat loosely called the propodium in the literature) comes into contact with the surface film. Air is then trapped by the anterior tip reaching above the surface film like a hand spread out to grasp. The foot closes over the bubble of air and brings it beneath the surface, passing it back into the funnel. This is a transverse depression lying across the middle of the foot into which open many glands (Thiele, 1897). Mucus from these, and from the anterior pedal mucous gland, forms a skin around the bubble, which is then freed for this to harden in contact with the water. The float appears to be attached to the posterior end of the sole, the surface of which is deeply pigmented and carries numerous longitudinal glandular ridges. Successive bubbles are pressed against one another and cemented together by further secretion as the propodium glides over them, and eventually mutual compression causes them to assume a polyhedral shape. During the early stages of this process the movements of the foot with its large epipodial lobes help to keep the animal at the surface. The fully formed float is strong and difficult to crush or puncture so that it successfully maintains the animal's position in rough seas, and must, in general, be an important orientating organ in view of the fact that neither statocysts nor effective eyes occur (Thiele, 1929–35). David (quoted by Wilson & Wilson, 1956) observed that many small *Ianthina* feeding on *Velella* had no floats and suggested that they may be a hindrance during feeding (when attachment to the siphonophore will keep the mollusc at the surface) and so are abandoned.

Three species of *Ianthina*, *I. janthina*, *I. exigua* and *I. pallida*, are occasional visitors to our shores. Two of these, *exigua* and *pallida*, attach egg capsules to a median longitudinal band of mucus on the underside of the float (Fraenkel, 1927*b*) which may have a length of 5 cm in *I. exigua* or 7 cm in *I. pallida*, the number of egg capsules being approximately 50/cm length in *I. exigua* and 60–80/cm in *I. pallida*. Each capsule in *exigua* contains 17 eggs on the average: in *pallida* the corresponding figure is 5,500 (Laursen, 1953). *I. janthina* is the most common visitor to this country and is viviparous (p. 378), the young being born as veligers with an operculum.

These prosobranchs are protandrous hermaphrodites and the reproductive processes are unusual in that during the male phase there is no penis, and spermatozeugmata are responsible for the transportation of sperm to the female and that fertilization seems to occur in the ovary (p. 378). In other internal features the ianthinids approach the scalids, possessing tubular salivary glands, no trace of oesophageal glands, a ptenoglossan radula and a tendency to produce a purple hypobranchial secretion. They also differ from other prosobranchs in that the spermatozeugmata and packets of larvae leave the mantle cavity on the left (inhalant) side (Wilson & Wilson, 1956). To escape in this way against the respiratory current they must be expelled by muscular contraction and perhaps directed to this side by the movements of the propodium observed by these authors. The normal escape route on the right is blocked by the epipodium. It is tempting to see in this the reason for the novel position of the oviducal aperture on the left side of the sole of the foot described by Laursen (1953) in *I. pallida*.

In contrast to *Ianthina* only isolated individuals of the two heteropods *Carinaria mediterranea* and *C. lamarcki* are found off Britain, and these do not occur at the surface. Indeed one specimen of *C. lamarcki* came from a depth of 1,000 m W of the Outer Hebrides (Hardy, 1956), and others from 250 m (information from Dr J. H. Fraser, who kindly lent the specimens). It is uncertain as to whether this is their normal depths at such latitudes. One suggestion is that they are carried with water of high salinity which passes outwards from the Mediterranean through the Straits of Gibraltar, beneath the influx of Atlantic water which replaces it, and travels northwards at a low level. It is surprising that these planktonic forms appear to maintain themselves in such changing conditions.

Like other heteropods *Carinaria mediterranea* (fig. 300) actively pursues its prey and the form of the body is considerably modified. It swims in an inverted position with the foot (pp, mpt) uppermost. The head-foot is large, elongated and somewhat laterally compressed and is transparent. The visceral mass is small and is covered by a patelliform shell which protects only the viscera and organs of the pallial complex, for neither head nor foot can be withdrawn into its shelter. The shell is glossy and characterized by a serrated dorsal keel (mk) marked with radial lines due to the extension of growth lines into it; at the apex is the persistent helicoid larval shell (pch). It is so fragile that whole specimens are come by only with difficulty and Woodward (1913) mentioned that as much as £100 has been paid by collectors for a single *Carinaria* shell. The enlargement of the head-foot is due to a post-tentacular elongation of the head as well as a smaller terminal enlargement to form a snout. There is a terminal mouth surrounded by a band of circular muscles which allows the protrusion of the large buccal mass. The prey is caught and pulled into the gut by the very powerful lateral and marginal teeth of the radula. The head bears a pair of retractile tentacles (t) and at the base of each is an eye (e) surrounded by a capsule and capable of being turned in all directions by its musculature. The eye can be protruded from the capsule or withdrawn for protection. The foot lies

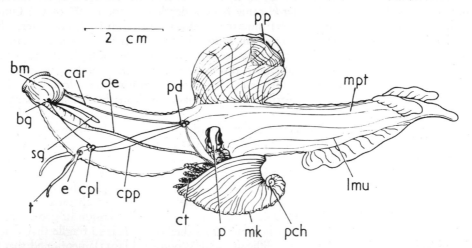

FIG. 300.—*Carinaria mediterranea:* male drawn in swimming position with the morphologically ventral
surface uppermost. The body wall is sufficiently transparent to allow most of the contents of the
head-foot to be seen except the visceral loop, which is too delicate. The shell obscures the organs
in the visceral mass which are shown in fig. 301. For clarity the columellar muscle and the muscles
of the head, except those of the buccal mass, have been omitted.

bg, buccal ganglion; bm, buccal mass; car, cephalic artery; cpl, cerebropleural ganglion; cpp,
cerebropleuropedal connective; ct, ctenidium; e, eye; lmu, longitudinal muscle; mk, median
keel on shell; mpt, metapodium; oe, oesophagus; p, penis; pch, protoconch; pd, pedal ganglion;
pp, propodium, forming sucker on mesopodium; sg, salivary gland; t, tentacle.

ventral to the visceral mass, where it expands into a large muscular fin, and also tapers posteriorly. Along the posteroventral edge of the fin in both sexes is a sucker (pp). It is said to be used by the copulating partners to secure a firm hold of one another and is aided in this by glands lying over its surface (Gegenbaur, 1855). It is confined to males in *Pterotrachea* where Krasucki (1911) has described a ganglion associated with its musculature. Franc (1949) has shown that in *Firoloides desmaresti* the fin is formed by the mesopodium and its sucker by the propodium, whilst the metapodium bears an oper-

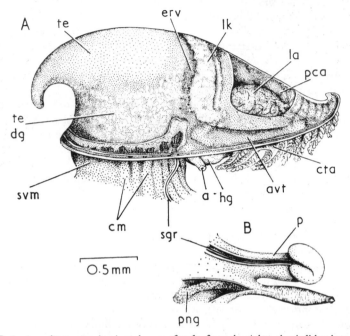

FIG. 301.—*Carinaria mediterranea*: A, visceral mass of male, from the right; the shell has been removed; B, details of penis, the appendage to which has been opened at its base.

a, anus; avt, afferent branchial vessel partly formed from transverse pallial vein; cm, columellar muscle; cta, ctenidial axis; dg, digestive gland; erv, efferent renal vein; hg, hypobranchial gland; la, auricle; lk, left kidney; p, penis; pca, pericardial cavity; png, gland on penial appendage; sgr, seminal groove; svm, stalk of visceral mass; te, testis.

culum, later lost. The outer layer of the body wall is composed of epithelium overlying a transparent connective tissue of a very specialized nature and is papillated. The muscles are deeper and are grouped in bundles running for the most part in a longitudinal or oblique direction, to form a sheath which encloses the spacious haemocoel, some being attached to the shell to form the horseshoe-shaped shell muscle (cm, fig. 301). The papillae are formed of chondroid tissue which is also found in other parts of the body, particularly (in *Pterotrachea*) the snout, which it helps to shape and make rigid for feeding (Krasucki, 1911). In the connective tissue are stellate cells surrounded by a clear jelly, which they secrete, and this is the main substance of the outer layer of the body wall. Embedded in it are other types of cells (Simroth, 1896-1907) and plates of a special reflecting tissue.

The ctenidium (ct, cta, figs. 300, 301A) projects from beneath the anterior part of the shell and is unusual in its structure and position. The axis, which is pectinate, extends across the opening of the shell and the branches, which are graded in length from the base of the axis to the tip, bear bipectinate filaments. The gill therefore resembles that of the diotocardians more than that of monotocardians. The mantle cavity is of negligible size, for the wall to which the gill is attached has grown forwards and downwards (bringing with it the heart) until it is almost level with the mouth of the cavity. The heart (la, fig. 301A), like the gill, is median and anterior and is of considerable size, in keeping with the haemocoel. The organs normally associated with the right side of the mantle cavity of a prosobranch—rectum (a), genital duct, renal opening and hypobranchial gland (hg)—are clustered in a very restricted area. This appears to be due to the hypertrophy of the left side of the mantle skirt and the ctenidium. The osphradium, however, retains its original position on the left edge of the mantle skirt and appears as a long narrow strip of ciliated and glandular cells.

The sexes of heteropods are separate and males of *Carinaria* are distinguished by the penis (p, figs. 300, 301B), which is split into dorsal and ventral halves and lies on the right side of the body, midway between the base of the fin and the free edge of the shell. An open seminal groove (sgr, fig. 301) passes from the male pore in the mantle cavity to the penis and continues along the median wall of the dorsal and stouter of the two branches, the true penis. Here the groove is broad and deep and ends distally at the swollen tip. The penis appendage bears at its tip the opening of a prostate gland (png) which is a blind tube extending into the haemocoel. No observations have been made on the function of this appendage. The secretion which it discharges may be prostatic, or it may be ejected in the vicinity of the female opening to secure the position of the penis during copulation.

Through the transparent body wall can be seen the long oesophageal region of the gut (oe, fig. 300), the strap-like salivary glands which open to the buccal cavity (sg), and much of the nervous system. The oesophagus is a straight tube without glandular outpouchings running back to the left side of the visceral mass, and the anterior part is swollen to form a crop; it is about half the length of the body. The animals are rapacious feeders capable of pursuing rapidly moving prey. Woodward (1913) stated that he took 6 small fish from the gut of a single *Carinaria*, each nearly as long as the mollusc itself. They were presumably packed into the oesophagus, where digestion occurs (Hirsch, 1915). *Pterotrachea* (found in the Mediterranean and N Atlantic) will seize living Heteronereis by the middle of the body so that the two halves fold together and the prey is swallowed whole. This is a rapid process and a worm 2·7 cm long may be swallowed by a *Pterotrachea* 6·6 cm long in 10–20 minutes. The whole body of the heteropod is flung into strong contractions, bending back and forth during the swallowing. The mollusc can also break pieces from larger masses of food which cannot be swallowed whole. The mid-gut, into which the digestive gland opens, is short and hidden in the visceral mass, and can be little but a passage-way between oeosophagus, digestive gland and the short intestine.

The nervous system of *Carinaria* has a most unusual plan, for with the post-tentacular elongation of the head the pedal ganglia (pd) are far removed from the cerebropleurals (cpl) and lie near the anterior end of the fin. Consequently the cerebropedal and pleuropedal connectives are elongated and have become united on each side (cpp). The visceral loop is normal but extremely long, since the ganglia on it lie in the stalk of the visceral mass. The nerves are very slender and cross in the neighbourhood of the ganglia.

Another feature which imparts a strange appearance to the system is the occurrence of pedovisceral connectives linking the supra-oesophageal ganglion to the left pedal and the sub-oesophageal ganglion to the right (Brüel, 1915, 1924a, b). This anomalous connexion may have a functional basis in making the correlation of pedal and visceral activities more effective.

A minor consequence of the elongation of the nerve ring which removes the pedal ganglia from the cerebrals is the fact that the nerve to the statocyst, which is very large, does not pass through the pedal ganglion on its way from the cerebral ganglion to the sense organ.

The eggs of *Carinaria* are laid in strings. Fertilization is internal and each egg is embedded in albumen and then provided with a shell. They escape from the female aperture in a single row close to one another (Gegenbaur, 1855) and surrounded by a protective secretion. Veligers with a bilobed velum develop in 3 days. The albumen and surrounding shell in *Pterotrachea* are secreted by glands attached separately to the oviduct but communicating with one another. The eggs passing down from the ovary, according to Krasucki (1911), enter the albumen gland and receive a layer of albumen, pass thence to the shell gland, where they are enclosed in a shell, and then return to the oviduct down which they pass to the mantle cavity.

Two prosobranchs which are dredged from soft substrata and do not occur intertidally are *Aporrhais* and *Turritella*. They are specialized for this habitat in different ways. *Turritella communis* is a sedentary filter feeder usually living just beneath the surface of muddy and sandy gravel, where its position can be detected by two depressions marking the inhalant and exhalant openings to the mantle cavity; the tip of the exhalant siphon is often visible. A veil of tentacles around the inhalant opening prevents the ingress of large particles and excessive silt. *Aporrhais pespelicani* lives at the surface of sandy mud, muddy sand or sand, or will construct itself a burrow just beneath the surface (see fig. 303C) with inhalant and exhalant channels further apart than those of *Turritella*. Yonge (1937) concluded that it remains there for a day or so at a time whilst the long proboscis searches around for food. This may be morsels of plants, though at the greater depths at which this genus is found (70–100 f) it must feed on other things, probably dead organic matter. Both prosobranchs have a shell with a long spire which may be dragged behind as they creep. In *Turritella* the shell (fig. 37A) is light yet progress appears laborious, for the foot is small. The shell of *Aporrhais* (figs. 29B, 302) is thick and heavy, and unique amongst British prosobranchs in the enormous expansion of the outer lip (ol), developed only in fully formed shells. The lip is produced into a broad flap with three angulated processes, also a spur running parallel with the spire and fused with it along the greater part of its length, and finally a terminal process (tol) which shields the inhalant pallial siphon and has its tip bent downwards. The mantle (me) spreads towards the edge of these extensions and the effective beat of its cilia is away from the mantle cavity. The opening to this cavity is constricted and the operculum (op) which closes it is a narrow, though stout, transverse strip with a surprisingly small area of attachment to the foot. When the animal is creeping it can be seen that the free blade-like part of the operculum projects upwards and to the left, away from the expanded lip of the shell.

*Aporrhais* can move over the surface in spasmodic jerks, displaying remarkable agility. When it does this the sole of the foot is placed firmly on the substratum, the shell and head lifted high off the ground by the upper part of the foot narrowing to form a stalk on which these pivot, and in a single swing forwards the mouth of the shell and the head are brought in front of the foot. The shell then sinks to the ground and with the aid of the enlarged outer lip maintains its position while the foot is lifted clear of the surface and brought forwards to the level of the snout. This completes a single step, and after a rest the sole is firmly pressed on the ground once more and the cycle recom-

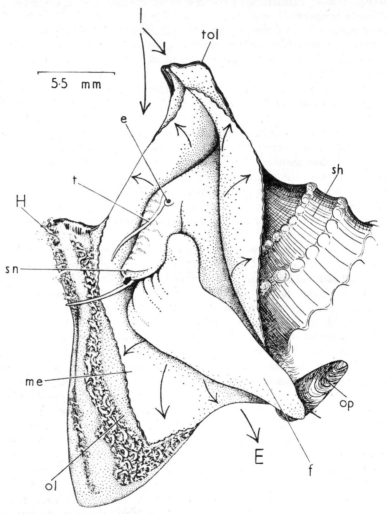

FIG. 302.—*Aporrhais pespelicani*: animal partly extended. Arrows on mantle edge show direction of ciliary rejection currents.

E, exhalant area; e, eye; f, foot; H, *Hydractinia* growing on outer lip; I, inhalant area; me, mantle edge; ol, outer lip showing thickening due to age; op, operculum; sh, shell; sn, snout; t, tentacle; tol, termnal projection of outer lip over inhalant area.

mences. The completion of one cycle takes about 10 secs, with a similar or longer rest period separating successive steps (Weber, 1925). Obviously this method of movement is correlated with the shape and weight of the shell. When the direction of movement is changed the head and visceral mass are rotated on the foot and may be pivoted round an obtuse angle left or right. If the shell be overturned the animal rights itself by extending the head and foot (in the usual manner for a prosobranch) stretching the foot posteriorly and bringing its tip to the substratum, always on the columellar side of the shell away from the expanded lip. Here it gains a firm purchase and will press the blade-like expansion of the operculum into the soil. Using this as a pivot the body is swung over.

The shell of *Aporrhais* thickens considerably with age and the sculpture of nodules and tubercules is worn down, partly with burrowing. The under surface of the expanded lip is also smoothed for this is dragged along the ground and covered to some extent by the mantle. It is perhaps surprising to find unworn grooves on this under surface covered by epizoic growth. Fig. 302 shows a colony of *Hydractinia* (H) near the edge of the thickened lip (ol) and adjacent to the area covered by the mantle (me), where it will benefit from the water currents created by the snail. Epizoic growths are not uncommon on the upper surface of the shell, many of them being obvious to the naked eye and sometimes they are so thickly clustered that the shell is recognizable only from its outline. Out of a haul of 60 *Aporrhais pespelicani* from Kames Bay, Isle of Cumbrae, Barnes & Bagenal (1952) found 30 thickly covered with *Balanus crenatus* and only 6 quite free. In other areas a higher percentage of shells is free from epifauna. The habitat in which the mollusc lives is poor in sites on which sessile animals needing a firm holdfast may settle and their colonization of the shell suggests that the prosobranch spends less time beneath the surface than was once thought (Yonge, 1937). The firmness of the substratum and the abundance of food, at or beneath the surface, may determine the extent to which burrowing occurs. It has been suggested that the consistent absence of sedentary organisms on young *Aporrhais*, in which the outer lip has not yet expanded, and their presence on the older shells in the same locality, may be due to a change in habitat (Barnes & Bagenal, 1952). Young, unworn shells of prosobranchs, however, are usually free of epizoic growth whatever their habitat. It would certainly seem that the breadth of the expanded lip would make burrowing more difficult and provide resistance against sinking. A second species *A. serresiana*, occurring on soft mud in deep water off the Shetland Isles, has an even more expanded lip with longer digitations and the shell is lighter and the animal more delicate. It tends to sink but then pushes forwards rather than burrowing downwards. According to Yonge (1937) *A. pespelicani* will actively burrow unless placed on soft mud. It moves obliquely downwards, the proboscis frequently pushing aside the muddy gravel or sand and making a way for the foot to move forward. The worn terminal process is the first part of the shell to be pressed into the substratum and then the expanded lip cuts its way through as the columellar muscle pulls somewhat jerkily on the shell. A succession of movements, often separated from one another by a considerable pause, brings the animal beneath the surface, where it takes up a horizontal position and its presence is indicated only by the displacement of the ground. Soon, however, at the edge of the mound which covers it the tip of the long snout appears as it makes an inhalant channel. An exhalant one is similarly constructed when the head is moved round under the expanded lip of the shell and the proboscis is pushed upwards (fig. 303c). A strong pallial flow of water is now set up and maintained by the lateral cilia on the filaments of the large ctenidium. The walls of the inhalant and exhalant channels are strengthened by the proboscis which moulds them and applies mucus from unicellar glands over its surface.

Secondary sexual differences in *Aporrhais pespelicani* concern not only the penis and the elaboration of the pallial genital ducts (p. 361) but also certain conspicuous ciliated areas leading from the exhalant region of the mantle cavity. In the male (fig. 179A) such an area (ca) lies between the anus (a) and base of the penis (p), and in the female (figs. 179B, 303B) a tract (ctr) leads down the side of the foot (f) to the anterior pedal mucous gland (apg, fig. 303A). It is probable that the eggs, which measure only 0·24 mm across and are surrounded by albumen and a tough outer covering, make their way along this gutter to be attached to sand grains or pieces of debris by secretion from the

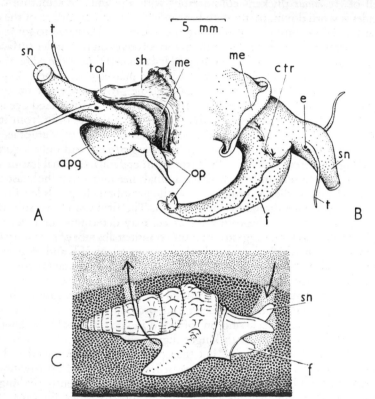

Fig. 303.—*Aporrhais pespelicani:* A, animal partly extended from shell showing extended snout; B, right side of anterior part of body of female showing ciliary tract from mantle cavity to anterior pedal gland; C, diagram of animal burrowed into substratum; arrows indicate direction of water and ciliary currents. C, after Yonge.

apg, anterior pedal mucous gland; ctr, ciliated tract; e, eye; f, foot; me, mantle edge; op, operculum; sh, shell; sn, snout; t, tentacle; tol, terminal expansion of outer lip of shell over inhalant area.

pedal gland; there is no ventral pedal gland which could effect this. They are deposited singly or 2 or 3 together (Lebour, 1937).

*Turritella communis* is gregarious and a hundred or so animals may be collected from a small area in a favourable locality. They occur at a depth ranging from 3–100 fathoms where, undisturbed by the tide, they may feed continuously, perhaps remaining buried in the same position for long periods of time. The many-whorled shells (fig. 37A) are referred to as 'screws' by old English naturalists. Their proportions reflect the shape of the mantle cavity which is long and tapering and is subdivided into inhalant and exhalant compartments by the large ctenidium. In a frontal view of the animal the openings of these two compartments are readily distinguishable, for the wide inhalant one is hung with a curtain of pinnate tentacles (pt, fig. 64). The ctenidial filaments, like those of other filter feeders, are narrow and elongated. They are laterally flattened and each is attached to the ctenidial axis by its base and fixed to the adjacent mantle skirt on the right of the axis by the basal third of its dorsal surface. In this way their long axes lie roughly parallel with the roof of the mantle cavity and their tips curve over to rest on the floor near the deep food-collecting gutter (fg, fig. 57 and see p. 100). Particles which enter this gutter from the gill and the ciliary currents on the floor of the mantle cavity are entangled in mucus. This is secreted by the hypobranchial gland (hg), by a strip of cells (the so-called endostyle) along the ctenidial axis and by the gill filaments and the walls of the groove. The food-string can be seen rotating forwards, following the course along the right side of the head, to collect in a spoon-shaped projection at the end of the groove which forms a platter from which the mollusc feeds. At intervals, one stroke of the radula pulls in a considerable length of rope from the platter and the groove.

The exhalant siphon (es), projecting a short distance from the shell, is a physiologically closed tube formed by two folds of pallial tissue. The force of the exhalant current is strengthened by the cilia over the rectum and the open pallial genital duct, so that the ovoid faecal pellets of compacted particles (fig. 127D) are shot clear of the animal's head. Their expulsion is reinforced by a slight but sudden retraction of the head-foot into the mantle cavity.

In captivity animals will burrow close to one another. The resultant disturbance in the water, due to the combined feeding currents, appears considerable, yet there is surprisingly little disturbance of the mud. The process of burrowing is rather slow, with minimal displacement of the substratum. The foot pushes diagonally downwards in a series of jerky movements until the spire disappears and a mound marks the position of the larger whorls. The foot then moves the mud away from the entrance to the mantle cavity, pushing it to the right in front of the head where a small heap accumulates, and secretion from the pedal gland consolidates the particles (Yonge, 1946). The head and foot are now partially withdrawn and the operculum brought forward so that its spinous edge acts as a subsidiary filter; the entrance to the mantle cavity is enlarged, and the mollusc lies apparently motionless. The exhalant stream of water displaces the mud to the right of the head so that a channel leading from the siphon is established.

The gregarious habit of *Turritella* and the delicate adjustment of organs associated with the mantle to guard against the rigours of living in a muddy situation may be correlated with the lack of a penis in the male and the open pallial duct in both sexes.

Lebour (1933c) suggested that the veligers of this prosobranch stay only a short time in the plankton and settle to the crawling stage when the shell has only about 2–2¼ whorls and the larvae are 2–3 weeks old. The larva has no special characteristics foreshadowing the adult structure and resembles many other prosobranch veligers. It would appear that the ciliary method of feeding characteristic of the adult is not adopted until the mollusc is older, and that the radula alone is responsible for collecting the food in the younger stages. Graham (1938) suggested that even in the adult the radula may be used at times for collecting food from the substratum and Lebour (1933c) has observed them browsing on the algal growth on the sides of plunger jars. Young individuals may be found living with the adults (Cullercoats) or may live apart from them (Plymouth, Millport). At the last place they have been collected with rissoids at 5 fathoms in Kames Bay.

Species of *Natica*, sometimes called necklace or sand–collar snails on account of their spawn masses (figs. 204E, F), are our only mesogastropods restricted to large sandy bays, where their empty shells provide one of the few types of home available for small hermit crabs. They are carnivores preying on lamellibranchs, which are hunted in the sand. In the British Isles there are 5 species, though 2, *N. pallida* and *N. fusca* are stated to be rare. These and *N. montagui* are dredged and do not occur on the shore; indeed *N. pallida* has been recorded elsewhere at a depth of 2,300 m. Probably these so–called rare animals

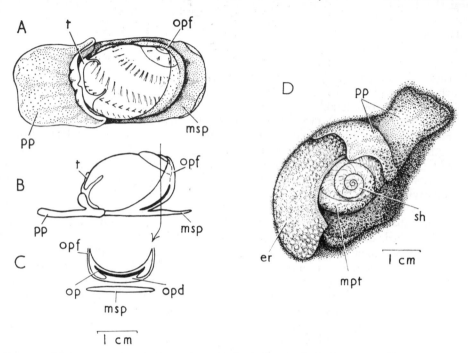

FIG. 304.—*Natica catena:* A, animal creeping, seen from above to show disposition of parts of foot; B, diagram of the same seen in left lateral view; C, ventral half of a vertical section at plane indicated by arrow; D, spawning beneath surface of sand.

er, egg ribbon; msp, mesopodium; mpt, metapodium; op, operculum; opd, operculigerous disc; opf, opercular fold of metapodium; pp, propodium; sh, shell; t, tentacle.

are more abundant than is realized. In the United States and Canada the family is well represented in numbers and species, some growing to a much larger size than any naticid does here (as much as 4 in across); in some areas the snails are a serious threat to the well-being of the clam industry.

*N. catena,* the larger of the two British species, specimens of which may be picked up near LWST, measures 1·5 in across the shell and *N. alderi* is about half this size. They may be seen moving, sometimes with remarkable rapidity, just beneath the surface of the sand and the course of each is marked by a trail which is left behind the heap of sand covering the shell. The prey would appear to be sensed at some distance for the mollusc may be seen in pursuit of a bivalve which is a foot or so away. Moreover, it has been found that areas recently colonized by *Venus* spp. are soon discovered by the carnivores which invade the area in numbers (A. D. Ansell, personal communication). In 1934 an abundant population of *N. alderi* occurred on the Hunterston Sands, Firth of Clyde, which survived until 1936, when it had become greatly reduced. It was apparently

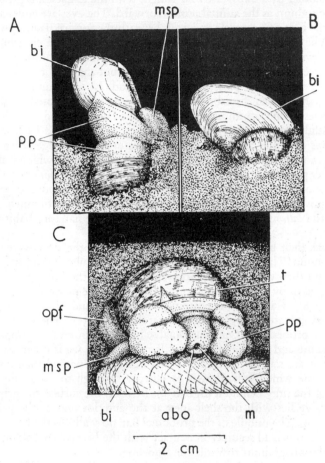

FIG. 305.—*Natica alderi:* stages in the manipulation of a bivalve prior to boring. A, the bivalve is gripped and raised preparatory to burrowing; B, the prosobranch is dragging the bivalve into the sand, having turned it so that it enters hinge first; C, the prosobranch has assumed the boring position, the proboscis is beginning to extend and is supported by the inturned corners of the propodium; the bivalve now lies with the hinge away from the prosobranch. After Ziegelmeier.

abo, accessory boring organ; bi, bivalve; m, mouth with radula; msp, mesopodium; opf, opercular fold; pp, propodium; t, tentacle.

feeding on the cockles (*Cardium edule*) in the sand and was itself eaten by overwintering swans.

The foot of *Natica* is exceptionally broad and large for the size of the shell (fig. 304). Not only is it used as a plough in moving through the sand, but an extension of the propodium (pp) is reflected over the shell anteriorly, covering the entrance to the mantle cavity, and an extension of the opercular lobe of the metapodium (opf, figs. 304, 305) covers the posterior part of the shell and conceals the operculum (op). In this way the shell is all but hidden. The cephalic tentacles (t) are widely separated, flattened and joined to one another by a transverse fold which, with the tentacles, is pressed against the shell by the propodium as the animal pushes forward. The eyes are covered, for they are small, each at the base of a tentacle and sunk beneath the surface tissues; in some naticids eyes are lost. The mantle cavity, so effectively isolated from the environment, is large and has a well developed gill (ct, fig. 180A). Delicate movements of the propodium regulate the pallial stream of water and keep from it all but the smallest particles which are stirred up by the animal as it passes through the sand. *N. catena* and *N. alderi* withdraw rapidly into the shell when disturbed and the opening is then closed by the operculum. In contrast species of the common American genus *Polinices* need considerable stimulation before withdrawing, and as the foot contracts and is folded back into the mantle cavity, fountains of water are ejected from pores around its edge (Ziegelmeier, 1958) for the foot has a water vascular system (Schiemenz, 1884, 1887) which is used to enlarge it. No such water pores have been found in British species. *P. josephinus* swims by undulating movements of the foot, mainly the propodium. The propodial expansion and the ability to swim is a convergent resemblance with the lower tectibranchs, the Bullidae; indeed the word *Natica* is supposed to be derived from the natatory habit of the mollusc (Jeffreys, 1867).

Naticids attack their bivalve prey beneath the surface of the sand, enveloping the shell with the propodium. The prey remains passive while a circular hole is drilled through the shell (p. 246) and then the proboscis, accurately fitted to the hole, ingests the contents. These are dragged in by the radula and pieces cut off by the powerful jaws. According to Ziegelmeier (1958), if a naticid is creeping in the sand and crosses the point where a bivalve is buried, it starts to dig at once in search of the prey. The sensitivity appears to be located in the propodium. Once the bivalve has been found it is gripped by the foot, covered with slime and the shell examined for damage to see if it can be eaten without boring. (Naticids are said to eat freshly killed flesh.) The naticid then converts its grip on the shell to one which will allow it to burrow through the sand (fig. 305A), which it does dragging the prey behind it (fig. 305B). Beneath the surface the grip is rearranged so that the bivalve lies with the shell apex at the anterior end of the propodium—the position for boring. The middle of the propodial flap now allows the proboscis to emerge (fig. 305C), and this is held securely in contact with the bivalve by folding the right and left halves of the propodium towards the mid-line.

Another prosobranch which lives in a somewhat similar habitat—muddy sand—and which may be encountered intertidally is the wentletrap shell, *Clathrus clathrus*. It is occasionally found in the SW of England but is rare in the N. Three other species of the same genus, which, one supposes, will probably prove to have the same habitat and habits as *C. clathrus*, but which are much more seldom seen, are *C. clathratulus*, *C. trevelyanus* and *C. turtonis*. *C. clathrus* is more commonly met on the shore during spring and summer, and this suggests that there may then be an onshore migration for spawning purposes. The spawn (fig. 211) consists of a series of small pyramidal egg cases encrusted with sand particles (Vestergaard, 1935; Clench & Turner, 1950) which is laid either on mud or muddy sand or on clean sand. In muddy environments the spawn is said to be laid on or near green weeds. From the capsules there emerge free-swimming veliger larvae which develop a smooth protoconch. Later the shell (fig. 142) develops a series of varices which give extra strength since its successive whorls are only just in contact one with the other, and may perhaps prevent boring by naticids by not allowing these predators to grip the shell correctly (Ankel, 1938*b*).

The mode of life of these animals is almost wholly unknown. Their internal anatomy (figs. 100, 101), partly described by Thiele (1928), and observations by Ankel (1936*a*) fit with those that we have ourselves made in suggesting that the animals are carnivores, and probably specialized carnivores. The facts upon which this rests are given on p. 260, but what the particular prey of the animal may be it is difficult to tell: Ankel (1936*a*, 1938*b*) suggested that *Clathrus* feeds upon sea anemones, but it hardly seems necessary to have the elaborate poison apparatus which it possesses to deal with such slow-moving prey, whilst other feeders on coelenterates seem to avoid the effects of their nematocysts without having to inject poisons into them. However, Thorson (1958) has observed an American scalid *Opalia crenimarginata* feeding on the anemone *Anthopleura xanthogrammica* by pushing the proboscis, which expands to considerable size, into the tissue of the host and 'sucking on its host for hours or even for days'. A feeding process which can be described as 'sucking' is a little difficult to understand in view of the absence of any structure in the gut comparable to the sucking bulb of pyramidellids, nor does it seem to involve the use of the powerful ptenoglossan radula which *Clathrus* possesses. If this were used in a more rapacious method of feeding the need for an anaesthetic (either from the salivary glands or the purple secretion of the hypobranchial gland as, perhaps, in *Ianthina*) would be understandable. The presence of the radula seems to make it likely that *Clathrus* has an alternative method of feeding on an active animal, perhaps an annelid or nemertine, which has to be quietened before it will let itself be hauled into the gut. This idea fits in with Thorson's further remarks that *Opalia* is only a temporary parasite and leaves the anemone on which it has been feeding to move freely over the beach.

# CHAPTER 23

# THE PROSOBRANCHS OF BRACKISH AND FRESH WATERS AND OF THE LAND

A NUMBER of prosobranch gastropods, all of which are herbivores or detritus feeders, have spread inland from their ancestral littoral home and colonized both freshwater and the land. Useful summaries of the habitats and distribution of these in the British Isles will be found in Boycott (1934, 1936) and in the census of the Conchological Society (1951). The 10 British species which live in freshwater retain the ctenidium, which indicates that they have reached this habitat by way of estuaries where there are a few other species capable of withstanding the fluctuations of salinity encountered there. In addition a number of marine forms penetrate the lower reaches of estuaries (e.g. *Patella vulgata, Gibbula umbilicalis, Littorina saxatilis, L. littorea, Buccinum undatum, Nassarius reticulatus*). These animals presumably retain isotonicity and their tissues can tolerate transitory low salt concentration, but their lack of osmotic independence means that they have not the ability to enter freshwater. However, one species, *Potamopyrgus jenkinsi*, appears to have overcome this barrier within recent times, for, though it was confined to brackish water until the end of the nineteenth century, it has subsequently spread with remarkable rapidity to both hard and soft freshwater masses, large and small. *Potamopyrgus* belongs to the Hydrobiidae, the same family as 3 more of our freshwater snails, 2 species of *Bithynia* (*B. tentaculata* and *B. leachi*) and *Bythinella scholtzi*, and also 4 brackish water species—*Hydrobia ulvae, H. ventrosa, Assiminea grayana* and *Pseudamnicola confusa*. Five of the 6 remaining freshwater species are lower meso-gastropods belonging to 2 families, the Valvatidae of the northern hemisphere and the Viviparidae which, except for S America (where ampullariids occupy corresponding niches), have a world-wide distribution. *Theodoxus fluviatilis*, the last species of our inland waters, is an advanced diotocardian occurring also in Europe and N Africa. Though in other groups of the animal kingdom freshwater animals have often given rise to terrestrial forms, in the prosobranchs it is from a littorinid stock that our 2 terrestrial species have evolved. The marine members of this family are typically shore-dwellers and some exhibit strong terrestrial tendencies.

Like the majority of animals which live in freshwater the prosobranchs have modified their reproductive methods. The need to suppress the free larval stage and to enclose eggs in capsules has required the development of copulatory organs and since the more primitive freshwater forms belong to groups in which these are not normally found they have been evolved from parts of the body not used for this purpose elsewhere in the prosobranchs (Neritidae, Viviparidae). The penis of *Bithynia* may also be anomalous as its innervation is unorthodox (p. 350). Additional modifications of reproductive behaviour are found in viviparity and parthenogenesis. Three of the species are viviparous (*Viviparus viviparus, V. contectus, Potamopyrgus jenkinsi*) and retain the young in the pallial oviduct until they are small snails, although viviparity occurs in only 2 of all the British marine species (*Littorina saxatilis, Ianthina janthina*). *P. jenkinsi* is also parthenogenetic. Freshwater forms produce few eggs compared with their marine relatives (and all are characterized by the relatively small size of the gonad). The eggs are heavily yolked and protected by a thick capsule which is securely fastened to weed or some other substratum.

Some pre-adaptation for freshwater and terrestrial conditions is found in the operculate snails of the intertidal zone of the rocky shore which are subjected to periods of desiccation and rain, and a considerable range of temperature. The external shell, which protects the larger part of the surface against the osmotic inflow of water, is responsible for their resistance to these conditions. Moreover the method of reproduction of species with no free larval stage ensures that the young never leave the part of the shore occupied by the parent, though sheltered crannies afford protection until the snails are large and their shells thick. The salt concentration in freshwater may be 500 times less than in the sea and this presents the most formidable barrier to the majority of molluscs. All which have overcome it (lamellibranchs and gastropods) have an external shell characterized by a well developed periostracum which guards against erosion, and they are able to maintain a considerable osmotic gradient between their body tissues and the external medium. For some it has been shown that absorbing cells in the external surface and in the kidney tubule take up salts from dilute solutions (Krogh, 1939), which is presumably the deciding factor in the colonization of inland waters.

An examination of the literature reveals a vast number of mutually contradictory accounts of the morphology and biology of the freshwater prosobranchs. This seems to be partly traceable to the fact that these animals are much more sensitive to variation in their environment than are their marine relatives and also to the fact that freshwater environments differ more among themselves than do their marine counterparts. For these reasons it is desirable to consider the locality in which a particular piece of work was carried out as an integral part of its results.

A few operculates can live in soft waters where the concentration of calcium salts is low. The most resistant of the British species in this respect is *Valvata piscinalis*, which is the only prosobranch of Loch Lomond (Hunter, 1953*b*; 1957). The calcium content of the water is 2·3–3·3 mg/l, yet *Valvata* has considerable stores of calcium carbonate in the body apart from its shell. These are found in cells of the digestive gland (Cleland, 1954) and in large connective tissue cells which penetrate all spaces amongst the viscera. This special connective tissue, which is also present in other freshwater prosobranchs, was described by Bourne (1908) in *Theodoxus fluviatilis* though he did not observe the calcareous concretions within it. They can be seen readily in living tissue, and in most freshwater species the refringent spherules are visible through the skin.

A richer fauna of prosobranchs is found in inland waters which are hard. These tend to have more plant growth and consequently more places for shelter, particularly against currents, and more humus which provides food. To what extent the degree of hardness is a precise factor in determining distribution is not known, nor easy to find out, since each habitat has a complexity of ecological factors which are difficult or impossible to study singly. In the Thames between Oxford and Reading 8 of the 10 species of prosobranchs occur and only the 2 rare ones, *Bythinella scholtzi* and *Valvata macrostoma*, are absent. In the case of *Bythinella* this may be due to the chance of its introduction in the N, rather than an unsuitability of the habitat. *V. macrostoma* is recorded only in marshes and drainage ditches with a good fauna in the counties of Hampshire and Sussex and in E Anglia.

The quiet and brackish waters of estuaries, salt marshes and saline pools are favoured by the 2 species of *Hydrobia*. The phenomenal abundance of one of these, *H. ulvae* (figs. 306B, 307A), has attracted the attention of many workers so that more is known about it

20

than the second, *H. ventrosa* (fig. 306c). In some places the distribution of the two over-laps. The association of *H. ulvae* with the sea lettuce *Ulva lactuca* accounts for its specific name, though this link is by no means as definite as was once thought and the mollusc

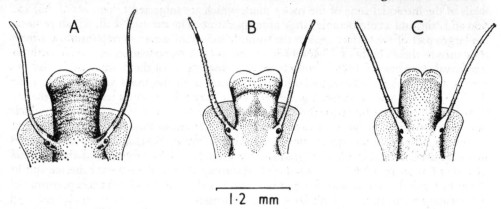

1·2 mm

FIG. 306.—Dorsal view of head of A, *Potamopyrgus jenkinsi*; B, *Hydrobia ulvae*; C, *H. ventrosa* to show pattern of pigmentation. In heavily pigmented animals the pattern may be more obscure.

will browse over the surface of other weeds such as *Enteromorpha*, and occurs in myriads on apparently bare mud. The shell is conical with an elongated blunt spire, the body whorl making up about half the height, which may be as much as 10 mm, and the

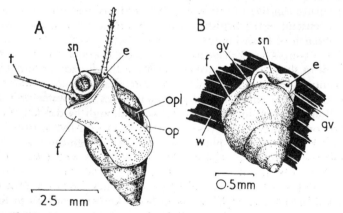

2·5 mm

0·5mm

FIG. 307.—A, *Hydrobia ulvae*: swimming and feeding on surface film. B, *Assiminea grayana*: male crawling, seen from above.

e, eye; f, foot; gv, groove from mantle cavity to edge of foot; op, operculum; opl, opercular lobe embracing anterior and lateral margins of operculum; sn, snout; t, tentacle with characteristic pigment patch; w, weed.

breadth 5 mm (though such a size is exceptional). It is rather thick and smooth and may be yellowish, brown, jet-black, reddish or even white in colour. Nicol (1936) recognized a difference in the distribution of the colour varieties in the lochs of North Uist. Here the strand form has a smooth, brown shell with very shallow sutures and is often 9 mm in height. Small numbers of this form may also be found in the lochs, where the typical individual has a rough eroded shell with deep sutures, and is dark reddish-brown; the erosion of the shell suggests that these individuals are parasitized (Rothschild, 1941*b*). Lambert (1930) found red the dominant colour in ditches on the marshes of the Thames estuary and attributed it to rust accumulating on the surface, which may also be green with algal growth. In females the spire of the shell is longer than in males and the whorls more tumid (Quick, 1920). The shell of *H. ventrosa* is smaller (8·4 × 3·2 mm), smooth, glossy and thin, with 6 rounded or ventricose whorls and the mouth auricular. It is horn coloured but appears dark with the pigmentation of the underlying tissues.

The different habitats of these 2 members of the family Hydrobiidae and of a third, *Potamopyrgus jenkinsi* (distinguished from each other by the pigmentation of the head (fig. 306) (Seifert, 1935)), may be illustrated by reference to the neighbourhood of the estuary of the River Adur at Shoreham, Sussex, where they were described by Ellis as occupying quite distinct areas and not occurring together (Ellis, 1932). In parts of the Ladywell Stream, not far from its junction with the estuary, and in dikes associated with it, *P. jenkinsi* was found living in water of a salinity of 0·88‰ or less, and usually associated with a fauna of freshwater insects. In a lagoon cut off from the estuary, but into which sea water percolated at high tide *H. ventrosa* **was** plentiful as a member of a marine fauna; the salinity of the water was 24·9‰. *H. ulvae* occurred in shallow pools on the saltings which are reached only by high spring tides and at other times may dry. After rain the salinity of the pools may fall to 13‰ and in hot weather, when a maximum temperature of 30°C has been recorded, it may rise as high as 34·7‰. *H. ulvae* flourishes in these extremes of salinity and temperature, sharing the habitat with a number of euryhaline crustaceans. Ellis also found it in a gravel pit on the river bank living amongst sea blite with the small, rare *Truncatella subcylindrica*. The salinity here at high spring tides was 24·8‰. During neap tides the floor of the basin dried and terrestrial arthropods invaded the area and were active whilst the molluscs were dormant.

Somewhat different salinity tolerances of these hydrobiids have been recorded in other localities in the British Isles and under experimental conditions suggesting that a combination of features regulates their distribution and not salinity alone. Although McMillan (1948*b*) found that under artificial conditions *H. ventrosa*, collected from Larne Lough, Co. Antrim, requires a minimum salinity of 24·5‰, which is similar to that in which it was living in the Adur estuary, yet this species occurs on peaty sand at Loch Obisary, North Uist, where the salinity is recorded as 10‰. Indeed Nicol (1936) found its salinity tolerance similar to that of *H. ulvae* (10–34‰). Johansen's records (1918) of the molluscs of Randers Fjord showed that *ulvae* can endure a salinity as low as 1‰, whereas the lowest record for *ventrosa* is 5‰. Jessen (1918) recorded the former species in freshwater in the Baltic, and Frömming (1956), in his study of the biology of mid-European snails, gave the salinity range for *H. ventrosa* as 10·9–2‰, and for *H. ulvae* water of full salinity to a salinity only as low as 10‰. *H. ulvae* is usually thought of as the more marine of the 2 species since it is less rarely cut off from the direct reach of the sea, and is indeed common on open beaches, where it may protect itself against the tide and desiccation by burrowing. *H. ventrosa*, on the other hand, lives in quiet lagoons not in direct communication with the sea and never where the salinity approaches that of normal sea water. In favourable places large numbers occur.

McMillan (1948*a*) has suggested that in the British Isles distinct biological races of *H. ulvae* can be distinguished, which differ in salinity tolerance, and perhaps the same holds for *H. ventrosa*. Her experimental results showed that a collection of *H. ulvae* from

Burton Marsh, Cheshire, behaved normally in 5% sea water (0·17‰), whereas another from 9 miles away was inactivated by 22% sea water (7·7‰), and a third from Holywood, Co. Down, died in water of this salinity. These differences in tolerance may be correlated with conditions in the habitat of each group of animals: only in Burton Marsh are the animals normally exposed to such low salinities; in the Holywood ditch they are subjected to inflows of normal sea water.

Thamdrup (1935), in his study of certain species of the Wattenfauna of Denmark, related oxygen consumption and temperature with habitat. The optimum temperature is highest for *Corophium*, *Pygospio* and *H. ulvae*, which are active at the surface of relatively dry, ebb tide areas—indeed this temperature is higher than the highest water temperature recorded for the area. Oxygen consumption rises abruptly with temperature and for *Hydrobia* it is calculated as 35 mg/kg/hr at 2°C and 490 mg/kg/hr at 20°C. Ellis (1925), working on the same species of *Hydrobia*, found that its acclimatization to freshwater is improved by warmth.

*Hydrobia ulvae* favours a rather firm mud or muddy sand and is also found in abundance on gravel and fragmented 'shillet' (clay slate) with silt (Spooner & Moore, 1940); in fact its distribution is almost independent of the nature of the ground. It dominates salt marshes, where large numbers congregate in the mud around plants or in other damp places, and is recorded on the shore of Plymouth Sound, though its presence in such marine habitats is linked with the local occurrence of freshwater. Its usual level on intertidal mud flats is near mid-tide, or on the upper third of the beach, and it is one of the dominant species of the *Macoma balthica* community or its *Scrobicularia* variation (Linke, 1939). In mud flats of the Cardiff area, however, the greatest frequency of the snail is towards low water, for the mud is too soft in the upper reaches of the shore (Rees, 1940). The areas it inhabits may be flooded only at spring tides, and so dry at neaps that the mud fissures, but *Hydrobia* can withstand long periods of exposure and survives in an apparently semi-desiccated state (Quick, 1920). In pools and damp hollows on the saltings conditions for growth are often more favourable than on mud flats and the snail attains a greater average size (Rothschild & Rothschild, 1939). *H. ulvae* is very sensitive to oxygen lack and appears to avoid putrid mud where *H. ventrosa* remains alive and apparently unharmed (Lambert, 1930), nor does it, like this species, appear to favour continuous immersion. *H. ventrosa*, perhaps owing to its smaller size, occurs on fine soft mud and often prefers weed to any other habitat. Nicol (1936) found it on all types of substratum except pure shell sand in the brackish water lochs of North Uist.

The intertidal area of St John's Lake in the Tamar Estuary, Plymouth, is only one of many localities around our coasts where a dense covering of *H. ulvae* spreads over acres of mud and fig. 308 shows the abundance of the species in a section across this Lake. The population density, which is based on numbers per sq m at 13 stations (indicated by vertical lines), is shown diagrammatically above the traverse. This survey was completed before the *Zostera* plague, when the ground between +1·0 m and −0·25 m was covered by a fairly continuous growth of *Zostera hornemanniana*. Here the density of *Hydrobia* appeared to increase, but the snail was also conspicuously abundant over stretches of mud devoid of such vegetation, and its numbers have not suffered significantly with the decline of the weed.

The behaviour of *Hydrobia ulvae* on exposed mud flats devoid of macroscopic vegetation shows how accurately it is adjusted to the changing conditions which prevail there. The snail creeps over the surface which is damp or covered by quiet water, but when the mud is stirred and the water made turbulent by the incoming tide, or if the surface dries, it burrows, sometimes to a depth of 1 cm. It emerges when favourable conditions return and creeps about, grazing on surface diatoms, blue-green algae or fine detritus; the long snout is swung from side to side and the movement of the radula and jaws can be seen through the surface tissues. As in other rissoaceans the tentacles have non-vibratile and vibratile cilia which sweep particles across them. In *H. ulvae* (figs. 306B, 307A) there is a hypertrophy of the ciliation of the left cephalic tentacle in the form of oblique lateral rows and this, together with the way in which the tentacle is used, suggests that it is of

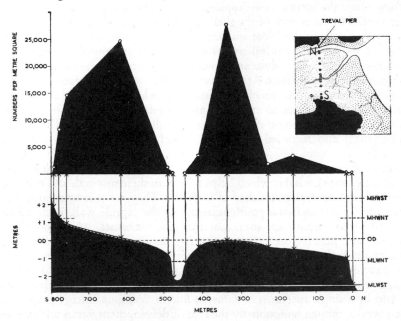

FIG. 308.—Graphs showing distribution of *Hydrobia ulvae* in St John's Lake, Tamar estuary, Cornwall. The lower half of the figure is a section along the line NS indicated in the map inset. Stations on this are marked by circles on the map; permanent water below MLW is white, land black and the dotted line on the stippled area is approximately MTL. The position of these stations is marked on the figure by arrow-headed lines and their distance from the channel at Treval pier is given in metres on the abscissa; ordinates on the left of the lower half of the figure give heights in metres from ordnance datum (OD); on the right tidal levels; ordinates for the upper half of the figure give number of snails per m². The broken line over the lower figure indicates occurrence of *Zostera*; white circles on the upper figure position of stations.

considerable sensory importance. The operculum (op) is not readily visible, for, when the animal creeps, its anterior and lateral edges are overhung by the opercular lobe of the foot (opl) as a protection against the ingress of silt between it and the underlying metapodium. The rapidity with which it creeps and the rhythmical movement of the snout (sn) are characteristic of rissoaceans, and a further similarity is the possession of a pallial tentacle which protrudes from the shell on the right side. Tracks are left over mud similar to those of *Littorina littorea*, but only 1·5–2 mm broad. They are often irregular and twisting, measuring 15 cm or so in length, though some may be twice as long (Linke, 1939). A trail of mucus (from the anterior pedal gland and a well developed sole gland) is laid along the path, and the closely-set, intertwining slime bands of countless snails form a network over the surface of the flat. Here, also, the spindle-shaped faecal pellets, which escape when the animal is active, accumulate in a layer sometimes 1 mm thick. On the Jadebusenwatt, Wilhelmshaven, where fantastic numbers of these *Hydrobia* occur, Linke (1939) described aggregations of pellets 15 cm deep. In drained areas, especially of soft mud, conspicuous pits, which are regularly spaced and often only a few millimetres apart, mark the positions of snails which are buried. Each lies in a more or less horizontal position with the mouth of the shell facing upwards. Snails which do not burrow when the surface dries (typically young ones recently settled on the shore) get air entrapped in the mouth of the shell, and the surface of the shell may dry, so that when water covers them they float and are lifted on the tide. On marshes they are soon caught up on the herbage, but on mud flats they may be dispersed over considerable distances. In stormy weather adults and young are scattered by the tide and they may be washed together in great masses. At the base of a dike wall on the Jadesbusenwatt Linke (1939) described an accumulation of living snails 20 m long, 2 m broad and on an average 2 cm thick, though in places 20 cm thick, and he estimated the number as 55,000,000. This phenomenal population on mud flats and marshes provides food for fish and birds, and Linke (1939) also recorded the opisthobranch *Retusa truncatula* as an importan predator.

The egg capsules of *Hydrobia ulvae* are fixed to the shells of other members of the community (fig. 204A), a habit which helps to ensure their survival, and occasional ones may be found elsewhere, as on the shell of a *Mytilus*. They are camouflaged and protected by particles of detritus and sand grains adhering to the capsule wall. Each contains 3–25 eggs, according to locality (p. 401). On the Jadebusenwatt, where breeding occurs between May and June (before and after this egg laying is rare), 92% of the snails have egg capsules attached to their shells in the former month. The range in numbers on each shell is 1–22 and a single capsule has 5–18 eggs. Linke (1939) calculated that a female will lay 300 eggs during a breeding period, which is few compared with the thousands which may be laid by a single specimen of *Littorina littorea*. Veligers emerge from the capsule in about 3 weeks, though undoubtedly the rate of development varies with the temperature, and Rothschild (1941a) stated that in captivity the larvae are freed 10 days after the eggs are fertilized. The pelagic phase may last a month or more (Linke, 1939), yet some authors have suggested that it is very short (Lebour, 1937; Thorson, 1946) and Smidt (1944) concluded that in certain places it may be suppressed. After the velum is lost the small snails with shells about 1 mm in length get washed about by the tide and dispersed. Smidt (1951) working on a population at Franø, Denmark, calculated that 10% of the eggs survive to the young snail stage, which is a high survival rate compared with that of lamellibranchs in the same habitat. The success of the species is partly due to its rapid multiplication and means of dispersal, for it will colonize newly available areas with remarkable speed. Such colonization has been recorded for the mud flats of the River Tamar and other estuaries in the Plymouth vicinity (Spooner & Moore, 1940), where during a long period of drought early in 1938 higher salinities than usual were registered upstream, and, in the same year, the species extended its range into these areas.

Rothschild (1941b) studied the growth rate of a population of *Hydrobia ulvae* inhabiting an isolated pool in the saltings of the River Tamar where conditions for growth are favourable. Here the main spawning period is autumn, though on nearby grounds it extends into the spring, and spring and summer are quoted as the breeding time in other parts of the British Isles. Rothschild found that by February the largest of the snails from the previous autumn spawning measure 1·25–1·75 mm long. Maximal growth occurs in

April–July when this autumn spat group overtakes the previous year groups and all merge to form a population in which the measurements for length of shell show a peak of about 5·75 mm. By November, when early individuals of the next spat fall are appearing on the bottom, a further growth of barely 0·25 mm has been made, and over the rest of the life span an increase of not more than 1 mm may occur. From the age of 17 months the snails begin to die off. In captivity they are known to live over 5 years (Quick, 1924). For the effects of parasites on this species see p. 603.

*Assiminea grayana* (fig. 307B), which is another brackish water species, has in comparison a very limited distribution. It is locally abundant on the E coast of England between Kent and the Humber and occurs at levels which are under water only at spring tides. Here it may be found in large numbers on grass and sedge stems and in the mud at their base. It seems to dislike immersion and in captivity crawls out of water to regions of high humidity, feeding on decaying herbage. It is the only British representative of the Assimineidae, a family closely related to the rissoids and resembling them in organization. However there are certain obvious differences. The tentacles are extremely short and broad, suggesting that each is represented only by the base which bears the eye; they are similar to the fully contracted tentacles of *Bythinella* (t, fig. 312C). The snout, unusually broad and bilobed, moves over the substratum as the animal creeps, and the foot is broad, short and abundantly supplied with glands of which the largest is the anterior gland provided with a lengthy sagittal duct; there are neither pallial nor metapodial tentacles. On both right and left sides a groove leaves the mantle cavity and passes forwards and downwards towards the sole of the foot (gv, fig. 307B), a feature which is also found in *Truncatella* (fig. 315A). There is no ctenidium, but 2 exhalant ciliated ridges, one on the mantle skirt and the other on the dorsal body wall, maintain water movements through the mantle cavity, the mantle epithelium acting as respiratory surface; on occasions, a bubble of air may be seen in the cavity. The intestine is long and elaborately coiled. The male is much smaller than the female and the penis is relatively enormous and arises from the mid-dorsal surface of the head; the prostate on the vas deferens is hypertrophied and, in a mature individual, is the largest gland in the body. The organization of the female duct resembles that of *H. ulvae* except that the pallial section is narrow, markedly muscular and runs through the centre of the glands which open into it; the muscles are concentrated in a circular layer beneath the ciliated epithelium lining the duct. The duct ends on a long papilla which is equally muscular and is probably to be related to the deposition of egg capsules in a semi-terrestrial habitat. The bursa copulatrix at the upper end of the pallial duct is extremely large and like many other organs is surrounded by the kidney sac which acts as a body cavity. The kidney, indeed, is a vast thin-walled space pushing amongst the viscera and resembling in this respect the kidney of the hydrobiids which live in fresh and brackish water. In this species, however, it is even larger, and, as in *Bithynia*, sends an extension forwards alongside the rectum and pallial genital duct. The kidney opens to the posterior end of the mantle cavity and only its central part adjacent to the opening is lined by excretory tissue. Unlike the freshwater hydrobiids *Assiminea* appears to have no special connective tissue in which calcareous matter is stored.

*Assiminea* spawns in late spring and summer. At the time of copulation the male mounts the shell of the female and inserts the penis into the oviduct whilst the female creeps about. The egg capsules, each with a single egg, may be deposited singly in the mud, dropping, as the animal crawls, from the right groove which leaves the mantle cavity in the vicinity of the anus and genital opening (Sander, 1950, 1952). Alternatively, a conglomerate mass of capsules, faecal pellets (which pass along the same groove) and mud may be packed together by the foot, so that up to 80 capsules may be aggregated. The wall of the capsule is tough and thick for the secretion which forms it is well compacted by the muscular oviduct.

*Truncatella subcylindrica* is a small hydrobiid snail, sometimes known as a 'looping snail' because of its method of locomotion, which recalls that of a looper caterpillar (fig. 315). It is restricted in the British Isles to a special type of habitat on the S coast of England, but is reasonably abundant where it does occur: it lives in muddy places at the level of high tide, where it may be only occasionally wet by sea water, and is commonly associated with the plants *Suaeda maritima* and *Halimione portulacoides* (Ellis, 1932). In these circumstances it is more exposed to air than water, but retains a small ctenidium in the mantle cavity and can withstand continuous immersion for a considerable period. When moving in air over the surface of the muddy ground on which it lives, it extends the snout, which is very extensible, and grips the substratum with its tip (fig. 315A); it then pulls the foot up to grasp the ground just behind the snout (fig. 315B), dragging the shell in its rear, releases the snout and starts the process once again. Sometimes the foot slides along the surface of the ground as it is drawn forwards, sometimes it is lifted clear. Related to this method of movement are the expanded tip of the snout and the small, rounded sole of the foot. According to Pilsbry (1948) the animals are said to creep in the ordinary way when placed in water, but this was not the case with those specimens which we have seen. The animals appear to feed on detritus of vegetable origin, and on small unicellular plants in which their habitat is rich, and their alimentary tract is similar to that of other rissoaceans, with a simple oesophagus, a crystalline style and a short intestine. The nervous system is concentrated with cerebral, pleural and parietal ganglia in contact on each side, though the visceral ganglia are in the usual posterior position. The eyes are large, crescentic and lie displaced towards the mid-line at the base of the tentacles (e, fig. 315C). The kidney is not large as in *Assiminea* and possesses a small nephridial gland. The viscera lie in a reticulate connective tissue.

The most unusual features of *Truncatella subcylindrica*, however, relate to the shell and the reproductive apparatus. The former, in the mature animal, is short and consists of about 3 whorls with almost parallel sides (fig. 314B), because of the fact that at maturity the snail breaks off the apical part of the spire having previously sealed the opening with a calcareous plate, an activity from which the generic name is derived. In young animals, before this truncation, the shell has the form of a tall cone, as in most hydrobiids, though more slender (fig. 314A). The sexes are separate and the male has a long penis with a well developed prostate on the vas deferens. In the female the genital duct (fig. 314C) is more complex: the ovarian duct (od) is connected to the pericardial cavity by a long gonopericardial duct (gpd), distal to which are a receptaculum seminis (rcs) in the form of a finger-shaped tube, and a pouch, presumably the bursa copulatrix (bcp). It then enters the capsule gland (cp) in which albumen and mucus-secreting parts may be distinguished, running through these as a ciliated ventral channel. Unexpectedly, however, the neck of the bursa copulatrix, the functional significance of which we have not established, connects with the left kidney (lk), an arrangement also found in *Circulus striatus* (Fretter, 1956; see fig. 188A), and there is also a duct linking the bursa copulatrix directly to the base of the receptaculum seminis. If the bursa is indeed used for the reception of seminal fluid this tube would then permit the sperm to migrate easily to the receptaculum. The eggs are presumably enclosed in capsules and deposited amongst the plants and stones on which the animals live, perhaps escaping from the mantle cavity by the ciliated groove which runs between the foot and the base of the proboscis (gv, fig. 315A) as in *Assiminea*. The larval stage is suppressed but no other observations on the reproduction of this species appear to have been made.

*Potamopyrgus jenkinsi* (Smith), rissoid-like in appearance and measuring about 5 mm in shell length, has been a popular species for study amongst field naturalists. Though Frömming (1956) suggested that it may have been introduced into this country as early as 1859, it was first described in 1889 from specimens taken from brackish water at Plumstead, in the marshes alongside the Thames (Smith, 1889). It was recorded in freshwater in 1893 when Daniel took it from a canal at Dudley. Its sudden appearance from an unknown source, rapid invasion of freshwater and subsequent abundance there aroused considerable interest. Small size and abundance favoured its rapid distribution for it may be easily caught up on the bills or feet of birds and transported elsewhere; for instance, Coates (1922) recorded the mollusc adhering to the outside and entangled in the lamellae of the bill of a scaup duck shot at Perth. In about 30 years *Potamopyrgus* spread through the greater part of England and Wales by active migration and passive transport, though it is still unrecorded from considerable areas in Scotland (W and N) where the first record was 1906 (Hunter & Warwick, 1957). There is a suggestion that its relatively slow spread in Scotland as compared with England may be due to the lack of a canal system which is so important in the distribution of a freshwater fauna (Boycott, 1936). The snail spread from the British Isles to other countries in NW Europe where the first records show it in brackish water (Bondesen & Kaiser, 1949; Hubendick, 1950) and later ones reveal its spread to freshwater, though in Sweden the species had not been observed in inland localities up to 1947 (Hubendick, 1947).

Taylor (1900) and Boycott (1917) were the first to observe the lack of males in this species, and later (1919) Boycott stated from experimental evidence that it is parthenogenetic; this was later confirmed by Quick (1920). With the exception of *Campeloma rufum* (Mattox, 1938) and members of the family Melaniidae (Jacob, 1957) it is the only undoubted parthenogenetic prosobranch which is known and like these species it is viviparous (Robson, 1920, 1923)—in the pallial oviduct there may be a brood of about 35–40 (bp, em, fig. 309). These features, together with the fact that this is one of the rare prosobranchs which may reproduce throughout the year, contribute to its abundance and rapid spread. According to Frömming (1956) the young are full-grown in 4–5 months and few individuals live longer than 7 months. In some areas it disappears as rapidly as it came and the reason for this is unknown, though such behaviour is commonly found in species recently introduced into a new habitat.

The shell, typically yellowish, is often so encrusted as to appear black, while other individuals in the vicinity remain clean; the deposit may obliterate the sutures and become concentrated in wart-like blotches. Warwick (1953) suggested that it is due to bacterial activity, which may be high in the mud where *Potamopyrgus* spends part of its time. The animal may be found on stones and weed, or buried in the superficial layers of mud and sediment of brackish or freshwaters where there is some current, and there may be numbers of these snails in the merest trickle; it is rarer in standing water. In favourable places it occurs in enormous numbers, blackening the weed and mud over which it crawls. It is known to provide food for carp (Dean, 1904) and large numbers are reported from the stomachs of trout (Whitehead, 1935). It can live and reproduce in salinities up to 17‰, but according to Adam (1942) none of the young hatching at a salinity above 18‰ attains maturity. Perhaps the occurrence of this species in North Uist (Nicol, 1936) in a salinity as high as 23‰, and in Randers Fjord in a salinity of 20‰

(Johansen, 1918), implies that factors other than salinity may be involved, or perhaps we are dealing with different races. It seems to be able to tolerate water with little calcium, for Boycott (1936) recorded it from Lough Leane at Killarney, along with 2 other prosobranchs—*Valvata piscinalis* and *V. cristata*—where the calcium content is only 7–11 mg/l. Moreover the density of the population in pits at Whitecross on Windermere was estimated at about 10,000/sq m in 1937 (Macan, 1950) and here, too, the water is soft.

There has been much discussion as to the origin of this prosobranch. There are suggestions that it is a mutant developed from *Hydrobia ventrosa* (Steusloff, 1927), though

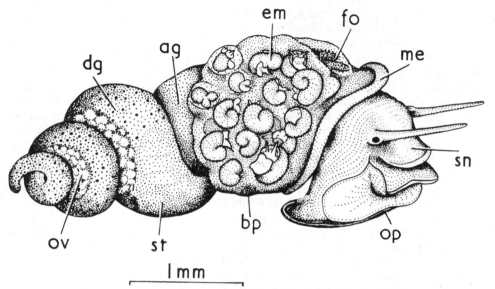

FIG. 309.—*Potamopyrgus jenkinsi:* animal removed from shell and seen from the right.
ag, albumen gland; bp, brood pouch; dg, digestive gland; em, embryo in brood pouch; fo, female aperture; me, mantle edge; op, operculum; ov, ovary; sn, snout; st, stomach.

Boettger (1951) considered that its shell characters are identical with those of *Potamopyrgus badia* Gould from S Island, New Zealand. Because of the theory that the species has been introduced, records of specimens from deposits of known age have become of great interest. Those from recent deposits in the British Isles have been summarized by Kennard (1941) though his conclusion that the species was living in England in Roman times has yet to be confirmed (Bondesen & Kaiser, 1949; Warwick, 1955). Uncertainty as to the origin of *P. jenkinsi* still remains.

The cytology of the parthenogenesis has been studied by Rhein (1935) and Sanderson (1939) who found that there is only one maturation division in oogenesis and that it is non-reductional. Sanderson found the number of chromosomes in the British individuals (36–44) twice that of the continental individuals (20–22) described by Rhein. She therefore suggested that there are 2 races, a diploid one living on the continent and a tetraploid one in the British Isles which, as Peacock (Sanderson, 1940) has pointed out, may prove to be more hardy and so a more successful form. However, Rhein's diploid race is described from only one locality, so further evidence is required for the confirmation of this suggestion. Undoubtedly the species is genetically unstable, and perhaps this may be associated with its tendency to die out in habitats for which it was initially adapted. It is represented in Britain by a number of strains which differ from one another phenotypically and genotypically (Warwick, 1952), and a single population may consist of one, two or even three strains living side by side. Moreover, each of the three may show substrains. The commonest has a shell like that pictured by Ellis (1926), which is slender and the sutures not deep; the mantle pigment is rather pale. A second, also abundant, and found in brackish and inland water, has a less slender shell with the whorls more convex and the sutures correspondingly deeper; the mantle surface is deeply pigmented. It grows more slowly, does not attain such a large size and appears to be less prolific. The third, occurring apparently only at St Bride's Bay, Pembrokeshire, is somewhat smaller and has very pale or patchy mantle pigmentation. In any of these shells there may be a keel represented by a row of bristles, or a slight ridge, or ridge and bristles may co-exist (all these are now regarded as var. *carinata* Marshall, 1889, and the last is sometimes distinguished as var. *aculeata* Overton, 1905). Starting at the third whorl this keel follows the coiling of the whorls near the periphery; rarely, accessory keels above and below this may occur. The keel is produced by a small blunt lobe in the mantle edge. Its occurrence in some individuals of a population has led to much speculation as to its origin, and since the snail breeds readily in captivity considerable work has been carried out in this connexion. However the results seem contradictory. Early workers (Robson, 1926; Boycott, 1929; Seifert, 1935) regarded the keel as due to the action of environmental factors such as salt concentration. Warwick (1944, 1952) was the first to suggest that genetical factors might be involved, acting in combination with algal metabolites in the water. Boettger (1949), on the other hand, considered it to be the result (in optimal conditions) of such environmental factors as food, oxygen, temperature and pH. In favour of this is the report of the occurrence of keeled and aculeate varieties of *Bithynia tentaculata* (Steusloff, 1939) and *Valvata piscinalis* (Haas, 1938) suggesting that shell sculpture and environmental factors are interlinked in other freshwater prosobranchs.

The keeled form was found before the smooth-shelled form both in the British Isles (Marshall, 1889) and in Belgium (Adam, 1942). It is interesting to note that *P. badia*, from which *P. jenkinsi* may have arisen (Boettger, 1951), has a keeled shell. Moreover Bondesen & Kaiser (1949) stated that all older records of *P. jenkinsi* mentioned the keel as typical of the shell and suggested that this was lost when the species invaded freshwater. Recent records from the British Isles and Europe show that the keeled shell is more common in brackish or polluted waters than in clean freshwater.

Recently a single male specimen of *Potamopyrgus jenkinsi* var. *carinata* Marshall has been recorded in the Thames at Sonning, Berkshire (Patil, 1958), though intensive search had previously been made for this sex, and subsequent search has also failed. Males must occur very infrequently, but the discovery of a single individual of this sex suggests that the species had originally separate sexes, and that parthenogenesis, evolved in comparatively recent times, has been accompanied by the gradual reduction in the number of males, which are becoming extinct. Males may even be extinct in the smooth-shelled form of the species. The general plan of the reproductive system of the male agrees with that of *Hydrobia ulvae* and *H. ventrosa*, and the testis, though small, shows active spermatogenesis; this is in accordance with the sporadically occurring males of species of *Melanoides* —*tuberculatus* and *lineatus*—in which the reproductive system is normal and similar to that of the males of related functionally bisexual species (Jacob, 1958). Krull (1935) and Thorson (1946) stated that *P. jenkinsi* may be hermaphrodite, though only Krull gave evidence for this, describing both eggs and sperm in the gonad and suggesting that self-fertilization takes place. The single male specimen which has been described is of average size for the variety *carinata*, has a well developed penis, a large prostate gland and shows no trace of oogenesis in the gonad. There is thus no suggestion that the species is hermaphrodite, and examination of small individuals to investigate whether sex change occurs failed to support this idea.

Correlated with the recent appearance and rapid spread of *Potamopyrgus jenkinsi* is, perhaps, its apparent freedom from parasitic trematodes. *Hydrobia ventrosa* and *H. ulvae* are often heavily infected, and Robson (1923) has found 90% of the former in which the gonad is entirely destroyed. Yet when the 3 hydrobiids are living together *P. jenkinsi* is immune.

*Bithynia tentaculata* is the largest of the British hydrobiids, for the shell may attain a height of 15 mm and a breadth of 6 mm; the second species, *B. leachi*, is about half this

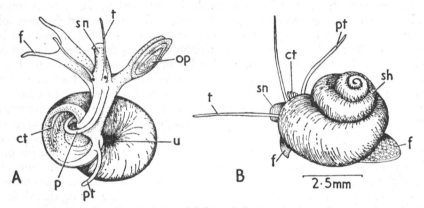

FIG. 310.—*Valvata piscinalis:* A, animal extended from shell; B, animal crawling, seen from the left. ct, anterior tip of ctenidium projecting from mantle cavity; f, foot; op, operculum; p, penis; pt, pallial tentacle; sh, shell; sn, snout; t, tentacle; u, umbilicus.

size. The shell is conical with a rounded base and has 5 or 6 convex whorls in the larger species and 4 or 5 in the smaller; the peristome is continuous; the operculum impregnated with calcium salts and concentrically ringed. *B. leachi* is distinguished by its more tumid whorls, a deeper suture, a sharply pointed apex to the short spire and a small umbilicus (this is scarcely discernible in *B. tentaculata*). Both species are calciphile and where their distribution coincides they may be found in the same habitat. However, *B. leachi* is more local and less abundant, especially in the N and W, and since it was introduced in Scotland it has become established only in limited localities. It favours water rich in plant growth, being more sensitive to oxygen lack than *B. tentaculata*, and avoids running water. Schäfer (1953a) showed that *B. tentaculata* is not affected by organic pollution and lives in the quieter stretches of rivers, quoting as maximum density in the River Lahn (W Germany) 81 animals in 250 cm². Both species may spread into slightly brackish water, and Johansen (1918) found them in salinities averaging 6–7‰ in Randers Fjord. He stated that they prefer a depth of 70–180 cm, but they are not uncommonly found to depths of 9–10 m.

In spring and summer *Bithynia* may be seen creeping over the surface of weed or stones and depositing egg capsules. Food is collected by the long snout, cleft in front, which incessantly searches the substratum when the animal is active. Intensive cleansing of an area will be observed before the female spawns for she carefully prepares the surface where the capsules are to be laid. They are fastened by the foot in tightly packed rows which are accurately arranged (fig. 207). An extension of the mantle edge on the right side forms a short siphon which directs the exhalant water current from the pallial cavity away from the head, carrying with it the ovoid faecal pellets, and it is from this region that the eggs are received by the foot.

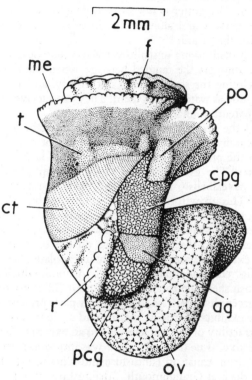

FIG. 311.—*Theodoxus fluviatilis:* animal removed from the shell and seen in dorsal view. The head has been fully retracted into the mantle cavity. Some organs are seen by transparency.
ag, albumen gland; cpg, capsule gland; ct, ctenidium; f, foot; me, mantle edge; ov, ovary; pcg, posterior lobe of capsule gland; po, pallial oviduct; r, rectum; t, tentacle.

An examination of the faecal pellets suggests that only the contents of ruptured plant cells are digested. Throughout the winter when there is little plant growth and water currents are stronger, the snails retreat to the surface layer of mud and go to deeper water. They feed on detritus, decaying weed and carrion. Particles stirred up from the bottom and entering the mantle cavity may also be collected and eaten by *B. tentaculata* (and presumably by *B. leachi*), though the importance of this method of feeding as compared with the selection of food by the radula is not known. Starmuhlner (1952) and Lilly (1953) were unable to prove that the mollusc did more than concentrate the detritus in the ciliated gutter which traverses the floor of the mantle cavity (fg, fig. 55). Lilly saw the concentrations of particles at the exhalant end of the groove removed by the foot, or wiped on to some object which the animal brushed against. However, Schäfer (1952) observed *B. tentaculata* eating them, and Hunter (1957) stated that in certain localities the greater part of the food of this species is obtained in this way. Werner (1953) suggested that this is only a supplementary method of feeding and Frömming (1956) agreed with this. Perhaps the frequency with which this method of feeding is used depends on the abundance of other foods and the nature of the suspended particles. The gill of *Bithynia* is large (ct), its lamellae triangular, each with a broad base and the tip hanging over the ciliated gutter. The gutter is not so well developed as in *Viviparus* where the ctenidial filaments are narrow and elongated as in other prosobranchs which filter the pallial flow of water for their food.

During winter floods snails living in shallower water may be drifted above the normal water course and left amongst the tangled herbage when the floods subside. They lie with the operculum closing the shell, though not tightly, and with the gut empty, yet activity is regained as soon as water covers them. They can survive in air of high humidity for several weeks, apparently unharmed.

Lilly (1953) studied the growth rate of a population of *B. tentaculata* at Wickford, Essex, and found that individuals which have a shell height of 6 mm or less in January have developed from the previous year's spawn, and that larger snails have survived a second or third winter. The growth rate is fairly constant throughout the year. By March some animals have shells 9 mm high and in its first spring the snail is mature, males before females. This growth rate is more rapid than that described by Hubendick (1948) for a population at Lake Malaren, Sweden, where the winter is more extreme. The average adult size of the snails in the two places is similar, the shell attaining a height of 10 mm. Hubendick found that growth rings on the operculum are unreliable for calculating age, since extra rings are unpredictably interpolated between the winter ones.

*Bythinella scholtzi* (fig. 312), the smallest British hydrobiid, which attains at most 3 mm in height, has a blackish shell due to an earthy deposit (Ellis, 1926), the cleaned surface being brown with a greenish tinge. The shell and soft parts present the general hydrobiid facies, but the former exhibits ventricose whorls and a blunt apex, and the latter shows an extraordinary contractility of the tentacles (t) and an excessive deposition of calcareous granules in the connective tissue (css). *Bythinella* was introduced from America and first recorded here in 1900 from canals in Lancashire and Cheshire (Jackson & Taylor, 1904) and later in a timber dock at Grangemouth, Stirlingshire (Waterston, 1934). In two of these places, Cheshire and Grangemouth, it was associated with the reed meadow grass *Glyceria*, of which it favoured the decaying leaves and stems. The snail lives well in captivity, and breeds. The egg capsules, deposited singly in late spring or early summer, have each a single egg which is large for the size of the snail. The capsule is attached by a flat base, circular in outline, and a keel projects across the convex upper surface (Jackson & Taylor, 1904). The young snail devours the albumen in which it is embedded and comes to fill the entire space within the tough outer wall before it escapes.

*Viviparus* is the largest of our freshwater prosobranchs, indeed of any in Europe, and lives longer. Jeffreys (1862) mentioned a specimen of *V. contectus* (p. 694) measuring as much as 2 in high and 1·75 in broad, and *V. viviparus* may be of similar dimensions— but is often slightly smaller. The shell of *V. contectus* is glossy and thin, the sutures deep and the whorls swollen, the apex pointed and the umbilicus distinct and deep; the dark green periostracum is rather thick and the brown spiral bands are seldom conspicuous (Watson, 1955). In contrast, the shell of *V. viviparus* is not very glossy, is thicker and whiter, the sutures not so deep, the apex blunt and the umbilicus scarcely visible; the periostracum is thinner and the spiral brown bands are often more conspicuous. The operculum of this second species is thicker and less nearly circular than that of *V. contectus*. Both live in hard water with slight to moderate current and may inhabit brackish areas, though they are very sensitive to any increase in salinity above 3‰. They are widely distributed in England (and throughout the greater part of Europe) and are often found together, for their habitats seem to be identical. However, *V. viviparus* has a wider distribution. It will live in reservoirs and has been recorded from standing water with a considerable accumulation of humous acids (pH 4·8).

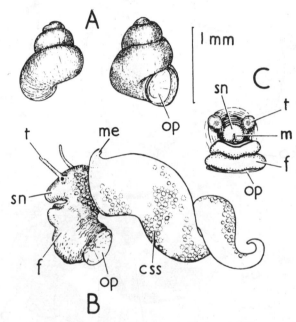

FIG. 312.—*Bythinella scholtzi:* A, shell in apertural (right) and abapertural (left) views; B, animal removed from the shell, seen from the left; C, animal seen from in front, to show shape of contracted tentacles. css, calcareous spherules; f, foot; m, mouth; me, mantle edge; op, operculum; sn, snout; t, tentacle.

Spoel (1958), working in Holland, found that *V. contectus* commonly reaches an age of 7 years, sometimes even 10, and *V. viviparus* an age of 6 years and sometimes 11; females live about half a year longer than males. He calculated this from growth rings on the shell and operculum, and stated that the darker winter rings are obvious and that 2–3 lying close together indicate a winter season during which there have been periods of activity and feeding. However Hubendick (1948) held that, as in *Bithynia*, the operculum is unreliable for calculating ages. A vast amount of similar work has been done in estimating the age of *Viviparus* from growth rings on the shell (Hazay, 1881; Goldfuss, 1900; Franz, 1938), but it seems unwise to adopt these as a criterion of age since they can be apparently produced at times other than winter. Spoel found that in both species of *Viviparus* the growth in height of the shell in spring exceeds that of the width, but in summer the width increases more rapidly; there are no differences in the height-width relationship in the two sexes, but Kessel (1933) said that females of both species are distinguishable on account of their more swollen whorls.

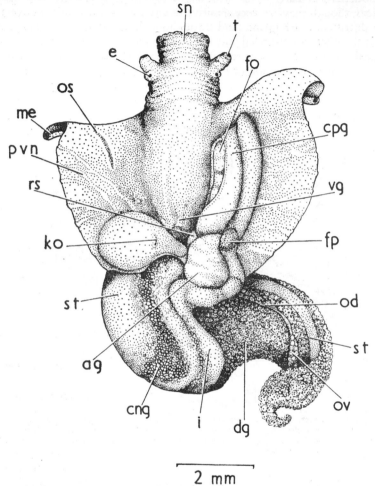

2 mm

FIG. 313.—*Pomatias elegans:* female removed from shell. The mantle cavity has been opened by a median cut. Some organs are seen by transparency.
ag, albumen gland; cng, concretion gland; cpg, capsule gland; dg, digestive gland; e, eye; fo, female aperture; fp, faecal pellet in rectum; i, intestine; ko, kidney opening; me, mantle edge; od, ovarian duct; os, osphradium; ov, ovary; pvn, pallial vessel; rs, receptaculum seminis; sn, snout; st, stomach; t, tentacle; vg, visceral ganglion.

Males of *Viviparus* are less numerous than females and may be distinguished by the right cephalic tentacle which is modified to form a penis (p, fig. 183) and appears short, blunt and deformed. Behind each tentacle is a neck lobe. The right, which is much longer than the left (is), is used as a siphon (es) which directs the exhalant flow of water and the faeces away from the body of the snail. In the possession of this siphon and also the food-collecting gutter in the mantle cavity, *Viviparus* resembles *Bithynia*. Both features may be associated with a habitat where there is considerable silt.

*Viviparus* indeed, appears to thrive in water where there is considerable particulate matter in suspension. It will be found crawling on stones, creeping over mud, or sometimes lying half-buried in the soft bottom partially retracted into the shell which has the aperture directed upwards. Food may be collected from the surface of stones or weed by the radula or it may be filtered from the pallial water current. As the snail creeps over the mud the anterior edge of the broad foot pushes just beneath the surface, stirring up clouds of particles over the head; behind it the snail leaves a sunken tract where the particles are compressed. Suspended matter is drawn into the mantle cavity with the inhalant flow of water. The ctenidial filaments are long and narrow, resembling those of the ciliary feeder *Crepidula* (ct, fig. 155). They are muscular and each can be seen moving independently of its neighbours. The tips of the filaments hang over a conspicuous food-collecting groove (fg) which runs diagonally across the floor of the mantle cavity from its deepest part to beneath the right cephalic tentacle. Cilia on adjacent strips of body wall direct mucus and particles into the groove. Sediment is caught on the gill filaments and carried to their tips, from where it falls off immediately or is passed forwards from filament to filament before ultimately reaching the groove. Here a food-mucus string is formed, carried forwards and rolled into a ball (fg, fig. 56). At intervals the animal turns its head and eats the accumulation (Cook, 1949). The radular teeth show little signs of wear and are probably used for picking up particulate matter rather than rasping hard surfaces. The radula is short, only a fifth the height of the shell, whereas in *Littorina* it is $2\frac{1}{4}$ times the shell height. When *Viviparus* remains half buried in the mud it may be feeding on suspended particles in the water, although appearing inert. No pallial tentacles guard the mantle cavity against excessive silt as in *Turritella communis*, but the entrance is partly obstructed by the head and foot.

Embryos which have not hatched by the end of summer are carried over the winter months in the brood pouch (bp, fig. 155) and the young are liberated in spring. This appears to be due to rising temperature. Jeffreys (1862) mentioned that Millet counted as many as 82 embryos of different sizes from a single *V. viviparus*. A few are freed at a time for they are not all of the same age. Each embryo is embedded in albumen which is used as food and then surrounded by a tough shell drawn out into a stalk. Sometimes the young are born in this cocoon, which then breaks. Embryos removed prematurely from the parent will complete their development in water, and it can be seen that when they are ready to hatch they break through the cocoon using the operculum (Heywood, personal communication). Newly emerged snails may differ from the older ones in some external features: in *contectus* the shell has spiral rows of recurved bristles (sbs, fig. 56) which overlie the positions later occupied by the coloured bands, and hanging from the edge of the mantle skirt on the right side there are 3 short tentacles (pt) (Cook, 1949, where the species is mistakenly called *viviparus*); both these features are inconspicuous in *viviparus* (Heywood, personal communication). The young of *contectus* have a shell with a sharply pointed spire and those of *viviparus* are flatly coiled (Spoel, 1958).

Hubendick (1948) studying a population of *V. viviparus* at Lake Malaren, Sweden, found that 33% of the total growth of an individual occurs before its first winter; this includes intra-uterine growth, which accounts for 14%. Between the first and second winter another 21% is added and a similar amount between the second and third.

Two of the 3 species of *Valvata*, *piscinalis* and *cristata*, have the widest distribution in Britain of all the freshwater prosobranchs, for they occur in both hard and soft water.

Ankel (1936a) stated that they live in brackish water with a salinity of about 2‰ in the North and Baltic Seas. The family to which they belong is of ancient origin, having been found in freshwater beds of the Oolitic period (Forbes & Hanley, 1850). In respect of the organization of the mantle cavity (fig. 156), many features of which may be associated with a muddy habitat, and also the complexity of the hermaphrodite reproductive system (p. 382), they stand apart from all other mesogastropods. One of their most diagnostic features is the bipectinate gill (ct, figs. 156, 310) which may project from the anterior edge of the shell when the animal is active. In some older drawings it is represented as projecting for nearly its entire length, which for a healthy snail appears to be an exaggeration. Frömming (1956) stated that it projects when distended by blood. There appears to be no correlation between the extent to which the gill is protruded and the degree of oxygenation of the water (Heywood, personal communication). The shell is primitive in having a loose winding of the whorls (most pronounced in *cristata* and least pronounced in *piscinalis*), an umbilicus and circular peristome (fig. 310). In *V. piscinalis* it is top-shaped with 5 or 6 rapidly increasing whorls which are rounded and have a conspicuous suture line. It may attain a breadth of 7 mm and the height exceeds the breadth only slightly. In *V. macrostoma* the shell is depressed with the spire only slightly raised, the umbilicus broadly open and the suture deep. The shell of *V. piscinalis* shows considerable variation in some localities and may be confused with this species, while that of *V. cristata* is markedly different for it has 5 whorls coiled in a disc-like fashion, the suture deep and the umbilicus very wide. The measurements given by Ellis (1926) for *cristata* are height 1·25 mm, breadth 2–4 mm, and for *macrostoma*, height 2 mm, breadth 3·5–4 mm.

When *Valvata* is active 3 long, extensile tentacles are seen to protrude from the body. Two are cephalic (t, fig. 310) and the third arises at the junction of the mantle skirt and body wall, in the position of an exhalant siphon. This pallial tentacle (pt) is extended upwards or laterally away from the body. Behind the right cephalic tentacle is the penis (p) which, in its resting condition, is directed posteriorly against the body wall so that its tip projects into the deepest part of the mantle cavity, for it is relatively longer than the penis of any other British prosobranch. The long narrow snout (sn) is wrinkled transversely and expands around the mouth. It appears to be continually in search of food, moving about between the 2 acute angles of the foot. The front edge of the foot (f) is deeply cleft and has a conspicuous double margin marking the opening of the pedal mucous gland. All exposed surfaces of the body have ciliary currents which cleanse them from silt. The cilia beat posteriorly over the foot, from left to right across the snout, across the cephalic tentacles from median to lateral edge and from base to tip on the pallial tentacle.

The gill extends only across the anterior third of the mantle cavity (ct, fig. 156) where it is attached to the roof by a short efferent membrane (efm) and to the rectum by an afferent membrane (afm). Between these attachments and the overlying pallial skirt a small pocket of mantle cavity is separated from the rest and into it the kidney opens posteriorly. The ctenidial axis and the filaments, which lack skeletal rods, are very mobile. The gill is moved freely within the limits of its attachments and its powerful ciliation can be seen as it projects from the shell. A strong current is directed forward along both afferent and efferent axes, carrying particles to the tip. In contrast to other Monotocardia there is no rejection current (A) associated with the inhalant current to the left of the head (Yonge, 1947) so that all particulate matter is swept across the floor by a strong current which beats towards the exhalant region on the right. Particles dropping from the tip of the gill are caught in this current or in a similar one on the head. The strength of the exhalant flow is increased and directed away from the body by the extremely extensile pallial tentacle, which may also have a tactile function. The anterior part of the mantle skirt is glandular and its secretion entangles particles and also the faeces, which are loosely compacted. The anus is on a papilla so that the pellets are swept clear of the body in the exhalant stream. The floor of the posterior part of the mantle cavity and the mantle above the ctenidium lack cilia.

During the autumn and winter months the snail may be found burrowing in the surface layer of mud and feeding there, yet the mantle cavity is kept clear of silt by the strong currents which sweep across its anterior parts and along the upturned pallial tentacle. There is no device for collecting and eating particles which enter the cavity. The snail grazes on detritus, diatoms, desmids and may rasp filamentous algae. In spring and early summer *Valvata* creeps on to plants (often entering into shallower water) and deposits egg capsules (fig. 208), or these may be fastened to any other solid object, even to the shells of bivalves. The young snails spend only a short period on the weed before they make their way down to the mud and may creep about on the surface for a time before eventually burying themselves. Cleland (1954), studying a population of *V. piscinalis* in the River Colne, Middlesex, found that all were beneath the surface by October. The older animals die off at this time and during the winter the next generation grows slowly. Growth increases in spring and the maximum size is reached by June.

*Theodoxus fluviatilis* is the only British representative of the Neritacea, a group of the Diotocardia which is of interest not only anatomically, since its members display a combination of primitive and advanced characters, but also ecologically, since they have exploited a variety of habitats. Such exploitation is partly attributable to their resistance to changing salinities, and to their method of reproduction, in respect of which they exhibit their most advanced characteristics. Three genera may be taken to illustrate the varieties of habitat in which members of the Neritidae are found: *Nerita*, a genus of tropical seas, occurs on rock in the littoral zone and some species ascend rivers and frequent brackish water and marshes; *Theodoxus*, the European representative, lives in brackish water and freshwater with a fairly high calcium content; and finally *Neritodryas*, which occurs in the E Indies, lives on bushes and high up in trees, sometimes remote from water. *Theodoxus* extends from the Baltic to the Mediterranean. It is found on the Dutch, Danish and Baltic coasts, and in a salinity as high as 13‰ in Randers Fjord (Johansen, 1918). In Finnish brackish waters (salinity 2–6‰) it is the most abundant species in the littoral zone, living amongst *Fucus vesiculosus*, though it is not found in the inland lakes where the water is soft and fresh (Segerstråle, 1949). The size of the snail and of its egg capsules is reduced in saline water. Johansen has shown that in a salinity of 0·2–0·5‰ the shell length averages 9·5 mm, whereas between 7 and 12‰ it averages only 7·4 mm. In saline waters, too, the shell is lighter in colour.

The distribution of *Theodoxus* in the British Isles appears to depend upon the conjunction of a certain degree of hardness and of movement in the water. Thus it occurs in rivers, lakes and canals wherever these conditions are satisfied, favouring the wave line and shallower parts of lakes—not below 7–8 m—and the more rapid reaches of rivers. It lives on stones, sunken wood and aquatic plants, moving slowly over the surface as it gathers its food of microscopic organisms and detritus and it will rasp the surface tissues of plants. It is sluggish in habit and avoids strong light. As the snail creeps the shell, semi-globular in shape, is scarcely raised from the ground, so that the large head and broad snout are not exposed and only the pointed tips of the tentacles are visible. The shell is strongly built, rarely exceeding 6 mm in height and 11 mm in length, and the spire is short and oblique. Its colour may be yellow, brown or (more rarely) black and it is flecked with white, pink or purple or may have darker bands. The columella forms a broad septum behind the semilunar aperture into which fits the partly calcified operculum, orange or yellow in colour. There are 3 convex whorls but their internal parts and the associated columella are absorbed so that the visceral mass is hardly spirally coiled. The mantle cavity is broad and moderately deep with the single bipectinate gill directed across it (ct, fig. 311). The ctenidium is attached to the posterior wall on the left side (see fig. 52) and is free anteriorly, giving considerable freedom of movement. There is no hypobranchial gland comparable to that of other prosobranchs. The epithelium of the mantle skirt has scattered gland cells and in the thickness of its posterior part are glandular tubules which open by a common duct into the mantle cavity. Since this opening is to the right of the 'organe creux' of Lenssen (1899), possible vestige of

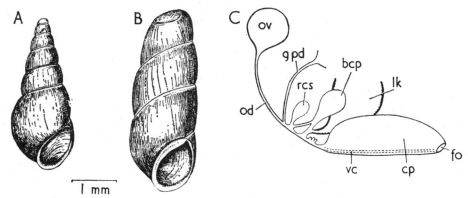

FIG. 314.—*Truncatella subcylindrica*: A, shell of young animal in apertural view; B, shell of mature animal in apertural view; C, diagram of female reproductive system.
bcp, bursa copulatrix; cp, capsule gland; fo, female opening; gpd, gonopericardial duct; lk, left kidney; od, ovarian duct; ov, ovary; rcs, receptaculum seminis; vc, ventral channel.

the right gill (ho, fig. 52), the gland is taken to represent the right hypobranchial gland (p. 123).

Males are distinguished from females by the penis, which is median to the base of the right tentacle and is stout proximally and tapering distally. Pairs may be seen copulating most freely during late spring and early summer. The egg capsules, which have their walls reinforced by grit from the crystal sac (csa, fig. 195), are securely attached to a firm substratum by the foot (fig. 209), and are most common then too, but a few may be found at other times of the year (Berg, 1938). They may be fastened to the shell of an individual of the same species and have been found on the shell of *Viviparus*. From each capsule a single snail hatches after an embryonic life of 3 weeks or more. According to Becker (1949) 2 generations may be passed through in 12 months provided that the temperature of the water does not fall below 12°C. The animals live for 2 years, a few surviving into a third.

There are only 2 terrestrial prosobranchs which are indigenous in Britain, *Pomatias elegans* and *Acicula fusca*. Two other land operculates, natives of S Europe, were discovered on a wall at Kearsney in Kent in 1918 by Mr H. C. Huggins. These were species of *Hartmannia*, *septemspiralis* (Razoumovsky) and *patula* (Draparnaud), and had probably been deliberately imported (Huggins, 1919). *Pomatias* and *Acicula* are members of the Littorinacea, a group represented in most diverse environments. *Pomatias elegans* spends much of its time burrowing in the upper 4 or 5 in of soil during cold or dry weather and appears on the surface when the atmosphere is warm and moist; normally 95% R.H. is necessary for activity (Kilian, 1951). This is reminiscent of the behaviour of the related winkle *Littorina saxatilis*, which will creep actively over the rock at low tide when a warm sea mist covers it, but otherwise lies motionless or even hidden in rock crevices when the tide retreats. *Pomatias* requires a soil of loose texture to burrow in and this is provided in calcareous soils by the flocculating action of calcium carbonate on the clay particles. Indeed the records of its occurrence show that the species is associated with soils having high calcium content: Kilian (1951) found it numerous when the calcium content is 21% and over, and absent at 6% or under. It is not recorded from inland calcareous sand, but occurs on marine sandhills in Devon (Longstaff, 1910) and Cornwall (Boycott, 1934), habitats well suited for burrowing, and, with their proximity to the sea, rich in fragments of calcareous shells. The snail is found in woods, alongside hedges and sometimes on open grassland where a thin layer of comparatively alkaline soil (pH 7·5–7·9) covers calcareous rock (Creek, 1951). In favourable localities it is abundant. It has a daily rhythm of activity which is maximal during the early morning and minimal around midday; it becomes more active in the evening and will creep about all night. In winter, when the soil temperature drops, it hibernates and can survive a temperature of −6°C; the heart beat falls considerably during hibernation and may be only 2–4/min, as against 53/min at 25–30°C (Kilian, 1951). The snail awakes from hibernation and becomes active again when the soil temperature rises to 10–12°C.

*Acicula fusca* has a shell only about 2 mm high. It is also found on calcareous soils amongst dead leaves and wood in damp, shady places (especially favouring beech woods), but prefers a more acid soil than *Pomatias*, so that although both species may occur in the same area they are rarely found together. Its habitat is so damp that it is almost aquatic for so small an animal, and certain specializations in its structure may be related to size as much as habitat.

The terrestrial environment requires adaptations in respiratory structures and in reproduction and also a considerable capacity for osmoregulation. Both *Pomatias* and *Acicula* (Creek, 1951, 1953) have lost the ctenidium, and the heart and kidney lie in the thickness of the mantle skirt, which is therefore highly vascularized and is the respiratory organ (a similar modification is found in some minute marine prosobranchs, p. 551). The mantle skirt is neither thickened anteriorly nor partially fused with the head as in pulmonates. The kidney opens (ko, fig. 313) into the posterior end of the mantle cavity as in other littorinaceans: this is unusual for a terrestrial gastropod in which there is no exhalant water current to carry away urine. In adult specimens of *Pomatias* the kidney concentrates large quantities of uric acid and this is also found in a special gland (cng), the concretion gland (Quast, 1924a, b; Kilian, 1951); in *Acicula* there are also large accumulations of crystals in the kidney tissue. These facts suggest that it is an accumulation kidney, and that the water which it excretes is almost pure. This could be used to keep the mantle cavity moist, and its surface is, indeed, always moist or even wet. In *Acicula* cilia on the head and hypobranchial gland set up currents in the water which probably facilitate gaseous exchange over the respiratory surface; the mantle cavity is narrow and deep and contains a large bubble of air which may be partially extruded as the animal creeps; this, like 'Notatmung' in fish, is probably a respiratory device. In both these terrestrial prosobranchs the osphradium and hypobranchial gland are retained.

The reproductive habits and processes are known only in the case of *Pomatias elegans*. In warm moist weather during spring and summer copulation may be frequently observed and during this period the females spawn. Each egg is laid in a large spherical capsule, about 2 mm in diameter (fig. 205), which is discharged into the mantle cavity from the swollen pallial oviduct. The opening of the duct occupies the greater part of its ventral wall. The capsule is forced out by muscular movements and passed down the

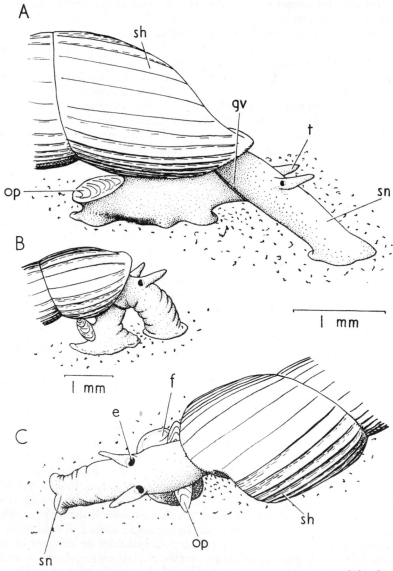

Fig. 315.—*Truncatella subcylindrica* to show method of locomotion: A, proboscis extended and gripping substratum; B, proboscis contracted and foot brought forward to its base; C, intermediate position in dorsal view.

e, eye; f, foot; gv, groove from mantle cavity; op, operculum; sh, shell; sn, snout; t, tentacle.

right side of the head to the foot. The sole of the foot is cleft by a deep groove into right and left halves, which are moved alternately in walking. A posterior pedal gland (composed of a number of tubules which penetrate the deeper tissues of the foot) opens into the groove, but it is uncertain whether this provides secretion for the final moulding of the egg capsule; it is present in both sexes. There seems no justification for Thiele's suggestion (1929–35) that it acts as a lung. The foot covers the capsule with a coating of soil before depositing it beneath the surface. The capsule wall is permeable to water and salts which pass in from the surrounding soil and there is also some factor present in natural soil water which is necessary for development. The egg of this terrestrial prosobranch is thus a typical non-cleidoic egg and may be provided with water in excess of the requirements of the embryo as a guard against temporary drought. Embryonic development is slow and takes 3 months, and as in some other members of the Littorinacea, *Littorina littoralis* and *L. saxatilis*, the larval stage is suppressed and the embryo develops into a miniature of the adult before it leaves the capsule. In *Pomatias*, however, the veliger stage is considerably modified, especially by the large cephalic vesicle which develops in the velar region (cv, fig. 232). A vesicle superficially similar is present in the embryo of other terrestrial gastropods and a variety of functions has been attributed to it. It has been considered as an adaptation to provide a greater surface area for the absorption of oxygen in *Helix pomatia* (Delsman, 1914); in *Agriolimax* (Carrick, 1938) it is vascular and contractile, functioning as a larval heart. In *Pomatias elegans* Creek (1951) has shown that the vesicle has an absorptive function and its cells become filled with albumen which is gradually used by the embryo.

Both these terrestrial prosobranchs feed on decaying vegetable matter, and *Pomatias* is known to digest the cellulose in its food, though it is uncertain as to whether this is done by the mollusc's own enzymes or by the bacteria which are present in the gut (Kilian, 1951). *Acicula* takes in minute particles and may select fungal hyphae from among decaying plants. Its gut, as in other small prosobranchs, is simplified. The glandular part of the oesophagus contains only mucous cells, the secretion from which may counteract the acidity of the decaying food. The stomach has neither gastric shield nor style, though there is a caecum homologous with that of winkles. In *Pomatias* the stomach is elaborated as in *Littorina* and in addition a style is present and consequently there are no oesophageal glands.

A peculiar tissue surrounds the intestine and borders the nephridium of *Pomatias elegans* and is conspicuous on account of the snow-white, rounded granules it contains. Claparède (1858) described it as the 'glande à concrétions'. Its cells contain glycogen, pigment and urates, and between them may be phagocytes with round or polymorphic nuclei. There are also bacteria which, according to Meyer (1925), are similar to those in the intestine. The concretion gland varies in size according to the season: it is maximal during autumn and decreases during hibernation (Kilian, 1951). It is thus affected by the food supply and increases with increased food. The gland would appear to be a temporary storage organ which can be called upon in times of reduced protein metabolism, and together with the nephridium it is responsible for excretion. There is a rich blood supply by which materials may enter or leave its tissues. Meyer (1925) suggested that the bacteria may aid in the transformative processes and so benefit the mollusc: they may produce enzymes which during periods of starvation transform waste material into substances of metabolic value. The snail is infected with these bacteria during its early life. None is present in the egg capsule though they occur on the outer surface, and the newly hatched individuals are said to eat this shell and so infect themselves.

# CHAPTER 24

# THE PARASITES OF PROSOBRANCHS

THE molluscs are notoriously the hosts of many helminth parasites and much of the economic importance of gastropods is due to the fact that they harbour stages in the life history of parasites dangerous to man and his domestic animals. They also appear to act as host to many protozoans and other invertebrates, but since these are seldom of any economic interest they have been much less investigated, and are probably more numerous than our present knowledge suggests. Indeed the soft body of a mollusc with its copious superficial secretions and its mantle cavity seems to offer attractive conditions for potential parasites or inquilines. Lists of species with these modes of life will be found in Pelseneer (1935) and except for the trematodes which merit more detailed discussion they will not be further referred to here.

The life cycle of digenetic trematodes is complicated by successive larval forms known as parthenitae which may multiply abundantly. The degree of complexity of the life history varies with the species and may involve one or two intermediate hosts which harbour the larvae, and a final host in which the adult lives. The first intermediate host is a mollusc, with only one known exception, in which it is a polychaete annelid (Linton, 1915; Martin, 1944). It is usually a gastropod, sometimes a lamellibranch or scaphopod, but never a cephalopod or amphineuran. This exclusion from two classes which are wholly marine has led to the suggestion that digenetic trematodes arose in freshwater, where they may have been associated with gastropods and lamellibranchs for a considerable time before they spread to marine habitats.

In some species the miracidium larva emerges from the egg after it has been ingested by the host, the hatching process being stimulated only by the environment provided by the gut of the mollusc. In others the larva hatches outside the host and by reacting to the specific chemical situation provided by the skin of the mollusc in which its further development is possible, attaches itself by the apical papilla and, with the aid of secretions, penetrates the tissues. The work of Wright (1959) indicates one way in which this selection of a host may be made, for he has demonstrated species-specific differences in the superficial mucus of the pulmonate genus *Lymnaea*. Host specificity varies, for in some flukes only one species of mollusc is suitable whereas in others more than one will serve, as in *Cercaria ubiquita* (Lebour, 1907) which will infect *Littorina littorea, L. littoralis, L. saxatilis* and *Hydrobia ulvae*.

Once within the mollusc the larvae usually make their way to the visceral haemocoel, which is of easy access either from the gut, the wall of which is easily penetrated, or from the exposed outer tissues of the body, and they settle in the blood spaces associated with the digestive gland or gonad. The parasite now undergoes extensive changes into the next larval stage, the sporocyst, which absorbs nourishment from the host and may be highly destructive. Within the sporocyst either daughter sporocysts or rediae develop and either of these may give rise to the final larval form, the cercaria. Consequently the sporocysts in the visceral mass of the mollusc may contain daughter sporocysts, rediae or cercariae. An interesting reproductive phenomenon has been reported by James (1960) in a gymnophalline parasite of *Littorina saxatilis*, only the third record so far known of a parasite of this subfamily in a gastropod, most previous records being from lamellibranchs. The cercariae are produced from a parthenite which has the same essential structure and which may, therefore, be a cercaria itself, in which the same kind of polyembryonic reproduction occurs as is commonly found in sporocysts and rediae.

In a few flukes the sporocyst stage does not occur, for a redia develops from the miracidium after penetration. A single miracidium usually gives rise, ultimately, to several thousand cercariae which leave the redia or daughter sporocyst. According to their species, these may remain in the mollusc or bore through the tissues and escape to the water. Once free, they may either enter a second intermediate host, within whose body they encyst, or they may encyst in the open water, often attached to weed, until ingested by the final host. A most remarkable illustration of the increase in numbers undergone within the molluscan host has been recorded for *Cercaria lophocerca* parasitizing *Littorina littorea* (Rothschild, 1942). A large winkle, the largest amongst hundreds, was isolated for 7 years and fed on sea lettuce, *Ulva*. During the first week of captivity the periwinkle emitted on the average 3,300 cercariae a day, and by the end of the first year 1,300,000 had been liberated (Meyerhof & Rothschild, 1940). More emerged through the following years though their number gradually decreased and fell to a daily output of about 830. Despite the drain on its constitution the mollusc continued to grow slightly and after 5 years, when it was still emitting cercariae, its shell had increased in size by 3·5 mm. This example of the resistance of a gastropod to heavy infection for a considerable length of time is typical of all molluscs, for their tissues are capable of rapid recovery after destruction. In some localities up to 40% of the edible winkles are infected, suggesting that there must be an astronomical number of cercariae liberated to the coastal waters.

For many trematodes the stages of the life history passed in the molluscan host are known, but nothing else, for the final host with the adult fluke and the second intermediate host (if any) have not been discovered. Authors give names, numbers or letters to the cercariae of such parasites, and if later the adult stage is found the name given to the cercaria is placed under the newly associated adult.

In general, trematode parasites settle in the sinuses surrounding the tubules of the digestive gland (fig. 316) and gonad, where they are in the direct path of nutrients which are being passed from the digestive gland to the gonad; which of these 2 glands is the first to be infected varies with the trematode. The parasite may destroy the gonad and then pass to the digestive gland, the destruction of which would be disastrous, or it may attack the digestive gland first. In the case of *Cercaria lophocerca* (Rees, 1936b) there is no serious blocking of the blood sinuses and the larvae are uniformly distributed throughout them. The digestive cells of the gland accumulate waste produced by the rediae, though the quantities are usually such that the cells can discharge it in the normal fashion to the lumina of the tubules.

Immobile sporocysts, increasing enormously in numbers, may not disperse, and those of *Cercaria emasculans*, which infects the winkle, block parts of the digestive gland, stop the blood flow to it and distend the blood sinuses to such an extent that the lumina of the surrounding tubules are obliterated. This isolated region of the gland is starved and its tissues degenerate whilst unparasitized regions are unaffected. Concentrations of the large rediae of *Himasthla leptosoma* may give similar effects. The total mass of larvae of a parasite may finally exceed the volume of the infected gland which, with the least pressure, may burst. Often physiological injury is greater than mechanical and is caused, frequently, by the mollusc being incapable of ridding its tissues of waste produced by the parasite at an ever increasing rate as infection continues.

Occasionally parthenites of the trematode invade other tissues: rediae of *Cercaria patellae* have been observed in the salivary glands of the limpet (Rees, 1934), and sporocysts of *Cercaria littorinae* are carried in the blood to the kidney of the winkle, in the sinuses of which they grow to maturity, apparently causing little harm (Rees, 1936b). Cercariae leave a gastropod by penetrating the tissues of the mantle, the gill or other parts so that damage to the tissue of the host is both mechanical and physiological.

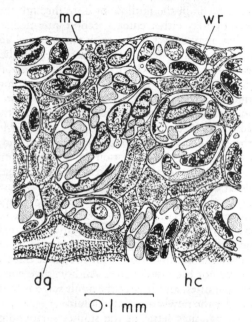

FIG. 316.—*Nucella lapillus:* part of a section of the digestive gland of an animal parasitized by the trematode *Parorchis acanthus.* From a slide prepared by Dr G. Rees.
    dg, tubule of digestive gland; hc, haemocoelic space; ma, mantle; wr, redia of parasite with cercariae.

In specimens of *Patella vulgata* containing *Cercaria patellae* (Rees, 1934) the digestive gland, the first region to suffer, becomes pale yellow and the rediae are visible as white threads. Waste from the parasite is taken up by the digestive cells of the gland and excreted to the lumina of the tubules. But, should excessive waste accumulate, there is cytolysis of the cells distally where its greatest concentration occurs, and protoplasm and food granules as well as excretory products are lost. The cell boundaries become irregular and in extreme cases a transverse partition grows across at the base of the cell enclosing the nucleus: the cell is no longer columnar but squamous in appearance. The parasite reproduces so rapidly that the tubules of the digestive gland disappear and are replaced by developing rediae and cercariae. The gonad of the limpet is invaded secondarily from the gland and the parasite, lodged in the intertrabecular spaces, intercepts its food supply. Starved of food and subjected to pressure from increasing numbers of the parasite the germinal epithelium atrophies and is ultimately destroyed.

In a study of various trematodes which infect *Littorina littorea* Rees (1936*b*) found that no rediae are associated with *Cercaria littorinae*, *C. emasculans* and *C. ubiquita*, whereas cercariae of *Himasthla leptosoma* and *C. lophocerca* develop in rediae and no sporocysts have been found. The rediae of these 2 parasites first attack the gonad of the snail and if this is female they may be seen filled with eggs and yolk sucked from the ovarian tubules by the muscular pharynx. The gonad is completely destroyed by both species and then the digestive gland invaded. This gland is bright orange when infected with the large rediae of *Himasthla leptosoma* which feed not only on the blood but on the tissues. The effect on the histology of the gland is, for either parasite, similar to that described in *Patella*. Winkles infected by the other 3 trematodes have the gonad preserved much longer, for the digestive gland is the organ primarily affected. The gonad is not eaten and its disappearance is due to secondary causes—pressure atrophy, accumulation of waste products and starvation. The sporocysts in which *Cercaria ubiquita* develops are the smallest of those larval parasites developed in the winkle, and the effects of parasitism are mildest.

To the trematodes the most advantageous hosts are the gregarious prosobranchs, which afford ample opportunity for infection. It is, therefore, not surprising that the admirable work of Rothschild has revealed the small spire shell, *Hydrobia ulvae*, as a most popular host since, in certain localities, it may occur in concentrations of up to 32,000/sq m as in the mud flats and saltings of the River Tamar, a habitat which is frequented by birds and fish, the definitive hosts of many trematodes. The life cycle of about half a dozen of these parasites in which the cercaria stage develops in *Hydrobia ulvae* (p. 608) is known, but many other types of cercariae, with unknown life histories, have been described from this species. The life cycles which are known involve, as the final host, a bird which frequents the saltings at low tide, where it defaecates among the swarms of *Hydrobia*. In the case of *Cryptocotyle jejuna* the faeces containing the eggs of the trematode are eaten by the snail and the miracidia liberated after ingestion. Asexual reproduction of the parasite involves sporocysts, rediae and then cercariae, thousands of which are the progeny of a single egg. A cercaria which has left the snail can live in water for about 8 hrs, during which time it penetrates the skin of a goby, and encysts beneath the scales. Such an encysted metacercaria is freed from the fish in the gut of a redshank which has devoured it. Two other parasites of *Hydrobia ulvae*, *Cercaria ephemera* (*Catatropis verrucosa?*) and *Cercaria oocysta* (*Maritrema oocysta?*), have no second intermediate host. The latter encyst within the snail, which is eaten by the redshank, the final host, and although the former escape they encyst immediately either on the mollusc shell or some nearby object, which may be the plant on which *Hydrobia* feeds. Geese and ducks become infected during feeding.

Another prosobranch which is known to harbour various kinds of cercariae is *Littorina littorea*, also an abundant and gregarious species, and mention has been made of the large size to which a heavily infected winkle may grow. Wesenberg-Lund (1934) was the first to point out that infected molluscs are sometimes abnormally large and suggested that this is due to them eating enormous quantities of food in order to satisfy the demands of the parasite. The larger the snail the greater the number of cercariae it can support, so that it is an advantage to the parasite to produce gigantism in the host. Gigantism was also observed in *Hydrobia ulvae* by Rothschild (1936*b*), who considered that it is associated with the destruction of the gonad by the parasite, which implies that nutrients instead of being used in the production of sex cells, are available for the general growth of the body. Spooner (Rothschild, 1941*c*), analysing Lysaght's data (1941) concerning *Littorina* *neritoides* parasitized by Cercaria B, revealed an apparent stimulation of growth as a result of parasitism. Lysaght (1943) found no evidence for this, since Cercaria B infects more female snails than males, and in the larger size groups of this winkle, females predominate. It is interesting to note that females infected by Cercaria B appear to be attractive to Metacercaria A, a larval trematode which otherwise shows a preference for the male. The winkle does not appear to be affected by the encysted metacercariae, which do not destroy the tissues, though the pressure of large numbers of cysts may cause some mechanical obstruction. The most interesting investigation revealing the effect of parasitism on the growth of a prosobranch was made by Rothschild (1941b) who studied the growth of *Hydrobia ulvae* from an isolated pool in the saltings of the River Tamar, where the conditions for growth were good. She found that after 10 months of age uninfected snails which had reached a length of 5·75 mm grew only 1–1·25 mm and gradually died off after the age of 17 months. Infected snails, probably no older than uninfected ones measuring 6·75 mm long, attained a length of 9–10 mm. The infection rate in this locality is high, and shows certain seasonal fluctuations which may be linked with migrations of wandering birds.

The more frequent infection with trematode larvae (parthenitae and cercariae) of larger rather than smaller individuals may be due to causes other than growth stimulation, and probably a number of factors are operative—one of these has already been mentioned in connexion with *Littorina neritoides*. Thus it is possible that the miracidium exerts intra- as well as interspecific selection. In some gastropods the young may be immune from attack by certain parasites (Kemp & Gravely, 1919), whereas in others the immunity belongs to older snails. Ameel (1934) failed to infect old specimens of *Pomatiopsis lapidaria* with the miracidia of *Paragonimus* sp., but obtained almost 100% infection in young snails of 1 mm in length. On the other hand Krull (1933, 1934) found a high mortality of the young of *Fossaria modicella* infected with *Cotylophoron cotylophorum* and *Fasciola hepatica* and all died before cercariae were produced. The rapid multiplication of the parasite within the tissues of the mollusc will be relatively more destructive in the younger host which, during the period of rapid growth, is in any case less resistant to environmental change than mature snails or those approaching maturity. The growth rate characteristic of most gastropods means that the younger stages are exposed to infection for a much shorter time than size suggests. Frequently too, young stages have a different habitat from larger individuals, sometimes a more sheltered one, and this means that they will be away from the infection centred around the adults. For instance *Turritella communis*, a gregarious prosobranch living on sublittoral mud banks, is infected with various cercariae, but individuals of a shell length less than about 30 mm appear to be unparasitized, perhaps because the young live away from the adults and do not come in contact with the eggs of the parasite (Wright, 1956). Owing to their larger size adults will be more attractive to the vertebrate host as food, and so more advantageous to the parasite. However, the age at which a mollusc becomes a successful host for the development of cercariae probably varies with the species of trematode as well as host. Rothschild (1941b) has shown that both *Hydrobia ulvae* and *Littorina neritoides* with a shell measuring less than 2 mm in height, will harbour larvae and produce cercariae. These observations were made in the field.

Recently Mr B. James[1] has made an extensive study of the trematode infection of *Littorina saxatilis* in the vicinity of Aberystwyth and has shown that not only the per-

---

[1] We are very grateful to Mr James for allowing us to use this unpublished work, and for discussing the matter with us.

centage infection but also the kind of larval trematode varies with the size of the snail, and that this may have an ecological significance. A collection of *L. saxatilis* var. *tenebrosa* from an area of 1 sq yard in the lower supralittoral zone illustrates the phenomenon. *Cercaria ubiquita* was found only in periwinkles with shells measuring 6·0–14·0 mm high, the heaviest infection (83%) being in the largest specimens. *C. littorinae-rudis* occurred in snails with a shell height of 4·5–10·0 mm, the heaviest infection (66%) in individuals 8·0–9·0 mm high. In snails 0·6–6·0 mm high an undescribed gymnophalline cercaria was found with the highest infection (40%) in medium sized individuals (2·5–3·5 mm). There is some evidence to suggest that the final host of the gymnophalline cercaria is the rock-pipit, a bird too small to feed on the larger snails. During the winter months its diet is small specimens of *L. saxatilis* and *L. neritoides* and it is then that the cercariae reach a stage which is infective to the final host. It has also been shown that each parasite has a vertical distribution which can be related to the habitat of the final host. *C. littorinae-rudis* and the gymnophalline cercaria occur in the upper region of distribution of the periwinkle, the highest infection of the former at about 20 ft above CD and the latter 15 ft. In neither of these trematodes is there a free-living stage in the life cycle, which would be a disadvantage at this level on the shore, and in both a bird is the final host. Two other trematodes infect snails living at a lower level: *C. ubiquita* with an upper distribution which overlaps the lower range of the 2 parasites already mentioned, but extends below them and has its highest infection at 12 ft above CD, and *C. podocotyle atomon* with highest infection at 8 ft above CD. These have free-swimming miracidia and cercariae in the life history: in the former a bird is the final host and in the latter, with the lowest distribution, a fish.

Wesenberg-Lund (1934) noticed the ballooning of certain whorls, the thinning and corroding of shells and also colour changes as effects of the presence of trematode parasites. Such abnormalities, which may cause an asymmetrical development of the spire, have been confirmed for *Hydrobia ulvae* by Rothschild (1936*b*), who attributed them to the pressure exerted by the parasite from within. Later (1938*b*, 1941*b*), however, she asserted that environmental conditions may be a contributory cause of defects.

In *Hydrobia ulvae*, females attain a larger size than males which are usually outnumbered in the largest size group of any sample (Rothschild, 1938*b*). More males than females are infected with larval trematodes, in fact the ratio may be as high as 16 : 1, and these individuals, displaying gigantism, obscure the true proportion of the sexes by reversing the characteristic sexual differences in size. Pelseneer (1928) first drew attention to the fact that males of gastropod molluscs are more frequently infected with trematodes than females. He mentioned *Turritella communis* as an exception, but Rothschild (1935*b*) disproved this. She found that specimens collected from Rame Head, Cornwall, gave an 8% infection with 4 species of closely related cercariae, and that out of 53 infected individuals 42 were male. In all of these the gonad was attacked. It would seem that the parasite enters male *Turritella* more readily than females, and Rothschild stated that this preference may be due to the fact that ova ripen only periodically in this prosobranch whereas the testis contains live sperm all the year round. Whether this is the explanation in all cases may be doubted.

Wherever they may lodge, trematode parasites directly or indirectly affect the gonad of the molluscan host causing partial or complete castration, and for this reason Pelseneer (1906*b*, 1928) gave the name *Cercaria emasculans* to a larval trematode from *Littorina littorea* which caused the penis of the male to be greatly reduced. The state of the gonad of the winkle normally influences the condition of the penis which is reduced in size out of the breeding season; reduction of the gonad by the parasite has thus the same effect. In the female the pallial oviduct is affected likewise as the ovary is destroyed, so that the sex of parasitized individuals may not be easy to determine. However, the parthenites of *C. emasculans* rarely cause such complete reduction of the secondary sexual organs as do the rediae of *Himasthla leptosoma* and *C. lophocerca* (Rees, 1936*b*) which devour the gonad and so destroy it completely. Rothschild (1936*b*) found that parasitized individuals of *Hydrobia ulvae* invariably have an abnormal penis, which is usually more or less reduced in size, and she suggested that some specimens without a penis and showing no external character of either sex may be castrated males. On the contrary Krull (1935) stated that parasitized females develop a non-functional penis and a similar masculinization transforms the right tentacle of the viviparid *Campeloma rufum* into a penis-like structure (Mattox, 1938).

Since the phenomenon of sex reversal is a normal occurrence in some gastropod molluscs it is not surprising to find authors suggesting that trematode parasites may be the cause of this in species in which it does not normally occur. Wesenberg-Lund (1931) found that in the hermaphrodite snail *Succinea putris* the female organs are first destroyed by the parasite *Leucochloridium paradoxum* while the production of sperm continues; finally, however, the mollusc may be totally sterilized. Krull (1935) regarded the infected individuals of *Hydrobia ulvae*, which show a reduced penis, as females which have changed sex to a certain degree though they never function as males. Moreover a single discovery by Rothschild (1938*b*) supports this idea, for she found an infected, gravid female with a small penis. If such change of sex occurs it explains the excess of parasitized males over females. However, Rothschild (1938*b*) regarded it as highly improbable that all infected snails with a reduced penis are sex-reversed females, and Rees (1936*b*) and Lysaght (1943) found no evidence of sex reversal in parasitized *Littorina littorea* and *L. neritoides*.

### A LIST OF THE OCCURRENCE OF TREMATODE LARVAE FROM PROSOBRANCHS IN THE BRITISH ISLES

#### Patella vulgata

1. *Cercaria patellae* Lebour, 1907; Loch Ryan, 6·25% infestation (Lebour, 1911). Aberystwyth, 0·5% (Rees, G., 1934). May be the larva of *Echinostophilla virgula* Lebour, 1909, from *Arenaria interpres interpres* (L.).

#### Gibbula cineraria

1. *Cercaria brachyura* Lespés, 1857; Loch Ryan—once; Millport, 2% (Lebour, 1911).
2. *Cercaria cotylura* Pagenstecher, 1862; Millport (Palombi, 1938).
3. *Cercaria pachycerca* Diesing, 1858; Loch Ryan (Palombi, 1938).

#### Gibbula umbilicalis

1. *Cercaria linearis* Lespés, 1857; Aberystwyth, in intertubular spaces of digestive gland. See *Littorina littorea* (1).
2. *Cercaria brachyura* Lespés, 1857; Aberystwyth, and see *G. cineraria* (1).
3. *Cercaria cotylura* Pagenstecher, 1862; see *G. cineraria* (2).
4. *Cercaria pachycerca* Diesing, 1858; see *G. cineraria* (3).

## Calliostoma zizyphinum

1. *Cercaria cotylura* Pagenstecher, 1862; Millport (Palombi, 1938).

## Viviparus viviparus

1. *Cercaria of Lecithodendrium chilostomum* (Mehl).
    First intermediate host: ? *V. viviparus* (see also *Bithynia tentaculata*) River Nene, Northamptonshire.
    Second intermediate host etc.: see *B. tentaculata*.

## Littorina littorea

1. *Cercaria linearis* Lespés, 1857; Budle Bay, 0·25% infestation; Millport (Lebour, 1911). Aberystwyth, 0·06% infestation (Rees, W. J., 1935).
2. *Cercaria ubiquita* Lebour, 1907; (see *Hydrobia ulvae*).
3. *Cercaria of ubiquita* group Rees, 1936; Aberystwyth, 0·06% infestation (Rees, W. J., 1936a). This may not be the same species as *C. ubiquita* Lebour, 1907. Rees suggested it may be the larva of *Spelotrema simile* (Jägerskiöld) (see *Hydrobia ulvae, H. ventrosa, Littorina saxatilis* and *L. littoralis*).
4. *Cercaria of Himasthla leptosoma* (Creplin); Budle Bay and Fenham Flats, 3% infestion; Loch Ryan, 5% (Lebour, 1911). Aberystwyth, 2·03% infestation (=*C. echinostomum secundum*) (Rees, W. J., 1935).
    Second intermediate hosts: *Mytilus edulis* L., *Cardium edule* L., *Mactra corallina* Montagu, *Mya arenaria* L., *Macoma balthica* (L.), (Lebour, 1908).
    Definitive hosts: *Haematopus ostralegus occidentalis* Neumann, *Larus argentatus argentatus* Pontoppidan etc.; see *Hydrobia ulvae* (Lebour, 1905).
5. *Cercaria emasculans* Pelseneer, 1906; Aberystwyth, 1·3% infestation (Rees, W. J., 1935).
6. *Cercaria lebourae* Stunkard, 1932; Aberystwyth, 0·13% infestation (Rees, W. J., 1935).
7. *Cercaria buccini* Lebour, 1911; Northumberland coast (Lebour, 1911). Aberystwyth, 0·06% infestation (Rees, W. J., 1935).
8. *Cercaria lophocerca* Lebour, 1907; Millport, 10·0% infestation (Lebour, 1911). Aberystwyth, 0·72% infestation (Rees, W. J., 1935). Drake's Island, Plymouth, 9·5% infestation; Trevol, Cornwall, 1·8% infestation; Rum Bay, Plymouth, 10·0% infestation (Rees, W. J., 1936a). (Rothschild is of the opinion that this is not the same species as in *Hydrobia ulvae*, but if it is, it is the larva of *Cryptocotyle lingua*).
9. *Cercaria littorinae* Rees, W. J., 1936b.

## Littorina saxatilis

1. *Cercaria (cotylomicrocercous* group) Cable, 1941; Aberystwyth (James).
    Second intermediate hosts: *Gammarus* spp., *Carinogammarus mucronatus, Amphithoe longimana.*
    Definitive hosts: *Cottus scorpius* L., *C. bubalis* Euphrasen, *Anguilla anguilla* (L.), *Entelurus aequoreus* (L.), *Gadus luscus* L., *G. merlangus* L., *G. virens* L., *G. pollachius* L., *Onos tricirratus* (Bloch), *O. mustelus* (L.), *Sparus auratus* L., *Gobius flavescens* Fabricius, *Pholis gunnellus* (L.), *Liparis montagui* Donovan, *Gasterosteus*

aculeatus L., *Spinachia spinachia* (L.), *Phrynorhombus norvegicus* (Günther), *Platichthys flesus* (L.), *Pleuronectes platessa* L., *Solea solea* (L.), *Limanda limanda* (L.), *Gaidrosparus mediterraneus* (L.).
Adult stage: *Podocotyle atomon* (Rudolphi, 1802).

2. *Cercaria littorinae-rudis* Lebour, 1911; Holy Island, Northumberland (Lebour, 1911).
   Second intermediate host: not known, but McIntosh (1865) suggested *Carcinus maenas.*
   Definitive host: suggested by Nicoll (1907) *Calidris alpina alpina* (L.) and *Charadrius hiaticula hiaticula* L.
   Other suggested hosts: *Numenius arquata arquata* (L.), *Anthus spinoletta petrosus* (Montagu), *Motacilla flava flava* L., *Larus ridibundus ridibundus* L. etc.
   Adult stage: probably *Spelotrema claviforme* (Brandes).

3. *Cercaria ubiquita* Lebour, 1907; (see Stunkard, 1957). Northumberland (Lebour, 1907). Plymouth (Rees, W. J., 1936a). Aberystwyth (Rees & James, personal communication).

4. *Cercaria roscovita* Stunkard, 1932. First described in *L.s.nigrolineata* at Roscoff; (intertubular lymph spaces of gonad and digestive gland). Suggested adult stage a plagiorchid. Aberystwyth (James).

5. *Cercaria lebourae* Stunkard, 1932. First described in *L. littorea* and *L. obtusa* (sic), Roscoff; (intertubular spaces of digestive gland and gonad). Monostome (*yenchingensis* group) (Rothschild, 1938a). Aberystwyth (James).

6. Unnamed, in interlobular spaces of gonad and digestive gland and in 'connective tissue lumen' of gonoduct of ♀ host. A gymnophalline cercaria. Adult unknown but other gymnophallines live in shore birds (James).

7. *Cercaria* of *ubiquita* group James, 1959. Aberystwyth, Plymouth.

### *Littorina littoralis*

1. *Cercaria littorinae-obtusatae* Lebour, 1911; Millport, 5% infestation (Lebour, 1911).
2. *Cercaria ubiquita* Lebour, 1907; Fenham Flats, Loch Ryan (Lebour, 1911). Aberystwyth (James).
3. *Cercaria* of *ubiquita* group Rees, 1936; Plymouth, 10·0% infestation (Rees, W. J., 1936a).
4. *Cercaria* of *pleurolophocerca* group; Plymouth (Rothschild, 1939b).

### *Littorina neritoides*

1. *Metacercaria A* Lysaght, 1941; Plymouth Breakwater (Lysaght, 1941).
2. *Cercaria B* (*ubiquita* group) Lysaght, 1941.
3. *Cercaria C* (allied to *C. emasculans*) Lysaght, 1941.
4. *Cercaria D* (*yenchingensis* group) Lysaght, 1941. Single infection recorded (Rothschild, 1938a).

### *Hydrobia ulvae*

1. *Cercaria oocysta* Lebour, 1907; Rothschild (1936a, b). Encysts in first host.
   Definitive host: possibly *Larus ridibundus ridibundus* L. (Rothschild, 1937).
   Adult stage: probably a species of *Maritrema* Nicoll, 1907 (Rothschild, 1937).
2. *Cercaria pirum* Lebour, 1907; Rothschild (1936a, b); Lebour (1911). Encysts in first host.

3. *Cercaria A* (*oocysta* group); Rothschild (1936*a*). Encysts in first host.
4. *Cercaria ubiquita* Lebour, 1907; Rothschild (1936*a*, *b*, 1938*b*).
    Second intermediate host: *Carcinus maenas* (L.), *Cancer pagurus* L. Plymouth.
    Definitive host: *Larus argentatus* Pontoppidan.
    Adult stage: *Spelotrema excellens* Nicoll, 1907.
5. *Cercaria B* ⎫
6. *Cercaria C* ⎬ (*ubiquita* group) Rothschild (1936*a*).
7. *Cercaria lophocerca* Lebour, 1907 (*non* Filippi); Rothschild (1936*a*, *b*).
    Second intermediate hosts: *Labrus bergylta* Ascanius, *Ctenolabrus rupestris* (L.),
    *Onos mustelus* (L.), *O. tricirratus* (Bloch), *Blennius pholis* L., *B. gattorugine* L.,
    *Pholis gunnellus* (L.), *Gobius flavescens* Fabricius (Rothschild, 1939*b*).
    Definitive hosts: *Larus marinus* L., *L. fuscus* L., *L. argentatus argentatus* Pontoppidan,
    *Sterna hirundo* L., *Rissa tridactyla tridactyla* (L.), *Alca torda* L., *Podiceps auritus* (L.),
    *Nycticorax nycticorax nycticorax* (L.); also in mammals.
    Adult stage: *Cryptocotyle lingua* (Creplin).
8. *Cercaria D* (*pleurolophocerca* group); Rothschild (1936*a*).
    Second intermediate host: *Gobius flavescens* Fabricius and other fishes (Rothschild,
    1938*d*).
    Definitive hosts: *Tringa totanus totanus* (L.), *Larus ridibundus ridibundus* L. (Roths-
    child, 1941*a*).
    Adult stage: *Cryptocotyle jejuna* Nicoll, 1907.
9. *Cercaria ephemera* Lebour, 1907 (*non* Nitzsch); Rothschild (1935*a*, 1936*a*, *b*); (may be
    identical with *C. imbricata* from *Bithynia tentaculata*). Encysts in free state (Roths-
    child, 1935*a*).
    Definitive host: various birds.
    Adult stage: Notocotylidae, possibly *Catatropsis verrucosa* (Frölich).
10. *Cercaria E* ⎫
11. *Cercaria F* ⎬ (*ephemera* group) Rothschild (1936*a*). Encyst in free state.
12. *Cercaria G* ⎭
13. *Cercaria* of *Himasthla leptosoma* (Creplin) (=*Cercaria* of *Echinostomum secundum*
    Lebour, 1907); Lebour (1911); Rothschild (1936*a*).
    Second intermediate hosts: *Abra tenuis* (Montagu), *Mytilus edulis* L., *Cardium
    edule* L., *Mya arenaria* L., *Paphia pallustra* (Montagu), (Lebour, 1908).
    Definitive hosts: *Larus ridibundus ridibundus* L., *L. argentatus argentatus* Pontoppidan,
    *Limosa lapponica lapponica* (L.), *Numenius arquata arquata* (L.), *Arenaria interpres
    interpres* (L.), *Crocethia alba* (Pallas), *Calidris canutus canutus* (L.), *Calidris alpina
    alpina* (L.).
14. *Cercaria H* (*echinostome* group); Rothschild (1936*a*).
15. *Cercaria I* ⎫
16. *Cercaria J* ⎬ (*metentera* group); Rothschild (1936*a*). Encyst in free state.
17. *Cercaria K* (*sagittarius* group); Rothschild (1936*a*). Encysts in free state.
18. *Cercaria L* ⎫
19. *Cercaria M* ⎪
20. *Cercaria N* ⎬ Cercariae of unknown systematic position; Rothschild (1936*a*).
21. *Metacercaria A* ⎪
22. *Metacercaria B* ⎭

    (1–22 recorded by Rothschild (1936*a*) from *Hydrobia ulvae* received from Ply-
mouth, Scotland and Wales. No exact locality given.)

21

23. *Cercaria sinitzini* Rothschild, 1938; St John's Lake, Plymouth, 0·5% infestation (Rothschild, 1938*e*).
Second intermediate host: a copepod?
Adult stage: one of the Hemiuridae.

24. *Cercaria coronanda* Rothschild, 1938; in 2 of several thousand.
Second intermediate host: *Gobius flavescens* Fabricius, and probably other fishes (Rothschild, 1938*c*).
Definitive host: a fish.
Adult stage: probably one of the Acanthostomatidae (Rothschild, 1940).

- 25. *Cercaria* of *Microcreadium parvum* Simer, 1929; St John's Lake, Plymouth (Rothschild, 1939*a*).

26. *Cercaria* sp. ⎫
27. *Cercaria* sp. ⎬ undescribed Notocotylidae (Rothschild, 1938*a*).

28. *Cercaria glandosa* Lebour, 1908; Fenham Flats (Lebour, 1911).
Adult stage: probably a species of *Gymnophallus* in a bird.

## Hydrobia ventrosa

1. *Cercaria ephemera* Lebour, 1907 (*non* Nitzsch); Plymouth (Rothschild, 1938*a*); (see *Hydrobia ulvae*).

2. *Cercaria* sp. (*imbricata* group); undescribed (Rothschild, 1938*a*).

3. *Cercaria ubiquita* Lebour, 1907; see *H. ulvae*.

4. *Cercaria lophocerca* Lebour, 1907; see *H. ulvae*.

## Bithynia tentaculata

1. *Cercaria* of *Lecithodendrium chilostomum* (Mehl).
First intermediate host: ? *B. tentaculata* (Brown, 1933), River Nene, Northamptonshire.
Second intermediate hosts: *Phryganea grandis* L., *Limnephilus rhombicus* (L.).
Definitive host: insectivorous bats.

2. *Cercaria vivacis* Iles, 1959; Roath Park lake, Cardiff; incidence low.

## Turritella communis

1. *Cercaria pythionike* Rothschild, 1935; Rame Mud, Plymouth, 2% infestation (Rothschild, 1935*b*).

2. *Cercaria herpsyllis* Rothschild, 1935; Rame Mud, Plymouth, 0·5% infestation (Rothschild, 1935*b*).

3. *Cercaria nicarete* Rothschild, 1935; Rame Mud, Plymouth, 1% infestation (Rothschild, 1935*b*).

4. *Cercaria ampelis* Rothschild, 1935; Rame Mud, Plymouth, 4% infestation (Rothschild, 1935*b*).

5. *Cercaria ranzii* Rothschild, 1935; Rame Mud, Plymouth, 1% infestation (Rothschild, 1935*b*).

6. *Cercaria doricha* Rothschild, 1935; Rame Mud, Plymouth, 5% infestation (Rothschild, 1935*b*).
Second intermediate host: possibly *Gadus luscus* L. (Rothschild & Sproston, 1941; Rothschild, 1941*c*).
Definitive hosts: *Lophius piscatorius* L., *Scophthalmus maximus* (L.), *Squatina squatina* (L.), *Gadus pollachius* L., *Raja* spp., *Trigla* spp.

7. *Cercaria turritellae* Hutton, 1955; Cawsand Bay, Plymouth, 0·5% infestation (Hutton, 1955).
8. *Cercaria doricha-pigmentata* Wright, 1956; Millport, 4·2% infestation (Wright, 1956).
9. *Cercaria cooki* Wright, 1956; St Bride's Bay and S Haven, Skomer (Wright, 1956).

### Natica alderi

1. *Cercaria* sp. W. J. Rees, 1937; (*cystophorus* type), Plymouth (description not published).

### Natica catena

1. *Cercaria* sp. W. J. Rees, 1937; Cawsand Bay, Plymouth (Dollfus, 1950).
   Second intermediate hosts: *Pseudocalanus* sp., *Balanus balanoides* (L.).

### Nucella lapillus

1. *Cercaria* of *Parorchis acanthus* (Nicoll, 1906); (=*C. purpurae* (Lebour, 1907)), Budle Bay, Fenham Flats, Loch Ryan, Millport, 20% infestation (Lebour, 1907). Aberystwyth, 9·5–12% infestation (Rees, G., 1937).
   Second intermediate hosts: *Cardium edule* L., *Mytilus edulis* L. (Lebour & Elmhirst, 1922). Encysts in free state.
   Definitive hosts: *Larus argentatus argentatus* Pontoppidan, *Larus canus canus* L.

### Urosalpinx cinerea

1. *Cercaria* of *Parorchis acanthus* (Nicoll, 1906); in 1 of 600 from Liverpool (Rees, G., 1939).

### Buccinum undatum

1. *Cercaria buccini* Lebour, 1911; Northumberland coast, 5% infestation (Lebour, 1911).
2. *Cercaria neptuneae* Lebour, 1911; Cullercoats (trawling grounds) (Lebour, 1911). May be larval stage of *Allocreadium* Looss, 1900 or of *Plagioporus* Stafford, 1904 (as *Lebouria* Nicoll, 1909), as suggested by Nicoll.
3. *Cercaria* of *Neophasis lageniformis* (Lebour, 1910) (=*Cercaria* of *Acanthopsolus lageniformis* Lebour, 1911); Cullercoats and Holy Island, 7% infestation. Probably no second intermediate host, the fish swallowing the whelk.
   Definitive host: *Anarhichas lupus* L.
4. *Cercaria* of *Zoogonoides viviparus* Olsson, 1868 (*microcercous* type) Plymouth, 75% infestation (Lebour, 1916–18).
   Second intermediate host: unknown.
   Definitive hosts: *Zeus faber* L., *Blennius gattorugine* L., *Blennius ocellaris* L., *Solea solea* (L.), *Microchirus variegatus* (Donovan), *Microstomus kitt* (Walbaum), *Pleuronectes platessa* L., *Scophthalmus maximus* (L.), *Hippoglossoides platessoides* (Fabricius), *Glyptocephalus cynoglossus* (L.), *Anarhichas lupus* L., *Callionymus lyra* L.

# CHAPTER 25

# THE RELATIONSHIPS OF PROSOBRANCHS

W E must now make some attempt to discuss the classification of the prosobranch gastropods and to evaluate their inter-relationships. After that task has been completed some indication will be given of the way in which they may perhaps be related to the other groups of the class.

The Gastropoda are usually recognized now-a-days as exhibiting 3 main patterns of body structure and are therefore classified into 3 large subclasses, the Prosobranchia, the Opisthobranchia and the Pulmonata, of which the Prosobranchia are undoubtedly the most primitive and the other 2 the more advanced. Both pulmonates and opisthobranchs probably have a prosobranch origin, but the extent to which it is common may be debated. A recent common ancestry would rightly lead to their being united in a single subclass, and this is, indeed, often done. The Gastropoda are then divided into a lower subclass, the Streptoneura (=Prosobranchia), so called because of the streptoneurous condition of the nervous system associated (like the forwardly directed gill to which the name prosobranch refers) with the torsion which they exhibit, and a higher subclass, the Euthyneura (=Opisthobranchia + Pulmonata), named thus because its members all show a euthyneurous condition of the nervous system. Euthyneury, however, appears to have been achieved by a real detorsion in opisthobranchs, but by internal rearrangement of the nervous system in the pulmonates so that their bodies except for this one particularity are still the bodies of gastropods which have retained torsion. Because this fact seems to suggest that pulmonates and opisthobranchs are clearly distinct, even if they may have shared a remote common origin from a prosobranch ancestry, the triple subdivision of the gastropod class will be used here.

It has been recognized for a long time that there are certainly 2 grades of organization within the subclass Prosobranchia, a lower grade in which the animals possess 2 sets of the organs composing the pallial complex—right and left ctenidia, right and left kidneys and so on—and a higher grade the members of which retain only the left half of the complex. On this basis rests a classification of prosobranchs which distinguishes the lower Diotocardia (a name derived from the presence of 2 auricles in the heart), from a higher group called the Monotocardia (a name which directs attention to the occurrence of only the left auricle). Alternative names for these 2 groupings are related to the fact that in animals of the lower grade the ctenidial axis bears a double row of filaments, whereas in the higher grade it carries only a single row. These differences led to the formation of the names Aspidobranchia and Scutibranchia (animals with shield-shaped gills) for the former, and Pectinibranchia and Ctenobranchia (animals with comb-like gills) for the latter. Aspidobranchia, Scutibranchia and Diotocardia are thus synonyms, as are Pectinibranchia, Ctenobranchia and Monotocardia.

The cleavage between the 2 grades is not absolute and annectent forms occur, as would be expected if the one group had evolved from the other by gradual modification of structure. These intermediate forms are members of the groups Trochacea and Neritacea, in which the right ctenidium has been lost along with the associated osphradium, but the 2 auricles are present and the Trochacea retain the 2 kidneys; the single gill which does remain is still aspidobranch (bipectinate) in arrangement.

Further analysis of both the diotocardian and monotocardian stocks allows them to be split into a series of sub-divisions, the degree of separation of which has always permitted argument. Sedgwick (1909) in his *Student's Text-Book* and Pelseneer (1906a) in his standard text-book on the molluscs subdivided both the diotocardians and the monoto-cardians into a number of groups of equal rank on the basis of radular structure. The diotocardians include 2 assemblages, one (the Docoglossa) characterized by the possession of a radula of that pattern, the other (the Rhipidoglossa) with a rhipidoglossate radula; the monotocardians are similarly split into the Taenioglossa, Ptenoglossa, Rachiglossa and Toxoglossa, with radulae of the sort indicated by their names, and the Gymnoglossa or Aglossa without any radula at all. This classification has the great merit of being based upon radular structure and is therefore usable with dried animals in which the radula is preserved, though it is not applicable, as the best classification should be, to the material of palaeontologist and neontologist alike. Nevertheless it has the unsatisfactory feature of subdividing the monotocardians into a large number of groups which do not all represent independent evolutionary trends, but some of which are merely develop-ments one from the other. For such reasons Thiele (1929-35) and Wenz (1938) suppressed these as taxonomic terms and left them merely as descriptions of radular structure, and made a classification of the prosobranchs which utilized 3 major sub-divisions, the Archaeogastropoda, the Mesogastropoda and the Stenoglossa, for which the name Neogastropoda has also been proposed. The synonymy of Thiele's and Pelseneer's classifications is best given in a table:

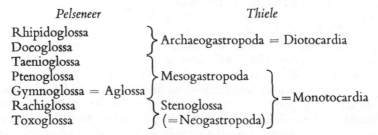

*Pelseneer*                                    *Thiele*

Rhipidoglossa
Docoglossa          } Archaeogastropoda = Diotocardia
Taenioglossa
Ptenoglossa         } Mesogastropoda
Gymnoglossa = Aglossa                          } = Monotocardia
Rachiglossa         } Stenoglossa
Toxoglossa          } (= Neogastropoda)

Cox (1960) uses the term Caenogastropoda for the monotocardian group.

Our preferred names for prosobranch groups are based first, on the contrast in heart and pallial structure and secondly, on the difference in radulae. This gives the following classification:

Prosobranchia } Diotocardia
              } Monotocardia } Taenioglossa (or Mesogastropoda)
                             } Stenoglossa (or Neogastropoda)

Here the group Taenioglossa includes such minor groupings as Ptenoglossa and Aglossa and is preferred to Mesogastropoda because of the antithesis which it offers to Stenoglossa.

We may now turn to the Diotocardia, a group which seems undoubtedly to contain the most primitive of living gastropods, though it is equally true that some of its members are amongst the most highly advanced and specialized. Diotocardians occur in 2 main facies, one like the Pleurotomariidae, Scissurellidae, Turbinidae, Cyclostrematidae, Trochidae and Neritidae, in which the shell has the ordinary helicoid spiral conformation, and the other like the Fissurellidae, Acmaeidae, Lepetidae and Patellidae, where it is simply conical and the animal is known as a limpet. The family Haliotidae, in which the shell is a rapidly growing spiral with an expanded terminal part, may perhaps be looked upon as a bridge between the 2 types. There can be little doubt that the spiral shell is the more primitive in view of its occurrence in such animals as the extinct Bellerophontacea, in the persistent larval shell of one specimen of *Neopilina galatheae*, and because of the fact that the conical shell of limpets is preceded by one which is spirally wound.

The whole organization of the diotocardian proclaims its primitive nature. The spiral shell, the double set of pallial structures, the circlet of epipodial tentacles, the eyes in the form of open pits, the setose tentacles, the polygyrous operculum, the lack of a penis, the eggs extruded singly, the trochophore larva and the posterior position of the anus within the mantle cavity are external characteristics which do this, whilst in its internal anatomy the following points may be mentioned as reflections of its primitive nature: the rhipidoglossan radula, the small salivary glands directly over the buccal cavity, the villi in the oesophageal glands, the well developed spiral caecum attached to the stomach, the passage of the rectum through the ventricle and the fact that the right kidney is still an excretory organ as well as an outlet for the reproductive cells. Other primitive features are the hypoathroid nervous system with poorly differentiated ganglia and ladder-like pedal cords, the lack of ganglia apart from the visceral on the visceral loop and the presence of a labial commissure; the sole gland is the only pedal gland; the membranes around the eggs are secreted by the eggs themselves or by the ovary, not by the genital duct; the shell has 2 shell muscles and there is nacre in it, and its pigments are not chemically bound to the calcareous material.

Within the Diotocardia there may be distinguished 3 grades, each with its particular evolutionary trends. Of these the most primitive is that which includes the animals placed by Thiele in his group Zeugobranchia (= Wenz's Pleurotomariacea), the families Pleurotomariidae, Scissurellidae, Haliotidae and Fissurellidae. The second grade is represented by the Patellacea, including the families Acmaeidae, Lepetidae and Patellidae, whilst the third grade includes 2 superfamilies, the Trochacea and the Neritacea, which contain the following families respectively: the former, Trochidae, Cyclostrematidae and Turbinidae; the latter, Neritidae (restricting the list to families represented in the British fauna). The first superfamily, the zeugobranchs, which contains 380 living species (Schilder, 1947), consists mainly of animals with spirally wound shells characterized by the presence of a slit (or series of holes representing a modified slit) which reflects a solution to the problem of pallial sanitation reached by the members of this superfamily and by none other amongst the prosobranchs. It also shows a tendency to the adoption of the limpet facies in the Haliotidae and this is consummated in the Fissurellidae, which includes some animals like *Diodora*, *Emarginula* and *Puncturella* with an almost perfect bilateral symmetry externally, though this is marred by internal variation in the size of paired structures. The group reached a maximal development in the period Silurian–Triassic and is much depleted since. Of the British members of the Zeugobranchia the Scissurellidae are the most primitive with their tight spiral shell, an operculum on the foot, and 2 shell muscles equal in size; the stomach has a spiral caecum and the left kidney is a large papillary sac. *Scissurella* shows some modification of its ctenidia in that the leaflets are finger-shaped rather than lamelliform and it is remarkable amongst prosobranchs in having all muscles except the columellar made of striped fibres.

Some approach towards the limpet mode of life is made by the Haliotidae in the rapid increase of the shell spiral, the loss of the operculum, the enlargement of the right shell muscle and foot into a powerful organ to grip the substratum and the hypertrophy of the epipodium as a sensory organ. Internally it still retains a generally primitive character, especially in having a spiral caecum in the stomach and a papillary sac. Both of these have been lost by members of the family Fissurellidae, associated with a considerable degree of advancement and specialization for the rock-clinging mode of life which they pursue. The bilateral symmetry of the shell and mantle cavity is also part of this adaptation, like the formation of a horseshoe-shaped shell muscle from the original right and left members of a pair. In addition, the Fissurellidae show two points not exhibited by any other zeugobranchs in the presence of a diverticulum within the buccal mass (p. 190) and the separation of the intestinal groove from the main part of the intestine to form a siphon (p. 233), although the adaptive significance of these two changes is not clear.

The Patellacea (containing 181 Recent species) represent another trend towards the limpet mode of life, but this must have had a different starting point from the zeugobranch limpets and it has followed a different course, although there is a certain degree of convergent similarity between the common and the keyhole limpets which represent the terminal members of the two series. The group appears in the Trias, presumably from a zeugobranch ancestor. The patellacean limpets have neither hole nor slit in their shells, and this allows them to colonize bare rocks on the upper parts of the shore with a success far beyond that attained by any zeugobranch, though it has compelled them to replace the ctenidia with pallial gills set around the margin of the mantle skirt. One ctenidium still persists in the Acmaeidae, sometimes with, sometimes without accompanying pallial gills, but this has been suppressed in the Patellidae where there are only pallial gills, though the vestiges of the 2 ctenidia are perhaps still incorporated in the structures known as osphradia. In the family Lepetidae, the members of which are all small, gills are totally lost, and it is perhaps worth recording that some malacologists regard the single ctenidium of the acmaeids as a novelty and not as homologous with those of other prosobranchs. Like other limpets, the Patellacea have a horseshoe-shaped shell muscle and the pallial margin has become greatly sensitized (e.g. *Acmaea*), accomplishing in this way what has been done by the exaggerated epipodium of the zeugobranchs. The epipodium has, indeed, been lost, and is functionally replaced by the mantle edge. The modification of the respiratory system has also made its effects felt in other parts of the body and the bilateral symmetry is even more superficial than in the fissurellids: thus the anus and the 2 excretory apertures lie to the right in the mantle cavity and the pericardial cavity and heart to the left. Various other anatomical points emphasize the great specialization and advance of the animals: the heart has only 1 auricle; the rectum does not penetrate the ventricle; the intestine has hypertrophied to form an extraordinarily elongated tube; the stomach has been all but lost; the gonad becomes ventral; the salivary glands are double, lie in the visceral mass and are linked to the buccal cavity by long ducts; the radula is docoglossate, the teeth all but immobile on the radular membrane, and the mode of action of the buccal mass, with protraction the effective movement for scraping the substratum, is unique amongst the prosobranchs. All these points show that the Patellacea have become a very advanced group. They form, indeed, when one considers the wealth of species and of individuals of *Acmaea* in the Pacific Ocean and *Patella* in the Atlantic, one of the most successful of all groups of prosobranchs.

The third grade of diotocardian is represented by the 2 superfamilies Trochacea (of which 929 species are found today) and Neritacea, in both of which there are discernible the same trends as have apparently led to the evolution of the Monotocardia. The Neritacea, indeed, exhibit so many features of this nature (as well as a number of peculiar ones of their own) as to suggest that their organization is fundamentally at the monotocardian level, but that they are classified as diotocardians rather than as monotocardians because of the way in which it has proved most convenient to draw up the definition of these 2 groups. Both groups are probably derived through the Trochonematacea from a zeugobranch ancestry.

The main trend towards the monotocardian condition which is represented within these superfamilies is the modification of the right moiety of the pallial complex. This is most marked in the Neritacea, where only a vestige of the right ctenidium occurs in the form of the 'organe creux' of the Neritidae and a few patches of glandular material represent the right hypobranchial gland. Only 1 kidney (the left) is present, and only 1 functional osphradium occurs. Two auricles, however, are still present in the heart and 2 muscles are attached to the shell. In the Trochacea the loss of structures on the right side is less and the animals of this superfamily still possess a right hypobranchial gland— in some cases to the exclusion of the left—2 auricles and a functional right kidney, and have lost only the gill and osphradium. Though known from the Triassic, whereas the Neritacea date from the Silurian, the Trochacea are in many other respects, too, a more primitive group than the Neritacea: they are typically marine; they have a tight spiral shell often with an umbilicus; the foot carries epipodial tentacles and sense organs; the ctenidium is aspidobranch; the eyes, though more advanced than those of the zeugobranchs and patellaceans, are still primitive in being open and are set on eye stalks separate from the cephalic tentacles; the stomach often retains a spiral caecum; their genital ducts are limited to the formation of a urinogenital papilla in the females of certain species and their eggs are fertilized externally and in most laid singly. The sole respects in which they offer some advance on the zeugobranchs, patellaceans and the neritaceans is in the possession of a single columellar muscle, in the presence of a large anteriorly directed intestinal loop and in the development of an anal gland.

Two families of undoubted Trochacea are represented in the British fauna, the Trochidae and the Turbinidae, the latter recognizable at once from the former by reason of the calcified operculum which its members carry; otherwise the organization of the 2 groups is remarkably similar. Within the Trochidae a number of different subfamilies contain a variety of animals popularly known as top shells; of these there is little doubt that the small members of the Margaritinae (*Margarites*) are the most primitive, with their smooth, globular shells, the complete absence of any tubular outgrowth from the ventral lip on the snout, and the presence of 6 pairs of epipodial tentacles, although they are advanced in having an extension to the lips of the right kidney which acts as a urinogenital papilla and in having suppressed the larval stage. The animals in the subfamily Trochinae are more advanced in their shell, in the presence of a spout-like ventral lip of the mouth, in the reduction of the epipodium and in the occurrence of egg ribbons and the suppression of the larva in the genus *Cantharidus*. Top shells of the Calliostomatinae are still more highly evolved as they possess conical shells without an umbilicus, a glandular urinogenital papilla, a tubular proboscidiform extension to the ventral lip, and are advanced in the development of an anterior pedal gland, in their stomach, in a shortened intestine and in the presence of a left dialyneury as well as the right one found in all the other subfamilies. In addition, the Calliostomatinae lay their eggs in strings, and have lost their larval stage.

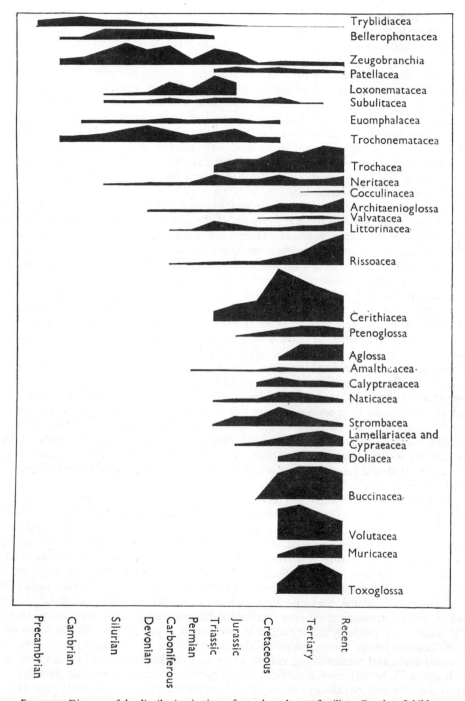

Fig. 317.—Diagram of the distribution in time of prosobranch superfamilies. Based on Schilder.

The Trochidae contain a further subfamily with British representatives, the Skeneinae; unfortunately the soft parts of these minute animals are not thoroughly known, so that it is not possible to assess their relationships to other trochids. Indeed, the fact that they are alleged to possess a penis makes their classification as trochids a somewhat dubious procedure and it may well be that they are truly mesogastropods of trochoid appearance rather than genuine members of the family. Much the same may be said of the animals placed in the family Cyclostrematidae. Of these *Circulus striatus* (= *Trochus duminyi* Requien) is said to be British. The animal described under this name by Thiele possesses a shell very similar to that carried by an animal described by Fretter (1956) the soft parts of which were wholly different from those of a trochid. It may be assumed that the conchological characters—which are about all that Thiele had to go on—misled him into placing this family within the Trochacea, and the animals ought properly to be transferred to the monotocardians.

The Neritacea is a group of very successful animals which abound in a great variety of habitats, particularly in the warmer parts of the globe, and are said to be represented by 582 species of living molluscs. Their only European representative is *Theodoxus fluviatilis* which, nevertheless, exhibits the trend shown by many members of the group to colonize brackish and freshwater and even to become terrestrial. This has led them into a considerable modification of body structure and produced an advanced type of prosobranch. The shell is spiral, devoid of nacre and is closable by an operculum with an inner projection. The walls separating the upper whorls of the shell from one another are often resorbed. The epipodial tentacles of lower groups have gone; the eyes, which are closed vesicles, are borne on stalks which become fused to the base of the tentacles. In the gut, there are no jaws and the salivary glands are reduced, though this may be compensated for by the development of other buccal glands; the oesophageal glands have become partly separated from the main part of the mid-oesophagus and the stomach has lost its spiral caecum; there is a crystal sac in relation to the rectum. In the nervous system the pleural ganglia have separated from the pedal and are connected by a pleural commissure—a very rare occurrence; the visceral loop has supra- and sub-oesophageal ganglia on it in addition to the visceral, and the sub-oesophageal is connected by a zygoneury to the right pleural ganglion. The sole ctenidium, on the left, is innervated from the left pleural ganglion, a fact which has given rise to some doubt as to its homology with other prosobranch ctenidia.

Adaptations for freshwater and terrestrial life affect mainly the respiratory, excretory and reproductive organs. The excretory organ consists of a single kidney on the left which is provided with a bladder, perhaps of osmoregulatory importance, and in the last system the important adaptations involve the presence of a penis, which is cephalic in origin, the manufacture of spermatophores and the elaboration of the female duct to allow copulation and the manufacture of egg capsules within which the eggs are laid and develop. The female is either diaulic or triaulic. In the Neritacea, too, parts of the pericardial and related coelomic cavities have expanded to give rise to large spaces which extend around the viscera: this indeed has proceeded to such an extent that the Neritacea may properly be regarded as coelomate prosobranchs. To do some other prosobranchs justice the extension of the right kidney sac amongst the viscera as in zeugobranchs and patellaceans gives rise to an almost identical result in a different way.

It seems likely that monotocardians have evolved from a diotocardian ancestry with trochoid relationships: alone of the diotocardians are the trochids sufficiently unspecialized to be regarded in this light. They may well be polyphyletic. The advance from the diotocardian to the monotocardian level of organization involved the completion of the trend towards the loss of the organs of the right side so that such parts as still remain in the trochids—right hypobranchial gland, right efferent pallial vein, right kidney as a functional excretory organ and right auricle—are lost altogether. As a consequence the rectum migrates to occupy a position near the extreme right of the mantle skirt, an area which it shares with the genital duct. This, in its turn, is able to expand into a series of glandular pouches which become prostatic in the male and allow the female to elaborate egg membranes and capsules within which the eggs are laid with food supplies. Because of this, internal fertilization becomes more or less obligatory and the trochophore larval stage is passed through whilst the egg is still protected by the capsule. The free larval stage of the mesogastropod is, therefore, a more advanced larva, the veliger.

In addition to these changes, which may be regarded as interlinked, a number of others have also taken place. Externally the epipodium is lost and the head and foot become bare of tentacles apart from the cephalic pair, the eye stalks and, in certain groups, occasional outgrowths from the metapodial region which are probably new developments rather than persistent epipodial vestiges. Internally the radula has become narrower, losing the vast array of marginal teeth characteristic of the rhipidoglossan type and now, in most monotocardians, containing only 7 teeth in each row. Their action has become more powerful and the animals are less given to microphagy than their ancestors. The salivary glands lie well behind the buccal mass and have long ducts which pass forwards through the nerve ring. The rectum never passes through the ventricle. The nervous system shows a change from the hypoathroid type of the diotocardian with the pleural and pedal ganglia forming a large mass under the anterior part of the gut and with the pedals extended into ganglion cords running the greater length of the foot and connected across the mid-line by numerous cross connexions. Instead, the pleural ganglia tend to migrate dorsally towards the cerebrals alongside which they ultimately come to lie, giving the condition known as epiathroid, whilst the pedal cords shorten to globular pedal ganglia and the original multiple commissures are reduced to 2 or 1. Supra-oesophageal and sub-oesophageal ganglia occur on the visceral loop. The shell alters in composition in never possessing nacre and the pigments which occur in it become intimately bound to the calcareous material so that they cannot be separated from it. The operculum becomes oligogyrous.

These are the principal changes in organization which mark the advance of the proso-branchs to mesogastropod level. They seem to have given rise to a stock which was physiologically effective and permitted a very varied adaptive radiation to occur. The original animals were marine and probably littoral, and while most of the modern mesogastropods have remained there, a large number have invaded freshwater, a few have become terrestrial—apparently by direct colonization of the land from the upper reaches of the shore rather than by the more ordinary route through freshwater—and a few have migrated to the deeper parts of the sea or become pelagic. Most are herbivorous and a few are still microphagous and have produced elaborate ciliary methods of collecting their food, but some monotocardians have become adapted to living on animal food, mainly sessile organisms such as coelenterates and tunicates, and a very few are parasitic. We may now turn to the relationships of these varied forms.

Primarily on the basis of the facts that pedal cords still exist in the nervous system with several cross-connexions, that the nervous system is dystenoid and retains a labial commissure and that neck lobes represent vestigial parts of an epipodial fold, the group Architaenioglossa (=Cyclophoracea of Wenz) is regarded as the most primitive of the

Monotocardia. Nevertheless the group (despite its ancient origin in the Devonian) is in several respects an advanced one; for example, all its members are either inhabitants of freshwater or of land, and although their shells are usually low cones, some have shells in which the most extraordinary development of coiling may occur, loosening the spiral into a corkscrew or even reversing direction: this seems to indicate not just advancement, but even gerontic change. In the males the penis is cephalic in origin. Most members of this superfamily (of which 1,562 species occur) are inhabitants of the warmer parts of the globe and have a general resemblance to one another, and in this respect the only British genus *Viviparus*, with 2 species, is typical of the group.

A second group of lowly monotocardians is the superfamily Valvatacea, which contains the single family Valvatidae with only 23 species in it and which appears in the Cretaceous. These, like most Architaenioglossa, are freshwater animals with an organization which is generally primitive, though in this case the simplicity may be that of small animals rather than that of truly primitive creatures. They show some of the characteristic features of freshwater animals, being hermaphrodite, without a free larval stage or even viviparous, and possessing an anterior projection of the kidney which may be osmoregulatory. The gut has no oesophageal glands, though it has no crystalline style, so that their absence is perhaps due just to the minuteness of the animal. The most outstanding feature of the valvatids, however, is the bipectinate gill, which is placed far forward on the mantle skirt so that its tip projects freely from the mantle cavity as the animals walk, giving in this way an appearance which is definitely diagnostic. Another feature of these animals, as of some other minute prosobranchs, is the presence of a tentacle set on the edge of the mantle skirt on the right side where it acts as a kind of exhalant siphon.

A larger superfamily of monotocardians is the Littorinacea (605 living species), which contains animals marked by nearly all the characteristic features of the mesogastropod and represents a stock neither primitive, advanced nor characterized by the evolution of specialization. They show some resemblance to Architaenioglossa, from which they may have evolved in the Carboniferous, though Cox (1960) followed Cossmann in deriving them from the diotocardian Trochonematacea. The Littorinacea is predominantly a group of marine animals, particularly common in the littoral region as the name which has been given to them is meant to suggest. Some, however, exhibit the same trend towards the invasion of freshwater and the land as was seen in the 2 preceding superfamilies, and one family, the Pomatiasidae, contains nothing but terrestrial members. Four families are included in the Littorinacea, and all 4 have at least one representative in the British fauna. Of these the 2 families Lacunidae and Littorinidae are the more primitive and the Pomatiasidae and Aciculidae are the more advanced. The Lacunidae and Littorinidae are very similar in general organization and, except for one littorinid (*Cremnoconchus*, not British), are marine. The Lacunidae occur lower on the shore than the littorinids and are often sublittoral; they have an umbilicus in the shell, which the littorinids have lost. Both groups retain open male ducts and still have, in the nervous system, a vestige of the original ladder-like arrangement in the form of a persistent post-pedal commissure. A certain number of advanced characters may be noted, especially in the littorinids, such as the development of an epiathroid nervous system, the elongation of part of the stomach to form a caecum extending far up the visceral mass and the appearance of an ovipositor on the right side of the head in females of certain species. Throughout the family runs a tendency towards the adoption of a more or less terrestrial mode of life which has involved uricotely, viviparity and alterations in the mode of respiration. This reaches its climax among British littorinids in *Littorina saxatilis* and *L. neritoides*. It was presumably by this route that the 2 other families of the Littorinacea, the Pomatiasidae and Aciculidae, reached their completely terrestrial mode of life, though both are very dependent upon wet conditions for survival and it may not be amiss to see a reminiscence of their marine origin in the strict dependence of members of the Pomatiasidae on calcareous soils. Associated with their terrestrial habitat these animals have lost the ctenidium, replacing it by pulmonary respiration through the walls of the mantle skirt wherein the extension of the kidney may play a part; the larval stage has been suppressed and the reproductive ducts have become elaborate; locomotion is improved by the presence of a large pedal gland. The Pomatiasidae are more primitive than the Aciculidae in retaining an osphradium, but the reverse is true in respect of the organization of the gut where the Aciculidae have jaws and oesophageal glands, both of which have disappeared in the Pomatiasidae in correlation with the presence of a crystalline style. The Pomatiasidae (or at least *Pomatias elegans*, the only member of the family which has been studied) are also peculiar in that their tissues seem to be inhabited by bacteria of metabolic importance.

We now come to one of the largest superfamilies of the mesogastropods, the Rissoacea (1,331 living species), which includes a vast number of different kinds of animals, predominantly marine in habitat, though extending not uncommonly into brackish water areas and freshwater. The first fossil rissoaceans appeared in the Carboniferous, but the group has expanded enormously since the end of the Secondary period. All rissoaceans are quite small, seldom exceeding 2–3 mm in height, and bear a close resemblance to one another. They are nearly all provided with small, smooth, conical shells without an umbilicus and are markedly gregarious in their way of life. They nearly all feed on detritus, largely but not exclusively of vegetable origin, and it appears likely that all of them possess a crystalline style and so have lost the oesophageal glands; the intestine is usually short. One of the characteristic features of the rissoaceans is their long narrow foot which is richly provided with pedal glands; of these the posterior pedal gland is particularly well developed and all these animals have the ability to spin ropes and webs with its secretion and clamber about the water with their support. The foot is particularly mobile and almost gives the impression of being jointed and divisible into separately operable anterior and posterior halves and right and left sides. Thanks to their mobility and small size the rissoaceans are able to exploit many sources of food which would be inaccessible and negligible to many larger creatures; they thus play on the shore and in the pools where they swarm, particularly in summer time, a role rather similar to that enacted on land by many kinds of insects. As in valvatids, and perhaps for the same reason, rissoaceans usually possess a pallial tentacle on the right side of the mantle skirt; tentacles also occur on the metapodial part of the foot by the operculum. A last noteworthy external feature of most rissoacean species is the very long, narrow penis of the males.

Internally the rissoacean nervous system is beginning to show the first steps towards a concentrated condition in the appearance of zygoneuries on both right and left sides. Apart from the features already mentioned in the plan of the alimentary system the only other point in internal anatomy which distinguishes the rissoaceans is the very greatly increased complexity of the female reproductive tract: in particular, the rissoaceans are the first group of monotocardians with the accessory genital structures constricted off the main duct. Considerable variation exists within the group as regards the detailed arrangement of the parts, but they are all distinguished by the fact that the receptaculum seminis and the bursa copulatrix are placed proximal to the capsule gland on the course of the female duct.

According to Thiele's classification the Rissoacea include no less than 8 families with representatives in the British fauna. Of these 8, 3 (Hydrobiidae, Rissoidae and Assimineidae) are closely related and are separable from one another only on relatively minor points; *Barleeia rubra*, however, differs so much from the other rissoids, especially in the complexity of its reproductive system, as probably to deserve separation into a distinct family Barleeidae. A fourth (Tornidae) appears to have some relationship with these 3 but departs from them significantly in a number of important characteristics, whilst the remaining 4 families (Skeneopsidae, Omalogyridae and Rissoellidae, with the probable addition of the Cingulopsidae) are doubtfully rissoacean, and perhaps in a few cases not even prosobranch. The truth is that the animals are so small and their soft parts so relatively little investigated that we may well be dealing with an artificial clumping of small prosobranchs showing a general similarity of external structure and not with a genetically related stock.

We may make a start in dealing with the Rissoacea by looking at the 3 families Hydrobiidae, Rissoidae and Assimineidae, which are all related. The hydrobiids have some marine species, but are mainly freshwater or live in brackish areas; the rissoids are marine and predominantly inhabit the littoral and sublittoral zones; the family Assimineidae includes only one British snail, *Assiminea grayana*, which lives on mud banks and amongst vegetation in brackish swampy areas, but its foreign members may be terrestrial. Of these families the hydrobiids are usually regarded as the most primitive, mainly because of the smooth architecture of their shells, the breadth of their foot and the fact that the pleuroparietal connectives in the nervous system are long. In the rissoids these connectives have shortened, the foot has become narrower, more agile and more glandular and possesses a metapodial tentacle. In this family the shell may be smooth, but it often shows ribs, striae or a cancellation produced by the interaction of these two types of decoration, and the aperture may be bent outwards below; all of these things are unknown or rare in the Hydrobiidae. The family Assimineidae is clearly more advanced than either of these in that its members have become to a certain extent adapted to a terrestrial life by losing the ctenidium (though retaining the osphradium). The foot has lost the subdivision into right and left halves that characterizes rissoids and the nervous system has become very concentrated. The penis arises from the mid-dorsal surface of the head instead of in the more typical right lateral position.

The family Tornidae is usually regarded as being properly classified along with the rissoaceans but our knowledge of the soft parts of the animals placed in it is woefully inadequate and is based almost entirely upon the description given by Woodward (1899) of *Tornus subcarinatus*; this contains a large number of points which mark the animal out as exceptional if it is a rissoacean at all. Thus the gill is bipectinate and can (as in *Valvata*) be protruded from the mantle cavity, the salivary glands are small, oesophageal glands are present though the animal is also said to possess a crystalline style, the nervous system is concentrated and the male has no penis. These facts seem to indicate a considerable degree of isolation of the tornids from the other rissoaceans although, as shown by Fretter & Patil (1958) they agree with the cingulopsids in some respects. However, these workers suggested that the true position of the Cingulopsidae may be more with the Littorinacea than with the Rissoacea and the same may therefore be true of the Tornidae.

The systematic position of the last group of families placed by Thiele within the Rissoacea is admitted even by him to be only dubiously correct. These are the Skeneopsidae, Omalogyridae and Rissoellidae, to which there now falls to be added the Cingulopsidae. The family Skeneopsidae, which contains only two or three genera of which one, *Skeneopsis*, is British, is perhaps the most primitive, though it is quite likely that some of its apparent simplicity (e.g. lack of pallial tentacle, lack of metapodial tentacle, lack of style) may be due to minuteness. To counter this simplicity, however, the animals are marked by some very peculiar features: the pedal glands have become enormously hypertrophied; there are no oesophageal glands though no crystalline style occurs; the female reproductive tract is very unusual in that it is diaulic with a special channel between the mantle skirt and the inner surface of the shell along which the penis of the male is passed during copulation; it also possesses a muscular pouch which seems to act as a pump for moving the various secretions along the genital ducts; the eggs are large and yolky. The Skeneopsidae retain separate sexes, but in the next two families, Omalogyridae and Rissoellidae, the animals are hermaphrodite and have large eggs. Further evolution has affected the organization of their mantle cavity in that both have lost ctenidium and osphradium and the circulation is maintained by means of ciliated ridges lying on the roof and floor of the cavity. The hypobranchial gland—perhaps in correlation with this—has hypertrophied, particularly in respect of the size of the cells of which it is composed. In the gut there is neither oesophageal gland nor style and the digestive gland may lie partly on the wall of the stomach instead of constricted from it. These, however, are conditions encountered in many minute gastropods of whatever group and as they are characteristic of all young animals are probably juvenile features retained into the adult because of its small size. In the Rissoellidae the penis is, as in other prosobranchs, a tubular structure attached to the right side of the foot, somewhat dorsally, and kept recurved, when not in use, in a groove along the floor of the mantle cavity into the proximal end of which the female duct opens. In *Omalogyra*, however, the penis is a retractile tubular structure lying within a sac and formed as an extension of the bursa copulatrix; it appears to suck sperm into itself and eject them later. Although quite unlike the penis of any other prosobranch this arrangement presents certain resemblances to the penis of some opisthobranchs.

There remains to be dealt with the family Cingulopsidae, recently created by Fretter & Patil (1958) for the reception of *Cingulopsis fulgida*, previously regarded as a member of the genus *Cingula* and therefore as a rissoid. The animal has, however, been shown to differ from true rissoids in so many ways—presence of oesophageal glands, lack of crystalline style, lack of penis, lack of jaws, diaulic female duct and structure of the radula—that it must obviously be put in a separate family which, like the last 3 with which we have been concerned, seems to have vague rissoacean affinities but not to be particularly closely related to other members of the superfamily. This state of affairs may perhaps be explicable if the position of the Rissoacea within the mesogastropods be examined.

Within his order Mesogastropoda Thiele distinguished 15 superfamilies, of which 1, the Heteropoda, is clearly specialized and apart, and another, the Aglossa, is also specialized for parasitism and probably neither natural nor wholly prosobranch. Of the remaining 13, 2 (Architaenioglossa and Valvatacea) have an obviously archaic look and must be thought of as the lower mesogastropods, while perhaps 8 (Ptenoglossa, Amaltheacea, Calyptraeacea, Strombacea, Naticacea, Lamellariacea, Cypraeacea and Doliacea) might be regarded as a group advanced in structure, though individual malacologists and conchologists might argue about its exact content. That leaves 3 superfamilies (Littorinacea, Rissoacea and Cerithiacea) as the central corpus of the order. The importance of these 3 superfamilies is also suggested by the relative numbers of genera contained in them. Schilder (1947) gave the number of living species in the lower grouping as 1,562 Architaenioglossa + 23 Valvatacea, total 1,585; in the higher grouping the figures are Ptenoglossa 272, Amaltheacea 86, Calyptraeacea 111, Strombacea 71, Naticacea 178, Lamellariacea + Cypraeacea 387, Doliacea 250, giving a total of 1,355. The central group gives the following: Littorinacea 605, Rissoacea 1,331, Cerithiacea 1,297, a total of 3,233. Any generalized prosobranch, therefore, particularly if it be small in size, is likely to be regarded by its describer as coming somewhere near the Rissoacea—Littorinacea—Cerithiacea within the mesogastropods.

The Cerithiacea, though perhaps less abundant now than in the Cretaceous, is a large group of the mesogastropods the members of which are mainly inhabitants of the warmer parts of the globe, only the genera *Turritella*, *Caecum*, *Bittium*, *Cerithiopsis*, *Cerithiella*, *Eumetula* and *Triphora*—7 out of 261—being found in this country. Many of the tropical and subtropical genera live in freshwater, an evolution more easily made in the tropics and therefore more frequently encountered in groups with tropical distribution. Those that are marine are not often found in the higher parts of the shore; rather are they met with at low levels and in the sublittoral and shallow water areas. In this country *Bittium reticulatum*, *Cerithiopsis tubercularis* and *Triphora perversa* may be found sparsely at LWST on the warmer S and W coasts; other species of *Cerithiopsis*, *Turritella communis* and *Caecum* spp. may be dredged. *Cerithiella metula* and *Eumetula arctica* are unusual in being boreal in distribution, but come from deeper waters and are very rare: they are the outposts of the group towards its northern limit of distribution.

The cerithiaceans are animals related to rissoaceans and perhaps derived through the Loxonematacea from the Pleurotomariacea and making their first appearance probably in the Permian. They are nearly all characterized by a tall, tower-like shell made up of many whorls; this is adapted for trailing across soft substrata or for burrowing into and through them. The mouth is usually round, with a slight tendency to an out-turning of the outer lip at the lower end in primitive forms like *Turritella*; this becomes more conspicuous in the more advanced types and in the higher families produces a structure almost like the siphonal canal of the Stenoglossa. In the more primitive forms the sculpture of the shell consists almost entirely of spiral elements of various size (fig. 37A); the more advanced families add to this a vertical factor, and a complex architecture may result (fig. 26C). In the family Vermetidae another tendency is apparent, a separation of the whorls of the shell so as to produce a corkscrew-like structure. The same is to be observed in snails of the family Caecidae, but in this case the older parts of the open spiral are successively snapped off and the opening so made is plugged with a calcareous seal: in this way the tube consists at any moment of only a short curved length. Ordinarily the cerithiacean shell has no umbilicus.

A number of points in the internal organization of the Cerithiacea appear referable to the fact that the body tends to be long and narrow to fit the shell. The males, except in *Caecum*, have no penis and there is a tendency in both sexes for the parts of the genital duct which traverse the mantle cavity to be open, ciliated grooves. No copulation can occur and this, it has been suggested by Fretter (1951b), is due to the fact that a penis could not be introduced successfully into so narrow a mantle cavity. The egg capsules which they produce are, perhaps for the same reason, small and contain a relatively small number of little eggs, although a limited number of freshwater cerithiaceans from warmer lands are viviparous and able to retain the developing eggs within the mantle cavity.

The nervous system is moderately concentrated throughout the superfamily, the parietal ganglia lying alongside the pleurals and linked to both by right and left zygoneuries. The visceral ganglion, however, has retained a posterior position at the inner end of the mantle cavity. Götze (1938) failed to find a visceral ganglion in *Caecum glabrum*, though this may perhaps have been due to its small size. The animals in this group are distinguished by a marked sperm dimorphism.

The family Turritellidae is usually regarded as the most primitive of the cerithiaceans, largely because of the simple spiral decoration of the shell and the structure of the radula, which has relatively simple teeth. The shell is very tall and this may be correlated with an elongation which has occurred in the mantle cavity in connexion with the development of a ciliary collection of food. The gill has become very long and a deep groove on the floor carries the food to the mouth. In the gut the salivary glands are small since most of the mucus used in feeding comes from this pallial groove, the oesophageal glands are absent and a crystalline style lies in the stomach. Since *Turritella* lives in a muddy environment, tentacles grow on the mantle edge and exclude much of the particulate matter which might otherwise be sucked into the mantle cavity and block the feeding apparatus. The operculum is edged with bristle-like extensions as in some vermetids. The whole length of the genital tract which runs along the mantle skirt is an open groove, with the bursa copulatrix and albumen gland also developed as open pouches from the mantle cavity. In several of these respects the turritellids come very close to the vermetids, though no member of that family occurs in the British fauna; in the possession of a crystalline style, too, they approach a number of the tropical melaniids and the family Caecidae, one genus of which, *Caecum*, is rarely found in British waters.

According to the account given by Götze (1938), however, this is one of the few ways in which *Caecum* and the cerithiaceans agree, so far as the soft parts are concerned. There is neither gill nor hypobranchial gland, salivary glands are absent, the nervous system is concentrated but lacks a visceral ganglion and there is a crystalline style. All these features are either clearly cerithiacean, like the broken shell, or, where they depart from this plan, can be easily explained on the basis of small size. It is not, however, possible to clear away other characteristics in the same way—the presence of a large, glandular penis in the male, the closed and glandular genital ducts of both sexes, and the lack of sperm dimorphism. These are highly unusual features for a cerithiacean and would seem to indicate that the caecids are not closely allied to the rest of the superfamily and may even be somewhat accidentally included within it on the basis of shell structure.

The great body of the cerithiaceans is included in the family Melaniidae, none of which is British and which departs somewhat from the rest of the group in being freshwater. The remaining British representatives occur in the 3 families Cerithiidae, Cerithiopsidae and Triphoridae, in all of which the shell shows a reticulation of pattern and a siphonal notch on the peristome. The cerithiids appear to be the most primitive, with normal radular teeth, an open genital groove in the mantle cavity, no proboscis and an oesophagus of the usual mesogastropod pattern. The female reproductive system is complicated by the formation of accessory copulatory pouches and a not very pronounced degree of sperm dimorphism seems to occur. The cerithiopsids are more elaborate. They feed largely on sponges instead of algae and they have a long proboscis to permit this; their radular teeth, too, have become long and claw-like to tear the sponge tissues; the oesophageal region has become complex and at least in some species the male uses the apyrene sperm, which are large, to form spermatozeugmata, ferrying the eupyrene sperm, in all probability, to the female duct. The triphorids are equally complex and are sinistral, with many peculiarities in the structure of their radula, an oesophageal structure unique among prosobranchs and a female duct which is partly open.

Although Cox (1960) seemed to suggest that the cerithiaceans are the earliest monotocardians it does not seem likely to the neontologist that *Turritella* and the other more simple cerithiaceans are fundamentally primitive in their organization.

Only 2 members of the next superfamily, the Strombacea, occur in British waters, and these are both members of the same genus, *Aporrhais*; most Strombacea—the remains of a group more flourishing in the Cretaceous—come from the Indopacific region and extend S to New Zealand, where they have been vigorously studied by Morton (1951*a, b*; 1956, 1959). To a certain extent they resemble the Cerithiacea (see Johansson, 1948*b*), both having a crystalline style in the gut, a microphagous habit and no oesophageal glands. The animals of the most primitive family, the Aporrhaidae, to which British members belong, are semi-sedentary in their habits like some cerithiaceans, but the more advanced strombaceans may be much more active and move—as *Aporrhais* can do too, on occasion—using their nail-like operculum as a lever to help them along, though in their case this often results in powerful leaps. The shell is commonly a tall, spirally wound cone with spiral striae and ribs, though the latter are frequently restricted to the adapical part of each whorl, where they give rise to characteristic tubercles. Its most outstanding feature, however, is the tendency for the peristomial region to be drawn out into long, finger-like projections in addition to a siphonal notch. These are often used to form a protective cover over the body when the animal burrows into mud or sand, maintaining contact with the surface by means of siphonal tubes. The snout is long.

The nervous system is like that of cerithiaceans but has the parietal ganglia rather further back in the body. The genital ducts are partly closed in the female of *Aporrhais* though there is a long, slit-like external aperture, but in the male an open ciliated groove leads to the tip of the penis; in other genera the female duct may be open too.

There now comes to be described a collection of monotocardian families in all of which an echinospira larva (p. 468) occurs. These are the Capulidae, Lamellariidae and Cypraeidae, to give them the names by which they are known in Thiele's *Handbuch*, all of which seem to have evolved about the Jurassic. In the systematic arrangement which he employed there each of these families falls into a separate superfamily, the Calyptraeacea, Lamellariacea and Cypraeacea respectively. Since the occurrence of this type of larva is rare its appearance in this way would seem to indicate a close genetic affinity between the groups. This led Schilder, an enthusiastic student of the cypraeids, to suggest (1936) that the genera related to *Erato* and *Trivia* (placed by Thiele in the subfamily Eratoinae of the Cypraeidae) which possess echinospira larvae, should be separated from the other cypraeids (subfamilies Amphiperatinae, Cypraeinae and one or two others), which do not, and transferred to the Lamellariacea, all of which have this characteristic type of larva. The Eratoinae do, indeed, separate themselves from the other members of the Cypraeacea not merely on this character but also on a number of others: of these the arrangement of the pedal ganglia and the osphradium are perhaps the most important of the differences in the soft parts. In the Eratoinae, as in the Lamellariacea, the pedal ganglia are short, ovoid bodies lying under the rest of the nerve ring and the osphradium is a curved bipectinate structure lying along the left side of a ctenidium slightly curved in the same way; in the Amphiperatinae and Cypraeinae on the other hand, the osphradium is triradiate in structure and lies in the concavity of a ctenidium moderately curved in the former subfamily and extremely curved in the latter. In these 2 subfamilies, too, the pedal part of the nervous system is drawn out into 2 long pedal cords with numerous cross-connexions which recall the ladder-like nervous system of many primitive archaeo-gastropods and mesogastropods. There are further differences in the radula, and the Cypraeinae appear to retain a number of other primitive features such as a gastric caecum and an open seminal groove in the male (Rau, 1934).

This simple re-arrangement of families proposed by Schilder in 1936 and backed by such powerful arguments would, at the time of its proposal, have united within the one superfamily Lamellariacea all the prosobranchs known to have an echinospira larva. The position, however, was changed significantly by the discovery by Lebour (1937) that *Capulus ungaricus*, belonging to the family Capulidae in the superfamily Calyptraeacea, also passed through an echinospira stage. Did this mean that *Capulus* should also be transferred to the Lamellariacea? Or was it likely that further investigation would show echinospira larvae turning up in several superfamilies, in which case the transference of the Eratoinae from Cypraeacea to Lamellariacea on the basis of its echinospira larva might have been a mistake? To answer this involves an examination of the structure of *Capulus* in relation to other Calyptraeacea and the Lamellariacea, undertaken by Graham (1954a), from which it seems that *Capulus* is properly classified among the calyptraeaceans, which it resembles much more than the lamellariaceans, though there are undoubted links between the 2 groups. The echinospira larva has not turned up in any other group of prosobranchs and so does seem to be a larval type characteristic of a certain area of the monotocardians and indicating a close degree of relationship of the superfamilies in which it is found.

Of the constituents of this 'echinospira' group or Echinospiracea, as we may call it, it is likely that the Calyptraeacea is the most primitive since the family Trichotropidae contains prosobranchs which show very little specialization of structure except in relation to feeding: they are microphagous and pick up with the radula food which has been collected on a small grooved proboscis made by extension of the ventral margin of the mouth. This is reminiscent of a similar extension of the lower lip found in some trochids. The trichotropid shell is spirally coiled and distinguished by the possession of a well developed periostracum drawn out into spiny processes. The foot is rather narrow and carries an operculum, but the animal, which is found on hard bottoms in the sub-littoral zone and in shallow water, is not very active. The contents of the mantle cavity show no particular specialization, though the osphradium has an advanced bipectinate shape; the edge of the mantle skirt is simple, not warty, nor with multicellular repugnatorial glands. Internally, the radula is short, the salivary glands small, the oesophagus glandular and there is no crystalline style. The nervous system shows some concentration, the cerebral and pleural ganglia on each side uniting to a single mass and zygoneuries linking these to the parietal ganglia on each side. There is a single columellar muscle; the sexes are separate and there is, in males, a seminal groove running to the apex of the penis. The larva is suppressed and the animals hatch in the crawling stage.

From some such relatively unmodified start the evolution of the calyptraeaceans can be traced along two pathways, one leading to the family Capulidae, the other to the family Calyptraeidae. Both lines involve an exaggeration of the tendency towards immobility and give rise to a limpet-like animal. In the last step, represented by the genus *Thyca*, the flat foot secretes a calcareous plate which fuses the animal on to the body of the echinoderm on which it lives in a semi-parasitic way, and so produces a kind of bivalved gastropod.

In the Capulidae, one genus of which, *Capulus* itself, is British, the shell has become cap-shaped, though still retaining some of its spiral coiling and the tendency towards generous production of periostracum noted in the Trichotropidae. It has, however, changed the foot to a rounded shape and lost the operculum, and it has become even less mobile than *Trichotropis*. It lives on hard bottoms, almost always on the shells of bivalves, and feeds to some extent at their expense, using a proboscis like that of a trichotropid but longer and lither, to take food from its host; in addition it has evolved a simple ciliary food-collecting mechanism. The radula is weak and, indeed, becomes completely lost in the fully parasitic genus *Thyca*. *Capulus* differs from *Trichotropis* in possessing an echinospira larva; *Thyca* does not. Both these genera are hermaphrodite.

The calyptraeids are also limpets, living more or less completely immobilized on rocks or stones or other suitable hard substrata in the case of *Calyptraea*, but forming chains of individuals piled one on the other in the genus *Crepidula*. They, too, have a round foot, a horseshoe-shaped shell muscle and a cap-shaped shell as in *Capulus*, but the shell differs in having no very great development of periostracum and in possessing an internal septum. The members of this family have no proboscis, having come to rely entirely on ciliary collection of food particles: they are, indeed, the classic example of this particular method of feeding in the prosobranchs and show to perfection all the adaptations for it. They possess a crystalline style, but in other respects their internal anatomy is like that of trichotropids or capulids except for the development of marginal pallial repugnatorial glands, the lack of oesophageal glands and their sexual arrangements. The calyptraeids all appear to be consecutive hermaphrodites, starting life as males and changing later to females. In *Crepidula*, in particular, a distinctive social life has been evolved in relation to this. The larvae are veligers.

The superfamily Lamellariacea, as defined by Thiele, is a small one containing rather less than a dozen genera of carnivorous prosobranchs, of which 2, *Velutina* and *Lamellaria*, are British. Even if, following Schilder, we transfer the Eratoinae from the Cypraeacea to the Lamellariacea we add only a further small number of genera, of which *Erato* and *Trivia* are British. They all live on tunicates, rasping at their flesh with the radula. Only *Erato* has a long proboscis with which it can reach into a tunicate polyp and rasp the most nutritious parts. The shell, though spirally wound, increases its curvature so rapidly as to appear auriculate or boat-shaped in *Velutina* and *Lamellaria*, in both of which a possible link with the calyptraeaceans is indicated by the presence of considerable periostracal material, noticeably absent from the shells of *Erato* and *Trivia*. In these, too, though the spiral of the shell rapidly grows (so as to conceal the spire in *Trivia*, though not *Erato*) the mouth is not expanded as in *Velutina* and *Lamellaria*, but undergoes the same kind of narrowing as it does in the undoubted cypraeids to produce a long, narrow aperture through which it seems impossible that the bulky body could be squeezed, and gives rise to the shape of shell popularly known as a cowrie. In *Velutina*, *Erato* and *Trivia* the shell is partly concealed by mantle folds when the animal is active, the folds being withdrawn on retirement within the shell, but in *Lamellaria* the mantle folds have fused over its outer surface so as to make the shell completely internal and the animal, on superficial examination, appears like a nudibranch. In these circumstances an operculum is obviously useless and is not present in the adult of any of these genera though it is a feature of the echinospira larva which they all possess. There are 2 shell muscles, right and left, and internally, the gut shows well developed oesophageal glands and the ganglia have been concentrated into a nerve ring with right and left zygoneuries linking pleural and parietal ganglia. This is more marked in *Lamellaria* than in *Trivia*. *Velutina* alone of this series is hermaphrodite, the others all having separate sexes. In *Velutina* and *Lamellaria* the coiling of the shell of the echinospira larva is nautiloid, in *Erato* and *Trivia* it is helicoid.

On Schilder's classification only one true cypraeacean occurs in the fauna of the British Isles—*Simnia patula*, a member of the family Amphiperatidae (=subfamily Amphiperatinae, fam. Cypraeidae of Thiele). This may be found living on the corals *Alcyonium* and *Eunicella* in shallow water off the SW coasts of England and Ireland. It is related to the familiar and beautiful cowrie shells of the tropics which come into the family Cypraeidae (sens. str.) of Schilder or the subfamily Cypraeinae of Thiele and none of which is British. As indicated above, there are marked differences both in the shell and in the soft parts of these groups as compared with the lamellariaceans in addition to the absence of an echinospira larva, and it seems right to regard the classification of this group of the mesogastropods to be as follows:

Calyptraeacea: Trichotropidae—without echinospira larva; periostracum conspicuous; pedal ganglia ovoid; mouth of shell oval; bipectinate osphradium; small proboscis.

Capulidae —with echinospira larva; periostracum conspicuous; pedal ganglia ovoid; wide-mouthed shell; bipectinate osphradium; long proboscis.

Calyptraeidae —without echinospira larva; periostracum not conspicuous; pedal ganglia ovoid; wide-mouthed shell; bipectinate osphradium; advanced ciliary feeders.

Lamellariacea: Lamellariidae —with nautiloid echinospira larva; periostracum conspicuous; pedal ganglia ovoid; wide-mouthed shell; bipectinate osphradium.

Eratoidae —with helicoid echinospira larva; no periostracum; pedal ganglia ovoid; narrow-mouthed shell; bipectinate osphradium.

Cypraeacea: Amphiperatidae ⎱ without echinospira larva; no periostracum; pedal
Cypraeidae ⎰ ganglia elongated; narrow-mouthed shell; triradiate osphradium.

There remain to be discussed only 4 groups of the mesogastropods, 3 of which are markedly specialized in a number of features and some of which seem to lead towards the opisthobranchs. The fourth is the Naticacea, a small group of carnivorous prosobranchs all placed within one family, Naticidae, and originating in the Trias. Except in respect of a number of adaptations correlated with their particular mode of life these animals present a very generalized appearance. In this country they are represented by a few species of the genus *Natica*, all of which are essentially alike and follow a similar way of living, and the rare *Amauropsis islandica*, which is dredged off sandy bottoms in northern waters and, though nothing is really known about it, would appear to be similar to the *Natica* species. These haunt sandy beaches and sublittoral zones, ploughing over and through the sand in search of the bivalves on which they feed and through the shells of which they bore by means of an accessory boring organ and the radula. To plough through the sand, and also to help in gripping their prey during boring, the propodium of the foot is greatly enlarged, in some exotic naticids (though not our British forms) some of the increased size being apparently genuinely due to the pumping of sea water into a series of water spaces. The enlarged propodium rises up over the animal's head and the entrance to the mantle cavity and so protects against sand during burrowing; the eyes are reduced.

The shell is smooth and somewhat swollen and retains an obvious umbilicus. The gut is adapted for a carnivorous mode of life with powerful jaws, a well developed oeso-phageal gland and a short intestine arising from a capacious stomach. The sexes are separate and one of the most characteristic features of the family is the egg collar manu-factured by the female; this consists of a large number of capsules each containing a number of eggs and cemented together into a mass which is squeezed into a collar shape and impregnated with sand as it emerges from the mantle cavity. The relationships of the Naticacea are obscure; that alleged to exist by Cox (1960), following Cossmann & Knight, with the neritaceans we find extremely difficult to accept on account of the extremely advanced nature of neritacean organization.

The 3 remaining groups of mesogastropods are the Ptenoglossa, Aglossa and Hetero-poda. The last consists of pelagic animals of a glassy transparency and gelatinous con-sistency, with reduced shell and visceral mass and well developed sense organs in con-nexion with their free-swimming predatory existence. They are only rarely found in British waters and their anatomy is described on p. 563. Their relationships are obscure, but may lie with the echinospira group. The Ptenoglossa (of Jurassic origin) also includes 2 pelagic genera, *Recluzia* and *Ianthina*, the latter occasionally drifting into British waters from its more normal southern home and stranding on the SW coasts of England and Ireland. Most ptenoglossans, however, are placed in the family Scalidae and are not pelagic, but live in the littoral and sublittoral regions. Their mode of life is very poorly known and observations on the feeding and reproduction of members of this family are very desirable. The scalids have a tall tower-like shell, sometimes with spiral lines but always with ribs. There is a long proboscis of an acrembolic type and when it is pro-truded there are visible, alongside the mouth, 2 stylets which bear the openings of a pair of salivary glands, which perhaps elaborate a toxic secretion used in predation. Similar stylets occur in the ianthinid *Recluzia*. The salivary glands are tubular. The radula is composed of recurved teeth all of one sort and forms a formidable grasping apparatus. No trace of oesophageal glands occurs. The animals are protandrous hermaphrodites and there is no penis. Spermatozeugmata are formed in the testis and these probably bear the eupyrene sperm to other animals.

In *Ianthina* spermatozeugmata are also found which seem to enter the genital tract and fertilize the eggs within the ovary. These animals are also protandrous hermaphrodites and have no penis. They have become distinctly modified for the pelagic existence which they lead: the shell is thin, violet in colour, and the foot modified into an organ for the production of bubbles of air enclosed in mucus which aggregate to form a float, keeping the animal near the surface of the water. The radula is ptenoglossan and the buccal mass has enlarged to accommodate it. This has the effect of increasing the dorsal part of the snout, so as to make the tentacles (which, incidentally, are bifid) appear as if they were set ventrolaterally, and also stretches the cerebral commissure. As in scalids, there are 2 pairs of salivary glands, no oesophageal glands, but a roomy stomach. The cerebral ganglia are united with the pleurals—perhaps as a result of the lateral thrust from the expanding buccal mass—but otherwise there is nothing unusual about the nervous system. Eyes are not visible, but in fact minute eyes do occur by the cerebral ganglia within the muscles of the body wall; statocysts appear to be absent. The hypobranchial gland of *Ianthina*, like that of the other ptenoglossans, produces a secretion of a striking violet colour.

Near *Ianthina* and *Clathrus* may perhaps be placed at least some of the members of the superfamily Aglossa of Thiele. In this group, which derives its name from the frequent absence of a radula in the animals which belong to it, there appears to be a general trend towards the adoption of a parasitic mode of life with the usual consequent alterations in bodily structure. Unfortunately these molluscs are not common, and it is fair to say that none of them has been amply studied recently. The family which Thiele places first in his *Handbuch* is the Aclididae, with one genus *Aclis*, a few species of which are British, though they are exceedingly rare and their soft parts are not well known. It is partly on them, however, that are based the possible relationships of this superfamily in that their high, spirally wound shell and the numerous, small and similar radular teeth, the long proboscis and the jaws seem to link them with the ptenoglossan prosobranchs on the one hand, whilst, on the other, the presence of a mentum and of a heterostrophic shell in some genera appears to link them with the pyramidellids. Their mode of life appears to be wholly unknown—beyond the suspicion that they are carnivores, and perhaps ectoparasitic like the pyramidellids—and so is much of their internal anatomy.

The next family of aglossan prosobranchs, Eulimidae (=Melanellidae) includes a number of animals found in the British Isles, all of which are definitely ectoparasitic in their way of living, and, like many prosobranchs which have taken to this, are associated with echinoderms. The group is a relatively recent one, the first fossils being found in late Secondary beds. The shell has a long spire and is smooth and highly polished and the external appearance of the animals is unexceptional. Internally, however, they have become highly modified, especially in the gut, in relation to their ectoparasitism. There is a long acrembolic proboscis which can be pushed far into the tissues of the host, there to suck up—since there is no radula to permit any other way—the food which the mollusc requires, the motive power being provided by a pump made from the transformed buccal region. Apart from this and the increase in length necessitated by the great elongation of the proboscis the gut of the eulimids is greatly simplified and shows few of the characteristic features of the prosobranch alimentary canal; oesophageal and salivary glands are absent and a stomach hardly discernible. The sexes are separate in the eulimids and the reproductive system is marked by open ducts. The nervous system is concentrated, and the pedal glands are hypertrophied.

At the base of the snout of *Balcis* or other eulimid there will be noticed a short projecting fold of tissue: this is the pseudopallium, and though of little importance in the eulimids it is a structure of increasing importance in the other families of the Aglossa. In the Eulimidae it appears to be no more than a stop preventing too deep an insertion of the proboscis or a seal allowing more effective sucking of food. In members of the family Stiliferidae, however, the pseudopallium has increased in size and is partly reflected over the shell as the animals move over the surface of the echinoderm which is their usual habitat. Apart from this increase in pseudopallium and a corresponding increase in the length of the proboscis few other significant changes have affected the organization of the animals found in this family; they have lost the operculum, however, and some at least have become hermaphrodite. Many of these animals are not well known anatomically.

The climax of this evolutionary trend towards parasitism is reached in the animals which are placed in the family Entoconchidae and which inhabit echinoderm hosts. Only one species of entoconchid has so far been found in the British fauna, *Enteroxenos östergreni*, which lives in holothurians, hanging into the coelomic cavity from the gut wall, as a wormlike object bearing little resemblance to anything molluscan, and showing few organs beyond what might be gut and gonads, for the creature is hermaphrodite. This state has probably been reached by an extension of the tendency (already visible in the Stiliferidae) of the pseudopallium to grow over the shell and form a cover within which the head, foot and visceral hump will lie and from which only the everted proboscis will project. Once this state has been reached, and given that the animal has now become an internal parasite for which movement is no longer necessary, then head, foot, shell and all the organs characteristic of the free-living prosobranch can degenerate and leave a bag of pseudopallial origin around such vestiges of gut and reproductive system as cannot be lost without the consequential death of the species. That these extraordinary creatures are undoubted prosobranchs, however, is made plain by the fact that their larval stages are normal.

The last family which is normally included in the superfamily Aglossa is the Pyramidellidae. Consideration of these, however, brings up the question of what is a prosobranch and what is an opisthobranch, which must be dealt with later. At the moment it is enough to mention those aspects of structure and biology which seem to relate them to the other aglossans. First of all may be noted the tall spire of the pyramidellid shell, with a reversed apex, as is also to be found in some members of the family Aclididae. The foot, again as in some aclidids, carries an operculum and a mentum. Unlike these animals, however, the pyramidellids have lost the ctenidium and, as in some other small prosobranchs, maintain the pallial circulation by means of ciliated ridges on the roof and floor of the mantle cavity. They have a long proboscis of the acrembolic type and no radula, but have modified their jaws into a stylet with which they attack their prey, sedentary animals of a variety of sorts, sucking their blood by means of a muscular pump made from part of the buccal cavity; the rest of the gut is simple and rather featureless as in many other aglossans. The pyramidellids are hermaphrodite and possess a retractile penis of a very unusual pattern. The nervous system is concentrated. They have free-swimming larvae.

With the Aglossa ends the series of prosobranchs which are usually placed within the order Mesogastropoda, a group which includes at the one extreme such relatively primitive forms as the Architaenioglossa, linking up with the diotocardians, and, at the other, such advanced and specialized groups as the Cypraeacea and Aglossa. Throughout the order there therefore exists a great range of variation in structure and way of living, yet there can be distinguished a general transition from a vegetarian and largely microphagous type of animal to one which has become carnivorous and to some extent parasitic. This has brought in its train changes in the gut, radula, salivary glands, oesophagus and stomach all being affected, and has also favoured the elongation of the snout into a proboscis which allows the animals to reach food otherwise inaccessible. Gastropods being what they are, the choice of prey open to these carnivorous types is restricted mainly to slow-moving or attached organisms and the elaboration of sense organs, brain and locomotor organs characteristic of carnivores belonging to other phyla is never present. Yet some increase in the efficiency of the nervous system is presumably marked by the concentration which it undergoes and a certain limited increase in sensitivity appears to affect at least some of the sense organs such as eyes and osphradium. The reproductive efficiency is certainly improved by the introduction of egg capsules, which allow the more vulnerable early developmental stages to be protected, and which permit, if it seems necessary, their complete deletion so that the young hatch in the crawling stage, as miniatures of their parents.

The prosobranchs which remain to be discussed fall into a third order, the Stenoglossa or Neogastropoda, a rather uniform group of carnivorous animals, which, to judge by their abundance of species (Thiele lists 168 genera) and individuals, have proved very successful. They are of late Secondary origin. They are practically without exception marine in their habitat and abound on all sorts of shores and shallow waters, preying largely on invertebrates, though many are scavengers and will accept any kind of flesh whilst still fresh. In the Stenoglossa there are usually placed 4 superfamilies, the Muricacea, Buccinacea, Volutacea and Toxoglossa, of which the first 3 (often called the Rachiglossa) have an organization so similar as to suggest that they are very closely related; the Toxoglossa stand more apart. Indeed the first 3 seem to be less sharply differentiated from one another than many mesogastropod superfamilies and perhaps might be regarded as forming a rachiglossan group within the neogastropods comparable to the 'echinospira' group within the mesogastropods.

The stenoglossan shell always possesses a siphonal groove at the lower end of the peristome in which is lodged, when the animal is expanded, a siphonal process of the mantle. This is often long and mobile and has a bipectinate osphradium at its base. The aperture of the shell is closed by an operculum in the more primitive genera, but this is lost in the more advanced ones; when present its nucleus lies close to or at one end. The shell is commonly decorated with spiral lines across which run ribs, sometimes producing a reticulate pattern, and this is the usual kind of shell seen in British gastropods; in many well-known exotic forms such as the cones, however, the shell has become quite smooth. Usually it has a high spire, and this becomes excessively so in the foreign terebrids; once again the cones are exceptional in that the spire is almost completely covered by the body whorl. The siphonal process may be short as it is in *Nucella* and *Nassarius*, or it may be drawn out into a long structure as in some of the foreign species of *Murex* (fig. 33A); in the cones a separate siphonal canal is hardly visible.

Internally one of the most characteristic features of the stenoglossan prosobranchs is their radula, which is relatively short and rarely contains more than 3 teeth per row, though even this is reduced in the toxoglossans. Where a median tooth occurs it is usually pectinate. The buccal mass lies in the apical part of a long proboscis but, unlike those of the mesogastropods, this is of the pleurembolic type. The front part of the gut has been greatly modified by the separation of the oesophageal gland to produce the so-called gland of Leiblein, connected to the oesophagus by a duct. This allows a migration of the oesophageal part of the gut through the nerve ring and has contributed to the formation of a proboscis. The stomach has become much simplified in structure, has lost many of the characteristic features of the mesogastropod stomach and is little more than a bag into which oesophagus, ducts from the digestive gland and intestine open and where the bulk of the digestive process goes on. The intestine is short and an anal gland with some excretory significance is sometimes found. The nervous system has become concentrated, with right and left zygoneuries, though the visceral ganglia still retain their primitive posterior situation. The sexes are separate and the ducts in both sexes are closed, though an opening from the male duct to the inner end of the mantle cavity may represent a vestige of an originally open seminal groove. The female duct is rich in glands, one of which ingests supernumerary spermatozoa. The eggs are rather large and are laid in capsules attached to hard substrata by means of a special gland in the sole of the foot. In many species the young pass through the veliger stage within these capsules and hatch as miniatures of the parent. The food supply which permits this is provided partly in the form of yolk granules within the egg, but sometimes by 'food eggs', that is eggs which undergo an abortive development and are eaten by the successful embryos.

The most primitive group of the Stenoglossa is the Muricacea, with only the 2 families, Muricidae and Magilidae, the latter being confined to tropical seas where its members live in association with corals. The members of the Muricidae, too, have a general preference for warmer waters and only 6 species belonging to 4 genera (*Ocenebra, Trophon, Nucella* and *Urosalpinx*) occur in this country, and of these one, *Urosalpinx*, is a relatively recent introduction from America. *Ocenebra*, too, does not occur except in southern and western areas of Britain. In this superfamily the shell often bears marked varices which form lamellae projecting from the shell as in *Ocenebra*, or spine rows as in many species of *Murex*; the same tendency affects the inner side of the outer lip of the peristome when the animal is sexually mature, leading to the formation of teeth partly blocking the aperture. The foot carries an operculum.

Internally a number of features characterize the muricaceans, most of them affecting the alimentary canal. In the radula the lateral teeth are always simple. The mid-oesophageal region shows plainly the scar where the glandular tissue was stripped from the food channel and its edges are rich in mucous glands, forming the so-called 'glande framboisée'. The gland of Leiblein is bulky and all its walls are clothed in glandular tissue. There are 2 pairs of salivary glands, an accessory pair of tubular glands opening by a common duct to the mid-ventral part of the mouth. There is no caecal appendage to the posterior oesophagus. The valve of Leiblein is well developed. Many of these features are to be associated with the habit which muricaceans have of reaching their prey by boring through shells; with this habit, too, is to be correlated the presence of an accessory boring organ located in a sac opening to the sole of the foot near its anterior end.

By contrast, the next superfamilies, Buccinacea and Volutacea, are carrion feeders rather than pure predators and have lost the equipment—accessory salivary glands and boring organ—which seems to be necessary for that activity. The oesophageal structure, too, tends to be simplified, the valve of Leiblein less developed, the scar on the mid-oesophagus less obvious and the gland of Leiblein less well developed and devoid of secreting tissue—presumably its function has been effectively taken over by the digestive gland. On the other hand an oesophageal caecum may be present. The shell is less apt to grow varices and there is, in the more advanced forms, a tendency to lose the operculum.

Of these 2 superfamilies only a few buccinaceans are members of the British fauna, no volutacean occurring here: the Buccinacea extend extensively into colder waters whereas the Volutacea are more frequent in the warmer parts of the globe. The superfamily Buccinacea includes 5 families—Columbellidae, Buccinidae, Galeodidae, Nassariidae and Fasciolariidae—of which the galeodids are the only one without a British representative. It must be admitted, however, that the only British columbellid, *Pyrene haliaeeti*, and the only British fasciolariid, *Troschelia berniciensis*, are so exceedingly rare that most malacologists have never seen a single specimen.

The last superfamily of the stenoglossan group is the Toxoglossa, which contains the 2 families Conidae and Terebridae. They are, on the whole, most frequently found in warm seas and only 6 genera of conids are represented in the British fauna. These are *Lora, Typhlomangelia, Mangelia, Philbertia, Thesbia* and *Haedropleura*, and once again it is necessary to say that specimens of *Haedropleura septangularis, Thesbia nana* and *Typhlomangelia nivalis*, which are the only species of these genera found, are very rare; specimens of *Mangelia* or *Philbertia* are the only British toxoglossans likely to be encountered.

Though the toxoglossans may be linked with the more primitive neogastropods through such a genus as *Drillia*, the majority of animals classified in this group have undergone a considerable evolutionary change, mainly in connexion with their very characteristic method of feeding. *Drillia* possesses a shell which is very like that of a muricacean with a short siphonal canal, spiral striae and ribs, the spire being rather short. The foot of the animal carries an operculum and the radula is like that of a rachiglossan in possessing a continuous radular membrane from which the teeth arise, a median tooth and a lateral and a marginal on each side, the laterals being pectinate: indeed, in having 5 teeth per row this radula is closer to the taenioglossan than is the rachiglossan. Few other details of the anatomy of this animal are known so that it is impossible to assess the closeness of its relationship to the other members of its order. The most outstanding resemblance between *Drillia* and the other toxoglossans is the elongation which the marginal teeth have undergone and the lanceolate shape of their free ends. In higher conids the operculum is lost and the radular apparatus undergoes a marked evolution which culminates in the production of a series of separate tubular teeth, not connected by a continuous radular membrane and derived from the elongate marginals of *Drillia*, all the others having been lost. As part of their way of feeding the whole front end of the alimentary canal has been altered, the salivary glands reduced, and the oesophagus has been so modified by the formation of the poison gland that it is difficult to homologize it with that of other types.

Apart from these changes, however, the organization of the cones in respect of the nervous and reproductive systems seems hardly to have altered from that of the lower stenoglossans. They therefore stand apart from the rachiglossans because of the evolution of their gut, but are otherwise neither particularly specialized nor advanced.

Before turning to the problem of the relationship of opisthobranchs and prosobranchs, the inter-relationships of the prosobranch superfamilies may be briefly dealt with.

As already indicated, the trochaceans form the group which, to our way of thinking, comes closest to the ancestors of the monotocardians. All the other diotocardian groups are too specialized, particularly in the way in which the left kidney has become reduced in size and the spiral coiling of the shell lost. The trochaceans themselves, in so far as they possess a papillary sac and a fringe of epipodial tentacles, approach the families Haliotidae, Scissurellidae and Pleurotomariidae and all these animals may therefore be taken as the modern representatives of a basal stock from which the monotocardians eventually emerged. The Neritacea, the remaining diotocardian group, is difficult to relate to the others but has followed, presumably, an approximately parallel evolution from a slightly different starting point.

Within the monotocardian group it is possible to indicate a few major groupings, as has already been suggested, which could reflect the polyphyletic origin of the order indicated by Cox (1960). These are: the group which we may call Echinospiracea, characterized by the possession of an echinospira larva and consisting of the superfamilies Lamellariacea and Calyptraeacea; another in which a crystalline style occurs and where the oesophageal glands are consequently reduced and in which a shell with a tall spire is commonly found. This group includes the Echinospiracea, Strombacea, Cerithiacea and Rissoacea. A third grouping may perhaps be suggested by the absence of a penis and the occurrence of spermatozeugmata in the Cerithiacea and Ptenoglossa, since this seems a phenomenon much more likely to be an indication of genetic affinity than to have been independently acquired.

If these 3 groupings be accepted as indicative of some degree of kinship, and if we restrict ourselves to those animals of British occurrence which have been discussed in these pages, we are then left with the following excluded groups: Architaenioglossa,

Valvatacea, Littorinacea, Naticacea and Aglossa. Of these the Littorinacea may perhaps be associated with the Cerithiacea-Rissoacea group, there being a number of ways in which they approach one another, and there is equally some justification for linking the Aglossa with the Cerithiacea-Ptenoglossa group. The 3 other superfamilies, however, appear to be more isolated and it is not easy to suggest where their affinities lie. The Naticacea are rather remote from the ancestral monotocardian and exhibit a number of advanced as well as specialized features. The Valvatacea and Architaenioglossa, however, are primitive monotocardians and still recall the diotocardians in several ways. They are best regarded as isolated evolutionary lines arising somewhere near the base of the monotocardian stem and exhibiting their own characteristic specialized features.

It is usually admitted that the opisthobranchs must have evolved from some proso-branch ancestry and it is interesting to see to what extent these two great divisions of the gastropods can be related to one another. Before doing this it is necessary to discuss typical opisthobranch organization. In these molluscs the shell tends to be reduced or, in many cases, wholly lost; when it does occur it is high-spired only in a small number of primitive families and is normally low-spired or involute. In many opisthobranchs it is small in relation to the volume of the soft parts, which cannot be entirely withdrawn into it for shelter. In these circumstances the absence of an operculum is understandable, but this is also a feature—and less easily explicable unless it relates to a burrowing habit— of some of the lower groups of opisthobranchs like the Ringiculidae, Hydatinidae and Diaphanidae, in which the entire body of the animal can be withdrawn into the shell. A heterostrophic protoconch is an outstanding characteristic of practically all opisthobranch shells and folds (or 'teeth') on the columella are of frequent occurrence—another reflec-tion of the fact that it is becoming too small to house the animal. When the shell is sufficiently well developed to possess an ornamented surface the decoration takes the form of spiral rather than longitudinal elements, and frequently no ornament at all occurs. This is more or less inevitable when still another opisthobranch character is noted—the tendency for the mantle to grow over and enclose the shell. When this happens it may lose its calcareous nature and be reduced to a thin plate of conchiolin. Finally, as in the nudibranchs, the shell may be lost, though the mantle may still retain the ability to secrete spicules of calcareous material within its thickness.

Accompanying these changes in the shell go others which affect the mantle cavity and the relative sizes of the various parts of the body. In the prosobranch the visceral hump is large and the head-foot of moderate size, the sole of the foot often being narrow; in the opisthobranchs, by contrast, the head-foot often becomes the larger of the two, broadening to provide space for many of the viscera, which move ventrally into the cephalopedal haemocoel. In the most primitive opisthobranchs the proportions of the prosobranch body are retained but the more advanced forms have the same bodily shape as a slug, in which head, foot and visceral hump are confluent.

The mantle cavity becomes shallow and gradually opens out on to the general surface of the body. At the same time it and its contents are displaced so as to face more and more to the right and, finally, almost backwards. By comparison with the prosobranch this brings about a detorsion of the body, a situation in which the auricle lies anterior to the gill and, as the parietal ganglia (especially the supra-oesophageal) follow the pallial organs which they innervate, a loss of the streptoneurous condition of the visceral loop. Some opisthobranchs, however, such as the Acteonidae, are still streptoneurous. Within the mantle cavity the ctenidium alters in appearance and becomes foliobranch instead of filamentous as it is in the prosobranchs. Because of the way in which the mantle cavity has become less deep a certain length of gill now projects from its mouth with the effect of decreasing the ventilation of the deeper parts. To compensate for the loss of ciliary surface which this extrusion of the gill causes, ciliated ridges often arise, more particularly in the lower opisthobranchs with deeper mantle cavities; these help in creating a pallial current. They are developed on the right side and so give what is predominantly an exhalant stream, whereas the ctenidium of prosobranchs lies on the left and makes a primarily inhalant current. A pallial tentacle on the right may extend the strips into an exhalant siphon. Perhaps the exogyrous caecum of the acteonids and hydatinids may be an alternative method of improving the ventilation of the mantle cavity in animals in which it is still moderately deep. The exposed parts of the body tend to develop repugnatorial glands of large size.

The alimentary canal of opisthobranchs is invariably characterized by the complete absence of any structures which can be homologized with the oesophageal glands of the prosobranchs. When one considers the way in which these glands and their homologues may be traced throughout the prosobranch series this is a rather extraordinary fact: it seems to find its only sensible solution in an evolution of the opisthobranchs from a stock of prosobranchs in which they had already been lost. A similar simplification of structure affects the stomach: the oesophageal and intestinal apertures tend to migrate towards one another and this results in the main part of the stomach appearing as a kind of caecum from the point where these 2 tubes converge. The stomach tends to be small and digestion occurs in an expanded oesophagus. The histology of the digestive gland is elaborate, and the salivary glands are often tubular.

The tendency towards concentration of the nervous system which was an obvious evolutionary trend in the prosobranchs is continued in the opisthobranchs by a migration of the pedal ganglia so that they come to lie alongside the cerebrals and the pleurals on the dorsal side of the alimentary canal. This produces a concentrated group of ganglia which are linked dorsally by the cerebral commissure and ventrally by the elongated pedal commissures and which always lies behind the buccal mass. In lower opisthobranchs the visceral ganglia may retain their ancestral posterior position but within the group an evolutionary trend brings them forward to join the nerve ring. The potentialities for greater and a higher level of nervous activity which this anatomical concentration of centres would permit seem to be destroyed by a simultaneous trend towards a reduction in the number of nerve cells contained in the ganglia.

In respect of sense organs the opisthobranchs differ from the prosobranchs in exhibiting, in their lowest members, tentacles which are flat instead of cylindrical and eyes which sink below the skin and come to lie on the dorsal surface of the cerebral ganglia. This insinking is accompanied by movement towards the mid-line so that the eyes lie median to the tentacles.

The opisthobranchs are hermaphrodite and though some may retain such primitive features as a seminal groove on the floor of the mantle cavity this is usually folded off to form a genital duct which lies in the haemocoel and which may become split into separate male and female channels. The penis, except in the acteonids, differs from that of prosobranchs in being invaginable. The eggs are laid in jelly masses rather than in capsules.

The opisthobranchs are a group of animals which are markedly marine in their habitat and show only the very slightest ability to tolerate brackish conditions. This may, perhaps, be correlated with the reduction and loss of the shell which throws too great an osmoregulatory burden on the excretory organs.

Having outlined the main features of the opisthobranch mollusc we may now examine a few groups from this subclass and from the prosobranchs in search of possible links. The passage from monotocardian to opisthobranch is, in many ways, so gradual as to let one approach this task with a certain optimism. Of the families which are generally accepted as opisthobranchs the most primitive are undoubtedly the Acteonidae, Ringiculidae, Hydatinidae and Diaphanidae. Their characteristic features may be sorted out into those which seem to link them with the prosobranchs, those which link them with the higher opisthobranchs and those which seem to be characteristic of the lower opisthobranchs themselves and which we may call transitional.

|  | *Prosobranch* | *Transitional* | *Opisthobranch* |
|---|---|---|---|
| *Acteonidae* | high-spired shell | ciliated strips in mantle cavity | tentacles flat |
|  | body retractile into shell | exhalant tentacle | eyes sunken |
|  | operculum present | exogyrous caecum | ctenidium foliobranch |
|  | mantle cavity faces forward | repugnatorial glands | no oesophageal glands |
|  | prosobranch |  | hermaphrodite |
|  | streptoneurous |  | separate vas deferens |
|  | penis external |  | albumen gland separate from genital duct |
|  | no pigmented hypobranchial gland |  | cerebropleural ganglia |
|  | seminal groove |  | long pedal commissures |
|  | separate vas deferens |  | no egg capsules |
|  | osphradium present |  | heterostrophic larval shell |
|  | no Hancock's organ |  |  |
| *Ringiculidae* | high-spired shell |  | tentacles flat |
|  | body retractile into shell |  | eyes sunken |
|  | mantle cavity faces forward |  | ctenidium not filamentous |
|  | prosobranch |  | no operculum |
|  | no pigmented hypobranchial gland |  | no oesophageal glands |
|  | streptoneurous |  | hermaphrodite |
|  |  |  | invaginable penis |
|  |  |  | no egg capsules |
|  |  |  | heterostrophic larval shell |
| *Hydatinidae* | body retractile into shell | spire reduced | no operculum |
|  |  | mantle grows over shell | no oesophageal glands |
|  |  | exhalant tentacle | hermaphrodite |
|  |  | tentacles ear-shaped | invaginable penis |
|  |  | exogyrous caecum | euthyneurous |
|  |  | eyes median | no egg capsules |
|  |  | Hancock's organ present |  |

| *Diaphanidae* | body retractile into shell | low-spired shell | tentacles flat |
| | foot narrow | pigmented hypobranchial gland | eyes sunken |
| | streptoneury in *Toledonia* | exhalant siphon | no operculum |
| | seminal groove | Hancock's organ present | no oesophageal glands |
| | osphradium | | hermaphrodite |
| | | | invaginable penis |
| | | | euthyneurous (ex. *Toledonia*) |
| | | | no egg capsules |

These characters may now be compared with those exhibited by certain groups of animals which are normally regarded as coming within the prosobranchs. The first of these groups is the pyramidellids. When their characters are tabulated in similar fashion they fall as follows:

| | *Prosobranch* | *Transitional* | *Opisthobranch* |
|---|---|---|---|
| *Pyramidellidae* | high-spired shell | ciliated strips in mantle cavity | eyes slightly sunken |
| | body retractile into shell | ear-shaped tentacles | no oesophageal glands |
| | mantle cavity faces forwards | pigmented hypobranchial gland | euthyneurous |
| | auricle anterior to ventricle | stomach simple but not a caecum | hermaphrodite |
| | operculum present | eyes median | invaginable penis |
| | foot narrow | tubular salivary glands | albumen gland separate from genital duct |
| | no Hancock's organ | | no egg capsules |
| | seminal groove | | heterostrophic larval shell |
| | osphradium | | |
| | pedal ganglia ventral | | |

The same may be done with the family Omalogyridae, though it is well to remember that their anatomy may well be affected by their small size.

| | *Omalogyridae* | | |
|---|---|---|---|
| | mantle cavity faces forward | ciliated strips in mantle cavity | eyes sunken |
| | body retractile within shell | pigmented hypobranchial gland | no oesophageal glands |
| | auricle anterior to ventricle | stomach simple but not a caecum | hermaphrodite |
| | operculum present | | invaginable penis |
| | foot narrow | | |
| | osphradium | | |
| | pedal ganglia ventral | | |
| | egg capsules | | |

When these anatomical features are tabulated in this way it is clear that both these families seem to show undoubted affinities with the opisthobranchs and, certainly so far as the pyramidellids are concerned, to be properly classified as opisthobranchs rather than as prosobranchs. They are an important annectent group, however, because, as was suggested above (p. 631) the pyramidellids link themselves to the families Scalidae, Ianthinidae, Eulimidae and Aclididae, in some members of each of which a hetero-strophic larval shell has been recorded, oesophageal glands are absent, a mentum may occur, pigmented hypobranchial glands are found, the ctenidium may be replaced by ciliated strips, the stomach is simple, the animals are hermaphrodite, eyes may be sunken and tubular salivary glands may occur. These animals in their turn show certain relation-ships to the Cerithiacea—witness the occurrence of spermatozeugmata in both groups, the similar shell, loss of oesophageal glands, the lack of penis—and to the Rissoacea. It is in this region of the prosobranchs that we would suggest, with Boettger (1954), that the origin of the opisthobranchs should be sought. In the Rissoacea-Cerithiacea grouping we have animals which qualify for the position of being ancestral to opisthobranchs by having a tall shell, in the rissoaceans frequently devoid of much ornament, with a horny operculum on a rather narrow foot, tentacles often provided with sensory cirri as in pyramidellids, a tendency to produce an exhalant pallial tentacle on the right side of the mantle cavity and even, on occasion, ciliated strips within. The ctenidium in the smaller forms is often reduced in size, a fact which would permit, if later animals became bigger once again, a re-development of the gill along the foliate lines shown by the opistho-branchs instead of the filamentous type of the prosobranch. The gut has lost the oesophageal glands because of the presence of a crystalline style, but, were the style to disappear because of a change in diet, the oesophagus would be the simple tube of the most lowly opisthobranchs, ready to evolve towards the gizzard and crop so commonly found in higher tectibranchs. The rissoacean-cerithiacean reproductive system is perhaps too specialized to provide an appropriate ancestry for that of the opisthobranch but such advanced features as it does show are not only compatible with but even foreshadow those of the opisthobranchs. The hermaphroditism of the latter group may indicate that in this respect they have undergone an independent evolution, another example of what de Beer (1954) called Watson's Rule, or it could be a persistence of a more fundamental state.

The question of how the opisthobranchs are related to the pulmonates is one at once too large and too irrelevant to the British prosobranchs to be profitably discussed here. But, though the two higher groups of gastropods seem to have been derived from a prosobranch ancestry by following different evolutionary paths, there is, nevertheless, sufficient resemblance between their more primitive members to suggest that both started from the same region of the prosobranchs—from some plastic group which was able to evolve, by retaining the marine habitat, towards a naked state and the agility and lightness which that permitted, and, by retaining the protective shell, towards the exploitation of freshwater and land which has made the pulmonates so successful a group.

# CLASSIFICATION

THE classification of the animals dealt with in this book is given below. In the main the system follows that used by Thiele (1929–35), but there are some respects in which it departs from his. In particular, regarding the mesogastropods and stenoglossans as merely suborders of a larger monotocardian group, we prefer to divide the prosobranchs into 2 orders, the Diotocardia and the Monotocardia, rather than into the 3 (Archaeogastropoda, Mesogastropoda and Stenoglossa) which he used. These suborders we call Taenioglossa and Stenoglossa; we are aware that the former group contains animals which do not possess a taenioglossate radula, though that which they do have may be derived from such a pattern. In addition to expressing zoological relationships (as we see them) more accurately, this avoids the mixing of different types of name in one classification. Occasionally we have included the names used by Wenz (1938) for the benefit of any palaeontologist who may consult the book. The superfamilies, families and genera are arranged in what seems to us to be the correct phylogenetic order, in so far as that is possible in a single linear list, but species within a genus are arranged in alphabetical order. Suggested groupings of superfamilies as discussed in Chapter 25 are indicated by reference marks. Species which occur in the Channel Islands but not elsewhere in the British Isles are not included.

## CLASS GASTROPODA

### Subclass PROSOBRANCHIA

#### Order DIOTOCARDIA (=ARCHAEOGASTROPODA)

Superfamily Zeugobranchia (=Pleurotomariacea)
   Scissurellidae: *Scissurella crispata* Fleming.
   Fissurellidae: *Emarginula conica* Lamarck, *E. crassa* Sowerby, *E. reticulata* Sowerby, *Puncturella noachina* (L.), *Diodora apertura* (Montagu).
Superfamily Patellacea (=Docoglossa)
   Patellidae: *Patella aspera* Lamarck, *P. intermedia* Jeffreys, *P. vulgata* L., *Patina pellucida* (L.).
   Acmaeidae: *Acmaea tessulata* (Müller), *A. virginea* (Müller).
   Lepetidae: *Lepeta caeca* (Müller), *L. fulva* (Müller), *Propilidium exiguum* (Thompson).
Superfamily Trochacea
   Trochidae: *Margarites groenlandicus* (Gmelin), *M. helicinus* (Fabricius), *M. olivaceus* (Brown), *Solariella amabilis* (Jeffreys), *Monodonta lineata* (da Costa), *Gibbula cineraria* (L.), *G. magus* (L.), *G. tumida* (Montagu), *G. umbilicalis* (da Costa), *Cantharidus clelandi* (Wood), *C. exasperatus* (Pennant), *C. montagui* (Wood), *C. striatus* (L.), *Calliostoma occidentale* (Mighels & Adams), *C. papillosum* (da Costa), *C. zizyphinum* (L.), *Skenea cutleriana* Clark, *S. millipunctata* (Friele), *S. nitens* (Philippi), *S. serpuloides* (Montagu).
   Turbinidae: *Tricolia pullus* (L.).
Superfamily Neritacea
   Neritidae: *Theodoxus fluviatilis* (L.).

Order MONOTOCARDIA

Suborder TAENIOGLOSSA (=MESOGASTROPODA)

Superfamily Architaenioglossa (=Cyclophoracea)
Viviparidae: *Viviparus contectus* (Millet), *V. viviparus* (L.).

Superfamily Valvatacea
Valvatidae: *Valvata cristata* Müller, *V. macrostoma* Mörch, *V. piscinalis* (Müller).

Superfamily Littorinacea
Lacunidae: *Lacuna crassior* (Montagu), *L. pallidula* (da Costa), *L. parva* (da Costa), *L. vincta* (Montagu).

Littorinidae: *Littorina littoralis* (L.), *L. littorea* (L.), *L. neritoides* (L.), *L. saxatilis* (Olivi).

Pomatiasidae: *Pomatias elegans* (Müller).

Aciculidae: *Acicula fusca* (Montagu).

*Superfamily Rissoacea
Hydrobiidae: *Hydrobia ulvae* (Pennant), *H. ventrosa* (Montagu), *Potamopyrgus jenkinsi* (Smith), *Bythinella scholtzi* (Schmidt), *Pseudamnicola confusa* (Frauenfeld), *Truncatella subcylindrica* (L.), *Bithynia leachi* (Sheppard), *B. tentaculata* (L.).

Rissoidae: *Cingula alderi* (Jeffreys), *C. cingillus* (Montagu), *C. inflata* (Monterosato), *C. proxima* (Forbes & Hanley), *C. semicostata* (Montagu), *C. semistriata* (Montagu), *C. vitrea* (Montagu), *Alvania abyssicola* (Forbes), *A. beani* (Hanley), *A. cancellata* (da Costa), *A. carinata* (da Costa), *A. cimicoides* (Forbes), *A. crassa* (Kanmacher), *A. jeffreysi* (Waller), *A. punctura* (Montagu), *A. zetlandica* (Montagu), *Rissoa albella* Lovén, *R. guerini* Récluz, *R. inconspicua* Alder, *R. lilacina* Récluz, *R. membranacea* (Adams), *R. parva* (da Costa), *R. sarsi* Lovén, [1]*Barleeia rubra* (Montagu).

Circulidae: *Circulus striatus* (Philippi).

Assimineidae: *Assiminea grayana* Fleming, *Paludinella littorina* (Chiaje).

Tornidae: *Tornus imperspicuus* (Chaster), *T. subcarinatus* (Montagu), *T. unisulcatus* (Chaster).

Incertae sedis: the systematic position of the 4 following families is uncertain though they are possibly more closely related to the Rissoacea than to other groups.

Cingulopsidae: *Cingulopsis fulgida* (Adams).

Skeneopsidae: *Skeneopsis planorbis* (Fabricius).

Omalogyridae: *Omalogyra atomus* (Philippi), *Ammonicera rota* (Forbes & Hanley).

Rissoellidae: *Rissoella diaphana* (Alder), *R. globularis* (Jeffreys), *R. opalina* (Jeffreys).

†*Superfamily Cerithiacea
Turritellidae: *Turritella communis* Risso.

Caecidae: *Caecum glabrum* (Montagu), *C. imperforatum* (Kanmacher).

Cerithiidae: *Bittium reticulatum* (da Costa).

Cerithiopsidae: *Cerithiopsis barleei* Jeffreys, *C. clarki* Forbes & Hanley, *C. jeffreysi* Watson, *C. metaxae* (Chiaje), *C. tubercularis* (Montagu), *Cerithiella metula* (Lovén), *Eumetula arctica* (Mörch).

Triphoridae: *Triphora perversa* (L.).

---

[1] The anatomy of this species is so different from that of other rissoids as to suggest that it might be better placed in a separate family Barleeidae.

Superfamily Strombacea
    Aporrhaidae: *Aporrhais pespelicani* (L.), *A. serresiana* (Michaud).
\*‡Superfamily Calyptraeacea
    Trichotropidae: *Trichotropis borealis* Broderip & Sowerby.
    Capulidae: *Capulus ungaricus* (L.).
    Calyptraeidae: *Calyptraea chinensis* (L.), *Crepidula fornicata* (L.).
‡Superfamily Lamellariacea
    Lamellariidae: *Velutina plicatilis* (Müller), *V. velutina* (Müller), *Lamellaria latens* (Müller), *L. perspicua* (L.).
    Eratoidae: *Erato voluta* (Montagu), *Trivia arctica* (Montagu), *T. monacha* (da Costa).
Superfamily Cypraeacea
    Cypraeidae: *Simnia patula* (Pennant).
Superfamily Naticacea
    Naticidae: *Amauropsis islandica* (Gmelin), *Natica alderi* Forbes, *N. catena* (da Costa), *N. fusca* Blainville, *N. montagui* Forbes, *N. pallida* Broderip & Sowerby.
†Superfamily Ptenoglossa (=Scalacea)
    Scalidae: *Cirsotrema commutatum* (Monterosato), *Clathrus clathratulus* (Kanmacher), *C. clathrus* (L.), *C. trevelyanus* (Leach), *C. turtonis* (Turton).
    Ianthinidae: *Ianthina exigua* Lamarck, *I. janthina* (L.), *I. pallida* Thompson.
Superfamily Aglossa (=Pyramidellacea)
    Aclididae: *Graphis albida* (Adams), *Aclis ascaris* (Turton), *A. minor* (Brown), *A. walleri* Jeffreys, *Pherusina gulsonae* (Clark), *Cima minima* (Jeffreys).
    Eulimidae: *Eulima glabra* (da Costa), *E. stenostoma* Jeffreys, *E. trifasciata* (Adams), *Balcis alba* (da Costa), *B. anceps* (Marshall), *B. collinsi* (Sykes), *B. compactilis* (Monterosato), *B. curva* (Monterosato), *B. devians* (Monterosato), *B. lubrica* (Monterosato), *B. monterosatoi* (Monterosato), *B. sinuosa* (Scacchi).
    Styliferidae: *Pelseneeria stylifera* (Turton).
Superfamily Doliacea (=Tonnacea)
    Cymatiidae: *Gyrina gigantea* (Lamarck).

Suborder STENOGLOSSA (=NEOGASTROPODA)

Superfamily Muricacea
    Muricidae: *Trophon barvicensis* (Johnston), *T. muricatus* (Montagu), *T. truncatus* (Ström), *Nucella lapillus* (L.), *Urosalpinx cinerea* (Say), *Ocenebra erinacea* (L.).
Superfamily Buccinacea
    Columbellidae: *Pyrene haliaeeti* (Jeffreys).
    Buccinidae: *Liomesus ovum* (Turton), *Beringius turtoni* (Bean), *Volutopsius norwegicus* (Gmelin), *Colus fenestratus* (Turton), *C. gracilis* (da Costa), *C. howsei* (Marshall), *C. islandicus* (Gmelin), *C. jeffreysianus* (Fischer), *Neptunea antiqua* (L.), *Buccinum humphreysianum* Bennett, *B. undatum* L., *Chauvetia brunnea* (Donovan).
    Nassariidae: *Nassarius incrassatus* (Ström), *N. pygmaeus* (Lamarck), *N. reticulatus* (L.).
    Fasciolariidae: *Troschelia berniciensis* (King).
Superfamily Toxoglossa (=Conacea)
    Conidae: *Haedropleura septangularis* (Montagu), *Lora rufa* (Montagu), *L. trevel-*

*liana* (Turton), *L. turricula* (Montagu), *Typhlomangelia nivalis* (Lovén), *Thesbia nana* (Lovén), *Mangelia attenuata* (Montagu), *M. brachystoma* (Philippi), *M. coarctata* (Forbes), *M. costulata* (Risso), *M. nebula* (Montagu), *M. powisiana* (Dautzenberg), *Philbertia asperrima* (Brown), *P. gracilis* (Montagu), *P. leufroyi* (Michaud), *P. linearis* (Montagu), *P. purpurea* (Montagu), *P. teres* (Forbes).

## Subclass OPISTHOBRANCHIA

Pyramidellidae: *Chrysallida clathrata* (Jeffreys), *C. decussata* (Montagu), *C. excavata* (Philippi), *C. eximia* (Jeffreys), *C. indistincta* (Montagu), *C. obtusa* (Brown), *C. spiralis* (Montagu), *Menestho clavula* (Lovén), *M. diaphana* (Jeffreys), *M. divisa* (Adams), *M. dolioliformis* (Jeffreys), *M. obliqua* (Alder), *M. warreni* (Thompson), *Odostomia acuta* Jeffreys, *O. albella* (Lovén), *O. conoidea* (Brocchi), *O. conspicua* Alder, *O. eulimoides* Hanley, *O. lukisi* Jeffreys, *O. nivosa* (Montagu), *O. plicata* (Montagu), *O. scalaris* Macgillivray, *O. truncatula* Jeffreys, *O. turrita* Hanley, *O. umbilicaris* (Malm), *O. unidentata* (Montagu), *Eulimella compactilis* Jeffreys, *E. gracilis* (Jeffreys), *E. laevis* (Brown), *E. macandrei* (Forbes), *E. nitidissima* (Montagu), *Turbonilla crenata* (Brown), *T. delicata* Monterosato, *T. elegantissima* (Montagu), *T. fenestrata* (Forbes), *T. fulvocincta* (Thompson), *T. innovata* Monterosato, *T. jeffreysi* (Forbes & Hanley), *T. rufescens* (Forbes).

\* Superfamilies characterized by the possession of a crystalline style.
† Superfamilies characterized by the occurrence of spermatozeugmata.
‡ Echinospiracea, characterized by presence of echinospira larva.

## HABITAT AND DISTRIBUTION LIST

T HE following list is intended to give information about those prosobranchs which occur in the British Isles and the surrounding seas. All have been included except a very small number recorded only once or twice which can be regarded as strays from other areas. Sarnian species are excluded.

The arrangement of the list is alphabetical. Each entry is arranged according to the following scheme. The first line contains the scientific name of the animal and its popular names. There then follows a list of other names by which the species has been called in the better known books and fauna lists. The names used by Forbes & Hanley in their *History of the British Mollusca* (1849–53) are distinguished by the initials F. & H., and those used by Jeffreys in his *British Conchology* (1862–69) by the letter J. in parentheses. *The list of names is not meant to be a synonymy in the technical sense,* and the order is simply alphabetical.

The first paragraph after the list of names gives the following information in this sequence—the kind of habitat in which the animal may be collected; its distribution in the British Isles, first in Great Britain, then in Ireland; an estimate of its frequency; its distribution outside the British Isles.

The second paragraph gives similarly—the breeding time; the way in which the eggs are laid and their whereabouts; the larvae and their time and place of occurrence.

The following abbreviations are used here and throughout the text: C, central; E, east; N, north; S, south; W, west; and in combination.

CD, chart datum; HWEST, high water of equinoctial spring tides; HWNT, high water of neap tides; HWST, high water of ordinary spring tides; LWEST, low water of equinoctial spring tides; LWNT, low water of neap tides; LWST, low water of ordinary spring tides; LW, low water; MTL, mid-tide level.

As far as possible the information in this list has been checked by personal observation, but much has perforce had to be taken from the literature. The most important publications are the following: Ankel (1936a), Boycott (1934, 1936), Chaster (1896), Chumley (1918), the Conchological Society's Census (1951), Cornet & Marche-Marchad (1951), Elliot, Laurie & Murdoch (1901), Ellis (1926), Forbes & Hanley (1849–53), Frömming (1956), Grossu (1956), Jeffreys (1862–69), Lebour (1937), Marine Biological Association (1957), Marshall (1893–1918), Moore (1937b), Sykes (1903), Thorson (1946), Winckworth (1932).

*Acicula fusca* (Montagu). Point snail.
  *Acicula lineata* (Draparnaud)
  *Acme fusca* (Montagu)
  *Acme lineata* (Draparnaud) (J.) (F. & H.)
  Among moss, leaves, under decaying wood and stones in old woods, especially beech; in damp situations more acid than those favoured by *Pomatias*. Locally in England, Wales, S and W Scotland, Ireland. Occasional. W Europe.
  Reproduction unknown.

*Aclis ascaris* (Turton). (J.) (F. & H.)

     Dredged, 23–100 fathoms, off all coasts; habitat unknown. Very rare. Norway to France.

     Reproduction unknown.

*Aclis gulsonae:* see *Pherusina gulsonae*

*Aclis minor* (Brown).

     *Aclis supranitida* (Wood) (J.) (F. & H.)

     Dredged, 15–75 fathoms, off all coasts; habitat unknown. Very rare. Scandinavia to Mediterranean.

     Breeding unknown. Egg capsules unknown. Free-swimming veligers not uncommon in offshore plankton, autumn (Plymouth).

*Aclis nitidissima:* see *Eulimella nitidissima*

*Aclis supranitida:* see *A. minor*

*Aclis unica:* see *Graphis albida*

*Aclis walleri* Jeffreys. (J.)

     Known only from a few specimens dredged N Scotland, habitat unknown. Very rare. Scandinavia to Sicily.

     Reproduction unknown.

*Acmaea tessulata* (Müller). Tortoiseshell limpet.

     *Acmaea testudinalis* (Müller) (F. & H.)

     *Patelloida tessulata* (Müller)

     *Tectura testudinalis* (Müller) (J.)

     Under stones on rocky shores and on shells, LWST or in pools above, and dredged to 20 fathoms, on all coasts N of Humber and N Wales, N Ireland. Common. N Atlantic.

     Breeds April–July (New England). Eggs attached. Free-swimming larvae.

*Acmaea virginea* (Müller). (F. & H.)

     *Patelloida virginea* (Müller)

     *Tectura virginea* (Müller) (J.)

     Gregarious, under stones, on shells, and on *Cystoseira ericoides* and *Chondrus crispus*, with *Lithothamnion*, on all rocky shores, LWST and sometimes above, and dredged to 30 fathoms, on all coasts. Common. N and S Atlantic.

     Breeds April–May (Roscoff). Eggs planktonic. Free-swimming larvae.

*Acme fusca:* see *Acicula fusca*

*Acme lineata:* see *Acicula fusca*

*Acme subcylindrica:* see *Truncatella subcylindrica*

*Acrybia islandica:* see *Amauropsis islandica*

*Actonia abyssicola:* see *Alvania abyssicola*

*Actonia punctura:* see *Alvania punctura*

*Adeorbis:* see *Tornus*

*Alvania abyssicola* (Forbes).

     *Actonia abyssicola* (Forbes)

     *Alvania subsoluta* (Aradas) var. *abyssicola*

     *Rissoa abyssicola* Forbes (J.) (F. & H.)

     *Rissoa subsoluta* Aradas var. *abyssicola*

     Dredged, 8–100 fathoms, on muddy bottoms, in Irish Sea, and off W Scotland, Ireland. Scarce. Scandinavia to Mediterranean.

Breeding and eggs unknown. Free-swimming veligers in plankton, late summer and autumn (Denmark).

*Alvania beani* (Hanley).

    *Alvania reticulata* (Montagu) (part)

    *Rissoa beani* Hanley (F. & H.)

    *Rissoa calathus* Forbes & Hanley (J.) (F. & H.)

    *Rissoa reticulata* (Montagu) (J.)

    Under stones in laminarian zone and dredged to 50 fathoms, off all coasts. Locally common. Scandinavia to Mediterranean.

    Reproduction unknown.

*Alvania cancellata* (da Costa).

    *Rissoa cancellata* (da Costa) (J.)

    *Rissoa crenulata* Michaud (F. & H.)

    Gregarious under stones on rocky shores, LWST—50 fathoms, on S and W coasts, Ireland. Local. British Isles to Mediterranean.

    Reproduction unknown.

*Alvania carinata* (da Costa).

    *Galeodina carinata* (da Costa)

    *Rissoa striatula* (Montagu) (J.) (F. & H.)

    Under stones embedded in sand on rocky shore, below LWNT and dredged to 12 fathoms, on S and W coasts, Ireland. Rare. British Isles to Mediterranean.

    Reproduction unknown.

*Alvania cimicoides* (Forbes).

    *Alvania reticulata* (Montagu) var. *cimicoides*

    *Rissoa cimicoides* Forbes (J.)

    *Rissoa sculpta* Philippi (F. & H.)

    On rocky shores and dredged to 50 fathoms, off S and W coasts. Rare. Scandinavia to Mediterranean.

    Reproduction unknown.

*Alvania costata: see A. crassa*

*Alvania crassa* (Kanmacher).

    *Alvania costata* (Adams)

    *Manzonia costata* (Adams)

    *Manzonia crassa* (Kanmacher)

    *Rissoa costata* (Adams) (J.) (F. & H.)

    Under stones and on weeds on rocky shores LWST, dredged to 25 fathoms, on all coasts. Occasional N, commoner S. Scandinavia to Mediterranean, Black Sea.

    Breeding and eggs unknown. Free-swimming veligers not uncommon in inshore plankton, late summer and autumn (Plymouth).

*Alvania jeffreysi* (Waller).

    *Rissoa jeffreysi* Waller (J.)

    Dredged, 70–85 fathoms, on sandy ground, off Shetland and Scilly Is. Very rare. Iceland to British Isles.

    Reproduction unknown.

*Alvania punctura* (Montagu).

    *Actonia punctura* (Montagu)

    *Alvania puncturata* Macgillivray

    *Arsenia punctura* (Montagu)

*Rissoa punctura* (Montagu) (J.) (F. & H.)

Among Bryozoa and *Laminaria*, LWST—40 fathoms, on shelly bottoms, on all coasts. Locally plentiful. Scandinavia to Mediterranean.

Breeds summer, early autumn (Plymouth). Egg capsules attached to weeds, high up shore. Free-swimming veligers common in plankton, summer and early autumn (Plymouth).

*Alvania puncturata:* see *A. punctura*

*Alvania reticulata:* see *A. beani*

*Alvania reticulata* var. *cimicoides:* see *A. cimicoides*

*Alvania sarsi:* see *Rissoa sarsi*

*Alvania subsoluta* var. *abyssicola:* see *A. abyssicola*

*Alvania zetlandica* (Montagu).

    *Manzonia zetlandica* (Montagu)

    *Rissoa zetlandica* (Montagu) (J.) (F. & H.)

Dredged, 7–70 fathoms, off S and W coasts, NE Scotland. Scarce. Scandinavia to W Mediterranean.

Reproduction unknown.

*Amauropsis islandica* (Gmelin).

    *Acrybia islandica* (Gmelin)

    *Natica helicoides* Johnston (F. & H.)

    *Natica islandica* (Gmelin) (J.)

Dredged, 7–100 fathoms, from sandy bottoms, off NE coasts. Rare. Panarctic-boreal.

Breeding unknown. Egg collar laid freely on bottom. Probably no free-swimming veligers.

*Ammonicera rota* (Forbes & Hanley).

    *Ammonicera tricarinata* (Webster)

    *Homalogyra rota* (Forbes & Hanley) (J.)

    *Omalogyra rota* (Forbes & Hanley)

    *Skenea rota* (Forbes & Hanley) (F. & H.)

    *Skenea tricarinata* Webster

Among weeds and detritus in rock pools, LWST, and dredged to 3 fathoms, on S and W coasts, SW Ireland. Scarce. British Isles to Mediterranean.

Reproduction unknown.

*Ammonicera tricarinata:* see *A. rota*

*Amnicola confusa:* see *Pseudamnicola confusa*

*Amnicola similis:* see *Pseudamnicola confusa*

*Amnicola taylori:* see *Bythinella scholtzi*

*Aporrhais macandreae:* see *A. serresiana*

*Aporrhais pescarbonis:* see *A. serresiana*

*Aporrhais pespelicani* (L.). (J.) (F. & H.). Pelican's foot shell.

    *Chenopus pespelicani* (L.)

Dredged, 4–70 fathoms, from sandy mud or muddy gravel, off all coasts. Locally abundant. Scandinavia to Mediterranean.

Breeds spring and early summer, maximum March (Plymouth). Egg capsules attached to sand grains. Free-swimming veligers in offshore plankton, summer (Plymouth).

*Aporrhais serresiana* (Michaud).
>*Aporrhais macandreae* Jeffreys (J.)
>*Aporrhais pescarbonis* Brongniart (F. & H.)
>*Chenopus pescarbonis* (Brongniart)
>Dredged, 7–100 fathoms, from soft mud, off Shetlands. Locally common. Norway to Mediterranean.
>Reproduction unknown, but free-swimming veligers probable.

*Arcularia reticulata:* see *Nassarius reticulatus*
*Argobuccinum giganteum:* see *Gyrina gigantea*
*Arsenia punctura:* see *Alvania punctura*
*Assiminea grayana* Fleming. (J.) (F. & H.). Sentinel shell.
>*Assemania grayana* (Fleming)
>On muddy banks and bottoms in brackish water at junction between fresh and salt, between Kent and Humber. Locally common. Low Countries.
>Breeds spring, summer (Wilhelmshaven). Egg capsules loose or compacted into groups on substratum. Free-swimming veligers.

*Assiminea littorina:* see *Paludinella littorina*
*Auriculina diaphana:* see *Menestho diaphana*
*Auriculina divisa:* see *Menestho divisa*
*Balcis alba* (da Costa).
>*Eulima alba* (da Costa)
>*Eulima polita* (L.) (J.) (F. & H.)
>*Melanella alba* (da Costa)
>*Melanella polita* (L.)
>Dredged, 7–65 fathoms, on muddy sand and gravel, off all coasts; associated with echinoderms. Locally common. Scandinavia to Mediterranean.
>Breeds spring, summer (Plymouth). Egg capsules unknown. Free-swimming veligers common in inshore and offshore plankton, spring and summer (Plymouth).

*Balcis anceps* (Marshall).
>*Eulima anceps* Marshall
>Dredged once, 31 fathoms, off Arran; habitat unknown. Very rare. British Isles to Mediterranean.
>Reproduction unknown.

*Balcis compactilis* (Monterosato).
>Dredged, 65 fathoms, the Minch, W Ireland; habitat unknown. Very rare. British Isles to Mediterranean.
>Reproduction unknown.

*Balcis curva* (Monterosato).
>*Eulima curva* Monterosato
>*Eulima philippii* var. *tumidosa* Marshall
>Recorded from Land's End and Scilly Isles; habitat unknown. Very rare. British Isles to Mediterranean.
>Reproduction unknown.

*Balcis devians* (Monterosato).
>*Balcis distorta* (Philippi)
>*Balcis incurva* (Renier)
>*Eulima distorta* (Deshayes) (J.) (F. & H.)
>*Eulima gracilis* Forbes

*Eulima incurva* (Renier)
*Eulima philippii* (Rayn & Ponzi)
*Melanella distorta* (Deshayes)
*Vitreolina devians* (Monterosato)
On and in various echinoderms, LWST—100 fathoms, on all coasts. Occasional. Scandinavia to Mediterranean.

Breeding and eggs unknown. Free-swimming veligers common in inshore plankton, spring and summer (Plymouth).

*Balcis distorta:* see *B. devians*
*Balcis incurva:* see *B. devians*
*Balcis lubrica* (Monterosato).
*Eulima intermedia* Cantraine (J.)
*Eulima nitida* Forbes
*Eulima polita* var. *nitida* Forbes & Hanley (F. & H.)
*Melanella intermedia* (Cantraine)
*Melanella lubrica* (Monterosato)
Dredged, 20–73 fathoms, on muddy sand, gravel, on all coasts. Rare. Scandinavia to Mediterranean.

Reproduction unknown.
*Balcis monterosatoi* (Monterosato).
*Eulima distorta* (Deshayes) var. *gracilis* (J.) (F. & H.)
*Eulima gracilis* Forbes
Dredged from deep water off W Scotland; habitat unknown. Not uncommon. Scandinavia to Mediterranean.

Reproduction unknown.
*Balcis sinuosa* (Scacchi).
*Balcis pernula* Monterosato
Dredged 7 fathoms off W Scotland; habitat unknown. Very rare.
Reproduction unknown.
*Barleeia rubra* (Montagu). (J.). Red spire shell.
*Barleeia unifasciata* (Montagu)
*Rissoa rubra* (Adams) (F. & H.)
On weeds at LWST on rocky shores of SW England, Ireland. Common. Southern Europe.

Breeds spring and early summer (Plymouth). Egg capsules attached to *Fucus*, *Calliblepharis*. No free-swimming larvae.
*Barleeia unifasciata:* see *B. rubra*
*Bela brachystoma:* see *Mangelia brachystoma*
*Bela coarctata:* see *Mangelia coarctata*
*Bela costata:* see *Mangelia coarctata*
*Bela costulata:* see *Mangelia costulata*
*Bela nebula:* see *Mangelia nebula*
*Bela powisiana:* see *Mangelia powisiana*
*Bela rufa:* see *Lora rufa*
*Bela septangularis:* see *Haedropleura septangularis*
*Bela striolata:* see *Mangelia costulata*
*Bela trevelyana:* see *Lora trevelliana*
*Bela turricola:* see *Lora turricula*

*Bela turricula:* see *Lora turricula*

*Bellardiella gracilis:* see *Philbertia gracilis*

*Beringius turtoni* (Bean).

  *Chrysodomus turtoni* (Bean)

  *Fusus turtoni* Bean (J.) (F. & H.)

  Dredged, 60–100 fathoms, on muddy bottoms, off NE coast. Very rare. Boreal N Atlantic.

  Breeding unknown. Egg capsules attached. No free-swimming larvae.

*Bithynia leachi* (Sheppard). (J.) (F. & H.)

  *Bithynia = Bythinia = Bithinia*

  In bigger lakes or slowly flowing water, extending to 2–3 m deep in summer, buried in mud in winter; calciphile. In England S of Yorkshire, locally at Grangemouth, Stirlingshire and in Wales, C Ireland. Common. Palaearctic.

  Breeds spring, summer. Egg capsules laid on weed. No free-swimming larvae.

*Bithynia tentaculata* (L.). (J.) (F. & H.)

  *Bithynia = Bythinia = Bithinia*

  On stones or weeds in large lakes, streams or ditches, extending to 10 m deep in summer, buried in mud in winter; calciphile. In S Scotland, England, E Wales, Ireland. Common. Palaearctic.

  Breeds spring, summer. Egg capsules laid on weed. No free-swimming larvae.

*Bittium reticulatum* (da Costa). Small needle whelk.

  *Cerithium reticulatum* da Costa (J.) (F. & H.)

  Gregarious under stones, in crevices on rocky shores, and on *Zostera* and *Codium* LWST, dredged to 10 fathoms, on S and W coasts, Ireland. Occasional. Norway to Mediterranean.

  Breeds January–May (Plymouth). Spawn laid on rocks or weeds, especially *Zostera*. Free-swimming veligers common in plankton, spring and summer (Plymouth).

*Brachystomia albella:* see *Odostomia albella*

*Brachystomia ambigua:* see *Odostomia eulimoides*

*Brachystomia eulimoides:* see *Odostomia eulimoides*

*Brachystomia lukisi:* see *Odostomia lukisi*

*Brachystomia rissoides:* see *Odostomia scalaris*

*Brochina glabra:* see *Caecum glabrum*

*Brochus glabrus:* see *Caecum glabrum*

*Brochus striatus:* see *Caecum imperforatum*

*Buccinofusus berniciensis:* see *Troschelia berniciensis*

*Buccinopsis dalei:* see *Liomesus ovum*

*Buccinum dalei:* see *Liomesus ovum*

*Buccinum fusiforme:* see *Colus fenestratus*

*Buccinum humphreysianum* Bennett. (J.) (F. & H.)

  Dredged, 18–90 fathoms, off W and N Scotland, Ireland; habitat unknown. Rare. N Atlantic.

  Breeding unknown. For egg capsules see Thorson (1935). No free-swimming larvae.

*Buccinum ovum:* see *Liomesus ovum*

*Buccinum undatum* L. (J.) (F. & H.). Common or white whelk or buckie.

On all types of shore, LW—1,200 fathoms on all coasts. Avoids brackish water but survives salinities <14‰. Locally abundant. N Atlantic.

Breeds October–May, according to locality. Egg capsules attached in clusters. No free-swimming larvae.

*Bythinella scholtzi* (Schmidt).
   *Amnicola taylori* (Smith)
   *Bythinella = Bithynella = Bithinella*
   *Bythinella steini* (Martens)
   *Hydrobia steini* Martens
   *Marstoniopsis steini* (Martens)
   *Paludestrina taylori* Smith
   *Pseudamnicola taylori* (Smith)
   In canals and docks Lancashire, Cheshire and Stirlingshire. N America, C and N Europe.

   Breeds spring and early summer. Egg capsules attached to substratum. No free-swimming larvae.

*Bythinella steini:* see *B. scholtzi*

*Caecum glabrum* (Montagu). (J.) (F. & H.)
   *Brochina glabra* (Montagu)
   *Brochus glabrus* (Montagu)
   Dredged, 3–35 fathoms, on sand and sandy gravel, off all coasts. Not common. Norway to Mediterranean.

   Breeds April–September (Heligoland). Egg capsules attached. Free-swimming veligers.

*Caecum imperforatum* (Kanmacher).
   *Brochus striatus* Brown
   *Caecum trachea* (Montagu) (J.) (F. & H.)
   Dredged, LWEST—3 fathoms, on sand and sandy gravel, off S and W coasts, Ireland. Not common. Southern N Atlantic, Mediterranean, Black Sea.

   Breeding and eggs unknown. Free-swimming veligers common.

*Caecum trachea:* see *C. imperforatum*

*Calliostoma conuloide:* see *C. zizyphinum*

*Calliostoma exasperatum:* see *Cantharidus exasperatus*

*Calliostoma miliare:* see *Cantharidus clelandi*

*Calliostoma granulatum:* see *C. papillosum*

*Calliostoma montagui:* see *Cantharidus montagui*

*Caloliostma occidentale* (Mighels & Adams).
   *Trochus alabastrum* Beck (F. & H.)
   *Trochus formosus* McAndrew & Forbes
   *Trochus occidentalis* Mighels & Adams (J.)
   Dredged, 40–90 fathoms, on stony ground, off NE England, E Scotland. Not uncommon locally. Boreal.

   Reproduction unknown.

*Calliostoma papillosum* (da Costa).
   *Calliostoma granulatum* (Born)
   *Trochus granulatus* Born (J.) (F. & H.)
   *Zizyphinus granulatus* (Born)

Dredged, 20–145 fathoms, on sandy gravel, SW England, Irish Sea, Clyde Sea Area. Scarce. British Isles to Mediterranean.

Breeds throughout year (Roscoff). Spawn ribbon attached (at three points). No free-swimming larvae.

*Calliostoma striatum:* see *Cantharidus striatus*

*Calliostoma zizyphinum* (L.). Painted top shell.

> *Calliostoma conuloide* (Lamarck)
> *Trochus conuloides* Lamarck
> *Trochus zizyphinus* L. (J.) (F. & H.)
> *Zizyphinum linnaei* Montagu
> *Zizyphinum conulus* (L.)

Under stones and in crevices on all rocky shores from MLWS (10% exposure) and in high rock pools in N and dredged to 85 fathoms, on muddy sand (Port Erin); extending into salinities $<$21‰, on all coasts, Ireland. Abundant. Scandinavia to Mediterranean.

Breeds spring and summer (Plymouth), May–October, maximum in July (Roscoff). Spawn ribbon attached (at one end). No free-swimming larvae.

*Calyptraea chinensis* (L.). (J.). Chinaman's hat.

> *Calyptraea sinensis* (L.) (F. & H.)
> *Patella chinensis* L.

On stones, shells, from LW to a few fathoms, on stony shores, SW England. Common locally. British Isles to Portuguese W Africa, Mediterranean, Black Sea.

Breeds April–September (Plymouth), spring–early summer (Roscoff). Egg capsules attached to stones, brooded by parent. No free-swimming larvae.

*Calyptraea sinensis:* see *C. chinensis*

*Cantharidus clelandi* (Wood).

> *Calliostoma miliare* (Brocchi)
> *Cantharidus miliaris* (Brocchi)
> *Clelandella clelandi* (Wood)
> *Trochus millegranus* Philippi (J.) (F. & H.)

Dredged, 2–150 fathoms, on muddy gravel and hard ground, off all coasts except SE England. Locally common. Scandinavia to Mediterranean.

Reproduction unknown.

*Cantharidus exasperatus* (Pennant).

> *Calliostoma exasperatum* (Pennant)
> *Cantharus (Jujubinus) exasperatus* (Pennant)
> *Jujubinus exasperatus* (Pennant)
> *Trochus exasperatus* Pennant (J.)
> *Trochus exiguus* Pulteney (F. & H.)

Under stones and on tufted algae (e.g. *Dictyopteris, Cystoseira*) on rocky shores, LWST, and dredged to 47 fathoms, SW England. Not common. British Isles to Mediterranean.

Breeds in spring, summer (Roscoff). Spawn attached to *Zostera*. No free-swimming larvae.

*Cantharidus miliaris:* see *C. clelandi*

*Cantharidus montagui* (Wood).

> *Calliostoma montagui* (Wood)
> *Cantharus (Jujubinns) moutagui* (Wood)

*Jujubinus montagui* (Wood)
>    *Trochus montacuti* Wood (J.) (F. & H.)
>    Dredged, 7-100 fathoms, off W coasts, S Ireland; habitat unknown. Occasional.
British Isles to Mediterranean.
>    Reproduction unknown.

*Cantharidus striatus* (L.).
>    *Calliostoma striatum* (L.)
>    *Cantharus (Jujubinus) striatus* (L.)
>    *Jujubinus striatus* (L.)
>    *Trochus striatus* L. (J.) (F. & H.)
>    *Zizyphinus aequistriatus* de Beauchamp
>    *Zizyphinus striatus* (L.)
>    Mainly on *Zostera*, LWST—15 fathoms, SW England, S Ireland. Occasional.
British Isles to Mediterranean.
>    Breeds June–September, maximum August (Roscoff). Spawn attached to weeds
or stones. No free-swimming larvae.

*Cantharus* spp.: see *Cantharidus* spp.

*Capulus ungaricus* (L.). Hungarian cap shell, bonnet limpet.
>    *Capulus hungaricus* (L.) (J.)
>    *Pileopsis hungaricus* (L.) (F. & H.)
>    Dredged, 7-85 fathoms, on rocks and shells, particularly on *Chlamys opercularis*,
off all coasts, Ireland. Not uncommon. Scandinavia to Mediterranean.
>    Breeds January–March (Plymouth). Egg capsules attached, brooded by parent.
Free-swimming echinospira larvae.

*Ceratia proxima*: see *Cingula proxima*

*Cerithiella metula* (Lovén).
>    *Cerithium metula* Lovén (J.) (F. & H.)
>    *Cerithium nitidum* McAndrew & Forbes
>    *Lovenella metula* (Lovén)
>    *Newtoniella metula* (Lovén)
>    Dredged, 45-125 fathoms, on gravelly sand with mud, off Shetland. Rare. Boreal.
>    Reproduction unknown.

*Cerithiopsis acicula*: see *C. tubercularis*

*Cerithiopsis barleei* Jeffreys. (J.)
>    Dredged, on *Suberites domuncula* (=*Ficulina ficus*), from shallow water, SW
England, SW Ireland. Not uncommon. Southern Europe.
>    Breeds spring, summer, autumn (Plymouth). Egg capsules attached to *Suberites
domuncula*. Free-swimming veligers common in plankton, spring–autumn (Plymouth).

*Cerithiopsis clarki* Forbes & Hanley. (F. & H.)
>    Based on shells taken at Exmouth, Torbay and Scilly Is. Presumably with habits
of *C. tubercularis*.

*Cerithiopsis costulata*: see *Eumetula arctica*

*Cerithiopsis jeffreysi* Watson.
>    *Cerithiopsis pulchella* Jeffreys. (J.)
>    Dredged, shallow water (30 fathoms), among sponges, SW England. Rare.
Southern Europe.
>    Reproduction unknown.

*Cerithiopsis metaxae* (Chiaje). (J.)

Dredged off Cornwall, Shetland; habitat unknown. Very rare. Southern Europe. Reproduction unknown.

*Cerithiopsis pulchella:* see *C. jeffreysi*

*Cerithiopsis tubercularis* (Montagu). (J.). Horn shell.

*Cerithiopsis acicula* Brusina

*Cerithiopsis tuberculare* (Montagu). (F. & H.)

Under stones on rocky beaches, LW—55 fathoms, usually associated with *Hymeniacidon sanguinea*, W coasts, Ireland. Occasional. Scandinavia to Mediterranean, Black Sea.

Breeds spring, summer (Plymouth). Egg capsules laid in holes on *Hymeniacidon*. Free-swimming veligers common in inshore and offshore plankton, spring, summer (Plymouth).

*Cerithium adversum:* see *Triphora perversa*

*Cerithium metula:* see *Cerithiella metula*

*Cerithium nitidum:* see *Cerithiella metula*

*Cerithium perversum:* see *Triphora perversa*

*Cerithium reticulatum:* see *Bittium reticulatum*

*Chauvetia brunnea* (Donovan).

*Chauvetia minima* (Montagu)

*Donovania minima* (Montagu)

*Lachesis minima* (Montagu) (J.) (F. & H.)

*Syntagma brunneum* (Donovan)

Under stones on boulder beaches, among sea weeds in rock pools, LWST, and dredged to 20 fathoms, SW England. Occasional. British Isles to Mediterranean.

Breeding unknown. Egg capsules attached. No free-swimming larvae?

*Chemnitzia acicula:* see *Eulimella laevis*

*Chemnitzia clathrata:* see *Chrysallida clathrata*

*Chemnitzia elegantissima:* see *Turbonilla elegantissima*

*Chemnitzia elegantissima* var. *pusilla:* see *Turbonilla innovata*

*Chemnitzia eximia:* see *Chrysallida eximia*

*Chemnitzia fenestrata:* see *Turbonilla fenestrata*

*Chemnitzia fulvocincta:* see *Turbonilla fulvocincta*

*Chemnitzia gracilis:* see *Turbonilla delicata*

*Chemnitzia gulsonae:* see *Pherusina gulsonae*

*Chemnitzia indistincta:* see *Chrysallida indistincta*

*Chemnitzia macandrei:* see *Eulimella macandrei*

*Chemnitzia nitidissima:* see *Eulimella nitidissima*

*Chemnitzia pusilla:* see *Turbonilla innovata*

*Chemnitzia rufa:* see *Turbonilla crenata* and *T. fulvocincta*

*Chemnitzia rufescens:* see *Turbonilla rufescens*

*Chemnitzia scalaris:* see *Turbonilla jeffreysi*

*Chemnitzia simillima:* see *Turbonilla delicata*

*Chemnitzia unica:* see *Graphis albida*

*Chenopus pescarbonis:* see *Aporrhais serresiana*

*Chenopus pespelicani:* see *Aporrhais pespelicani*

*Chrysallida clathrata* (Jeffreys).

*Chemnitzia clathrata* (Jeffreys) (F. & H.)

*Odostomia clathrata* Jeffreys (J.)
*Parthenina clathrata* (Jeffreys)
Recorded from Birterbuy Bay, Co. Galway, 15 fathoms, and St Andrews. Very rare. British Isles to Mediterranean.
Reproduction unknown.

*Chrysallida decussata* (Montagu).
*Odostomia decussata* (Montagu)  (J.) (F. & H.)
*Parthenina decussata* (Montagu)
*Pyrgulina decussata* (Montagu)
Dredged, 7–45 fathoms, on sandy and shelly ground, S and W coasts, Ireland; habitat unknown. Locally common. British Isles.
Reproduction unknown.

*Chrysallida excavata* (Philippi).
*Ividella excavata* (Philippi)
*Ividia excavata* (Philippi)
*Miralda excavata* (Philippi)
*Odostomia excavata* (Philippi) (J.) (F. & H.)
Dredged, 1–25 fathoms, SW England, Clyde Sea Area, Ireland; habitat unknown. Scarce. British Isles to Mediterranean.
Reproduction unknown.

*Chrysallida eximia* (Jeffreys).
*Chemnitzia eximia* (Jeffreys)
*Odostomia eximia* (Jeffreys) (J.)
*Parthenina eximia* (Jeffreys)
*Pyrgulina eximia* (Jeffreys)
*Rissoa eximia* Jeffreys
Dredged, 27–72 fathoms, N Scotland; habitat unknown. Very rare. Norway to British Isles.
Reproduction unknown.

*Chrysallida indistincta* (Montagu).
*Chemnitzia indistincta* (Montagu) (F. & H.)
*Odostomia indistincta* (Montagu) (J.)
*Parthenina indistincta* (Montagu)
*Pyrgulina indistincta* (Montagu)
In rock pools, LWST, and dredged on shelly mud and fine sand to 72 fathoms, on all coasts. Locally not uncommon. Scandinavia to Mediterranean, Black Sea.
Reproduction unknown.

*Chrysallida obtusa* (Brown).
*Chrysallida tenuistriata* Milaschewich
*Odostomia interstincta* (Montagu) (J.) (F. & H.)
*Parthenina interstincta* (Montagu)
*Parthenina obtusa* (Brown)
*Pyrgulina interstincta* (Montagu)
*Pyrgulina obtusa* (Brown)
On rocky beaches, LWST, and dredged to 45 fathoms, on all coasts, Ireland; with oysters. Locally common. N Atlantic, Mediterranean, Black Sea.
Reproduction unknown.

*Chrysallida spiralis* (Montagu).
> *Odostomia spiralis* (Montagu) (J.) (F. & H.)
> *Partidula spiralis* (Montagu)
> *Partulida spiralis* (Montagu)
> *Pyrgulina spiralis* (Montagu)
> *Spiralina spiralis* (Montagu)
> *Spiralinella spiralis* (Montagu)
> On rocky beaches, LWST or below, in association with *Sabellaria*, on all coasts, Ireland. Not uncommon. Scandinavia to Iberia.
> Reproduction unknown.

*Chrysallida tenuistriata*: see *C. obtusa*

*Chrysodomus antiquus*: see *Neptunea antiqua*

*Chrysodomus turtoni*: see *Beringius turtoni*

*Cima minima* (Jeffreys).
> *Odostomia minima* Jeffreys (J.)
> In *Laminaria* holdfasts, LWST or below, on SW and W coasts. Rare. British Isles.
> Reproduction unknown.

*Cincinna piscinalis*: see *Valvata piscinalis*

*Cingula alderi* (Jeffreys).
> *Cingula obtusa* (Cantraine)
> *Parvisetia alderi* (Jeffreys)
> *Pseudosetia alderi* (Jeffreys)
> *Pseudosetia obtusa* (Cantraine)
> *Rissoa obtusa* Cantraine
> *Rissoa soluta* Philippi (J.) (F. & H.)
> *Setia obtusa* (Cantraine)
> Laminarian zone and below, SW England, W and NE Scotland, SW Ireland; habitat unknown. Rare. Norway to Mediterranean.
> Reproduction unknown.

*Cingula cingillus* (Montagu).
> *Cingula trifasciata* (Adams)
> *Rissoa cingillus* (Montagu) (J.) (F. & H.)
> Gregarious under stones and in crevices, especially if silty, MT and above to 4 fathoms, on all coasts; in association with *Jaera, Lumbricillus*. Common. Iceland to Mediterranean.
> Breeds spring (Plymouth). Egg capsules laid in rock crevices. No free-swimming larvae.

*Cingula fulgida*: see *Cingulopsis fulgida*

*Cingula inflata* (Monterosato).
> *Setia inflata* (Monterosato)
> Dredged, 7–10 fathoms, on coarse gravel, Clyde Sea Area. Rare. British Isles to Mediterranean.
> Reproduction unknown.

*Cingula obtusa*: see *C. alderi*

*Cingula proxima* (Forbes & Hanley).
> *Ceratia proxima* (Forbes & Hanley)
> *Hyala proxima* (Forbes & Hanley)
> *Onoba proxima* (Forbes & Hanley)

*Rissoa proxima* Forbes & Hanley (J.) (F. & H.)

Dredged, 6–90 fathoms, on mud with shells and muddy sand, on SW and W coasts, Ireland. Very rare. Iceland to W Mediterranean.

Reproduction unknown.

*Cingula semicostata* (Montagu).

   *Onoba candida* (Brown)

   *Onoba striata* (Adams)

   *Rissoa striata* (Adams) (J.) (F. & H.)

Gregarious under stones rich in diatoms, among brown and green algae in coralline pools and in crevices especially where silty, on all rocky shores, LW and above—25 fathoms, on all coasts. Abundant. Iceland to Mediterranean.

Breeds March–May (Plymouth). Egg capsules attached to sand grains. No free-swimming larvae.

*Cingula semistriata* (Montagu).

   *Rissoa semistriata* (Montagu) (J.) (F. & H.)

Gregarious under stones and amongst fucoids, in crevices especially where silty, LW or above—55 fathoms, on all coasts. Common in S, rare N. Norway to Mediterranean.

Breeds spring–autumn (Plymouth). Egg capsules attached to weeds or other substratum. Free-swimming veligers in plankton (Plymouth).

*Cingula trifasciata:* see *C. cingillus*

*Cingula vitrea* (Montagu).

   *Hyala vitrea* (Montagu)

   *Onoba vitrea* (Montagu)

   *Rissoa vitrea* (Montagu) (J.) (F. & H.)

Dredged, 6–65 fathoms, on mud, S and W coasts, S and W Ireland. Rare and local. W European coasts (except N Sea and Channel), Mediterranean.

Reproduction unknown, but free-swimming larvae seem to occur.

*Cingulopsis fulgida* (Adams).

   *Cingula fulgida* (Adams)

   *Parvisetia fulgida* (Adams)

   *Rissoa fulgida* (Adams) (J.) (F. & H.)

   *Setia fulgida* (Adams)

On algae (*Dictyota dichotoma*) and in coralline pools below MT, on rocky shores, SW England, W Scotland, SW Ireland. Common in S. British Isles to Mediterranean.

Breeds April (Plymouth). Egg capsules attached to corallines. No free-swimming larvae.

*Cioniscus albidus:* see *Graphis albida*

*Cioniscus unicus:* see *Graphis albida*

*Circulus striatus* (Philippi).

   *Delphinula duminyi* Requien

   *Trochus duminyi* (Requien) (J.)

Recorded only from Bundoran, Mayo and Antrim. British Isles to Mediterranean.

Reproduction unknown.

*Cirillia linearis:* see *Philbertia linearis*

*Cirsotrema commutatum* (Monterosato).

   *Gyroscala commutata* (Monterosato)

*Scala pseudoscalaris* (Brocchi)
*Scalaria pseudoscalaris* (Brocchi) (J.)
Habitat unknown; SW England. Very rare. British Isles to Mediterranean.
Reproduction unknown.
*Clathrus clathratulus* (Kanmacher).
  *Epitonium clathratulum* (Kanmacher)
  *Scala clathratula* (Kanmacher)
  *Scalaria clathratula* (Kanmacher) (J.) (F. & H.)
In rock crevices and between stones, LW—25 fathoms, S and W coasts. Scarce.
British Isles to Mediterranean.
Reproduction unknown.
*Clathrus clathrus* (L.). Wentletrap.
  *Epitonium commune* (Lamarck)
  *Scala clathrus* (L.)
  *Scala communis* (Lamarck)
  *Scalaria communis* Lamarck (J.) (F. & H.)
Dredged, LWST—40 fathoms, on mud or sandy mud, on all coasts. Rare in N,
occasional in S, more frequent in spring. Scandinavia to Mediterranean.
Breeds April–July (Roscoff), June–August or later (Plymouth). Egg capsules laid
on mud near green weeds, or on sand. Free-swimming veligers.
*Clathrus trevelyanus* (Leach).
  *Scala trevelyana* (Leach)
  *Scalaria trevelyana* Leach (J.) (F. & H.)
Dredged, 14–100 fathoms, off all coasts on muddy sand. Rare. Norway to
Mediterranean.
Reproduction unknown.
*Clathrus turtonis* (Turton).
  *Scala turtoni* (Turton)
  *Scala turtonis* (Turton)
  *Scalaria tenuicosta* Michaud
  *Scalaria turtonae* (Turton) (J.)
  *Scalaria turtonis* (Turton) (F. & H.)
Dredged, from below LWST—45 fathoms, off S and W coasts, NE England and
E Scotland; habitat unknown but presumably as for *C. clathrus*. Rare. Norway to
Mediterranean.
Reproduction unknown.
*Clathurella anceps:* see *Philbertia teres*
*Clathurella formosa:* see *Philbertia asperrima*
*Clathurella leufroyi:* see *Philbertia leufroyi*
*Clathurella linearis:* see *Philbertia linearis*
*Clathurella purpurea:* see *Philbertia purpurea*
*Clathurella reticulata:* see *Philbertia asperrima*
*Clelandella clelandi:* see *Cantharidus clelandi*
*Columbella haliaeeti:* see *Pyrene haliaeeti*
*Columbella nana:* see *Thesbia nana*
*Colus fenestratus* (Turton).
  *Buccinum fusiforme* Broderip (F. & H.)
  *Fusus fenestratus* Turton (J.)

*Neptunea fusiformis* Broderip
*Sipho fusiformis* (Broderip)
*Tritonofusus fusiformis* (Broderip)
Known only from isolated specimens dredged, 10–50 fathoms, at widely separated places in N Atlantic. Very rare. Boreal.
Reproduction unknown.

*Colus gracilis* (da Costa).
*Fusus gracilis* (da Costa) (J.)
*Fusus islandicus* auctt. nec Chemnitz (F. & H.)
*Neptunea gracilis* (da Costa)
*Sipho gracilis* (da Costa)
*Tritonofusus gracilis* (da Costa)
Dredged, 20–150 fathoms, off Northumbrian and Scottish coasts, rarely further S; habitat unknown. Common, rare in S. Scandinavia to British Isles.
Breeding unknown. Egg capsules attached to stones and corallines. No free-swimming larvae.

*Colus howsei* (Marshall).
*Fusus propinquus* Alder (J.) (F. & H.)
*Neptunea propinqua* (Alder)
*Sipho propinquus* (Alder)
*Siphonorbis howsei* (Marshall)
*Siphonorbis propinquus* (Alder)
*Tritonofusus propinquus* (Alder)
Dredged, 6–30 fathoms, on soft bottoms, off NE England, Scotland. Occasional. Scandinavia to British Isles.
Breeding unknown. Egg capsules attached to empty bivalve shells. No free-swimming larvae.

*Colus islandicus* (Gmelin).
*Fusus islandicus* Chemnitz (J.) (F. & H.)
*Neptunea islandica* (Chemnitz)
*Sipho islandicus* (Chemnitz)
*Tritonofusus islandicus* (Chemnitz)
Only rare specimens from British localities (Shetland). Mainly belongs to infauna of clay bottoms from below LWST—600 fathoms or more, in arctic areas. Rare. Panarctic.
Breeding unknown. Egg capsules attached to stones. No free-swimming larvae.

*Colus jeffreysianus* (Fischer).
*Fusus buccinatus* Lamarck (in error) (J.)
*Sipho jeffreysianus* (Fischer)
*Siphonorbis jeffreysianus* (Fischer)
Dredged, 18 fathoms, on sandy grounds, bryozoan beds, off S and W England, SW Ireland. Occasional. Southern Europe.
Reproduction unknown.

*Comarmondia gracilis:* see *Philbertia gracilis*
*Cremula clavula:* see *Menestho clavula*
*Crepidula fornicata* (L.). Slipper limpet.
Gregarious in chains, and solitary, on stony beaches at LW, and on hard and soft

bottoms to 5 fathoms, E and S coasts of England. Abundant in SE, decreasing W and N. Stands salinities ≮25‰. N America.

Breeds April–October (Essex). Egg capsules attached, brooded by parent. Free-swimming veligers in plankton early summer (Essex).

*Cryptothyra* spp.: see *Lamellaria* spp.

*Cyclostoma achatinum*: see *Viviparus viviparus*

*Cyclostoma elegans*: see *Pomatias elegans*

*Cyclostoma reflexum*: see *Pomatias elegans*

*Cyclostoma viviparum*: see *Viviparus contectus*

*Cyclostrema* spp.: see *Skenea* spp.

*Cypraea europea*: see *Trivia arctica* and *T. monacha*

*Defrancia gracilis*: see *Philbertia gracilis*

*Defrancia leufroyi*: see *Philbertia leufroyi*

*Defrancia linearis*: see *Philbertia linearis*

*Defrancia purpurea*: see *Philbertia purpurea*

*Defrancia reticulata*: see *Philbertia asperrima*

*Defrancia teres*: see *Philbertia teres*

*Delphinoidea* spp.: see *Skenea* spp.

*Delphinula duminyi*: see *Circulus striatus*

*Delphinula nitens*: see *Skenea nitens*

*Diodora apertura* (Montagu). Keyhole limpet.
   *Fissurella graeca* (L.) (J.)
   *Fissurella mamillata* Risso
   *Fissurella reticulata* (da Costa) (F. & H.)
Under stones and rocks, especially where a little silt occurs, on all rocky shores, LWST, and dredged to 50 fathoms, on S and W coasts, Ireland. Not uncommon. Stands salinities ≮21‰. British Isles to Mediterranean, Black Sea.

Breeds December–May (Plymouth). Eggs attached to rocks. No free-swimming larvae.

*Donovania minima*: see *Chauvetia brunnea*

*Ebalina nitidissima*: see *Eulimella nitidissima*

*Emarginula conica* Lamarck.
   *Emarginula rosea* Bell (J.) (F. & H.)
   *Emarginula rubra* Lamarck
Under stones and rocks on rocky shores, LWST, and dredged to 50 fathoms, SW and W coasts. Occasional. British Isles to Mediterranean.

Reproduction unknown.

*Emarginula crassa* Sowerby. (J.) (F. & H.)
   *Emarginula crassalta* Wood
Under stones and rocks on rocky shores, LWST, and dredged to 100 fathoms, W Scotland, Shetland, Ireland. Uncommon. Scandinavia to British Isles.

Reproduction unknown.

*Emarginula reticulata* Sowerby. (F. & H.). Slit limpet.
   *Emarginula fissura* (L.) (J.)
   *Emarginula mülleri* Forbes
Under stones and rocks, on all rocky shores, especially where a little silt occurs; dredged on stones and shells, LWST—90 fathoms, on all coasts. Not uncommon. Scandinavia to Mediterranean.

Reproduction unknown.

*Emarginula rosea:* see *E. conica*
*Emarginula rubra:* see *E. conica*
*Epheria crassior:* see *Lacuna crassior*
*Epheria vincta:* see *Lacuna vincta*
*Epitonium* spp.: see *Clathrus* spp.
*Erato voluta* (Montagu).
     *Erato laevis* (Donovan)
     *Marginella laevis* (Donovan) (J.) (F. & H.)
     *Voluta laevis* Donovan
     Dredged, 1–90 fathoms, on gravelly or sandy bottoms, off all coasts. Scarce, rare in N.  British Isles to Mediterranean.
     Breeding and eggs unknown. Free-swimming echinospira larvae frequent in offshore plankton, spring, summer (Plymouth).
*Eugyrina gigantea :* see *Gyrina gigantea*
*Eulima alba:* see *Balcis alba*
*Eulima anceps:* see *Balcis anceps*
*Eulima bilineata:* see *E. trifasciata*
*Eulima curva:* see *Balcis curva*
*Eulima distorta:* see *Balcis devians*
*Eulima distorta* var. *gracilis:* see *Balcis monterosatoi*
*Eulima glabra* (da Costa).
     *Eulima subulata* (Donovan) (J.) (F. & H.)
     *Leiostraca glabra* (da Costa)
     *Strombiformis glaber* (da Costa)
     Dredged, 5–90 fathoms, S and W coasts, NE England, Ireland. Rare. British Isles to Mediterranean.
     Reproduction unknown.
*Eulima gracilis:* see *Balcis monterosatoi* and *B. devians*
*Eulima incurva:* see *Balcis devians*
*Eulima intermedia:* see *Balcis lubrica*
*Eulima nitida:* see *Balcis lubrica*
*Eulima nitidissima:* see *Eulimella nitidissima*
*Eulima philippii:* see *Balcis devians*
*Eulima philippii* var. *tumidosa:* see *Balcis curva*
*Eulima polita:* see *Balcis alba* and *B. lubrica*
*Eulima stenostoma* Jeffreys. (J.)
     *Haliella stenostoma* (Jeffreys)
     *Strombiformis stenostomus* (Jeffreys)
     Recorded only off Shetlands and N Norway, 70–90 fathoms: habitat unknown.
     Reproduction unknown.
*Eulima subulata:* see *E. glabra*
*Eulima trifasciata* (Adams).
     *Eulima bilineata* (Adams) (J.) (F. & H.)
     *Leiostraca bilineata* (Adams)
     *Strombiformis bilineatus* (Adams)
     Under stones on rocky beaches, and dredged, LWST—80 fathoms, on all coasts, Ireland. Scarce. Scandinavia to W Mediterranean.
     Reproduction unknown.

*Eulimella acicula:* see *E. laevis*
*Eulimella affinis:* see *E. gracilis*
*Eulimella clavula:* see *Menestho clavula*
*Eulimella commutata:* see *E. gracilis* and *E. laevis*
*Eulimella compactilis* Jeffreys.
> *Odostomia compactilis* (Jeffreys)
> *Odostomia scillae* var. *compactilis* Jeffreys (J.)
> Recorded only from the Hebrides, dredged; habitat unknown.
> Reproduction unknown.

*Eulimella gracilis* (Jeffreys).
> *Eulimella affinis* (Philippi) (F. & H.)
> *Eulimella commutata* (Monterosato) var. *ventricosa* (Forbes)
> *Eulimella ventricosa* (Forbes)
> *Odostomia acicula* (Philippi) var. *ventricosa* (Forbes) (J.)
> *Odostomia ventricosa* (Forbes)
> *Parthenia ventricosa* Forbes
> Dredged, 15–80 fathoms, S and W coasts, on fine sandy mud. Rare. Scandinavia to Mediterranean.
> Reproduction unknown.

*Eulimella laevis* (Brown).
> *Chemnitzia acicula* (Philippi)
> *Eulimella acicula* (Philippi) (F. & H.)
> *Eulimella commutata* (Monterosato)
> *Odostomia acicula* (Philippi) (J.)
> Dredged from muddy sand, S and W coasts. Scarce. Scandinavia to Mediterranean, Black Sea.
> Reproduction unknown.

*Eulimella macandrei* (Forbes).
> *Chemnitzia macandrei* (Forbes)
> *Eulimella scillae* (Scacchi) (F. & H.)
> *Odostomia scillae* (Scacchi) (J.)
> Dredged, 18–27 fathoms, on muddy sand, NE England, E and W Scotland. Rare. Scandinavia to Mediterranean.
> Reproduction unknown.

*Eulimella nitidissima* (Montagu).
> *Aclis nitidissima* (Montagu) (F. & H.)
> *Chemnitzia nitidissima* (Montagu)
> *Ebalina nitidissima* (Montagu)
> *Eulima nitidissima* (Montagu)
> *Odostomia nitidissima* (Montagu) (J.)
> Among *Corallina* and *Gigartina* LWST, and dredged to 45 fathoms on fine sand, S and W coasts. Rare. Scandinavia to W Mediterranean.
> Breeds spring–early summer (Plymouth). Egg capsules attached. Free-swimming veligers.

*Eulimella scillae:* see *E. macandrei*
*Eulimella ventricosa:* see *E. gracilis*
*Eumargarita* spp.: see *Margarites* spp.

*Eumetula arctica* (Mörch).
>  *Cerithiopsis costulata* (Möller) (J.)
>  *Laskeya arctica* (Mörch)
>  Dredged, 82–86 fathoms, on fine muddy sand, off Shetland. Very rare. Boreal. Reproduction unknown.

*Evalea* spp.: see *Menestho* spp.

*Fissurella:* see *Diodora*

*Fusus antiquatus:* see *Neptunea antiqua*

*Fusus antiquus:* see *Neptunea antiqua*

*Fusus asperrimus:* see *Philbertia asperrima*

*Fusus berniciensis:* see *Troschelia berniciensis*

*Fusus buccinatus:* see *Colus jeffreysianus*

*Fusus cinereus:* see *Urosalpinx cinerea*

*Fusus fenestratus:* see *Colus fenestratus*

*Fusus gracilis:* see *Colus gracilis*

*Fusus islandicus:* see *Colus gracilis* and *C. islandicus*

*Fusus norvegicus:* see *Volutopsius norvegicus*

*Fusus propinquus:* see *Colus howsei*

*Fusus turtoni:* see *Beringius turtoni*

*Galeodina carinata:* see *Alvania carinata*

*Gibbula cineraria* (L.). Top shell.
>  *Trochus cinerarius* L. (J.) (F. & H.)
>  On weeds and under stones on all weedy, rocky shores, LWNT–LWEST, in high rock pools in N, 30–0% exposure, and extending to 70 fathoms, on all coasts, Ireland. Lower than *G. umbilicalis*. Abundant. Iceland to Mediterranean.
>  Breeds all the year round (Plymouth), spring (Clyde). Eggs planktonic. Free-swimming trochophores occur but are unknown.

*Gibbula lineata:* see *Monodonta lineata*

*Gibbula magus* (L.). Painted top shell.
>  *Trochus magus* (L.) (J.) (F. & H.)
>  On rocks, rough bottoms and on muddy sand at LWEST and dredged from coarse shell sand or gravel down to 40 fathoms, on S and W coasts, Ireland. Fairly common. British Isles to Mediterranean.
>  Breeds spring and autumn (Plymouth), June (Roscoff). Eggs planktonic, common in spring and autumn. Larvae unknown.

*Gibbula obliquata:* see *G. umbilicalis*

*Gibbula tumida* (Montagu).
>  *Trochus tumidus* Montagu (J.) (F. & H.)
>  Dredged, 4–95 fathoms, on muddy and stony ground, off all coasts, Ireland. Occasional, commoner in N. Iceland to Mediterranean.
>  Breeds spring and autumn (Plymouth). Eggs laid in gelatinous masses. No free-swimming larvae.

*Gibbula umbilicalis* (da Costa). Top shell.
>  *Gibbula obliquata* (Montagu)
>  *Gibbula umbilicata* (Montagu)
>  *Trochus obliquatus* Montagu
>  *Trochus umbilicatus* Montagu (J.) (F. & H.)
>  On weeds and under stones on rocky beaches, HWNT–above LWEST, 55–0%

exposure, higher than G. *cineraria*; also dredged to 20 fathoms; on S and W coasts, Ireland. Tolerates salinities ≮10‰. Abundant. British Isles to Iberia.

Breeds throughout the year, maximum in winter (Plymouth); April–June (Roscoff). Eggs planktonic. Larvae unknown.

*Goniostoma membranaceum*: see *Rissoa membranacea*

*Graphis albida* (Adams).
> *Aclis unica* (Montagu) (J.) (F. & H.)
> *Chemnitzia unica* (Montagu)
> *Cioniscus albidus* (Adams)
> *Cioniscus unicus* (Montagu)

In detritus in rock pools and amongst seaweed at LW and dredged—28 fathoms on SW, W and NE coasts. Rare and local. Southern Atlantic coasts of Europe.

Reproduction unknown.

*Gyrina gigantea* (Lamarck).
> *Argobuccinum giganteum* (Lamarck)
> *Eugyrina gigantea* (Lamarck)
> *Ranella gigantea* Lamarck

Dredged 50–100 fathoms off S Ireland. Habitat unknown. Very rare. E Atlantic S of Ireland, Mediterranean.

Reproduction unknown. Free-swimming veligers.

*Gyroscala commutata*: see *Cirsotrema commutatum*

*Haedropleura septangularis* (Montagu).
> *Bela septangularis* (Montagu)
> *Mangelia septangularis* (Montagu) (F. & H.)
> *Pleurotoma ecostata* (da Costa)
> *Pleurotoma septangularis* (Montagu) (J.)

Dredged, 6–40 fathoms off SW and W coasts, Ireland; habitat unknown. Rare. Norway to Mediterranean.

Reproduction unknown.

*Haliella stenostoma*: see *Eulima stenostoma*

*Helcion pellucidum*: see *Patina pellucida*

*Hima* (=*Hinia*) spp.: see *Nassarius* spp.

*Homalogyra atomus*: see *Omalogyra atomus*

*Homalogyra rota*: see *Ammonicera rota*

*Hyala proxima*: see *Cingula proxima*

*Hyala vitrea*: see *Cingula vitrea*

*Hydrobia confusa*: see *Pseudamnicola confusa*

*Hydrobia jenkinsi*: see *Potamopyrgus jenkinsi*

*Hydrobia minuta*: see *H. ventrosa*

*Hydrobia similis*: see *Pseudamnicola confusa*

*Hydrobia stagnalis*: see *H. ventrosa* and *H. ulvae*

*Hydrobia stagnorum*: see *H. ventrosa*

*Hydrobia steini*: see *Bythinella scholtzi*

*Hydrobia ulvae* (Pennant). (J.). Spire shell.
> *Hydrobia stagnalis* (Küster)
> *Paludestrina ulvae* (Pennant)
> *Paludina ulvae* (Pennant)
> *Peringia ulvae* (Pennant)

*Rissoa barleei* Jeffreys

*Rissoa ulvae* (Pennant) (F. & H.)

*Sabanaea* (=*Sabinea*) *ulvae* (Pennant)

On muddy sand and muddy flats especially where wet, in estuaries and salt marshes, often with *Ulva*. Stands salinities $\ll 1\cdot5\%$. Usually above MT but extends to 70 fathoms; on all coasts. Abundant. Scandinavia to Mediterranean, Baltic Sea.

Breeds late spring and summer. Egg capsules attached to shells of the same species. Free-swimming larvae, probably short-lived, or suppressed according to circumstances.

*Hydrobia ventrosa* (Montagu). (J.). Spire shell.

*Hydrobia minuta* Totten

*Hydrobia stagnalis* (Baster)

*Hydrobia stagnorum* (Gmelin)

*Paludestrina stagnalis* (Baster)

*Paludestrina ventrosa* (Montagu)

*Paludina balthica* Nilsson

*Rissoa ventrosa* (Montagu) (F. & H.)

Among algae and on mud in quiet brackish water; not usually in pure sea water. Widely spread over E, S coasts of England, Bristol Channel, Anglesey, Outer Hebrides and N Ireland. Locally abundant. W Europe.

Breeds May–July. Egg capsules attached to stones or shells of the same species. No free-swimming larvae.

*Ianthina exigua* Lamarck. (F. & H.)

*Ianthina bifida* Nuttall

*Ianthina nitida* Adams

Cast on shores of SW England, S Wales and Ireland. Cosmopolitan, in warm seas. Egg capsules attached to float.

*Ianthina janthina* (L.). Violet snail.

*Ianthina bicolor* Menke

*Ianthina bicolor* Monterosato

*Ianthina britannica* Forbes & Hanley

*Ianthina communis* Lamarck (F. & H.)

*Ianthina fragilis* Lamarck

*Ianthina planispirata* Adams & Reeve

*Ianthina rotundata* Leach (J.)

*Ianthina trochoidea* Reeve

*Ianthina vulgaris* Gray

Cast on shores of SW England, S Wales and Ireland. Cosmopolitan, in warm seas. Viviparous, with free-swimming veligers.

*Ianthina pallida* Thompson. (F. & H.)

*Ianthina pallida* var. *minor* Monterosato

*Ianthina striolata* Adams & Reeve

Cast on shores of SW England, S Wales and Ireland. Cosmopolitan, in warm seas. Egg capsules attached to float. No free-swimming larvae.

*Ividella excavata*: see *Chrysallida excavata*

*Ividia excavata*: see *Chrysallida excavata*

*Jeffreysia* spp.: see *Rissoella* spp.

*Jeffreysina* spp.: see *Rissoella* spp.

*Jordaniella nivosa:* see *Odostomia nivosa*

*Jordaniella truncatula:* see *Odostomia truncatula*

*Jordanula nivosa:* see *Odostomia nivosa*

*Jordanula truncatula:* see *Odostomia truncatula*

*Jujubinus* spp.: see *Cantharidus* spp.

*Lachesis minima:* see *Chauvetia brunnea*

*Lacuna crassior* (Montagu). (J.) (F. & H.). Chink shell.
>    *Epheria crassior* (Montagu)
>    *Lacuna glacialis* Möller
>    Among stones and old shells in muddy sand, LW–50 fathoms, on all coasts. Nowhere common, but very rare in S. Greenland to N France.
>    Reproduction unknown.

*Lacuna divaricata:* see *L. vincta*

*Lacuna pallidula* (da Costa). (J.) (F. & H.). Chink shell.
>    *Lacuna patula* (Thorpe)
>    *Lacuna retusa* Brown
>    *Nerita pallidula* da Costa
>    On *Laminaria* and other fucoids and on *Fucus*-covered rocks, LW–40 fathoms, on all coasts, Ireland. Occasional, seasonally plentiful. N Atlantic.
>    Breeds late winter to summer. Spawn laid on fucoids. No free-swimming larvae.

*Lacuna parva* (da Costa). Chink shell.
>    *Lacuna puteolus* (Turton) (J.) (F. & H.)
>    On weeds, especially *Chondrus* and *Nitophyllum*, LWST, SW and W England, Scotland, Ireland. Occasional, seasonally plentiful. Scandinavia to Iberia.
>    Reproduction unknown.

*Lacuna retusa:* see *L. pallidula*

*Lacuna vincta* (Montagu). (F. & H.). Chink shell.
>    *Epheria vincta* (Montagu)
>    *Lacuna divaricata* (Fabricius) (J.)
>    On rocks covered with weed, especially *Fucus, Ceramium, Polysiphonia, Chordaria* and *Zostera,* LW–21 fathoms, on all coasts, Ireland. Occasional. Endures salinities ≮20‰. Boreal, N Atlantic.
>    Breeds January to early summer (Plymouth). Spawn laid on *Fucus, Laminaria* and *Zostera.* Veligers common in the plankton.

*Lamellaria latens* (Müller).
>    *Cryptothyra latens* (Müller)
>    *Lamellaria perspicua* (L.) (male) (J.)
>    *Lamellaria tentaculata* Montagu (F. & H.)
>    *Marsenia complanata* Leach
>    LW and dredged with *Alcyonium,* to 90 fathoms, on all coasts, Ireland. Occasional. Scandinavia to Mediterranean.
>    Breeding and spawn unknown. Echinospira larvae common in offshore plankton (Plymouth).

*Lamellaria perspicua* (L.). (J.)
>    *Cryptothyra perspicua* (L.)
>    *Lamellaria tentaculata* Montagu (F. & H.)
>    *Marsenia perspicua* (L.)

Under loose stones, especially where compound ascidians abound, LWST–90 fathoms, on all coasts, Ireland. Not uncommon. Throughout Northern Hemisphere.

Breeds all the year round, maximal spring and summer. Egg capsules sunk in test of compound ascidians, especially didemnids; echinospira larvae common in plankton (Plymouth).

*Laskeya arctica:* see *Eumetula arctica*

*Leiostraca bilineata:* see *Eulima trifasciata*

*Leiostraca glabra:* see *Eulima glabra*

*Lepeta caeca* (Müller). (J.)

Dredged, 18–90 fathoms, on sandy bottoms, W Scotland. Very rare. Panarctic.

Reproduction unknown, but probably no free-swimming larvae occur.

*Lepeta fulva* (Müller).

*Pilidium fulvum* (Müller) (F. & H.)

*Scutellina fulva* (Müller)

*Tectura fulva* (Müller) (J.)

Dredged, 10–80 fathoms, on stony ground, off W and N Scotland, Ireland. Scarce. Scandinavia to France.

Reproduction unknown.

*Leufroyia leufroyi:* see *Philbertia leufroyi*

*Liomesus ovum* (Turton).

*Buccinopsis dalei* (Sowerby) (J.)

*Buccinum dalei* Sowerby (F. & H.)

*Buccinum ovum* Turton *non* Middendorff

Dredged, 40–100 fathoms, on sand and mud, N Sea and SW Ireland. Very rare. Boreal.

Breeding and larvae unknown. Egg capsules fastened to maternal shell (Jeffreys, 1867).

*Liostomia clavula:* see *Menestho clavula*

*Littorina aestuarii:* see *L. littoralis*

*Littorina fabalis:* see *L. littoralis*

*Littorina groenlandica:* see *L. saxatilis*

*Littorina jugosa:* see *L. saxatilis*

*Littorina littoralis* (L.). (F. & H.). Flat winkle or periwinkle.

*Littorina aestuarii* Jeffreys (J.)

*Littorina fabalis* (Turton) (F. & H.)

*Littorina obtusata* (L.) (J.)

*Littorina obtusata* var. *littoralis* (L.)

*Littorina palliata* (Say) (F. & H.)

On fucoids, mainly *Ascophyllum nodosum* and *Fucus vesiculosus*, and in pools, on rocky and stony shores, HWNT—above LWST, 65–<5% exposure, lower than *L. saxatilis* and along with *L. littorea*, also dredged to 40 fathoms; on all coasts, Ireland. Abundant. Endures salinities <10‰. Iceland to Mediterranean.

Breeds March–October. Spawn attached to weeds, usually *Fucus serratus*. No free-swimming larvae.

*Littorina littorea* (L.). (J.) (F. & H.). Common or edible winkle or periwinkle.

*Littorina ustulata* (Lamarck)

On rocks, among stones and weeds, from HWNT–above LWEST, 65–<5% exposure, commonly lower than *L. saxatilis* and along with *L. littoralis* but extends lower; mainly on rocky shores, but occasionally on wet muddy sand, also dredged to 35 fathoms, on all coasts. Abundant. Endures salinities $<$10‰. N Atlantic.

Breeds November–May, mainly February–March (Plymouth), March (Port Erin), January–July (Millport). Egg capsules planktonic. Free-swimming veligers common in plankton, spring (Plymouth).

*Littorina neritoides* (L.). (J.) (F. & H.). Small winkle or periwinkle.

> *Littorina petraea* (Montagu)
> *Melarhaphe neritoides* (L.)

In crevices in rocks above high water, occasionally extending below and with *Lichina confinis* and *L. pygmaea*; 4 ft above HWEST to HWST, 100–95% exposure; often in empty barnacle shells; on exposed rocky shores on all coasts, Ireland. Locally common. Scandinavia to Mediterranean, Black Sea.

Breeds winter (Plymouth). Egg capsules planktonic. Free-swimming veligers in plankton.

*Littorina nigrolineata*: see *L. saxatilis*
*Littorina obtusata*: see *L. littoralis*
*Littorina palliata*: see *L. littoralis*
*Littorina patula*: see *L. saxatilis*
*Littorina petraea*: see *L. neritoides*
*Littorina rudis*: see *L. saxatilis*
*Littorina saxatilis* (Olivi). (F. & H.). Rough winkle or periwinkle.

> *Littorina groenlandica* Menke
> *Littorina jugosa* (Montagu) (=*L. s. tenebrosa*)
> *Littorina nigrolineata* Gray
> *Littorina patula* Thorpe (F. & H.) (=*L. s. patula*)
> *Littorina rudis* (Maton) (J.) (F. & H.)
> *Littorina saxatilis* Johnston (F. & H.) (=*L. s. saxatilis*)
> *Littorina similis* Jeffreys (J.)
> *Littorina sulcata* Leach (J.)
> *Littorina tenebrosa* (Montagu) (F. & H.) (=*L. s. tenebrosa*)

On rocks near high water, from 3 ft above HWEST to MTL, 100–50% exposure, above *L. littoralis* and *L. littorea*, on all rocky shores on all coasts, Ireland. Abundant. N Atlantic.

Breeds throughout the year, perhaps interrupted June to mid-August (Whitstable), and also December to March (Millport). Viviparous. No free-swimming larvae.

*Littorina similis*: see *L. saxatilis*
*Littorina sulcata*: see *L. saxatilis*
*Littorina tenebrosa*: see *L. saxatilis*
*Littorina ustulata*: see *L. littorea*
*Lora rufa* (Montagu).

> *Bela rufa* (Montagu)
> *Mangelia rufa* (Montagu) (F. & H.)
> *Pleurotoma rufa* (Montagu) (J.)

Dredged, LWST–20 fathoms, on sandy bottoms, off all coasts, Ireland. Rare, especially in N. Scandinavia to France.

Reproduction unknown.

*Lora trevelliana* (Turton).

> *Bela trevelyana* (Turton)

*Lora trevelyana* (Turton)
> *Mangelia trevelliana* (Turton) (F. & H.)
> *Pleurotoma trevelyana* (Turton) (J.)

Dredged, 3–75 fathoms, on muddy sand and in *Macoma* communities on clay bottoms, off NE England, Scotland. Rare and local. Panarctic.

Breeding unknown. Egg capsules attached. Free-swimming veligers in plankton; suppressed in Arctic.

*Lora turricula* (Montagu).
> *Bela turricola* (Montagu)
> *Bela turricula* (Montagu)
> *Mangelia turricula* (Montagu) (F. & H.)
> *Pleurotoma turricula* (Montagu) (J.)

Dredged, 10–150 fathoms, on sandy bottoms, off all coasts except S and SW England. Rare. Boreal.

Breeds early summer (Clyde). Egg capsules attached to shells, etc. Free-swimming veligers in plankton.

*Lovenella metula:* see *Cerithiella metula*

*Lunatia* spp.: see *Natica* spp.

*Mangelia attenuata* (Montagu). (F. & H.)
> *Mangilia attenuata* (Montagu)
> *Pleurotoma attenuata* (Montagu) (J.)

Dredged, 7–30 fathoms, on muddy gravel, muddy sand and mud, off S and W coasts, Ireland. Rare. Scandinavia to Mediterranean.

Reproduction unknown.

*Mangelia brachystoma* (Philippi). (F. & H.)
> *Bela brachystoma* (Philippi)
> *Mangilia brachystoma* (Philippi)
> *Pleurotoma brachystoma* (Philippi) (J.)
> *Pleurotoma brachystomum* (Philippi)

Dredged, 10–60 fathoms, on mud and muddy gravel and sand, off S and W coasts, NE England, E Scotland, Ireland. Scarce. Scandinavia to Mediterranean.

Breeding and egg capsules unknown. Free-swimming veligers in plankton.

*Mangelia coarctata* (Forbes).
> *Bela coarctata* (Forbes)
> *Bela costata* (Donovan)
> *Mangelia costata* (Donovan) (F. & H.)
> *Philbertia costata* (Donovan)
> *Pleurotoma coarctata* (Forbes)
> *Pleurotoma costata* (Donovan) (J.)

Dredged, 5–50 fathoms, on muddy sand, sand or sandy gravel, off all coasts, Ireland. Locally common. Scandinavia to Mediterranean.

Reproduction unknown.

*Mangelia costata:* see *M. coarctata*

*Mangelia costulata* (Risso).
> *Bela costulata* (Risso)
> *Bela striolata* (Scacchi)
> *Mangelia striolata* (Scacchi) (F. & H.)
> *Pleurotoma costulata* (Risso)

*Pleurotoma striolata* (Scacchi) (J.)

Dredged, 10–20 fathoms, off S and W coasts; habitat unknown. Rare. Scandinavia to Mediterranean.

Reproduction unknown.

*Mangelia elongata:* see *M. nebula*

*Mangelia gracilis:* see *Philbertia gracilis*

*Mangelia lactea:* see *M. nebula*

*Mangelia laevigata:* see *M. nebula*

*Mangelia leufroyi:* see *Philbertia leufroyi*

*Mangelia linearis:* see *Philbertia linearis*

*Mangelia nana:* see *Thesbia nana*

*Mangelia nebula* (Montagu). (F. & H.)

    *Bela nebula* (Montagu)

    *Mangelia elongata* (Jeffreys)

    *Mangelia lactea* Reeve

    *Mangelia laevigata* (Philippi)

    *Mangelia vittata* Hinds

    *Pleurotoma nebula* (Montagu) (J.)

Dredged, LWST–50 fathoms, on muddy gravel and sand, off all coasts except N Scotland. Rare. Scandinavia to Mediterranean.

Breeds summer (Plymouth). Egg capsules attached. Free-swimming veligers common in offshore and inshore plankton, summer (Plymouth).

*Mangelia nebula* var. *laevigata:* see *M. powisiana*

*Mangelia powisiana* (Dautzenberg).

    *Bela powisiana* (Dautzenberg)

    *Mangelia nebula* var. *laevigata* (Philippi) (F. & H.)

    *Pleurotoma laevigata* (Philippi) (J.)

In sand between tide marks, also dredged, 5–50 fathoms, on muddy gravel, SW England, Clyde. Locally common. Southern Europe.

Reproduction unknown.

*Mangelia purpurea:* see *Philbertia purpurea*

*Mangelia rufa:* see *Lora rufa*

*Mangelia septangularis:* see *Haedropleura septangularis*

*Mangelia striolata:* see *M. costulata*

*Mangelia teres:* see *Philbertia teres*

*Mangelia trevelliana:* see *Lora trevelliana*

*Mangelia turricula:* see *Lora turricula*

*Mangelia vittata:* see *M. nebula*

*Mangilia* spp.: = *Mangelia* spp.

*Manzonia costata:* see *Alvania crassa*

*Manzonia crassa:* see *Alvania crassa*

*Manzonia zetlandica:* see *Alvania zetlandica*

*Margarita* spp.: see *Margarites* spp.

*Margarites groenlandicus* (Gmelin).

    *Eumargarita groenlandica* (Gmelin)

    *Margarita groenlandica* (Gmelin)

    *Trochus groenlandicus* Gmelin (J.)

    *Trochus undulatus* Sowerby (F. & H.)

In *Laminaria* holdfasts and also in *Desmarestia* and *Fucus* epifauna, LWST-40 fathoms, off W and N Scotland, one record S Devon. Not uncommon, local. Panarctic.

Breeding unknown. Spawn attached to algae. No free-swimming larvae.

*Margarites helicinus* (Fabricius). Pearly top shell.
  *Eumargarita helicina* (Fabricius)
  *Margarita helicina* (Fabricius)
  *Trochus helicinus* Fabricius (J.) (F. & H.)
  *Trochus margaritus* Gray

Amongst weed and under loose stones in lower littoral and laminarian zones, on coasts N of the Humber and the Bristol Channel, N Ireland. Common. Panarctic.

Breeds spring (Cullercoats and Isle of Man). Spawn fixed to weeds and stones. No free-swimming larvae.

*Margarites olivaceus* (Brown).
  *Margarita olivacea* (Brown)

Dredged, 1-60 fathoms, on stones with weed on clay bottoms, off N Scotland and Hebrides. Rare. Panarctic.

Reproduction unknown.

*Marginella laevis:* see *Erato voluta*

*Marsenia complanata:* see *Lamellaria latens*

*Marsenia perspicua:* see *Lamellaria perspicua*

*Marstoniopsis steini:* see *Bythinella scholtzi*

*Melanella* spp.: see *Balcis* spp.

*Melarhaphe neritoides:* see *Littorina neritoides*

*Menestho clavula* (Lovén).
  *Cremula clavula* (Lovén)
  *Eulimella clavula* (Lovén) (F. & H.)
  *Liostomia clavula* (Lovén)
  *Odostomia clavula* (Lovén) (J.)
  *Turbonilla clavula* Loven

Dredged, 6-90 fathoms, on muddy sand, off SW England, W Scotland, SW Ireland; originally collected with *Pennatula*. Very rare, less so in W Scotland and SW Ireland. Scandinavia to British Isles.

Reproduction unknown.

*Menestho diaphana* (Jeffreys).
  *Auriculina diaphana* (Jeffreys)
  *Evalea diaphana* (Jeffreys)
  *Odostomia diaphana* Jeffreys (J.)
  *Ondina diaphana* (Jeffreys)

Dredged in sandy mud, 3-90 fathoms, off S and W coasts, NE Scotland; habitat unknown. Local, rare. British Isles.

Reproduction unknown.

*Menestho divisa* (Adams).
  *Auriculina divisa* (Adams)
  *Evalea divisa* (Adams)
  *Odostomia insculpta* (Montagu) (J.) (F. & H.)
  *Ondina divisa* (Adams)

In seaweeds at LWST and dredged to 90 fathoms, off all coasts, Ireland; habitat unknown. Rare. Scandinavia to British Isles.

Reproduction unknown.

*Menestho dolioliformis* (Jeffreys).
> *Noemia dolioliformis* (Jeffreys)
> *Noemiamea dolioliformis* (Jeffreys)
> *Oda dolioliformis* (Jeffreys)
> *Odostomia dolioliformis* Jeffreys (J.) (F. & H.)

Between tide marks on small weeds in rock pools, SW and W coasts, NE Scotland. Rare. British Isles to Mediterranean.

Reproduction unknown.

*Menestho obliqua* (Alder).
> *Evalea obliqua* (Alder)
> *Odostomia obliqua* Alder (J.) (F. & H.)
> *Ondina obliqua* (Alder)

Dredged on fine sand, down to 20 fathoms, SW and W coasts, Northumberland; habitat unknown. Very rare. S Sweden to N France.

Reproduction unknown.

*Menestho warreni* (Thompson).
> *Odostomia obliqua* Alder var. *warreni* (Thompson) (J.)
> *Odostomia warreni* (Thompson) (F. & H.)

From rock pools, LWST, widely diffused on S and W coasts, Ireland. Not uncommon. British Isles to Mediterranean.

Reproduction unknown.

*Miralda excavata:* see *Chrysallida excavata*

*Monodonta lineata* (da Costa). Top shell.
> *Gibbula lineata* (da Costa)
> *Osilinus lineatus* (da Costa)
> *Trochocochlea lineata* (da Costa)
> *Trochus crassus* Pulteney
> *Trochus lineatus* (da Costa) (J.) (F. & H.)

On rocks and stones just below HWNT, 60–50% exposure, S and W coast of England and Wales between Poole and the Mersey, Ireland except Antrim. Very local but common where found. British Isles to Iberia.

Breeds spring (Plymouth). Eggs planktonic. Free-swimming larvae.

*Murex:* see *Ocenebra*

*Nassa* spp.: see *Nassarius* spp.

*Nassarius incrassatus* (Ström). Dog whelk.
> *Hima incrassata* (Ström)
> *Nassa ambigua* (Pulteney)
> *Nassa incrassata* (Ström) (J.) (F. & H.)

Under stones and in crevices on rocky shores, especially where silt occurs, LW, dredged, on shells and stones, to 50 fathoms, on all coasts, Ireland. Common. Iceland–Mediterranean.

Breeds spring and summer (Plymouth). Egg capsules attached to weeds, hydroids, Bryozoa, etc. Free-swimming veligers common in inshore plankton, spring and summer (Plymouth).

23

*Nassarius pygmaeus* (Lamarck). Dog whelk.
    *Hima pygmaea* (Lamarck)
    *Nassa pygmaea* (Lamarck) (J.) (F. & H.)
    *Nassa varicosa* (Turton)
    Dredged, 2–60 fathoms, on sandy bottoms, off SW England, Clyde sea area, Ireland. Rather rare. Scandinavia to Mediterranean.
    Breeding unknown. Egg capsules attached to shells at 3–4 fathoms. Free-swimming veligers.

*Nassarius reticulatus* (L.). Dog whelk.
    *Arcularia reticulata* (L.)
    *Hima reticulata* (L.)
    *Hinia reticulata* (L.)
    *Nassa nitida* Jeffreys (J.)
    *Nassa reticulata* (L.) (J.) (F. & H.)
    In silted places on rocky shores where there is decaying organic matter; often just under the surface of the sand; from LW–20 fathoms, on all coasts, Ireland. In estuaries surviving in salinities $>10‰$. Common. Eastern N Atlantic S of Trondhjem, Mediterranean, Black Sea.
    Breeds spring, summer (Plymouth, Clyde). Egg capsules in clusters on rock or other firm substratum, e.g. weed, shells. Free-swimming velgiers very common in inshore plankton, spring and summer (Plymouth).

*Natica alderi* Forbes. (J.). Necklace shell.
    *Lunatia alderi* (Forbes)
    *Natica intermedia* Philippi
    *Natica nitida* (Donovan) (F. & H.)
    *Natica poliana* Chiaje
    *Natica pulchella* Risso
    *Polinices nitida* (Donovan)
    On sand and gravel, LWST–90 fathoms, on all coasts, Ireland. Not uncommon locally. Scandinavia to Mediterranean.
    Breeds spring and early summer. Egg masses free on sand. Free-swimming veligers common in plankton.

*Natica catena* (da Costa). (J.). Necklace shell.
    *Lunatia catena* (da Costa)
    *Natica monilifera* Lamarck (F. & H.)
    *Polinices* (=*Polynices*) *catena* (da Costa)
    From large sandy bays, LWST–104 fathoms, on all coasts, Ireland. Local, but not uncommon. Scandinavia to W Mediterranean.
    Breeds spring and early summer. Egg collar free on sand. Free-swimming veligers probably suppressed.

*Natica fusca* Blainville.
    *Lunatia fusca* (Blainville)
    *Lunatia sordida* (Philippi)
    *Natica sordida* Philippi (J.) (F. & H.)
    Dredged, 7–104 fathoms, on muddy sand, off SW England, W Scotland, Ireland. Rare. British Isles to Mediterranean, Black Sea.
    Reproduction unknown.

*Natica groenlandica:* see *N. pallida*

*Natica helicoides:* see *Amauropsis islandica*

*Natica intermedia:* see *N. alderi*

*Natica islandica:* see *Amauropsis islandica*

*Natica monilifera:* see *N. catena*

*Natica montagui* Forbes. (F. & H.)

    *Lunatia montagui* (Forbes)

    *Natica montacuti* Forbes (J.)

    *Polinices montagui* (Forbes)

    Dredged, 8–100 fathoms, on muddy, sandy or gravelly bottoms, off all coasts, Ireland. Common in N, less common S. Scandinavia to Mediterranean.

    Breeding unknown. Egg collars free on bottom. Free-swimming veligers.

*Natica nitida:* see *N. alderi*

*Natica pallida* Broderip & Sowerby.

    *Lunatia pallida* (Broderip & Sowerby)

    *Natica groenlandica* Beck in Möller (J.)

    *Natica pusilla* Gould (F. & H.)

    *Polinices groenlandica* Möller

    Dredged, 40–60 fathoms, on muddy sand and clay bottoms in the *Macoma* community, off NE England and Shetlands. Rare. Panarctic.

    Breeding unknown. Egg collars free on bottom. No free-swimming veligers.

*Natica poliana:* see *N. alderi*

*Natica pulchella:* see *N. alderi*

*Natica pusilla:* see *N. pallida*

*Natica sordida:* see *N. fusca*

*Neptunea antiqua* (L.). Red whelk or buckie.

    *Chrysodomus antiquus* (L.)

    *Fusus antiquatus* (L.)

    *Fusus antiquus* (L.) (J.) (F. & H.)

    *Neptunea despecta* (L.)

    In laminarian zone also dredged, 5–7 fathoms, on all coasts except S and SW England and S Wales. Common. Scandinavia to France.

    Breeds early spring. Egg capsules attached. No free-swimming larvae.

*Neptunea despecta:* see *N. antiqua*

*Neptunea fusiformis:* see *Colus fenestratus*

*Neptunea gracilis:* see *Colus gracilis*

*Neptunea islandica:* see *Colus islandicus*

*Neptunea norvegica:* see *Volutopsius norwegicus*

*Neptunea propinqua:* see *Colus howsei*

*Nerita pallidula:* see *Lacuna pallidula*

*Neritina fluviatilis:* see *Theodoxus fluviatilis*

*Newtoniella metula:* see *Cerithiella metula*

*Noemia dolioliformis:* see *Menestho dolioliformis*

*Noemiamea dolioliformis:* see *Menestho dolioliformis*

*Nucella lapillus* (L.). Dog whelk, dog winkle, horse winkle.

    *Polytropa lapillus* (L.)

    *Purpura lapillus* (L.) (J.) (F. & H.)

    *Thais lapillus* (L.)

On rocky shores, from HWNT to several fathoms, associated with barnacles and mussels, on all coasts, Ireland. In estuaries surviving in salinities ≮10‰. Abundant. N Atlantic.

Breeds throughout the year. Egg capsules in clusters in rock crevices. No free-swimming veligers.

*Ocenebra erinacea* (L.). Sting winkle, rough whelk-tingle.

>*Murex erinaceus* L. (J.) (F. & H.)
>
>*Ocinebra erinacea* (L.)
>
>*Tritonalia erinacea* (L.)

On rocks and under stones in association with small bivalves, avoiding exposure, LW–50 fathoms, on SE, S and W coasts, Ireland. Endures salinities ≮21‰. Common in S, rare N. Scandinavia to Mediterranean.

Breeds late spring and summer (Plymouth), March–May (Roscoff). Egg capsules attached to rock crevices, stones, shells. No free-swimming veligers.

*Oda dolioliformis:* see *Menestho dolioliformis*

*Odostomia acicula:* see *Eulimella laevis*

*Odostomia acicula* var. *ventricosa:* see *Eulimella gracilis*

*Odostomia acuta* Jeffreys. (J.) (F. & H.)

>Dredged, 3–60 fathoms, on SW and W coasts and NE Scotland, Ireland. Rare. Scandinavia to W Mediterranean.
>
>Reproduction unknown.

*Odostomia albella* (Lovén). (J.)

>*Brachystomia albella* (Lovén)
>
>*Odostomia rissoides* var. *albella* Alder (F. & H.)
>
>*Turbonilla albella* Lovén
>
>*Zastoma albellum* (Lovén)

Under stones on rocky shores, LWST, on all coasts. Not uncommon, but local. Scandinavia to W Mediterranean.

Reproduction unknown.

*Odostomia clathrata:* see *Chrysallida clathrata*

*Odostomia clavula:* see *Menestho clavula*

*Odostomia compactilis:* see *Eulimella compactilis*

*Odostomia conoidea* (Brocchi). (J.) (F. & H.)

>Dredged, 18–80 fathoms, with *Astropecten irregularis* on mud, SW and W coasts, Ireland. Rare. Scandinavia to Mediterranean.
>
>Reproduction unknown.

*Odostomia conspicua* Alder. (J.) (F. & H.)

>Dredged, 9–75 fathoms, off S and W coasts and NE Scotland, N Ireland. Rare. Scandinavia to Mediterranean.
>
>Breeding unknown.

*Odostomia cylindrica:* see *O. nivosa*

*Odostomia decussata:* see *Chrysallida decussata*

*Odostomia diaphana:* see *Menestho diaphana*

*Odostomia dolioliformis:* see *Menestho dolioliformis*

*Odostomia eulimoides* Hanley. (F. & H.)

>*Brachystomia ambigua* (Maton & Rackett)
>
>*Brachystomia eulimoides* (Hanley)
>
>*Odostomia pallida* (Montagu) (J.)

On ears of *Pecten maximus* and *Chlamys opercularis*, on all coasts, Ireland. Rather common. Scandinavia to Mediterranean.

Breeds late spring and summer (Plymouth). Spawn laid on valves of host. Free-swimming veligers.

*Odostomia excavata:* see *Chrysallida excavata*

*Odostomia eximia:* see *Chrysallida eximia*

*Odostomia fenestrata:* see *Turbonilla fenestrata*

*Odostomia gulsonae:* see *Pherusina gulsonae*

*Odostomia indistincta:* see *Chrysallida indistincta*

*Odostomia insculpta:* see *Menestho divisa*

*Odostomia interstincta:* see *Chrysallida obtusa*

*Odostomia lactea:* see *Turbonilla elegantissima*

*Odostomia lukisi* Jeffreys. (J.)

    *Brachystomia lukisi* (Jeffreys)

With *Pomatoceros* on rocky shores, LW–30 fathoms, on all coasts. Not uncommon locally.

Reproduction unknown.

*Odostomia minima:* see *Cima minima*

*Odostomia nitidissima:* see *Eulimella nitidissima*

*Odostomia nivosa* (Montagu). (J.)

    *Jordaniella nivosa* (Montagu)

    *Jordanula nivosa* (Montagu)

    *Odostomia cylindrica* Forbes & Hanley (F. & H.)

LWST and below, SW and W coasts, E coast north of Yorkshire, Ireland; habitat unknown. Rare. British Isles.

Reproduction unknown.

*Odostomia obliqua:* see *Menestho obliqua*

*Odostomia obliqua* var. *warreni:* see *Menestho warreni*

*Odostomia oblongula* Marshall.

Dredged once, 72 fathoms, in the Minch; habitat unknown.

Reproduction unknown.

*Odostomia pallida:* see *O. eulimoides*

*Odostomia plicata* (Montagu). (J.) (F. & H.)

With *Pomatoceros*, LW–7 fathoms, on all coasts. Scarce. British Isles to Mediterranean.

Breeds summer. Egg capsules attached. Larvae unknown.

*Odostomia pusilla* Philippi.

(Not the animal described by Jeffreys under this name for which see *Turbonilla innovata*.)

Recorded from S and W coasts; muddy sand in shallow water. Scarce.

Reproduction unknown.

*Odostomia rissoides:* see *O. scalaris*

*Odostomia rissoides* var. *albella:* see *O. albella*

*Odostomia rufa:* see *Turbonilla crenata*

*Odostomia rufa* var. *fulvocincta:* see *Turbonilla fulvocincta*

*Odostomia scalaris* Macgillivray.

    *Brachystomia rissoides* (Hanley)

    *Odostomia rissoides* Hanley (J.) (F. & H.)

With *Mytilus edulis*, on all coasts, Ireland. Not uncommon locally. Scandinavia to Mediterranean.

Breeds summer. Spawn attached. Free-swimming veligers at salinities >20‰; no free larvae at salinities ≯16‰.

*Odostomia scalaris* (Philippi): see *Turbonilla jeffreysi*

*Odostomia scalaris* var. *rufescens*: see *Turbonilla rufescens*

*Odostomia scillae*: see *Eulimella macandrei*

*Odostomia scillae* var. *compactilis*: see *Eulimella compactilis*

*Odostomia spiralis*: see *Chrysallida spiralis*

*Odostomia truncatula* Jeffreys. (J.) (F. & H.)
> *Jordaniella truncatula* (Jeffreys)
> *Jordanula truncatula* (Jeffreys)
> Dredged, off SW England, Yorkshire; habitat unknown. Rare. British Isles.
> Reproduction unknown.

*Odostomia turrita* Hanley. (J.)
> *Odostomia unidentata* (Montagu) var.? (F. & H.)
> On weeds and under stones at LWST in S and dredged to 40 fathoms in N, probably on all coasts, Ireland. Not uncommon locally. Denmark to W Mediterranean.
> Breeding, egg capsules, unknown. Free-swimming veligers common in N Sea plankton.

*Odostomia umbilicaris* (Malm). (J.)
> Dredged, 6–60 fathoms, off SW England, W and NE Scotland. (With *Mytilus adriaticus* in Sweden.) Rather scarce. Scandinavia to British Isles.
> Reproduction unknown.

*Odostomia unidentata* (Montagu). (J.) (F. & H.)
> With *Pomatoceros*, LWST–15 fathoms, on all coasts, Ireland. Not uncommon. Scandinavia to France.
> Reproduction unknown.

*Odostomia unidentata* var.?: see *O. turrita*

*Odostomia ventricosa*: see *Eulimella gracilis*

*Odostomia warreni*: see *Menestho warreni*

*Omalogyra atomus* (Philippi).
> *Homalogyra atomus* (Philippi) (J.)
> *Skenea nitidissima* (Adams) (F. & H.)
> In pools, from MTL and below, with *Ulva* and *Zostera*, on rocky shores, on all coasts, Ireland. Common in summer, scarce winter; less common in N. Greenland to Mediterranean.
> Breeds late spring, summer (Plymouth). Egg capsules attached. No free-swimming larvae.

*Omalogyra rota*: see *Ammonicera rota*

*Ondina* spp.: see *Menestho* spp.

*Onoba candida*: see *Cingula semicostata*

*Onoba proxima*: see *Cingula proxima*

*Onoba striata*: see *Cingula semicostata*

*Onoba vitrea*: see *Cingula vitrea*

*Osilinus lineatus*: see *Monodonta lineat*

*Ovula patula*: see *Simnia patula*

*Paludestrina confusa* : see *Pseudamnicola confusa*
*Paludestrina jenkinsi:* see *Potamopyrgus jenkinsi*
*Paludestrina stagnalis:* see *Hydrobia ventrosa*
*Paludestrina taylori:* see *Bythinella scholtzi*
*Paludestrina ulvae:* see *Hydrobia ulvae*
*Paludestrina ventrosa:* see *Hydrobia ventrosa*
*Paludina actalina:* see *Viviparus viviparus*
*Paludina balthica:* see *Hydrobia ventrosa*
*Paludina contecta:* see *Viviparus contectus*
*Paludina listeri:* see *Viviparus contectus*
*Paludina ulvae:* see *Hydrobia ulvae*
*Paludina vivipara:* see *Viviparus viviparus*
*Paludinella littorina* (Chiaje).
    *Assiminea littorina* (Chiaje) (J.)
    *Rissoa littorea* (Chiaje) (F. & H.)
    Under stones, in earth, in caves, with *Truncatella, Leucophytia, Phytia* and *Otina,*
SW England. Not common. British Isles to Mediterranean.
    Reproduction unknown.
*Parthenia ventricosa:* see *Eulimella gracilis*
*Parthenina clathrata:* see *Chrysallida clathrata*
*Parthenina decussata:* see *Chrysallida decussata*
*Parthenina eximia:* see *Chrysallida eximia*
*Parthenina indistincta:* see *Chrysallida indistincta*
*Parthenina interstincta:* see *Chrysallida obtusa*
*Parthenina obtusa:* see *Chrysallida obtusa*
*Partidula spiralis:* see *Chrysallida spiralis*
*Partulida spiralis:* see *Chrysallida spiralis*
*Parvisetia alderi:* see *Cingula alderi*
*Parvisetia fulgida:* see *Cingulopsis fulgida*
*Patella aspera* Lamarck. China limpet.
    *Patella athletica* Bean (F. & H.)
    *Patella depressa* Jeffreys *non* Pennant (J.)
    *Patella vulgata* L. var. *depressa* Jeffreys
    On rocks and in pools and runnels of water on rocky shores from about HWNT–
LWST or just below. Usually in wet places, and rarely on rocks which dry out
wholly; avoids the most sheltered places, extends higher up beach in exposed
situations; on all coasts except between Isle of Wight and Humber, Ireland.
Abundant. British Isles, France.
    Breeds most of the year, maximally summer, resting in January. Eggs planktonic.
Free-swimming trochophores.
*Patella athletica:* see *P. aspera*
*Patella chinensis:* see *Calyptraea chinensis*
*Patella depressa* Jeffreys: see *P. aspera*
*Patella depressa* Pennant: see *P. intermedia*
*Patella intermedia* Jeffreys. Black-footed limpet.
    *Patella depressa* Pennant
    *Patella vulgata* L. (part) (F. & H.)
    *Patella vulgata* var. *intermedia* Jeffreys (J.)

On rocks and in pools on rocky shores, HWNT–LWST. Extends on to bare rock; avoids the most sheltered and polluted places; SW England, and Wales to Anglesey. Common.

Breeds most of the year, maximally summer, not resting in January. Eggs planktonic. Free-swimming trochophores.

*Patella laevis:* see *Patina pellucida*

*Patella pellucida:* see *Patina pellucida*

*Patella tarentina:* see *P. vulgata*

*Patella vulgata* L. (J.) (F. & H.). Common limpet, flither, papshell.

     *Patella tarentina* Lamarck

On rocks and in pools on rocky shores from HWNT–LWST, 90–5% exposure, on pebbles not subjected to too much movement. Extends on to bare rocks at high levels, also into sheltered and polluted waters, withstands salinities $< 3‰$. On all coasts, Ireland. Abundant. Scandinavia to Iberia.

Breeds winter, October–January, resting spring, early summer. Eggs planktonic. Free-swimming trochophores.

*Patella vulgata* var. *depressa* Jeffreys: see *P. aspera*

*Patella vulgata* var. *intermedia* Jeffreys: see *P. intermedia*

*Patelloida:* see *Acmaea*

*Patina laevis:* see *P. pellucida*

*Patina pellucida* (L.). Blue-rayed limpet.

     *Helcion pellucidum* (L.) (J.)

     *Patella laevis* Pennant

     *Patella pellucida* L. (F. & H.)

     *Patina laevis* (Pennant)

Adult animals on fronds, stipes and under stipes of *Laminaria*, preferring *L. saccharina*, *L. digitata* and *Rhodymenia palmata* in that order, young on fucoids or rocks at LW, on all coasts, Ireland. Common. Scandinavia to Mediterranean.

Breeds throughout the year (Plymouth) maximum winter, spring. Eggs planktonic. Free-swimming trochophores in plankton throughout the year (Plymouth); very common August (Kattegat).

*Pelseneeria stylifera* (Turton). Urchin snail.

     *Rosenia stylifera* (Turton)

     *Stilifer stilifer* (Turton)

     *Stilifer stylifer* (Turton)

     *Stilifer turtoni* Broderip (J.)

     *Stylifer turtoni* Broderip (F. & H.)

     *Turtonia stylifera* (Turton)

Among spines of living echinoids (*Echinus esculentus*, *Psammechinus miliaris*) dredged, 20–80 fathoms, probably off all coasts. Rare. W European coasts.

Breeding unknown. Egg capsules attached to echinoids. Free-swimming veligers.

*Peringia ulvae:* see *Hydrobia ulvae*

*Phasianella pullus:* see *Tricolia pullus*

*Pherusina gulsonae* (Clark).

     *Aclis gulsonae* (Clark) (J.)

     *Chemnitzia gulsonae* Clark

     *Odostomia gulsonae* (Clark) (F. & H.)

Dredged, 12–90 fathoms on fine sand, off SW and W coasts, Ireland. Rare. British Isles.

Reproduction unknown.

*Philbertia anceps:* see *P. teres*

*Philbertia asperrima* (Brown).

    *Clathurella formosa* (Reuss)
    *Clathurella reticulata* (Renier)
    *Defrancia reticulata* (Renier) (J.)
    *Fusus asperrimus* Brown (F. & H.)
    *Philbertia reticulata* (Renier)

Dredged, 3–86 fathoms, on hard ground with mud, off S and W coasts, SW Ireland. Rare. Scandinavia to Mediterranean.

Breeding, egg capsules unknown. Free-swimming veligers, uncommon in summer plankton (Plymouth).

*Philbertia costata:* see *Mangelia coarctata*

*Philbertia gracilis* (Montagu).

    *Bellardiella gracilis* (Montagu)
    *Comarmondia gracilis* (Montagu)
    *Defrancia gracilis* (Montagu) (J.)
    *Mangelia gracilis* (Montagu) (F. & H.)

Dredged, 12–35 fathoms, on mud with stones and gravel, off all coasts. Scarce. British Isles to Mediterranean.

Breeds spring, summer (Plymouth). Egg capsules attached. Free-swimming veligers common in outside plankton, summer (Plymouth).

*Philbertia leufroyi* (Michaud).

    *Clathurella leufroyi* (Michaud)
    *Defrancia leufroyi* (Michaud) (J.)
    *Leufroyia leufroyi* (Michaud)
       also as *lefroyi*
    *Mangelia leufroyi* (Michaud) (F. & H.)
    *Pleurotoma leufroyi* Michaud

Under stones on rocky shores, and dredged down to 90 fathoms, on all coasts, Ireland. Scarce. Scandinavia to Mediterranean.

Breeds spring, summer (Plymouth). Egg capsules unknown. Free-swimming veligers.

*Philbertia linearis* (Montagu).

    *Cirillia linearis* (Montagu)
    *Clathurella linearis* (Montagu)
    *Defrancia linearis* (Montagu) (J.)
    *Mangelia linearis* (Montagu) (F. & H.)
    *Pleurotoma linearis* (Montagu)

Under stones and on weeds in rock pools and dredged, 15–80 fathoms, on shelly bottoms, muddy sand and with Bryozoa, on all coasts, Ireland. Not uncommon. Iceland to Mediterranean.

Breeds spring, summer (Plymouth). Egg capsules attached to shells. Free-swimming veligers common in inshore and offshore plankton, spring and summer (Plymouth).

*Philbertia purpurea* (Montagu).

  *Clathurella purpurea* (Montagu)
  *Defrancia purpurea* (Montagu) (J.)
  *Mangelia purpurea* (Montagu) (F. & H.)
  *Pleurotoma purpurea* (Montagu)

Under stones and in rock crevices LWST, and dredged on stony, shelly ground to 70 fathoms, on S and W coasts, Ireland. Scarce, less so in S. Scandinavia to Mediterranean.

Breeding unknown. Egg capsules attached. Free-swimming veligers.

*Philbertia reticulata:* see *P. asperrima*

*Philbertia teres* (Forbes).

  *Clathurella anceps* (Eichwald)
  *Defrancia teres* (Forbes) (J.)
  *Mangelia teres* (Forbes) (F. & H.)
  *Philbertia anceps* (Eichwald)
  *Pleurotoma teres* Forbes
  *Teres anceps* (Eichwald)

Dredged, 15–100 fathoms, on stony, shelly ground, off SW and W coasts, NE England and Scotland, Ireland. Scarce. Scandinavia to Mediterranean.

Reproduction unknown.

*Pileopsis hungaricus:* see *Capulus ungaricus*
*Pilidium fulvum:* see *Lepeta fulva*
*Pleurotoma attenuata:* see *Mangelia attenuata*
*Pleurotoma brachystoma* (=*brachystomum*): see *Mangelia brachystoma*
*Pleurotoma coarctata:* see *Mangelia coarctata*
*Pleurotoma costata:* see *Mangelia coarctata*
*Pleurotoma costulata:* see *Mangelia costulata*
*Pleurotoma ecostata:* see *Haedropleura septangularis*
*Pleurotoma laevigata:* see *Mangelia powisiana*
*Pleurotoma leufroyi:* see *Philbertia leufroyi*
*Pleurotoma linearis:* see *Philbertia linearis*
*Pleurotoma nana:* see *Thesbia nana*
*Pleurotoma nebula:* see *Mangelia nebula*
*Pleurotoma nivalis:* see *Typhlomangelia nivalis*
*Pleurotoma purpurea:* see *Philbertia purpurea*
*Pleurotoma rufa:* see *Lora rufa*
*Pleurotoma septangularis:* see *Haedropleura septangularis*
*Pleurotoma striolata:* see *Mangelia costulata*
*Pleurotoma teres:* see *Philbertia teres*
*Pleurotoma trevelyana:* see *Lora trevelliana*
*Pleurotoma turricula:* see *Lora turricula*
*Polinices* (=*Polynices*) spp.: see *Natica* spp.
*Polytropa lapillus:* see *Nucella lapillus*
*Pomatias elegans* (Müller). Round-mouthed snail.

  *Cyclostoma elegans* (Müller) (J.) (F. & H.)
  *Cyclostoma reflexum* (L.)

Gregarious, among dead leaves and loose earth in hedges, banks and undergrowth, wherever calcium content of soil is >7%. Locally abundant in England and Wales, mainly S and E England. S and W Europe, N Africa and Asia Minor.

Breeds February–August (SE England). Eggs laid in soil. No free-swimming larvae.

*Potamopyrgus jenkinsi* (Smith).
> *Hydrobia jenkinsi* Smith
> *Paludestrina jenkinsi* (Smith)
> *Potamopyrgus crystallinus carinatus* Marshall
> *Rissoa ventricosa* var.

In brackish water and in rivers, streams, canals, ditches or standing water throughout British Isles. Abundant except locally in N Scotland, C Ireland. Europe from Flanders to Riga and N to 61°, W Mediterranean.

Breeds throughout the year, parthenogenetic and viviparous. No free-swimming larvae.

*Propilidium exiguum* (Thompson).
> *Propilidium ancyloide* (Forbes) (J.) (F. & H.)

Dredged, LWEST–100 fathoms, on stones and shells, off Scottish and Irish coasts. Rare. Scandinavia to Mediterranean.

Reproduction unknown.

*Pseudamnicola confusa* (Frauenfeld).
> *Amnicola confusa* Frauenfeld
> *Amnicola similis* (Draparnaud)
> *Hydrobia confusa* (Frauenfeld)
> *Hydrobia similis* (Draparnaud) (J.)
> *Paludestrina confusa* (Frauenfeld)
> *Pseudamnicola similis* (Draparnaud)
> *Rissoa anatina* (Draparnaud) (F. & H.)

In muddy ditches, in brackish or almost fresh water in SE, E England, S Ireland. Locally common. Low countries, S Europe.

Reproduction unknown.

*Pseudamnicola similis:* see *P. confusa*
*Pseudamnicola taylori:* see *Bythinella scholtzi*
*Pseudosetia alderi:* see *Cingula alderi*
*Pseudosetia obtusa:* see *Cingula alderi*
*Puncturella noachina* (L.). (J.) (F. & H.)

Dredged, 14–90 fathoms, on hard and soft bottoms, off the coasts of NE England, and Scotland. Not uncommon. In cold waters of both hemispheres.

Reproduction unknown.

*Purpura:* see *Nucella*
*Pyrene haliaeeti* (Jeffreys).
> *Columbella haliaeeti* Jeffreys (J.)

Dredged, 85–95 fathoms, from gravelly sand off the Shetlands. Rare. Northern.

Reproduction unknown. Related *P. rosacea* has attached capsules and no free-swimming larvae (Thorson, 1944).

*Pyrgisculus* spp.: see *Turbonilla* spp.
*Pyrgiscus rufus:* see *Turbonilla crenata*
*Pyrgiscus scalaris:* see *Turbonilla jeffreysi*
*Pyrgostelis interrupta:* see *Turbonilla fulvocincta*
*Pyrgostelis interrupta* var. *rufa:* see *Turbonilla crenata*

*Pyrgostelis scalaris:* see *Turbonilla jeffreysi*
*Pyrgostelis scalaris* var. *rufescens:* see *Turbonilla rufescens*
*Pyrgulina decussata:* see *Chrysallida decussata*
*Pyrgulina eximia:* see *Chrysallida eximia*
*Pyrgulina fenestrata:* see *Turbonilla fenestrata*
*Pyrgulina indistincta:* see *Chrysallida indistincta*
*Pyrgulina interstincta:* see *Chrysallida obtusa*
*Pyrgulina obtusa:* see *Chrysallida obtusa*
*Pyrgulina spiralis:* see *Chrysallida spiralis*
*Ranella gigantea:* see *Gyrina gigantea*
*Rissoa abyssicola:* see *Alvania abyssicola*
*Rissoa albella* Lovén. (J.)
  *Rissoa inconspicua* var. *tenuis* Alder (F. & H.)
  At LWST–8 fathoms, SW and W coasts, Ireland; habitat unknown. Rare. Scandinavia to Mediterranean.
  Breeding unknown. Spawn attached. Free-swimming veligers.
*Rissoa albella* var. *sarsi:* see *R. sarsi*
*Rissoa albula:* see *R. inconspicua*
*Rissoa anatina:* see *Pseudamnicola confusa*
*Rissoa barleei:* see *Hydrobia ulvae*
*Rissoa beani:* see *Alvania beani*
*Rissoa calathus:* see *Alvania beani*
*Rissoa cancellata:* see *Alvania cancellata*
*Rissoa cimicoides:* see *Alvania cimicoides*
*Rissoa cingillus:* see *Cingula cingillus*
*Rissoa costata:* see *Alvania crassa*
*Rissoa costulata:* see *R. guerini*
*Rissoa crenulata:* see *Alvania cancellata*
*Rissoa eximia:* see *Chrysallida eximia*
*Rissoa fulgida:* see *Cingulopsis fulgida*
*Rissoa guerini* Récluz.
  *Rissoa costulata* Alder (J.) (F. & H.)
  On algae, especially *Codium tomentosum*, on *Zostera* and under stones, at LW on S and W coasts, S Ireland. Fairly common locally. British Isles to Mediterranean.
  Breeds February–April (Plymouth). Egg capsules laid on weeds. Free-swimming veligers common in plankton spring–autumn (Plymouth).
*Rissoa inconspicua* Alder. (J.) (F. & H.)
  *Rissoa albula* (Maton & Rackett)
  On hard bottoms with algae, and on sandy and shell gravel, below LWST to 23 fathoms, off all coasts, Ireland. Common. Scandinavia to Mediterranean.
  Breeds summer (Denmark). Egg capsules on *Zostera*, debris or on shells of other animals of same species. Free-swimming veligers common in plankton, autumn (Plymouth), summer (Denmark).
*Rissoa inconspicua* var. *tenuis:* see *R. albella*
*Rissoa interrupta:* see *R. parva*
*Rissoa jeffreysi:* see *Alvania jeffreysi*
*Rissoa labiosa:* see *R. membranacea*

*Rissoa lilacina* Récluz.

 *Rissoa rufilabrum* (Leach) (F. & H.)

 *Rissoa violacea* Desmarest (J.)

 Amongst algae and *Zostera*, LWST–20 fathoms, on S and W coasts, Ireland. Not uncommon in N, uncommon in S. Scandinavia to Mediterranean.

 Reproduction unknown.

*Rissoa littorea:* see *Paludinella littorina*

*Rissoa membranacea* (Adams). (J.)

 *Goniostoma membranaceum* (Adams)

 *Rissoa labiosa* (Montagu) (F. & H.)

 *Rissoa octona* (L.)

 *Zippora membranacea* (Adams)

 On *Zostera* and other weeds, LWST and below, on all coasts, Ireland. Common in S, less so in N, and not common since onset of *Zostera* disease. Extends into brackish water ≮12‰. Scandinavia to Mediterranean, Black Sea.

 Breeds throughout year (Plymouth). Spawn laid on *Zostera* leaves. Free-swimming veligers among *Zostera* leaves, not in open plankton.

*Rissoa obtusa:* see *Cingula alderi*

*Rissoa octona:* see *R. membranacea*

*Rissoa parva* (da Costa). (J.) (F. & H.)

 *Rissoa interrupta* (Adams)

 *Turboella parva* (da Costa)

 On weeds (especially *Plocamium coccineum* and *Nitophyllum laceratum*), on *Zostera*, under stones, in rock pools and in rock crevices, at MTL and extending to 12 fathoms on all coasts, Ireland. Abundant in summer. Scandinavia to Mediterranean.

 Breeds all the year, maximum spring, summer (Plymouth). Egg capsules attached to weed, especially in rock pools, or shells of other animals of same species. Free-swimming veligers common in plankton, summer–autumn (Plymouth).

*Rissoa proxima:* see *Cingula proxima*

*Rissoa punctura:* see *Alvania punctura*

*Rissoa reticulata:* see *Alvania beani*

*Rissoa rubra:* see *Barleeia rubra*

*Rissoa rufilabrum:* see *R. lilacina*

*Rissoa sarsi* Lovén.

 *Alvania sarsi* Lovén

 *Rissoa albella* var. *sarsi* Lovén (J.)

 Among *Zostera* and weeds between tide-marks on S and W coasts. Scarce. Scandinavia to Mediterranean.

 Breeds October (Plymouth). Egg capsules laid on weeds. Free-swimming veligers common in inshore and offshore plankton, winter and spring (Plymouth).

*Rissoa sculpta:* see *Alvania cimicoides*

*Rissoa semistriata:* see *Cingula semistriata*

*Rissoa soluta:* see *Cingula alderi*

*Rissoa striata:* see *Cingula semicostata*

*Rissoa striatula:* see *Alvania carinata*

*Rissoa subsoluta* var. *abyssicola:* see *Alvania abyssicola*

*Rissoa ulvae:* see *Hydrobia ulvae*

*Rissoa ventricosa* var.: see *Potamopyrgus jenkinsi*

*Rissoa ventrosa:* see *Hydrobia ventrosa*

*Rissoa violacea:* see *R. lilacina*

*Rissoa vitrea:* see *Cingula vitrea*

*Rissoa zetlandica:* see *Alvania zetlandica*

*Rissoella diaphana* (Alder).

     *Jeffreysia diaphana* (Alder) (J.) (F. & H.)

     On weeds in rock pools, below MTL, on all coasts, SW Ireland. Common locally in summer, less abundant in E. British Isles to Mediterranean.

     Breeds spring and summer (Plymouth). Egg capsules attached to green or red algae. No free-swimming larvae.

*Rissoella globularis* (Jeffreys).

     *Jeffreysia globularis* Jeffreys (J.)

     *Jeffreysina globularis* (Jeffreys) (F. & H.)

     On *Laminaria* off Skye and Shetland. Rare.

     Reproduction unknown.

*Rissoella opalina* (Jeffreys).

     *Jeffreysia opalina* (Jeffreys) (J.) (F. & H.)

     *Jeffreysina opalina* (Jeffreys)

     On weeds in rock pools, below MTL, on S and W coasts. Common in summer.

     Breeds spring, summer (Plymouth). Egg capsules attached to green and red algae. No free-swimming larvae.

*Rosenia stylifera:* see *Pelseneeria stylifera*

*Sabanaea* (= *Sabinea*) *ulvae:* see *Hydrobia ulvae*

*Scala* spp.: see *Clathrus* spp.

*Scala pseudoscalaris:* see *Cirsotrema commutatum*

*Scalaria pseudoscalaris:* see *Cirsotrema commutatum*

*Scalaria* spp.: see *Clathrus* spp.

*Scissurella crispata* Fleming. (J.) (F. & H.)

     Dredged, 7–100 fathoms, on stones and from shelly sand and clay bottoms, off W and N coasts of Scotland, W and N Ireland. Very rare. Greenland to Southern Europe.

     Reproduction unknown.

*Scutellina fulva:* see *Lepeta fulva*

*Setia fulgida:* see *Cingulopsis fulgida*

*Setia inflata:* see *Cingula inflata*

*Setia obtusa:* see *Cingula alderi*

*Simnia patula* (Pennant). Poached-egg shell.

     *Ovula patula* (Pennant) (J.) (F. & H.)

     Dredged, mainly with *Alcyonium*, 10–30 fathoms, off SW coasts of England and Ireland. Scarce. British Isles to Mediterranean.

     Breeds February–July (Plymouth). Egg capsules attached to *Alcyonium* and *Eunicella*. Free-swimming veligers common in offshore plankton, spring and summer (Plymouth).

*Sipho fusiformis:* see *Colus fenestratus*

*Sipho gracilis:* see *Colus gracilis*

*Sipho islandicus:* see *Colus islandicus*

*Sipho jeffreysianus:* see *Colus jeffreysianus*

*Sipho propinquus:* see *Colus howsei*

*Siphonorbis howsei:* see *Colus howsei*

*Siphonorbis jeffreysianus:* see *Colus jeffreysianus*

*Siphonorbis propinquus:* see *Colus howsei*

*Skenea cutleriana* Clark. Dolphin shell.

    *Cyclostrema cutlerianum* (Clark) (J.) (F. & H.)

    Dredged, 10–40 fathoms, off S and W coasts; habitat unknown. Rare. Scandinavia to Mediterranean.

    Reproduction unknown.

*Skenea divisa:* see *S. serpuloides*

*Skenea millipunctata* (Friele).

    *Cyclostrema millepunctatum* Friele

    Recorded once from W of Isle of Man; also dredged off Oban; habitat unknown. Very rare. Boreal.

    Reproduction unknown.

*Skenea nitens* (Philippi). Dolphin shell.

    *Cyclostrema nitens* (Philippi) (J.)

    *Delphinoidea nitens* (Philippi)

    *Delphinula nitens* Philippi

    *Trochus pusillus* (Jeffreys) (F. & H.)

    On algae in rock pools below LW and dredged to 55 fathoms on S and W coasts, Ireland. Scarce. British Isles to Mediterranean.

    Reproduction unknown.

*Skenea nitidissima:* see *Omalogyra atomus*

*Skenea planorbis:* see *Skeneopsis planorbis*

*Skenea rota:* see *Ammonicera rota*

*Skenea serpuloides* (Montagu). Dolphin shell.

    *Cyclostrema serpuloides* (Montagu) (J.)

    *Delphinoidea serpuloides* (Montagu)

    *Skenea divisa* (Adams) (F. & H.)

    On weeds on rocky shores, and dredged, LW–25 fathoms, on all coasts, W Ireland. Occasional. Scandinavia to Mediterranean.

    Breeding unknown. Spawn laid on membranous weeds. Larvae unknown.

*Skenea tricarinata:* see *Ammonicera rota*

*Skeneopsis planorbis* (Fabricius).

    *Skenea planorbis* (Fabricius) (J.) (F. & H.)

    On finer weeds below MTL and dredged to 16 fathoms, on all coasts. Abundant in summer. N Atlantic.

    Breeds spring and summer, occasionally earlier and later (Plymouth). Egg capsules attached to filamentous algae. No free-swimming larvae.

*Solariella amabilis* (Jeffreys).

    *Trochus amabilis* Jeffreys (J.)

    Dredged off Shetland, 85–95 fathoms on fine gravelly sand. Rare. N Europe.

    Reproduction unknown: related species appear to have no free larvae.

*Spiralina spiralis:* see *Chrysallida spiralis*

*Spiralinella spiralis:* see *Chrysallida spiralis*

*Stilifer* (= *Stylifer*) *stilifer* (= *stylifer*): see *Pelseneeria stylifera*

*Stilifer* (= *Stylifer*) *turtoni:* see *Pelseneeria stylifera*

*Strombiformis* spp.: see *Eulima*

*Syntagma brunneum:* see *Chauvetia brunnea*
*Tectura fulva:* see *Lepeta fulva*
*Tectura testudinalis:* see *Acmaea tessulata*
*Tectura virginea:* see *Acmaea virginea*
*Teres anceps:* see *Philbertia teres*
*Thais:* see *Nucella*
*Theodoxus fluviatilis* (L.).
    *Neritina fluviatilis* (L.) (J.) (F. & H.)
    *Theodoxa fluviatilis* (L.)
    On and under stones, on sunk wood, plants and in sponges, mainly in rivers but also in canals and in lakes, especially on wave line. Calciphile. Not going deeper than 20 ft. Also found in brackish water. Locally common in England except Devon, Cornwall, in Loch of Stennis, Orkney, and C Ireland. Europe.
    Breeds late spring, summer. Egg capsules attached to shells of other animals of same species, or to stones or weeds. No free-swimming larvae.
*Thesbia nana* (Lovén).
    *Columbella nana* (Lovén) (J.)
    *Mangelia nana* (Lovén) (F. & H.)
    *Pleurotoma nana* (Lovén)
    Dredged, 30–45 fathoms, off Orkney and Shetland; habitat unknown. Very rare. Scandinavia, Iceland, British Isles.
    Reproduction unknown.
*Tornus imperspicuus* (Chaster).
    *Adeorbis imperspicuus* Chaster
    Dredged, Irish Sea and off Co. Galway; habitat unknown. Rare. British Isles to Mediterranean.
    Reproduction unknown.
*Tornus subcarinatus* (Montagu).
    *Adeorbis subcarinatus* (Montagu) (J.) (F. & H.)
    On rocks and in burrows at LW and below and on shell gravel, on S and W coasts, Ireland. Rare. British Isles to Mediterranean.
    Breeding and egg capsules unknown. Free-swimming veligers common in inshore plankton (Plymouth).
*Tornus unisulcatus* (Chaster).
    *Adeorbis unisulcatus* Chaster
    Dredged 17 fathoms off W coast, Ireland. Habitat unknown. Rare. British Isles to Mediterranean.
    Reproduction unknown.
*Tragula fenestrata:* see *Turbonilla fenestrata*
*Trichotropis borealis* Broderip & Sowerby. (J.) (F. & H.)
    Dredged, 10–80 fathoms, on stony and shelly bottoms, off Northumbrian and all Scottish coasts. Not uncommon. Northern N Atlantic.
    Breeding unknown. Egg capsules attached to bivalve shells. No free-swimming larvae.
*Tricolia pullus* (L.). Pheasant shell.
    *Phasianella pullus* (L.) (J.) (F. & H.)
    *Turbo pullus* L.
    On rocks, on algae (especially *Laminaria*, *Chondrus crispus*, *Padina pavonia* and

*Prilota plumosa*) at LWST and dredged down to 19 fathoms on S and W coasts, NE Scotland, Ireland. Common in S in spring, rare in N at all times. British Isles to Mediterranean.

Breeding unknown. Eggs planktonic. Free-swimming veligers.

*Triphora perversa* (L.).
> *Cerithium adversum* (Montagu) (F. & H.)
> *Cerithium perversum* (L.) (J.)
> *Triforis perversa* (L.)

Under stones and in other shady positions, associated with sponges and algae, at LWST on rocky shores and dredged on hard grounds to 55 fathoms off S and W coasts, Ireland. Occasional. Scandinavia to Mediterranean.

Breeds spring to autumn (Plymouth). Egg capsules attached. Free-swimming veligers common in plankton spring to autumn (Plymouth).

*Tritonalia erinacea: see Ocenebra erinacea*
*Tritonofusus fusiformis: see Colus fenestratus*
*Tritonofusus gracilis: see Colus gracilis*
*Tritonofusus islandicus: see Colus islandicus*
*Tritonofusus propinquus: see Colus howsei*

*Trivia arctica* (Montagu). Cowry, stick-farthing, nun, groat, John o' Groat's buckie, maiden.
> *Cypraea europaea* Montagu (part) (J.) (F. & H.)
> *Trivia europaea* (Montagu) (part)

On rocks and in crevices on rocky shores at LWST and below, on all coasts, usually associated with compound ascidians. Moderately common. Scandinavia to Mediterranean.

Breeds winter (Plymouth). Egg capsules unknown. Free-swimming echinospira larvae fairly common in inshore plankton (Plymouth) autumn–spring.

*Trivia monacha* (da Costa). Cowry, stick-farthing, nun, groat, John o' Groat's buckie, maiden.
> *Cypraea europaea* Montagu (part) (J.) (F. & H.)
> *Trivia europaea* (Montagu) (part)

On rocks and in crevices on rocky shores mainly at LWST on S and W coasts. Usually associated with compound ascidians. Not uncommon. British Isles to Mediterranean.

Breeds spring, summer (Plymouth, Isle of Man). Egg capsules deposited in compound ascidians especially *Diplosoma* and *Botryllus*. Free-swimming echinospira larvae fairly common in inshore plankton (Plymouth), in all months.

*Trochocochlea lineata: see Monodonta lineata*
*Trochus alabastrum: see Calliostoma occidentale*
*Trochus amabilis: see Solariella amabilis*
*Trochus cinerarius: see Gibbula cineraria*
*Trochus conuloides: see Calliostoma zizyphinum*
*Trochus crassus: see Monodonta lineata*
*Trochus duminyi: see Circulus striatus*
*Trochus exasperatus: see Cantharidus exasperatus*
*Trochus exiguus: see Cantharidus exasperatus*
*Trochus formosus: see Calliostoma occidentale*
*Trochus granulatus: see Calliostoma papillosum*

*Trochus groenlandicus:* see *Margarites groenlandicus*
*Trochus helicinus:* see *Margarites helicinus*
*Trochus lineatus:* see *Monodonta lineata*
*Trochus magus:* see *Gibbula magus*
*Trochus margaritus:* see *Margarites helicinus*
*Trochus millegranus:* see *Cantharidus clelandi*
*Trochus montacuti* (=*montagui*): see *Cantharidus montagui*
*Trochus obliquatus:* see *Gibbula umbilicalis*
*Trochus occidentalis:* see *Calliostoma occidentale*
*Trochus pusillus:* see *Skenea nitens*
*Trochus striatus:* see *Cantharidus striatus*
*Trochus tumidus:* see *Gibbula tumida*
*Trochus umbilicatus* (=*umbilicalis*): see *Gibbula umbilicalis*
*Trochus undulatus:* see *Margarites groenlandicus*
*Trochus zizyphinus:* see *Calliostoma zizyphinum*
*Trophon bamffium:* see *T. truncatus*
*Trophon barvicensis* (Johnston). (J.) (F. & H.)
> *Trophon muricatus* (Montagu) var. *barvicensis*
> *Trophonopsis muricata* var. *barvicensis*
> Dredged, 7–55 fathoms, on stony bottoms, off NE England and all Scottish coasts, Ireland. Scarce. Scandinavia, Iceland, British Isles.
> Reproduction unknown.
*Trophon clathratus:* see *T. truncatus*
*Trophon echinatus:* see *T. muricatus*
*Trophon muricatus* (Montagu). (J.) (F. & H.). Spindle shell.
> *Trophon echinatus* (Sowerby) (=*echinatum* auctt.) (F. & H.)
> *Trophonopsis muricata* (Montagu)
> Dredged, 12–70 fathoms, on muddy sand and hard bottoms, off S and W coasts, Ireland. Rare. Scandinavia to Mediterranean.
> Breeds February–June (Plymouth). Egg capsules attached. No free-swimming larvae.
*Trophon muricatus* var. *barvicensis:* see *T. barvicensis*
*Trophon truncatus* (Ström). (J.). Spindle shell.
> *Trophon bamffius* (Donovan) (=*bamffium* auctt.) (F. & H.)
> *Trophon clathratus* (L.) (F. & H.)
> *Trophonopsis clathrata* (L.)
> Dredged, 2–80 fathoms, on stony bottoms, off W coast, NE England and E Scotland, Ireland. Scarce. N Atlantic.
> Breeding unknown. Egg capsules attached to stones or shells. No free-swimming larvae.
*Trophonopsis clathrata:* see *Trophon truncatus*
*Trophonopsis muricata:* see *Trophon muricatus*
*Trophonopsis muricata* var. *barvicensis:* see *Trophon barvicensis*
*Troschelia berniciensis* (King).
> *Buccinofusus berniciensis* (King)
> *Fusus berniciensis* King (J.) (F. & H.)
> Dredged, down to 100 fathoms, on sandy or muddy grounds, off NE England and E Scotland. Very rare. Norway to British Isles.
> Breeding unknown. Egg capsules attached. No free-swimming larvae.

*Truncatella subcylindrica* (L.). Looping snail.
 *Acme subcylindrica* (L.)
 *Truncatella montagui* Forbes & Hanley (F. & H.)
 *Truncatella truncata* (Montagu)
 *Truncatella truncatula* (Draparnaud) (J.)
  Under stones, weed, boards, on muddy shores at and above HW though not in direct contact with the sea, with *Halimione portulacoides* and *Suaeda maritima*, on S coast of England. Very local. British Isles to Mediterranean.
  Reproduction unknown.
*Turbo pullus:* see *Tricolia pullus*
*Turboella parva:* see *Rissoa parva*
*Turbonilla acuta:* see *T. delicata*
*Turbonilla albella:* see *Odostomia albella*
*Turbonilla clavula:* see *Menestho clavula*
*Turbonilla crenata* (Brown).
 *Chemnitzia rufa* (Philippi) (part) (F. & H.)
 *Odostomia rufa* (Philippi) (J.)
 *Pyrgisculus crenatus* (Brown)
 *Pyrgiscus rufus* (Philippi)
 *Pyrgostelis interrupta* (Totten) var. *rufa*
 *Turbonilla rufa* (Philippi)
  Dredged, 3–40 fathoms, from sandy mud, off S and W coasts. Scarce, commoner in S. Scandinavia to Mediterranean.
  Breeding, eggs unknown. Free-swimming veligers.
*Turbonilla delicata* Monterosato.
 *Chemnitzia gracilis* Philippi
 *Chemnitzia simillima* Montagu
 *Turbonilla acuta* (Donovan)
  Dredged, 12 fathoms, off Ireland; habitat unknown. Rare. British Isles to Mediterranean.
  Reproduction unknown.
*Turbonilla elegantissima* (Montagu).
 *Chemnitzia elegantissima* (Montagu) (F. & H.)
 *Odostomia lactea* (L.) (J.)
 *Turbonilla lactea* (L.)
  Under stones and in crevices on muddy rocky shores at LWST, extending to 10 fathoms, on all coasts, Ireland; associated with *Amphitrite gracilis*, *Cirratulus cirratus* and *Audouinia tentaculata*. Uncommon except in SW England. Scandinavia to Mediterranean.
  Breeding and eggs unknown. Short free-swimming veliger stage occurs (Plymouth).
*Turbonilla fenestrata* (Forbes).
 *Chemnitzia fenestrata* (Forbes) (F. & H.)
 *Odostomia fenestrata* Forbes (J.)
 *Pyrgulina fenestrata* (Forbes)
 *Tragula fenestrata* (Forbes)
  Dredged, 7–12 fathoms, on muddy ground, off SW and W coasts. Very rare. Southern Europe.
  Breeding unknown. Egg capsules attached.

*Turbonilla fulvocincta* (Thompson).
> *Chemnitzia fulvocincta* (Thompson)
> *Chemnitzia rufa* (Philippi) (part) (F. & H.)
> *Odostomia rufa* (Philippi) var. *fulvocincta* (J.)
> *Pyrgisculus fulvocinctus* (Thompson)
> *Pyrgostelis interrupta* (Totten)
> Dredged, 18–90 fathoms, from sandy mud, off Scotland, N and E Ireland. Scarce, common in N. Scandinavia to British Isles.
> Reproduction unknown.

*Turbonilla innovata* Monterosato.
> *Chemnitzia elegantissima* var. *pusilla* Philippi (F. & H.)
> *Chemnitzia pusilla* Philippi
> *Odostomia pusilla* (Philippi) (J.)
> *Turbonilla pusilla* (Philippi)
> Under stones and in rock crevices at LWST in SW England. Rare. British Isles to Mediterranean.
> Reproduction unknown.

*Turbonilla jeffreysi* (Forbes & Hanley).
> *Chemnitzia scalaris* Philippi (F. & H.)
> *Odostomia scalaris* (Philippi) (J.)
> *Pyrgisculus jeffreysi* (Forbes & Hanley)
> *Pyrgiscus scalaris* (Philippi)
> *Pyrgostelis scalaris* (Philippi)
> Dredged, 3–50 fathoms, from muddy gravel, off SW and W coasts; associated with hydroids, especially *Halecium*. Not uncommon locally. N Atlantic, Mediterranean.
> Reproduction unknown.

*Turbonilla lactea:* see *T. elegantissima*

*Turbonilla pusilla:* see *T. innovata*

*Turbonilla rufa:* see *T. crenata*

*Turbonilla rufescens* (Forbes).
> *Chemnitzia rufescens* Forbes (F. & H.)
> *Odostomia scalaris* var. *rufescens* (J.)
> *Pyrgisculus rufescens* (Forbes)
> *Pyrgostelis scalaris* var. *rufescens*
> Dredged, 20–60 fathoms, off W Scottish coasts, N Ireland; habitat unknown. Scarce. N Atlantic.
> Reproduction unknown.

*Turritella communis* Risso. (F. & H.). Screw shell or auger.
> *Turritella terebra* (L.) (J.)
> Gregarious, 3–100 fathoms, in muddy bottoms, off all coasts, Ireland. Locally abundant. Scandinavia to Mediterranean.
> Breeds summer (Plymouth). Egg capsules attached to substratum. Free-swimming veligers in plankton for very short time.

*Turtonia stylifera:* see *Pelseneeria stylifera*

*Typhlomangelia nivalis* (Lovén).
> *Pleurotoma nivalis* Lovén (J.)

Dredged, 78 fathoms, from fine muddy sand, off Shetland. Very rare. Iceland to British Isles.

Reproduction unknown.

*Urosalpinx cinerea* (Say). American whelk-tingle, oyster drill.

> *Fusus cinereus* Say

On oyster banks and stony ground LWST and below, off Essex coasts. Common. E North America.

Breeds spring, summer (Essex). Egg capsules attached to shells, stones. No free-swimming larvae.

*Valvata cristata* Müller. (J.) (F. & H.)

In slowly flowing and still freshwater, throughout British Isles (except Cornwall). Not uncommon in S, rare in N. Palearctic.

Reproduction as in *V. piscinalis*.

*Valvata macrostoma* Mörch.

> *Valvata macrostoma* Steenbuch
> *Valvata pulchella* Studer

In marshes and ditches, on leaves, on the sides and bottoms of drains, in SE England. Very local. N Europe.

Reproduction unknown, but presumably as in *V. piscinalis*.

*Valvata piscinalis* (Müller). (J.) (F. & H.). Valve snail.

> *Cincinna piscinalis* (Müller)

In running water and large lakes, mainly on weeds in summer, buried in mud in winter, throughout the British Isles (rare in N Scotland). Common locally. Palaearctic.

Breeds summer. Egg capsules laid on weeds, stones and mollusc shells. No free-swimming larvae.

*Valvata pulchella:* see *V. macrostoma*
*Velutella flexilis:* see *Velutina plicatilis*
*Velutina capuloidea:* see *V. velutina*
*Velutina flexilis:* see *V. plicatilis*
*Velutina haliotoidea:* see *V. velutina*
*Velutina laevigata:* see *V. velutina*
*Velutina plicatilis* (Müller). (J.)

> *Velutella flexilis* (Montagu)
> *Velutina flexilis* (Montagu) (F. & H.)

Dredged, 12–25 fathoms, on hard ground, off NE England and off all Scottish coasts; associated with *Tubularia indivisa* and other hydroids. Rare. Panarctic-boreal.

Reproduction unknown.

*Velutina velutina* (Müller).

> *Velutina capuloidea* (Blainville)
> *Velutina haliotoidea* (Fabricius)
> *Velutina laevigata* (Pennant) (J.) (F. & H.)

On hard bottoms, LWEST–44 fathoms, on all coasts, Ireland; associated with ascidians. Scarce in S, common in N. N Atlantic, Mediterranean.

Breeds summer, egg capsules sunk in test of the ascidian *Styela coriacea*. Free-swimming echinospira larvae not common in inshore plankton, summer and autumn (Plymouth).

*Vitreolina devians:* see *Balcis devians*

*Vivipara vera:* see *Viviparus contectus*

*Viviparus contectus* (Millet). River snail.

    *Cyclostoma viviparum* (L.) of Draparnaud
    *Paludina contecta* (Millet) (J.)
    *Paludina listeri* Forbes & Hanley (F. & H.)
    *Vivipara vera* Frauenfeld
    *Viviparus crystallinus* (Gray)
    *Viviparus fasciatus* auctt. angl.
    *Viviparus lacustris* Beck

    In running freshwater, but also in standing water and into brackish water $\not> 3\text{‰}$. Calciphile, but also occurs in water with humous acids of pH 4·8. Locally common in England S of Lancashire and Yorkshire, rare in SW. Europe and Africa.

    Breeds spring, summer. Viviparous. No free-swimming larvae.

*Viviparus viviparus* (L.). River snail.

    *Cyclostoma achatinum* Draparnaud
    *Paludina actalina* (Draparnaud)
    *Paludina vivipara* (L.) (part) (J.) (F. & H.)
    *Viviparus fasciatus* (Müller)

    In running freshwater, large ditches, but extends into brackish water $\not> 3\text{‰}$. Calciphile. Not uncommon in England S of Lancashire and Yorkshire. Palaearctic.

    Breeds spring, summer. Viviparous. No free-swimming larvae.

*Voluta laevis:* see *Erato voluta*

*Volutopsis:* see *Volutopsius*

*Volutopsius norwegicus* (Gmelin).

    *Fusus norvegicus* (Gmelin) (J.) (F. & H.)
    *Neptunea norvegica* (Gmelin)
    *Volutopsis norvegica* (Gmelin)

    Dredged, 50–85 fathoms, on fine muddy sand, off NE England and Shetland. Very rare. Panarctic.

    Breeding unknown. Egg capsules attached to old shells or other hard, flat substrata. No free-swimming larvae.

*Zastoma albellum:* see *Odostomia albella*

*Zippora membranacea:* see *Rissoa membranacea*

*Zizyphinum conulus:* see *Calliostoma zizyphinum*

*Zizyphinum linnaei:* see *Calliostoma zizyphinum*

*Zizyphinus aequistriatus:* see *Cantharidus striatus*

*Zizyphinus granulatus:* see *Calliostoma papillosum*

*Zizyphinus striatus:* see *Cantharidus striatus*

# BIBLIOGRAPHY

ABBOTT, R. T. 1954. *American Seashells*. New York, van Nostrand.

ABE, N. 1931. Ecological observations on *Acmaea dorsuosa* Gould. *Sci. Rep. Tohoku Imp. Univ.* (4), **6**, pp. 403–427.

ABOLIŅŠ-KROGIS, A. 1958. The morphological and chemical characteristics of organic crystals in the regenerating shell of *Helix pomatia* L. *Acta zool., Stockh.*, **39**, pp. 19–38.

ADAM, W. 1942. Notes sur les gastéropodes XI. Sur la répartition et le biologie de *Hydrobia jenkinsi* Smith en Belgique. *Bull. Mus. R. Hist. nat. Belg.*, **18**, pp. 1–18.

ADANSON, M. 1757. *Histoire naturelle du Sénégal (Coquillages). Avec le relation abrégée d'un voyage fait en ce pays pendant les années* 1749–53. Paris, C. J. B. Bauche.

AGERSBORG, H. P. K. 1929. Factors in the evolution of the prosobranchiate mollusc, *Thais lapillus. Nautilus*, **43**, pp. 45–49.

ALBRECHT, P. G. 1921. Chemical study of several marine mollusks of the Pacific coast. *J. biol. Chem.*, **45**, pp. 395–405.

ALBRECHT, P. G. 1923. Chemical study of several marine mollusks of the Pacific coast. The liver. *J. biol. Chem.*, **57**, pp. 789–794.

ALEXANDER, W. B., B. A. SOUTHGATE & R. BASSINDALE. 1935. Survey of the River Tees. Pt. 2. The estuary—chemical and biological. *Tech. Pap. Wat. Pollut. Res., Lond.*, **5**, pp. 1–171.

ALPERS, F. 1931a. Über die Nahrungsaufnahme von *Conus mediterraneus* Brug., eines toxoglossen Prosobranchiers. *Pubbl. Staz. zool. Napoli*, **11**, pp. 436–455.

ALPERS, F. 1931b. Zur Kenntnis der Anatomie von *Conus lividus* Brug., besonders des Darmkanals. *Jena. Z. Naturw.*, **65**, pp. 587–658.

ALPERS, F. 1932. Zur Biologie des *Conus mediterraneus* Brug. *Jena. Z. Naturw.*, **67**, pp. 346–363.

AMAUDRUT, A. 1898. La partie antérieure du tube digestif et la torsion chez les mollusques gastéropodes. *Ann. Sci. nat. Zool.* (7), **8**, pp. 1–291.

AMEEL, D. J. 1934. *Paragonimus*, its life history and distribution in North America and its taxonomy (Trematoda : Troglotrematidae). *Amer. J. Hyg.*, **19**, pp. 279–317.

ANCEY, G. F. 1906. Observations sur les mollusques gastropodes sénestres de l'époque actuelle. *Bull. sci. Fr. Belg.*, **40**, pp. 187–205.

ANDERSEN, K. 1924a. Entwicklungsgeschichtliche Untersuchungen an *Paludina vivipara*. i Teil. Die Formengestaltung der Sumpfschnecke (*Paludina vivipara*) während der Larvenzeit. *Morph. Jb.*, **53**, pp. 211–258.

ANDERSEN, K. 1924b. Entwicklungsgeschichtliche Untersuchungen an *Paludina vivipara*. ii Teil. Die Entwicklung des Nervensystems bei *Paludina vivipara*, zugleich eine kritische Studie über die Torsion und Chiastoneurie der Gastropoden. *Morph. Jb.*, **54**, pp. 157–204.

ANDREWS, E. A. 1934. Shell repair by the snail *Pleurodonta rostrata* Pfr. *Biol. Bull., Wood's Hole*, **67**, pp. 294–299.

ANDREWS, E. A. 1935a. Shell repair by the snail *Neritina. J. exp. Zool.*, **70**, pp. 75–107.

ANDREWS, E. A. 1935b. The egg capsules of certain Neritidae. *J. Morph.*, **57**, pp. 31–59.

ANKEL, W. E. 1924. Spermatozoen-Dimorphismus und Befruchtung bei *Bythinia tentaculata* L. und *Viviparus viviparus* L. *Senckenbergiana*, **6**, pp. 1–12.

ANKEL, W. E. 1925. Zur Befruchtungsfrage bei *Viviparus viviparus* L. nebst Bemerkungen über die erste Reifungsteilung des Eies. *Senckenbergiana*, **7**, pp. 37–54.

ANKEL, W. E. 1926. Spermiozeugmenbildung durch atypische (apyrene) und typische Spermien bei *Scala* und *Janthina. Verh. dtsch. zool. Ges., Zool. Anz.* Suppl. **2**, pp. 193–202.

ANKEL, W. E. 1929. Über die Bildung der Eikapsel bei *Nassa*-Arten. *Verh. dtsch. zool. Ges., Zool. Anz.* Suppl. **4**, pp. 219–230.

ANKEL, W. E.  1930*a*.  Die atypische Spermatogenese von *Janthina* (Prosobranchia, Ptenoglossa). *Z. Zellforsch.*, **11**, pp. 491–608.

ANKEL, W. E.  1930*b*.  Nähreierbildung bei *Natica catena* (da Costa). *Zool. Anz.*, **89**, pp. 129–135.

ANKEL, W. E.  1930*c*.  Über das Vorkommen und die Bedeutung zwittriger Geschlechtzellen bei Prosobranchiern. *Biol. Zbl.*, **50**, pp. 513–531.

ANKEL, W. E.  1933.  Untersuchungen über Keimzellbildung und Befruchtung bei *Bythinia tentaculata* L.  II. Gibt es in der Spermatogenese von *Bythinia tentaculata* eine Polymegalie? *Z. Zellforsch.*, **17**, pp. 160–198.

ANKEL, W. E.  1935.  Das Gelege von *Lamellaria perspicua*. *Z. Morph. Ökol. Tiere*, **30**, pp. 635–647.

ANKEL, W. E.  1936*a*.  Prosobranchia.  In GRIMPE, G. & E. WAGLER: *Die Tierwelt der Nord- und Ostsee*, **IX**b1.  Leipzig, Akademische Verlagsgesellschaft.

ANKEL, W. E.  1936*b*.  Die Fresspuren von *Helcion* und *Littorina* und die Funktion der Radula. *Verh. dtsch. zool. Ges., Zool. Anz.* Suppl. **9**, pp. 174–182.

ANKEL, W. E.  1937*a*.  Wie bohrt *Natica*? *Biol. Zbl.*, **57**, pp. 75–82.

ANKEL, W. E.  1937*b*.  Der feinere Bau des Kokons der Purpurschnecke *Nucella lapillus* (L.) und seine Bedeutung für das Laichleben.  *Verh. dtsch. zool. Ges., Zool. Anz.* Suppl. **10**, pp. 77–86.

ANKEL, W. E.  1937*c*.  Wie frisst *Littorina*?  1. Radula-Bewegung und Fresspuren.  *Senckenbergiana*, **19**, pp. 317–333.

ANKEL, W. E.  1938*a*.  Erwerb und Aufnahme der Nahrung bei den Gastropoden.  *Verh. dtsch. Zool. Ges., Zool. Anz.* Suppl. **11**, pp. 223–295.

ANKEL, W. E.  1938*b*.  Beobachtungen an Prosobranchiern der schwedischen Westküste. *Ark. Zool.*, **30**A (9), pp. 1–27.

ANKEL, W. E.  1947.  Über einen 'Anklebe'-Reflex von *Gibbula*. *Arch. Molluskenk.*, **76**, pp. 167–168.

ANKEL, W. E.  1948.  Die Nahrungsaufnahme der Pyramidelliden. *Verh. dtsch. zool. Ges., Zool. Anz.* Suppl. **13**, pp. 478–484.

ARNOLD, D. C.  1957.  The response of the limpet, *Patella vulgata* L., to waters of different salinities. *J. mar. biol. Ass. U.K.*, **36**, pp. 121–128.

AUBIN, P. A.  1892.  The limpet's power of adhesion. *Nature, Lond.*, **45**, pp. 464–465.

BACCI, G.  1947.  L'inversione del sesso ed il ciclo stagionale dell gonade in *Patella coerulea* L. *Pubbl. Staz. zool. Napoli*, **21**, pp. 183–217.

BACCI, G.  1951.  L'ermafroditismo di *Calyptraea chinensis* L. e di alni Calyptraeidae. *Pubbl. Staz. zool. Napoli*, **23**, pp. 66–90.

BÄCKER, R.  1903.  Die Auge einiger Gastropoden. *Arb. zool. Inst. Univ. Wien*, **14**, pp. 259–290.

BAKKER, K.  1959.  Feeding habits and zonation in some intertidal snails. *Arch. néerl. Zool.*, **13**, pp. 230–257.

BALDWIN, E.  1957.  *Dynamic Aspects of Biochemistry*.  Cambridge, University Press.

BALL, E. G. & B. MEYERHOF.  1940.  The occurrence of cytochrome and other haemochromogens in certain marine forms. *Biol. Bull., Wood's Hole*, **77**, p. 321.

BALLANTINE, D. & J. E. MORTON.  1956.  Filtering, feeding and digestion in the lamellibranch *Lasaea rubra*. *J. mar. biol. Ass. U.K.*, **35**, pp. 241–274.

BARKMAN, J. J.  1955.  On the distribution and ecology of *Littorina obtusata* (L.) and its subspecific units. *Arch. néerl. Zool.*, **11**, pp. 22–86.

BARNES, H. & T. B. BAGENAL.  1952.  The habits and habitats of *Aporrhais pes-pelicani* (L.). *Proc. malac. Soc. Lond.*, **29**, pp. 101–105.

BATAILLON, C.  1921.  Spermies couplées et hétérochromosome dans la lignée typique d'une Turritelle. *C.R. Soc. Biol., Paris*, **84**, pp. 219–222.

BECK, K.  1912.  Anatomie der deutschen *Buliminus*-Arten. *Jena. Z. Naturw.*, **48**, pp. 187–262.

BECKER, K.  1949.  Untersuchungen über das Farbmuster und das Wachstum der Molluskenschale. *Biol. Zbl.*, **68**, pp. 263–288.

BEEDHAM, G. E. 1958a. Observations on the mantle of the Lamellibranchia. *Quart. J. micr. Sci.*, **99**, pp. 181-197.

BEEDHAM, G. E. 1958b. Observations on the non-calcareous component of the shell of the Lamellibranchia. *Quart. J. micr. Sci.*, **99**, pp. 341-357.

BEER, G. R. DE. 1954. *Archaeopteryx* and evolution. *Advanc. Sci. Lond.*, **42**, pp. 1-11.

BELDING, D. L. 1930. The soft shelled clams of Massachusetts. *Commonwealth of Mass. mar. Fish. Ser.*, **1**.

BENNETT, M. F. 1954. The rhythmic activity of the quahog, *Venus mercenaria*, and its modification by light. *Biol. Bull.*, *Wood's Hole*, **107**, pp. 174-191.

BERG, K. 1938. Studies on the bottom animals of Esrom Lake. *K. danske vidensk. Selsk.*, Sect. Sci. (9), **8**, pp. 1-255.

BERNARD, F. 1888. Recherches anatomiques sur la *Valvata piscinalis*. *C.R. Acad. Sci.*, *Paris* **107**, pp. 191-194.

BERNARD, F. 1890. Recherches sur les organes palléaux des gastéropodes prosobranches. *Ann. Sci. nat. Zool.* (7), **9**, pp. 89-404.

BERNER, L. 1942. La croissance de la coquille chez les gastéropodes. *Bull. Inst. océanogr. Monaco*, **816**, pp. 1-16.

BERRY, A. J. 1956. Some factors affecting the distribution of *Littorina saxatilis* (Olivi). *Ph.D. Thesis, University of London.*

BEVELANDER, G. 1952. Calcification in molluscs. III. Intake and deposition of $Ca^{45}$ and $P^{32}$ in relation to shell formation. *Biol. Bull.*, *Wood's Hole*, **102**, pp. 9-15.

BEVELANDER, G. & P. BENZER. 1948. Calcification in marine molluscs. *Biol. Bull.*, *Wood's Hole*, **94**, pp. 176-183.

BIEDERMANN, N. W. 1905. Studien zur vergleichenden Physiologie der peristaltischen Bewegungen. II. Die lokomotorischen Wellen der Schneckensohle. *Pflüg. Arch. ges. Physiol.*, **107**, pp. 1-56.

BLOCH, I. 1896. Die embryonale Entwicklung der Radula von *Paludina vivipara*. *Jena. Z. Naturw.*, **30**, pp. 350-392.

BLOCHMANN, F. 1882. Über die Entwicklung der *Neritina fluviatilis* Mül. *Z. wiss. Zool.*, **36**, pp. 125-174.

BOBRETZKY, N. 1877. Studien über die embryonale Entwicklung der Gastropoden. *Arch. mikr. Anat.*, **13**, pp. 75-169.

BOETTGER, C. R. 1930. Die Lage der Bohrstelle beim Angriff der Raubschnecken aus der Familie Naticidae. *Z. wiss. Zool.*, **136**, pp. 453-463.

BOETTGER, C. R. 1949. Hinweise zur Frage der Kielbildung auf der Schale der Wasserschnecke *Potamopyrgus crystallinus jenkinsi* (E. A. Smith). *Arch. Molluskenk.*, **22**, pp. 63-72.

BOETTGER, C. R. 1951. Die Herkunst und Verwandtschaftsbeziehungen der Wasserschnecke *Potamopyrgus jenkinsi* (Smith), nebst einer Angabe über ihr Auftreten im Mediterrangebiet. *Arch. Molluskenk.*, **80**, pp. 57-84.

BOETTGER, C. R. 1954. Die Systematik der euthyneuren Schnecken. *Verh. dtsch. zool. Ges.*, *Zool. Anz.* Suppl. **18**, pp. 253-280.

BØGGILD, O. B. 1930. The shell structure of the mollusks. *K. danske vidensk. Selsk.* (9), **2**, pp. 235-325.

BOHN, G. 1904. Périodicité vitale des animaux soumis aux oscillations du niveau des hautes mers. *C.R. Acad. Sci.*, *Paris*, **139**, pp. 610-611.

BONDESEN, P. 1940. Preliminary investigations into the development of *Neritina fluviatilis* L. in brackish and fresh water. *Vidensk. Medd. dansk naturh. Foren. Kbh.*, **104**, pp. 283-318.

BONDESEN, P. & E. W. KAISER. 1949. *Hydrobia* (*Potamopyrgus*) *jenkinsi* Smith in Denmark illustrated by its ecology. *Oikos*, **1**, pp. 252-281.

BONSE, H. 1935. Ein Beitrag zum Problem der Schneckenbewegung. *Zool. Jb.* (*Zool. Physiol.*), **54**, pp. 349-384.

BOUCHILLOUX, S. & J. ROCHE. 1955. Contribution à l'étude biochimique de la pourpre des *Murex*. *Bull. Inst. océanogr. Monaco*, **1054**, pp. 1-23.

BOURNE, A.   1894.   On certain points in the development and anatomy of some earthworms. *Quart. J. micr. Sci.*, **36**, pp. 11–33.

BOURNE, G. C.   1908.   Contribution to the morphology of the group Neritacea of aspidobranch gastropods. Part I. The Neritidae. *Proc. zool. Soc. Lond.*, pp. 810–887.

BOURNE, G. C.   1910.   On the anatomy and systematic position of *Incisura (Scissurella) lyttel-tonensis. Quart. J. micr. Sci.*, **55**, pp. 1–47.

BOUTAN, L.   1886.   Recherches sur l'anatomie et le développement de la Fissurelle. *Arch. Zool. exp. gén.* (2), **3**, pp. 1–173.

BOUTAN, L.   1892.   Sur le développement de l'Haliotide, et sur l'utilité du Scaphandre dans les recherches zoologiques. *C.R. Ass. franc. Ad. Sci.*, **2**, pp. 522–525.

BOUTAN, L.   1899.   La cause principale de l'asymétrie des mollusques gastéropodes. *Arch. Zool. exp. gén.* (3), **7**, pp. 203–342.

BOUTAN, L.   1900.   Gastéropodes. La Patelle commune. In *Zoologie Descriptive*, **2**, edited by L. Boutan. Paris, O. Doin.

BOUTAN, L.   1919.   Considérations nouvelles sur les affinités réciproques des mollusques gastéro-podes. *Act. Soc. linn. Bordeaux*, **71**, pp. 5–116.

BOUTAN, L.   1923.   Nouvelle étude sur les perles naturelles et sur les perles de culture. *Ann. Sci. nat. Zool.* (10) **6**, pp. 1–94.

BOUVIER, E. L.   1885.   Note sur le système nerveux des Toxiglosses, et considérations générales sur le système nerveux des gastéropodes prosobranches. *Bull. Soc. philom.*, Paris, **10**, pp. 44–56.

BOUVIER, E. L.   1886.   Contributions à l'étude des prosobranches pténoglosses. *Bull. Soc. malac. Fr.*, **3**, pp. 77–130.

BOUVIER, E. L.   1887.   Système nerveux, morphologie générale et classification des gastéropodes prosobranches. *Ann. Sci. nat. Zool.* (7), **3**, pp. 1–510.

BOUVIER, E. L. & H. FISCHER.   1902.   L'organisation et les affinités des gastéropodes primitifs d'après l'étude anatomique du *Pleurotomaria beyrichi. J. Conchyliol.*, **50**, pp. 117–272.

BOYCOTT, A. E.   1917.   Where is the male of *Paludestrina jenkinsi? J. Conch.*, **15**, p. 216.

BOYCOTT, A. E.   1919.   Parthenogenesis in *Paludestrina jenkinsi. J. Conch.*, **16**, p. 54.

BOYCOTT, A. E.   1929.   The inheritance of ornamentation in var. *aculeata* of *Hydrobia jenkinsi* Smith. *Proc. malac. Soc. Lond.*, **18**, pp. 230–234.

BOYCOTT, A. E.   1934.   The habitats of land Mollusca in Britain. *J. Ecol.*, **22**, pp. 1–38.

BOYCOTT, A. E.   1936.   The habitats of the fresh-water Mollusca in Britain. *J. Anim. Ecol.*, **5**, pp. 116–186.

BOYCOTT, A. E., C. DIVER, S. L. GARSTANG & F. M. TURNER.   1930.   The inheritance of sinistrality in *Limnaea peregra* (Mollusca, Pulmonata). *Philos. Trans.* B, **219**, pp. 51–131.

BOZLER, E.   1930.   Untersuchungen zur Physiologie der Tonusmuskeln. *Z. vergl. Physiol.*, **12**, pp. 579–602.

BREGENZER, A.   1916.   Anatomie und Histologie von *Bythinella dunkeri. Zool. Jb.* (Anat. Ont.), **39**, pp. 237–292.

BROUARDEL, J.   1948.   Etude du mode d'infestation des Patelles par l'*Urceolaria patellae* (Cuénot). Influence de l'espèce de Patelle. *Bull. Lab. marit. Dinard*, **30**, pp. 1–6.

BROCK, F.   1933.   Analyse des Beute- und Verdauungsfeldes der Wellhornschnecke *Buccinum undatum* L. *Verh. dtsch. zool. Ges., Zool. Anz.* Suppl. **6**, pp. 243–250.

BROCK, F.   1936.   Suche, Aufnahme und enzymatische Spaltung der Nahrung durch die Well-hornschnecke *Buccinum undatum* L. *Zoologica, Stuttgart*, **34** (92), pp. 1–136.

BROWN, C. H.   1952.   Some structural proteins of *Mytilus edulis. Quart. J. micr. Sci.*, **43**, pp. 487–503.

BROWN, F. A., Jr., M. FINGERMAN, M. I. SANDEEN & H. M. WEBB.   1953.   Persistent diurnal and tidal rhythms of colour change in the fiddler crab *Uca pugnax. J. exp. Zool.*, **123**, pp. 29–60.

BROWN, F. A., Jr.   1954.   Persistent activity rhythms in the oyster. *Amer. J. Physiol.*, **178**, pp. 510–514.

BROWN, F. J. 1933. On the excretory system and life history of *Lecithodendrium chilostomum* (Mehl) and other bat trematodes, with a note on the life history of *Dicrocoelium dendriticum* (Rudolphi). *Parasitology*, **25**, pp. 317–328.

BRÜEL, L. 1915. Über das Nervensystem der Heteropoden. I. *Pterotrachea*. *Zool. Anz.*, **45**, pp. 530–548.

BRÜEL, L. 1924a. Über das Nervensystem der Heteropoden. II. Das Nervensystem von *Carinaria* und seine Herleitung von den Prosobranchiern. *Zool. Anz.*, **59**, pp. 113–127.

BRÜEL, L. 1924b. Über das Nervensystem der Heteropoden. II. Das Nervensystem von *Carinaria* und seine Herleitung von den Prosobranchiern (Schluss). *Zool. Anz.*, **59**, pp. 190–199.

BUDDENBROCK, W. VON. 1915. Die Statocyste von *Pecten*, ihre Histologie und Physiologie. *Zool. Jb. (Zool. Physiol.*), **35**, pp. 301–356.

BURGER, J. W. & C. S. THORNTON. 1935. A correlation between the food eggs of *Fasciolaria tulipa* and the apyrene spermatozoa of prosobranch molluscs. *Biol. Bull., Wood's Hole*, **68**, pp. 253–257.

BUTLER, P. A. 1954. The southern oyster drill. *Proc. nat. Shellfish Ass.*, **1953**, pp. 67–75.

CARLSON, A. J. 1905a. The physiology of locomotion in gasteropods. *Biol. Bull., Wood's Hole*, **8**, pp. 85–92.

CARLSON, A. J. 1905b. Comparative physiology of the invertebrate heart. The innervation of the invertebrate heart. *Biol. Bull., Wood's Hole*, **8**, pp. 123–167.

CARRICK, R. 1938. The life-history and development of *Agriolimax agrestis* L., the grey field slug. *Trans. roy. Soc. Edinb.*, **59**, pp. 563–597.

CARRIERE, J. 1889. Über Molluskenaugen. *Arch. mikr. Anat.*, **33**, pp. 378–402.

CARRIKER, M. R. 1943. On the structure and function of the proboscis in the common oyster drill *Urosalpinx cinerea* Say. *J. Morph.*, **73**, pp. 441–506.

CARRIKER, M. R. 1946. Observations on the functioning of the alimentary system of the snail *Lymnaea stagnalis appressa* Say. *Biol. Bull., Wood's Hole*, **91**, pp. 88–111.

CARRIKER, M. R. 1951. Observations on the penetration of tightly closing bivalves by *Busycon* and other predators. *Ecology*, **32**, pp. 73–83.

CARRIKER, M. R. 1955. Critical review of biology and control of oyster drills *Urosalpinx* and *Eupleura*. *Spec. sci. Rep. U.S. Dept. Inst. Fish.*, **148**, pp. 1–150.

CARRIKER, M. R. 1959. Comparative functional morphology of the drilling mechanism in *Urosalpinx* and *Eupleura* (muricid gastropods). *Proc. XVth int. Cong. Zool. Lond.*, pp. 373–376.

CASTEEL, D. B. 1904. The cell-lineage and early larval development of *Fiona marina*, a nudibranch mollusk. *Proc. nat. Acad. Sci. Philad.*, **56**, pp. 325–405.

CATE, J. TEN. 1922. Quelques observations sur la locomotion de l'escargot des vignes. *Arch. néerl. Physiol.*, **7**, pp. 103–111.

CATE, J. TEN. 1923. Quelques recherches sur la locomotion des limaces. *Arch. néerl. Physiol.*, **8**, pp. 377–393.

CAULLERY, M. & P. PELSENEER. 1910. Sur la ponte et le développement du vignot (*Littorina littorea*). *Bull. sci. Fr. Belg.*, **44**, pp. 357–360.

CHARIN, N. 1926. Über die Nahrung des Embryo von *Paludina vivipara*. *Bull. Soc. Nat. Voronèje*, **1**, pp. 60–66.

CHASTER, G. W. 1896. *Adeorbis unisulcatus*, new species, from the Irish coast. *J. Conch.*, **8**, p. 373.

CHIPPERFIELD, P. N. J. 1952. The breeding of *Crepidula fornicata* (L.) in the river Blackwater, Essex. *J. mar. biol. Ass. U.K.*, **30**, pp. 49–71.

CHUMLEY, J. 1918. *The Fauna of the Clyde Sea Area*. Glasgow, University Press.

CLAPAREDE, E. 1858. Beitrag zur Anatomie des *Cyclostoma elegans*. *Arch. Anat. Physiol., Lpz.*, **2**, pp. 1–34.

CLARK, W. C. 1958. Notes on the mantle cavities of some trochid and turbinid Gastropoda. *Proc. malac. Soc. Lond.*, **33**, pp. 57–64.

CLARKE, A. H. & R. J. MENZIES. 1959. *Neopilina* (*Vema*) *ewingi*, a second living species of the paleozoic class Monoplacophora. *Science*, **129**, pp. 1026–1027.

CLELAND, D. M. 1954. A study of the habits of *Valvata piscinalis* (Müller), and the structure and function of the alimentary canal and reproductive system. *Proc. malac. Soc. Lond.*, **30**, pp. 167–203.

CLENCH, W. J. 1946. The poison cone shell. *Occ. Pap. Mollusks Harv.*, **1**, pp. 49–80.

CLENCH, W. J. 1947. The genera *Purpura* and *Thais* in the Western Atlantic. *Johnsonia*, **2**, pp. 61–91.

CLENCH, W. J. & R. D. TURNER. 1948. The genus *Truncatella* in the Western Atlantic. *Johnsonia*, **2**, pp. 149–164.

CLENCH, W. J. & R. D. TURNER. 1950. The genera *Sthenorytis*, *Cirsotrema*, *Acirsa*, *Opalia* and *Amaea* in the Western Atlantic. *Johnsonia*, **2**, pp. 221–246.

COATES, H. 1922. Exhibit. *J. Conch.*, **16**, p. 319.

COE, W. R. 1938a. Conditions influencing change of sex in mollusks of the genus *Crepidula*. *J. exp. Zool.*, **77**, pp. 401–424.

COE, W. R. 1938b. Influence of the association on the gastropods having protandric consecutive sexuality. *Biol. Bull., Wood's Hole*, **75**, pp. 274–285.

COE, W. R. 1942. The reproductive organs of the prosobranch mollusk *Crepidula onyx* and their transformation during the change from male to female phase. *J. Morph.*, **70**, pp. 501–512.

COE, W. R. 1944. Sexual differentiation in mollusks. II. Gastropods, amphineurans, scaphopods, and cephalopods. *Quart. Rev. Biol.*, **19**, pp. 85–97.

COE, W. R. 1948. Nutrition and sexuality in protandric gastropods of the genus *Crepidula*. *Biol. Bull., Wood's Hole*, **94**, pp. 158–160.

COE, W. R. 1953. Influences of association, isolation and nutrition on the sexuality of snails of the genus *Crepidula*. *J. exp. Zool.*, **122**, pp. 5–19.

COLE, H. A. 1942. The American whelk tingle, *Urosalpinx cinerea* (Say), on British oyster beds. *J. mar. biol. Ass. U.K.*, **25**, pp. 477–501.

COLE, H. A. 1952. The American slipper limpet on Cornish oyster beds. *Fish. Invest., Lond.*, ser. 2, **17**, 7, pp. 1–13.

COLE, H. A. 1956. Benthos and the shellfish of commerce. In M. GRAHAM: *Sea Fisheries, their Investigations in the United Kingdom*. London, Arnold.

COLE, H. A. & R. H. BAIRD. 1953. The American slipper limpet (*Crepidula fornicata*) in Milford Haven. *Nature, Lond.*, **172**, p. 687.

COLE, H. A. & D. A. HANCOCK. 1955. *Odostomia* as a pest of oysters and mussels. *J. mar. biol. Ass. U.K.*, **34**, pp. 25–31.

COLE, H. A. & D. A. HANCOCK. 1956. Progress in oyster research in Britain 1949–54, with special reference to the control of pests and diseases. *Rapp. Cons. Explor. Mer*, **140**, pp. 24–29.

COLGAN, N. 1910. Notes on the adaptability of certain littoral Mollusca. *Irish Nat.*, **19**, pp. 127–133.

COLMAN, J. 1933. The nature of the intertidal zonation of plants and animals. *J. mar. biol. Ass. U.K.*, **18**, pp. 435–476.

COLMAN, J. 1940. On the faunas inhabiting intertidal seaweeds. *J. mar. biol. Ass. U.K.*, **24**, pp. 129–183.

COLTON, H. S. 1908. How *Fulgur* and *Sycotypus* eat oysters, mussels and clams. *Proc. nat. Acad. Sci., Philad.*, **60**, pp. 3–10.

COLTON, H. S. 1916. On some varieties of *Thais lapillus* in the Mount Desert region, a study of individual ecology. *Proc. nat. Acad. Sci., Philad.*, **68**, pp. 440–451.

COLTON, H. S. 1922. Variation in the dog whelk *Thais* (*Purpura* auct.) *lapillus*. *Ecology*, **3**, pp. 146–157.

COMFORT, A. 1951. The pigmentation of molluscan shells. *Biol. Rev.*, **26**, pp. 285–301.

CONCHOLOGICAL SOCIETY OF GREAT BRITAIN AND IRELAND. 1951. Census of the distribution of British non-marine Mollusca. *J. Conch.*, **23**, pp. 171–244.

CONKLIN, E. G. 1897. The embryology of *Crepidula. J. Morph.*, **13**, pp. 1–226.

COOK, P. M. 1949. A ciliary feeding mechanism in *Viviparus viviparus* (L.). *Proc. malac. Soc. Lond.*, **27**, pp. 265–271.

COOKE, A. H. 1895. *Molluscs*. In S. F. HARMER & A. E. SHIPLEY: *The Cambridge Natural History*, **3**. London, Macmillan & Co.

COOKE, A. H. 1917. *Patella vulgata*, Linnæus, and its so-called variety, *Patella depressa*, Pennant. *Proc. malac. Soc. Lond.*, **12**, pp. 135–137.

COOKE, A. H. 1920. Evolution in the molluscan radula. *J. Conch.*, **16**, pp. 145–150.

COPELAND, M. 1919. Locomotion in two species of the gastropod genus *Alectrion* with observations on the behaviour of pedal cilia. *Biol. Bull., Wood's Hole*, **37**, pp. 126–138.

COPELAND, M. 1922. Ciliary and muscular locomotion in the gastropod genus *Polinices. Biol. Bull., Wood's Hole*, **42**, pp. 132–142.

CORNET, R. & I. MARCHE-MARCHAD. 1951. Inventaire de la faune marine de Roscoff. Mollusques. *Trav. Sta. biol. Roscoff*, suppl. **5**, pp. 1–81.

COX, L. R. 1955. Observations on gastropod descriptive terminology. *Proc. malac. Soc. Lond.*, **31**, pp. 190–202.

COX, L. R. 1960. Thoughts on the classification of the Gastropoda. *Proc. malac. Soc. Lond.*, **33**, pp. 239–261.

CRAMPTON, H. E. 1894. Reversal of cleavage in a sinistral gasteropod. *Ann. N.Y. Acad. Sci.*, **8**, pp. 167–170.

CREEK, G. A. 1951. The reproductive system and embryology of the snail *Pomatias elegans* (Müller). *Proc. zool. Soc. Lond.*, **121**, pp. 599–640.

CREEK, G. A. 1953. The morphology of *Acme fusca* (Montagu) with special reference to the genital system. *Proc. malac. Soc. Lond.*, **29**, pp. 228–240.

CROFTS, D. R. 1929. *Haliotis. L.M.B.C. Memoir*, **29**. Liverpool, University Press.

CROFTS, D. R. 1937. The development of *Haliotis tuberculata*, with special reference to the organogenesis during torsion. *Philos. Trans. B*, **208**, pp. 219–268.

CROFTS, D. R. 1955. Muscle morphogenesis in primitive gastropods and its relation to torsion. *Proc. zool. Soc. Lond.*, **125**, pp. 711–750.

CROSSE, H. & P. FISCHER. 1882. Note complémentaire sur la résorption des parois internes du test chez les *Olivella. J. Conchyliol.*, **30**, p. 177.

CUENOT, L. 1891. Etudes sur le sang et les glandes lymphatiques dans la série animale. *Arch. Zool. exp. gén.* (2), **9**, pp. 13–90.

CUENOT, L. 1899. L'excrétion chez les mollusques. *Arch. Biol., Paris*, **16**, pp. 49–96.

CUENOT, L. 1914. Les organes phagocytaires des mollusques. *Arch. Zool. exp. gén.*, **54**, pp. 267–305.

CUVIER, G. L. C. F. D. 1798. *Tableau Elémentaire de l'Histoire Naturelle des Animaux*. Paris, Baudonin.

DAKIN, W. J. 1912. *Buccinum. L.M.B.C. Memoir*, **20**. London, Williams & Norgate.

DALL, W. H. 1889. Reports on the results of dredging, under the supervision of Alexander Agassiz, in the Gulf of Mexico (1877–78) and in the Caribbean Sea (1879–80), by the U.S. Coast Survey Steamer 'Blake', Lieut.-Commander C. D. Sigsbee, U.S.N., and Commander J. R. Bartlett, U.S.N., commanding. XXIX. Report on the Mollusca. Part II. Gastropoda and Scaphopoda. *Bull. Mus. comp. Zool. Harvard*, **18**, pp. 1–492.

DALL, W. H. 1924. The value of the nuclear characters in the classification of marine gastropods *J. Wash. Acad. Sci.*, **14**, pp. 177–180.

DANIEL, A. T. 1893. *Hydrobia jenkinsi* Smith in an inland locality. *J. Conch.*, **7**, p. 325.

DAS, S. M. & G. SESHAPPA. 1947. A contribution to the biology of *Patella*: on population distribution and sex-proportions in *Patella vulgata* Linnaeus at Cullercoats, England. *Proc. zool. Soc. Lond.*, **117**, pp. 653–662.

DAUTERT, E. 1929. Die Bildung der Keimblätter bei *Paludina. Zool. Jb. (Anat. Ont.)*, **50**, pp. 433–496.

DAUTZENBERG, P. & H. FISCHER. 1914. Etude sur le *Littorina abtusata* et ses variations. *J. Conchyliol.*, **62**, pp. 87–128.

DAVIES, A. M. 1939. Some palaeontological problems. *Proc. malac. Soc. Lond.*, **23**, pp. 336–344.

DAVIS, J. R. A. 1895. The habits of limpets. *Nature, Lond.*, **51**, pp. 511–512.

DAVIS, J. R. A. & H. J. FLEURE. 1903. *Patella. L.M.B.C. Memoir*, **10**. Liverpool, University Press.

DEAN, J. D. 1904. Fish and their relation to *Paludestrina jenkinsi. J. Conch.*, **11**, p. 15.

DEAN, J. D. 1936. Conchological cabinets of the last century. *J. Conch.*, **20**, pp. 225–252.

DEINSE, A. B. VAN. 1913. Again: regeneration of the shell of *Anodonta* and other deformation of shells. *Zool. Anz.*, **42**, pp. 36–42.

DELAGE, Y. 1887. Sur une fonction nouvelle des otocystes comme organes d'orientation locomotrice. *Arch. Zool. exp. gén.* (2), **5**, pp. 1–26.

DELSMAN, H. C. 1914. Entwicklungsgeschichte von *Littorina obtusata. Tijdschr. ned. dierk. Ver.*, **13**, pp. 170–340.

DESHPANDE R. D. 1957. Observations on the anatomy and ecology of British trochids. *Ph.D. Thesis, University of Reading.*

DIEHL, M. 1956. Die Raubschnecke *Velutina velutina* das Feind und Bruteinmieter der Ascidie *Styela coriacea. Kieler Meeresforsch.*, **12**, pp. 180–185.

DIMELOW, E. J. 1959. Some aspects of the biology of *Antedon bifida* (Pennant). *Ph.D. Thesis, University of Reading.*

DODD, J. M. 1956. Studies on the biology of limpets. II. Breeding of *Patella vulgata* L. in Britain. III. Hermaphroditism in the three British species of *Patella. J. mar. biol. Ass. U.K.*, **35**, pp. 149–176 and 327–340.

DODD, J. M. 1957. Artificial fertilisation, larval development and metamorphosis in *Patella vulgata* L. and *Patella coerulea* L. *Pubbl. Staz. zool. Napoli*, **29**, pp. 172–186.

DODGSON, K. S. & B. SPENCER. 1954. Studies on sulphatases. 7. A preliminary account of the glycosulphatase of *Littorina littorea. Biochem. J.*, **57**, pp. 310–315.

DOLLFUS, R. PH. 1950. Hôtes et distribution géographique des cercaires cystophores. *Ann. Parasit. hum. comp.*, **25**, pp. 276–296.

DONGEN, A. VAN. 1956. The preference of *Littorina obtusata* for Fucaceae. *Arch. néerl. Zool.*, **11**, pp. 373–386.

DONS, C. 1913. Zoologisker notiser II. Om egglaegningen hos enkelte Buccinider. *Tromsø Mus. Aarsh.*, **35** & **36**, pp. 11–22.

DOTTERWEICH, H. & E. ELSSNER. 1935. Die Mobilisierung des Schalenkalkes für die Reaktionsregulation der Muscheln (*Anodonta cygnea*). *Biol. Zbl.*, **55**, pp. 138–163.

DRUMMOND, I. M. 1903. Notes on the development of *Paludina vivipara*, with special reference to the urinogenital organs and theories of gasteropod torsion. *Quart. J. micr. Sci.*, **46**, pp. 97–143.

DUBOIS, R. 1902a. Sur le mécanisme intime de la formation de la pourpre chez *Murex brandaris. C.R. Soc. Biol., Paris*, **54**, pp. 82–83.

DUBOIS, R. 1902b. Sur le mécanisme intime de la formation de la pourpre. *C.R. Acad. Sci., Paris*, **134**, pp. 245–246.

DUBOIS, R. 1903a. Sur la formation de la pourpre de *Purpura lapillus. C.R. Acad. Sci., Paris*, **136**, pp. 117–118.

DUBOIS, R. 1903b. Sur le vénin de la glande à pourpre de *Purpura lapillus. C.R. Soc. Biol., Paris*, **55**, p. 81.

DUBOIS, R. 1909. Recherches sur la pourpre et sur quelques autres pigments animaux. *Arch. Zool. exp. gén.*, **42**, pp. 471–590.

DUGES, A. 1829. Observations sur la structure et la formation de l'opercule chez les mollusques. *Ann. Sci. nat. Zool.* (1), **18**, pp. 113–133.

DUVAL, M. 1924. Recherches sur le milieu intérieur des invertébrés marins. Comparaison entre la teneur en chlorure de sodium de ce milieu et celle de l'eau de mer extérieure. *Bull. Sta. biol. Arcachon Bordeaux*, **21**, pp. 33–39.

EBLING, F. J. 1945. Formation and nature of the opercular chaetae of *Sabellaria alveolata*. *Quart. J. micr. Sci.*, **85**, pp. 153–176.

EBLING, F. J., J. A. KITCHING, R. D. PURCHON & R. BASSINDALE. 1948. The ecology of the Lough Ine rapids with special reference to water currents. 2. The fauna of the *Saccorhiza* canopy. *J. Anim. Ecol.*, **17**, pp. 223–244.

EIGENBRODT, H. 1941. Untersuchungen über die Funktion der Radula einiger Schnecken. *Z. Morph. Ökol. Tiere*, **37**, pp. 735–791.

ELLIOT, G. F. S., M. LAURIE & J. B. MURDOCH. 1901. *Fauna, Flora and Geology of the Clyde Area*. Glasgow, Local Committee for the meeting of the British Association.

ELLIS, A. E. 1925. Experimental acclimatization in *Sabanaea ulvae* (Pennant) to freshwater. *Ann. Mag. nat. Hist.* (9), **15**, pp. 496–497.

ELLIS, A. E. 1926. *British Snails. A Guide to the Non-Marine Gastropoda*. Oxford, Clarendon Press.

ELLIS, A. E. 1932. The habitats of Hydrobiidae in the Adur estuary. *Proc. malac. Soc. Lond.*, **20**, pp. 11–18.

ERLANGER, R. VON. 1891*a*. Zur Entwickelung von *Paludina vivipara*. *Morph. Jb.*, **17**, pp. 337–379 and 636–680.

ERLANGER, R. VON. 1891*b*. Zur Entwickelung von *Paludina vivipara*. Vorläufige Mittheilung. *Zool. Anz.*, **14**, pp. 280–283.

ERLANGER, R. VON. 1892. On the paired nephridia of prosobranchs, the homologies of the only remaining nephridium of most prosobranchs, and the relation of the nephridia to the gonad and genital duct. *Quart. J. micr. Sci.*, **33**, pp. 587–623.

ERLANGER, R. VON. 1894. Zum Bildung des Mesoderms bei der *Paludina vivipara*. *Morph. Jb.*, **22**, pp. 113–118.

ERSPAMER, V. 1947. Ricerche chimiche e farmacologiche sugli estratti di ghiandola ipo-branchiale di *Murex (Truncularia) trunculus* (L.), *Murex (Bolimes) brandaris* (L.) e *Tritonalia erinacea* (L.). *Pubbl. Staz. zool. Napoli*, **20**, pp. 91–101.

ERSPAMER, V. 1952. Wirksame Stoff der hinteren Speicheldrüsen der Octopoden und der Hypobranchialdrüse der Purpurschnecken. *Arzneimittelforsch.*, **2**, pp. 253–258.

ESLICK, A. 1940. An ecological study of *Patella* at Port St. Mary, Isle of Man. *Proc. Linn. Soc. Lond.*, Sess. 152, pp. 45–58.

EVANS, R. G. 1947. The intertidal ecology of selected localities in the Plymouth neighbour-hood. *J. mar. biol. Ass. U.K.*, **27**, pp. 173–218.

EVANS, R. G. 1948. The lethal temperatures of some common British littoral molluscs. *J. Anim. Ecol.*, **17**, pp. 165–173.

EVANS, R. G. 1953. Studies on the biology of British limpets—the genus *Patella* on the south coast of England. *Proc. zool. Soc. Lond.*, **123**, pp. 357–376.

FÄNGE, R. 1957. An acetylcholine-like salivary poison in the marine gastropod *Neptunea antiqua*. *Nature, Lond.*, **180**, pp. 196–197.

FÄNGE, R. 1958. Paper chromatography and biological extracts of the salivary gland of *Neptunea antiqua* (Gastropoda). *Acta zool. Stockh.*, **39**, pp. 39–46.

FÄNGE, R. & A. MATTISSON. 1958. Studies on the physiology of the radula-muscle of *Buccinum undatum*. *Acta zool. Stockh.*, **39**, pp. 53–64.

FERNANDO, W. 1931*a*. The origin of the mesoderm in the gastropod *Viviparus* ( =*Paludina*). *Proc. roy. Soc. B*, **107**, pp. 381–390.

FERNANDO, W. 1931*b*. The development of the kidney in *Ampullaria (Pila) gigas*. *Proc. zool. Soc. Lond.*, pp. 745–750.

FISCHER, E. 1928. Recherches de bionomie et d'océanographie littorales sur La Rance et le littoral de la Manche. *Ann. Inst. océanogr. Monaco*, **5**, pp. 201–429.

FISCHER, E. 1931. Sur la pénétration des diverses espèces marines sessiles dans les estuaires et sa limitation par l'eau douce. *Ann. Inst. océanogr. Monaco*, **10**, pp. 213–243.

FISCHER, H. 1892. Recherches sur la morphologie du foie des gastéropodes. *Bull. sci. Fr. Belg.*, **24**, pp. 260–346.

FISCHER, P. 1865. Note sur les moeurs du *Murex erinaceus*. *J. Conchyliol.*, **13**, pp. 5–8.

FISCHER, P. 1887. *Manuel de Conchyliologie*. Paris, Savy.

FISCHER, P.-H. 1922. Sur les gastropodes perceurs. *J. Conchyliol.*, **67**, pp. 3–56.

FISCHER, P.-H. 1925. Sur la rôle de la glande purpurigène des *Murex* et des Pourpres. *C.R. Acad. Sci.*, *Paris*, **180**, pp. 1369–1371.

FISCHER, P.-H. 1940a. Structure et évolution de l'épithelium de l'opercule chez *Purpura lapillus* L. *Bull. Soc. zool. Fr.*, **65**, pp. 199–204.

FISCHER, P.-H. 1940b. Observations sur la ponte de quelques Muricidés. *Bull. Soc. zool. Fr.*, **65**, pp. 205–211.

FISCHER, P.-H. 1948. Données sur la résistance et le vitalité des mollusques. *J. Conchyliol.*, **88**, pp. 100–140.

FISCHER, P.-H., M. DUVAL & A. RAFFY. 1933. Etudes sur les échanges respiratoires des Littorines. *Arch. Zool. exp. gén.*, **74**, pp. 627–634.

FISCHER-PIETTE, E. 1935a. Histoire d'une moulière. Observations sur une phase de déséquilibre faunique. *Bull. biol.*, **69**, pp. 154–180.

FISCHER-PIETTE, E. 1935b. Systématique et biogéographie—les Patelles d'Europe et d'Afrique du Nord. *J. Conchyliol.*, **79**, pp. 5–66.

FISCHER-PIETTE, E. 1941a. Croissance, taille maximum, et longévité possible de quelques animaux intercotideaux en fonction du milieu. *Ann. Inst. océanogr. Monaco*, **21**, pp. 1–28.

FISCHER-PIETTE, E. 1941b. Observations biométriques sur Patelles de la Manche. *J. Conchyliol.*, **84**, pp. 300–306.

FISCHER-PIETTE, E. 1946. Review of Biology of *Patella* in Great Britain, par J. Orton, *Nature*, vol. **158**, p. 173, 3 Août 1946. *J. Conchyliol.*, **87**, pp. 83–84.

FISCHER-PIETTE, E. 1948. Sur les éléments de prospérité des Patelles et sur leur spécificité. *J. Conchyliol.*, **88**, pp. 45–96.

FLATTELY, F. W. & C. L. WALTON. 1922. *The Biology of the Sea-shore*. London, Sidgwick & Jackson.

FLEISCHMANN, A. 1932. Vergleichende Betrachtungen über das Schalenwachstum der Weichtiere (Mollusca). II. Deckel (Operculum) und Haus (Concha) der Schnecken (Gastropoden). *Z. Morph. Ökol. Tiere*, **25**, pp. 549–622.

FLEURE, H. J. 1903. Notes on the relations of the kidney in *Haliotis tuberculata* etc. *Quart. J. micr. Sci.*, **46**, pp. 77–97.

FLORKIN, M. 1935. Influences des variations de l'abaissement cryoscopique du milieu extérieur sur celui du sang et de l'urine de l'Anodonte. *Bull. Acad. Belg. Cl. Sci.*, **1935**, pp. 432–435.

FLORKIN, M. & G. BESSON. 1935. Le liquid extrapalléal de l'Anodonte n'est pas identique au sang de cet animal. *C.R. Soc. Biol.*, *Paris*, **118**, pp. 1222–1223.

FLORKIN, M. & G. DUCHATEAU. 1949. Sur l'osmorégulation de l'Anodonte. *Physiol. comp. Oecol.*, **1**, pp. 29–45.

FOL, H. 1880. Sur le développement des gastropodes pulmonés. *Arch. Zool. exp. gén.* (1), **8**, pp. 103–232.

FORBES, E. & S. HANLEY. 1849–53. *A History of British Mollusca, and their Shells*. 4 Vols. Vol. 2 (1849), 3 (1850), 4 (1852, 1853). London, van Voorst.

FRAENKEL, G. 1927a. Beiträge zur Geotaxis und Phototaxis von *Littorina*. *Z. vergl. Physiol.*, **5**, pp. 585–597.

FRAENKEL, G. 1927b. Biologische Beobachtungen an *Ianthina*. *Z. Morph. Ökol. Tiere*, **7**, pp. 597–608.

FRAISSE, P. 1881. Über Molluskenaugen mit embryonalem Typus. *Z. wiss. Zool.*, **35**, pp. 461–477.

FRANC, A. 1940. Recherches sur le développement d'*Ocinebra aciculata*, Lamarck (mollusque gastéropode). *Bull. biol.*, **74**, pp. 327–345.

FRANC, A. 1941a. Sur les reins larvaires de certains mollusques prosobranches. *C.R. Soc. Biol.*, *Paris*, **135**, pp. 1487–1489.

FRANC, A. 1941*b*. Sur la formation des oothèques des mollusques prosobranches. *C.R. Soc. Biol., Paris*, **135**, pp. 1609-1611.

FRANC A. 1943. Etudes sur le développement de quelques prosobranches mediterranéens. *Thèse, Université d'Alger.*

FRANC, A. 1949. Notes histologiques sur la métamorphose de *Firoloida desmaresti* Lesueur (mollusque hétéropode). *Bull. Soc. zool. Fr.*, **74**, pp. 141-146.

FRANC, A. 1950. Ponte et larves planctoniques de *Philbertia purpurea* (Montagu). *Bull. Lab. marit. Dinard*, **33**, pp. 23-25.

FRANC, A. 1952*a*. Notes éthologiques et anatomiques sur *Tritonalia (Ocinebrina) aciculata* (Lk.). (Mollusque prosobranche). *Bull. Lab. marit. Dinard*, **36**, pp. 31-34.

FRANC, A. 1952*b*. Notes écologiques et anatomiques sur *Philbertia purpurea* (Montagu). (Moll. Ctenobr.). *Bull. Mus. Hist. nat. Paris*, **24**, pp. 302-305.

FRANK, E. J. 1914. Beiträge zur Anatomie der Trochiden. *Jena. Z. Naturw.*, **51**, pp. 377-486.

FRANZ, V. 1938. Die europäische Flussdeckelschnecke (*Viviparus fasciatus*) im starkem Strom des Njemen. *Arch. Molluskenk.*, **70**, pp. 9-30.

FRANZÉN, A. 1955. Comparative morphological investigations into the spermiogenesis among Mollusca. *Zool. Bidr. Uppsala*, **30**, pp. 399-456.

FRANZÉN, A. 1956. On spermiogenesis, morphology of the spermatozoon, and biology of fertilization among invertebrates. *Zool. Bidr. Uppsala*, **31**, pp. 356-482.

FREDERICQ, H. 1939. Action des nerfs du coeur d'*Aplysia limacina*. Analyse au moyen de la caféine. *Arch. int. Physiol.*, **49**, pp. 299-304.

FREEMAN, J. A. & K. M. WILBUR. 1948. Carbonic anhydrase in molluscs. *Biol. Bull., Wood's Hole*, **94**, pp. 55-59.

FRETTER, V. 1939. The structure and function of the alimentary canal of some tectibranch molluscs, with a note on excretion. *Trans. roy. Soc. Edinb.*, **59**, pp. 599-646.

FRETTER, V. 1941. The genital ducts of some British stenoglossan prosobranchs. *J. mar. biol. Ass. U.K.*, **25**, pp. 173-211.

FRETTER, V. 1946*a*. The pedal sucker and anal gland of some British Stenoglossa. *Proc. malac. Soc. Lond.*, **27**, pp. 126-130.

FRETTER, V. 1946*b*. The genital ducts of *Theodoxus*, *Lamellaria* and *Trivia*, and a discussion on their evolution in the prosobranchs. *J. mar. biol. Ass. U.K.*, **26**, pp. 312-351.

FRETTER, V. 1948. The structure and life history of some minute prosobranchs of rock pools: *Skeneopsis planorbis* (Fabricius), *Omalogyra atomus* (Philippi), *Rissoella diaphana* (Alder) and *Rissoella opalina* (Jeffreys). *J. mar. biol. Ass. U.K.*, **27**, pp. 597-632.

FRETTER, V. 1951*a*. Some observations on the British cypraeids. *Proc. malac. Soc. Lond.*, **29**, pp. 14-20.

FRETTER, V. 1951*b*. Observations on the life history and functional morphology of *Cerithiopsis tubercularis* (Montagu) and *Triphora perversa* (L.). *J. mar. biol. Ass. U.K.*, **29**, pp. 567-586.

FRETTER, V. 1951*c*. *Turbonilla elegantissima* (Montagu), a parasitic opisthobranch. *J. mar. biol. Ass. U.K.*, **30**, pp. 37-47.

FRETTER, V. 1952. Experiments with $P^{32}$ and $I^{131}$ on species of *Helix*, *Arion* and *Agriolimax*. *Quart. J. micr. Sci.*, **93**, pp. 133-146.

FRETTER, V. 1953*a*. Experiments with radioactive strontium ($^{90}$Sr) on certain molluscs and polychaetes. *J. mar. biol. Ass. U.K.*, **32**, pp. 367-384.

FRETTER, V. 1953*b*. The transference of sperm from male to female prosobranch, with reference, also, to the pyramidellids. *Proc. Linn. Soc. Lond.*, Sess. 164, 1951-52, pp. 217-224.

FRETTER, V. 1955*a*. Observations on *Balcis devians* (Monterosato) and *Balcis alba* (Da Costa). *Proc. malac. Soc. Lond.*, **31**, pp. 137-144.

FRETTER, V. 1955*b*. Some observations on *Tricolia pullus* (L.) and *Margarites helicinus* (Fabricius). *Proc. malac. Soc. Lond.*, **31**, pp. 159-162.

FRETTER, V. 1956. The anatomy of the prosobranch *Circulus striatus* (Philippi) and a review of its systematic position. *Proc. zool. Soc. Lond.*, **126**, pp. 369-381.

FRETTER, V. & A. GRAHAM. 1949. The structure and mode of life of the Pyramidellidae, parasitic opisthobranchs. *J. mar. biol. Ass. U.K.*, **28**, pp. 493–532.

FRETTER, V. & A. M. PATIL. 1958. A revision of the systematic position of the prosobranch gastropod *Cingulopsis* (=*Cingula*) *fulgida* (J. Adams). *Proc. malac. Soc. Lond.*, **33**, pp. 114–126.

FRIZA, F. 1932. Zur Kenntnis des Conchiolins der Muschelschalen. *Biochem. Z.*, **246**, pp. 29–37.

FRÖMMING, E. 1956. *Biologie der mitteleuropäischen Süsswasserschnecken.* Berlin, Duncker & Humblot.

GABE, M. 1951a. Données histologiques sur la neurosécrétion chez les Pterotracheidae (hétéropodes). *Rev. canad. Biol.*, **10**, pp. 391–410.

GABE, M. 1951b. Données histologiques sur les organes du complexe palléal chez la Fissurelle. *Bull. Lab. marit. Dinard*, **35**, pp. 1–14.

GABE, M. 1953a. Particularités morphologiques des cellules neurosécrétrices chez quelques prosobranches monotocardes. *C.R. Acad. Sci., Paris*, **236**, pp. 333–335.

GABE, M. 1953b. Particularités histologiques des cellules neurosécrétrices chez quelques gastéropodes opisthobranches. *C.R. Acad. Sci., Paris*, **236**, pp. 2161–2163.

GABE, M. 1954. La neurosécrétion chez les invertébrés. *Ann. biol.*, **30**, pp. 5–62.

GABE, M. & M. PRENANT. 1949. Contribution à l'étude cytologique et histochimique du tube digestif des polyplacophores. *Arch. Biol., Paris*, **60**, pp. 39–77.

GALLIEN, L. & M. DE LARAMBERGUE. 1936. Cycle et dimorphisme sexuel chez *Lacuna pallidula* da Costa (Littorinidae). *C.R. Acad. Sci., Paris*, **203**, pp. 409–412.

GALLIEN, L. & M. DE LARAMBERGUE. 1938. Biologie et sexualité de *Lacuna pallidula* da Costa (Littorinidae). *Trav. Sta. zool. Wimereux*, **13**, pp. 293–306.

GALTSOFF, P. S., H. F. PRYTHERCH & J. B. ENGLE. 1937. Natural history and methods of controlling the common oyster drills (*Urosalpinx cinerea* Say and *Eupleura caudata* Say). *Cir. U.S. Bur. Fish.*, **25**, pp. 1–24.

GARNAULT, P. 1887. Recherches anatomiques et histologiques sur le *Cyclostoma elegans*. *Acta Soc. linn. Bordeaux*, **41**, pp. 11–158.

GARSTANG, W. 1928. The origin and evolution of larval forms. Presidential Address, Section D. *Brit. Ass. Rep., Glasgow*, pp. 77–98.

GARSTANG, W. 1951. *Larval Forms.* Oxford, Blackwell.

GEDDES, P. 1879. On the mechanism of the odontophore in certain Mollusca. *Trans. zool. Soc. Lond.*, **10**, pp. 485–491.

GEGENBAUR, C. 1855. *Untersuchungen über Pteropoden und Heteropoden.* Leipzig, Engelmann.

GEORGE, J. C. & C. JURA. 1958. A histochemical study of the capsule fluid of the egg of a land snail *Succinea putris* L. *Proc. Acad. Sci. Amst.*, **61**, C, pp. 598–603.

GEORGE, W. C. & J. H. FERGUSON. 1950. The blood of gastropod molluscs. *J. Morph.*, **86**, pp. 315–327.

GERMAIN, L. 1930. Mollusques terrestres et fluviatiles. *Faune de France*, **22**, pp. 1–444.

GERSCH, M. 1934. Zur experimenteller Veränderung der Richtung der Wellenbewegung auf der Kriechsole von Schnecken und zur Rückwartsbewegung von Schnecken. *Biol. Zbl.*, **54**, pp. 511–518.

GERSCH, M. 1936. Der Genitalapparat und die Sexualbiologie der Nordseetrochiden. *Z. Morph. Ökol. Tiere*, **31**, pp. 106–150.

GERSCH, M. 1959. Neurohormone bei wirbellosen Tieren. *Verh. dtsch. zool. Ges., Zool. Anz.* Suppl. **23**, pp. 40–76.

GIARD, A. 1875. Sur l'embryologie du *Lamellaria perspicua*. *C.R. Acad. Sci., Paris*, **80**, pp. 736–739.

GIBSON, R. J. H. 1887. Anatomy and physiology of *Patella vulgata*. Part I, Anatomy. *Trans. roy. Soc. Edinb.*, **32**, pp. 601–638.

GIESE, M. 1915. Der Genitalapparat von *Calyptraea sinensis* Linn., *Crepidula unguiformis* Lam. und *Capulus hungaricus* Lam. *Z. wiss. Zool.*, **114**, pp. 169–231.

GIGLIOLI, M. E. C. 1949. Some observations on the biology of the whelk *Polynices heros* Say (1822) and *Polynices triseriata* Say (1826), at Belliveau Cove, Nova Scotia. *MS Rep. Fish. Res. Bd. Canada*, **398**, pp. 1–140.

GIGLIOLI, M. E. C. 1955. The egg masses of the Naticidae (Gastropoda). *J. Fish. Res. Bd. Canada*, **12**, pp. 287–327.

GISLÉN, T. 1930. Epibioses of the Gullmar Fjord I. A study in marine sociology. *Skriftser. Kristinebergs zoologiska Station* 1877–1927, **3**, pp. 1–123.

GLANCY, J. B. 1953. Oyster production and oyster drill control. *Conv. Pap. nat. Shellf. Ass.*, New Orleans.

GLASER, O. C. 1906. Über den Kannibalismus bei *Fasciolaria tulipa* (var. *distans*) und deren larve Exkretionsorgane. *Z. wiss. Zool.*, **80**, pp. 80–121.

GOLDFUSS, O. 1900. *Die Binnenmollusken Mitteldeutschlands*. Leipzig, Engelmann.

GOMPEL, M. M. 1937. Recherches sur la consommation d'oxygène de quelques animaux aquatiques littoraux. *C.R. Acad. Sci.*, Paris, **205**, pp. 816–818.

GOODRICH, E. S. 1895. On the coelom, genital ducts and nephridia. *Quart. J. micr. Sci.*, **37**, pp. 477–510.

GOSTAN, G. 1958. Correlation entre la croissance d'un prosobranche (*Rissoa parva* da Costa) et le développement des organes internes. *C.R. Acad. Sci.*, Paris, **247**, pp. 2193–2195.

GÖTZE, E. 1938. Bau und Leben von *Caecum glabrum* (Montagu). *Zool. Jb. (Syst.)*, **71**, pp. 55–122.

GOULD, H. N. 1919. Studies on sex in the hermaphrodite mollusc *Crepidula plana*. III. Transference of the male-producing stimulus through sea-water. *J. exp. Zool.*, **29**, pp. 113–120.

GOULD, H. N. 1947. Conditions affecting the development of the male phase in *Crepidula plana*. *Biol. Bull., Wood's Hole*, **93**, p. 194.

GOULD, H. N. 1952. Studies on sex in the hermaphrodite mollusk *Crepidula plana*. IV. Internal and external factors influencing growth and sex development. *J. exp. Zool.*, **119**, pp. 93–160.

GOWANLOCH, J. N. 1927. Contributions to the study of marine gastropods. II. The intertidal life of *Buccinum undatum*, a study in non-adaptation. *Contr. canad. Biol. Fish.*, N.S., **3**, pp. 167–177.

GOWANLOCH, J. N. & F. R. HAYES. 1926. Contributions to the study of marine gastropods. I. The physical factors, behaviour and intertidal life of *Littorina*. *Contr. canad. Biol. Fish.*, N.S., **3**, pp. 133–165.

GRABAU, A. W. 1902. Characters of the gastropod shell. *Amer. Nat.*, **36**, pp. 917–945.

GRABAU, A. W. 1928. The significance of the so-called ornamental characters in the molluscan shell. *Bull. Peking Soc. nat. Hist.*, **2**, pp. 27–36.

GRAHAM, A. 1932. On the structure and function of the alimentary canal of the limpet. *Trans. roy. Soc. Edinb.*, **57**, pp. 287–308.

GRAHAM, A. 1938. On a ciliary process of food-collecting in the gastropod *Turritella communis* Risso. *Proc. zool. Soc. Lond.*, A, **108**, pp. 453–463.

GRAHAM, A. 1939. On the structure of the alimentary canal of style-bearing prosobranchs. *Proc. zool. Soc. Lond.*, B, **109**, pp. 75–112.

GRAHAM, A. 1941. The oesophagus of the stenoglossan prosobranchs. *Proc. roy. Soc. Edinb.*, B, **61**, pp. 1–23.

GRAHAM, A. 1949. The molluscan stomach. *Trans. roy Soc. Edinb.*, **61**, pp. 737–778.

GRAHAM, A. 1954a. The anatomy of the prosobranch *Trichotropis borealis* Broderip and Sowerby, and the systematic position of the Capulidae. *J. mar. biol. Ass. U.K.*, **33**, pp. 129–144.

GRAHAM, A. 1954b. Some observations on the reproductive tract of *Ianthina janthina* (L.). *Proc. malac. Soc. Lond.*, **31**, pp. 1–6.

GRAHAM, A. & V. FRETTER. 1947. The life history of *Patina pellucida* (L.). *J. mar. biol. Ass. U.K.*, **26**, pp. 590–601.

GRAY, J. E. 1850. On the operculum of the gasteropodous Mollusca and an attempt to prove that it is homologous or identical with the second valve of Conchifera. *Ann. Mag. nat. Hist.* (2), **5**, pp. 476–483.

GRENACHER, H. 1886. Abhandlungen zur vergleichenden Anatomie des Auges. II. Das Auge der Heteropoden. *Abh. naturf. Ges. Halle*, **17**, pp. 1–64.

GROBBEN, C. 1888. Die Pericardialdrüse der Lamellibranchiaten. Ein Beitrag zur Kenntniss der Anatomie dieser Molluskenclasse. *Arb. zool. Inst. Univ. Wien*, **7**, pp. 355–444.

GROBBEN, C. 1891. Die Pericardialdrüse der Gastropoden. *Arb. zool. Inst. Univ. Wien*, **9**, pp. 35–56.

GROSSU, A. V. 1956. *Fauna republicii populare Romîne. Mollusca*, **3**, 2. *Gastropoda Prosobranchia si Opisthobranchia.* Bucureşti, Academiei Republicii Populare Romîne.

GURJANOVA, E., I. SACHS & P. USCHAKOV. 1930. Das Littoral des Kola Fjords. III. *Trav. Soc. Nat. Leningrad*, **60**, pp. 17–107.

GWATKIN, H. M. 1914. Some molluscan radulae. *J. Conch.*, **14**, pp. 139–148.

HAAS, F. 1938. Über potentielle Skulpturbildung bei *Valvata (Cincinna) piscinalis antiqua* (Sow.). *Arch. Molluskenk.*, **70**, pp. 41–45.

HALLER, B. 1884. Untersuchungen über marine Rhipidoglossen. I. *Morph. Jb.*, **9**, pp. 1–98.

HALLER, B. 1886. Untersuchungen über marine Rhipidoglossen. II. *Morph. Jb.*, **11**, pp. 321–430.

HALLER, B. 1888. Die Morphologie der Prosobranchier, gesammelt auf einer Erdumsegelung durch die König. italienische Korvette 'Vettor Pisani'. I. *Morph. Jb.*, **14**, pp. 54–169.

HALLER, B. 1894. *Studien über docoglosse und rhipidoglosse Prosobranchier.* Leipzig, Engelmann.

HAMMERSTEN, O. D. & J. RUNNSTRÖM. 1926. Zur Embryologie von *Acanthochiton discrepans* Brown. *Zool. Jb. (Anat. Ont.)*, **47**, pp. 261–318.

HANCOCK, D. A. 1954. The destruction of oyster spat by *Urosalpinx cinerea* (Say) on Essex oyster beds. *J. Cons. int. Explor. Mer*, **20**, pp. 186–196.

HANCOCK, D. A. 1956. The structure of the capsule and the hatching process in *Urosalpinx cinerea* (Say). *Proc. zool. Soc. Lond.*, **127**, pp. 565–571.

HANCOCK, D. A. 1957. Studies in the biology and ecology of certain marine invertebrates, with particular reference to those associated with oyster culture. *Ph.D. Thesis, University of Reading.*

HANCOCK, D. A. 1959. The biology and control of the American whelk tingle *Urosalpinx cinerea* (Say) on English oyster beds. *Fish. Invest. Lond.* (2), **22**, no. 10, pp. 1–66.

HANKO, B. 1913. Über die Regeneration des Operkulums bei *Murex brandaris. Arch. Entw Mech. Org.*, **35**, pp. 740–747.

HANKS, J. E. 1957. The rate of feeding of the common oyster drill *Urosalpinx cinerea* (Say) at constant water temperatures. *Biol. Bull., Wood's Hole*, **112**, pp. 330–335.

HANSON, J. & J. LOWY. 1957. Structure of smooth muscles. *Nature, Lond.*, **180**, pp. 906–909.

HANSON, J., J. T. RANDALL & S. T. BAYLEY. 1952. The microstructure of the spermatozoa of the snail *Viviparus. Exp. Cell Res.*, **3**, pp. 65–78.

HARDY, A. [C.] 1956. *The Open Sea. Its Natural History: the World of Plankton.* London, Collins.

HASEMAN, J. D. 1911. The rhythmical movements of *Littorina littorea* synchronous with ocean tides. *Biol. Bull., Wood's Hole*, **21**, pp. 113–121.

HATTON, H. 1938. Essais de bionomie explicative sur quelques espèces intercotidales d'algues et d'animaux. *Ann. Inst. océanogr. Monaco*, **17**, pp. 241–348.

HAYES, F. R. 1927a. The negative geotropism of the periwinkle: a study in littoral ecology. *Trans. Nova Scotian Inst. Sci.*, **16**, pp. 155–173.

HAYES, F. R. 1927b. The effect of environmental factors on the development and growth of *Littorina littorea. Trans. Nova Scotian Inst. Sci.*, **17**, pp. 6–13.

HAYES, F. R. 1929. Contributions to the study of marine gastropods. III. Development, growth, and behaviour of *Littorina. Contr. canad. Biol.*, N.S., **4**, pp. 413–430.

HAZAY, J. 1881. Die Molluskenfauna von Budapest. Biologischer Teil. *Malak. Bl.*, N.F., **4**, pp. 43–221.

HAZELHOFF, E. H. 1938. Über die Ausnutzung des Sauerstoffs bei verschiedenen Wassertieren. *Z. vergl. Physiol.*, **26**, pp. 306–327.

HEATH, H. 1899. The development of *Ischnochiton*. *Zool. Jb.* (*Anat. Ont.*), **12**, pp. 567-656.

HENKING, H. 1894. Beiträge zur Kenntnis von *Hydrobia ulvae* Penn. und deren Brutpflege. *Ber. naturf. Ges. Freiburg i. B.*, **8**, pp. 89-110.

HENSCHEL, J. 1932. Untersuchungen über den chemischen Sinn von *Nassa reticulata*. *Wiss. Meeresuntersuch. Abt. Kiel*, **21**, pp. 131-159.

HENSEN, V. 1865. Über das Auge einiger Cephalopoden. *Z. wiss. Zool.*, **15**, pp. 155-242.

HERMITTE, L. C. D. 1946. Venomous marine molluscs of the genus *Conus*. *Trans. Soc. trop. Med. Hyg. Lond.*, **39**, pp. 485-512.

HERRICK, J. C. 1906. Mechanism of the odontophoral apparatus in *Sycotypus canaliculatus*. *Amer. Nat.*, **40**, pp. 707-737.

HERTLING, H. 1928. Beobachtungen und Versuche an den Eiern von *Littorina* und *Lacuna*. Bedeutung der Eihüllen. Entwicklung im naturlichen und abgeänderten Medium. *Wiss. Meeresuntersuch. Abt. Helgoland*, **17**, pp. 1-49.

HERTLING, H. 1931. Über den Einfluss des veränderten Mediums auf die Entwicklung von *Lacuna divaricata*, besonders auf die Bildung der Schale. *Wiss. Meeresuntersuch. Abt. Helgoland*, **18**, pp. 1-27.

HERTLING, H. & W. E. ANKEL. 1927. Bemerkungen über den Laich und die Jugendformen von *Littorina* und *Lacuna*. *Wiss. Meeresuntersuch. Abt. Helgoland*, **16**, pp. 1-13.

HESSE, R. 1900. Untersuchungen über die Organe der Lichtempfindung bei niederen Thieren. VI. Die Augen einiger Mollusken. *Z. wiss. Zool.*, **68**, pp. 379-477.

HESSE, R., W. C. ALLEE & K. P. SCHMIDT. 1937. *Ecological Animal Geography*. New York, John Wiley & Sons.

HEWATT, W. G. 1940. Observations on the homing limpet, *Acmaea scabra* Gould. *Amer. midl. Nat.*, **24**, pp. 205-208.

HILGER, C. 1885. Beiträge zur Kenntnis des Gastropodenauges. *Morph. Jb.*, **10**, pp. 351-371.

HIRASE, S. 1932. The adaptive modifications of the gastropod *Stilifer celebensis* Kükenthal, parasitic on the starfish *Certonardea semiregularis* (Müller & Troschel). *Proc. malac. Soc. Lond.*, **20**, pp. 73-76.

HIRSCH, G. C. 1915. Die Ernährungsbiologie fleischfressender Gastropoden (*Murex*, *Natica*, *Pterotrachea*, *Pleurobranchaea*, *Tritonium*). I Teil. Makroskopischer Bau, Nahrungsaufnahme, Verdauung, Sekretion. *Zool. Jb.* (*Zool. Physiol.*), **35**, pp. 357-504.

HOFFMANN, H. 1930. Über dem Fluchtreflex bei *Nassa*. *Z. vergl. Physiol.*, **11**, pp. 662-688.

HOFFMANN, H. 1932. Über die Radulabildung bei *Lymnaea stagnalis*. Jena. *Z. Naturw.*, **67**, pp. 535-550.

HOFFMANN, H. 1937. Über die Stammesgeschichte der Weichtiere. *Verh. dtsch. zool. Ges.*, *Zool. Anz.* Suppl. **10**, pp. 33-69.

HOFFMANN, H. 1938. Beiträge zur Kenntnis der Chitonen. 2. Zur Frage der Anheftung der Chitonen an die Unterlage. *Z. Morph. Ökol. Tiere*, **34**, pp. 647-662.

HÖRSTADIUS-KJELLSTRÖM, G. & S. HÖRSTADIUS. 1940. Untersuchungen über die Eiweissverdauung *in vivo* und *in vitro* bei einigen Gastropoden. *Pubbl. Staz. zool. Napoli*, **18**, pp. 151-249.

HOUSSAY, F. 1884. Recherches sur l'opercule et les glandes du pied des gastéropodes. *Arch. Zool. exp. gén.* (2), **2**, pp. 171-288.

HOWES, N. H. 1939. The ecology of a saline lagoon in south-east Essex. *J. Linn. Soc.* (*Zool.*), **40**, pp. 383-445.

HUBENDICK, B. 1945. Phylogenie und Tiergeographie der Siphonariidae. Zur Kenntnis der Phylogenie in der Ordnung Basommatophora und des Ursprungs der Pulmonatengruppe. *Zool. Bidr. Uppsala*, **24**, pp. 1-216.

HUBENDICK, B. 1947. Die Verbreitungsverhältnisse der limnischen Gastropoden in Südschweden. *Zool. Bidr. Uppsala*, **24**, pp. 419-559.

HUBENDICK, B. 1948. Über den Bau und das Wachstum des Konzentrischen Operculartypus bei Gastropoden. *Ark. Zool.*, **40** A, (10), pp. 1-28.

HUBENDICK, B.   1950.   The effectiveness of passive dispersal in *Hydrobia jenkinsi*.   *Zool. Bidr. Uppsala*, **28**, pp. 493–504.

HUBENDICK, B.   1958.   On the molluscan adhesive epithelium.   *Ark. Zool.*, A.S., **11**, pp. 31–36.

HUGGINS, H. C.   1919.   Occurrence of *Hartmannia septemspiralis* (Razoumovsky) and *H. patula* (Drap.) in England.   *J. Conch.*, **16**, pp. 51–52.

HULBERT, G. C. E. B. & C. M. YONGE.   1937.   A possible function of the osphradium in the Gastropoda.   *Nature, Lond.*, **139**, p. 840.

HUNTER, W. R.   1953*a*.   Notes on the Mollusca of the Garvelloch Islands.   *J. Conch.*, **23**, pp. 379–386.

HUNTER, W. R.   1953*b*.   On migrations of *Lymnaea peregra* (Müller) on the shores of Loch Lomond.   *Proc. roy. Soc. Edinb.*, B, **65**, pp. 84–105.

HUNTER, W. R.   1957.   Studies on freshwater snails at Loch Lomond.   *Glasg. Univ. Publ. Stud. Loch Lomond*, **1**, pp. 56–95.

HUNTER, W. R. & T. WARWICK.   1957.   Records of '*Potamopyrgus jenkinsi*' (Smith) in Scottish fresh waters over fifty years (1906–56).   *Proc. roy. Soc. Edinb.*, B, **66**, pp. 360–373.

HUTTON, R. F.   1955.   *Cercaria turritellae* n. sp., a 'huge-tailed', monostome larva from *Turritella communis* Risso.   *J. mar. biol. Ass. U.K.*, **34**, pp. 249–255.

HUXLEY, T. H.   1853.   On the morphology of the cephalous Mollusca, as illustrated by the anatomy of certain Heteropoda and Pteropoda collected during the voyage of H.M.S. 'Rattle-snake' in 1846–50.   *Philos. Trans.*, **143**, pp. 29–65.

HYKEŠ, O. V.   1929.   Adrenalin und das Weichtierherz.   *Biol. Listy*, **14**, p. 385.

HYKEŠ, O. V.   1930.   L'adrénaline et le coeur des mollusques.   *C.R. Soc. Biol.*, *Paris*, **103**, pp. 360–363.

HYKEŠ, O. V.   1932.   Adrenalwirkung am Herzen der Avertebraten.   *Čas. Lék. česk.*, p. 129; *Ber. wiss. Biol.*, **22**, p. 144.

HYMAN, L. H.   1940.   *The Invertebrates. I. Protozoa through Ctenophora.*   New York, McGraw-Hill.

HYMAN, O. W.   1923.   Spermic dimorphism in *Fasciolaria tulipa*.   *J. Morph.*, **37**, pp. 307–383.

ILES, C.   1959.   The larval trematodes of certain fresh-water molluscs. I. The furcocercariae.   *Parasitology*, **49**, pp. 478–504.

ILYIN, P.   1900.   Das Gehörbläschen als Gleichgewichtsorgan bei den Pterotracheiden.   *Zbl. Physiol.*, **13**, pp. 691–694.

INO, T.   1949.   The effect of food on growth and coloration of the topshell (*Turbo cornutus* Solander).   *J. mar. Res.*, **8**, pp. 1–5.

IREDALE, T.   1911.   On the value of the gastropod apex in classification.   *Proc. malac. Soc. Lond.*, **9**, pp. 319–323.

ISHIKI, H.   1936.   Sex changes in Japanese slipper limpets *Crepidula aculeata* and *Crepidula walshi*.   *J. Sci. Hiroshima Univ.*, Ser. B, Div. I, **3**, pp. 91–99.

JACOB, J.   1957.   Cytological studies of Melaniidae (Mollusca) with special reference to parthenogenesis and polyploidy. I. Oogenesis of the parthenogenetic species of '*Melanoides*' (Prosobranchia-Gastropoda).   *Trans. roy. Soc. Edinb.*, **63**, pp. 341–352.

JACOB, J.   1958.   Cytological studies of Melaniidae (Mollusca) with special reference to parthenogenesis and polyploidy. II. A study of meiosis in the rare males of the polyploid race of '*Melanoides tuberculatus*' and *Melanoides lineatus*.   *Trans. roy. Soc. Edinb.*, **63**, pp. 433–444.

JACKSON, J. W. & F. TAYLOR.   1904.   Observations on the habits and reproduction of *Paludestrina taylori*.   *J. Conch.*, **11**, pp. 9–11.

JAECKEL, S.   1952.   Über Vergiftungen durch *Conus*-Arten (Gastr. Pros.) mit einem Beiträge zur Morphologie und Physiologie ihres Giftapparates.   *Zool. Anz.*, **149**, pp. 206–216.

JÄGERSTEN, G.   1937.   Zur Kenntnis der Parapodialborsten bei *Myzostomum*.   *Zool. Bidr. Uppsala*, **16**, pp. 283–299.

JAMES, B. L.   1960.   A new cercaria of the subfamily Gymnophallinae (Trematoda : Digenea) developing in a unique 'parthenita' in *Littorina saxatilis* (Olivi).   *Nature, Lond.*, **185**, pp. 181–182.

JEFFREYS, J. G. 1862-69. *British Conchology*. Vols. 1-5. 1 (1862), 2 (1863), 3 (1865), 4 (1867), 5 (1869). London, van Voorst.

JENKINS, H. L. 1955. Digestive system of *Littorina littorea* (L.). *M.Sc. Thesis, University of Wales*.

JENSEN, A. S. 1951. Do the Naticidae (Gastropoda Prosobranchia) drill by chemical or mechanical means? *Vidensk. Medd. dansk naturh. Foren. Kbh.*, **113**, pp. 251-261.

JESSEN, A. 1918. Udstroekningen af Randers Fjord i Litorinatiden. *Randers Fjords Naturhistorie*, 1B. Copenhagen, C. A. Reitzel.

JOHANSEN, A. C. 1918. Bløddyrene i Randers Fjord. *Randers Fjords Naturhistorie*, 5G. Copenhagen, C. A. Reitzel.

JOHANSSON, J. 1939. Anatomische Studien über die Gastropodenfamilien Rissoidae und Littorinidae. *Zool. Bidr. Uppsala*, **18**, pp. 289-296.

JOHANSSON, J. 1942. Von diaulen Geschlechtsapparaten bei den Prosobranchiern. *Ark. Zool.*, **34**A (12), pp. 1-10.

JOHANSSON, J. 1946. Von den Geschlechtsorganen bei *Turritella communis* nebst Bemerkungen über die diaulen Geschlechtsorgane der Neritaceen. *Ark. Zool.*, **38**A (12), pp. 1-11.

JOHANSSON, J. 1947. Über den offenen Uterus bei einigen Monotocardiern ohne Kopulationsorgan. *Zool. Bidr. Uppsala*, **25**, pp. 102-110.

JOHANSSON, J. 1948a. Über die Geschlechtsorgane der Hydrobiiden und Rissoiden und den ursprünglichen Hermaphroditismus der Prosobranchier. *Ark. Zool.*, **40**A (15), pp. 1-13.

JOHANSSON, J. 1948b. Über die Geschlechtsorgane von *Aporrhais pespelecani* nebst einigen Betrachtungen über die phylogenetische Bedeutung der Cerithiacea und Architaenioglossa. *Ark. Zool.*, **41**A (8), pp. 1-13.

JOHANSSON, J. 1950. On the embryology of *Viviparus* and its significance for the phylogeny of the Gastropoda. *Ark. Zool.*, A.S., **1**, pp. 173-177.

JOHANSSON, J. 1953. On the genital organs of some mesogastropods: *Cerithium vulgatum* Brug., *Triphora perversa* (L.) and *Melanella* (*Eulima*) *intermedia* (Cantr.). *Zool. Bidr. Uppsala*, **30**, pp. 1-23.

JOHANSSON, J. 1955. Garnault's duct and its significance for the phylogeny of the genital system of *Valvata*. *Zool. Bidr. Uppsala*, **30**, pp. 457-464.

JOHANSSON, J. 1956a. Genital organs of two *Alvania* species, and a comparison with related families (Moll. Pros.). *Ark. Zool.*, A.S., **9**, pp. 377-387.

JOHANSSON, J. 1956b. On the anatomy of *Tympanotonus fuscatus* (L.), including a survey of the open pallial oviducts of the Cerithiacea. *Atlantide Report*, no. 4, pp. 149-166.

JONES, E. I., R. A. McCANCE & L. R. B. SHACKLETON. 1935. The role of iron and silica in the structure of the radular teeth of certain marine molluscs. *J. exp. Biol.*, **12**, pp. 59-64.

JONES, N. S. 1948. Observations on the biology of *Patella vulgata* at Port St. Mary, Isle of Man. *Proc. Lpool. biol. Soc.*, **56**, pp. 60-77.

JORDAN, H. J. 1913. *Vergleichende Physiologie der wirbelloser Tiere. I. Die Ernährung*. Jena, Fischer.

JORDAN, H. J. & H. BEGEMANN. 1921. Über die Bedeutung des Darmes von *Helix pomatia*. *Zool. Jb. (Zool. Physiol.)*, **38**, pp. 565-582.

JORDAN, H. J. & G. C. HIRSCH. 1927. Einige vergleichendphysiologische Probleme der Verdauung bei Metazoen. *Handb. norm. pathol. Physiol.*, **3**B (2).

JORDAN, H. J. & H. J. LAM. 1918. Über die Darmdurchlässigkeit bei *Astacus fluviatilis* und *Helix pomatia*. *Tijdschr. nederl. dierk. Ver.*, **16**, pp. 281-292.

JULLIEN, A. 1948. Recherches sur les fonctions de la glande hypobranchiale chez *Murex trunculus*. *C.R. Soc. Biol., Paris*, **142**, pp. 102-103.

JULLIEN, A. & D. VINCENT. 1938. Sur l'action de l'acétylcholine sur le coeur des mollusques. Antagonisme: curare-acétylcholine. *C.R. Acad. Sci., Paris*, **206**, pp. 209-211.

KEMP, S. & F. H. GRAVELY. 1919. On the possible spread of schistosomiasis in India. *Indian J. med. Res.*, **7**, pp. 251-264.

KENNARD, A. S. 1941. The geological record of *Potamopyrgus jenkinsi* in the British Isles. *Proc. malac. Soc. Lond.*, **24**, p. 156.

KESSEL, E. 1933. Über die Schale von *Viviparus viviparus* L. und *Viviparus fasciatus* Müll. *Z. Morph. Ökol. Tiere*, **27**, pp. 129–198.

KESSEL, E. 1942. Über Bau und Bildung des Prosobranchier-Deckels. *Z. Morph. Ökol. Tiere*, **38**, pp. 197–250.

KESSEL, E. 1944. Über Periostracum-Bildung. *Z. Morph. Ökol. Tiere*, **40**, pp. 348–360.

KILIAN, F. 1951. Untersuchungen zur Biologie von *Pomatias elegans* (Müller) und ihrer 'Kronkrementdrüse'. *Arch. Molluskenk.*, **80**, pp. 1–16.

KNIGHT, J. B. 1947. Bellerophont muscle scars. *J. Paleont.*, **21**, pp. 264–267.

KNIGHT, J. B. 1952. Primitive fossil gastropods and their bearing on gastropod classification. *Smithson. misc. Coll.*, **117**, no. 13, pp. 1–56.

KNIGHT, J. B. & E. L. YOCHELSON. 1958. A reconsideration of the relationships of the Monoplacophora and the primitive Gastropoda. *Proc. malac. Soc. Lond.*, **33**, pp. 37–48.

KNIGHT-JONES, E. W. 1954. Relations between metachronism and the direction of ciliary beat in Metazoa. *Quart. J. micr. Sci.*, **95**, pp. 503–521.

KOEHLER, R. & C. VANEY. 1908. Description d'un nouveau genre de prosobranches, parasite sur certains échinides (*Pelseneeria* n.g.). *Bull. Inst. océanogr. Monaco*, **118**, pp. 1–16.

KOEHLER, R. & C. VANEY. 1912. Nouvelles formes de gastéropodes ectoparasites. *Bull. sci. Fr. Belg.*, **46**, pp. 191–217.

KOHN, A. J. 1956. Piscivorous gastropods of the genus *Conus*. *Proc. nat. Acad. Sci.*, **42**, pp. 168–171.

KOHN, A. J. 1959. The ecology of *Conus* in Hawaii. *Ecol. Monogr.*, **29**, pp. 47–90.

KOLLMANN, M. 1908. Recherches sur les leucocytes et le tissu lymphoide des invertébrés. *Ann. Sci. nat. Zool.* (9), **8**, pp. 1–240.

KORRINGA, P. 1952. Recent advances in oyster biology. *Quart. Rev. Biol.*, **27**, pp. 266–308; 339–365.

KOSTITZINE, J. 1934. Le cycle génital femelle de la pourpre. *C.R. Soc. Biol., Paris*, **115**, p. 264.

KOSTITZINE, J. 1940. Sur la ponte de la pourpre. *Bull. Soc. zool. Fr.*, **65**, pp. 80–84.

KOSTITZINE, J. 1949. Contribution à l'étude de l'appareil reproducteur femelle de quelques mollusques prosobranches marins. *Arch. Zool. exp. gén.*, **86**, pp. 145–167.

KRASUCKI, A. 1911. Untersuchungen über Anatomie und Histologie der Heteropoden. *Bull. Acad. Sci. Cracovie, ser. B, Sci. nat.*, 5B, pp. 391–448 and 6B, pp. 449–450.

KRIJGSMAN, B. J. 1925. Die Arbeitsrhythmus der Verdauungsdrüsen bei *Helix pomatia*. *Z. vergl. Physiol.*, **2**, pp. 264–302.

KRIJGSMAN, B. J. 1928. Die Arbeitsrhythmus der Verdauungsdrüsen bei *Helix pomatia*. II. Teil: Sekretion, Resorption und Phagocytose. *Z. vergl. Physiol.*, **8**, pp. 187–280.

KRIJGSMAN, B. J. & G. A. DIVARIS. 1955. Contractile and pacemaker mechanisms of the heart of molluscs. *Biol. Rev.*, **30**, pp. 1–39.

KROGH, A. 1939. *Osmotic Regulation in Aquatic Animals*. Cambridge, University Press.

KRULL, H. 1935. Anatomische Untersuchungen an einheimischen Prosobranchiern und Beiträge zur Phylogenie der Gastropoden. *Zool. Jb. (Anat. Ont.)*, **60**, pp. 399–464.

KRULL, W. H. 1933. New snail and rabbit hosts for *Fasciola hepatica* Linn. *J. Parasit.*, **20**, pp. 49–52.

KRULL, W. H. 1934. Life history studies on *Cotylophoron cotylophorum* (Fischoeder, 1901) Stiles and Goldberger, 1910. *J. Parasit.*, **20**, pp. 173–180.

KRUMBACH, T. 1918. Napfschnecken in der Gezeitenwelle und der Brandungszone der Karstküste. *Zool. Anz.*, **49**, pp. 96–112; 113–123.

KUSCHAKEWITSCH, S. 1910. Zur Kenntnis der sogenannten 'wurmförmigen' Spermien der Prosobranchier. *Anat. Anz.*, **37**, pp. 318–324.

KÜTTLER, A. 1913. Die Anatomie von *Oliva peruviana* Lamarck. *Zool. Jb.*, Suppl. **13** (*Fauna chilensis*, 4), pp. 477–544.

LABBE, A. 1926. Contributions à l'étude de l'allélogénèse. 2ᵉ mémoire: croissance et environnement. Essai d'une théorie des adaptations. *Bull. biol.*, **60**, pp. 1-87.

LACAZE-DUTHIERS, H. DE. 1859. Système nerveux de l'Haliotide et sur la pourpre. *Ann. Sci. nat. Zool.* (4), **12**, pp. 5-84.

LACAZE-DUTHIERS, H. DE. 1872. Otocystes ou capsules auditives des mollusques (gastéropodes). *Arch. Zool. exp. gén.*, **1**, pp. 97-166.

LAMBERT, F. J. 1930. Animal life in the marsh ditches of the Thames estuary. *Proc. zool. Soc. Lond.*, pp. 801-808.

LAMY, E. 1928. La ponte chez les gastéropodes prosobranches. *J. Conchyliol.*, **72**, pp. 25-196.

LANG, A. 1891. Versuch einer Erklärung der Asymmetrie der Gastropoden. *Vjschr. naturf. Ges. Zürich*, **36**, pp. 339-371.

LANG, A. 1896. *Text-book of comparative Anatomy*, **2**. London, Macmillan.

LANKESTER E. R. 1872. A contribution to the knowledge of haemoglobin. *Proc. roy. Soc.*, **21**, pp. 70-81.

LANKESTER, E. R. 1893. Note on the coelom and vascular system of Mollusca and Arthropoda. *Quart. J. micr. Sci.*, **34**, pp. 427-432.

LAURSEN, D. 1953. The genus *Ianthina*. *Dana-Report* no. **38**, pp. 1-40.

LAWRENCE-HAMILTON, J. 1892. The limpet's strength. *Nature, Lond.*, **45**, p. 487.

LEBOUR, M. V. 1905. Notes on Northumberland trematodes. *Northumberland Sea Fish. Rep.*, **1905**, pp. 100-105.

LEBOUR, M. V. 1907. Larval trematodes of the Northumberland Coast. *Trans. nat. Hist. Soc. Northumb.*, N.S., **1**, pp. 437-454.

LEBOUR, M. V. 1908. A contribution to the life history of *Echinostomum secundum* Nicoll. *Parasitology*, **1**, pp. 352-358.

LEBOUR, M. V. 1910. *Acanthopsolus lageniformis* n. sp. A trematode in the catfish. *Northumberland Sea Fish. Rep.*, **1909**, pp. 29-35.

LEBOUR, M. V. 1911. A review of the British marine cercariae. *Parasitology*, **4**, pp. 416-456.

LEBOUR, M. V. 1916-18. A trematode larva from *Buccinum undatum* and notes on trematodes from post-larval fish. *J. mar. biol. Ass. U.K.*, **11**, pp. 514-517.

LEBOUR, M. V. 1931a. The larval stages of *Nassarius reticulatus* and *Nassarius incrassatus*. *J. mar. biol. Ass. U.K.*, **17**, pp. 797-818.

LEBOUR, M. V. 1931b. The larval stages of *Trivia europaea*. *J. mar. biol. Ass. U.K.*, **17**, pp. 819-832.

LEBOUR, M. V. 1932a. The larval stages of *Simnia patula*. *J. mar. biol. Ass. U.K.*, **18**, pp. 107-115.

LEBOUR, M. V. 1932b. The eggs and early larval stages of two commensal gastropods, *Stilifer stylifer* and *Odostomia eulimoides*. *J. mar. biol. Ass. U.K.*, **18**, pp. 117-122.

LEBOUR, M. V. 1933a. The British species of *Trivia*, *T. arctica* and *T. monacha*. *J. mar. biol. Ass. U.K.*, **18**, pp. 477-484.

LEBOUR, M. V. 1933b. The life-histories of *Cerithiopsis tubercularis* (Montagu), *C. barleei* Jeffreys and *Triphora perversa* (L.). *J. mar. biol. Ass. U.K.*, **18**, pp. 491-498.

LEBOUR, M. V. 1933c. The eggs and larvae of *Turritella communis* Lamarck and *Aporrhais pes-pelicani* (L.). *J. mar. biol. Ass. U.K.*, **18**, pp. 499-506.

LEBOUR, M. V. 1933d. The eggs and larvae of *Philbertia gracilis* (Montagu). *J. mar. biol. Ass. U.K.*, **18**, pp. 507-510.

LEBOUR, M. V. 1934a. Rissoid larvae as food of young herring. The eggs and larvae of Plymouth Rissoidae. *J. mar. biol. Ass. U.K.*, **19**, pp. 523-540.

LEBOUR, M. V. 1934b. The eggs and larvae of some British Turridae. *J. mar. biol. Ass. U.K.*, **19**, pp. 541-554.

LEBOUR, M. V. 1935a. The echinospira larvae of Plymouth. *Proc. zool. Soc. Lond.*, pp. 163-174.

LEBOUR, M. V. 1935b. The larval stages of *Balcis alba* and *B. devians*. *J. mar. biol. Ass. U.K.*, **20**, pp. 65-70.

LEBOUR, M. V. 1935c. The breeding of *Littorina neritoides*. *J. mar. biol. Ass. U.K.*, **20**, pp. 373-378.

LEBOUR, M. V. 1936. Notes on the eggs and larvae of some Plymouth prosobranchs. *J. mar. biol. Ass. U.K.*, **20**, pp. 547–565.

LEBOUR, M. V. 1937. The eggs and larvae of the British prosobranchs with special reference to those living in the plankton. *J. mar. biol. Ass. U.K.*, **22**, pp. 105–166.

LEBOUR, M. V. 1945. The eggs and larvae of some prosobranchs from Bermuda. *Proc. zool. Soc. Lond.*, **114**, pp. 462–489.

LEBOUR, M. V. 1947. Notes on the inshore plankton of Plymouth. *J. mar. biol. Ass. U.K.*, **26**, pp. 527–547.

LEBOUR, M. V. & R. ELMHIRST. 1922. A contribution towards the life history of *Parorchis acanthus* Nicoll, a trematode in the herring gull. *J. mar. biol. Ass. U.K.*, **12**, pp. 829–832.

LEMCHE, H. 1957. A new living deep-sea mollusc of the Cambro-Devonian class Monoplacophora. *Nature, Lond.*, **179**, pp. 413–416.

LEMCHE, H. 1959. Protostomian relationships in the light of *Neopilina*. *Proc. XVth int. Cong. Zool. Lond.*, pp. 381–389.

LEMCHE, H. & K. WINGSTRAND. 1959. The comparative anatomy of *Neopilina galatheae* Lemche, 1957 (Mollusca Monoplacophora). *Proc. XVth int. Cong. Zool. Lond.*, pp. 378–380.

LENSSEN, J. 1899. Système digestif et système génital de la *Neritina fluviatilis*. *Cellule*, **16**, pp. 179–232.

LETELLIER, A. 1889. Recherches sur la pourpre produite par le *Purpura lapillus*. *C.R. Acad. Sci., Paris*, **109**, pp. 82–84.

LETELLIER, A. 1890. Recherches sur la pourpre produite par le *Purpura lapillus*. *Arch. Zool. exp. gén.* (2), **8**, pp. 361–408.

LEVER, J. 1957. Some remarks on neurosecretory phenomena in *Ferrissia* (Gastropoda Pulmonata). *Proc. Acad. Sci. Amst.*, **60**, C, pp. 510–522.

LEWIS, J. R. 1954a. Observations on a high-level population of limpets. *J. Anim. Ecol.*, **23**, pp. 85–100.

LEWIS, J. R. 1954b. The ecology of exposed rocky shores of Caithness. *Trans. roy. Soc. Edinb.*, **62**, pp. 695–723.

LEYON, H. 1947. The anatomy of the cerebral nerves of Gastropoda. *Zool. Bidr. Uppsala*, **25**, pp. 394–401.

LHOSTE, L.-J. 1944. Sur la microstructure interne du test des gastéropodes. *C.R. Acad. Sci., Paris*, **219**, pp. 351–352.

LHOSTE, L.-J. 1946. Les microstructures des Patelles. *J. Conchyliol.*, **87**, pp. 29 and 38.

LILLY, M. M. 1953. The mode of life and the structure and functioning of the reproductive ducts of *Bithynia tentaculata* (L.). *Proc. malac. Soc. Lond.*, **30**, pp. 87–110.

LILLY, S. J., J. F. SLOANE, R. BASSINDALE, F. J. EBLING & J. A. KITCHING. 1953. The ecology of the Lough Ine rapids with special reference to water currents. IV. The sedentary fauna of sublittoral boulders. *J. Anim. Ecol.*, **22**, pp. 87–122.

LINKE, O. 1933. Morphologie und Physiologie des Genitalapparates der Nordseelittorinen. *Wiss. Meeresuntersuch. Abt. Helgoland*, **19**, Nr. 5, pp. 3–52.

LINKE, O. 1934a. Beiträge zur Sexualbiologie der Littorinen. *Z. Morph. Ökol. Tiere*, **28**, pp. 170–177.

LINKE, O. 1934b. Über die Beziehungen zwischen Keimdrüse und Soma bei Prosobranchiern. *Verh. dtsch. zool. Ges., Zool. Anz.* Suppl. **7**, pp. 164–175.

LINKE, O. 1935a. Der Laich von *Littorina* (*Melaraphe*) *neritoides* L. *Zool. Anz.*, **112**, pp. 57–62.

LINKE, O. 1935b. Zur Morphologie und Physiologie des Genitalapparates der Süsswasserlittorinide *Cremnoconchus syhadrensis* Blanford. *Arch. Naturg.*, N.F., **4**, pp. 72–87.

LINKE, O. 1939. Die Biota des Jadebusenwattes. *Helgoland. wiss. Meeresunters.*, **I**, pp. 201–348.

LINTON, E. 1915. Sporocysts in an annelid. *Biol. Bull., Wood's Hole*, **28**, pp. 115–118.

LISSMANN, H. W. 1945. The mechanism of locomotion in gastropod molluscs. I. Kinematics. *J. exp. Biol.*, **21**, pp. 58–69.

LISSMANN, H. W. 1946. The mechanism of locomotion in gastropod molluscs. II. Kinetics. *J. exp. Biol.*, **22**, pp. 37–50.

List, T. 1902. Die Mytiliden. *Fauna und Flora des Golfes von Neapel*, **27**.

Longstaff, M. J. 1910. Non-marine Mollusca found in the parish of Mortehoe, North Devon. *J. Conch.*, **13**, pp. 15–23.

Loppens, K. 1922. Note sur la variabilité et l'éthologie de *Patella vulgata*. *Ann. Soc. zool. malac. Belg.*, **53**, pp. 57–68.

Loppens, K. 1926. La perforation des coquilles de mollusques par les gastropodes et les éponges. *Ann. Soc. zool. Belg.*, **57**, pp. 14–18.

Lucas, J. A. W. 1954. Het genus *Patella* in Nederland. *Basteria*, **18**, pp. 36–40.

Lysaght, A. M. 1941. The biology and trematode parasites of the gastropod *Littorina neritoides* (L.) on the Plymouth Breakwater. *J. mar. biol. Ass. U.K.*, **25**, pp. 41–67.

Lysaght, A. M. 1943. The incidence of larval trematodes in males and females of the gastropod *Littorina neritoides* (L.) on the Plymouth Breakwater. *Parasitology*, **35**, pp. 17–22.

McGee-Russell, S. 1954. A cytological study of the tissues concerned in the secretion of shell in the snail *Helix*. *D. Phil. Thesis, University of Oxford*.

McIntosh, W. C. 1865. The trematode larva and ascaris of *Carcinus maenas*. *Quart. J. micr. Sci.*, **5**, pp. 201–204.

McMillan, N. F. 1938–39. Early records of *Crepidula* in English waters. *Proc. malac. Soc. Lond.*, **23**, p. 236.

McMillan, N. F. 1939. The British species of *Lamellaria*. *J. Conch.*, **21**, pp. 170–173.

McMillan, N. F. 1944. The distribution of *Monodonta* (*Trochus*) *lineata* (da Costa) in Britain. *Northw. Naturalist*, **19**, pp. 290–292.

McMillan, N. F. 1948a. Possible biological races in *Hydrobia ulvae* (Pennant) and their varying resistance to lowered salinity. *J. Conch.*, **23**, pp. 14–16.

McMillan, N. F. 1948b. The resistance of *Hydrobia ventrosa* (Montagu) to low salinities. *J. Conch.*, **23**, p. 16.

McMurrich, J. P. 1886. A contribution to the embryology of the prosobranch gasteropods. *Stud. biol. Lab. Johns Hopkins Univ.*, **3**, pp. 403–450.

Macan, T. T. 1950. Ecology of the freshwater Mollusca in the English Lake District. *J. Anim. Ecol.*, **19**, pp. 124–146.

Manigault, P. 1933. La tension du gaz carbonique condition de la régénération de la coquille chez les *Helix*. *Trav. Sta. biol. Roscoff*, **11**, pp. 53–59.

Manigault, P. 1939. Recherches sur le calcaire chez les mollusques. Phosphatase et précipitation calcique. Histochimie du calcium. *Ann. Inst. océanogr. Monaco*, **18**, pp. 331–426.

Mansour, K. 1945. The zooxanthellae, morphological peculiarities and food and feeding habits of the Tridacnidae with reference to other lamellibranchs. *Proc. Egypt. Acad. Sci.*, **1**, pp. 1–11.

Mansour-Bek, J. J. 1934. Über die proteolytischen Enzyme von *Murex anguliferus* Lamk. *Z. vergl. Physiol.*, **20**, pp. 343–369.

Marine Biological Association. 1957. *Plymouth Marine Fauna*. Plymouth, M.B.A.

Marshall, J. T. 1889. On *Hydrobiae* and *Assimineae* from the Thames valley. *J. Conch.*, **6**, pp. 140–142.

Marshall, J. T. 1893. Additions to 'British Conchology'. *J. Conch.*, **7**, pp. 241–265.

Marshall, J. T. 1894. Additions to 'British Conchology'. *J. Conch.*, **7**, pp. 379–385.

Marshall, J. T. 1895. Alterations in 'British Conchology'. *J. Conch.*, **8**, pp. 24–41.

Marshall, J. T. 1898a. Additions to 'British Conchology'. *J. Conch.*, **9**, pp. 61–74.

Marshall, J. T. 1898b. Additions to 'British Conchology'. *J. Conch.*, **9**, pp. 120–138.

Marshall, J. T. 1899a. Additions to 'British Conchology'. *J. Conch.*, **9**, pp. 165–171.

Marshall, J. T. 1899b. Additions to 'British Conchology'. *J. Conch.*, **9**, pp. 222–232.

Marshall, J. T. 1900a. Additions to 'British Conchology'. *J. Conch.*, **9**, pp. 284–296.

Marshall, J. T. 1900b. Additions to 'British Conchology'. *J. Conch.*, **9**, pp. 332–338.

Marshall, J. T. 1901. Additions to 'British Conchology'. *J. Conch.*, **10**, pp. 122–128.

Marshall, J. T. 1902. Additions to 'British Conchology'. *J. Conch.*, **10**, pp. 190–193.

MARSHALL, J. T. 1910–12. Additions to 'British Conchology'. *J. Conch.*, **13**, pp. 179–190, 192–209, 223–231, 294–306, 324–338.

MARSHALL, J. T. 1913–15. Additions to 'British Conchology'. *J. Conch.*, **14**, pp. 65–77, 200–213, 324–329.

MARSHALL, J. T. 1916–18. Additions to 'British Conchology'. *I. Conch.*, **15**, pp. 44–47, 87–89, 168–174, 198–203.

MARTIN, W. E. 1944. Studies on trematodes of Wood's Hole. IV. Additional observations upon *Cercaria loossi* Stunkard developing in an annelid. *Trans. Amer. micr. Soc.*, **63**, pp. 237–243.

MARTIN, A. W., D. M. STEWART & F. M. HARRISON. 1954. Kidney function in the giant African snail. *J. cell. comp. Physiol.*, **44**, pp. 345–346.

MATTOX, N. T. 1938. Morphology of *Campeloma rufum*, a parthenogenetic snail. *J. Morph.*, **62**, pp. 243–261.

MEDEM, F. GRAF V. 1945. Untersuchungen über die Ei- und Spermawirkstoffe bei marinen Mollusken. *Zool. Jb. (Zool. Physiol.)*, **61**, pp. 1–44.

MENDEL, L. B. & H. C. BRADLEY. 1905a. Experimental studies in the physiology of the molluscs. First paper. *Amer. J. Physiol.*, **13**, pp. 17–29.

MENDEL, L. B. & H. C. BRADLEY. 1905b. Experimental studies in the physiology of the molluscs. Second paper. *Amer. J. Physiol.*, **14**, pp. 313–327.

MENDEL, L. B. & H. C. BRADLEY. 1906. Experimental studies in the physiology of the molluscs. Third paper. *Amer. J. Physiol.*, **17**, pp. 167–176.

MENG, K. 1958. 5-hydroxytryptamin und Acetylcholin als Wirkungsantagonisten beim *Helix*-Herzen. *Naturwissenschaften*, **45**, p. 470.

MENKE, H. 1911. Physikalische und physiologische Faktoren bei der Anheftung von Schnecken der Brandungszone. *Zool. Anz.*, **37**, pp. 19–30.

MEVES, F. 1903. Über oligopyrene und apyrene Spermien und über ihre Entwicklung nach Beobachtungen an *Paludina* und *Pygaera*. *Arch. mikr. Anat.*, **61**, pp. 1–84.

MEYER, A. 1913. Das Renogenitalsystem von *Puncturella noachina* L. *Biol. Zbl.*, **33**, pp. 564–576.

MEYER, E. 1901. Studien über den Korperbau der Anneliden. V. Das Mesoderm der Ringelwürmer. *Mitt. zool. Stat. Neapel*, **14**, pp. 247–585.

MEYER, K. F. 1925. The bacterial symbiosis in the concretion deposits of certain operculate land molluscs of the families Cyclostomatidae and Annulariidae. *J. infect. Dis.*, **36**, pp. 1–107.

MEYERHOF, E. & M. ROTHSCHILD. 1940. A prolific trematode. *Nature, Lond.*, **146**, pp. 367–368.

MILNE-EDWARDS, H. 1846. Sur la circulation chez les mollusques (chez les Patelles et les Haliotides). *Ann. Sci. nat. Zool.* (3), **8**, pp. 37–53.

MISTAKIDIS, M. N. 1951. Quantitative studies of the bottom fauna of Essex oyster grounds. *Fish. Invest. Lond.* (2), **17**, no. 6, pp. 1–47.

MISTAKIDIS, M. N. & D. A. HANCOCK. 1955. Reappearance of *Ocenebra erinacea* (L.) off the east coast of England. *Nature, Lond.*, **175**, p. 734.

MONTALENTI, G. 1960. Perspectives of research on sex problems in marine animals. In A. A. BUZZATI-TRAVERSO: *Perspectives in Marine Biology*. Berkeley & Los Angeles, University of California Press.

MOORE, H. B. 1931. The systematic value of molluscan faeces. *Proc. malac. Soc. Lond.*, **19**, pp. 281–290.

MOORE, H. B. 1932. The faecal pellets of the Trochidae. *J. mar. biol. Ass. U.K.*, **18**, pp. 235–241.

MOORE, H. B. 1934. The relation of shell growth to environment in *Patella vulgata*. *Proc. malac. Soc. Lond.*, **21**, pp. 217–222.

MOORE, H. B. 1936. The biology of *Purpura lapillus*. I. Shell variation in relation to environment. *J. mar. biol. Ass. U.K.*, **21**, pp. 61–89.

MOORE, H. B. 1937a. The biology of *Littorina littorea*. Part I. Growth of the shell and tissues, spawning, length of life and mortality. *J. mar. biol. Ass. U.K.*, **21**, pp. 721–742.

MOORE, H. B. 1937b. *Marine Fauna of the Isle of Man*. Liverpool, University Press.

MOORE, H. B. 1938a. The biology of *Purpura lapillus*. Part II. Growth. *J. mar. biol. Ass. U.K.*, **23**, pp. 57–66.

MOORE, H. B. 1938b. The biology of *Purpura lapillus*. Part III. Life history and relation to environmental factors. *J. mar. biol. Ass. U.K.*, **23**, pp. 67–74.

MOORE, H. B. 1938c. Algal production and food requirements of a limpet. *Proc. malac. Soc. Lond.*, **23**, pp. 117–118.

MOORE, H. B. 1939. Faecal pellets in relation to marine deposits. In P. D. TRASK: *Recent Marine Sediments: a Symposium*. London, Murby for the American Association of Petroleum Geologists, Tulsa, Oklahoma.

MOORE, H. B. 1940. The biology of *Littorina littorea*. Part II. Zonation in relation to other gastropods on stony and muddy shores. *J. mar. biol. Ass. U.K.*, **24**, pp. 227–237.

MOQUIN-TANDON, A. 1855. *Histoire naturelle des mollusques terrestres et fluviatiles de France.* Paris, Baillière.

MORGAN, C. L. 1894. The homing of limpets. *Nature, Lond.*, **51**, p. 127.

MORIN, G. & A. JULLIEN. 1931. Sur l'automatisme des sinus contractiles de l'embryon de la limace agreste dans les solutions de concentration et de composition saline variées. *C.R. Soc. Biol., Paris*, **106**, pp. 1038–1040.

MORIN, G. & A. JULLIEN. 1932. Recherches sur l'automatisme du coeur isolé de *Murex trunculus*. *Arch. int. Physiol.*, **35**, pp. 143–157.

MORITZ, C. E. 1939. Organogenesis in the gasteropod, *Crepidula adunca* Sowerby. *Univ. Calif. Publ. Zool.*, **43**, pp. 217–248.

MORSE, E. S. 1880. The gradual dispersion of certain mollusks in New England. *Bull. Essex Inst.*, **12**, pp. 3–8.

MORTON, J. E. 1951a. The ecology and digestive system of the Struthiolariidae (Gastropoda). *Quart. J. micr. Sci.*, **92**, pp. 1–25.

MORTON, J. E. 1951b. The structure and adaptations of the New Zealand Vermetidae. Part I. The genus *Serpulorbis*. Part II. The genera *Stephopoma* and *Pyxipoma*. Part III. *Novastoa lamellosa* and its affinities. *Trans. roy. Soc. N.Z.*, **79**, pp. 1–51.

MORTON, J. E. 1955. The functional morphology of the British Ellobiidae (Gastropoda Pulmonata) with special reference to the digestive and reproductive systems. *Philos. Trans.* B, **239**, pp. 89–160.

MORTON, J. E. 1956. The evolution of the Struthiolariidae: *Perissodonta* and *Tylospina*. *Proc. roy. Soc. N.Z.*, **83**, pp. 515–524.

MORTON, J. E. 1958. Torsion and the adult snail: a re-evaluation. *Proc. malac. Soc. Lond.*, **33**, pp. 2–10.

MORTON, J. E. 1959. The adaptations and relationships of the Xenophoridae (Mesogastropoda). *Proc. malac. Soc. Lond.*, **33**, pp. 89–101.

MOSELEY, H. N. 1877. On the colouring matter of marine animals. *Quart. J. micr. Sci.*, **17**, pp. 1–23.

MURRAY, J. & J. HJORT. 1912. *The Depths of the Ocean.* London, Macmillan.

NAEF, A. 1913. Studien zur generellen Morphologie der Mollusken. 1. Teil: Über Torsion und Asymmetrie der Gastropoden. *Ergebn. Zool.*, **3**, pp. 73–164.

NAEF, A. 1926. Studien zur generellen Morphologie der Mollusken. 3. Teil: Die typischen Beziehungen der Weichtiere untereinander und das Verhältnis ihrer Urformen zu anderen Cölomaten. *Ergebn. Zool.*, **6**, pp. 27–124.

NATHUSIUS-KÖNIGSBORN, W. VON. 1877. *Untersuchungen über nicht celluläre Organismen namentlich Crustaceen-Panzer, Molluskenschalen und Eihüllen.* Berlin, Weigardt, Hempel & Parey.

NEEDHAM, J. 1935. Problems of nitrogen catabolism in invertebrates. II. Correlation between uricotelic metabolism and habitat in the phylum Mollusca. *Biochem. J.*, **29**, pp. 238–251.

NEEDHAM, J. 1938. Contributions of chemical physiology to the problem of reversability in evolution. *Biol. Rev.*, **13**, pp. 225–251.

NEKRASSOW, A. D. 1928. Vergleichende Morphologie der Laiche von Süsswassergastropoden. *Z. Morph. Ökol. Tiere*, **13**, pp. 1–35.

NELSON, T. C.  1918.  On the origin, nature and function of the crystalline style of lamellibranchs.  *J. Morph.*, **31**, pp. 53-111.

NEWCOMBE, C. L., C. E. MILLER & D. W. CHAPPEL.  1936.  Preliminary report on respiratory
studies of *Littorina irrorata*.  *Nature, Lond.*, **137**, p. 33.

NEWELL, G. E.  1958a.  The behaviour of *Littorina littorea* (L.) under natural conditions and its
relation to position on the shore.  *J. mar. biol. Ass. U.K.*, **37**, pp. 229-239.

NEWELL, G. E.  1958b.  An experimental analysis of the behaviour of *Littorina littorea* (L.) under
natural conditions and in the laboratory.  *J. mar. biol. Ass. U.K.*, **37**, pp. 241-266.

NICOL, E. A. T.  1936.  The brackish-water lochs of North Uist.  *Proc. roy. Soc. Edinb.*, **66**,
pp. 169-195.

NICOLL, W.  1907.  Observations on the trematode parasites of British birds.  *Ann. Mag. nat.
Hist.* (7), **20**, pp. 245-271.

NISBET, R. H.  1953.  The structure and function of the buccal mass in some gastropod molluscs.
I.  *Monodonta lineata* (da Costa).  *Ph. D. Thesis, University of London.*

NORTH, W. J.  1954.  Size distribution, erosive activities, and gross metabolic efficiency of the
marine intertidal snails, *Littorina planaxis* and *L. scutulata*.  *Biol. Bull., Wood's Hole*, **106**,
pp. 185-197.

NOWIKOFF, M.  1912.  Studien über das Knorpelgewebe von Wirbellosen.  *Z. wiss. Zool.*, **103**,
pp. 661-717.

ODHNER, N. H.  1932.  Zur Morphologie und Systematik der Fissurelliden.  *Jena. Z. Naturw.*,
**67**, pp. 292-309.

OHBA, S.  1952.  Analysis of activity rhythm in the marine gastropod, *Nassarius festivus*, inhabiting
the tide pool. I. On the effect of tide and food in the daytime rhythm of activity.  *Annot.
zool. Jap.*, **25**, pp. 289-297.

OHBA, S.  1954.  Analysis of activity rhythm in the marine gastropod, *Nassarius festivus*, inhabiting
the tide pool. II. Nocturnal activity and its artificial control by light.  *Biol. J. Okayama
Univ.*, **1**, pp. 209-216.

ÖKLAND, F.  1933.  Litoralstudien an der Skagerrakküste Norwegens: die Verbreitung von
*Purpura lapillus*, *Patella vulgata* und den *Littorina*-Arten in Tromö.  *Zoogeographica*, **1**, pp. 579-
601.

OLMSTED, J. M. D.  1917.  Notes on the locomotion of certain Bermudian mollusks.  *J. exp.
Zool.*, **24**, pp. 223-236.

OLDFIELD, E.  1959.  The embryology of *Lasaea rubra* (Montagu) and the functional morphology
of *Kellia suborbicularis* (Montagu), *Montacuta ferruginosa* (Montagu) and *M. substriata* (Montagu)
(Mollusca, Lamellibranchiata).  *Ph.D Thesis, University of London.*

ORTON, J. H.  1909.  On the occurrence of protandric hermaphroditism in the mollusc *Crepidula
fornicata*.  *Proc. roy. Soc.* B, **81**, pp. 468-484.

ORTON, J. H.  1912a.  An account of the natural history of the slipper limpet (*Crepidula fornicata*),
with some remarks on its occurrence on the oyster grounds on the Essex coast.  *J. mar. biol.
Ass. U.K.*, **9**, pp. 437-443.

ORTON, J. H.  1912b.  The mode of feeding of *Crepidula*, with an account of the current-producing
mechanism in the mantle cavity, and some remarks on the mode of feeding in gastropods and
lamellibranchs.  *J. mar. biol. Ass. U.K.*, **9**, pp. 444-478.

ORTON, J. H.  1913a.  On the breeding habits of *Echinus miliaris*, with a note on the feeding habits
of *Patella vulgata*.  *J. mar. biol. Ass. U.K.*, **10**, pp. 254-257.

ORTON, J. H.  1913b.  On ciliary mechanisms in brachiopods and some polychaetes, with a
comparison of the ciliary mechanisms on the gills of molluscs, Protochordata, brachiopods
and cryptocephalous polychaetes, and an account of the endostyle of *Crepidula* and its allies.
*J. mar. biol. Ass. U.K.*, **10**, pp. 283-311.

ORTON, J. H.  1920.  Sex-phenomena in the common limpet (*Patella vulgata*).  *Nature, Lond.*,
**104**, p. 373.

ORTON, J. H.  1927.  The habits and economic importance of the rough whelk-tingle (*Murex
erinaceus*).  *Nature, Lond.*, **120**, pp. 653-654.

ORTON, J. H. 1928a. Observations on *Patella vulgata*. Part I. Sex-phenomena, breeding and shell-growth. *J. mar. biol. Ass. U.K.*, **15**, pp. 851–862.

ORTON, J. H. 1928b. Observations on *Patella vulgata*. Part II. Rate of growth of shell. *J. mar. biol. Ass. U.K.*, **15**, pp. 863–874.

ORTON, J. H. 1929a. Habitats and feeding habits of *Ocenebra erinacea*. *Nature, Lond.*, **124**, pp. 370–371.

ORTON, J. H. 1929b. Observations on *Patella vulgata*. Part III. Habitat and habits. *J. mar. biol. Ass. U.K.*, **16**, pp. 277–288.

ORTON, J. H. 1930. On the oyster drills in the Essex estuaries. *Essex Nat.*, **22**, p. 298.

ORTON, J. H. 1932. Studies on the relation between organisms and environment. *Proc. Lpool. biol. Soc.*, **46**, pp. 1–16.

ORTON, J. H. 1946. Biology of *Patella* in Great Britain. *Nature, Lond.*, **158**, pp. 173–174.

ORTON, J. H. 1950a. Recent breeding phenomena in the American slipper limpet, *Crepidula fornicata*. *Nature, Lond.*, **165**, p. 433.

ORTON, J. H. 1950b. The recent extension in the distribution of the American slipper limpet, *Crepidula fornicata*, into Lyme Bay in the English Channel. *Proc. malac. Soc. Lond.*, **28**, pp. 168–184.

ORTON, J. H. & H. N. LEWIS. 1931. On the effect of the severe winter of 1928–29 on the oyster drills (with a record of five years' observations on sea-temperature on the oyster beds) of the Blackwater estuary. *J. mar. biol. Ass. U.K.*, **17**, pp. 301–313.

ORTON, J. H., A. J. SOUTHWARD & J. M. DODD. 1956. Studies on the biology of limpets. Part II. The breeding of *Patella vulgata* L. in Britain. *J. mar. biol. Ass. U.K.*, **35**, pp. 149–176.

ORTON, J. H. & R. WINCKWORTH. 1928. The occurrence of the American oyster pest *Urosalpinx cinerea* (Say) on English oyster beds. *Nature, Lond.*, **122**, p. 241.

OTTO, H. & C. TÖNNIGES. 1906. Untersuchungen über die Entwicklung von *Paludina vivipara*. *Z. wiss. Zool.*, **80**, pp. 411–514.

OVERTON, H. 1905. Note on a variety of *Paludestrina jenkinsi*, E. A. Smith. *J. Malacol.*, **12**, p. 15.

OWEN, G. 1956. Observations on the stomach and digestive diverticula of the Lamellibranchia. II. The Nuculidae. *Quart. J. micr. Sci.*, **97**, pp. 541–567.

OWEN, G. 1958. Observations on the stomach and digestive gland of *Scutus breviculus* (Blainville). *Proc. malac. Soc. Lond.*, **33**, pp. 103–114.

PALOMBI, A. 1938. Gli stadi larvali dei Trematodi del Golfo di Napoli. 2°. Contributo allo studio della morfologia, biologia e sistematica delle cercarie marine. *Rev. Parasit.*, **11**, pp. 189–206.

PARKER, G. H. 1911. The mechanism of locomotion in gastropods. *J. Morph.*, **22**, pp. 155–170.

PATANÈ, L. 1933. Sul comportamento di *Littorina neritoides* L. mantenuta in ambiente subaero ed in altro condizioni sperimentali. *R.C. Accad. Lincei* (6), **17**, pp. 961–967.

PATIL, A. M. 1958. The occurrence of a male of the prosobranch *Potamopyrgus jenkinsi* (Smith) var. *carinata* Marshall in the Thames at Sonning, Berkshire. *Ann. Mag. nat. Hist.* (13), **1**, pp. 232–240.

PATTEN, W. 1886a. The embryology of *Patella*. *Arb. zool. Inst. Wien*, **6**, pp. 149–174.

PATTEN, W. 1886b. Eyes of molluscs and arthropods. *Mitt. zool. Stat. Neapel*, **6**, pp. 542–756.

PEILE, A. J. 1937. Some radula problems. *J. Conch.*, **20**, pp. 292–304.

PELLEGRINI, O. 1948. Ricerche statistiche sulla sessualità di *Patella coerulea* L. *Boll. Zool.*, **15**, pp. 115–121.

PELLEGRINI, O. 1949. Ermafroditismo proterandrico in *Calyptraea chinensis* (L.) (Gasteropoda Prosobranchiata). *Boll. Zool.*, **16**, pp. 49–59.

PELSENEER, P. 1895. Hermaphroditism in Mollusca. *Quart. J. micr. Sci.*, **37**, pp. 19–46.

PELSENEER, P. 1896. Les reins, les glandes génitales et leurs conduits dans les mollusques. *Zool. Anz.*, **19**, pp. 140–145.

PELSENEER, P. 1898–99. Recherches morphologiques et phylogénétiques sur les mollusques archaïques. *Mém. Sav. étr. Acad. R. Belg.*, **57**, pp. 1–112.

PELSENEER, P. 1902. Sur l'exagération du dimorphisme sexuel chez un gastéropode marin. *J. Conchyliol.*, **50**, pp. 41–43.

PELSENEER, P. 1906a. Mollusca. In E. R. LANKESTER: *A Treastise on Zoology*, **5**. London, A. & C. Black.

PELSENEER, P. 1906b. Trématodes parasites de mollusques marins. *Bull. sci. Fr. Belg.*, **40**, pp. 161–186.

PELSENEER, P. 1910. Glandes pédieuses et coques ovigères des gastropodes. *Bull. sci. Fr. Belg.*, **44**, pp. 1–9.

PELSENEER, P. 1911. Recherches sur l'embryologie des gastropodes. *Mém. Acad. R. Belg. Cl. Sci.* (2), **3**, pp. 1–167.

PELSENEER, P. 1914. De quelques *Odostomia* et d'un Monstrilide. *Bull. sci. Fr. Belg.*, **48**, pp. 1–8.

PELSENEER, P. 1925. Gastropodes marins carnivores *Natica* et *Purpura*. *Ann. Soc. zool. Belg.*, **55**, pp. 37–39.

PELSENEER, P. 1926a. La proportion relative des sexes chez les animaux et particulièrement chez les mollusques. *Mém. Acad. R. Belg. Cl. Sci.* (2), **8**, pp. 1–258.

PELSENEER, P. 1926b. Notes d'embryologie malacologique. *Bull. biol.*, **60**, pp. 88–112.

PELSENEER, P. 1928. Les parasites des mollusques et les mollusques parasites. *Bull. Soc. zool. Fr.*, **53**, pp. 158–189.

PELSENEER, P. 1932. Le métamorphose préadulte des Cypraeidae. *Bull. biol.*, **66**, pp. 149–163.

PELSENEER, P. 1935. *Essai d'Ethologie zoologique d'après l'Etude des Mollusques*. Acad. R. Belg. Cl. Sci. Publ. Fondation Agathon de Potter, **1**, pp. 1–662.

PEREZ, C. & J. KOSTITZINE. 1930. Processus de résorption dans l'ovaire de la Turritelle. *C.R. Soc. Biol.*, Paris, **104**, pp. 1270–1272.

PERRIER, R. 1889. Recherches sur l'anatomie et l'histologie du rein des gastéropodes Proso-branchiata. *Ann. Sci. nat. Zool.* (7), **8**, pp. 61–192.

PETERSEN, C. G. J. 1911. Some experiments on the possibility of combating the harmful animals of the fisheries, especially the whelks in the Limfjord. *Rep. Danish biol. Sta.*, **19**, pp. 1–20.

PETERSEN, C. G. J. 1918. The sea bottom and its production of fish-food. *Rep. Danish biol. Sta.*, **25**, 1–62.

PFEIL, E. 1922. Die Statocyste von *Helix pomatia* L. *Z. wiss. Zool.*, **119**, pp. 79–113.

PICKEN, L. E. R. 1937. The mechanism of urine formation in invertebrates. II. The excretory mechanism of certain Mollusca. *J. exp. Biol.*, **14**, pp. 20–34.

PIERON, H. 1909. Contribution à la biologie de la Patelle et de la Calyptrée. *Arch. Zool. exp. gén.*, **41**, pp. 18–24.

PIERON, H. 1933. Notes éthologiques sur les gastéropodes perceurs et leur comportement avec utilisation de méthodes statistiques. *Arch. Zool. exp. gén.*, **75**, pp. 1–20.

PILSBRY, H. A. 1948. Land Mollusca of North America (North of Mexico). II, 2. *Monogr. Acad. nat. Sci. Philad.*, **3**, pp. 521–1113.

PLATE, L. H. 1895. Bemerkungen über die Phylogenie und die Entstehung der Asymmetrie der Mollusken. *Zool. Jb. (Anat. Ont.)*, **9**, pp. 162–206.

POPE, T. E. B. 1910–11. The oyster drill and other predatory Mollusca. *Rep. U.S. Bur. Fish. Wash.* (Unpublished.)

PORTMANN, A. 1925. Der Einfluss der Nähreier auf die Larvenentwickelung von *Buccinum* und *Purpura*. *Z. Morph. Ökol. Tiere*, **3**, pp. 526–541.

PORTMANN, A. 1927. Die Nähreierbildung durch atypische Spermien bei *Buccinum undatum* L. *Z. Zellforsch.*, **5**, pp. 230–243.

PORTMANN, A. 1930. Die Larvennieren von *Buccinum undatum* L. *Z. Zellforsch.*, **10**, pp. 401–410.

PORTMANN, A. 1931a. Die Entstehung der Nähreier bei *Purpura lapillus* durch atypische Befruch-tung. *Z. Zellforsch.*, **12**, pp. 167–178.

PORTMANN, A. 1931b. Die atypische Spermatogenese bei *Buccinum undatum* L. und *Purpura lapillus* L. *Z. Zellforsch.*, **12**, pp. 307–326.

PORTMANN, A. 1955. La métamorphose 'abritée' de *Fusus* (Gast. Prosobranches). *Rev. suisse Zool.*, **62**, fasc. suppl., pp. 236–252.

POTTS, W. T. W. 1954a. The inorganic composition of the blood of *Mytilus edulis* and *Anodonta cygnea*. *J. exp. Biol.*, **31**, pp. 376-385.

POTTS, W. T. W. 1954b. The energetics of osmotic regulation in brackish- and fresh-water animals. *J. exp. Biol.*, **31**, pp. 618-630.

PRASHAD, B. 1932. *Pila* (The apple snail). *Indian zool. Mem.*, **4**. Lucknow, Methodist Publishing House.

PRENANT, M. 1924a. L'activité sécrétrice dans l'épithelium supérieur de la gaine radulaire chez l'escargot (*Helix pomatia* L.). *Bull. Soc. zool. Fr.*, **49**, pp. 336-341.

PRENANT, M. 1924b. Contributions à l'étude cytologique du calcaire. I. Quelques formations calcaires du conjonctif chez les gastéropodes. *Bull. biol.*, **58**, pp. 331-380.

PRENANT, M. 1925. Sur la permanence des odontoblastes de la radula. *Bull. Soc. zool. Fr.*, **50**, pp. 164-167.

PROSSER, C. L. 1950. *Comparative Animal Physiology*. Philadelphia & London, W. B. Saunders.

PRUVOT, G. 1913. Sur la structure et la formation des soies de 'Nereis'. *IXth Cong. int. Zool. Monaco*, pp. 348-355.

PRUVOT-FOL, A. 1925. Morphogénèse des odontoblastes chez les Mollusques. *Arch. Zool. exp. gén.*, **64**, pp. 1-7.

PRUVOT-FOL, A. 1926. Le bulbe buccal et la symétrie des mollusques. I. La radula. *Arch. Zool. exp. gén.*, **65**, pp. 209-343.

PRUVOT-FOL, A. 1954. Le bulbe buccal et la symétrie des mollusques. II. *Arch. Zool. exp. gén.*, **91**, pp. 235-330.

QUAST, P. 1924a. Chemische Untersuchungen des Organextrakts der Konkrementendrüse und des Nephridium von *Cyclostoma elegans* Drap. *Z. Biol.*, **80**, pp. 211-222.

QUAST, P. 1924b. Der Konkrementendrüse von *Cyclostoma elegans*. *Z. ges. Anat.* I. *Z. Anat. EntwGesch.*, **72**, pp. 169-198.

QUAST, P. 1928. Farbstoffinjectionsversuche bei *Cyclostoma elegans* Drap. *Pflüg. Arch. ges. Physiol.*, **200**, pp. 642-648.

QUICK, H. E. 1920. Notes on the anatomy and reproduction of *Paludestrina* (*Hydrobia*) *stagnalis*. *J. Conch.*, **16**, pp. 96-97.

QUICK, H. E. 1924. Length of life of *Paludestrina ulvae*. *J. Conch.*, **17**, p. 169.

RAMAMOORTHI, K. 1955. Studies in the embryology and development of some melaniid snails. *J. zool. Soc. India*, **7**, pp. 25-34.

RAMMELMEYER, H. 1925. Zur Morphologie der *Puncturella noachina*. *Zool. Anz.*, **64**, pp. 105-114.

RANDLES, W. B. 1905. Some observations on the anatomy and affinities of the Trochidae. *Quart. J. micr. Sci.*, **48**, pp. 33-78.

RASETTI, F. 1957. Additional fossils from the Middle Cambrian Mt. Whyte formation of the Canadian Rocky Mountains. *J. Paleont.*, **31**, pp. 955-972.

RASMUSSEN, E. 1944. Faunistic and biological notes on marine invertebrates. I. *Vidensk. Medd. dansk naturh. Foren. Kbh.*, **107**, pp. 207-233.

RASMUSSEN, E. 1951. Faunistic and biological notes on marine invertebrates. II. The eggs and larvae of some Danish marine gastropods. *Vidensk. Medd. dansk naturh. Foren. Kbh.*, **113**, pp. 201-249.

RASSBACH, R. 1912a. Beiträge zur Kenntnis der Schale und Schalenregeneration von *Anodonta cellensis* Schröt. *Z. wiss. Zool.*, **103**, pp. 363-448.

RASSBACH, R. 1912b. Zur Kenntnis der Schalenregeneration bei der Teichmuschel (*Anodonta cellensis*). *Zool. Anz.*, **39**, pp. 35-38.

RAU, A. 1934. Anatomisch-histologische Untersuchungen an Cypraeen. *Jena. Z. Naturw.*, **69**, pp. 83-168.

REAUMUR, R. 1711. De la formation et de l'accroissement des coquilles des animaux tant terrestres qu'aquatiques, soit de mer soit de rivière. *Mém. Hist. Acad. Sci.*, Année 1709, pp. 364-400.

REES, C. B. 1940. A preliminary study of the ecology of a mud-flat. *J. mar. biol. Ass. U.K.*, **24**, pp. 185-199.

Rees, F. G. 1934. *Cercaria patellae* Lebour, 1911, and its effects on the digestive gland and gonads of *Patella vulgata*. *Proc. zool. Soc. Lond.*, pp. 45–53.

Rees, G. 1937. The anatomy and encystment of *Cercaria purpurae* Lebour, 1911. *Proc. zool. Soc., Lond.*, B, **107**, pp. 65–73.

Rees, G. 1939. Studies on the germ cell cycle of the digenetic trematode *Parorchis acanthus* Nicoll. Part 1. Anatomy of the genitalia and gametogenesis in the adult. *Parasitology*, **31**, pp. 417–433.

Rees, W. J. 1935. The anatomy of *Cercaria buccini* Lebour, 1911. *Proc. zool. Soc. Lond.*, pp. 309–312.

Rees, W. J. 1936a. Notes on the ubiquitous cercaria from *Littorina rudis*, *L. obtusata* and *L. littorea*. *J. mar. biol. Ass. U.K.*, **20**, pp. 621–624.

Rees, W. J. 1936b. The effect of parasitism by larval trematodes on the tissues of *Littorina littorea* (Linné). *Proc. zool. Soc. Lond.*, pp. 357–368.

Remane, A. 1950. Die Entstehung der Metamerie der Wirbellosen. *Verh. dtsch. zool. Ges.*, *Zool. Anz.* Suppl. **14**, pp. 16–23.

Rhein, A. 1935. Diploide Parthenogenese bei *Hydrobia jenkinsi* Smith. *Naturwissenschaften*, **23**, p. 100.

Rijnberk, G. van. 1919. Petites contributions à la physiologie comparée. IV. Sur le mouvement de locomotion de l'escargot terrestre *Helix aspersa*. *Arch. néerl. Physiol.*, **3**, pp. 539–552.

Risbec, J. 1937. Les irrégularités et les anomalies du développement embryonnaire chez *Murex erinaceus* L. et chez *Purpura lapillus* L. *Bull. Lab. marit. Dinard*, **17**, pp. 25–38.

Risbec, J. 1953a. Observations sur l'anatomie des Terebridae néocalédoniens. *Bull. Mus. Hist. nat.*, *Paris*, **25**, pp. 576–583.

Risbec, J. 1953b. Note sur la biologie et l'anatomie de *Ianthina globosa* (Gast. Prosobranches). *Bull. Soc. zool. Fr.*, **78**, pp. 194–201.

Risbec, J. 1954. Observations sur les Eulimidae (Gastéropodes) de Nouvelle-Calédonie. *Bull. Mus. Hist. nat.*, *Paris*, **26**, pp. 109–116.

Roaf, H. E. 1906. A contribution to the study of the digestive gland in Mollusca and decapod Crustacea. *Biochem. J.*, **1**, pp. 390–397.

Roaf, H. E. 1908. The hydrolytic enzymes of invertebrates. *Biochem. J.*, **3**, pp. 462–472.

Robert, A. 1900. Gastéropodes. Le troque. In L. Boutan: *Zoologie Descriptive*, **2**. Paris, Doin.

Robert, A. 1902. Recherches sur le développement des troques. *Arch. Zool. exp. gén.* (3), **10**, pp. 269–538.

Robertson, J. D. 1941. The function and metabolism of calcium in the Invertebrata. *Biol. Rev.*, **16**, pp. 106–133.

Robertson, J. D. 1949. Ionic regulation in some marine invertebrates. *J. exp. Biol.*, **26**, pp. 182–200.

Robertson, R. 1957. Gastropod host of an *Odostomia*. *Nautilus*, **70**, pp. 96–97.

Robinson, E. 1955. Observations on the toxoglossan gastropod *Mangelia brachystoma* (Philippi) and on the stenoglossan *Trophon muricatus* (Montagu). *M. Sc. Thesis, University of London*.

Robson, G. C. 1920. On the anatomy of *Paludestrina jenkinsi*. *Ann. Mag. nat. Hist.* (9), **5**, pp. 425–431.

Robson, G. C. 1922a. On the anatomy and affinities of *Paludestrina ventrosa* Montague. *Quart. J. micr. Sci.*, **66**, pp. 159–185.

Robson, G. C. 1922b. On the style-sac and intestine in Gastropoda and Lamellibranchia. *Proc. malac. Soc. Lond.*, **15**, pp. 41–46.

Robson, G. C. 1923. Parthenogenesis in the mollusc *Paludestrina jenkinsi*. Part I. *J. exp. Biol.*, **1**, pp. 65–77.

Robson, G. C. 1926. Parthenogenesis in the mollusc *Paludestrina jenkinsi*. Part II. The genetical behaviour, distribution, etc., of the keeled form ('var. *carinata*'). *J. exp. Biol.*, **3**, pp. 149–159.

ROHLACK, S. 1959. Über das Vorkommen von Sexualhormonen bei der Meeresschnecke *Littorina littorea* L. *Z. vergl. Physiol.*, **42**, pp. 164–180.

ROSEN, B. 1932. Zur Verdauungsphysiologie der Gastropoden. *Zool. Bidr. Uppsala*, **14**, pp. 1–67.

ROSEN, B. 1937. Vergleichende Studien über die Proteinasen von Gastropoden und dekapoden Crustaceen. *Z. vergl. Physiol.*, **24**, pp. 602–612.

ROSEN, N. 1910. Zur Kenntnis der parasitischen Schnecken. *Acta Univ. lund.*, *N.F. Afd.*, **2**, pp. 1–67.

RÖSSLER, R. 1885. Die Bildung der Radula bei den cephalophoren Mollusken. *Z. wiss. Zool.*, **41**, pp. 447–482.

ROTARIDES, M. 1934. Zum Formproblem des Schneckenfusses. *Zool. Anz.*, **108**, pp. 165–178.

ROTHSCHILD, A. & M. ROTHSCHILD. 1939. Some observations on the growth of *Peringia ulvae* (Pennant) 1777 in the laboratory. *Novit. zool.*, **41**, pp. 240–247.

ROTHSCHILD, M. 1935a. Notes on the excretory system of *Cercaria ephemera* Lebour, 1907 (nec Nitzsch). *Parasitology*, **27**, pp. 171–174.

ROTHSCHILD, M. 1935b. The trematode parasites of *Turritella communis* Lmk. from Plymouth and Naples. *Parasitology*, **27**, pp. 152–170.

ROTHSCHILD, M. 1936a. Preliminary note on the trematode parasites of *Peringia ulvae* (Pennant), 1777. *Novit. zool.*, **39**, pp. 268–269.

ROTHSCHILD, M. 1936b. Gigantism and variation in *Peringia ulvae* Pennant 1777, caused by infection with larval trematodes. *J. mar. biol. Ass. U.K.*, **20**, pp. 537–546.

ROTHSCHILD, M. 1937. Note on the excretory system of the trematode genus *Maritrema* Nicoll, 1907, and the systematic position of the Microphallinae Ward, 1901. *Ann. Mag. nat. Hist.* (10), **19**, pp. 355–365.

ROTHSCHILD, M. 1938a. Notes on the classification of cercariae of the superfamily Notocotyloidea (Trematoda), with special reference to the excretory system. *Novit. zool.*, **41**, pp. 75–83.

ROTHSCHILD, M. 1938b. Further observations on the effect of trematode parasites on *Peringia ulvae* (Pennant) 1777. *Novit. zool.*, **41**, pp. 84–102.

ROTHSCHILD, M. 1938c. The excretory system of *Cercaria coronanda* n. sp. together with notes on its life-history and the classification of cercariae of the superfamily Opisthorchioidea Vogel 1934 (Trematoda). *Novit. zool.*, **41**, pp. 148–163.

ROTHSCHILD, M. 1938d. Preliminary note on the life-history of *Cryptocotyle jejuna* Nicoll, 1907 (Trematoda). *Ann. Mag. nat. Hist.* (11), **I**, p. 238.

ROTHSCHILD, M. 1938e. *Cercaria sinitzini* n. sp. a cystophorous cercaria from *Peringia ulvae* (Pennant 1777). *Novit. zool.*, **41**, pp. 42–57.

ROTHSCHILD, M. 1939a. Large and small flame cells in a cercaria (Trematoda). *Novit. zool.*, **41**, p. 376.

ROTHSCHILD, M. 1939b. A note on the life cycle of *Cryptocotyle lingua* (Creplin), 1825 (Trematoda). *Novit. zool.*, **41**, pp. 178–180.

ROTHSCHILD, M. 1940. A note on the systematic position of *Cercaria coronanda* Rothschild, 1938. *Proc. helminthol. Soc. Washington*, **7**, pp. 13–14.

ROTHSCHILD, M. 1941a. The metacercaria of a pleurolophocerca cercaria parasitizing *Peringia ulvae* (Pennant, 1777). *Parasitology*, **33**, pp. 439–441.

ROTHSCHILD, M. 1941b. Observations on the growth and trematode infections of *Peringia ulvae* (Pennant), 1777, in a pool in the Tamar Saltings, Plymouth. *Parasitology*, **33**, pp. 406–415.

ROTHSCHILD, M. 1941c. The effect of trematode parasites on the growth of *Littorina neritoides* (L.). *J. mar. biol. Ass. U.K.*, **25**, pp. 69–80.

ROTHSCHILD, M. 1942. A seven-year-old infection of *Cryptocotyle lingua* Creplin in the winkle *Littorina littorea* L. *J. Parasit.*, **28**, p. 350.

ROTHSCHILD, M. & N. G. SPROSTON. 1941. The metacercaria of *Cercaria doricha* Roths., 1934, or a closely related species. *Parasitology*, **33**, pp. 359–362.

ROTTMANN, G. 1901. Über die Embryonalentwicklung der Radula bei den Mollusken. I. Die Entwicklung der Radula bei den Cephalopoden. *Z. wiss. Zool.*, **70**, pp. 236–262.

RÜCKER, A. 1883. Über die Bildung der Radula bei *Helix pomatia*. *Ber. oberhess. Ges. Nat.-u. Heilk.*, **22**, pp. 209–229.

RUDOLPHI, C. A. 1802. Fortsetzung der Beobachtungen. *Wiedemann's Arch. Zool. Zoot.*, **2**, (2), pp. 1–67.

RUSSELL, E. S. 1907. Environmental studies on the limpet. *Proc. zool. Soc. Lond.*, pp. 856–870.

RUSSELL, E. S. 1909. The growth of the shell of *Patella vulgata* L. *Proc. zool. Soc. Lond.*, pp. 235–253.

SACHWATKIN, V. A. 1920. Das Urogenitalsystem von *Ampullaria gigas* Spix. *Acta zool.*, Stockh., **1**, pp. 67–130.

SAHM, W. 1932. Bau und Wachstum des Deckels. In A. FLEISCHMANN: Vergleichende Betrachtungen über das Schalenwachstum der Weichtiere (Mollusca). II. Deckel (Operculum) und Haus (Concha) der Schnecken (Gastropoden). *Z. Morph. Ökol. Tiere*, **25**, pp. 549–622.

SANDEEN, M. I., G. C. STEPHENS & F. A. BROWN, JR. 1954. Persistent daily and tidal rhythms of oxygen consumption in two species of marine snails. *Physiol. Zool.*, **27**, pp. 350–356.

SANDER, K. 1950. Beobachtungen zur Fortpflanzung von *Assiminea grayana* Leach. *Arch. Molluskenk.*, **79**, pp. 147–149.

SANDER, K. 1952. Beobachtungen zur Fortpflanzung von *Assiminea grayana* Leach (2). *Arch. Molluskenk.*, **81**, pp. 133–134.

SANDERSON, A. R. 1939. The cytology of parthenogenesis in the snail *Potamopyrgus jenkinsi* Smith. *Advanc. Sci. Lond.*, **1**, p. 46.

SANDERSON, A. R. 1940. Maturation in the parthenogenetic snail *Potamopyrgus jenkinsi* Smith and in the snail *Peringia ulvae* (Pennant). *Proc. zool. Soc. Lond.*, **110**, pp. 11–15.

SARASIN, P. 1882. Entwickelungsgeschichte der *Bithynia tentaculata*. *Arb. zool. Inst. Würzburg*, **6**, pp. 1–68.

SAUNDERS, A. M. C. & M. POOLE. 1910. The development of *Aplysia punctata*. *Quart. J. micr. Sci.*, **55**, pp. 497–539.

SCHÄFER, H. 1952. Ein Beitrag zur Ernährungsbiologie von *Bithynia tentaculata* L. (Gastropoda Prosobranchia.) *Zool. Anz.*, **148**, pp. 299–303.

SCHÄFER, H. 1953a. Beobachtungen zur Ökologie von *Bithynia tentaculata*. *Arch. Molluskenk.*, **82**, pp. 67–70.

SCHÄFER, H. 1953b. Beiträge zur Ernährungsbiologie einheimischer Süsswasserprosobranchier. *Z. Morph. Ökol. Tiere*, **41**, pp. 247–264.

SCHARRER, B. 1935. Über das Hanströmsche Organ X bei Opisthobranchiern. *Pubbl. Staz. zool. Napoli*, **15**, pp. 135–142.

SCHARRER, B. 1937. Über sekretorisch tätige Nervenzellen bei wirbellosen Tieren. *Naturwissenschaften*, **25**, pp. 131–138.

SCHARRER, B. 1954. Neurosecretion in invertebrates: a survey. *Pubbl. Staz. zool. Napoli*, **24**, suppl., pp. 38–40.

SCHEPOTIEFF, A. 1903. Untersuchungen über den feineren Bau der Borsten einiger Chätopoden und Brachiopoden. *Z. wiss. Zool.*, **74**, pp. 656–710.

SCHEPOTIEFF, A. 1904. Untersuchungen über die Borstentaschen einiger Polychäten. *Z. wiss. Zool.*, **77**, pp. 586–605.

SCHIEMENZ, P. 1884. Über die Wasseraufnahme bei Lamellibranchiaten und Gastropoden (einschliesslich der Pteropoden). *Mitt. zool. Stat. Neapel*, **5**, pp. 509–543.

SCHIEMENZ, P. 1887. Über die Wasseraufnahme bei Lamellibranchiaten und Gastropoden (einschliesslich der Pteropoden). Zweiter Theil. *Mitt. zool. Stat. Neapel*, **7**, pp. 423–472.

SCHIEMENZ, P. 1891. Wie bohrt *Natica* die Muscheln an? *Mitt. zool. Stat. Neapel*, **10**, pp. 153–169.

SCHILDER, F. A. 1936. Anatomical characters of the Cypraeacea which confirm the conchological classification. *Proc. malac. Soc. Lond.*, **22**, pp. 75–112.

SCHILDER, F. A. 1947. Die Zahl der Prosobranchier in Vergangenheit und Gegenwart. *Arch. Molluskenk.*, **76**, pp. 37–44.

SCHITZ, V. 1920a. Sur la spermatogénèse chez *Cerithiopsis vulgata* Brug., *Turritella triplicata* Brocchi (*mediterranea* Monterosato) et *Bittium reticulatum* da Costa. *Arch. Zool. exp. gén.*, **58**, pp. 489-520.

SCHITZ, V. 1920b. Sur la spermatogénèse chez *Murex trunculus* L., *Aporrhais pespelecani* L., *Fusus* sp. et *Nassa reticulata* L. *Arch. Zool. exp. gén.*, **59**, pp. 477-508.

SCHNABEL, H. 1903. Über die Embryonalentwicklung der Radula bei den Mollusken. II. Die Entwicklung der Radula bei der Gastropoden. *Z. wiss. Zool.*, **74**, pp. 616-655.

SEDGWICK, A. 1909. *A Student's Text-book of Zoology.* London, Swan Sonnenschein.

SEGAL, E. 1956. Adaptive differences in water-holding capacity in an intertidal gastropod. *Ecology*, **37**, pp. 174-178.

SEGERSTRÅLE, S. G. 1949. The brackish-water fauna of Finland. *Oikos*, **1**, pp. 127-141.

SEIFERT, R. 1935. Bemerkungen zur Artunterscheidung der deutschen Brackwasser-Hydrobien. *Zool. Anz.*, **110**, pp. 233-239.

SESHAPPA, G. 1947. Oviparity in *Littorina saxatilis* (Olivi). *Nature, Lond.*, **160**, p. 335.

SHARMAN, M. 1956. Note on *Capulus ungaricus* (L.). *J. mar. biol. Ass. U.K.*, **35**, pp. 445-450.

SHAW, H. O. N. 1915. On the anatomy of *Conus tulipa*, Linn., and *Conus textile*, Linn. *Quart. J. micr. Sci.*, **60**, pp. 1-60.

SHOTWELL, J. A. 1950. Distribution of volume and relative linear measurement changes in *Acmaea*, the limpet. *Ecology*, **31**, pp. 51-61.

SIMROTH, H. 1882. Über die Bewegung und das Bewegungsorgan des *Cyclostoma elegans* und der einheimischen Schnecken überhaupt. *Z. wiss. Zool.*, **36**, pp. 1-67.

SIMROTH, H. 1895. Die Gastropoden der Plankton-Expedition. *Ergebn. Atlant. Planktonexped.*, **2**, pp. 1-206.

SIMROTH, H. 1896-1907. Gastropoda Prosobranchia. In H. G. BRONN: *Klassen und Ordnungen des Tierreichs*, **3**. Leipzig, Akademische Verlagsgesellschaft.

SIMROTH, H. 1911. Die Gastropoden des nordischen Planktons. *Nordisches Plankton*, **5**, pp. 1-36.

SIOLI, H. 1935. Über den Chemismus der Reparatur von Schalendefekten bei *Helix pomatia*. *Zool. Jb. (Zool. Physiol.)*, **54**, pp. 507-534.

SKRAMLIK, E. VON. 1941. Über den Kreislauf bei den Weichtieren. *Ergebn. Biol.*, **18**, pp. 88-286.

SMIDT, E. 1938. Notes on the reproduction and rate of growth in *Rissoa membranacea* (Adams) (Gastropoda Prosobranchiata) in the Sound. *Vidensk. Medd. dansk naturh. Foren. Kbh.*, **102**, pp. 169-181.

SMIDT, E. L. B. 1944. Biological studies of the invertebrate fauna of the harbour of Copenhagen. *Vidensk. Medd. dansk naturh. Foren. Kbh.*, **107**, pp. 235-316.

SMIDT, E. L. B. 1951. Animal production in the Danish Waddensee. *Medd. Komm. Havundersøg., Kbh.*, Ser. Fiskeri, **11**, no. 6, pp. 1-151.

SMITH, E. A. 1889. Notes on British *Hydrobiae* with a description of a supposed new species. *J. Conch.*, **6**, pp. 142-145.

SMITH, F. G. W. 1935. The development of *Patella vulgata*. *Philos. Trans.* B, **225**, pp. 95-125.

SMITH, J. E. & G. E. NEWELL. 1955. The dynamics of the zonation of the common periwinkle (*Littorina littorea* (L.)) on a stony beach. *J. Anim. Ecol.*, **24**, pp. 35-56.

SOLLAS, I. B. J. 1907. The molluscan radula: its chemical composition, and some points in its development. *Quart. J. micr. Sci.*, **51**, pp. 115-136.

SOOS, L. 1936. Zur Anatomie der Ungarischen Melaniiden. *Allatt. Közlem.*, **33**, pp. 103-128.

SOUTHWARD, A. J. 1958. Note on the temperature tolerances of some intertidal animals in relation to environmental temperatures and geographical distribution. *J. mar. biol. Ass. U.K.*, **37**, pp. 49-66.

SOUTHWARD, A. J. & D. J. CRISP. 1954. The distribution of certain intertidal animals around the Irish coast. *Proc. roy. Irish Acad.*, **57**, B, 1, pp. 1-29.

SOUTHWARD, A. J. & J. H. ORTON. 1954. The effects of wave action on the distribution and numbers of the commoner animals living on the Plymouth breakwater. *J. mar. biol. Ass. U.K.*, **33**, pp. 1-19.

SPEK, J. 1921. Beiträge zur Kenntis der chemischen Zusammensetzung und Entwicklung der Radula der Gastropoden. *Z. wiss. Zool.*, **118**, pp. 313-363.

SPENGEL, J. W. 1881. Die Geruchsorgane und das Nervensystem der Mollusken. *Z. wiss. Zool.*, **35**, pp. 333-383.

SPILLMANN, J. 1905. Zur Anatomie und Histologie des Herzens und der Hauptarterien der Diotocardier. *Jena. Z. Naturw.*, **40**, pp. 537-588.

SPITZER, J. M. 1937. Nitrogen excretion and distribution of molluscs. *Zool. Jb. (Zool. Physiol.)*, **57**, pp. 457-496.

SPOEL, S. VAN DER. 1958. Groei en ouderdom bij *Viviparus contectus* (Millet, 1813) en *Viviparus viviparus* (Linné, 1758). *Basteria*, **22**, pp. 77-90.

SPOONER, G. M. & H. B. MOORE. 1940. The ecology of the Tamar estuary. VI. An account of the macrofauna of the intertidal muds. *J. mar. biol. Ass. U.K.*, **24**, pp. 283-330.

STAIGER, H. 1950a. Chromosomenzahlen stenoglosser Prosobranchier. *Experientia*, **6**, pp. 54-59.

STAIGER, H. 1950b. Chromosomenzahl-Varianten bei *Purpura lapillus*. *Experientia*, **6**, pp. 140-145.

STAIGER, H. 1950c. Zur Determination der Nähreier bei Prosobranchiern. *Rev. suisse Zool.*, **57**, pp. 496-503.

STAIGER, H. 1951. Cytologische und morphologische Untersuchungen zur Determination der Nähreier bei Prosobranchiern. *Z. Zellforsch.*, **35**, pp. 496-549.

STAIGER, H. 1954. Die Chromosomendimorphismus beim Prosobranchier *Purpura lapillus* in Beziehung zur Ökologie der Art. *Chromosoma*, **6**, pp. 419-478.

STAIGER, H. 1955. Reziproke Translokationen in naturlichen Populationen von *Purpura lapillus* (Prosobranchia). *Chromosoma*, **7**, pp. 181-197.

STAIGER, H. 1957. Genetical and morphological variation in *Purpura lapillus* with respect to local and regional differentiation of population groups. *Année biol.*, **33**, pp. 251-258.

STARMÜHLNER, F. 1952. Zur Anatomie, Histologie und Biologie einheimischer Prosobranchier. *Öst. zool. Z.*, **3**, pp. 546-590.

STARMÜHLNER, F. 1956. Zur Molluskenfauna des Felslitorals und submariner Höhlen am Capo di Sorrento (I. Teil). Ergebnisse der Österr. Tyrrhenia-Expedition 1952 Teil IV. *Öst. zool. Z.*, **6**, pp. 147-249. II. Teil. *Öst. zool. Z.*, **6**, pp. 631-713.

STEPHENS, G. C., M. I. SANDEEN & H. M. WEBB. 1953. A persistent tidal rhythm of activity in the mud snail *Nassa obsoleta*. *Anat. Rec.*, **117**, p. 635.

STEPHENSON, T. A. 1924. Notes on *Haliotis tuberculata*. *J. mar. biol. Ass. U.K.*, **13**, pp. 480-495.

STEUSLOFF, U. 1927. Die Bedeutung der *Paludestrina jenkinsi* E. A. Smith für unsere Vorstellungen über Artentstehung und Artverbreitung. *Verh. int. Ver. Limnol.*, **3**, pp. 454-459.

STEUSLOFF, U. 1939. *Potamopyrgus crystallinus crystallinus* J. T. Marshall mit Kalkkielen auf der Schale. *Arch. Molluskenk.*, **71**, pp. 82-86.

STINSON, R. H. 1946. Observations on the natural history of clam drills. *MS Rep. Fish. Res. Bd. Canada*, p. 383.

STROHL, J. 1914. Die Exkretion. In H. WINTERSTEIN: *Handbuch der vergleichenden Physiologie*, **II**, 2. Berlin, Gustav Fischer.

STRUNK, C. 1935. Studien über die Niere der Wellhornschnecke (*Buccinum undatum*). *Zool. Zbl.*, **55**, pp. 53-57.

STUNKARD, H. W. 1957. The morphology and life-history of the digenetic trematode, *Microphallus similis* (Jägerskiöld, 1900) Baer, 1943. *Biol. Bull., Wood's Hole*, **112**, pp. 254-266.

SUZUKI, S. 1934. On the innervation of the heart of limpets. *Sci. Rep. Tohoku Imp. Univ.* (4) (Biol.), **9**, pp. 117-121.

SUZUKI, S. 1935. The innervation of the heart of molluscs. *Sci. Rep. Tohoku Imp. Univ.* (4) (Biol.), **10**, pp. 15-27.

SYKES, E. R. 1903. Notes on British Eulimidae. *Proc. malac. Soc. Lond.*, **5**, pp. 348-353.

TATTERSALL, W. M. 1920. Notes on the breeding habits and life history of the periwinkle. *Sci. Invest. Fish. Br. Ire.*, **1**, pp. 1-11.

TAYLOR, F. 1900. *Paludestrina jenkinsi* Smith at Droylsden, Lancashire. *J. Conch.*, **9**, p. 340.

TECHOW, G. 1910. Zur Kenntnis der Schalenregeneration bei den Gastropoden. *Arch. Entwick-Mech.*, **31**, pp. 258–288.

THAMDRUP, H. M. 1935. Beiträge zur Ökologie der Wattenfauna. *Medd. Komm. Havundersøg.*, Kbh., ser. Fiskeri, **10**, no. 2, pp. 1–125.

THIELE, J. 1897. Beiträge zur Kenntnis der Mollusken. III. Über Hautdrüsen und ihre Derivative. *Z. wiss. Zool.*, **62**, pp. 632–670.

THIELE, J. 1928. Über ptenoglosse Schnecken. *Z. wiss. Zool.*, **132**, pp. 73–94.

THIELE, J. 1929–35. *Handbuch der Systematischen Weichtierkunde.* 4 parts. 1 (1929), 4 (1935). Jena, Fischer.

THIEM, H. 1917a. Beiträge zur Anatomie und Phylogenie der Docoglossen. I. Zur Anatomie von *Helcioniscus ardosiaeus* Hombron et Jaquinot unter Bezugnahme auf die Bearbeitung von Erich Schuster in den Zoolog. Jahrb., Supplement XIII, Bd. IV, 1913: Jena. *Z. Naturw.*, **54**, pp. 333–404b.

THIEM, H. 1917b. Beiträge zur Anatomie und Phylogenie der Docoglossen. II. Die Anatomie und Phylogenie der Monobranchen. (Akmäiden und Scurriiden nach der Sammlung Plates.) Jena. *Z. Naturw.*, **54**, pp. 405–630.

THOMAS, I. M. 1948. The adhesion of limpets. *Aust. J. Sci.*, **11**, pp. 28–29.

THOMPSON, D'A. W. 1942. *On Growth and Form.* Cambridge, University Press.

THORSON, G. 1935. Studies on the egg-capsules and development of Arctic marine prosobranchs. *Medd. Grønland*, **100**, no. 5, pp. 1–71.

THORSON, G. 1936. The larval development, growth, and metabolism of Arctic marine bottom invertebrates. *Medd. Grønland*, **100**, no. 6, pp. 1–155.

THORSON, G. 1940a. Studies on the egg masses and larval development of Gastropoda from the Iranian Gulf. *Danish sci. Invest. Iran*, **2**, pp. 159–238.

THORSON, G. 1940b. Notes on the egg-capsules of some North-Atlantic prosobranchs of the genus *Troschelia, Chrysodomus, Volutopsis, Sipho* and *Trophon*. *Vidensk. Medd. naturh. Foren. Kbh.*, **104**, pp. 251–265.

THORSON, G. 1944. Marine Gastropoda Prosobranchiata. *Medd. Grønland*, **121**, no. 13, pp. 1–181.

THORSON, G. 1946. Reproduction and larval development of Danish marine bottom invertebrates. *Medd. Komm. Havundersøg.*, Kbh., ser. Plankton, **4**, pp. 1–523.

THORSON, G. 1950. Reproductive and larval ecology of marine bottom invertebrates. *Biol. Rev.*, **25**, pp. 1–45.

THORSON, G. 1958. Parasitism in the marine gastropod-family Scalidae. *Vidensk. Medd. naturh. Foren. Kbh.*, **119**, pp. 55–58.

TÖNNIGES, C. 1896. Die Bildung des Mesoderms bei *Paludina vivipara*. *Z. wiss. Zool.*, **61**, pp. 541–605.

TOTZAUER, R. J. 1902. Nieren- und Gonadenverhältnisse von *Haliotis*. *Zool. Anz.*, **25**, pp. 487–488.

TOURAINE, J. 1952. Les glandes pédieuses des gastéropodes prosobranches monotocardes. *Bull. Soc. zool. Fr.*, **77**, pp. 240–241.

TRINCHESE, S. 1878. Anatomia e fisiologia della *Spurilla neapolitana*. *Mem. Accad. Bologna* (3), **9**, pp. 1–48.

TRUEMAN, E. R. 1942. The structure and deposition of the shell of *Tellina tenuis*. *J. roy. micr. Soc.*, **62**, pp. 69–92.

TRUEMAN, E. R. 1949. The ligament of *Tellina tenuis*. *Proc. zool. Soc. Lond.*, **119**, pp. 717–742.

TSCHACHOTIN, S. 1908. Die Statocyste der Heteropoden. *Z. wiss. Zool.*, **90**, pp. 343–422.

TULLBERG, T. 1881. Studien über den Bau und das Wachstum des Hummerpanzers und der Molluskenschalen. *K. svenska VetenskAkad. Handl.*, **19**, (3), pp. 1–57.

TURNER, H. J. 1953. The drilling mechanism of the Naticidae. *Ecology*, **34**, pp. 222–223.

VANDEBROEK, G. 1936. Organogénèse des follicules sétigères chez *Eisenia foetida* Sav. *Mém. Mus. Hist. nat. Belg.* (2), **3**, pp. 559–568.

VANEY, C. 1913. L'adaptation des gastropodes au parasitisme. *Bull. sci. Fr. Belg.*, **47**, pp. 1–87.

VANSTONE, J. H. 1894. Some points in the anatomy of *Melongena melongena*. *J. Linn. Soc. (Zool.)*, **24**, pp. 369–373.

VERLAINE, L. 1936. L'instinct et l'intelligence chez les Mollusques. Les gastéropodes perceurs de coquilles. *Mém. Mus. Hist. nat. Belg.* (2), **3**, pp. 387–394.

VESTERGAARD, K. 1935. Über den Laich und die Larven von *Scalaria communis* (Lam.), *Nassarius pygmaeus* (Lam.) und *Bela turricola* (Mont.). *Zool. Anz.*, **109**, pp. 217–222.

VILLEE, C. A. & T. C. GROODY. 1940. The behaviour of limpets with reference to their homing instinct. *Amer. midl. Nat.*, **24**, pp. 190–204.

VILLEPOIX, M. DE. 1892. Recherches sur la formation et l'accroissement de la coquille des mollusques. *J. Anat. Paris*, **28**, pp. 461–518 and pp. 582–674.

VLES, F. 1907. Sur les ondes pédieuses des mollusques reptateurs. *C.R. Acad. Sci., Paris*, **145**, pp. 276–278.

WAELE, A. DE. 1930. Le sang d'Anodonte et la formation de la coquille. *Mém. Acad. R. Belg. Cl. Sci.* (2), **10**, no. 3, pp. 1–52.

WAGGE, L. E. 1951. The activity of amoebocytes and of alkaline phosphatases during the regeneration of the shell in the snail, *Helix aspersa. Quart. J. micr. Sci.*, **92**, pp. 307–321.

WALNE, P. R. 1956. The biology and distribution of the slipper limpet *Crepidula fornicata* in Essex rivers with notes on the distribution of the larger epi-benthic invertebrates. *Fish. Invest. Lond.* (2), **20**, no. 6, pp. 1–50.

WARWICK, T. 1944. Inheritance of the keel in *Potamopyrgus jenkinsi* (Smith). *Nature, Lond.*, **154**, pp. 798–799.

WARWICK, T. 1952. Strains in the mollusc *Potamopyrgus jenkinsi* (Smith). *Nature, Lond.*, **169**, pp. 551–552.

WARWICK, T. 1953. The nature of shell incrustations in some aquatic molluscs. *Proc. malac. Soc. Lond.*, **30**, pp. 71–73.

WARWICK, T. 1955. *Potamopyrgus jenkinsi* (Smith) in recent deposits in Suffolk. *Proc. malac. Soc. Lond.*, **31**, pp. 22–25.

WATERSTON, J. & J. W. TAYLOR. 1906. Land and freshwater molluscs of St. Kilda. *Ann. Scot. nat. Hist.*, pp. 21–24.

WATERSTON, R. 1934. Occurrence of *Amnicola taylori* (E. A. Smith) and *Bithynia leachi* (Sheppard) in Scotland. *J. Conch.*, **20**, pp. 55–56.

WATSON, H. 1955. The names of the two common species of *Viviparus. Proc. malac. Soc. Lond.*, **31**, pp. 163–174.

WEBER, H. 1925. Über arhythmische Fortbewegung bei einigen Prosobranchiern. Ein Beitrag zur Bewegungsphysiologie der Gastropoden. *Z. vergl. Physiol.*, **2**, pp. 109–121.

WEBER, H. 1927. Der Darm von *Dolium galea* L., eine vergleichend anatomische Untersuchung unter besonderer Berücksichtigung der *Tritonium*-Arten. *Z. Morph. Ökol. Tiere*, **8**, pp. 663–804.

WEGMANN, H. 1884. Contributions à l'histoire naturelle des Haliotides. *Arch. Zool. exp. gén.* (2), **2**, pp. 289–378.

WEGMANN, H. 1887. Notes sur l'organisation de la *Patella vulgata* L. *Rec. zool. suisse*, **4**, pp. 269–303.

WEISE, W. 1924. Das Nervensystem von *Calyptraea sinensis* Lin. und *Aporrhais pes-pelicani* Lam. *Z. wiss. Zool.*, **128**, pp. 570–600.

WELSH, J. H. 1953. The action of acetylcholine antagonists on the heart of *Venus mercenaria. Brit. J. Pharmacol.*, **8**, pp. 327–333.

WELSH, J. H. 1956. Neurohormones of invertebrates. I. Cardio-regulators of *Cyprina* and *Buccinum. J. mar. biol. Ass. U.K.*, **35**, pp. 193–201.

WELSH, J. H. 1957. Neurohormones or transmitter agents. In B. T. SCHEER: *Recent Advances in Invertebrate Physiology.* Eugene, Oregon, University of Oregon.

WENZ, W. 1938. Gastropoda 1, 2. In O. H. SCHINDEWOLF: *Handbuch der Paläozoologie*, **6**. Berlin, Borntraeger.

WERNER, B. 1939. Über die Entwicklung und Artunterscheidung von Muschellarven des Nordseeplanktons, unter besonderer Berücksichtigung der Schalenentwicklung. *Zool. Jb. (Anat. Ont.)*, **66**, pp. 1–54.

WERNER, B. 1952. Ausbildungsstufen der Filtrationsmechanismen bei filtrierenden Prosobranchiern. *Verh. dtsch. zool. Ges., Zool. Anz.* Suppl. **17**, pp. 529–546.

WERNER, B. 1953. Über den Nahrungserwerb der Calyptraeidae (Gastropoda Prosobranchia). Morphologie, Histologie und Funktion der am Nahrungserwerb beiteiligten Organe. *Helgoländ. wiss. Meeresunters.*, **4**, pp. 260–315.

WERNER, B. 1955. Über die Anatomie, die Entwicklung und Biologie des Veligers und der Veliconcha von *Crepidula fornicata* L. (Gastropoda Prosobranchia). *Helgoländ. wiss. Meeresunters.*, **5**, pp. 169–217.

WERNER, B. 1959. Das Prinzip des endlosen Schleimfilters beim Nahrungserwerb wirbelloser Meerestiere. *Int. Rev. ges. Hydrobiol.*, **44**, pp. 181–216.

WESENBERG-LUND, C. 1931. Contributions to the development of the Trematoda Digenea. Part I. The biology of *Leucochloridium paradoxum*. *K. dansk. Vidensk. Selsk.*, **4**, no. 3, pp. 1–142.

WESENBERG-LUND, C. 1934. Contributions to the development of the Trematoda Digenea. Part II. The biology of the freshwater cercariae in Danish freshwaters. *K. dansk. Vidensk. Selsk.*, **5**, no. 3, pp. 1–223.

WESENBERG-LUND, C. 1939. *Die Biologie der Süsswassertiere. Wirbellose Tiere.* Wien, Springer.

WESTBLAD, E. 1922. Zur Physiologie der Turbellarien. I. Die Verdauung. II. Die Exkretion. *Lunds Univ. Årssk.*, N.F. (2), **18**, 6, pp. 9–212.

WHEATLEY, J. M. 1947. Investigations on *Polynices* and clams at Belliveau Cove, N.S. *MS Rep. Fish. Res. Bd. Canada*, p. 371.

WHITEHEAD, H. 1935. An ecological study of the invertebrate fauna of a chalk stream near Great Driffield, Yorkshire. *J. Anim. Ecol.*, **4**, pp. 58–78.

WHITAKER, M. B. 1951. On the homologies of the oesophageal glands of *Theodoxus fluviatilis* (L.). *Proc. malac. Soc. Lond.*, **29**, pp. 21–34.

WHITTAKER, V. P. & I. A. MICHAELSON. 1954. Studies in urocanylcholine. *Biol. Bull., Wood's Hole*, **107**, p. 134.

WIERZEJSKI, A. 1905. Embryologie von *Physa fontinalis* L. *Z. wiss. Zool.*, **83**, pp. 502–706.

WILBUR, K. M. & L. H. JODREY. 1955. Studies on shell formation. V. The inhibition of shell formation by carbonic anhydrase inhibitors. *Biol. Bull., Wood's Hole*, **108**, pp. 359–365.

WILCZYNSKI, J. C. 1955. On sex behaviour and sex determination in *Crepidula fornicata*. *Biol. Bull., Wood's Hole*, **109**, pp. 353–354.

WILLCOX, M. A. 1898. Zur Anatomie von *Acmaea fragilis*. *Jena. Z. Naturw.*, **32**, pp. 411–456.

WILLCOX, M. A. 1905a. Biology of *Acmaea testudinalis* Müller. *Amer. Nat.*, **39**, pp. 325–333.

WILLCOX, M. A. 1905b. Homing of *Fissurella* and *Siphonaria*. *Science*, **22**, p. 90.

WILLEM, V. 1892a. Contributions à l'étude physiologique des organes des sens chez les mollusques. I. La vision chez les gastropodes pulmonés. *Arch. Biol.*, **12**, pp. 57–98.

WILLEM, V. 1892b. Contributions à l'étude physiologique des organes des sens chez les mollusques. II. Les gastropodes pulmonés perçoivent-ils les rayons ultra-violets? *Arch. Biol.*, **12**, pp. 99–122.

WILLEM, V. 1892c. Contributions à l'étude physiologique des organes des sens chez les mollusques. III. Observations sur la vision et les organes visuels de quelques mollusques prosobranches et opisthobranches. *Arch. Biol.*, **12**, pp. 123–149.

WILSMANN, T. 1942. Der Pharynx von *Buccinum undatum*. *Zool. Jb. (Anat. Ont.)*, **68**, pp. 1–48.

WILSON, D. P. 1929. A habit of the common periwinkle (*Littorina littorea* Linn.). *Nature, Lond.*, **124**, p. 443.

WILSON, D. P. & M. A. WILSON. 1956. A contribution to the biology of *Ianthina janthina* (L.). *J. mar. biol. Ass. U.K.*, **35**, pp. 291–305.

WILSON, E. B. 1904. On germinal localization in the egg. II. Experiments on the cleavage mosaic in *Patella*. *J. exp. Zool.*, **1**, pp. 197–268.

WINCKWORTH, R. 1932. The British marine Mollusca. *J. Conch.*, **19**, pp. 211–252.

WINKLER, L. R. & E. D. WAGNER. 1959. Filter paper digestion by the crystalline style in *Oncomelania*. *Trans. Amer. micr. Soc.*, **78**, pp. 262–268.

WOODWARD, B. B. 1892. On the mode of growth and the structure of the shell in *Velates conoideus* Lamk. and other Neritidae. *Proc. zool. Soc. Lond.*, pp. 528–540.

WOODWARD, B. B. 1913. *The Life of the Mollusca*. London, Methuen.

WOODWARD, M. F. 1899. On the anatomy of *Adeorbis subcarinatus* Montagu. *Proc. malac. Soc. Lond.*, **3**, pp. 140–146.

WOODWARD, M. F. 1901a. The anatomy of *Pleurotomaria beyrichii* Hilg. *Quart. J. micr. Sci.*, **44**, pp. 215–268.

WOODWARD, M. F. 1901b. Note on the anatomy of *Voluta ancilla* (Sol.), *Neptuneopsis gilchristi* Sby., and *Volutilithes abyssicola* (Ad. and Rve.). *Proc. malac. Soc. Lond.*, **4**, pp. 117–125.

WOODWARD, S. P. 1851–56. *A Manual of the Mollusca*. London, Lockwood.

WOODWARD, S. P. 1875. *A Manual of the Mollusca*. 3rd edition. London, Lockwood.

WRIGHT, C. A. 1956. Studies on the life-history and ecology of the trematode genus *Renicola* Cohn, 1904. *Proc. zool. Soc. Lond.*, **126**, pp. 1–49.

WRIGHT, C. A. 1959. The application of paper chromatography to a taxonomic study in the molluscan genus *Lymnaea*. *J. Linn. Soc. (Zool.)*, **44**, pp. 222–237.

WRIGHT, F. S. 1936. Report on the Maldon (Essex) periwinkle fishery. *Fish. Invest., Lond.* (2), **14**, no. 6, pp. 1–37.

WRIGLEY, A. 1932. Spiral sculpture and lip-denticulation of the Cymatiidae. *Proc. malac. Soc. Lond.*, **20**, pp. 127–128.

WRIGLEY, A. 1934. Spiral sculpture and colour markings of the Cassididae. *Proc. malac. Soc. Lond.*, **21**, pp. 111–114.

WRIGLEY, A. 1942. English Eocene *Hastula* with remarks on the coloration of the Terebridae. *Proc. malac. Soc. Lond.*, **25**, pp. 17–24.

WRIGLEY, A. 1948. The colour patterns and sculpture of molluscan shells. *Proc. malac. Soc. Lond.*, **27**, pp. 206–217.

WYATT, H. V. 1957. The biology and reproduction of *Calyptraea chinensis*. *Challenger Soc. Rep.*, **3**, p. 33.

YASIRO, H. 1939. Fatal bite of *Conus geographus* (in Japanese). *Venus*, **9**, p. 165. (Summarized in *Proc. malac. Soc. Lond.*, **24**, p. 32.)

YONGE, C. M. 1925a. The hydrogen ion concentration in the gut of certain lamellibranchs and gastropods. *J. mar. biol. Ass. U.K.*, **13**, pp. 938–952.

YONGE, C. M. 1925b. The digestive diverticula in the lamellibranchs. *Trans. roy. Soc. Edinb.*, **54**, pp. 703–718.

YONGE, C. M. 1926. Structure and physiology of the organs of feeding and digestion in *Ostrea edulis*. *J. mar. biol. Ass. U.K.*, **14**, pp. 295–386.

YONGE, C. M. 1928. Feeding mechanisms in the invertebrates. *Biol. Rev.*, **3**, pp. 21–76.

YONGE, C. M. 1930. The crystalline style of the Mollusca and a carnivorous habit cannot normally co-exist. *Nature, Lond.*, **125**, pp. 444–445.

YONGE, C. M. 1932. Notes on feeding and digestion in *Pterocera* and *Vermetus*, with a discussion on the occurrence of the crystalline style in the Gastropoda. *Sci. Rep. Gt. Barrier Reef Exped.*, **1**, pp. 259–281.

YONGE, C. M. 1937. The biology of *Aporrhais pes-pelicani* (L.) and *A. serresiana* (Mich.). *J. mar. biol. Ass. U.K.*, **21**, pp. 687–704.

YONGE, C. M. 1938. Evolution of ciliary feeding in the Prosobranchia, with an account of feeding in *Capulus ungaricus*. *J. mar. biol. Ass. U.K.*, **22**, pp. 453–468.

YONGE, C. M. 1939a. The protobranchiate Mollusca: a functional interpretation of their structure and evolution. *Philos. Trans. B*, **230**, pp. 79–147.

YONGE, C. M. 1939b. On the mantle cavity and its contained organs in the Loricata (Placophora). *Quart. J. micr. Sci.*, **81**, pp. 367–390.

YONGE, C. M. 1946. On the habits of *Turritella communis* Risso. *J. mar. biol. Ass. U.K.*, **26**, pp. 377–380.

YONGE, C. M. 1947. The pallial organs in the aspidobranch Gastropoda and their evolution throughout the Mollusca. *Philos. Trans.* B, **232**, pp. 443–518.

YONGE, C. M. 1953. Form and habit in *Pinna carnea* Gmelin. *Philos. Trans.* B, **237**, pp. 335–374.

YONGE, C. M. 1954. Physiological anatomy of the alimentary canal in invertebrates. *Tabul. biol.*, *Hague*, **21**, no. 20, pp. 1–24.

ZIEGELMEIER, E. 1954. Beobachtungen über den Nahrungserwerb bei der Naticide *Lunatia nitida* Donovan (Gastropoda Prosobranchia). *Helgoländ. wiss. Meeresunters.*, **5**, pp. 1–33.

ZIEGELMEIER, E. 1958. Zur Lokomotion bei Naticiden (Gastropoda Prosobranchiata) (Kurze Mitteilung über Schwimmbewegungen bei *Polynices josephinus* Risso). *Helgoländ. wiss. Meeresunters.*, **6**, pp. 202–206.

ZIEGENHORN, A. & H. THIEM. 1926. Beiträge zur Systematik und Anatomie der Fissurellen. *Jena. Z. Naturw.*, **62**, pp. 1–78.

ZUBKOV, A. A. 1934. Studies on the comparative physiology of the heart: the pace-maker of the heart of the snail (*Helix pomatia*). *Coll. Pap. Lab. comp. Physiol. Timiriasev biol. Inst.*, pp. 52–61.

# AUTHOR INDEX

# SUBJECT INDEX

Numbers in italics refer to pages with text-figures

# SYSTEMATIC INDEX

Numbers in italics refer to pages with text-figures